Abnormal Psychology

Sixth Canadian Edition

GORDON L. FLETT

York University

NANCY L. KOCOVSKI

Wilfrid Laurier University

with contributions from

KIRK R. BLANKSTEIN

University of Toronto Mississauga

WILEY

Dedicated from Gordon Flett to
Kathy, Hayley, and Alison, and my dearly departed sister Karen.

Dedicated from Nancy Kocovski to
Jim, Abby, Alex, and Andrew

VICE PRESIDENT AND DIRECTOR	George Hoffman
DIRECTOR	Veronica Visentin
SENIOR MANAGER	Karen Staudinger
ASSOCIATE DEVELOPMENTAL EDITOR	Courtney Luzzi
EDITORIAL ASSISTANT	Ethan Lipson
SENIOR MARKETING MANAGER	Patty Maher
CONTENT MANAGER	Dorothy Sinclair
PRODUCTION EDITOR & MEDIA SPECIALIST	Meaghan MacDonald
PRODUCT DESIGNER	Wendy Ashenberg
INTERIOR & COVER DESIGN	Wiley/Joanna Vieira
COVER IMAGE	©agsandrew/Shutterstock
TYPESETTER	Aptara
PRINTER	LSC Communications

Library and Archives Canada Cataloguing in Publication

Davison, Gerald C., author
  Abnormal psychology / Gordon L. Flett, Nancy Kocovski, Gerald C. Davison, John M. Neale. — Sixth Canadian edition.

Revision of: Abnormal psychology / Gerald C. Davison, Kirk R. Blankstein, Gordon L. Flett, John M. Neale. — Fifth Canadian edition. — Toronto: John Wiley & Sons Canada, 2013.

Includes bibliographical references and index.

Issued in print and electronic formats.

ISBN 978-1-119-33515-3 (paperback).—ISBN 978-1-119-33533-7 (pdf)
  1. Psychology, Pathological—Textbooks. I. Flett, Gordon L. (Gordon Leslie), 1957-, author II. Kocovski, Nancy, 1973-, author III. Neale, John M., 1943-, author IV. Title.

RC454.D33 2017   616.89   C2016-905804-2   C2016-905805-0

Printed in the United States of America
10 9 8 7 6 5 4 3 2 1

GORDON L. FLETT is a Professor of Psychology at York University in Toronto. He is currently the Director of the LaMarsh Centre for Child and Youth Research at York University. He has served as Associate Dean of Research and Graduate Education in York's Faculty of Health and as Director of Undergraduate Studies in the Department of Psychology at York University. He received the Outstanding Teaching Award from the Faculty of Arts at York University in 1993 and again in 1997. Dr. Flett has taught courses in abnormal psychology, introduction to personality, and personality theory and behavioural disorders at the undergraduate level, as well as courses in personality theory and research and in the self-concept at the graduate level. He received his B.Sc., M.A., and Ph.D. from the University of Toronto, and he began his appointment at York University in 1987.

In 1996, Dr. Flett was recognized by the American Psychological Society as one of the top 25 scholars in psychology, based on the number of publications over a five-year period. In 1999, he received the Dean's Award for Outstanding Research from the Faculty of Arts at York University. In 2004, Dr. Flett was awarded a Tier I Canada Research Chair in Personality and Health, which he currently holds, and in 2007, he was nominated and made a Fellow of the Association for Psychological Science in recognition of his "distinguished contributions to psychological science."

His research interests include the role of personality factors in depression, as well as the continuity of depression, and the interpersonal aspects of anxiety. Dr. Flett is a member of York's LaMarsh Centre for Child and Youth Research and he is extensively involved in raising awareness about the mental health problems of children and adolescents, including serving as one of the guest editors of a 2013 special issue of the *Canadian Journal of School Psychology* focused on the role of schools in a new mental health strategy. Dr. Flett has also served as guest editor of four special issues on perfectionism for the *Journal of Rational-Emotive & Cognitive-Behavior Therapy*. He also served as guest editor of a 2016 special issue on perfectionism of the *Journal of Psychoeducational Assessment*. One of his current projects is a collaborative venture with the York Region District School Board funded by the Ontario Ministry of Education that is focused on increasing resilience among children and youth.

Dr. Flett is perhaps most recognized for his seminal contributions to research and theory on the role of perfectionism in psychopathology. His collaborative work with Dr. Paul Hewitt (University of British Columbia) has helped establish that perfectionism is multidimensional with salient interpersonal components that contribute to personal and interpersonal maladjustment. Their work on perfectionism has received international attention and has been the subject of numerous media stories, including coverage on CTV, CNN, NPR, and the BBC.

Dr. Flett has published over 250 journal articles and chapters and he was the lead editor of the first academic book on perfectionism, published in 2002. He is also co-author of a new clinically focused book with Paul Hewitt and Samuel Mikail titled *Perfectionism: A Relational Approach to Conceptualization, Assessment, and Treatment*. His work with Dr. Hewitt on perfectionism has led to the creation of the Multidimensional Perfectionism Scale, the Child-Adolescent Perfectionism Scale, the Perfectionism Cognitions Inventory, and the Perfectionistic Self-Presentation Scale. Dr. Flett is also the co-creator of the Endler Multidimensional Anxiety Scales (EMAS)—Social Anxiety Scales. He has also worked extensively with Dr. Marnin Heisel on the development of the Geriatric Suicide Ideation Scale and related research.

In addition to his academic interests, Dr. Flett has been involved actively in the school system. Dr. Flett served for many years as the chair of the school council at Middlebury Public School in Mississauga, Ontario, and he was the spokesperson for the Parents of Peel, an advocacy group for parents interested in improving and protecting public education. In 1999, his civic contributions were acknowledged when Dr. Flett was awarded the City of Mississauga Certificate of Recognition for "Outstanding Commitment to the Community." Dr. Flett was honoured with the Community and Leadership Award from Toastmasters International in May 2006.

NANCY KOCOVSKI is Associate Professor of Psychology at Wilfrid Laurier University in Waterloo, Ontario. She received her Honours B.Sc. in Psychology from Queen's University at Kingston, Ontario, and her M.A. and Ph.D. in clinical psychology from York University in Toronto. Dr. Kocovski completed her predoctoral clinical internship at the Centre for Addiction and Mental Health (CAMH), and a postdoctoral fellowship in the Anxiety Disorders Clinic at CAMH focused on cognitive models of social anxiety, funded by the Social Sciences and Humanities Research Council (SSHRC). She is a member of the College of Psychologists of Ontario and is a founding member of the Canadian Association of Cognitive and Behavioural Therapies (CACBT), and a CACBT-certified cognitive-behavioural therapist.

Dr. Kocovski first taught abnormal psychology in 2000 and has centred her teaching in this area, in the form of large lecture classes and small seminar classes. She began her appointment at Laurier in 2004 and served as Undergraduate Academic Advisor (2013–2016). She received a merit award from Laurier for her dedication in this role, her second merit award. She has held adjunct appointments at the University of Waterloo (2005–2009) related to the supervision of graduate students on assessment and therapy cases, and at Ryerson University (2009–2012) related to her research. Also related to her program of research, she held a Research Scientist (Affiliate Status) appointment at CAMH (2005–2010). Dr. Kocovski has served on the Research Grants Review Committee for the Ontario Mental Health Foundation, as a conference abstract reviewer for the Association for Behavioral and Cognitive Therapies, and an ad hoc reviewer for SSHRC and various academic journals. Starting in 2005, she served as a member of the board of directors for the Centre for Opportunities, Respect and Empowerment (CORE), a non-profit agency in Toronto that serves adults with mental illness and/or developmental disabilities. She was Chair of the Board in 2009–2010.

Her early clinical training strongly focused on cognitive behaviour therapy (CBT) for anxiety disorders, through extended practicum training at the Anxiety Disorders Clinic at CAMH. For her internship, she completed major rotations in CBT for depression and Dialectical Behavior Therapy for borderline personality disorder, as well as a minor rotation in concurrent disorders (comorbid mental health and addiction). Dr. Kocovski subsequently became interested in mindfulness and acceptance-based treatments and completed intensive workshops in mindfulness-based cognitive therapy and acceptance and commitment therapy (ACT), mostly with the goal of applying these approaches to the treatment of social anxiety disorder (SAD).

Dr. Kocovski maintains an active research program focused on social anxiety, mindfulness and acceptance-based treatments, and CBT. She received a New Investigator Fellowship from the Ontario Mental Health Foundation and an Early Researcher Award from the Ontario Ministry of Research and Innovation for her work on the development of mindfulness and acceptance-based group therapy for SAD. She has also held funding from SSHRC. Her collaborative work with Dr. Jan Fleming has led to several publications on the treatment of SAD (including *Behaviour Research and Therapy*, 2015). In 2013, they published *The Mindfulness and Acceptance Workbook for Social Anxiety and Shyness* to increase the accessibility of this intervention. They received the Association for Behavioral and Cognitive Therapies (ABCT) Self-Help Book Recommendation (formerly known as ABCT Self-Help Seal of Merit Award). Dr. Kocovski was profiled for her work on social anxiety and ACT in a book entitled *The Research Journey of Acceptance and Commitment Therapy (ACT)* (2015). Dr. Kocovski continues to focus her research on the treatment of SAD, in particular examining predictors of treatment outcome and mechanisms of change, including self-compassion and post-event rumination.

Dr. Kocovski remains active in clinical practice. In addition to her delivery of social anxiety group treatment as part of her research program, she works as a clinical psychologist in private practice at CBT Associates of Toronto (Unionville location). She lives in Unionville with her husband and three children.

GERALD C. DAVISON is Professor of Psychology and Gerontology at the University of Southern California (USC). Previously he was Professor and Chair of the Department of Psychology at USC and served also as Director of Clinical Training. He also served as Dean of the USC Davis School of Gerontology. He earned his B.A. in social relations from Harvard and his Ph.D. in psychology from Stanford. He is a Fellow of the American Psychological Association, a Charter Fellow of the Association for Psychological Science, and a Distinguished Founding Fellow of the Academy of Cognitive Therapy. Among his other honours are the USC Associates Award for Excellence in Teaching, and the Outstanding Educator Award and the Lifetime Achievement Award of the Association for Behavioral and Cognitive Therapies. Among his more than 150 publications is his book *Clinical Behavior Therapy*, co-authored in 1976 with Marvin Goldfried and reissued in expanded form in 1994. It is one of two publications that have been recognized as Citation Classics by the Social Sciences Citation Index. He is also on the editorial board of several professional journals. His research has emphasized experimental and philosophical analyses of psychopathology, assessment, therapeutic change, and the relationships between cognition and a variety of behavioural and emotional problems via his articulated thoughts in simulated situations paradigm.

JOHN M. NEALE was Professor of Psychology at the State University of New York at Stony Brook, retiring in 2000. He was born in Toronto in 1943. He received his B.A. from the University of Toronto in 1965 and his M.A. and Ph.D. from Vanderbilt University. He went to graduate school after working at a residential treatment centre for emotionally disturbed children. He won numerous awards, including the American Psychological Association's Early Career Award (1974), the Distinguished Scientist Award from the American Psychological Association's Society for a Science of Clinical Psychology (1991), and the Sustained Mentorship Award from the Society for Research in Psychopathology (2011). Besides his numerous articles in professional journals, he published books on the effects of televised violence on children, research methodology, schizophrenia, case studies in abnormal psychology, and psychological influences on health. Schizophrenia was a major focus of his research, and he also conducted research on the influence of stress on health. Dr. Neale passed away in November 2011.

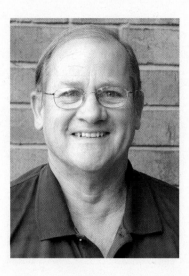

KIRK R. BLANKSTEIN is Professor Emeritus of Psychology at the University of Toronto Mississauga (UTM). He received his Honours B.A. from McMaster University and M.A. and Ph.D. in Clinical Psychology from the University of Waterloo. He completed his clinical internship at Duke University Medical Center in 1970 following a period as a Research Associate at the Institute of Psychiatry in London, England. One of his passions has been teaching undergraduate students and training future psychologists. He began his teaching career as an introductory psychology instructor and although he has taught over 20 different undergraduate and graduate courses, he was primarily responsible for the abnormal psychology part of the program, including introduction to abnormal psychology, separate courses on adult disorders and disorders of children, and a fourth-year special topics in abnormal psychology course. Cross-appointed to the Forensic Science Program, he taught students about psychopaths and serial killers. Professor Blankstein enjoyed enlivening his lectures with tongue-in-cheek references to himself and his family, using their names in association with illustrative cases and examples, and in test questions and assignments.

Professor Blankstein is a past recipient of the UTM Teaching Excellence Award. In 2003 he was recognized as an Exceptional Teacher in celebration of "175 Years of Great Teaching" at the University of Toronto. In 2007, he received the inaugural Leadership in Faculty Teaching Award from the Government of Ontario awarded to "faculty who influence, motivate and inspire students and demonstrate leadership in teaching methods for the diverse student body." In 2005, Professor Blankstein received the prestigious Northrop Frye Award in recognition of his contributions to the integration of teaching and research. The award recognizes faculty who have set "themselves apart through innovation in teaching and commitment to conveying the excitement and importance of research to undergraduate and graduate students." Many of his students have gone on to distinguished careers as professional psychologists, physicians, social workers, lawyers, criminologists, a High Commissioner, and an Ontario court judge.

Preface

Davison and Neale's classic text *Abnormal Psychology* introduced the field of abnormal psychology to over one million readers over several decades. Kirk Blankstein and Gordon Flett responded to calls for a text with a greater focus on Canadian issues by adapting this classic work. The publication in 2002 of the first edition of Davison, Neale, Blankstein, & Flett, *Abnormal Psychology*, Canadian Edition, meant that Canadian students could now benefit from the structure and principles of the classic text but within the context of extensive Canadian content that highlighted the unique aspects of the people of Canada.

The Canadian adaptation of the Davison and Neale text has been a leading choice of professors and instructors teaching abnormal psychology over the past 15 years. The publication of this new volume, the sixth edition, represents a substantial change in several key respects. Most notably, Kirk Blankstein's retirement led eventually to the recruitment of Nancy Kocovski as a key contributor to this new edition. The content of this volume and its structure were updated and revised to further reflect emerging research assessing aspects of the *DSM-5* as well as some of the structural changes it introduced. Each new edition of the text reflects revisions that are needed to keep up to date on emerging developments in the field and in Canadian society, but they also reflect our continuing mission: to constantly seek new ways to meet students' learning needs. Our overarching goal is to write the chapters as clearly and concisely as possible in ways that are highly engaging for today's student.

Goals of the Book

Our other main goals in writing *Abnormal Psychology*, Sixth Canadian Edition, were to continue to build upon the strengths of a classic text and present abnormal psychology from a unique Canadian perspective with a contemporary emphasis. Acknowledged strengths are as follows:

A Scientific, Clinical Approach

The study of abnormal psychology is a science and this edition, like its predecessors, retains a strong commitment to the scientific approach and Davison and Neale's original goal of encouraging readers to think critically and consider the merits of various viewpoints. Tough choices have to be made when selecting from among the vast literature and these choices are guided by the need to accurately represent the field and continue to make a fair and comprehensive presentation of the various conceptualizations in contemporary psychopathology.

Paradigms as an Organizing Principle

One of the reasons we have used the Davison text over many years and sought to use it as a base for our Canadian text is that it has always been consistent with our orientation toward abnormal psychology and with our teaching philosophy. A recurrent theme in the book is the importance of major points of view or, to use Kuhn's (1962) phrase, "paradigms." Our experience in teaching undergraduates has made us very aware of the importance of making explicit the unspoken assumptions underlying any quest for knowledge. In our handling of the paradigms, we have tried to make their premises clear. Long after specific facts are forgotten, the student should retain a grasp of the basic problems in the field of psychopathology and understand that the answers one arrives at are constrained by the questions one poses and the methods employed to ask those questions. Throughout the book we discuss four major paradigms: psychoanalytic, learning (behavioural), cognitive, and biological (neuroscientific).

An Authoritative, Contemporary Approach

Abnormal Psychology, Sixth Canadian Edition, furthers its reputation as one of the most current, authoritative overviews of the theories and research in psychopathology and intervention. It maintains the widely praised scientific clinical approach that blends the clinical and empirical/experimental, as the authors examine each disorder from multiple perspectives. The field of abnormal psychology continues to evolve and expand at a phenomenal rate. As always, additions and modifications to this text are significant and not merely cosmetic. Why? Because it is vitally important to incorporate a wide range of new findings in this edition to ensure that this text is an accurate source of contemporary developments.

New to this Edition

Preparation for the new edition starts as soon as the previous edition is published. It begins with an exhaustive evaluation of the contents of the previous edition by several reviewers, including current users of the text. We have been responsive to their insightful feedback while remaining consistent with the sage approach and framework used historically by Davison and Neale.

This new edition reflects some significant changes in two key regards. First, the content of the various chapters has been changed to more closely reflect the changes that occurred as a result of the publication of the *DSM-5*. Specifically, the anxiety disorder chapter has been updated so that it no longer includes material related to obsessive-compulsive disorder and post-traumatic stress disorder, but it does include some anxiety disorders and phobias that are now more prominent. A separate chapter (Chapter 6) has been written to address new developments with respect to obsessive-compulsive disorder and other disorders it is grouped with (i.e., hoarding disorder, body dysmorphic disorder, trichotillomania, and excoriation). Chapter 9 is now titled "Stress-Related Disorders and Health Psychology" and includes our description and analysis of post-traumatic stress disorder. Finally, two previous chapters have been combined into a new Chapter 3 titled "Clinical Assessment, Classification, and Diagnosis."

Second, the book's structural format has been improved by embracing a student-friendly focus. Specifically, each chapter now begins with a series of clearly outlined learning objectives and the chapter summaries have been reorganized to align with these learning objectives. In addition, the specific components of each chapter and associated headings in the chapter have been modified to reflect the learning objectives. These changes in structure and organization are helpful given the extensive information that readers encounter in each chapter.

The structural changes to the book reflect the fact that it is continuously assessed by various individuals to ensure that we retain a high level of readability and continue to highlight the relevance of the material by incorporating case studies and case vignettes of interest to our readers. Other additions and changes to the book are outlined below.

Contemporary Focus

As a reflection of the important developments, over 350 new references have been integrated throughout the text, with the vast majority of these references published in the last three years. New material was added only if it represented important new research or key themes. As always, we continue to emphasize meaningful new research conducted in Canada, while also incorporating international developments, in order to provide a contemporary representation of the current state of the field.

Historically, with each revision of this text, three or more chapters are selected and extensive changes and updates are made. However, in this instance, as noted above, chapters have been reconfigured to parallel the *DSM-5* framework and extensive changes have been made throughout the text.

Organization by Learning Objectives

As noted above, this edition has been enhanced by the addition of learning objectives. These learning objectives are outlined at the start of each chapter, and the material within the chapter is organized by the learning objectives, as is the summary at the end of each chapter. Today's student will benefit from these explicit statements instructing them of their learning goals for each chapter.

Content Revision

Content areas have been considerably strengthened, and this is especially apparent in Chapter 5, Chapter 9, and Chapter 17. Our decision to update and expand the biological perspective that began in the second edition has continued in this edition and this continuing emphasis reflects key advances in the field. Any book purporting to be representative must have increased coverage of advances in neuroscience and genetic research but it is also important to consider these developments within broad conceptual frameworks such as the biopsychosocial model that is outlined later in the book.

Chapter 17 has been updated and modified to reflect contemporary advances in the treatment of disorders. This new chapter reflects updates and evaluations of classic therapeutic approaches, but it also reflects emerging themes. For instance, there is an extended description of compassion-focused therapy and a description and evaluation of therapy delivered online.

A central aim in revising the content was to provide expanded descriptions of several "hot" topics. We further explored those topics already included in the previous edition, but also added emerging issues, including key issues specific to Canada. Key emerging themes of growing significance and new developments discussed at length in this edition include the introduction of assisted suicide legislation in Canada (Chapter 8), the heroin epidemic and the excessive use of OxyContin and other painkillers in Canada and the United States (Chapter 12), the mental health crisis facing our children and adolescents (Chapter 15), and Bill C-54 and the treatment of people who have engaged in violent attacks but were deemed not criminally responsible due to mental disorder (Chapter 18).

Organization of the Text

In Part 1 (Chapters 1–4), we place the field in historical context, present the concept of paradigms in science, describe the major paradigms in psychopathology and intervention, discuss the role of cultural factors in a Canadian setting, and introduce our readers to Canada's mental health care system. The most significant change here is that two chapters from previous editions have now been combined into an integrated Chapter 3 that discusses issues related to assessment, classification, and diagnosis. This combined chapter represents the interconnectedness of assessment, classification, and diagnosis. The previous Chapter 5 from the fifth edition has become Chapter 4 in this new edition.

Specific disorders and their treatment are discussed in Parts 2 and 3 (Chapters 5–16). The anxiety disorders chapter (Chapter 5) is the first specific disorders chapter presented. Note that this updated chapter differs in many ways that go beyond the fact that this was Chapter 6 in the previous edition. As noted above, a new Chapter 6 titled "Obsessive-Compulsive and Related Disorders" has been added and Chapter 9 has been extensively modified. Chapter 9 is now titled "Stress-Related Disorders and Health Psychology."

The final section, Part 4, consists of Chapters 17 and 18. Chapter 17 discusses process and outcome research on treatment and controversial issues surrounding the therapy enterprise. Chapter 17 has been extensively updated and rewritten to make it more "student friendly." In Chapter 18, legal and ethical issues are discussed and extensive Canadian content is provided. This closing chapter is devoted to an in-depth study of the complex interplay between scientific findings and theories on the one hand, and the role of ethics and the law on the other hand.

Features of this Book

In addition to the content and organization, a variety of pedagogical features support the approach of this text. These features are designed to make it easier for students to master and enjoy the material.

Canadian Focus Boxes

There are two types of boxes in the text that focus solely on placing the material in a Canadian context. Canadian Perspectives explore past and current practices in the treatment of abnormal psychology in Canada. Canadian Contributions highlight the research contributions Canadians have made in the field. Several of these boxes have been updated with recent anecdotes and key developments from news reports to illustrate important mental health issues in Canada today.

Student Perspectives Boxes

One of the most substantial revisions to the previous edition of this book was the addition of Student Perspectives boxes in several chapters. This material was retained based on the favourable feedback we received about this unique feature. The various topics have been updated to reflect recent developments. A wide range of issues is explored, including binge drinking on university and college campuses and the growing problem of the abuse of attention-deficit/hyperactivity disorder medication as a type of study aid.

Focus on Discovery Boxes

There are many in-depth discussions of selected topics encased in Focus on Discovery boxes throughout the book. This continuing feature allows us to involve the reader in topics that are sometimes very specialized, in a way that does not detract from the flow of the regular text. Sometimes a Focus on Discovery box expands on a point in the text; sometimes it deals with an entirely separate but relevant issue, often a controversial one; and often it presents material of particular interest to the Canadian student.

Chapter-Opening Cases and in-Text Cases

Several chapters open with extended case illustrations. These accounts provide a clinical context for the theories and research that occupy most of our attention in the chapters and help make vivid the real-life implications of the empirical work of psychopathologists and clinicians.

Chapter Summaries

Revised summaries appear at the end of each chapter. As noted above, these chapter summaries have been modified to reflect the learning objectives that are at the beginning of each chapter. We continue to suggest that the student beginning a new chapter read the learning objectives and the summary before beginning the chapter itself to get a good overview.

Key Terms

When an important term is introduced, it is boldfaced and defined or discussed immediately. Most such terms appear again later in the book, in which case they will not be highlighted in this way. All of these terms are listed after each chapter summary as key terms and are defined in the end-of-text glossary. The page number on which the term is defined appears in this list.

References

As noted above, our commitment to current and forward-looking scholarship is reflected in the inclusion of hundreds of new references among the more than 4,000 references. We have continued to emphasize important Canadian references when they are warranted.

Acknowledgements

It is a pleasure to recognize the contributions of a number of colleagues who helped with their valuable comments and feedback in the writing of six Canadian editions. We would like to acknowledge a number of our colleagues whose thoughtful comments and expert feedback helped us in writing the previous Canadian edition. They are John Conklin, Camosun College; Nukte Edguer, Brandon University; Ross Keele, University of Saskatchewan; Ron Laye, University of the Fraser Valley; and Timothy Parker, University of Alberta.

Many thanks to the staff at John Wiley & Sons Canada, Ltd. for their ongoing enthusiastic support of this project. Members of the very impressive team at Wiley we would like to thank include Karen Staudinger, Editorial Manager, who has shown her continuing faith in this project over the years. We also thank Andrea Grzybowski and Courtney Luzzi, Developmental Editors, for their exemplary efforts on the project. Courtney's patience and advice is particularly appreciated. We also thank Karyn Morrison for her assistance with permissions. We also offer our continuing gratitude to Patty Maher, Marketing Manager, and of course all the sales representatives who brought the text to you. The exceptional editorial contributions and professionalism of Laurel Hyatt deserve special mention. We would also like to extend our special thanks to Beth Visser (Lakehead University) for compiling the Instructor's Manual, Carrie Scherzer (Mount Royal University) for updating the Test Bank, Joel Goldberg (York University) for working on the PowerPoints, Carolyn Ensley for updating the Practice Quizzes, and Wendy Tarrel (Nova Scotia Community College) for working on the Concept Check, Discussion Questions, Research Activities, and Video Mapping. Also, we would be remiss if we did not acknowledge Joel's contributions to the revised *The Student's Guide to DSM-5*.

Our sincere gratitude is extended to the authors who graciously provided us with preprints that described their research; this was a great help to us as we wrote the manuscript. These people are too numerous to name, but you know who you are! We continue to extend a special thank you to the Honourable Mr. Justice Richard Schneider for his contributions over the years to Chapter 18.

Most importantly, more than thanks is due to family members for their endless support and encouragement throughout the writing of this edition of this text. We are exceptionally fortunate, plain and simple. In terms of the Flett family, thank you Kathy, for your patience, affection, timely advice, and the reminder that there is much more to life than writing books. Thank you Hayley for your love and support and the insights you can provide with respect to legal and human rights issues. And thank you, Alison Flett, a master's student in psychology at Wilfrid Laurier University, for your timely suggestions and feedback from the student perspective and your enthusiasm for abnormal psychology.

As for Nancy, thank you Jim for your support of my writing and career. Our young children—our daughter, Abby, and twin boys, Alex and Andrew—add so much joy to our lives but finding enough time to work can be daunting. I would not have been able to take this on without your support and the support of my parents who happily look after the kids with a moment's notice. I would also like to acknowledge the students at Laurier. I love teaching abnormal psychology and have learned a lot from the students who have taken it over the years. I am looking forward to their continued feedback in the coming years.

Finally, a special note of gratitude is extended to Kirk Blankstein for getting this project started many years ago and developing it over the years. Kirk, your extensive influence and commitment to students is still reflected throughout this book and it will always be evident.

GORDON FLETT AND NANCY KOCOVSKI

March 2017

Brief Contents

Contents

18 Legal and Ethical Issues 561

Introduction: Definitional and Historical Considerations, and Canada's Mental Health System

LEARNING OBJECTIVES

1. Understand what constitutes abnormal behaviour.
2. Compare the history of psychopathology across centuries.
3. Describe current attitudes toward people with psychological disorders, including how stigma and self-stigma are potential barriers to help-seeking.
4. Describe mental health problems and their treatment in Canada.
5. Describe the issues and challenges in the delivery of psychotherapy.

Every day of our lives we try to understand other people. Acquiring insight into what we consider normal, expected behaviour is difficult. It is even more difficult to understand human behaviour that is beyond the normal range.

This book deals with abnormality as it applies to psychological disorders, including their description, causes, and treatment. As you will see, we know with certainty much less about our field than we would like. As we approach the study of **psychopathology**—the field concerned with the nature and development of abnormal behaviour, thoughts, and feelings—we do well to keep in mind that the subject offers few hard and fast answers.

Another challenge we face in studying abnormal psychology is the need to remain objective. Our subject matter is personal and it is powerfully affecting, making objectivity difficult but no less necessary. The disturbing effects of abnormal behaviour intrude on our own lives. Who has not experienced irrational thoughts, fantasies, and feelings? Who has not felt profound sadness that is more extreme than circumstances can explain? Most of you will have known someone whose behaviour was upsetting and impossible to fathom, and realize how frustrating and frightening it is to try to help a person suffering psychological difficulties.

This feeling of familiarity with the subject matter adds to its intrinsic fascination—undergraduate courses in abnormal psychology are among the most popular in psychology departments and indeed in the entire university or college curriculum. But it has one distinct disadvantage. All of us bring to our study preconceived notions of what the subject matter is. We have developed certain ways of thinking and talking about behaviour, certain words and concepts that somehow seem to fit.

As scientists, we have to grapple with the difference between what we may feel is the appropriate way to talk about human behaviour and experience and what may be a more productive way of defining it in order to study and learn about it. The concepts and labels we use in the scientific study of abnormal behaviour must be free of the subjective feelings of appropriateness ordinarily attached to certain human phenomena. As you read this book and try to understand the mental disorders it discusses, you may be asked to adopt frames of reference different from those to which you are accustomed.

We will now turn to a discussion of what we mean by the term "abnormal behaviour." Then we will look briefly at how our view of abnormality has evolved through history to the more scientific perspectives of today. We then continue with a discussion of current attitudes toward people with psychological problems and with an introduction to the system of mental health care in Canada. Chapter 1 concludes with a discussion of the issues and challenges in the delivery of psychotherapy.

Before we embark on this journey, it is important to note that this is an exceptionally good time to be a student learning about abnormal psychology, especially in Canada. Important research discoveries continue to emerge, in part fuelled by developments in neuroscience. The field is also under great scrutiny as a result of the introduction in May 2013 of the next edition of the diagnostic system, the *Diagnostic and Statistical Manual of Mental Disorders, Fifth Edition (DSM-5;* see www.dsm5.org). Moreover, mental health issues are very much at the forefront of the public consciousness at present, and this is partly due to the efforts of heroic famous Canadians such as Clara Hughes (see photo) and the many individuals and corporations who are determined to make a difference. Arguably, there has been no time in our past when public interest and determination to make positive changes in mental health has been higher. Another important development is that due to the exceptional efforts of the Mental Health Commission of Canada and individuals across our nation, Canada finally has its first comprehensive Mental Health Strategy (see http://strategy. mentalhealthcommission.ca/). And even politicians seemed poised to do their part. For instance, Canada is now seriously considering a national suicide prevention strategy as a result of public support for a nonpartisan motion put forth in October 2011 by then-federal Liberal leader Bob Rae.

These efforts and initiatives are important because the challenges still facing us are very significant ones. Some challenges require filling key gaps in knowledge, but more importantly, the remaining challenges are the sheer prevalence of psychological problems among people of various ages in Canada and elsewhere. We will see that the number of people who require treatment and other services for mental health issues far outweighs the services that are available. Ideally, we will get to the point that, collectively, we will have all of the resources needed to put timely preventions in place and thereby substantially decrease the suffering that accompanies mental illness.

1.1 What Is Abnormal Behaviour?

One of the more difficult issues facing us is how to define abnormal behaviour. Several characteristics have been proposed as components. No single one is adequate, although each has merit and captures some part of what might be a full definition. Consequently, abnormality is usually determined by the presence of several characteristics at one time. Our best definition of **abnormal behaviour** includes such characteristics as statistical infrequency, violation of norms, personal distress, disability or dysfunction, and unexpectedness.

Statistical Infrequency

One aspect of abnormal behaviour is that it is *infrequent* in the general population. The **normal curve**, or bell-shaped curve, places the majority of people in the middle as far as any particular characteristic is concerned; very few people fall at either extreme. An assertion that a person is normal implies that he or she does not deviate much from the average in a particular trait or behaviour pattern.

Statistical infrequency is used explicitly in diagnosing mental retardation. Figure 1.1 shows the normal distribution of intelligence quotient (IQ) measures in the population. Though a number of criteria are used to diagnose mental retardation, low intelligence is a principal one. When an individual's IQ is below 70, his or her intellectual functioning is considered sufficiently subnormal to be designated as mental retardation.

THE CANADIAN PRESS IMAGES/Dominic Chan

Clara Hughes, Olympic champion, also champions awareness of mental health issues and has been open about her own bouts with depression. She is shown here in October 2012 speaking to graduates when receiving an honorary Doctor of Laws degree from York University for her tireless efforts. Among other things, in 2014 her "Big Ride" had her go across Canada by bike to heighten awareness of mental health issues. Her new 2015 autobiography *Open Heart Open Mind* details the challenges she has faced.

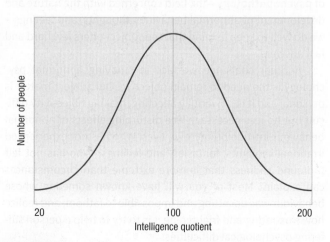

FIGURE 1.1   The distribution of intelligence among adults, illustrating a normal, or bell-shaped, curve.

Although some infrequent behaviours or characteristics of people do strike us as abnormal, in some instances, the relationship breaks down. Having great athletic ability is infrequent (see photo), but few would regard it as part of the field of abnormal psychology. Only certain infrequent behaviours, such as experiencing hallucinations or deep depression, fall into the domain considered in this book. Unfortunately, the statistical component gives us little guidance in determining which infrequent behaviours psychopathologists should study.

Violation of Norms

Another characteristic to consider is whether the behaviour *violates social norms* or threatens or makes anxious those observing it. Violation of norms explicitly makes abnormality a relative concept; various forms of unusual behaviour can be tolerated, depending on the prevailing cultural norms. Yet violation of norms is at once too broad and too narrow. Criminals and prostitutes, for example, violate social norms but are not usually studied within the domain of abnormal psychology, and the highly anxious person, who is generally regarded as a central character in the field of abnormal psychology, typically does not violate social norms and would not be bothersome to many lay observers.

In addition, cultural diversity can affect how people view social norms. What is the norm in one culture may be abnormal in another. This subtle issue is addressed throughout the book (see especially Chapters 2 and 3).

Personal Suffering

Another characteristic is *personal suffering;* that is, behaviour is abnormal if it creates great distress and torment in the person experiencing it. Personal distress clearly fits many of the forms of abnormality considered in this book—people experiencing anxiety disorders and depression truly suffer greatly—but some disorders do not necessarily involve distress. The psychopath, for example, treats others cold-heartedly and may continually violate the law without experiencing any guilt, remorse, or anxiety whatsoever. And not all forms of distress—for example, hunger or the pain of childbirth—belong to the field.

Disability or Dysfunction

Disability—that is, impairment in some important area of life (e.g., work or personal relationships) because of an abnormality—can also be a component of abnormal behaviour. Substance-use disorders are defined in part by the social or occupational disability (e.g., poor work performance, serious arguments with one's spouse) created by substance abuse and addiction. Similarly, a phobia can produce both distress and disability; for example, a severe fear of flying may prevent someone from taking a job promotion. Like suffering, disability applies to some, but not all, disorders. Transvestism

(cross-dressing for sexual pleasure), for example, which is currently diagnosed as a mental disorder if it distresses the person, is not necessarily a disability. Most transvestites are married, lead conventional lives, and usually cross-dress in private. Other characteristics that might in some circumstances be considered disabilities—such as being short if you want to be a professional basketball player—do not fall within the domain of abnormal psychology. We do not have a rule that tells us which disabilities belong and which do not.

Unexpectedness

We have just described how not all distress or disability falls into the domain of abnormal psychology. Distress and disability are considered abnormal when they are *unexpected* responses to environmental stressors (Wakefield, 1992). For example, an anxiety disorder is diagnosed when the anxiety is unexpected and out of proportion to the situation, as when a person who is well off worries constantly about his or her financial situation.

We have considered here several key characteristics of a definition of abnormal behaviour. Again, none by itself yields a fully satisfactory definition, but together they offer a useful framework for beginning to define abnormality. In this volume we will study a list of human problems that are currently considered abnormal. The disorders on the list will undoubtedly change with time, for the field is continually evolving, and it is not possible to offer a simple definition of abnormality that captures it in its entirety. The characteristics presented constitute a partial definition, but they do not equally apply to every diagnosis.

Focus on Discovery 1.1 describes the education and training of professionals who study and treat mental disorders. Goering, Wasylenki, and Durbin (2000) estimated that approximately 3,600 practising psychiatrists, about 13,000 psychologists and psychological associates, and about 11,000 nurses specialize in the mental health area in Canada. Thousands of

John Berry/Getty Images

Although abnormal behaviour is infrequent, so, too, is great athletic talent, such as that of the proud members of the Canadian multiple gold medal-winning Olympic women's hockey team. Therefore, infrequency is not a sufficient definition of abnormal behaviour.

Focus on Discovery 1.1

The Mental Health Professions

The training of **clinicians,** the various professionals authorized to provide psychological services, takes different forms. Here, we discuss several types of clinicians, the training they receive, and a few related issues.

To be a **clinical psychologist** typically requires a Ph.D. or Psy.D. degree, which entails four to seven years of graduate study. However, in Canada, professional regulation of the psychology profession is within the jurisdiction of the provinces and territories and, depending upon regulatory statutes, a psychologist may have either a doctoral- or a master's-level degree (Hunsley & Johnston, 2000). In some jurisdictions the title "psychologist" is reserved for doctoral-level registrants, whereas master's-level registrants are referred to as "psychological associates." Specific curriculum requirements vary across jurisdictions. Gauthier (2002) concluded that there was effectively no consensus among the provinces on the minimal academic requirements, the required length of supervised practice, and the timing of such practice (i.e., before or after the degree is achieved).

The 1995 Agreement on Internal Trade stipulated that a framework for mobility had to be developed so that the credentials of professional psychologists from one part of Canada would be recognized in other parts of Canada. A Mutual Recognition Agreement was signed in June 2001. According to Gauthier (2002), this requires a person to obtain five core competencies in order to become a registered psychologist: (1) interpersonal relationships, (2) assessment and evaluation (including diagnosis), (3) intervention and consultation, (4) research, and (5) ethics and standards.

Training for a Ph.D. in clinical psychology requires a heavy emphasis on laboratory work, research design, statistics, and the empirically based study of human and animal behaviour. The Ph.D. is basically a research degree, and candidates are required to research and write a dissertation on a specialized topic. But candidates in clinical psychology learn skills in two additional areas, which distinguishes them from other Ph.D. candidates in psychology. First, they learn techniques of **assessment** and **diagnosis** of mental disorders. Second, they learn how to practise **psychotherapy**, a primarily verbal means of helping troubled individuals change their thoughts, feelings, and behaviour to reduce distress and to achieve greater life satisfaction. Students take courses in which they master specific techniques under close professional supervision; then, during an intensive internship or post-doctoral training, they gradually assume increasing responsibility for the care of clients.

Other clinical graduate programs are more focused on practice. These programs offer the relatively new degree of Psy.D. (doctor of psychology). The curriculum is similar to that required of Ph.D. students, with less emphasis on research and more on clinical training. The Ph.D. approach is based on a scientist-practitioner model, while the Psy.D. approach is based on a scholar-practitioner model, which is described below. Note that a survey of clinical psychology students in Ph.D. programs in Canada found that most students enrolled in current programs were satisfied with their level of science training, and as was the case in the United States, students felt that the training received was slightly more weighted toward research than toward clinical practice (Peluso, Carleton, & Asmundson, 2010).

The Canadian Psychological Association (CPA) Psy.D. Task Force (1998) described a scholar-practitioner as a "flexible, socially responsible, thinking practitioner who derives his/her skills from core knowledge in scientific psychology. This comprehensively trained professional is capable of performing in a number of roles, and would not be trained simply to be a technician in specific areas" (p. 13). As of 2007 there were two Psy.D. programs in Canada, at the Université du Quebec and Université Laval, both offered in French. Later, Memorial University initiated a Psy.D. program in 2009 and in 2013, a Psy.D. program was introduced in Vancouver at a campus of the Adler School of Professional Psychology.

According to the CPA, psychologists are Canada's single largest group of licensed and specialized mental health care providers. Further, psychologists are the primary researchers and providers of evidence-based psychological treatments.

A **psychiatrist** holds an MD degree and has had postgraduate training, called a residency, in which he or she has received supervision in the practice of diagnosis and psychotherapy. By virtue of the medical degree, and in contrast with psychologists, psychiatrists can also continue functioning as physicians—giving physical examinations, diagnosing medical problems, and the like. Most often, however, the primary aspect of medical practice in which psychiatrists engage is prescribing **psychoactive drugs**, chemical compounds that can influence how people feel and think. Nonetheless, a study (Hadjipavlou & Ogrodniczuk, 2007) concluded that current psychiatry residents in Canada have a strong interest in psychotherapy training.

A **psychoanalyst** has received specialized training at a psychoanalytic institute. The program usually involves several years of clinical training as well as the in-depth psychoanalysis of the trainee. It can take up to 10 years of graduate work to become a psychoanalyst and there are proportionally fewer psychoanalysts in modern times.

A **social worker** obtains an M.S.W. (master of social work) degree. Programs for **counselling psychologists** are somewhat similar to graduate training in clinical psychology but usually have less emphasis on research and the more severe forms of psychopathology. How does counselling psychology differ from clinical psychology in Canada? First, they differ in number. A survey reported in 2012 compared 22 accredited clinical psychology programs and 4 counselling psychology programs in Canada (see Bedi, Klubben, & Barker, 2012). While there are many similarities, there also key differences. Another key difference is that counselling programs tend to be terminal, meaning that students earn a master's degree and there is no doctoral progress that follows. Also, clinical psychology programs tend to have a large proportion of their faculty members registered as clinical psychologists (see Bedi et al., 2012).

social workers also work in the mental health field. Goering et al. (2000) also noted that, "The major proportion of primary mental health care in Canada is delivered by general practitioners (GPs)" (p. 350). Psychiatrists (who are medical doctors) have a great deal of clinical autonomy. The majority are self-employed professionals whose clinical income is usually based on billing their provincial health plan. As noted by Latimer (2005), "Psychiatrists are essentially free to choose the patient population they wish to care for, and how" (p. 566).

Analyses of the results of the National Population Health Survey (NPHS; Statistics Canada, 1995) indicated that approximately 2% of respondents had consulted with a psychologist one or more times in the preceding 12 months (Hunsley, Lee, & Aubry, 1999)—equivalent to almost 515,000 people in the Canadian population aged 12 and older. Hunsley and colleagues concluded, however, that psychological services are vastly underused. They also determined that psychological services are more available in urban areas than in rural areas and that psychiatrists tend to practise in major urban centres. Thus, many areas of Canada are underserved by two important mental health professions.

There has been a lively and sometimes acrimonious debate concerning the merits of allowing clinical psychologists with suitable training to prescribe psychoactive drugs (see Westra, Eastwood, Bouffard, & Gerritsen, 2006). Predictably, granting **prescriptive authority** to psychologists is opposed by psychiatrists for various reasons (see McGrath, 2010). It is also opposed by many psychologists, who view it as an ill-advised dilution of the behavioural science focus of psychology. Is it possible for a non-MD to learn enough about biochemistry and physiology to monitor the effects of drugs and protect clients from adverse side effects and drug interactions? This debate will undoubtedly continue for some time; at present, prescriptive authority has been granted to psychologists in three U.S. jurisdictions (New Mexico, Louisiana, and the U.S. territory of Guam) (see McGrath, 2010).

1.2 History of Psychopathology

"Those who cannot remember the past are condemned to repeat it."

—*George Santayana,* The Life of Reason

The search for the causes of deviant behaviour has gone on for a long time. Before the age of scientific inquiry, all good and bad manifestations of power beyond the control of humankind—eclipses, earthquakes, storms, fire, serious and disabling diseases, the passing of the seasons—were regarded as supernatural. Behaviour seemingly outside individual control was subject to similar interpretation. Many early philosophers, theologians, and physicians who studied the troubled mind believed that deviancy reflected the displeasure of the gods or possession by demons.

Early Demonology

The doctrine that an evil being, such as the devil, may dwell within a person and control his or her mind and body is called **demonology**. Examples of demonological thinking are found in the records of the early Chinese, Egyptians, Babylonians, and Greeks. Among the Hebrews, deviancy was attributed to possession of the person by bad spirits, after God in his wrath had withdrawn protection. Christ is reported to have cured a man with an unclean spirit by casting out the devils from within him and hurling them into a herd of swine (Mark 5:8–13).

Following from the belief that abnormal behaviour was caused by possession, its treatment often involved **exorcism**, the casting out of evil spirits by ritualistic chanting or torture. Exorcism typically took the form of elaborate rites of prayer, noisemaking, forcing the afflicted to drink terrible-tasting brews, and on occasion more extreme measures, such as flogging and starvation, to render the body uninhabitable to devils.

Trepanning of skulls (the making of a surgical opening in a living skull by some instrument) by Stone Age or neolithic cave dwellers was quite widespread. One popular theory is that it was a way of treating conditions such as epilepsy, headaches, and psychological disorders attributed to demons within the cranium. It was presumed that the individual would return to a normal state by creating an opening through which evil spirits could escape. Trepanning was presumably introduced into the Americas from Siberia. Although the practice was most common in Peru and Bolivia, three Aboriginal specimens have been found in Canada, all on the Pacific coast in British Columbia (see illustration). One skull is that of a young male believed to be of high rank, since he received a "copper burial" (his forehead and chest were covered by thin sheets of copper). Despite the extensive focus in Aboriginal cultures on possession by spirits, the widely accepted interpretation of the historical data has been disputed. Kidd (1946) suggested that the trepannings "were done to relieve pressure resulting from depressed fractures caused by war clubs" (p. 515).

Somatogenesis

In the fifth century B.C., Hippocrates (ca. 460–377 B.C.), often regarded as the father of modern medicine, separated medicine from religion, magic, and superstition. He rejected the prevailing Greek belief that the gods sent serious physical diseases and mental disturbances as punishment and insisted instead that such illnesses had natural causes and hence should be treated like other, more common maladies, such as colds and constipation. Hippocrates regarded the brain as the organ of consciousness, of intellectual life and emotion; thus, he thought that deviant thinking and behaviour were indications of some kind of brain pathology. Hippocrates is often considered one of the very earliest proponents of **somatogenesis**—the notion that something wrong with the soma, or physical body, disturbs thought and action (see photo). **Psychogenesis**, in contrast, is the belief that a disturbance has psychological origins.

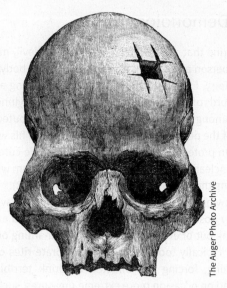

The Auger Photo Archive

Was trepanning by the Aboriginals of British Columbia performed to allow evil spirits to escape the body?

Jeremy Horner/Corbis/VCG/Getty Images

The Greek physician Hippocrates held a somatogenic view of abnormal behaviour, considering psychopathology a disease of the brain.

Hippocrates classified mental disorders into three categories: mania, melancholia, and phrenitis (or brain fever). Through his teachings, the phenomena of abnormal behaviour became more clearly the province of physicians than of priests.

Hippocrates's physiology was rather crude, however, for he conceived of normal brain functioning, and therefore of mental health, as dependent on a delicate balance among four humours, or fluids, of the body: blood, black bile, yellow bile, and phlegm. An imbalance produced disorders and an associated temperament or personality style. If a person was sluggish and dull, for example, the body supposedly contained a preponderance of phlegm and a phlegmatic temperament. A preponderance of black bile was the explanation for melancholia; too much yellow bile explained irritability and anxiousness; and too much blood, changeable temperament.

Hippocrates's humoral physiology did not withstand later scientific scrutiny. However, his basic premise—that human behaviour is markedly affected by bodily structures or substances and that abnormal behaviour is produced by some kind of physical imbalance or even damage—did foreshadow aspects of contemporary thought.

The Dark Ages and Demonology

Historians have often suggested that the death of Galen (130–200 A.D.), the second-century Greek who is regarded as the last major physician of the classical era, marked the beginning of the Dark Ages for Western European medicine and for the treatment and investigation of abnormal behaviour. Over several centuries of decay, Greek and Roman civilization ceased to exist. The churches gained in influence, and the papacy was declared independent of the state. Christian monasteries, through their missionary and educational work, replaced physicians as healers and as authorities on mental disorder. The monks cared for and nursed the sick. A few monasteries were

repositories for the classic Greek medical manuscripts, even though the monks may not have made use of the knowledge within these works. When monks cared for the mentally disordered, they prayed over them and touched them with relics or they concocted fantastic potions for them to drink in the waning phase of the moon. The families of the deranged might take them to shrines. Many of the mentally ill roamed the countryside, becoming more and more disturbed.

The Persecution of Witches   During the thirteenth and the following few centuries, a populace that was already suffering from social unrest and recurrent famines and plagues again turned to demonology to explain these disasters. People in Europe became obsessed with the devil. Witchcraft, viewed as instigated by Satan, was seen as a heresy and a denial of God. Faced with inexplicable and frightening occurrences, people tended to seize on whatever explanation was available. The times conspired to heap enormous blame on those regarded as witches, and these unfortunates were persecuted with great zeal.

In 1484 Pope Innocent VIII exhorted the clergy of Europe to leave no stone unturned in the search for witches. He sent two Dominican monks to northern Germany as inquisitors. Two years later they issued a comprehensive and explicit manual, *Malleus Maleficarum* ("the witches' hammer"), to guide the witch hunts. This legal and theological document came to be regarded by Catholics and Protestants alike as a textbook on witchcraft. Those accused of witchcraft were to be tortured if they did not confess (see artwork); those convicted and penitent were to be imprisoned for life; and those convicted and

Illumination from a 15th-century manuscript showing Christ exorcising a demon from a possessed youth.

In the dunking test, if the woman did not drown, she was thought to be in league with the devil, the ultimate no-win situation.

unrepentant were to be handed over to the law for execution. The manual specified that a person's loss of reason was a symptom of demonic possession and that burning was the usual method of driving out the supposed demon. Although records of the period are not reliable, it is thought that over the next several centuries, hundreds of thousands of women, men, and children were accused, tortured, and put to death.

Witchcraft and Mental Illness
The prevailing interpretation for some time in the later Middle Ages was that the mentally ill were generally considered witches (Zilboorg & Henry, 1941). Detailed examination of this historical period, however, indicates that many of the accused were not mentally ill. Careful analyses of the witch hunts reveal that many more sane than insane people were tried. The delusion-like confessions were typically obtained during brutal torture; words were put on the tongues of the tortured by their accusers and by the beliefs of the times. Indeed, in England, where torture was not allowed, the confessions did not usually contain descriptions indicative of delusions or hallucinations (Schoeneman, 1977).

Other information, moreover, indicates that witchcraft was not the primary interpretation of mental illness. From the thirteenth century on, as the cities of Europe grew larger, hospitals began to come under secular jurisdiction. Municipal authorities, gaining in power, tended to supplement or take over some of the activities of the church, one of these being the care of the ill. English laws during this period allowed both the dangerously insane and the incompetent to be confined in a hospital. Notably, the people who were confined were not described as being possessed (Allderidge, 1979).

Beginning in the thirteenth century, "lunacy" trials to determine a person's sanity were held in England. The trials were conducted under the Crown's right to protect the mentally impaired, and a judgement of insanity allowed the Crown to become guardian of the lunatic's estate (Neugebauer, 1979). The defendant's orientation, memory, intellect, daily life, and habits were at issue in the trial. Strange behaviour was typically linked to physical illness or injury or to some emotional shock. In all the cases that Neugebauer examined, only one referred to demonological possession. The preponderance of evidence thus indicates that this explanation of mental disturbance was not as dominant during the Middle Ages as was once thought.

While our focus is on what took place centuries ago, it is important to realize that there are some places in the world where this practice continues today. For instance, northern Ghana has six witch camps over 100 years old that hold 800 women. These camps were finally slated to close in 2012. Ghana has acknowledged the need for greater public education, in part due to incidents such as what took place in 2010 when Madam AmaHemmah, a 78-year-old woman, was accused of being a witch and was burned alive (see Dixon, 2012).

Development of Asylums

Until the end of the Crusades in the fifteenth century, there were very few mental hospitals in Europe, although there were thousands of hospitals for lepers. In the twelfth century, England and Scotland had 220 leprosy hospitals for a population of 1.5 million. After the principal Crusades had been waged,

A tour of St. Mary of Bethlehem (Bedlam) provides amusement for two upper-class women in Hogarth's 18th-century painting.

Charles Phelps Cushing/ClassicStock/Getty Images

leprosy gradually disappeared from Europe, probably because with the end of the wars came a break with the eastern sources of the infection. With leprosy no longer of such great social concern, attention seems to have turned to the mad.

Confinement of the mentally ill began in earnest in the fifteenth and sixteenth centuries. Leprosariums were converted to **asylums**, refuges established for the confinement and care of the mentally ill. Many of these asylums took in a mixed lot of disturbed people and beggars. Beggars were regarded as a great social problem at the time; in sixteenth-century Paris the population of fewer than 100,000 included 30,000 beggars (Foucault, 1965). These asylums had no specific regimen for their inmates other than to get them to work, but during the same period, hospitals geared more specifically for the confinement of the mentally ill also emerged.

Bethlehem and Other Early Asylums   The Priory of St. Mary of Bethlehem was founded in 1243. In 1547 Henry VIII handed it over to the City of London, thereafter to be a hospital devoted solely to the confinement of the mentally ill. The conditions in Bethlehem were deplorable. Over the years the word **bedlam**, a contraction and popular name for this hospital, became a descriptive term for a place or scene of wild uproar and confusion. Bethlehem eventually became one of London's great tourist attractions, by the eighteenth century rivalling both Westminster Abbey and the Tower of London. Even as late as the nineteenth century, viewing the violent patients and their antics was considered entertainment, and tickets of admission to Bedlam were sold (see artwork). Similarly, in the Lunatics' Tower constructed in Vienna in 1784, patients were confined in the spaces between inner square rooms and the outer walls, where they could be viewed by passersby.

It should not be assumed that the inclusion of abnormal behaviour within the domain of hospitals and medicine necessarily led to more humane and effective treatment. Medical treatments were often crude and painful. Benjamin Rush (1745–1813), who began practising medicine in Philadelphia in 1769, is considered the father of American psychiatry. He

believed that mental disorder was caused by an excess of blood in the brain. Consequently, his favoured treatment was to draw great quantities of blood (Farina, 1976)! Further, he believed that many "lunatics" could be cured by being frightened. A New England doctor of the nineteenth century implemented this prescription in an ingenious manner: "On his premises stood a tank of water, into which a patient, packed into a coffin-like box pierced with holes, was lowered. He was kept under water until the bubbles of air ceased to rise, after which he was taken out, rubbed, and revived—if he had not already passed beyond reviving!" (Deutsch, 1949, p. 82).

Moral Treatment   Philippe Pinel (1745–1826) is considered a primary figure in the movement for humanitarian treatment of the mentally ill in asylums. According to Cohen, Patel, and Minas (2014), it was in 1838 that France created a state-run asylum system. But individual asylums existed before then, and in 1793, while the French Revolution raged, Pinel was put in charge of a large asylum in Paris known as La Bicetre (see artwork). It has long been asserted that Pinel removed the chains of the people imprisoned there. Although Pinel actually adopted the practice, it appears that it was a former patient orderly, Jean-Baptiste Pussin, who first removed the chains (Weiner, 1994). Pinel also began to treat the patients as sick human beings rather than as beasts. Many who had been completely unmanageable became calm and much easier to handle. They strolled through the hospital and grounds with no inclination to create disturbances or harm anyone. Light and airy rooms replaced dungeons. Some patients who had been incarcerated for years were eventually discharged.

Pinel also believed that the patients in his care were essentially normal people who should be approached with compassion and understanding, and treated with dignity as individual human beings. According to Charland (2010), a scholar from the University of Western Ontario, Pinel was a pioneer in promoting a view of mental illness as affective disorder and a form of mental alienation. Psychopathology stems from "affections moral" or passions. Specific passions include anger, hate, wounded pride, seeking vengeance, disgust with life, and irresistible tendencies toward suicide.

Pinel also surmised that if patients' reason had left them because of severe personal and social problems and the presence of these passions, it might be restored to them through comforting counsel and purposeful activity. However, for all the good Pinel did for people with mental illness, he was not a complete paragon of enlightenment and egalitarianism. The more humanitarian treatment he reserved for the upper classes; patients of the lower classes were still subjected to terror and coercion as a means of control.

In the wake of Pinel's revolutionary work in La Bicetre, the hospitals established in Europe and the United States were for a time relatively small and privately supported. A prominent merchant and Quaker, William Tuke (1732–1822), shocked by the conditions at York Asylum in England, proposed to the Society of Friends that it found its own institution. In 1796 the York Retreat was established on a country estate, providing mentally ill people with a quiet and religious atmosphere in which to live, work, and rest. Patients discussed their difficulties with attendants, worked in the garden, and took walks through the countryside. Charland (2007) described the moral treatment offered at the York Retreat as a form of affective conditioning informed by "benevolent theory" steeped in religious ethics.

In the United States the Friends' Asylum, founded in 1817 in Pennsylvania, and the Hartford Retreat, established in 1824 in Connecticut, were patterned after the York Retreat. Other U.S. hospitals were influenced by the sympathetic and attentive treatment provided by Pinel and Tuke. In accordance with this approach, which became known as **moral treatment**, patients had close contact with the attendants, who talked and read to them and encouraged them to engage in purposeful activity; residents led as normal lives as possible and in general took responsibility for themselves within the constraints of their disorders. According to Charland (2007), Pinel believed that a central aspect of moral treatment was restoring a patient's sense of self-esteem by letting her or him demonstrate self-restraint.

Despite the emphasis on moral treatment in the early nineteenth century, drugs were also used frequently in mental hospitals. Two findings emerged from a review of detailed case records of the York Retreat from 1880 to 1884 (Renvoise & Beveridge, 1989). First, drugs were the most common treatment and included alcohol, cannabis, opium, and chloral hydrate (knockout drops). Second, the outcomes were not very favourable; fewer than one-third of the patients were discharged as improved or recovered.

Moral treatment was abandoned in the latter part of the nineteenth century. Ironically, the efforts of Dorothea Dix (1802–77), a crusader for improved conditions for people with mental illness, helped effect this change (see illustration). Dix, a Boston schoolteacher, taught a Sunday-school class at the local prison and was shocked at the deplorable conditions in which the inmates lived. Her interest spread to the conditions of patients in private mental hospitals and to the mentally ill people of the time who had nowhere to go for treatment. Dix

In the 19th century, Dorothea Dix was a tireless social reformer who lobbied for improvement of the deplorable treatment of mentally ill people.

Encyclopaedia Britannica/UIG/Getty Images

campaigned vigorously to improve the lot of people with mental illness; she personally helped see that 32 state hospitals were built to take in the many patients whom the private ones could not accommodate. Unfortunately, state hospital staff members were unable to provide the individual attention that was a hallmark of moral treatment (Bockhoven, 1963). Moreover, the hospitals came to be administered by physicians who were interested in the biological aspects of illness and in the physical, rather than the psychological, well-being of mental patients. The money that once paid the salaries of personal attendants now paid for equipment and laboratories. Nonetheless, on March 2, 2009, as part of National Women's History Month and its 100th anniversary celebration, Mental Health America honoured the significant contributions of Dorothea Dix to the field.

For a limited time, there were attempts to apply moral treatment in certain regions of Canada, but these were undermined by the political and economic decisions of those in power. LaJeunesse (2002) documented how attempts at moral treatment in Alberta in the early twentieth century were undercut by Premier Arthur Sifton's decision to focus on larger institutions, where patients were crowded into buildings with inadequate space. Dr. Henry Hunt Stabb made heroic efforts to institute moral treatment and non-restraint at the Lunatic Asylum in St. John's, Newfoundland (see O' Brien, 1989). He presided at this site until his death in 1892, but his efforts were hindered by inadequate financial resources and more patients than the hospital could reasonably accommodate. Also, beginning in the late 1870s, the hospital often played a custodial role, as Stabb was made to take in low-functioning patients deemed untreatable.

Historical Picture Services/Stock Montage

Pinel's freeing of the patients at La Bicetre is often considered to mark the beginning of more humanitarian treatment of people with mental illness.

Asylums in Canada

"This, you must remember, that patients here within, Are here, because we all were born into a world of sin. . . . Now come inside the building, and enter into the halls, You will see many patients, whose sorrows for pity calls. But pay no attention, to what might be said of you, Some of them had fine intellects 'fore trouble their minds o'erthrew. . . ."

—Graeme L., 1907, patient at the Toronto Hospital for the Insane (Rheaume, 2000)

A network of asylums was eventually established in Canada. According to Cohen et al. (2014), mentally ill people were admitted to hospital in Quebec as early as 1714, but psychiatric asylums emerged in the decades following 1840, and eventually there was a network of asylums. The history of the development of this network is a history of the institutionalization of people with serious psychological disorders. However, as pointed out by Sussman (1998), the process "began with humane intentions as part of a progressive and reformist movement, which attempted to overcome neglect and suffering in the community, jails, penitentiaries, almshouses, poorhouses, and hospitals" (p. 260). Dorothea Dix described poignant and shameful examples of this neglectful community care and human suffering in her eloquent 1850 memorial prayer to the Nova Scotia Legislative Assembly (see Canadian Perspectives 1.1).

Canadian Perspectives 1.1

Dorothea Dix and the Development of the Asylums in Canada: Light into the Darkness?

"One lost mind whose star is quenched Has lessons for mankind."

—Dorothea Dix, 1850 (Hurd, 1916, Volume I, p. 492)

When Dorothea Dix visited "the Canadas" in 1843 and 1844, she discovered appalling conditions suffered by the "insane" incarcerated in the Toronto jail and the Quebec Lunatic Asylum (Hurd, 1916, Volume I).

On January 21, 1850, Dix presented a compelling "memorial prayer" on behalf of the mentally ill to the Nova Scotia legislature and requested construction of a public mental hospital (see photo). She stated that "[t]hroughout the province, in short, I found cases incurable through long neglect, doomed to a life-long burden to themselves through suffering, and a life-long charge either upon their friends or the public for care and maintenance" (Hurd, 1916, Volume I, p. 485). Dix also discussed moral treatment and the consequences of failure to obtain help at an early point. Her emphasis on early detection and treatment over 150 years ago is consistent with current views (e.g., see the discussion of early risk detection and intervention for schizophrenia in Chapter 11). Dix appealed to the members to consider what it was like to be mentally ill in Canada:

"In imagination, for a short hour, place yourselves in their stead; enter the horrid, noisome cell, invest yourselves with the foul, tattered garments which scantily serve the purposes of decent protection; cast yourselves upon the loathsome pile of filthy straw; find companionship in your own cries and groans, . . . then, if self-possession is not overwhelmed under the imaginary miseries of what are the actual distresses of the insane, return to the consciousness of your sound intellectual health, and answer if you will longer refuse or delay to make adequate appropriations for the establishment of a provincial hospital for those who are deprived of reason, and thereby of all that gladdens life or makes existence a blessing."

(Hurd, 1916, Volume I, p. 493)

NSA, J.M. Margeson, photographer – the Halifax Poor Asylum, 1899

The Halifax Poor House being rebuilt in 1899 following a fire in 1882.

This appears to be Dorothea Dix's only *public* appeal to a Canadian province. She did take an active role in selecting the site for the Nova Scotia hospital and helped Henry Hunt Stabb raise funds for the St. John's, Newfoundland, asylum (see O'Brien, 1989).

Thinking Critically

1. Imagine yourself back in 1850 Nova Scotia. You're suffering with a major psychiatric disorder such as schizophrenia, living under conditions similar to those described by Dorothea Dix. What would it be like for you? What could realistically be done to help you?

2. Given the establishment of a public "asylum," what model of care would you propose? How should the "inmates" be "treated"?

3. Assuming that people in the community treated you with humanity and compassion, cared for you, and supported you, do you think that it would be possible for you to live among them?

Around this time, J. F. Lehman (1840) wrote the first textbook published in Canada with a focus on the care and control of mentally ill people. Unfortunately, Lehman recommended stringent discipline and harsh treatments, including flogging. Although his views failed to stimulate much popular or medical support, as we will see, many strategies employed in Canada during the twentieth century were just as harsh and a few were much more severe and had tragic consequences.

Sussman (1998) argued that the development of services for the mentally ill in Canada and British North America was largely ad hoc, with little cross-fertilization of ideas from province to province. During the 1840s through to the 1880s, when most of the formal asylums were first established, all of the jurisdictions could be characterized as having a need to develop separate facilities with better conditions for the mentally ill. As noted by Sussman (1998), "This segregated form of care, the psychiatric institution known as the asylum, was the very beginning of state provisions for mentally ill people in a vast and sparsely populated country" (p. 261).

The earliest precursor to the nineteenth-century asylums was the Hotel-Dieu, established in Quebec City in 1714 by the Duchess d'Aiguillon, niece of Cardinal Richelieu, the effective ruler of New France. The facility cared for indigents and crippled people in addition to "idiots." Similar "hospitals" were built in other parts of Quebec, using a contracting-out system whereby the King of France paid religious orders of the French Roman Catholic Church to care for the mentally ill. However, following the 1763 Treaty of Paris, the English assumed power over the area and the British influence on care practices prevailed.

Asylums in Canada were built during the institution-building period prior to the First World War. Alberta was the last province to open an asylum for the insane, which meant that mentally ill people no longer had to be transported from Alberta to Manitoba by the Royal North West Mounted Police. Typically, asylum superintendents were British-trained physicians who modelled the asylums after British forms of structure, treatment, and administration, although Bartlett (2000), in a comparative analysis of structures in Ontario and England, concluded that they functioned differently and reflected very different norms of social governance.

In Upper Canada, power rested with the asylum doctor. A few years before Confederation, the Annual Report of the Board of Inspectors of Asylums, Prisons, & c., for the Year 1864 (1865) included a memorandum "on the necessity of providing additional accommodation for lunatics in Upper and Lower Canada" (p. iii). The inspectors gave a glowing report on behalf of the medical superintendent of the Provincial Lunatic Asylum in Toronto, the principal asylum in Upper Canada. However, the superintendent reported that both the Chief Asylum and the University Branch (a smaller asylum near the University of Toronto) were "dangerously overcrowded" and lamented the fact that this overcrowding was responsible for a striking increase in the death list (composed mostly of females) and for the impaired general health of the inmates. The average cost of caring for each patient to the province in 1864 was $152.88!

Over the years since the asylum was opened in 1841, the superintendent calculated the discharge rate to be 52%. Almost 20% of the inmates died while in the institution, a large number due to "general paresis of the insane" and to a condition called "phthisis."

Concerns exist today that Canada has developed a two-tier medical system in which the wealthy have more opportunity for, and quick access to, superior quality care (e.g., Adams & Laghi, 2000). Such a system had the force of law in the era of institution building, at least in Upper Canada (present-day Ontario). In 1853 the legislature passed the Private Lunatic Asylums Act to accommodate the wealthy in alternatives to the public asylums. As a consequence of the preferential legislation, the Homewood Retreat, a profit-oriented, independent, private asylum, was established in 1883 at Guelph, Ontario. Dr. Lett, the first medical superintendent, believed in the humane care of patients. Despite his resistance to the "cult of curability" ascribed to by practitioners of moral therapy, he encouraged his staff to employ the principles of moral therapy in order to provide symptomatic relief to his wealthy charges (Warsh, 1989).

The history of the development of institutions for the mentally disordered in Canada can be characterized in terms of two distinctive trends: (1) with the advent of the asylums, provisions for the mentally ill were separate from provisions for the physically ill, indigents, and criminals; and (2) the process was segregated from the wider community—"The institution and the community were two separate and distinct solitudes" (Sussman, 1998, p. 262).

Canadian Perspectives 1.2 examines mental institutions in Canada in the latter part of the twentieth century versus mental health services at present.

The Beginning of Contemporary Thought

Recall that in the West, the death of Galen and the decline of Greco-Roman civilization temporarily ended inquiries into the nature of both physical and mental illness. Not until the late Middle Ages did any new facts begin to appear, discovered thanks to an emerging empirical approach to medical science that gathered knowledge by direct observation. One development that fostered progress was the discovery by the Flemish anatomist and physician Vesalius (1514–64) that Galen's presentation of human anatomy was incorrect. Galen had presumed that human physiology mirrored that of the apes he studied. It took more than a thousand years for autopsy studies of humans—not allowed during Galen's time—to begin to prove that he was wrong. Further progress came from the efforts of the English physician Thomas Sydenham (1624–89). He was particularly successful in advocating an empirical approach to classification and diagnosis, one that subsequently influenced those interested in mental disorders.

Canadian Perspectives 1.2

The Mental Hospital in Canada: The Twentieth Century Versus Today

Despite the humane motives that stimulated the institution-building period in Canada, the results during much of the twentieth century were not very positive, especially from a patient's perspective. Provincial mental hospitals became extremely overcrowded, and in too many instances individual treatment was unavailable, with the exception of some radical treatments (such as lobotomy) and whatever psychoactive drugs were available in different eras. Drugs became the central means of treatment, especially after the introduction of the antipsychotic phenothiazines in the 1950s. As Sussman (1998) noted, "Eventually, institutionalization in Canada became a synonym for an inhumane response to mentally ill people, often because of a scarcity of resources" (p. 262).

Provinces varied in their responsiveness to mental illness. Mills (1997) applauded the province of Saskatchewan for being highly progressive and having a number of Canadian "firsts." Most notably, with changes implemented under the leadership of Premier Tommy Douglas, Saskatchewan was the first province to use more humane treatment and it implemented Canada's first provincially funded psychiatric research program in the 1950s. Overcrowded conditions were also found there but steps were taken to improve institutional environments. Saskatchewan is also where the initial research took place on attitudes toward mentally ill people. This research sought to learn how people would respond to the deinstitutionalization of patients placed in the community (see Cumming & Cumming, 1957).

According to Sealy (2012), the process of deinstitutionalization has been going on for more than 40 years in Canada. The goal of deinstitutionalization is to shift care from psychiatric hospitals into the community. The process of rapid deinstitutionalization occurred in five provinces (Alberta, British Columbia, Ontario, Nova Scotia, and Saskatchewan). Dramatic reductions in places for psychiatric patients took place when this change in policy was first implemented. According to Wasylenki, Goering, and MacNaughton (1994), the capacity of Canadian mental hospitals went from about 50,000 beds to about 15,000 beds between 1960 and 1976. At the same time, beds in general hospital psychiatric units increased from fewer than 1,000 to almost 6,000. Budget cuts in the 1980s and 1990s caused the trend of deinstitutionalization to continue. However, the enthusiasm for deinstitutionalization was tempered by evidence that many discharged people led lives of poverty in the community, with a significant number included among the homeless and the prison population.

A process of **transinstitutionalization** has also taken place. That is, while the number of beds has declined in various institutions, a shift has occurred and more care is now provided in psychiatric units of general hospitals rather than in psychiatric hospitals. Sealy (2012) reported that across Canada, the average days of care provided in psychiatric hospitals went from 418 days per 1,000 Canadians in 1994–95 to 215 days in 1998–99 and 99 days in 2002–03. Meanwhile, the average days of care in psychiatric units in general hospitals went from 176 days per 1,000 people in the population in 1994–95 to 127 days in 1998–99 and 118 days in 2002–03. The amount of care provided over this time frame decreased by an estimated 77% in psychiatric hospitals versus about 34% in hospital units.

East Wing of the 1868 addition to the Provincial Asylum in Toronto (opened 1850), as seen in 1971.

Photo by R. Essex. Courtesy of Archives of the Centre for Addiction and Mental Health (CAMH), Toronto.

A somewhat specialized mental hospital, sometimes called a prison or forensic hospital, is reserved for people who have been arrested and judged unable to stand trial and for those who have been acquitted of a crime because they are "not criminally responsible on account of mental disorder." Although these patients have not been sent to prison, their lives are controlled by guards and tight security. Treatment of some kind is supposed to take place during their incarceration. In Canada there are three maximum-security forensic hospitals, in Ontario, Quebec, and British Columbia. Also, in Ontario, forensic services are provided through small, medium-security regional forensic units based in the provincial psychiatric hospitals (e.g., METFORS—Metropolitan Toronto Forensic Service).

A recent assessment of the forensic mental health hospital in British Columbia indicated that substantial improvements have taken place over the years. This study found that both the patients and service providers held favourable views of the social climate in the hospital (see Livingston, Nijdam-Jones, & Brink, 2012). Overall, the study concluded that forensic mental health hospitals are not necessarily inhospitable environments for patient-centred care. There are issues, however, involving safety; some staff members in the Livingston et al. (2012) study expressed concerns about their own well-being. Similar concerns have been expressed by workers elsewhere. For instance, in Hamilton, Ontario, workers demanded safer conditions in May 2012 after one mental health patient used his bare hands to beat another patient to death. Here it is important to not make the inferential leap that most mental patients are violent or potentially violent; in fact, as we see later in this chapter, just the opposite is true.

At present, the role of the remaining **provincial psychiatric hospitals** is "tertiary"; that is, they "provide specialized treatment and rehabilitation services for individuals whose needs for care are too complex to be managed in the community" (Goering et al., 2000, p. 349). As provincial governments continue to develop portable and community-based tertiary care and "delink" delivery from particular settings (Goering et al., 2000), the provincial psychiatric hospitals' role will be increasingly minimized.

The trend toward community care has fuelled a debate on the value of **community treatment orders** (CTOs), a legal tool issued by a medical practitioner that establishes the conditions under which a mentally ill person may live in the community, including requirements for compliance with treatment (O'Reilly, 2004). The consequence for a patient of failing to follow the CTO is being returned to a psychiatric facility for assessment. We examine this emotionally charged, contentious issue in detail in Chapter 18.

One thing is certain. The "asylums" as we have known them over the past 150 years are a thing of the past as the trend toward societal integration continues.

Thinking Critically

1. Current institutions such as the Centre for Addiction and Mental Health (CAMH) in Toronto refer to people with psychological problems or psychiatric disorders—historically and traditionally called "patients"—as "clients." This term has also been used commonly in the past by many practising psychologists, particularly by those who adopt a less biological, medically oriented approach. The authors of this textbook also prefer the term "client" and will use it throughout the remainder of the book whenever appropriate. Do you agree with this decision? Why or why not?

2. How should chronic patients (now referred to as clients) be managed and treated so that their dignity is respected but society is protected?

3. In 1988 the federal government published *Mental Health for Canadians: Striking a Balance* (Epp, 1988). It claimed that closure of psychiatric hospitals was not offset by "strengthening community resources" and that psychiatric patients (clients) "face a life of deprivation, danger and neglect." Is there still a huge gap between deinstitutionalization, outpatient care, and community care? If so, how would you close it? Does society have a responsibility for the treatment of the vulnerable mentally ill?

An Early System of Classification

One of those impressed by Sydenham's approach was the German physician Wilhelm Griesinger, who insisted that any diagnosis of mental disorder specify a biological cause—a clear return to the somatogenic views first espoused by Hippocrates. A textbook of psychiatry, written by Griesinger's well-known follower Emil Kraepelin (1856–1926) and first published in 1883, furnished a classification system in order to establish the biological nature of mental illnesses.

Kraepelin discerned among mental disorders a tendency for a certain group of symptoms, called a **syndrome**, to appear together regularly enough to be regarded as having an underlying physical cause, much as a particular medical disease and its syndrome may be attributed to a biological dysfunction. He regarded each mental illness as distinct from all others, having its own genesis, symptoms, course, and outcome. Even though cures had not been worked out, at least the course of the disease could be predicted.

Kraepelin proposed two major groups of severe mental diseases: dementia praecox, an early term for schizophrenia, and manic-depressive psychosis (now called bipolar disorder). He postulated a chemical imbalance as the cause of schizophrenia and an irregularity in metabolism as the explanation of manic-depressive psychosis. Kraepelin's scheme for classifying these and other mental illnesses became the basis for the present diagnostic categories, described in Chapter 3.

General Paresis and Syphilis

Although the workings of the nervous system were understood somewhat by the mid-1800s, not enough was known to reveal all the expected abnormalities in structure that might underlie various mental disorders. Degenerative changes in the brain cells associated with senile and presenile psychoses and some structural pathologies that accompany mental retardation were identified, however. Perhaps the most striking medical success was the discovery of the full nature and origin of syphilis, a venereal disease that had been recognized for several centuries.

The story of this discovery provides a wonderful picture of the empirical approach, the basis for contemporary science. Since 1798 it was known that a number of mental patients manifested a syndrome characterized by a steady deterioration of both physical and mental abilities and that these patients suffered multiple impairments, including delusions of grandeur and progressive paralysis. Soon after these symptoms were recognized, it was observed that these patients never recovered. In 1825 this deterioration in mental and physical health was designated a disease, **general paresis**. Although it was established in 1857 that some patients with paresis had earlier had syphilis, there were many competing theories for the origin of paresis. For example, in attempting to account for the high rate of the disorder among sailors, some supposed that seawater might be the cause. And Griesinger, in trying to explain the higher incidence among men, speculated that liquor, tobacco, and coffee might be implicated.

In the 1860s and 1870s, Louis Pasteur established the **germ theory of disease**, which set forth the view that disease is caused by infection of the body by minute organisms. This theory laid the groundwork for demonstrating the relation between syphilis and general paresis. In 1905, the specific micro-organism that causes syphilis was discovered. A causal link had been established between infection, destruction of certain areas of the brain, and a form of psychopathology. If one type of psychopathology had a biological cause, so could others. Somatogenesis gained credibility, and the search for more biological causes was off and running.

Psychogenesis

The search for somatogenic causes dominated the field of abnormal psychology until well into the twentieth century, no doubt partly because of the stunning discoveries made about general paresis. But in the late eighteenth and throughout the nineteenth century, some investigators considered mental illnesses to have an entirely different origin. Various psychogenic points of view, which attributed mental disorders to psychological malfunctions, were fashionable in France and Austria.

Mesmer and Charcot   Many people in Western Europe were at that time subject to hysterical states; they suffered from physical incapacities, such as blindness or paralysis, for which no physical cause could be found. Franz Anton Mesmer (1734–1815), an Austrian physician practising in Vienna and Paris in the late eighteenth century, believed that hysterical disorders were caused by a particular distribution of a universal magnetic fluid in the body. Moreover, he felt that one person could influence the fluid of another to bring about a change in the other's behaviour. Mesmer conducted meetings cloaked in mystery and mysticism at which afflicted patients sat around a covered *baquet*, or tub. Iron rods protruded through the cover of the baquet from bottles underneath that contained various chemicals. Mesmer would enter a room, take various rods from the tub, and touch afflicted parts of his patients' bodies. The rods were believed to transmit animal magnetism and adjust the distribution of the universal magnetic fluid, thereby removing the hysterical disorder. Whatever we may think of what seems today to be a questionable theoretical explanation and procedure, Mesmer apparently helped many people overcome their hysterical problems.

You may wonder about our discussing Mesmer's work under the rubric of psychogenic causes, since Mesmer regarded hysterical disorders as strictly physical. Because of the setting in which Mesmer worked with his patients, however, he is generally considered one of the earlier practitioners of modern-day hypnosis (see artwork). The word "mesmerize" is an older term for "hypnotize." (The phenomenon itself, however, was known to the ancients of probably every culture and was part of the sorcery and magic of conjurers, fakirs, and faith healers.)

Mesmer was regarded as a quack by his contemporaries, but the study of hypnosis gradually became respectable. A great Parisian neurologist, Jean Martin Charcot (1825–93),

The French psychiatrist Jean Charcot lectures on hysteria in this famous painting. Charcot was an important figure in reviving interest in psychogenesis.

Bettmann/Getty Images

also studied hysterical states, including anaesthesia (loss of sensation), paralysis, blindness, deafness, convulsive attacks, and gaps in memory. Charcot initially espoused a somatogenic point of view. One day, however, some of his enterprising students hypnotized a normal woman and prompted her to display certain hysterical symptoms. Charcot was deceived into believing that she was an actual hysterical patient. When the students showed him how readily they could remove the woman's symptoms by waking her, Charcot changed his mind about hysteria and became interested in non-physiological interpretations of these very puzzling phenomena (see artwork).

Breuer and the cathartic method   At about this time, in Vienna, a physician named Josef Breuer (1842–1925) treated a young woman who had become bedridden with a number of hysterical symptoms. Her legs and right arm and side were paralyzed, her sight and hearing were impaired, and she often had difficulty speaking. She also sometimes went into a dreamlike state, or "absence," during which she mumbled to herself, seemingly preoccupied with troubling thoughts. During one treatment session, Breuer hypnotized Anna O. and repeated some of her mumbled words. He succeeded in getting her to talk more freely—ultimately, with considerable emotion—about some very upsetting past events. Frequently, on awakening from these hypnotic sessions, she felt much better. With Anna O. and other hysterical patients, Breuer found that the relief and cure of symptoms seemed to last longer if, under hypnosis, they were able to recall the precipitating event for the symptom and if their original emotion was expressed. The experience of reliving an earlier emotional catastrophe and releasing the emotional tension caused by suppressed thoughts about the event was called *catharsis*. Breuer's method became known as the **cathartic method**. In 1895 one of his colleagues joined him in the publication of *Studies in Hysteria*, a book considered a milestone in abnormal psychology. In the next chapter we examine the thinking of Breuer's collaborator, Sigmund Freud.

Jean Loup Charmet/Science Source

Mesmer's procedure for transmitting animal magnetism was generally considered a form of hypnosis.

Many people go about the study of abnormal psychology without considering the nature of the perspective, conceptual framework, or paradigm (see Chapter 2) they have adopted. The choice of a paradigm, however, has important consequences for the way in which abnormal behaviour is defined, investigated, and treated. Canadian Perspectives 1.3 examines, from a historical perspective, some of the treatment strategies that developed as a result of adopting a particular paradigm, and leads us to consider the lesson of history. It raises ethical issues and concerns that we will address in detail in Chapter 18.

Canadian Perspectives 1.3

The Lesson of History: A View from the Twenty-First Century

"CIA brainwash settlement 'a flea': Spy agency escaped lightly in lawsuit, Winnipegger says"

—*The Canadian Press, October 6, 1988*

"Brainwash 'guinea pig' seeks more damages: Canadian victim of CIA experiment in late 1950s tries to launch class-action suit against Ottawa"

—*The Canadian Press, January 8, 2007 to Moore, January 8, 2007*

These Canadian Press reports describe the settlement of a lawsuit resulting from what is probably the greatest abuse of psychiatric power in Canadian history. Similar abuses occurred in the United States and elsewhere during the same era and, tragically, are common in some parts of the world even today. However, before proceeding to tell the CIA story, we should point out that a majority of psychiatric patients in Canada were treated with decency and humanity within the constraints of scientific knowledge and accepted clinical practice at the time.

Dr. Ewen Cameron, a world-renowned Montreal psychiatrist, was head of the Allan Memorial Institute at McGill University in the 1950s and early 1960s (see photo). At one point, he was president of the Quebec, Canadian, American, and World Psychiatric Associations. In 1955 he initiated a nine-year series of experiments on unsuspecting psychiatric patients, apparently in a misguided attempt to discover breakthrough treatments or a "cure" for mental illness. None of his patients or their families was asked for consent, nor were they informed of the experimental treatments involved that went far beyond the limits of acceptable treatments. Dr. Cameron's quest led

to a bizarre theory of "beneficial brainwashing" that had tragic consequences for hundreds of Canadians. Many years later, it was determined that his shocking mind-control experiments were funded secretly by the U.S. Central Intelligence Agency and the federal government of Canada. The CIA believed that these brainwashing strategies might be used on "enemies" during the Cold War (Gillmor, 1987).

What did Dr. Cameron—and his staff—do that was of such great interest to the CIA? He administered massive doses of hallucinogenic drugs, such as LSD. He administered intensive, repeated courses of electroconvulsive therapy (ECT), or "shock treatment," often three times each day, while patients were kept in a drug-induced coma for as long as three months. He also administered so-called psychic driving, in which subliminal messages, such as "You killed your mother," were repeated over and over while the patient was in the drug-induced state (Collins, 1988). The alleged purpose of these "treatments" was to "wipe away" the troubled past of his patients. It succeeded. Linda Macdonald, who initiated a lawsuit against the federal government, claimed that the experiments erased her memory for the first 26 years of her life. She received over 100 electroshock treatments and was kept in a drug-induced sleep for 86 days. Theoretically, Dr. Cameron would bestow a "new," healthy personality on her. Macdonald claimed, however, that there was no subsequent care directed at the psychological difficulties that brought her to the institute in the first place, or for the effects of Dr. Cameron's experiments on her. Victims claimed that they suffered permanent damage. Those still alive (several committed suicide) remain in psychiatric hospitals or attempt to live in the community but require extensive support.

The role of the CIA was not discovered until 1977. In 1988 the U.S. government settled out of court for a total of $750,000 with a group of nine former patients who had initiated a lawsuit in 1980. At the time, Val Orlikow, a former patient and the wife of a then Winnipeg Member of Parliament, stated that with the settlement, the CIA had merely "flicked a flea off the sleeve of their jacket" (The Canadian Press, 1988). She told CBC's investigative news program *the fifth estate* that Dr. Cameron had let her down. "It was an awful thing to realize, when I found this out, that the man whom I had thought cared about what happened to me didn't give a damn. I was a fly, just a fly." Her granddaughter Sarah Anne Johnson later told the Globe and Mail that her grandmother had been an avid reader but after her treatment, she lost her ability to read. It would take her a week to read a simple note or a month to read a newspaper (Milroy, 2009).

In 1992 the Canadian government finally agreed to a settlement of up to $100,000 per person. Neither the CIA nor the Canadian government apologized to the surviving patients who lost their identities and their dignity, or to the families of approximately 150 former patients who died. In 1998, following an exposé on *the fifth estate,* CBC Television aired a miniseries dramatizing the work of Dr. Cameron and the occurrences in his "Sleep Room." In early

(Continued)

McGill News/McGill University Archives, PR019175

2007 another victim sought approval to launch a class-action lawsuit against the federal government of Canada. She and more than 250 others had been denied compensation by the government because they had not suffered "total depatterning" and were not rendered to a child-like state (The Canadian Press, 2007).

Several radical approaches for the treatment of serious mental disorders were introduced during the twentieth century. Lobotomy or psychosurgery is particularly controversial. In this surgical procedure, the tracts connecting the frontal lobes to lower centres of the brain are destroyed. Egas Moniz of Lisbon introduced prefrontal lobotomy into psychiatry in 1935. The first lobotomies in Canada were performed in Ontario in 1944 on 19 female patients from various mental hospitals. Simmons (1987) demonstrated that psychosurgery was used in Ontario for several reasons, including out of curiosity, to observe the consequences to patients.

Three operations conducted in 1981 were the last lobotomies performed in Ontario (Simmons, 1987). Lobotomies were effectively banned in all public psychiatric hospitals.

What is the lesson of history with respect to society's "treatment" of the mentally ill? The examples presented here, together with examples from the more distant past and knowledge of circumstances surrounding events, point to two main conclusions:

1. Periods in which people exhibiting psychologically disordered behaviour were persecuted and treated cruelly (e.g., witch hunts, bloodletting, asylums) have often alternated with periods of humanitarian reform and care for suffering people (e.g., Hippocrates's humanitarian treatments, Pinel's reform of the asylums).

2. Cycles of persecution, neglect, and humanitarianism in the treatment of the mentally ill have occurred irrespective of the helping agency, whether religious, medical, or psychological.

Thinking Critically

1. Are you aware of any "treatment" of people with psychological disorders that illustrates the wisdom of paying attention to Santayana's famous dictum about the need to remember the past? Is continued progress in Canada inevitable? What economic, political, and social circumstances could potentially contribute to a lack of progress?

2. What steps would you take to ensure that tragic incidents, such as the "treatments" employed by Dr. Cameron, never occur again in Canada?

3. Do you think that lobotomy was ever justified? (After you think critically about this issue, refer to the discussion of ethical dilemmas of research and therapy in Chapter 18.)

1.3 Current Attitudes toward People with Psychological Disorders

"Changing attitudes to mental illness continues to be our biggest challenge. Discrimination, ignorance and fear remain the enemies that we have to conquer."

—Bill Gaudette, National President, Canadian Mental Health Association, May 2001

Many Canadians are suspicious of people with psychological disorders. Their concerns have been reinforced by incidents involving threats, violence, and other examples of frightening behaviour on the part of seriously mentally ill people, many of whom had refused to take or were no longer taking their prescribed medications. We will likely never forget the media reports of the tragic, horrific, brutal case of 40-year-old Vince Li, who killed and then mutilated the body of a young passenger named Tim McLean, whom he didn't even know, on a bus in Manitoba in 2008. At Li's trial, it was revealed that he told a psychiatrist that he was commanded by God to kill the young man because he was a force of evil:

"Suddenly the sunshine came in the bus and the voice said, 'Quick. Hurry up. Kill him and then you'll be safe.' It was so quick, such an angry voice, and I had to do what it said. I was told that if I didn't listen to the voice, I would die immediately."

(Puxley, 2009, March 6, p. A2)

The judge, with the agreement of both the Crown and the defence, declared Li not criminally responsible on account of mental disorder. Psychiatrists testified that Li was suffering from untreated **schizophrenia**. Li spent seven years at Selkirk Mental Health Centre and it was announced in early 2016 that Li would soon be moving to independent living in the community. As we will see, cases such as this one, and numerous others that you can probably recall, are actually extremely rare. Unfortunately, they can leave an indelible impression on people and impact negatively on our attitudes toward people with mental health issues or psychological problems.

Consistent with other minority groups in Canada, people with psychological disorders often face negative **stereotyping** and **stigmatization**. For example, according to the Centre for Addiction and Mental Health in Toronto (CAMH, 2000), the social stigma surrounding depression is the primary reason why only one-third of the estimated three million people in Canada who suffer from depression seek help. According to a report on the 2002 Mental Health and Well-being Survey (Government of Canada, 2006), over 50% of Canadians who suffered from mood, anxiety, or substance dependence disorders in the previous year felt embarrassed about their problems and reported facing discrimination. One Canadian study (Bahm & Forchuk, 2009) found that people with both a psychiatric and a physical disability faced more perceived stigma and discrimination than those with a psychiatric disability alone.

A much publicized example of the issue of stereotyping and stigmatizing of the mentally ill was the 2000 movie *Me, Myself & Irene* starring Canadian actor Jim Carrey. The character played by Carrey develops a "split personality" and fights against himself. A coalition of Canadian health organizations and advocacy groups, including the Canadian Mental Health Association, demanded that disclaimers be attached to the film, arguing it reinforces negative stereotypes of people suffering from psychiatric disorders, in particular the schizophrenias.

Carrey's character is misidentified as having schizophrenia rather than **dissociative identity disorder** (see Chapters 7 and 11). One unfortunate and particularly ironic aspect of this example is Carrey's own struggles with depression (see Canadian Contributions 1.1).

Mental illness can occur regardless of fame, fortune, or power, and there are many examples of well-known Canadians, or their loved ones, who have experienced a diagnosable psychological disorder (see Nunes & Simmie, 2002). Canadian Contributions 1.1 identifies some of these celebrities, all of whom have acknowledged their adjustment problems despite the possible stigma associated with admitting a mental health problem.

Canadian Contributions **1.1**

The Advocacy of Well-Known Canadians with Mental Health Problems

Clara Hughes is not alone. A growing number of Canadian celebrities have been open about their history of mental health problems and have advocated for more treatment resources and greater awareness of the impact that mental illness has on our citizens. As noted above, actor Jim Carrey suffered from depression, which he discussed during a 2009 interview on *60 Minutes.* Carrey revealed that he spent years on Prozac but now relies on spiritual forms of coping. Another example is Margot Kidder, the actress from Yellowknife who is famous for her role as Superman's girlfriend in the *Superman* movies starring the late Christopher Reeve. Kidder's problems with bipolar disorder led to her temporary retention in a psychiatric facility. She has campaigned against the drug treatments she received.

Another celebrity from the same era is Margaret Trudeau, who married then-Prime Minister Pierre Trudeau in 1971 when she was only 22 years old. Of course, she is now the mother of Prime Minister Justin Trudeau. Margaret Trudeau has been open about her long history of battles with bipolar depression, including her symptoms while being the Prime Minister's wife. In 2006, she recalled, "It was never talked about in those days, and barely recognized, no matter what sector of society you lived in. And so, in the public eye and under public scrutiny, I tried to manage as best I could" (Berthiaume, 2006, p. A6).

Margaret Trudeau is the mother-in-law of another notable Canadian with a history of mental health problems. Sophie Grégoire, wife of Prime Minister Justin Trudeau, admitted her history with an eating disorder in 2006. Grégoire has worked extensively in recent years on behalf of the Montreal-based BACA Eating Disorders Clinic.

Canadian entertainers have been particularly open about the mental health challenges they have faced. Perhaps the most well-known is comedian Howie Mandel. Mandel suffers from obsessive-compulsive disorder and it is his fear of contamination that made him uneasy about shaking the hands of contestants on the show *Deal or No Deal* (and he shaves his head so that germs will not get in his hair!). Meanwhile, actor Keanu Reeves, who is known

primarily for his role in the *Matrix* movies, acknowledged that he was plunged into depression when he turned 40 years old.

Mary Walsh (formerly of *This Hour Has 22 Minutes* and co-star in several films) is another celebrity with a history of mental health issues. Walsh had a difficult upbringing in St. John's, Newfoundland. She took her first drink at the age of 13 and eventually came to abuse alcohol. In 2005, she was given the Centre for Addiction and Mental Health's Courage to Come Back Award. In 2015–2016, in recognition of her advocacy work, Walsh was the Honorary Canadian Psychological Association President. She addressed the annual convention in June 2016 in Victoria and urged for national reform to improve access to mental health care.

Singer Alanis Morissette revealed her battles with anorexia and bulimia in 2005. She acknowledged that as a teenage prodigy, she struggled with the symptoms when she was between the ages of 14 and 18, and much of it was due to the need to meet high expectations. She stated, "The pressure was hardcore. For four to six months at a time, I would barely eat, so I constantly felt dizzy. I lived on a lot of Melba toast, carrots and black coffee" (*Vancouver Sun,* 2005, p. C3). Morissette has fought against the unrealistic body image pressures prescribed for females. More recently, in 2012, Morissette revealed her struggles with postpartum depression.

Other Canadians in the music industry have similarly revealed their difficulties. Steven Page, former frontman for the Barenaked Ladies, acknowledged his struggles with bipolar depression in 2011. Canadian rocker Matthew Good revealed that he has struggled with anxiety and depression for years and he dealt with it by becoming a seemingly tireless worker. Good was eventually hospitalized after ingesting 50 Ativan pills. He has since recovered (Patch, 2009, D4).

Some scholars have suggested that the professional performers who are vulnerable often experience psychological distress because of the heightened self-consciousness and self-focused attention that comes from being in the public spotlight. Given the potential stigma associated with admitting a mental health problem, it is particularly impressive when these celebrities acknowledge their issues and instead shine that same spotlight on the significant psychological disorders that afflict people in Canada and around the world. Congratulations to all of them!

The Public Perception

Many common misconceptions or myths of mental illness can be dispelled. For example, as noted above, it is a common belief that people with psychological disorders are unstable and dangerous. We will revisit this issue in subsequent chapters but at this point we can state that recent research does not provide confirmation of this widespread idea, although there is a small but significant relation between schizophrenia and violent acts (see Taylor, 2008, for review). A major American epidemiological study (Elbogen & Johnson, 2009) found that the incidence of violence was higher for people with severe mental illness; however, the effect was significant only for those with co-occurring substance abuse or dependence. As suggested earlier, the majority of mentally ill people never perpetrate violent acts; in fact, they are more likely to be victims (Taylor, 2008).

Another insidious myth is the belief that people with psychological disorders can never be "cured" and can never contribute meaningfully to society again. As you read the research findings presented in this text, you will readily conclude that such a belief is a major misconception. Further, you will no doubt be able to cite examples of people who, though never "cured" of their psychological problems, nevertheless went on to make significant contributions to humanity. One such individual was Clarence Hincks. He suffered from serious, chronic psychological problems but was able to devote his life to helping the mentally ill and to trying to change the public's attitudes toward them. Hincks was a founder and long-term medical director of the **Canadian Mental Health Association** (CMHA).

A survey released for the 50th anniversary of Mental Health Week in Canada, in May 2001 (CMHA, 2001), found that the majority of Canadians believe that maintaining mental health is "very important" (95% of women and 88% of men). However, relative to a 1997 survey, fewer Canadians were willing to tell their bosses (only 42%) or friends (only 50%) if they were receiving help for depression. Women were more willing to admit to receiving treatment than men.

A 2008 national Ipsos Reid online survey, commissioned by the Canadian Medical Association (see Kirkey, 2008), indicated the extent of current negative attitudes and discrimination. The following were some of the findings.

- Almost 50% of Canadians (46%) believe "we call some things mental illness because it gives some people an excuse for poor behaviour and personal failings."

- About 50% indicated they would avoid socializing with (42%) or marrying (55%) someone who is mentally ill.

- Twenty-seven percent are afraid to even be around someone with a serious mental illness.

- About 50% would decline to tell friends or co-workers about a family member suffering from a mental illness (but 72% would share a cancer diagnosis).

- Most wouldn't hire a doctor, a lawyer, a financial adviser, someone to care for or teach their child, or even a landscaper who has a mental illness!

Dr. David Goldbloom, who has served as the chair of the Mental Health Commission of Canada, summarized the message from this survey about Canadians' attitudes toward mental illness: "They're not going to talk about it. They're not going to disclose. And they're not going to disclose as long as there is a culture of shame, secrecy and stigma" (Kirkey, 2008, p. A1). However, on the bright side, 72% of survey respondents agreed that funding to treat mental illness should be comparable to funding for physical illnesses such as cancer (see Zon, 2009).

Anti-Stigma Campaigns

Over the past decade, there have been numerous widely publicized campaigns in Canada and throughout the world to try to destigmatize mental illness. Michael Wilson, a prominent former federal minister of finance, lost a young son, who suffered from depression, to suicide. Wilson has been a tireless crusader to help reduce the stigma associated with depression. Wilson encourages people to seek help for themselves or for loved ones and friends. He served as chair of a multi-year campaign launched by CAMH and various partners to remove barriers that impede people from seeking treatment for mental health and addiction problems.

Kevin Bieksa, formerly of the Vancouver Canucks NHL team, is actively engaged in fighting schema. Bieksa became involved with and filmed a video appeal for the site Mindcheck.ca following the death of his friend and former teammate Rick Rypien, who took his own life in 2011 after struggling for years with depression. It is important for athletes to continue the fight against mental health stigma in light of recent research with student athletes indicating that the culture and values of highly competitive sport can create an atmosphere that promotes and maintains stigma (Delenardo & Terrion, 2014).

Another crusader is actress Glenn Close, who was in Ottawa in June 2012 to attend an international anti-stigma conference hosted by the Mental Health Commission of Canada (see photo). Close was accompanied by two family members who have suffered from mental illness. Close is striving to influence public awareness through her non-profit organization BringChange2Mind. She has also indicated that in retrospect, she should have refused the role of Alex Forrest in the movie *Fatal Attraction* due to the extreme way that the movie depicted mental illness (see Anderssen, 2012).

The reduction of the stigma of schizophrenia is the continuing focus of a global campaign by the World Psychiatric Association. Meanwhile, in Canada, Heather Stuart from Queen's University is the national leader in fighting stigma (see photo). Stuart was named in 2012 as the Bell Mental Health and Anti-Stigma Research Chair, which is the first research chair created in the world that is focused on assessing and remediating mental health stigma. An intriguing aspect of Stuart's personal story is that she grew up next to the Homewood Sanitorium in Guelph, Ontario, where her mother worked as an administrator. Stuart recounted that "I would meet the patients every day when I went to see my mother ... They were pleasant and kind people and I made friends with them. It never occurred to me that there was a social division between us" (Curtis, 2012; www.universityaffairs.ca. Indeed, contact with

Joe Lofaro/Metro News

Actress Glenn Close with her sister, Jessie Close, and her nephew, Calen Pick, at an international conference on eliminating mental health stigma in Ottawa.

people who have psychological problems is a factor that mitigates against stigma.

A preventive intervention developed by Stuart (2006a) sought to reduce stigma in high school students through a video-based active learning program (The Schizophrenia Society of Canada's Reaching Out program) that chronicled the challenges of actual people with schizophrenia. Exposure to the program resulted in increased knowledge of schizophrenia and its treatment and less social distancing (and presumably less stigma). Female students showed greater gains in understanding than males. Although it is not known whether a lasting improvement in knowledge resulted, this study illustrates the potential of such programs with young people. Indeed, programs that send speakers to talk in public about mental health have been used worldwide and effectively improve knowledge and attitudes of students toward the mentally ill (see Sartorius & Schultze, 2005).

The opportunity to hear from a mental health consumer was part of a program that was used effectively in a recent intervention conducted in schools in Hamilton, Ontario. In this instance, high school students heard in person the autobiographical account of a married woman in her forties who was diagnosed with schizophrenia in her late teens (see Hartman et al., 2013). She described her experiences and challenges with mental illness, including the initial onset of symptoms, such as auditory hallucinations, and the problems she faced throughout the process of arriving at her diagnosis. She was also very forthcoming about times when her mental illness led to suicide attempts and hospitalizations. Her story concludes with an account of her recovery. She is happily married and she works as a full-time health care worker. She is doing quite well and the psychotic symptoms remain under control as long as she takes her medication.

Two aspects of this autobiographical first-hand account are particularly compelling. First, this brave woman described what happened when she started to experience her symptoms while at university. She recounted, "In my final year of university I was trying to study for final exams and write my thesis. But the voices in my head were so horrible and the visions so great I had to tell someone. I phoned my parents. I came home that weekend and was in a doctor's office by Monday" (Hartman, 2012, p. 93). Most students can easily imagine how distressing this would be if it happened to them.

Courtesy of Heather Stuart

Heather Stuart, who holds the Bell Mental Health and Anti-Stigma Research Chair, is a crusader for the rights of mentally ill people. Stuart met many such people as a child as a result of visiting her mother, who worked at the Homewood Sanitorium.

Second, she discussed at length the upset associated with continuing exposure to stigma. Specifically, she recounted the following:

> *"I hear the comments all the time, both at work and when I am with friends. Things like 'psycho', 'crazy', 'one side of the brain isn't listening to the other side', 'schizo's shouldn't be driving'. These words and ideas hurt me immensely, I'm stuck here taking pills and going to counselling for the rest of my life and to top it off I can't tell anyone about my problem because people think I'm going to attack them! I can't say anything because of fear that I will be alienated from all my friends and coworkers, not to mention the chance of getting some sort of promotion in the organization is probably out the window! So please as health care workers and as people please stop this vicious style of talk and understand that I am a productive person in society and should be treated as such. Thank you!"*
>
> *(Hartman, 2012, p. 94).*

Once again, you can easily imagine how you would feel if this happened to you.

The research component of the Hartman et al. (2013) study showed that students who took part in this prevention did have improved knowledge and less social distancing from people with mental illness, indicating decreased stigma. Conclusions are restricted somewhat due to the lack of a no-intervention control group in this study. A control group that does not receive the intervention is needed for comparison purposes. A control group was not included because it was deemed that all students should have this learning opportunity. One of the most unique elements of this study is that it also assessed **self-stigma**, which is the tendency to internalize mental health stigma and see oneself in more negative terms as a result of experiencing a psychological problem. Hartman et al. (2013) found the intervention also yielded substantial reductions in self-stigma, suggesting that exposure to these programs can result in more self-compassion. Research is now beginning to identify factors that seem to protect against self-stigma such as being securely attached to significant others instead of having insecure anxious attachments to others (Zhao et al., 2015).

Media images of mental illness with a focus on dangerousness, criminality, and unpredictability, and that model negative reactions to people with psychological problems such as fear, rejection, and ridicule, can inhibit help-seeking behaviours, medication adherence, and recovery (see Stuart, 2006b). However, "The media have produced some of the most sensitive, educational and award-winning material on mental illness and the mentally ill" (Stuart, 2006b, p. 99). Thus, the media can play a strong role as allies in anti-stigma activities and can challenge prejudice and discrimination, project positive human-interest stories that promote understanding and compassion, and encourage help-seeking and self-esteem in the mentally ill.

Anti-stigma campaigns in Canada are escalating. Heather Stuart and other advocates have joined with the Mental Health Commission of Canada to spread the Opening Minds (OM) Anti-Stigma Initiative (see Stuart et al., 2014). OM is working with more than 100 community partners and their affiliates. Extensive research is also underway in order to further our understanding of stigma and how to combat it. A recent review paper by one of the world leaders in this area (Patrick Corrigan) and his colleagues reminds us that there are both individual and system factors that promote stigma and concerns about stigma and it is essential to view stigma as involving complex phenomena (see Corrigan, Druss, & Perlick, 2014). Because it is such an important topic, the American Psychological Association has recently introduced a new journal called *Stigma and Health* and Patrick Corrigan was selected as editor of this important new journal.

So, do you believe that the Canadian public's perception of people with psychological problems has become more positive and supportive in the past 15 years? Attitudes only change when they are challenged! It is our hope and expectation that you will treat all people, including those with psychiatric disorders, whether real or imagined, with decency and dignity. We further hope that many of you will take an active role in advocating for, or helping, people with psychological problems.

Mental Health Literacy

How much do people actually know about mental health and related issues? The term **mental health literacy** has been created to refer to the accurate knowledge that a person develops about mental illness and its causes and treatment. What do we know about mental health literacy in general? A review concluded that more positive and informed attitudes are found among younger people, more educated people, people with training, and those with personal experience, perhaps due to having a family member with some form of illness. This review also concluded that there is a reasonably high level of knowledge about depression, but surprising ignorance of disorders such as schizophrenia and social anxiety. Finally, the prevailing view is that mental health is a reflection of biological and genetic causes, but a substantial proportion of people attribute mental health problems to early family experience (see Furnham & Telford, 2011).

What about Canadians? In 2008, the Canadian Alliance on Mental Illness and Mental Health presented its report on Mental Health Literacy in Canada. Funded by Health Canada, the report is the culmination of approximately four years of research, planning, and consultation across Canada. While this study was supposed to assess mental health literacy, the focus was more on beliefs rather than the accuracy of the beliefs. Among the conclusions were the following:

- Most Canadians see mental health as a medical problem (66% recommend medical intervention for schizophrenia, 61% for depression, and 46% for anxiety).

- Many Canadians are cautious about the use of psychiatric medications (e.g., while 60% believe that antidepressants can be helpful, 51% agree that they can be harmful).

- Canadians prefer a holistic treatment approach but are largely unaware of the range of available treatment options.

- About 90% of Canadians believe that anyone can suffer from a mental disorder.

- Common mental problems, such as anxiety or depression, are viewed as more likely caused by psychosocial factors whereas mental illnesses such as schizophrenia are viewed as more serious and more likely caused by biomedical factors.

As of 2008, Canada has a national integrated strategy, but how much do people actually know about mental health issues? Useful information was provided by a team of York University researchers who conducted the first national study of mental health literacy that compared younger people (18–24 years old) and older people (25–64 years old) (see Marcus, Westra, Eastwood, & the Mobilizing Minds Research Group, 2012). Overall, while few age differences were found, it seems that Canadians have a good understanding of depression; the recognition of depression was substantially better than the recognition of anxiety or schizophrenia. In general, the respondents correctly identified major mental health problems at moderate rates and about two-thirds of the participants were accurate at estimating mental health disorders in Canada. Thus, while there is considerable mental health literacy in Canada, there is also considerable room for improvement.

How will such improvements actually occur? One way is to develop and deliver mental health education programs in elementary schools and high schools. A recent study conducted with the assistance of four Ontario school boards indicates that this approach has substantial promise. The delivery of a mental health literacy program called The Guide resulted in lasting improvements in students' knowledge of and attitudes toward mental health problems (McLuckie, Kutcher, Wei, & Weaver, 2014).

1.4 Mental Health Problems and Their Treatment in Canada

The Extent of Mental Health Problems in Canada

"Conservatively, we estimate that 7.5 million Canadians suffer from depression, anxiety, substance abuse or another mental health disorder."

—Phil Upshall, National Executive Director of the Mood Disorders Society of Canada, and chair of Mental Illness Awareness Week (Canadian Psychiatry Aujourd'hui, October 2008)

Canada as a Whole So just how many people in Canada have mental health problems? An initial broad look at Canada as a whole came from the Canadian Community Health Survey (CCHS) (Cycle 1.2), which was the first comprehensive Canadian *national* study to use a full current version of the Composite International Diagnostic Interview (developed by the World Health Organization). For this reason and because of the large sample size (nearly 37,000 community-dwelling respondents), the CCHS 1.2 provided the best available description of selected disorders in Canada for many years (see Gravel & Beland, 2005, for a description).

However, another study was conducted in 2012 by Statistics Canada. The 2012 Canadian Community Health Survey—Mental Health (CCHS-MH) collected information from Canadians aged 15 and older on the prevalence of six mental disorders (within the 12 months prior to the interview as well as overall lifetime): depression, bipolar disorder, generalized anxiety disorder, alcohol abuse or dependence, cannabis abuse or dependence, and other drug abuse or dependence (excluding cannabis). Disorders assessed in 2002 but not this time included panic disorder, social phobia, and agoraphobia, as well as eating attitude problems, and problem gambling or moderate risk for problem gambling.

The results are summarized in Table 1.1. Some major findings were as follows (see Pearson, Janz, & Ali, 2013):

- About 1 out of every 10 Canadians aged 15 and over (about 2.8 million people) reported *symptoms* consistent with one of the disorders during the previous 12 months.

TABLE 1.1	Rates of Selected Mental or Substance Use Disorders, Lifetime and 12 Month, Canada, Household Population 15 and Older, 2012	
	Lifetime (%)	12-Month (%)
Mental or substance use disorders[1]	**33.1**	**10.1**
Substance use disorder[2]	21.6	4.4
Alcohol abuse or dependence	18.1	3.2
Cannabis abuse or dependence	6.8	1.3
Other drug abuse or dependence (excluding cannabis)	4.0	0.7
Mood disorder[3]	12.6	5.4
Major depressive episode	11.3	4.7
Bipolar disorder	2.6	1.5
Generalized anxiety disorder	8.7	2.6

[1]**Mental or substance use disorders** is comprised of: substance use disorders, mood disorders, and generalized anxiety disorder. However, these three disorders cannot be added to create this rate because these three categories are not mutually exclusive, meaning that people may have a profile consistent with one or more of these disorders.

[2]**Substance use disorder** includes alcohol abuse or dependence, cannabis abuse or dependence, and other drug abuse or dependence.

[3]**Mood disorder** includes depression (major depressive episode) and bipolar disorder.

Source: Statistics Canada, Canadian Community Health Survey—Mental Health, 2012.

- 1 in 3 Canadians met criteria for a disorder at some point in their lifetimes.
- About 1 in 5 Canadians met lifetime criteria for a substance use disorder. This amounts to approximately 6 million Canadians.
- About 1 in 7 Canadians met lifetime criteria for a major depressive episode or a bipolar disorder.
- Females, relative to males, had higher rates of mood disorders and generalized anxiety disorder. Males had higher rates of substance abuse.
- About 1 in 3 Canadians had a need for treatment that was unmet, either in whole or in part.

Clearly, mental health and addiction problems are widespread in Canada and point to the need for a dramatic escalation of prevention and intervention efforts. The number of people with unmet needs is equally alarming. Comparable levels of unmet need were identified in another study conducted with 571 Canadians (see Fleury et al., 2016). About 3 out of 10 reported an unmet need for counselling. However, higher levels of unmet need were found among younger people, and people with an addiction.

Regional Differences   Does the mental health of the population differ from one region of Canada to another? Do the provinces and territories differ from one another in terms of mental health? These questions are difficult to answer. There are, of course, some obvious differences in certain parts of Canada. In Chapter 2, for example, we will discuss the high level of mental health problems among some of Canada's Aboriginal people. However, Stephens, Dulberg, and Joubert (1999) did not find any major independent association between mental health and a respondent's province of residence.

There are, however, a few consistent differences. One of these is the good mental health in both Newfoundland and Labrador and Prince Edward Island. People in these two provinces reported the most happiness and the least distress. Quebec is noteworthy because it reported very high levels of self-esteem and mastery but the least happiness and most distress. The initial results of an intriguing new study suggest that mental health problems may be more prevalent in Quebec but the results could be influenced by an oversampling of people with lower socio-economic status (SES). Caron et al. (2012) reported the initial results of the first Epidemiological Catchment Area Study of mental health in Canada. This study is being conducted with a randomly selected sample of 2,433 people from the southwest sector of Montreal. Overall, Caron et al. (2012) found that the rate of psychological distress was 38%, which was almost double the rate found in the earlier Canadian Community Health Survey—Mental Health. The rate of diagnosable mental disorder was 17% (versus 11% in the general population). The study found that SES mattered. When compared with people with an annual income of $70,000 or more, people with less than $19,000 per year were 4.3 times more at risk of having a diagnosable mental disorder. The risk inherent among people who live in poverty is explored in more detail both later in this chapter and in Chapter 2.

Cost of Mental Health Problems

"A newly coined term, 'presenteeism,' describes those who currently work but are depressed and non-productive."

—Patrick J. White, President of the Canadian Psychiatric Association, February 2008

What is the cost of mental health problems in Canada? The cost in misery and human suffering among both the people who experience psychological problems and those they touch—their family, friends, and even strangers—is *incalculable*. An Ontario Ministry of Health study (1994) reported that disability costs to society, which often go unrecognized owing to the stigma attached to symptoms of mental disorders and their treatment, include (1) personal misery, (2) disruption of family life, (3) lower quality of life, and (4) loss of productivity. Regarding the last point, in Ontario the monthly total number of work days lost by people with mental disorders was estimated at more than 1.8 million in 1990.

Cost can also be expressed in terms of the disease burden for people: how it impacts life expectancy and the quality of life. A study from Ontario estimated that the burden of mental illness and addictions is 1.5 times greater than the combined burden of all cancers (see Ratnasingham et al., 2012). The five disorders with the highest amount of burden were depression, bipolar disorder, alcohol use disorders, social phobia, and schizophrenia. Depression by itself was deemed to have a higher level of burden than the combined burden of four types of cancer.

How does mental illness compare with other difficulties? Ormel et al. (2008) reported on the administration of epidemiological surveys in 15 countries through the World Health Organization Mental Health Survey initiative. It was found that respondents in both high-income and low- and middle-income countries attributed higher disability to mental disorders than to commonly occurring physical disorders. Further, this higher disability was limited to disability in social and personal role functioning. Productive role functioning was generally comparable for mental and physical disorders. Despite higher disability, mental disorders were generally under-treated in all countries.

The situation begs an answer to an urgent question: How can we ensure that care for Canadians with psychological disorders is both cost-efficient and effective? We must also ask ourselves: How much should we invest in finding and disseminating better treatments in order to reduce these costs, and how much should we invest in the prevention of disorders in the first place? These issues will be examined further in a later segment of this chapter.

Transformations in Canada's Mental Health System

The Romanow Report   The Government of Canada established the Commission on the Future of Health Care in

Canada in 2001 and appointed the former premier of Saskatchewan, Roy Romanow, as commissioner (see photo). The mandate was to engage Canadians in a national dialogue and to assess options for a long-term, sustainable, universally accessible, publicly funded health care system. Although the commission intended to examine mental health issues, various stakeholders formed an alliance (the Canadian Alliance on Mental Illness and Mental Health or CAMIMH) to address what they saw as two key policy weaknesses in the mental health area in Canada (see Canadian Psychiatric Association, 2002): (1) a fragmented constituency, and (2) the lack of a comprehensive national plan. CAMIMH is an alliance of five national organizations representing major consumer, family, community, and medical constituencies: the Canadian Mental Health Association, the Mood Disorders Association of Canada, the Schizophrenia Society of Canada, the National Network of Mental Health, and the Canadian Psychiatric Association. The accord reached meant that for the first time, these diverse interests could speak in a unified way about policies in Canada that affect the mentally ill. Among other things, the organization called for a national, coordinated action plan on mental illness and mental health. Other stakeholders in the mental health field, such as the Canadian Psychological Association, as well as private citizens, made presentations and submissions to Romanow at public hearings as he criss-crossed the country.

Romanow released his final report on November 28, 2002 (Romanow, 2002). A comprehensive template for the development of health care in Canada, it reaffirmed and expanded upon the five principles of the Canada Health Act. It also proposed sweeping changes to medicare and made 47 specific recommendations. Perhaps the central element of the report was the proposal to expand medicare coverage beyond just physicians

Fred Chartrand /The Canadian Press

Health care commissioner Roy Romanow recommended crucial changes to Canada's system.

and hospitals. We focus here on the mental health implications. Calling mental health the "orphan child of medicare," Romanow recommended that it be made a priority within the system. Of particular relevance, he recommended broadening medicare to include a limited number of home care services and, eventually, some drug treatments and a national drug agency.

The report's proposed expansion of the Canada Health Act would specifically include home care coverage for mental health case management and intervention services (over $500 million of new funding) as part of a $1-billion home care transfer. Romanow also proposed the establishment of a new program to provide direct support to informal caregivers (e.g., family and friends) to allow them to be away from work to provide necessary home care assistance at critical times. Although he stopped short of full pharmacare, he recommended a $1-billion "catastrophic drug transfer" to cover 50% of the cost of drug insurance plans in excess of $1,500 per person a year, a strategy that would improve access to necessary medications for people with severe, chronic psychiatric disorders such as schizophrenia and bipolar disorder. The report also called for an improvement in services to rural and remote communities, including Aboriginal communities. Consistent with our previous discussion of best practice models and evidence-based treatment, the report stated that the principle of **accountability** must be added to the Canada Health Act.

Numerous mental health professional and advocacy groups (e.g., CAMIMH) endorsed these and other key recommendations and urged the Minister of Health to include them in any proposed implementation plans, in order to offer hope to people with serious mental illnesses (see Canadian Psychological Association, 2003). Further, the proposed transformation strategies (such as for primary care and services to remote areas) were presumed to offer a chance to improve integration of primary care and mental health reforms. However, Romanow subsequently expressed frustration because his recommendations had not been implemented (Romanow, 2006; Walkom, 2003).

The Senate Committee Final Report

On May 9, 2006, the Senate Committee on Social Affairs, Science and Technology released its final report relating to mental health, mental illness, and addiction in Canada. Michael Kirby was chair (see photo) and Wilbert Keon deputy chair of the three-year study that culminated in the most comprehensive report on mental health in Canada ever completed. The committee held public hearings in every province and territory, offered two online questionnaires, received briefs (including from CMHA, CAMIMH, and CPA), conducted literature searches, and explored international innovations before preparing the report *Out of the Shadows at Last: Transforming Mental Health, Mental Illness and Addiction Services in Canada*, also known as the Kirby Report (Kirby & Keon, 2006). In a subsequent interview, Kirby stated:

> *"We managed to ignore the issue of mental health for a very long time. If you look at the services on the ground, they are hugely fragmented. There is no cohesive, patient-oriented system. Mental health*

THE CANADIAN PRESS/Sean Kilpatrick

Michael Kirby chaired the Senate study that resulted in a 2006 comprehensive report on mental health in Canada. After retiring from the Senate, he was subsequently appointed chair of the Mental Health Commission of Canada. Most recently, he was promoted to officer of the Order of Canada, which recognizes a lifetime of achievement and merit of a high degree, especially in service to Canada or to humanity at large.

> has not been at the top of the political agenda. The overwhelming reason for that is the stigma of mental health, which is the reason it has never had the kind of public support that other health issues, such as cancer, have had. The second reason is that services for the mentally ill do not fall under a single department—some aspects address health, others relate to housing or training."
>
> (Andresen, 2006, p. 39)

The Senate committee put forward 118 specific recommendations for transforming Canada's mental health system. Two recommendations were key—the creation of the Mental Health Commission of Canada and the Mental Health Transition Fund.

1. Mental Health Commission of Canada: The commission would pave the way for a national action plan. It would complement work being done by people and existing structures at all government levels and be designed according to two key principles: an independent not-for-profit organization at arm's length from governments and existing stakeholder organizations, and one with a central focus on those living with mental illness and their families. The committee recommended that the commission be composed of 19 members (one-third from governments and two-thirds without any government connection), independent of narrowly focused interest groups.

   The mission of the commission would be to:

   • Act as facilitator, enabler, and supporter of a national approach to mental health issues.
   • Be a catalyst for reform of mental health policies and improvements in service delivery.

• Educate all Canadians about mental health and increase mental health literacy.
• Diminish the stigma and discrimination faced by mentally ill Canadians and their families.

   The commission was agreed to by all the provinces and territories, except Quebec (for constitutional reasons). Its important work has been mentioned in several places in this chapter.

2. Mental Health Transition Fund: The Mental Health Transition Fund was created to allow the federal government to make a time-limited investment to cover transition costs and to speed the process of developing a community-based system of mental health service delivery. The provinces and territories would decide how to allocate the funds.

1.5   Delivery of Psychotherapy: Issues and Challenges

> "The best practice will continue to be based on the best science."
>
> —Alan E. Kazdin on evidence-based treatment and practice (2008, p. 157)

Restructuring health care services has implications for people treated with psychotherapy or a combination of psychological and biological interventions. Evaluation of the effectiveness of psychotherapy has become a significant issue because of the increasing demands placed on psychotherapists by both the universal health care system and third-party insurance companies (Hunsley & Johnston, 2000). Psychotherapists are being asked to restrict themselves to the most effective and efficient treatments. Professional organizations are becoming involved as well. For example, the Section on Clinical Psychology of the Canadian Psychological Association has been spearheading efforts to reach consensus on which treatments are supported by enough controlled data to be regarded as an **evidence-based treatment** or psychological practice (Hunsley, Dobson, Johnston, & Mikail, 1999; also see Epp & Dobson, 2010; Hunsley & Lee, 2007).

Since time-limited psychotherapy is available as an alternative to classic psychodynamic treatment, which sometimes requires many years, provincial governments concerned about cost-effectiveness are limiting or attempting to limit the use of classical analysis and other forms of long-term psychotherapy within the medicare system. Medication-based treatments benefit from the major marketing efforts of huge pharmaceutical companies. In contrast, evidence-based psychological and psychosocial interventions rarely reach the average client in a timely fashion and when they do, research on the quality of care for various disorders sometimes shows gaps between treatments shown to be efficacious in clinical research trials and the care provided people with these problems "in the real world," leading Unutzer (2008) to question if "this tremendous activity in clinical research is having an impact on the millions of patients living with depression and anxiety disorders or if this important work is 'getting lost in translation'" (p. 726).

What do the data indicate? Hunsley and Lee (2007) examined 35 "effectiveness" studies on a variety of disorders and concluded that improvement rates as a result of cognitive behavioural therapy were comparable in actual clinical practice to the improvement rates or outcomes ("efficacy") obtained in randomized, tightly controlled clinical trials within an experimental setting. (Cognitive behavioural therapy, which seeks to change people's thought patterns to help overcome some disorders, is discussed in later chapters.) The issues are complex. As noted by Kazdin (2008), "Researchers and clinicians alike see dangers in prescriptive and inflexible treatments" (p. 146). In fact, most psychological treatments are implemented in a flexible way (see Murphy et al., 2009). We will revisit these issues in Chapter 17.

Wait Times for Treatment

One of the most vexing problems for those who require mental health services is the problem of wait times. The Fraser Institute provides an annual report each year (see *Waiting Your Turn: Wait Times for Health Care in Canada,* see Barua & The Fraser Institute, 2015) and it includes an emphasis on access to psychiatric services. The national median wait time for those seeking psychiatric treatment (i.e., the time to begin a treatment program after being referred by a general practitioner to a psychiatric specialist) in 2015 was 19.8 weeks, which far exceeds what specialists believe is appropriate. More specific findings included the following:

- The shortest wait times were in Ontario, British Columbia, and Manitoba (15.8, 18.5, and 19.5 weeks, respectively).
- The longest wait times were in Newfoundland and Labrador (59.0 weeks) followed by New Brunswick (51.0 weeks). Data were not available for Prince Edward Island, which tends to historically have one of the longest wait times.
- The time spent waiting for treatment after an appointment with a specialist was longer than the wait to see a specialist after GP referral.
- The median wait time to see a psychiatrist on an urgent basis was 2.0 weeks, whereas on an elective basis it was 8.2 weeks.
- Among specific treatments surveyed, patients waited longest to enter a housing program (20.0 weeks), whereas wait times were shortest for pharmacotherapy (4.1 weeks). Wait times for an eating disorders program was 16.0 weeks.

The same conclusion reached in previous years was once again reached following the latest reports—that is, people in Canada continue to wait far too long for necessary treatment. (Barua & Fraser Institute, 2015).

The problem of long wait times continues to be a pressing national concern. It became the headline story in February 2016 when some Ontario parents said that a key factor when their daughter attacked students at her school was the hopelessness she experienced while waiting over a year and still not receiving mental health treatment. A group called the Wait Time Alliance concluded in 2014 that no significant progress has occurred in terms of reducing wait times (see www.waittimealliance.ca). Reports of wait times from at least three months to over a year have surfaced and seem far too common. Wait times of over one year for treatment for eating disorders have been discussed widely in the media. A federal report quotes psychiatrist Wendy Spettigue as having told the Parliamentary committee studying eating disorders that when the wait list for eating disorder treatment hit the one-year level, the Children's Hospital of Eastern Ontario decided to close its program because the situation was simply unacceptable; as a result, those on the waiting list were sent back to their family doctors in order to receive more immediate care (Report of the Standing Committee on the Status of Women, 2014). A web-based survey of 379 agencies in Canada found that only about 3 in 10 agencies providing treatment to children and adolescents were mostly or always able to meet the wait time benchmarks set out by the Canadian Psychiatric Association (Kowalewski, McLennan, & McGrath, 2011). Long wait times are believed to be playing a role in recent trends suggesting that there is a dramatic 53% increase in children and adolescents presenting to hospital emergency rooms due to mental health problems (Canadian Institute for Health Information, 2015). Clearly, a very important question to keep asking is what is happening in each province to proactively address unmet needs and shorten wait times in order to address not only current concerns but also anticipated concerns as the Canadian population continues to grow and there is an increasing proportion of older Canadians. The lack of timely access for seniors is also a very salient and growing concern.

Help-Seeking and Perceived Need for Help

The problem of lengthy wait times would be substantially greater if everyone in Canada who needed it asked for help. Extensive evidence indicates that the majority of people who need help do not seek it. For instance, the Ontario Health Survey (*Mental Health Supplement*) determined that 7.8% of respondents used mental health services in the past year (Lin et al., 1996). About half of those seeking help had a concurrent psychiatric diagnosis. The vast majority sought help from outpatient service providers. Over 75% of those with a disorder in the past year did not seek help; however, 27.1% of those who sought help did not qualify for a diagnosis. Lin et al. (1996) concluded that there is a mismatch between people's needs and the care received. Although the strongest predictor of help-seeking was psychiatric diagnosis, help-seeking was also associated with marital disruption and poverty.

Another study confirms that professional services are underused. The Women's Health Study conducted in Ontario found that only about 5 out of 10 women with at least one lifetime psychiatric disorder sought mental health services (Frise et al., 2002). The presence of three or more disorders—called "comorbid" if they exist simultaneously—was associated with increased likelihood of seeking help, but it was still the case that 35% of women with three or more disorders did not seek help.

This problem of underuse may be underestimated because women are actually more willing to seek help than men. An analysis of data from the *Mental Health Supplement* to the Ontario Health Survey confirmed the existence of gender differences in the use of outpatient mental health services for mood disorders, anxiety disorders, substance-use disorders, and anti-social behaviours (Rhodes, Goering, To, & Williams, 2002). Moreover, these gender differences remain evident after controlling for differences in type of mental disorder and associated differences in social and economic factors. Vasiliadis, Tempier, Lesage, and Kates (2009) reported that men are less likely to consult with a family physician and other resources (although not with a psychiatrist). They concluded that there is a need to design promotional campaigns emphasizing the need for men to seek mental health care.

One of our motives in writing this book is to highlight issues that pertain to young people aged 15 to 24 years old, who are considered to be in a category that researchers refer to as "emerging adults." Many readers of this book are in the emerging adult category. What is known about the mental health needs and service use of emerging adults? Bergeron et al. (2005) examined a subsample of young Canadians (aged 15 to 24 years) from the CCHS data set who were identified as having a mood disorder, an anxiety disorder, or a substance-related disorder in the 12 months preceding the survey. They concluded that there is a particular need for interventions to encourage service use in young men, young persons living with their parents or unrelated others, and young people diagnosed with an anxiety or a substance-related disorder (relative to those with a mood disorder). The need to encourage help-seeking among young men was also noted by Marcus et al. (2012) in their study of mental health literacy because of a tendency for young adult males to prefer to solve mental health problems on their own.

Findlay and Sunderland (2014) investigated the mental health supports and service use for Canadians between the ages of 15 to 24 years by examining results from the 2012 Canadian Community Health Survey—Mental Health. Overall, 12% reported consulting health professionals about emotional, mental health, or substance abuse problems in the past year, but 27% consulted informal sources such as family or friends. The decision to consult other people was predicted by three factors (i.e., having a chronic physical condition, having a higher level of distress, or having experienced a traumatic experience in childhood). Two findings are particularly troubling. First, many young people relied solely on the Internet, and hopefully acquired accurate information. The authors highlighted the fact that the Internet is not regulated and as a result, there is a need to develop e-health literacy in young people (as well as people in general). Second, only about half of those with a mental disorder and only 1 in 4 with a substance disorder used professional services. Thus, it seems that many young people are not seeking help and a substantial proportion of these young

people may be hiding their distress behind a front or façade. As we see below, this may help set the stage for deaths due to suicide.

Completed suicide is the second-leading cause of death for young Canadians (see Cheung & Dewa, 2007), and as indicated above, many depressed and suicidal adolescents and young adults do not receive mental health services. Cheung and Dewa (2007) used data from the CCHS to identify young people, aged 15 to 24 years, who screened positive for depression and suicidality in the past 12 months. Their findings confirmed that almost 50% of adolescents and young adults with depression and suicidality do not access any mental health services. Another stark indication of the consequences of the failure to seek help can be found in statistics from Ontario. An analysis was conducted of the 370 adolescent suicides that took place between the years 2000 to 2006 (Soor et al., 2012). Analyses were based on data obtained from the Office of the Chief Coroner of Ontario. Among Canadians of all ages, there is usually a 3:1 or 4:1 gender difference in completed suicides (that is, males are three to four times as likely as females to commit suicide). However, this study found that among younger people, there was increased suicide among females, with there being a 2:1 ratio of suicide among adolescent males versus females. More importantly, it was found that only 66 of the 370 adolescents who took their lives had previously received psychological treatment of any kind. Given that the vast majority did not receive any form of treatment, there is a strong possibility that many of the adolescents who killed themselves had a suicide without any apparent warning signs. The major clinical implications of these data are obvious: there is a need to increase service use in depressed and suicidal young people and reduce the unwillingness to seek help.

To what extent do you university students and college students seek help when it is needed? This issue is the focus of Student Perspectives 1.1.

The greater risk associated with low SES seems to be due, at least in part, to widespread socio-economic disparities in accessing the system. Steele, Glazier, and Lin (2006) made the point that simply having a system that theoretically provides universal and equitable coverage is not enough. Their study, conducted in Toronto, found that people with high SES, relative to people living in the lowest SES neighbourhoods, were 1.6 times more likely to use psychiatric services (even though poverty contributes to a greater prevalence of mental disorder). It seems that little has changed in recent years. These data point to the need to develop outreach programs that target low-income people and implement innovations that enhance their access to treatment.

The Human Costs of Deinstitutionalization and Limited Access to Service

As stated previously, Canada has undergone an extensive process of psychiatric bed reduction and closure. Unfortunately, the consequences of **deinstitutionalization** in an

Student Perspectives 1.1

Help-Seeking Attitudes and Behaviours in University and College Students

We have seen that only a relatively small proportion of those who need to seek help actually do so. Is it any different for university and college students? Unfortunately, the situation is the same and research here sometimes yields findings that seem paradoxical, at least on the surface. An investigation of 302 Australian university students found that as levels of suicide ideation went up, respondents reported less willingness to seek help from family, friends, and professional mental health care providers. This tendency was exacerbated among those who had suicide ideation and high levels of depressive symptoms (Wilson & Deane, 2010). The pattern of findings is consistent with a follow-up study of over 5,000 high school students that found once again that as depression levels increase, there is less willingness to seek help from anyone (Sawyer et al., 2012). It seems that many students are suffering in silence and they are not getting help.

Eisenberg and his colleagues conducted a much broader investigation. Online surveys assessed students from 26 campuses around the United States. Overall, among those deemed in need, only 36% received any treatment in the previous year and the proportion of students who used psychotherapy was about the same as the proportion who used medication. Predictors of not seeking help included low perceived urgency and a negative attitude about the usefulness of help (Eisenberg, Hunt, Speer, & Zivin, 2011).

What are some other predictors of negative help-seeking attitudes among students? A comprehensive analysis of 19 previous studies involving over 7,000 participants focused on nine predictors. Nam et al. (2013) found that almost all nine factors were associated with more negative help-seeking attitudes, but the three most robust predictors were self-stigma (i.e., internalized stigma beliefs), negative beliefs about anticipated benefits, and low levels of trait self-disclosure. Recent data indicate that anticipated benefits still facilitate help-seeking, while perceived barriers to help-seeking tend to contribute to more negative overall attitudes (Kim & Zane, in press). This study was conducted in the United States and found that Asian American students, relative to White American students, had less favourable attitudes overall.

One barrier for university and college students seeking psychological treatment is the coverage available to students through extended health insurance programs. A recent national survey found that most available programs in Canada cover the costs of drug treatment up to a yearly maximum of $3,000 in the majority of instances. However, the modal level of treatment coverage for psychological treatment was between $300 and $500. Thus, very few plans allow for necessary psychological treatment (see Nunes et al., 2014).

Thinking Critically

1. Do you believe that other students do in fact secretly hold stigmatizing beliefs and would react negatively to a fellow student who sought help? Or is today's university student less likely to hold negative opinions?

2. If you were going to design a brochure for students to get them to seek help, what key messages would you emphasize? What would you tell students who say they are simply too busy to get help? Do you have insights that might help explain why males are less likely to get help?

---

era of escalating needs for services are multiple and include homelessness and a lack of supported housing, the jailing of the mentally ill, the failure to achieve an ideal of community-focused care for people with mental disorders, a lack of home care, insufficient intensive case management, too few community-based crisis response systems, concerns about community treatment orders, and so forth. Although deinstitutionalization was a well-intended attempt to reintegrate the mentally ill with the rest of Canadian society and to prevent involuntary hospitalization and treatment, to this point many professionals and "psychiatric survivors" or "consumers" would consider it an abject failure. We will revisit some of these issues in Chapter 18.

At the beginning of this century, there were approximately 370 general-hospital psychiatric units in Canada, providing about 10,000 inpatient beds with provincially mandated services that include inpatient care, outpatient care, daycare, emergency care, and consultation (Goering et al., 2000). However, the preferred mental health service model is one that emphasizes intensive local community supports and services, along with the general-hospital psychiatric units and regional tertiary care centres (the provincial psychiatric hospitals or their replacements).

The most recent Canadian Institute for Health Information analysis (from 2008) reported that psychiatric patients are being discharged earlier. The shorter general hospital stays were hypothesized to be due to the pressure to free up hospital beds, which frequently results in people being discharged prematurely. As noted by Dr. Patrick White, President of the Canadian Psychiatric Association, "there's continuous pressure to get patients admitted, treated and out" (Tam, 2008).

We will briefly mention two national problems that are the subject of a more extensive analysis in Chapter 18: (1) homelessness and mental illness and (2) the jailing of mentally ill people. It is important to take a closer look at homelessness and mental illness due to the magnitude of the problems and the continuing need for services and effective solutions. Clearly, for some people, mental illness had contributed to homelessness, while for others, the experience of becoming homeless has contributed to mental health problems. But, of course, it is important to reiterate that only a proportion of people who are homeless are mentally ill.

While much of the research on homelessness is cross-sectional and focused on only one time point, a longitudinal study conducted with young people in the United States indicates that it is possible to use psychological vulnerabilities to identify those who are more likely to become homeless. Participants were first assessed in 1994–95 when they were between the ages of 11 to 18 and then they were followed up in 2001 when they were now in the age range of 18 to 28 years old. It was found at follow-up that among the more than 10,000 participants, 428 had been homeless at some point since first being assessed. All of the risk factors evaluated at Time 1 were significant individual predictors of subsequent homelessness, including higher levels of depression, lower levels of self-esteem, delinquency, substance use, and poorer neighbourhood quality. A regression analysis showed that the three most robust and independent predictors were poor family relationship quality, school adjustment problems, and experiences of victimization (see van den Bree et al., 2009). Thus, for many, homelessness is a reflection of earlier challenges and earlier vulnerabilities, but we must also allow for the fact that for many, homelessness is simply rooted in misfortune or possibly starting out life in a family dealing with poverty.

Multiple factors have contributed to an increase in the number of mentally ill homeless people in Canada. While the primary focus is on deinstitutionalization, organizations such as the Canadian Alliance on Mental Illness and Mental Health point to the period in the 1990s when provincial governments decreased welfare benefits and did not invest sufficiently in social housing (see www.camimh.ca).

Another pressing problem is the use of incarceration as a way of addressing mental health problems among prisoners. This is a problem experienced in many areas of the world. A shocking report in 2010 from E. Fuller Torrey and his associates, which was based on data from 2004–05, concluded that in the United States, there are many more mentally ill people in jails and in prisons than in hospitals (see Torrey et al., 2010). How many more? They reported that there were 300% more patients with serious mental illness incarcerated than in hospitals. An editorial in the journal *Current Psychiatry* called this a crisis that has reached the point where the incarceration of mentally ill people is at the levels that existed in the 1840s (see Nasrallah, 2012). The editorial stated that deinstitutionalization has gone too far and asked, "Why are we building more jails and prisons instead of therapeutic communities?" (p. 4). In 2010, there was only one psychiatric bed per 3,000 Americans, whereas in 1955, there was one psychiatric bed per 300 Americans. This editorial concluded with a plea for a modern-day Dorothea Dix to illuminate this problem.

The issue of incarcerating mentally ill people became an extremely salient one in Canada as a result of the case of Ashley Smith, who strangled herself in 2007 at the Grand Valley Institution for Women in Kitchener, Ontario. In total, Smith had been shuffled between an estimated 17 prisons and treatment centres in the past year. Prison staff members were seemingly in a position to intervene but did not stop the suicide from occurring. Did her extensive history of aggressive behaviour and acting out merit a more proactive approach that would have resulted in better treatment? Do you think her death could have been prevented?

Public debate about this situation continues at the national level. In October 2012, the Canadian Psychological Association and the Canadian Psychiatric Association issued a joint appeal for urgent action to address the mental health needs of mentally ill people in jails and prisons. In the meantime, the 2012 national report from the Office of the Correctional Investigator indicates that the problems in Canada are growing at a troubling rate (see Correctional Investigator of Canada, 2012). Rates of mental illness detected at intake doubled between 1997 and 2008. Overall, 13% of male inmates and 29% of women inmates have mental health problems at intake. The mental health needs of women are particularly acute. Estimates indicate that 50% of federally sentenced women report histories of self-harm, and over half report a current or past addiction. In addition, 85% report a history of physical abuse and 68% report a history of sexual abuse.

The Correctional Investigator of Canada, Howard Sapers, identified seven urgent mental health needs in his report, including the following:

- Create intermediate health care units.
- Increase capacity at regional treatment centres.
- Recruit and retain more mental health professionals.
- Expand the range of alternative mental health service delivery partnerships with the provinces and territories.

As noted above, these issues will be re-examined in Chapter 18 where the focus is on legal and ethical issues, including the issue of the rights of mental patients.

Community Psychology and Prevention

Much of our discussion of therapy and interventions has focused on situations in which professionals make themselves available to clients in offices, clinics, or hospitals. This type of service delivery, long referred to as "the waiting mode" (Rappaport & Chinsky, 1974), is characteristic of traditional therapy, whether inpatient or outpatient. **Community psychology** in contrast, operates in "the seeking mode." Rather than waiting for people to initiate contact, community psychologists seek out problems, or even potential problems. They often focus on **prevention**, in contrast to the more usual situation of trying to reduce the severity or duration of an existing problem. We must focus to a much greater degree on preventive measures if we are ever going to solve the problem of mental illness in Canada. In particular, there is a need for programs that promote the psychological, social, and physical well-being of all people in Canada.

Although we have had some success, we have a long way to go. For example, despite a proclamation by governments in Canada that child poverty would be eliminated by the year 2000, it actually increased (Denton, 2000). Nonetheless, there are ongoing programs that promise to fulfill prevention goals in the future. Here is one example. In 1995 the federal government established Aboriginal Head Start to help the development and school readiness of Aboriginal children by meeting their psychological, emotional, social, health, and nutritional needs. The initiative is intended to "encourage the development of locally controlled projects in First Nations communities that strive to instill a sense of pride, a desire to learn, provide parenting skills, foster emotional and social development, increase confidence, and improve family relationships" (Health Canada, 1998, p. 1). The program has continued to expand and, as of 2010, receives $59 million annually for over 9,000 children in more than 300 Aboriginal Head Start programs.

We will examine prevention and community psychology programs throughout this book. These programs often focus on attempting to reduce "risk" factors and to facilitate the development of "protective" factors (see Chapter 2). Examples of these programs include:

- efforts to prevent educational deficits and associated social and economic disadvantages
- eating-disorder prevention programs
- programs for the early detection and prevention of schizophrenia
- school-based prevention and early intervention programs for anxiety
- school-based programs for the prevention of cigarette smoking
- the establishment of suicide prevention centres with telephone hotlines that desperate people can use to survive a suicidal crisis
- a parent and child training program for francophones in Montreal to prevent early onset of delinquent behaviour.

Consistent with the Aboriginal Head Start program, many prevention programs in Canada focus on children (see Prilleltensky & Nelson, 2000). According to Nelson, Lavoie, and Mitchell (2007), Quebec led the way in progressive prevention policies, including its $7 per day childcare program, and in developing an infrastructure for community-based prevention programs. Further, while numerous programs emphasize interventions that reduce the incidence of disorder, governments in Canada, led by the federal government (see Government of Canada, 2006), are increasingly focusing on *mental health promotion;* that is, they are concentrating on enhanced functioning, well-being, and optimal functioning. (For a discussion of the distinctions between prevention and promotion and Canadian guidelines and proposals, see Epp [1988], *Mental Health for Canadians: Striking a Balance.*) Unfortunately, widespread prevention and promotion programs are simply not possible in Canada with the current resources available. Nonetheless, the contributions of community psychologists are numerous

and varied, especially in Quebec, which has made a greater commitment to promotion and prevention in health care and social policies relative to other provinces (see Nelson et al., 2007).

A New Beginning: Canada's Mental Health Strategy

A good place to end this chapter is by providing a summary of Canada's new beginning that was unveiled in 2012. The announcement of Canada's national mental health strategy was long overdue but it is clear that the time is right for building momentum for progress on the mental health front. You are encouraged to read the full document when time permits (see http://strategy.mentalhealthcommission.ca/pdf/strategy-images-en.pdf). You will see that this extensive document, titled *Changing Directions, Changing Lives,* is built on six key strategic directions. These strategic directions represent important values and goals that touch on many themes included throughout this book. The six strategic directions are the following:

- Promote mental health across the lifespan in homes, schools, and workplaces, and prevent mental illness and suicide wherever possible.
- Foster recovery and well-being for people of all ages living with mental health problems and illness, and uphold their rights.
- Provide access to the right combination of services, treatments, and supports, when and where people need them.
- Reduce disparities in risk factors and access to mental health services, and strengthen the response to the needs to diverse communities and Northerners.
- Work with First Nation, Inuit, and Metis citizens to address their distinct mental health needs, acknowledging their unique circumstances, rights, and cultures.
- Mobilize leadership, improve knowledge, and foster collaboration at all levels.

This plan will work only to the extent that public and private resources are dedicated to the mental health and well-being of people in Canada. Resources need not be entirely financial, so if you have the opportunity to volunteer your time, you should definitely consider doing so. In fact, volunteerism is a protective factor that improves most people's mental health, especially when they are simply motivated by the desire to help (Weinstein & Ryan, 2010).

Summary

1.1 The study of psychopathology is a search for why people behave, think, and feel in unexpected, sometimes bizarre, and typically self-defeating ways. Much less is known than we would like. Several

characteristics are considered in evaluating whether a behaviour is abnormal: statistical infrequency, violation of societal norms, personal distress, disability or dysfunction, and unexpectedness. Each characteristic tells us something about what can be considered abnormal, but none by itself provides a fully satisfactory definition. It is impossible to offer a simple definition that captures abnormality in its entirety.

1.2 The field of abnormal psychology has its origins in ancient demonology and crude medical theorizing. Since the beginning of scientific inquiry into abnormal behaviour, two major points of view have vied for attention: the somatogenic, which assumes that every mental aberration is caused by a physical malfunction; and the psychogenic, which assumes that the person's body is intact and that difficulties are to be explained in psychological terms. The somatogenic viewpoint originated in the writings of Hippocrates. After the fall of Greco-Roman civilization, it became less prominent, but then re-emerged in the eighteenth and nineteenth centuries through the writings of such people as Kraepelin. The psychogenic viewpoint is akin to early demonology. Its more modern version emerged in the nineteenth century from the work of Charcot and the seminal writings of Breuer and Freud. A number of issues and events are of historical and current relevance to students in a Canadian setting or to students who are particularly interested in developments in Canada. For example, Dorothea Dix played an influential role and there was a confluence of factors that led to the development of the first asylums, and that ushered in the institution-building era in Canada. Despite humane motives, the long-term results were not very positive, as can be seen by the treatment provided in some provincial psychiatric hospitals in the latter part of the twentieth century. In Canada the current emphasis is on psychiatric hospital bed reduction and closure.

1.3 There is ongoing concern about mental health stigma (i.e., negative attitudes and stereotypes about mentally ill people). Stigma internalized into a self-view is known as self-stigma. Extensive anti-stigma initiatives and mental health literacy campaigns are taking place in Canada and elsewhere. While significant progress has been made, it is still the case that a very substantial proportion of people endorse stereotyped views of mentally ill people and a proportion of these people turn these inappropriate views on themselves when they suffer mental illness.

1.4 The mental health system in Canada is closely tied to medicare, the universal health care system. The system will face many challenges in the future. There is a need for an increased focus on and funding for community-based interventions and prevention programs. The report from the Commission on the Future of Health Care in Canada (the Romanow Report) recommended that mental health be made a priority within the system. Specific recommendations included broadening medicare to include a limited number of home care services and some drug treatments. The Senate Committee Final Report (the Kirby Report) relating to mental health, mental illness, and addiction made 118 recommendations, including establishing a Canadian mental health commission to focus national attention on mental illness, and a proposal to fund the development of a community-based system of mental health service delivery.

1.5 There are many challenges related to psychotherapy and providing treatment. Deinstitutionalization and decreased government support have complicated the mental health problems experienced by certain homeless people. The timely delivery of services and growing wait lists are related challenges. Canada also has many improvements to make in terms of delivering mental health services to prisoners in jails and prisons and ensuring that people who should receive treatment do not instead end up incarcerated in a correctional facility. One positive development in the treatment of mental health problems was the release of the document *Changing Directions, Changing Lives,* which outlines our new national mental health strategy. This strategy has at its centre six strategic directions that emphasize such themes as mental health promotion, access to services and treatment, and the reduction of disparities in risk factors while remaining mindful of the rights of people from unique cultures.

Key Terms

abnormal behaviour
accountability
assessment
asylums
bedlam
Canadian Mental Health Association
cathartic method
clinical psychologist
clinicians
community psychology
community treatment order
counselling psychologist
deinstitutionalization
demonology

diagnosis
dissociative identity disorder
evidence-based treatment
exorcism
general paresis
germ theory of disease
medicare
mental health literacy
moral treatment
normal curve
prescriptive authority
prevention
provincial psychiatric hospital
psychiatrist

psychoactive drugs
psychoanalyst
psychogenesis
psychopathology
psychotherapy
schizophrenia
self-stigma
social worker
somatogenesis
stereotyping
stigmatization
syndrome
transinstitutionalization
trepanning

Reflections: Past, Present, and Future

1. Think about the material presented in this chapter and develop your own comprehensive definition of abnormal psychology. When you have finished the exercise, turn to Chapter 3 and think about how disorders are described and classified.

2. Think of someone you have heard about (or possibly someone you know) who appears to suffer from a psychological disorder or to behave abnormally at times. How would you conceptualize that person's disorder or behaviour in terms of the somatogenic and psychogenic hypotheses? We will examine modern scientific perspectives in the next chapter. You should know that current views typically integrate several perspectives or paradigms.

3. Is mental health the "orphan child" of medicare? Would you and your family and friends be willing to pay an extra nickel a drink to help cover most of the cost of the Senate Committee's proposed Mental Health Transition Fund?

4. How should we try to help the person who has a psychological disorder or problem? Are you in favour of biological interventions, psychological treatments, self-help, or social change? Do our views about the causes of psychological disorders affect our beliefs in how they should be treated?

Current Paradigms and Integrative Approaches

LEARNING OBJECTIVES

1. Explain what a paradigm is and the role of paradigms.

2. Describe the biological paradigm and how it is studied.

3. List the key assumptions of the cognitive-behavioural paradigm.

4. Describe the psychoanalytic paradigm and why it is still relevant.

5. Describe the humanistic paradigm and its treatment implications.

6. Explain how and why the paradigm adopted is important.

7. Discuss psychosocial influences on mental health.

8. Explain how the cultural context can contribute to mental health problems.

9. Identify and explain two integrative paradigms.

In Chapter 2, we consider current paradigms of abnormal behaviour and treatment. A paradigm is a set of basic assumptions—a general perspective that defines how to conceptualize and study a subject, how to gather and interpret relevant data, even how to think about a particular subject. Our discussion of paradigms lays the groundwork for the examination of the major categories of disorders and intervention. Following our discussion of paradigms, we will examine factors outside the person that influence mental health and integrative models that reflect how factors combine to contribute to mental health.

2.1 The Role of Paradigms

Science is bound by the limitations imposed on scientific inquiry by the current state of knowledge. It is also bound by whether the scientist can remain objective when trying to understand and study abnormal behaviour. Unfortunately, science is not a completely objective and certain enterprise. Rather, as suggested by philosopher of science Thomas Kuhn (1962), subjective factors as well as limitations in our perspective on the universe enter into the conduct of scientific inquiry.

Central to any application of scientific principles, in Kuhn's view, is the notion of **paradigm**, the conceptual framework or approach within which the scientist works. A paradigm is a set of basic assumptions that outline the particular universe of scientific inquiry. It has profound implications for how scientists operate, for "[people] whose research is based on shared paradigms are committed to the same rules and standards for scientific practice" (Kuhn, 1962, p. 11). Paradigms specify what problems scientists will investigate and how they will go about the investigation. Paradigms are an intrinsic part of a science, serving the vital function of indicating the rules to be followed.

A paradigm injects inevitable biases into the definition and collection of data and may also affect the interpretation of facts. In other words, the meaning or import given to data may depend to a considerable extent on a paradigm. In this chapter, we will describe the major paradigms of abnormal psychology and provide an idea of how they operate. We first present four major types of paradigms: biological, cognitive-behavioural, psychoanalytic, and humanistic. The psychodynamic and humanistic paradigms have become less influential over the years, but have some modern applications and themes that continue to have a significant impact.

Our discussion of each paradigm will conclude with an evaluation section. These sections will focus on the paradigm itself and, briefly, on treatment. Treatments will be evaluated in greater detail in the chapters dealing with specific disorders as well as in Chapter 17.

Current thinking about abnormal behaviour tends to be multi-faceted, and contemporary views of abnormal behaviour and its treatment tend to integrate several paradigms. Accordingly, later in this chapter we will describe two highly influential paradigms—the diathesis–stress and biopsychosocial—that provide the basis for an integrative approach.

2.2 The Biological Paradigm

"Biology will not replace psychology within our explanatory systems. Rather we will slowly clarify, through progress in neuroscience, how the brain implements psychological functions. That iterative process will deepen our understanding of both biological and psychological processes."

—*Kenneth S. Kendler, 2008, p. 700*

The **biological paradigm** of abnormal behaviour is a continuation of the somatogenic hypothesis. This broad perspective holds that mental disorders are caused by aberrant biological processes. This paradigm has often been referred to as the **medical model** or **disease model**.

The study of abnormal behaviour is linked historically to medicine. Early and contemporary workers have used the model of physical illness as the basis for understanding deviant behaviour. Within the field of abnormal behaviour, the terminology of medicine is pervasive. Medical illnesses can differ widely from one another in their causes. However, they all share one characteristic: in all of them, some biological process is disrupted or not functioning normally. That is why we call this the biological paradigm.

The biological paradigm was the dominant paradigm in Canada and elsewhere from the late 1800s until at least the middle of the twentieth century. An extreme example of its influence is Hall's (1900) use of gynaecological procedures to treat "insanity" in women from British Columbia. He maintained that "insanity exists when the Ego is dominated and controlled by the influence from a diseased periphery nerve tract or center . . . the removal of a small part of the physical disease might result in the restoration of the balance of power to such an organism and diminish if not remove the abnormal psychic phenomena" (Hall, 1900, p. 3). Removal of ovarian cysts or the entire ovaries was employed as treatment for melancholia, mania, and delusions. In one such example, "Mrs. D" was reported to have delusions that her husband was trying to poison her, and she would frequently wander away from home. Her behaviour was attributed to a cyst "the size of a walnut," and both her ovaries were removed as the form of treatment.

Contemporary Approaches to the Biological Paradigm

More sophisticated approaches are used today, of course, and there is now an extensive literature on biological factors relevant to psychopathology. Heredity probably predisposes a person to have an increased risk of developing schizophrenia (see Chapter 11), depression may result from chemical imbalances within the brain (Chapter 8), anxiety disorders may stem from a defect within the autonomic nervous system that causes a person to be too easily aroused (Chapter 5), and dementia can be traced to impairments in structures of the brain (Chapter 16). In each case, the psychopathology is viewed as caused by the disturbance of some biological process. Those working with the biological paradigm assume that answers to puzzles of psychopathology will be found within the body. In this section, we will look at three areas of research within this paradigm in which the data are particularly interesting: behaviour genetics, molecular genetics, and biochemistry.

Behaviour Genetics   When the ovum, the female reproductive cell, is joined by the male's spermatozoon, a zygote, or fertilized egg, is produced. It has 46 chromosomes, the number characteristic of a human being. Each chromosome is made up of thousands of **genes**, the carriers of the genetic information (DNA) passed from parents to child.

Behaviour genetics is the study of individual differences in behaviour that are attributable in part to differences in genetic makeup. The total genetic makeup of an individual, consisting of inherited genes, is referred to as the genotype. An individual's **genotype** is his or her unobservable genetic constitution; in contrast, an individual's **phenotype** is the totality of his or her observable, behavioural characteristics, such as level of anxiety. The genotype is fixed at birth, but it should not be viewed as a static entity. Genes controlling various features of development switch off and on at specific times to control aspects of physical development. An example of genetic research is a project led by Kerry Jang (see photo) and John Livesley that examines genetic factors in personality dysfunction.

The phenotype changes over time and is viewed as the product of an interaction between the genotype and the environment. For example, an individual may be born with the capacity for high intellectual achievement, but whether he or she develops this genetically given potential depends on such environmental factors as upbringing and education. Hence, any measure of intelligence is best viewed as an index of the phenotype.

It is critical to recognize that various clinical syndromes are disorders of the phenotype, not of the genotype. Thus, it is not correct to speak of the direct inheritance of schizophrenia or anxiety disorders; at most, only the genotypes for these disorders can be inherited. Whether these genotypes will eventually engender the phenotypic behaviour disorder will depend on environment and experience. A predisposition, also known as a *diathesis,* may be inherited, but not the disorder itself.

The study of behaviour genetics has relied on four basic methods to uncover whether a predisposition for psychopathology is inherited: comparison of members of a family,

Courtesy Kerry Jang

Behaviour genetics studies the degree to which characteristics such as physical resemblance or psychopathology are shared by family members because of shared genes. The University of British Columbia twin study led by Kerry Jang (shown here) and John Livesley is a long-term investigation of the contribution of shared genes to personality factors and behavioural disorders.

comparison of pairs of twins, the investigation of adoptees, and linkage analysis. The **family method** can be used to study a genetic predisposition among members of a family because the average number of genes shared by two blood relatives is known. Children receive a random sample of half their genes from one parent and half from the other; therefore, on average, siblings as well as parents and their children are identical in 50% of their genetic background. People who share 50% of their genes with a given individual are called *first-degree relatives* of that person. Relatives not as closely related share fewer genes. Nephews and nieces share 25% of the genetic makeup of an uncle and are called *second-degree relatives*. If a predisposition for a mental disorder can be inherited, a study of the family should reveal a relationship between the number of shared genes and the prevalence of the disorder in relatives.

The starting point in such investigations is the collection of a sample of individuals who bear the diagnosis in question. These people are referred to as **index cases**, or **probands**. Then, relatives are studied to determine the frequency with which the same diagnosis might be applied to them. If a genetic predisposition to the disorder being studied is present, first-degree relatives of the index cases should have the disorder at a rate higher than that found in the general population. For example, about 10% of the first-degree relatives of index cases with schizophrenia can be diagnosed as having schizophrenia, compared with about 1% of the general population.

In the **twin method**, both **monozygotic (MZ) twins** and **dizygotic (DZ) twins** are compared. MZ, or identical, twins develop from a single fertilized egg and, typically, they are genetically the same. DZ, or fraternal, pairs develop from separate eggs

and are on average only 50% alike genetically, no more alike than any other two siblings. MZ twins are always the same sex, but DZ twins can be either the same or the opposite sex. Twin studies begin with diagnosed cases and then search for the presence of the disorder in the other twin. When the twins are similar diagnostically, they are said to be concordant. To the extent that a predisposition for a mental disorder can be inherited, **concordance** for the disorder should be greater in genetically identical MZ pairs than in DZ pairs. When the MZ concordance rate is higher than the DZ rate, the characteristic being studied is said to be heritable. We will see in later chapters that the concordance for many forms of psychopathology is higher in MZ twins than in DZ twins. Extensive research at the University of British Columbia has been conducted on over 2000 twins. This work led by Kerry Jang (2012) has provided some revealing findings, including data suggesting that resilience has a genetic component (see Jang, 2012).

It was indicated above that MZ twins are typically the same in terms of genetic background, but this is not always the case. A growing number of studies have identified MZ twins who differ both genetically and epigenetically in terms of developmental changes in gene expression (see Bruder et al., 2008; Haque, Gottesmann, & Wong, 2009). So while it is usually the case, it is not always the case that identical twins are identical! Factors that account for genetic variations include physiological abnormalities that occurred during gestation and fetal development that result in the twins not really having the same genes. Differences detected between adult MZ twins could reflect differences in life experiences and the timing of life experiences that influence how the genes are expressed throughout life. While the genetic similarities are much greater among MZ versus DZ twins, there is great information value when there are slight genetic differences between MZ twins and one develops a physical difficulty or mental health affliction that is not found in their twin brother or sister.

Although the methodology of the family and twin studies is clear, as indicated above, the data they yield are not always easy to interpret. Let us assume that children of parents with panic disorder (see Chapter 5) are themselves more likely than average to have panic disorder. Does this mean that a predisposition for this anxiety disorder is genetically transmitted? Not necessarily. The greater number of children with panic disorder could reflect the child-rearing practices of the panic disorder parents, as well as the children's imitation of adult behaviour. In other words, the data show that panic disorder runs in families, but that a genetic predisposition is not necessarily involved.

The ability to offer a genetic interpretation of data from twin studies hinges greatly on what is called the *equal environment assumption*. The equal environment assumption is that the environmental factors that are partial causes of concordance are equally influential for MZ pairs and DZ pairs. This does not mean that the environments of MZ and DZ twins are equal in all respects. The equal environment assumption would assert that MZ pairs and DZ pairs have equivalent numbers of stressful life experiences.

Researchers using the **adoptees method** study children with abnormal disorders who were adopted and reared apart from their parents. Though infrequent, this situation has the benefit of eliminating the effects of being raised by disordered parents. If a high frequency of panic disorder were found in children reared apart from parents who also had panic disorder, we would have support for the theory that a genetic predisposition figures in the disorder. (The study of MZ twins reared apart would also be valuable, but this situation has little practical value because it so rarely can be tested in the study of psychopathology. Research involving separated twins does, however, exist in the study of the inheritance of personality traits, as we will see in Chapter 13.)

Molecular Genetics

Molecular genetics is a highly advanced approach that goes beyond mere attempts to show whether a disorder has a genetic component; it tries to specify the particular gene or genes involved and the precise functions of these genes.

Each cell consists of the 46 chromosomes (23 pairs) with thousands of genes per chromosome. The chromosomes are our genetic material and one of each pair comes from a person's mother and father. An *allele* is any one of several DNA codings that occupy the same position or location on a chromosome. A person's genotype is his or her set of alleles.

Genetic polymorphism is the variability that occurs among members of the species. It involves differences in the DNA sequence that can manifest in very different forms among members in the same habitat. It entails mutations in a chromosome that can be induced or naturally occurring.

For many years, genetic discoveries involving humans have primarily been the product of extensive lines of research conducted initially with animals. Discoveries are made in animal research, and then, where feasible, the generalizability and applicability to humans has been evaluated.

Linkage analysis is a method in molecular genetics used to study people. Researchers using this method typically study families in which a disorder is heavily concentrated. They collect diagnostic information and blood samples from affected individuals and their relatives and use the blood samples to study the inheritance pattern of characteristics whose genetics are fully understood, referred to as *genetic markers*. Eye colour, for example, is known to be controlled by a gene in a specific location on a specific chromosome. If the occurrence of a form of psychopathology among relatives goes along with the occurrence of another characteristic whose genetics are known (the genetic marker), it is concluded that the gene predisposing individuals to the psychopathology is on the same chromosome and in a similar location on that chromosome (i.e., it is linked) as the gene controlling the other characteristic. Linkage analysis was used in a study in Toronto that established an association between obsessive-compulsive disorder (OCD) and the gamma-aminobutyric acid (GABA) type B receptor 1 (GABBR1) gene (Zai et al., 2005). Another study of genetic linkage in adolescents and young adults found that a locus on chromosome 9 is associated with enhanced risk for externalizing psychopathology (i.e., aggression and conduct disorder) (see Stallings et al., 2005). We will see several additional examples of linkage analysis in subsequent chapters, especially when we discuss mood disorders (Chapter 8) and schizophrenia (Chapter 11).

Note that researchers in this area often hypothesize *gene–environment interactions.* This is the notion that a disorder or related symptoms are the joint product of a genetic vulnerability and specific environmental experiences or conditions. According to Moffitt, Caspi, and Rutter (2006), when such interactions were found in the past, they were viewed as rare and atypical, but these authors argued convincingly that such interactions are much more common and important (both theoretically and practically) than previously imagined. The possibility of gene–environment interactions is becoming a predominant theme in depression literature, as illustrated by an intriguing study by Hayden et al. (2008). This study posits a link among the serotonin transporter promoter (5-HTTLPR) genotype, the development of cognitive vulnerabilities, stressful events, and depression.

A focus on gene–environment interactions is important in qualifying the perceived influence of genetic factors. A new article by Linda Booij from Queen's University and her associates discusses complex gene–environment interactions as they relate to serotonin (5-HT) and the need to examine the role of serotonin across various developmental stages. Indeed, it has been established that receptors, proteins, and enzymes vary in their developmental patterns. Booij, Tremblay, Szyf, and Benkelfat (2015) also emphasize how environmental disruptions can affect serotonin in ways that set the stage for psychopathology.

One concern is that an exclusive focus on genetic factors promotes the notion that illness and mental illness are predetermined. One Canadian survey indicated that 3 out of 5 respondents believed that genetic factors pose a moderate risk or high risk for health problems, including depression (Etchegary, Lemyre, Wilson, & Krewski, 2009). Nevertheless, it was still concluded that most people do not hold overly deterministic views of the causes of illness. This is encouraging, because believing that "biology is destiny" could limit the extent to which people try to modify lifestyle and environmental factors that contribute to health and mental health problems.

Genetic Differences Reflected in Temperament

In Chapter 1, the role of biological factors in personality differences was introduced in our overview of the views of Hippocrates that linked imbalances in bodily fluids with characteristic temperament styles. Current research on temperament is also based on the notion that individual differences among people are largely attributable to genetically predetermined differences that are detectable almost as soon as children are born.

Rothbart and Putnam (2002) defined **temperament** as constitutionally based differences in reactivity and self-regulation. Temperament differences are reflected in differences in the style of expressing behaviours (i.e., whether someone reacts strongly or weakly to emotionally upsetting events). Pioneering work by Thomas and Chess (1989) led to the identification of three temperament styles corresponding to three general types of young children: (1) the difficult child; (2) the easy child; and (3) the hard-to-warm-up child, who is more reserved. Contemporary research has linked these temperament styles with personality traits and tendencies that have clear implications for understanding abnormal behaviour.

Robins, John, Caspi, Moffitt, and Stouthamer-Loeber (1996) analyzed data from 300 adolescent boys in the United States and found three types or categories: (1) the **resilient type**, (2) the **overcontrolling type**, and (3) the **undercontrolling type**. Resilient children cope well with adversity, while overcontrolled children are overly inhibited and prone to distress, and undercontrolled children are impulsive and can seem out of control at times. The undercontrolled type is prone to acting out and aggressive behaviours. Donnellan and Robins (2010) summarized results confirming that the resilient type is quite adaptive and high functioning (i.e., high IQ and high self-esteem and school performance) but the overcontrolled type is linked with shyness, loneliness, and moderate self-esteem and school performance, while the undercontrolled type is associated with delinquency and externalizing problems, school conduct difficulties, and lower levels of IQ and school performance. We will return to these biologically based personality types in a later segment of this chapter that focuses on integrative models.

Neuroscience and Biochemistry in the Nervous System

Neuroscience is the study of the brain and the nervous system. Neuroscience can come in numerous forms, including cognitive developmental neuroscience, molecular neuroscience, and cellular neuroscience. The nervous system is composed of billions of neurons. Although neurons differ in some respects, each **neuron** has four major parts: (1) the cell body; (2) several dendrites (the short and thick extensions); (3) one or more axons of varying lengths (usually only one long and thin axon extending a considerable distance from the cell body); and (4) terminal buttons on the many end branches of the axon (Figure 2.1). When a neuron is appropriately stimulated at its cell body or through its dendrites, a **nerve impulse**, which is a change in the electric potential of the cell, travels down the axon to the terminal endings. Between the terminal endings of the sending axon and the cell membrane of the receiving neuron, there is a small gap, called the **synapse** (see Figure 2.2).

For a nerve impulse to pass from one neuron to another and for communication to occur, the impulse must have a way of bridging the synaptic gap. The terminal buttons of each axon contain synaptic vesicles, small structures that are filled with **neurotransmitters**, chemical substances that allow a nerve impulse to cross the synapse. Nerve impulses cause the synaptic vesicles to release molecules of their transmitter substances, and these molecules flood the synapse and diffuse toward the receiving, or postsynaptic, neuron. The cell membrane of the postsynaptic cell contains proteins, called receptor sites, that are configured so that specific neurotransmitters can fit into them. When a neurotransmitter fits into a receptor site, a message can be sent to the postsynaptic cell. What actually happens to the postsynaptic neuron depends on its integrating thousands of similar messages. Sometimes these messages

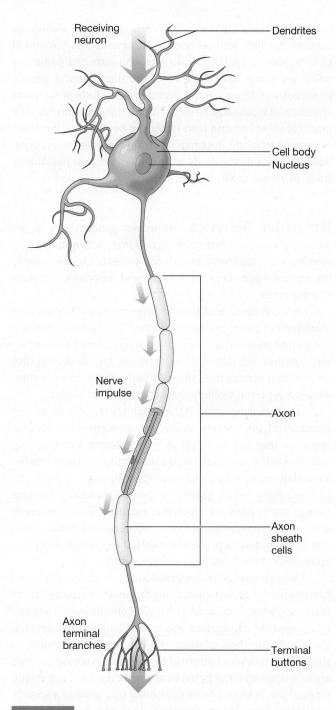

FIGURE 2.1   The neuron, the basic unit of the nervous system.

are excitatory, leading to the creation of a nerve impulse in the postsynaptic cell; at other times, the messages can be inhibitory, making the postsynaptic cell less likely to fire. Inhibitory neurotransmitters act as mood stabilizers or balancers, while excitatory neurotransmitters stimulate the brain.

Once a presynaptic neuron (the sending neuron) has released its neurotransmitter, the last step is for the synapse to be returned to its normal state. Not all of the released neurotransmitter has found its way to postsynaptic receptors. Some of what remains in the synapse is broken down by enzymes, and some is pumped back into the presynaptic cell through a process called **reuptake**.

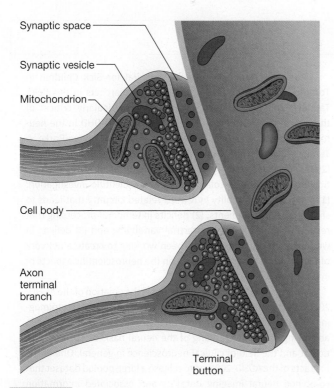

Synaptic space

Synaptic vesicle

Mitochondrion

Cell body

Axon terminal branch

Terminal button

FIGURE 2.2 A synapse, showing the terminal buttons of two axon branches in close contact with a very small portion of the cell body of another neuron.

Several key neurotransmitters have been implicated in psychopathology. Norepinephrine, a neurotransmitter of the peripheral **sympathetic nervous system**, is involved in producing states of high arousal and is involved in anxiety disorders. Both serotonin and dopamine are neurotransmitters in the brain. Serotonin may be involved in depression, and dopamine in schizophrenia. Another important brain transmitter is GABA, which inhibits some nerve impulses and is implicated in anxiety disorders.

Some of the theories linking neurotransmitters to psychopathology have proposed that a given disorder is caused by either too much or too little of a particular transmitter (e.g., mania results from too much norepinephrine, and anxiety disorders from too little GABA). Neurotransmitters are synthesized in the neuron through a series of metabolic steps, beginning with an amino acid. Each reaction along the way to producing an actual transmitter is catalyzed by an enzyme, speeding up the metabolic process. Too much or too little of a particular transmitter could result from an error in these metabolic pathways. Similar disturbances in the amounts of specific transmitters could result from alterations in the usual processes by which transmitters are deactivated after being released into the synapse. For example, a failure to pump leftover neurotransmitter molecules back into the presynaptic cell (reuptake) would leave excess transmitter molecules in the synapse. Then, when a new nerve impulse caused further neurotransmitter substances to be released into the synapse, the postsynaptic neuron would, in a sense, get a double dose of neurotransmitter, making it more likely for a new nerve impulse to be created.

Finally, contemporary research has focused to a large extent on the possibility that the receptors are at fault in some psychopathologies. If the receptors on the postsynaptic neuron were too numerous or too easily excited, the result would be akin to having too much transmitter released. There would simply be more sites available with which the neurotransmitter could interact, increasing the chances that the postsynaptic neuron would be stimulated. The delusions and hallucinations of schizophrenia may result from an overabundance of dopamine receptors.

For many years, researchers and clinicians have attempted to observe directly or make inferences about the functioning of the brain and other parts of the nervous system in their efforts to understand both normal and abnormal psychological functioning. Focus on Discovery 2.1 illustrates the biological paradigm and the relevance of neuroscience in abnormal behaviour by examining recent research in attention-deficit/hyperactivity disorder (ADHD). This disorder is the most commonly diagnosed behavioural disorder in childhood and is described in more detail in Chapter 15.

Biological Approaches to Treatment

An important implication of the biological paradigm is that prevention or treatment of mental disorders should be possible by altering bodily functioning. Certainly, if a deficiency in a particular biochemical substance is found to underlie or contribute to some problem, it makes sense to attempt to correct the imbalance by providing appropriate doses of the deficient chemical. In such cases, a clear connection exists between the cause of a disorder (a biological defect) and its treatment (a biological intervention).

Most biological interventions in common use, however, have not been derived from precise knowledge of what causes a given disorder. Nonetheless, the use of psychoactive drugs continues to increase. In 1985, psychoactive drugs were prescribed in the United States at about 33 million physician visits, and in 1994, at almost 46 million (Pincus et al., 1998). A particular concern is the rapid increase in the prescription and use of psychoactive drugs among children and adolescents. This trend is evident across several countries including Canada, though there are wide variations; for instance, the rates of drug use are lower in various European countries versus the United States (see Steinhausen, 2015).

A growing body of research has emerged on the role of **deep brain stimulation** in the treatment of certain disorders and health conditions. This practice involves planting battery-operated electrodes in the brain that deliver low-level electrical impulses. This approach may prove to be quite effective though the specific processes and mechanisms implicated in improvement have yet to be identified. Initial, groundbreaking research on the use of deep brain stimulation to alleviate treatment-resistant depression was conducted in Toronto and follow-up research over several years continues to indicate that this is quite effective. This research found that more

Focus on Discovery 2.1

The Neuroscience of Attention-Deficit/ Hyperactivity Disorder (ADHD)

At present, theory and research on the neuroscience of ADHD is one of the most exciting areas of inquiry in the field of the neuroscience of abnormal behaviour. Poissant, Emond, and Joyal (2008) reviewed existing evidence and concluded that there is extensive evidence implicating frontostriatal circuitry in ADHD (i.e., the lateral prefrontal cortex, the dorsal anterior cingulated cortex, and the caudate nucleus). According to the authors, other research highlights the potential significance of pervasive reductions in volume throughout the cerebrum and cerebellum. One intriguing study that received widespread interest found that ADHD clients experience delays in cortical maturation, as reflected by attaining peak levels of cortical thickness at an older age (Shaw et al., 2007). The sequence of development was the same for those with and without ADHD, but it was delayed by up to five years in ADHD clients. The delay in cortical maturation was most evident in the lateral prefrontal cortex, which is the region responsible for working memory and attention. It has been assumed for many years that young people with ADHD eventually catch up and they have a delay but not a lasting difference. However, new research indicates that many adolescents with ADHD go on to have structural brain deficits in adulthood and this accounts for some memory deficits that have been detected. These structures may be implicated among those adults with ADHD (see Roman-Urrestarazu et al., 2015).

Related research on the cognitive neuroscience of attention has focused on the role of the dopaminergic and the noradrenergic neurotransmitter systems (Vaidya & Stollstorff, 2008). The dopaminergic hypothesis is that ADHD is due to a dopamine deficit believed to be genetic in origin.

Rosemary Tannock from the Hospital for Sick Children in Toronto is one of the leading Canadian researchers in this field. Tannock and her colleagues have been particularly critical of the lack of theoretical models of the causes of ADHD in the neuroscience field (see Coghill, Nigg, Rothenberger, Sonuga-Barke, & Tannock, 2005). In one widely cited paper, Castellanos and Tannock (2002) suggested that three particular features of ADHD are particularly amenable to collaborative neuroscientific investigation: (1) a specific abnormality in reward-related circuitry that leads to shortened delay gradients; (2) deficits in temporal processing that result in high intrasubject-intertrial variability; and (3) deficits in working memory. Tannock has been working to create a network of Canadian researchers focusing on the neuroscientific aspects of inattention.

An important recent development is the creation of the ADHD-200. This is a grassroots consortium of 200 functional neuroimaging investigators from three continents who share an interest in advancing our understanding of the neural basis of ADHD in particular and the field of clinical neuroscience in general. One of the first acts of the ADHD-200 was to release a large pooled dataset that combined neural imaging datasets and associated information from around the world. They then held a global competition that included submissions from scholars from a range of disciplines, including mathematics and computer science. The winning team was from Johns Hopkins University. They developed a highly predictive tool that uses brain-imaging data to determine ADHD diagnoses with a high level of specificity with a very low risk of false positives (i.e., falsely identifying normally developing children as ADHD positive). These efforts stand as a shining example of how large-scale collaborations can advance new knowledge that is in the public interest (see ADHD-200 Consortium, 2012).

---

than half of the participants with treatment-resistant depression improved enough to go back to their jobs (see Kennedy et al., 2011; Mayberg et al., 2005). Research has suggested that treatment is effective if it modulates the subgenual cingulate region (Brodmann area 25) that seems to be overactive in treatment-resistant depression (see Mayberg et al., 2005). However, a recent study has cast some doubt on the usefulness of deep brain stimulation, so further inquiry is needed. This study is relatively unique in that it involved a randomized controlled trial and no significant difference in degree of improvement was found for the 15 people in the deep brain stimulation group and the 15 people in the control group (referred to as the sham condition) (see Dougherty et al., 2015). Unfortunately, only 3 of the 15 people in the deep brain stimulation group had improvements. Clearly, more research is warranted.

Contemporary approaches to biological assessment are discussed in detail in Chapter 3. These approaches involve attempts to make inferences about the functioning of the nervous system (e.g., neuropsychological assessment) or to "see" the actual structure and functioning of the brain and other parts of the nervous system (e.g., magnetic resonance imaging [MRI]). Neuroimaging studies have become an increasingly important area of psychiatric research over the past 30 years and have advanced our understanding of several disorders. For example, Zipursky (2007) noted that due to findings from brain-imaging research, antipsychotic medications can now be prescribed at a fraction of the dosages considered standard just 10 years ago. Further, neuroimaging research is beginning to show the involvement of prefrontal and limbic regions in the perception and modulation of psychological stress (see Dedovic, D'Aguiar, & Pruessner, 2009) and to identify differences that might have significance related to the difference in vulnerability to psychological disorders in women and men (vanStegeren, 2009).

The general public in Canada has become more aware of the potential usefulness of neuroimaging as a result of Daniel Levitin's pioneering work and his book *This Is Your Brain on Music*. Levitin is a cognitive neuroscientist at McGill University in Montreal whose work is providing novel information on the functioning of the auditory cortex. Neuroimaging has not yet had a major impact on the diagnosis of psychiatric disorders.

Evaluating the Biological Paradigm

Over the past several decades, biological researchers have made exceptional progress in elucidating brain-behaviour relationships and the role of specific genetic factors. Biologically based research on both causes and treatment of psychopathology is proceeding rapidly. Although we view these developments in a positive light, we also want to caution against reductionism. **Reductionism** is the view that whatever is being studied can and should be reduced to its most basic elements or constituents. Advances in neuroscience have raised concerns that the role of psychological factors is not receiving enough consideration in some fields. Recently, for instance, in the field of eating disorders, Harris and Steele (2014) authored a commentary paper titled "Have we lost our minds? The siren song of reductionism in eating disorder research and theory." They noted that the last 10 years has seen a shift from focusing on the mind to now focusing on the brain in the etiology and expression of eating disorders. However, they still acknowledge the merits of the biopsychosocial paradigm that is described at the end of this chapter.

Although reductionism is an influential viewpoint among biological psychiatrists, in philosophical circles, it has been severely criticized. Once basic elements, such as individual nerve cells, are organized into more complex structures or systems, such as neural pathways or circuits, the properties of these systems cannot be deduced from the properties of the constituents. The whole is often greater than the sum of its parts. Ian Gold (2009), who holds a Canada Research Chair in philosophy and psychiatry at McGill University, concluded succinctly that "there is little reason to think that any significant portion of psychiatric theory will be reduced to neuroscience or genetics" (p. 506). Similarly, Joel Paris (2009) concluded that the applied neuroscience model is most appropriate to severe mental disorders, that psychiatric disorders cannot be reduced to abnormalities in neuronal or molecular activity, and that psychological problems need to be understood at multiple levels.

We now consider psychological paradigms. The cognitive-behavioural paradigm is highly influential today and is regarded as a generally effective, evidence-based approach. We provide an overview of the **behavioural** (sometimes referred to as the **learning) paradigm** and cognitive (sometimes referred to separately as the cognitive paradigm) approaches that were eventually combined or integrated into the cognitive-behavioural paradigm. Our discussion of paradigms concludes with other psychological paradigms (i.e., the psychodynamic and humanistic-existential), which have less influence today than in the past, but that still provide us with some important insights, principles, and treatment approaches. All of these approaches emphasize the role of social factors, including socio-cultural considerations and internal psychological processes. The role of early experience is central to both biological and psychological paradigms. Ultimately, our challenge will be to integrate the different biological and psychosocial approaches or viewpoints into a comprehensive, theoretically consistent, integrative paradigm.

2.3 The Cognitive-Behavioural Paradigm

"Cognitive-behavioural therapy (CBT) has a wide-ranging empirical base, supporting its place as the evidence-based treatment of choice for the majority of psychological disorders."

—Waller, 2009, p. 119

Contemporary versions of cognitive-behavioural therapy are primarily cognitive in their emphasis, but key principles from a behavioural or learning perspective have been incorporated as well.

The Behavioural Perspective

Psychologists operating primarily from a behavioural perspective view abnormal behaviour as responses learned in the same ways other human behaviour is learned.

The Rise of Behaviourism   John B. Watson (1878–1958) is a key figure in the rise of behaviourism. As a response to the focus on **introspection** favoured by many others in the field of human psychology, in 1913, Watson promoted a focus on behaviourism by extrapolating from the work of psychologists who were investigating learning in animals. Because of his efforts, the dominant focus of psychology switched from thinking to learning. **Behaviourism** can be defined as an approach that focuses on observable behaviour rather than on consciousness. Three types of learning have attracted the research efforts of psychologists.

Classical conditioning   One type of learning, **classical conditioning**, was discovered by the Russian physiologist and Nobel laureate Ivan Pavlov (1849–1936) at the turn of the century. In Pavlov's studies of the digestive system, a dog was given meat powder to make it salivate. Before long, Pavlov's laboratory assistants became aware that the dog began salivating when it saw the person who fed it. As the experiment continued, the dog began to salivate even earlier, when it heard the footsteps of its feeder. Intrigued by these findings, Pavlov decided to study the dog's reactions systematically. In the first of many experiments, a bell was rung behind the dog, and then the meat powder was placed in its mouth (see image). After this procedure had been repeated a number of times, the dog began salivating as soon as it heard the bell.

In this experiment, because the meat powder automatically elicits salivation with no prior learning, the powder is termed an **unconditioned stimulus** (UCS) and the response to it, salivation, an **unconditioned response** (UCR). When the offering of meat powder is preceded several times by the ringing of a bell, a neutral stimulus, the sound of the bell alone

Ivan P. Pavlov, Russian physiologist and Nobel laureate, was responsible for extensive research and theory in classical conditioning.

(the **conditioned stimulus**, CS) is able to elicit the salivary response (the **conditioned response**, CR) (see Figure 2.3). The CR usually differs somewhat from the UCR (Rescorla, 1988), but these subtleties are beyond the needs of this book. As the number of paired presentations of the bell and the meat powder increases, the number of salivations elicited by the bell alone increases. **Extinction** is what happens to the CR when the repeated soundings of the bell are later not followed by meat powder; fewer and fewer salivations are elicited, and the CR gradually disappears.

A famous experiment, conducted by John Watson and Rosalie Rayner (1920), discovered that classical conditioning could instill pathological fear. They introduced a white rat to an 11-month-old boy, Little Albert, who indicated no fear of the animal. Whenever the boy reached for the rat, the experimenter made a loud noise (the UCS) by striking a steel bar behind

Albert's head, causing him great fright (the UCR). After five such experiences, Albert became very frightened (the CR) by the sight of the white rat, even when the steel bar was not struck. The fear initially associated with the loud noise had come to be elicited by the previously neutral stimulus, the white rat (now the CS). This study suggests the possible association between classical conditioning and the development of certain emotional disorders, including phobias. Contemporary research in abnormal psychology has continued to implicate classical conditioning in the development of anxiety disorders (see Mineka & Oehlberg, 2008). The role of classical conditioning may be more pervasive than realized; indeed, a study conducted in Toronto indicated that the abnormal tendency of people with schizophrenia to make context-inappropriate associations may be an example of classical conditioning gone awry as strong associations are made to seemingly neutral stimuli (Jensen et al., 2008).

Operant conditioning   Over 60 years ago, B. F. Skinner (1904–1990; see photo) introduced **operant conditioning**, so named because it applied to behaviour that operates on the environment. He reformulated the **law of effect** by shifting the focus from the linking of stimuli and responses (S-R connections) to the relationships between responses and their consequences or contingencies. This subtle distinction reflects Skinner's contention that stimuli do not so much get connected to responses as they become the occasions for responses to occur, if in the past they have been reinforced. Skinner introduced the concept of **discriminative stimulus** to refer to external events that in effect tell an organism that if it performs a certain behaviour, a certain consequence will follow.

Skinner distinguished two types of reinforcement that influence behaviour. **Positive reinforcement** is the strengthening of a tendency to respond by virtue of the presentation of a pleasant event, called a *positive reinforcer*. For example, a water-deprived pigeon will tend to repeat behaviours (operants) that are followed by the availability of water. **Negative reinforcement** also strengthens a response, but it does so

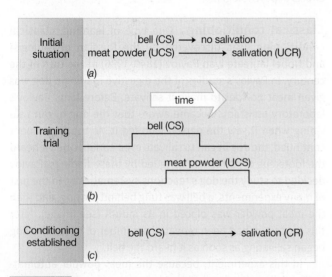

B. F. Skinner was responsible for the study of operant behaviour and the extension of this approach to education, psychotherapy, and society as a whole.

FIGURE 2.3 The process of classical conditioning. (a) Before learning, the meat powder (UCS) elicits salivation (UCR), but the bell (CS) does not. (b) A training or learning trial consists of presentations of the CS, followed closely by the UCS. (c) Classical conditioning has been accomplished when the previously neutral bell elicits salivation (CR).

Aggressive responses in children are often rewarded, which makes such behaviour more likely to occur in the future.

via the removal of an aversive event, such as the cessation of electric shock. Skinner called such consequences *negative reinforcers*. Extrapolating his work with pigeons to human behaviour, Skinner argued that freedom of choice is a myth and that all behaviour is determined by the reinforcers provided by the environment.

Operant conditioning can produce abnormal behaviour. Consider a key feature of conduct disorder, a high frequency of aggressive behaviour (see Chapter 15). Aggression is often rewarded, as when one child hits another to get a toy (see photo). (Getting the toy is the reinforcer.)

Modelling　In real life, learning often goes on even in the absence of reinforcers. We all learn by watching and imitating others, a process called vicarious learning or **modelling**. Experimental work by Albert Bandura and others (see Canadian Contributions 2.1) has demonstrated that witnessing someone perform certain activities can increase or decrease diverse kinds of behaviour. Albert Bandura and Menlove (1968) used a modelling treatment to reduce fear of dogs in children. After witnessing a fearless model engage in various activities with a dog, initially fearful children became more willing to approach and handle a dog. Modelling may explain the acquisition of abnormal behaviour (see Askew & Field, 2008, for a review of the underlying mechanisms). Children of parents with phobias or substance-abuse problems may acquire similar behaviour patterns, in part through modelling.

Behaviour Therapy　A new way of treating psychopathology, called **behaviour therapy**, emerged in the 1950s. In its initial form, this therapy applied procedures based on classical and operant conditioning to alter clinical problems. Sometimes the term **behaviour modification** is used as well, particularly by therapists who employ operant conditioning as a means of treatment. Behaviour therapy is an attempt to change abnormal behaviour, thoughts, and feelings by applying in a clinical context the methods used and the discoveries made by experimental psychologists in their study of both normal and abnormal behaviour.

It is helpful to distinguish three theoretical approaches in behaviour therapy: in addition to the role of modelling, discussed above, there are counterconditioning and exposure, as well as the application of operant conditioning. Cognitive behaviour therapy is often considered a fourth aspect of behaviour therapy, but we will discuss it separately in the section on the cognitive approach because of its focus on thought processes.

Counterconditioning and exposure

"Embodying the principle of exposure, today's treatments affirm that the conquest of our fears requires confrontation with the things we fear the most."

—Richard J. McNally, 2007, p. 750

Because behavioural approaches assume that behaviour is the result of learning, treatment often involves relearning a new, more adaptive response. **Counterconditioning** is relearning achieved by eliciting a new response in the presence of a particular stimulus. A response (R1) to a given stimulus (S) can be eliminated by eliciting a new response (R2) in the presence of that stimulus, as diagrammed in Figure 2.4. For example, in an early and now famous demonstration, Mary Cover Jones successfully treated a young boy's fear of rabbits by feeding him in the presence of a rabbit. The animal was at first kept several feet away and then gradually moved closer on successive occasions. In this way, the fear (R1) produced by the rabbit (S) was replaced by the stronger positive feelings evoked by eating (R2).

The counterconditioning principle is behind an important behaviour therapy technique, **systematic desensitization**, developed by Joseph Wolpe (1958; see photo). A person who suffers from anxiety works with the therapist to compile a list of feared situations, starting with those that arouse minimal anxiety and progressing to the most frightening. The person is also taught to relax deeply. Step by step, while relaxed, the person imagines the graded series of anxiety-provoking situations. The relaxation tends to inhibit any anxiety that might otherwise be

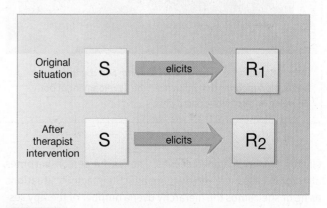

FIGURE 2.4　Schematic diagram of counterconditioning, whereby an original response (R1) to a given stimulus (S) is eliminated by evoking a new response (R2) to the same stimulus.

Canadian Contributions 2.1

Albert Bandura: The World's Greatest Living Psychologist?

According to Haggbloom et al. (2002), Albert Bandura (see photo) is the world's greatest living psychologist—fourth in the twentieth century in terms of his impact (behind Skinner, Piaget, and Freud). Born in Mundare, Alberta, in 1925, he obtained his early education in a one-room schoolhouse in this northern Alberta farming community. According to Bandura's (2007) autobiographical statement, his father worked laying railroad tracks for the trans-Canada rail line after emigrating from Poland, while his mother worked in the general store in town. As a student, Bandura received his B.A. degree in 1949 from the University of British Columbia and his Ph.D. from the University of Iowa in 1952. He joined the faculty at Stanford University in 1953, where he remains to this day. Albert Bandura has received many awards for his scientific contributions. He has served as president of the American Psychological Association and honorary president of the Canadian Psychological Association. He was named an Officer of the Order of Canada in 2014. U.S. President Barack Obama presented Bandura with the National Medal of Science in 2016.

Bandura's seminal work is based on the premise that it is important to study clinical phenomena in experimental situations. His initial work focused on social learning theory and on the idea that much of what we learn is through the process of imitation.

Other people provide us with a range of behaviours that can be imitated. Bandura's initial observations were published in books co-authored with his first graduate student, Canadian

Albert Bandura developed social learning and cognitive self-regulation theories that influenced the development of both learning and cognitive paradigms.

Photo by Jon Brenneis/Life Magazine/Time & Life Pictures/Getty Images, Inc.

Richard Walters (Bandura & Walters, 1959, 1963). Their classic 1963 book, *Social Learning and Personality Development,* was critical of the psychodynamic approach and offered an empirically based alternative.

In many respects, research on social learning theory is synonymous with the famous Bobo doll study conducted by Bandura, Ross, and Ross (1961). In this study, children who witnessed an adult being aggressive with a plastic Bobo doll were observed imitating this aggression while playing with other children. Bandura and associates conducted several other classic studies designed to test how situational factors contributed to observational learning (e.g., witnessing a model who is rewarded for aggression). These variations led Bandura to conclude that there are four key processes in observational learning: (1) attention (noticing the model's behaviour); (2) retention (remembering the model's behaviour); (3) reproduction (personally exhibiting the behaviour); and (4) motivation (repeating imitated behaviours if they received positive consequences).

Bandura's more recent work is a cognitive self-regulation theory known as social cognitive theory that focuses on the concept of human agency and **self-efficacy**, an individual's perceived sense of being capable (see Bandura, 1986, 2001). Self-regulation is a multi-stage process that involves self-observation, self-judgement by comparing personal achievements and behaviours with standards and goals, and self-response in the form of self-reinforcement and praise or self-punishment and criticism. In a wide variety of contexts, self-control therapies have been applied that focus on improving an individual's sense of personal efficacy in order to lessen distress and promote adaptive behaviours.

Bandura's (2006) more recent work examines human agency from an expanded perspective that incorporates various forms of efficacy, which supplement individual differences in personal efficacy. Fostering a sense of group efficacy and collective efficacy (i.e., the power of the people as a whole) can create enormous social change for the betterment of societies. You are encouraged to review the possible developments that Bandura links with group and collective agency.

Bandura continues to be an authoritative voice in the field of psychology. He has authored a new book titled *Moral Disengagement* that addresses the issue of how some people are able to do great harm to other people and society as a whole yet are still able to live with themselves (see Bandura, 2015).

Bandura's focus on both social learning and self-regulation underscores the close interplay between external forces (models in our environment to be imitated) and internal forces (personal beliefs about the self) in adaptive and maladaptive behaviours. The focus on personal, group, and collective agency promotes the view that we are key players who can act proactively to determine the factors and influences in our lives.

elicited by the imagined scenes. The fearful person becomes able to tolerate increasingly more difficult imagined situations as he or she climbs the hierarchy over a number of therapy sessions. Wolpe hypothesized that counterconditioning underlies the efficacy of desensitization; a state or response antagonistic to anxiety is substituted for anxiety as the person is exposed

gradually to stronger and stronger doses of what he or she fears. Some experiments (e.g., Davison, 1968) suggest Wolpe's hypothesis, but other explanations are possible. Most contemporary theorists believe that exposure per se to what the person fears is important. Relaxation is then considered merely a useful way to encourage a frightened individual to confront

Joseph Wolpe, one of the pioneers in behaviour therapy, is known particularly for systematic desensitization, a widely applied behavioural technique.

what he or she fears (Wilson & Davison, 1971). This technique is useful in reducing a wide variety of fears. Indeed, the treatment of anxiety disorders with exposure-based therapies has been a major success story in clinical psychology (see McNally, 2007). However, in a review of the cognitive processes in exposure therapy, Hofmann (2008) concluded that exposure therapy is "a form of cognitive intervention that specifically changes the expectancy of harm" (p. 1999).

Another type of counterconditioning, **aversive conditioning**, also played an important historical role in the development of behaviour therapy. In aversive conditioning, a stimulus attractive to the client is paired with an unpleasant event, such as a drug that produces nausea, in the hope of endowing it with negative properties. For example, a problem drinker who wishes to stop drinking might be asked to smell alcohol while he or she is being made nauseous by a drug. Aversive techniques have been employed to reduce smoking, drug use, and socially inappropriate desires, such as those of pedophiles.

Operant conditioning as an intervention   Several behavioural procedures derive from operant conditioning (see image). Much of this work has been done with children. Making positive reinforcers contingent on behaviour is used to increase the frequency of desirable behaviour. For example, a socially withdrawn child could be reinforced for playing with others. Problems treated with this method include autism, learning disabilities, mental retardation, bedwetting, aggression, hyperactivity, tantrums, and social withdrawal. The main premise is that the same learning conditions and processes that created maladaptive behaviour can also be used to change maladaptive behaviour (i.e., unlearning the behaviour).

The Cognitive Perspective

"The mind is its own place, and in itself

Can make a Heav'n of Hell, a Hell of Heav'n."

—John Milton, *Paradise Lost*

Cognition is a term that groups together the mental processes of perceiving, recognizing, conceiving, judging, and reasoning. The **cognitive paradigm** focuses on how people (and animals) structure their experiences, how they make sense of them, and how they relate their current experiences to past ones that have been stored in memory. (See the Brief Case Example for an illustration of how trying to change a client's cognition can be an effective treatment option.)

The Basics of Cognitive Theory   At any given moment, we are bombarded by far more stimuli than we can possibly respond to. How do we filter this overwhelming input, put it into words or images, form hypotheses, and arrive at a perception of what is out there? Cognitive psychologists consider the learning process much more complex than the passive formation of new stimulus–response associations. Cognitive psychologists regard the learner as an active interpreter of a situation, with the learner's past knowledge imposing a perceptual funnel on the experience. The learner fits new information into an organized network of already accumulated knowledge, often referred to as a **schema**, or cognitive set (Neisser, 1976). New information may fit the schema, but if it does not, the learner reorganizes the schema to fit the information or construes the information in such a way as to fit the schema. The cognitive approach may remind you of our earlier discussions of paradigms; scientific paradigms are similar

Time out is an operant procedure wherein the consequence for misbehaviour is removal to an environment with no positive reinforcers.

Brief Case Example

Dressing For Success?

The client was a 47-year-old woman from Saskatchewan with chronic schizophrenia. She had been hospitalized for nine years. One of her main symptoms was that she always wore excessive amounts of clothing. How excessive? When she first appeared at the hospital, it was reported that her clothes included:

> "... several sweaters, shawls, dresses, undergarments and stockings. The clothing also included sheets and towels wrapped around her body, and a turban-like head-dress made up of several towels. In addition, the patient carried two to three cups in one hand while holding a bundle of miscellaneous clothing, and a large purse in the other." (Ayllon, 1963, p. 58).

The average weight of her clothing at the beginning of treatment was 11 kg!

A behaviour intervention resulted in dramatic reductions in the amount of clothing worn by the client. Food reinforcement was used. The client was weighed prior to meals. If she did not meet the weight criterion set for her, the nurse told the client, "Sorry, you weigh too much. You'll have to weigh less." Failure to comply meant missing the meal (i.e., not obtaining the reinforcement). As indicated, the intervention was quite successful. The client went eventually from 11 kg to 1.5 kg of clothing.

This example also serves as an illustration of the behavioural concept of **successive approximations**. Initially, the client was allowed access to the meal room if she removed 1 kg of clothing. Once this goal was achieved (along with no longer bringing her own cups), the criterion was made more stringent on successive trials until the goal of 1.5 kg of clothing was achieved.

---

in function to a cognitive schema, for they act as filters to our experience of the world.

Currently, cognitive explanations are quite predominant and appear more and more often in the search for the causes of abnormality and for new methods of intervention. A widely held view of depression, for example, places the blame on a particular cognitive set, namely, the individual's overriding sense of hopelessness. Many people who are depressed believe that they have no important effect on their surroundings regardless of what they do. Their destiny seems to them to be out of their hands, and they expect their future to be negative. If depression does develop from a sense of hopelessness, this fact could have implications for how clinicians treat the disorder. Cognitive theorizing will be included in discussions of most of the disorders described in this book.

Beck's Cognitive Therapy

The psychiatrist Aaron Beck (see photo) developed a cognitive therapy (CT) for depression based on the idea that a depressed mood is caused by distortions in the way people perceive life experiences (Beck, 1976; Salkovskis, 1996). For example, a depressed person may focus exclusively on negative happenings and ignore positive ones, or interpret positive experiences in a negative manner. This is illustrated by revelations made in her autobiography by Canadian prima ballerina Karen Kain (see Kain, 1994). Kain admitted having experienced severe depression and had this to say about occasions when her performance did not meet her own exacting standards:

> "Sometimes my lacklustre performance would be evident, and the applause would be muted, merely polite. But at other times—and these were even worse for a perfectionist like me—people would give me a warm reception, perhaps even stand and

> applaud, when I knew I'd been dreadful, and I would interpret their enthusiasm as proof positive that I'd never been any good. I had always danced badly, and somehow nobody had ever noticed."

> (Kain, 1994, p. 158)

Beck's therapy (examined in detail in Chapter 8) tries to persuade clients to change their opinions of themselves and the way in which they interpret life events. When a depressed person expresses feelings that nothing ever goes right, for example, the therapist offers counter-examples, pointing out how the client has overlooked favourable happenings. The general goal of Beck's therapy is to provide clients with experiences, both inside and outside the consulting room, that will alter their negative schemas and dysfunctional beliefs and attitudes.

The role of cognitive factors is clearly evident in the following case study of Thomas, an elderly man suffering jointly from depression and a medical condition.

> "Thomas was a 68-year-old married man, diagnosed with Parkinson's disease four years previously. As a consequence of his disease he had become uncertain and fearful of others' reactions to him in professional and social situations and he had increasingly avoided such situations. This had profoundly affected his self-concept; he was experiencing many features of depression.
>
> A cognitive formulation of Thomas' presenting problems suggested that at a core level, central to his sense of self, Thomas had assimilated the belief that his acceptability as a person was conditional on being respected and regarded as competent in all domains and at all times. His career as a

carpenter and his retirement interests involved fine motor skills that had been essentially lost through the progression of his Parkinson's disease . . .

Thomas attended 16 therapy meetings over eight months. Initially meetings were weekly, but later meetings were biweekly and then monthly. The steps in cognitive therapy were: (1) education about social anxiety, depression, and the cognitive model to normalize Thomas' experience, (2) diary keeping of thoughts, feelings and behaviour across a range of upsetting situations to help Thomas further understand his beliefs and their role in his psychological difficulties, (3) reducing avoidance of feared situations in graded homework assignments and, (4) testing and challenging hypothesized conditional and core beliefs."

(Kuyken & Beck, 2007, pp. 27–28)

Because this approach focused on the role of dysfunctional thoughts and beliefs, the main emphasis of therapy is replacing these thoughts with more adaptive thoughts. Thus, Beck dismissed the old psychoanalytic theory (see section "The Psychoanalytic Paradigm") that depression is self-directed hostility. He replaced it with a model of negative cognitive bias—an automatic misprocessing of information. In a seminal 2008 paper entitled, "The evolution of the cognitive model of depression and its neurobiological correlates," Beck (2008) linked his cognitive constructs to current brain imaging studies that demonstrate overreaction of the amygdala to negative stimuli.

Rational-Emotive Behaviour Therapy

Theory of rational-emotive behaviour therapy Albert Ellis was another leading cognitive therapist. His principal thesis was that sustained emotional reactions are caused by internal sentences that people repeat to themselves, and these self-statements reflect sometimes unspoken assumptions—**irrational beliefs**—about what is necessary to lead a meaningful life. In Ellis's rational-emotive therapy (RET), subsequently renamed **rational-emotive behaviour therapy (REBT)** (Dryden, David, & Ellis, 2010; Ellis, 1995), the aim is to eliminate self-defeating beliefs through a rational examination of them. Anxious persons, for example, may create their own problems by making unrealistic demands on themselves or others, such as "I must win the love of everyone." Or a depressed person may say several times a day, "What a worthless jerk I am." Ellis proposes that people interpret what is happening around them, that sometimes these interpretations can cause emotional turmoil, and that a therapist's attention should be focused on these beliefs rather than on historical causes or, indeed, on overt behaviour (Ellis, 1962).

Ellis used to list a number of irrational beliefs that people can harbour. One very common notion was that they must be thoroughly competent in everything they do. Ellis suggested that many people actually believe this untenable assumption

Photo courtesy of The Beck Institute for Cognitive Behavior Therapy

Aaron Beck developed a cognitive theory of depression and a cognitive therapy for the biases of depressed people. At the time of writing, Beck was 95 years old and continues to publish and consult on clients.

and evaluate every event within this context. Thus, if a person makes an error, it becomes a catastrophe because it violates the deeply held conviction that he or she must be perfect (Ellis, 2002). It sometimes comes as a shock to clients to realize that they actually believe such strictures and have thus run their lives in a way that makes it is virtually impossible to live comfortably or productively.

More recently, Ellis (2002) shifted from a cataloguing of specific beliefs to the more general concept of demandingness—the "musts" or "shoulds" that people impose on themselves and others. Thus, instead of wanting something to be a certain way, feeling disappointed when it is not, and then engaging in behaviour that might bring about the desired outcome, the person demands that it be so. This unrealistic, unproductive demand is hypothesized to create severe emotional distress and behavioural dysfunction.

Clinical implementation of REBT After becoming familiar with the client's problems, the therapist presents the basic theory of rational-emotive behaviour therapy so that the client can understand and accept it. The following transcript is from a session with a young man who had inordinate fears about speaking in front of groups. The therapist guides the client to view his inferiority complex in terms of the unreasonable things he may be telling himself. The therapist's thoughts during the interview are indicated in italics within square brackets.

Client:	My primary difficulty is that I become very uptight when I have to speak in front of a group of people. I guess it's just my own inferiority complex.
Therapist:	[*I don't want to get sidetracked at this point by talking about that conceptualization of his problem. I'll just try to finesse it and make a smooth transition to something else.*] I don't know if I would call it an inferiority complex, but I do believe that people can, in a sense, bring on their own upset and anxiety in certain kinds of situations. When you're in a particular situation, your anxiety is often not the result of the situation itself, but rather the way in which you interpret the situation—what you tell yourself about the situation. For example, look at this pen. Does this pen make you nervous?
Client:	No.
Therapist:	Why not?
Client:	It's just an object. It's just a pen.
Therapist:	It can't hurt you?
Client:	No . . .
Therapist:	It's really not the object that creates emotional upset in people, but rather what you think about the object. [*Hopefully, this Socratic-like dialogue will eventually bring him to the conclusion that self-statements can mediate emotional arousal.*] Now this holds true for . . . situations where emotional upset is caused by what a person tells himself about the situation. Take, for example, two people who are about to attend the same social gathering. Both of them may know exactly the same number of people at the party, but one person can be optimistic and relaxed about the situation, whereas the other one can be worried about how he will appear, and consequently be very anxious. [*I'll try to get him to verbalize the basic assumption that attitude or perception is most important here.*] So, when these two people walk into the place where the party is given, are their emotional reactions at all associated with the physical arrangements at the party?
Client:	No, obviously not.
Therapist:	What determines their reactions, then?
Client:	They obviously have different attitudes toward the party.
Therapist:	Exactly, and their attitudes—the ways in which they approach the situation—

greatly influence their emotional reactions. (Goldfried & Davison, 1994, pp. 163–165)

Having persuaded the client that his or her emotional problems will benefit from rational examination, the therapist proceeds to teach the person to substitute for irrational self-statements an internal dialogue meant to ease the emotional turmoil. Therapists who implement Ellis's ideas differ greatly on how they persuade clients to change their self-talk. Some therapists, like Ellis himself, argue with clients, cajoling and teasing them, sometimes in very blunt language. Others, believing that social influence should be more subtle and that individuals should participate more in changing themselves, encourage clients to discuss their own irrational thinking and then gently lead them to discover more rational ways of regarding the world (Goldfried & Davison, 1994).

Once a client verbalizes a different belief or self-statement during a therapy session, it must be made part of everyday thinking. Ellis and his followers provide clients with homework assignments designed to help them experiment with the new self-talk and to experience the positive consequences of viewing life in less catastrophic ways. Ellis emphasizes the importance of getting the client to behave differently, both to test out new beliefs and to learn to cope with life's disappointments. This is how this approach becomes both cognitive and behavioural. In practice, Beck's cognitive therapy also employs behavioural strategies and is now considered to be a leading cognitive behaviour therapy approach.

Cognitive Behaviour Therapy Classical behavioural therapies emphasize the direct manipulation of overt behaviour and occasionally of covert behaviour, with thoughts and feelings being construed as internal behaviours (referred to as mediational learning). They pay relatively little attention to direct alteration of the thinking and reasoning processes of the client. Theorists such as Bandura were influential in promoting the notion that external events are also represented and reflected internally by cognitions, and when focusing on a particular person, it is important to consider the interplay of behaviours and cognitions. **Cognitive-behavioural therapy (CBT)** does incorporate theory and research on cognitive and behavioural processes and represents a blend of cognitive and learning principles. Cognitive behaviour therapists pay attention to private events—thoughts, perceptions, judgements, self-statements, and even tacit (unconscious) assumptions—and have studied and manipulated these processes in their attempts to understand and modify overt and covert disturbed behaviour. **Cognitive restructuring** is a general term for changing a pattern of thought that is presumed to be causing a disturbed emotion or behaviour. This restructuring is implemented in several ways by CBT therapists.

CBT is quite popular and it continues to grow in influence in Canada and elsewhere. Jaimes, Larose-Hebert, and Moreau (2015) conducted a survey of the theoretical orientations of clinical psychologists in Quebec over the past 20 years.

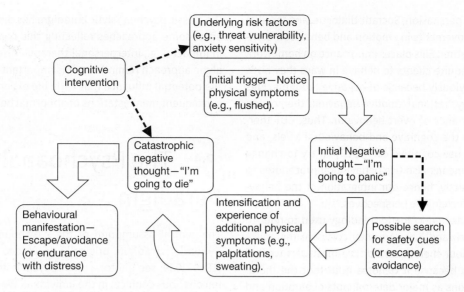

FIGURE 2.5 Cognitive-Behavioural Model (Carter et al., 2008.) This material is reproduced with permission of John Wiley & Sons, Inc.

The implementation of CBT more than doubled; it went up from 18.4% to 38%.

The Cognitive-Behaviour Integrated Approach

Carter, Forys, and Oswald (2008) conducted a review of the cognitive-behavioural paradigm. They made the astute observation that cognitive-behavioural models, when applied to various disorders, differ in terms of how much emphasis is placed on cognitive versus behavioural factors. However, they observed that all of these models are based on the basic premise that the person is influenced as much and perhaps more by his or her perception of events than the objective features of these events.

Figure 2.5 is a proposed cognitive-behavioural model of panic disorder (Carter et al., 2008). Panic disorder is described in more detail in Chapter 5. It is clearly shown in Figure 2.5 that catastrophic cognitions (e.g., "I'm going to die") are at the root of this disorder, but clear behavioural manifestations play a role in the form of escape and avoidance behaviours as panic mounts. Feedback arrows suggest that cognitions influence behaviours but these avoidance and escape behaviours also further contribute to the ongoing experience of catastrophic cognitions.

Evaluating the Cognitive-Behavioural Paradigm

While the learning explanation of abnormal behaviour has led to many treatment innovations, the fact that a treatment based on learning principles is effective in changing behaviour does not mean that the behaviour was itself learned in a similar way. For example, while the mood of depressed people may be elevated by rewards for increased activity, this cannot be considered evidence that the depression was initially produced by an absence of rewards. How does a person's observation of a model lead to changes in his or her overt behaviour? As mentioned in Canadian Contributions 2.1, Bandura and Walters (1963) asserted that an observer could somehow learn new behaviour by watching others. However, in order for imitation to occur, cognitive processes must become engaged, including the ability to remember later on what had happened. Findings of research on social learning led some behavioural researchers and clinicians to include cognitive variables in their analyses of psychopathology and therapy. However, some criticisms of the cognitive component of the cognitive-behavioural paradigm should also be noted. The concepts on which it is based (e.g., schema) are abstract and not always well defined. Furthermore, cognitive explanations of psychopathology do not always explain much. That a depressed person has a negative schema tells us that the person thinks gloomy thoughts. However, such a pattern of thinking is actually part of the diagnosis of depression. What is distinctive in the cognitive perspective is that the thoughts are given causal status; they are regarded as causing the other features of the disorder, such as sadness. Left unanswered is the question of where the negative schema came from in the first place. Cognitive explanations of psychopathology tend to focus more on current determinants of a disorder and less on its historical antecedents.

Is the cognitive point of view basically different and separate from the learning perspective? Much of what we have just considered suggests that it is. The growing field of CBT gives us pause, however, because its researchers study the complex interplay of beliefs, expectations, perceptions, and attitudes on the one hand, and overt behaviour on the other. For example, as a leading advocate of changing behaviour through cognitive means, Bandura (1977) uses his concept of self-efficacy (see Canadian Contributions 2.1) to argue that different therapies produce improvement by increasing people's belief that they can achieve desired goals. At the same time, though, he argues that changing behaviour through behavioural techniques is the most powerful way to enhance self-efficacy. Therapists such as Ellis, in contrast, emphasize direct alteration of cognitions (through argument, persuasion, Socratic dialogue, and the like) to bring about improvements in emotion and behaviour. Complicating matters further, Ellis places importance on homework assignments that require clients to behave in ways they have been unable to previously because of negative thoughts. Ellis renamed his therapy "rational-emotive behaviour therapy" to highlight the importance of overt behaviour. Thus, CBT therapists work at both the cognitive and behavioural levels, and most of those who use cognitive concepts and try to change beliefs with verbal means also use behavioural procedures to alter behaviour directly, hence our integration of the behavioural (learning) and cognitive perspectives.

This issue is reflected in the terminology used to refer to people such as Beck and Ellis. Are they cognitive therapists or cognitive behaviour therapists? For the most part we will use the latter term because it denotes both that the therapist regards cognitions as major determinants of emotion and behaviour and that he or she maintains the focus on overt behaviour that has always characterized behaviour therapy. Nonetheless, Beck, even though he assigns many behavioural tasks as part of his therapy, is usually referred to as the founder of cognitive therapy (CT); Ellis's rational-emotive therapy (RET) was once considered separate from behaviour therapy.

However, the issue is not just a matter of terminology. A placebo-controlled comparison study (Dimidjian et al., 2006) found behavioural activation (a treatment condition that uses the basic behavioural components of CT with an increased focus on avoidance behaviours in the context of a behavioural rationale) to be as effective as antidepressants and superior to CT in the treatment of depressed adults. And Beck himself (e.g., Beck, Kovacs, & Weissman, 1979; DeRubeis, Webb, Tang, & Beck, 2010) recommended that therapists use more behavioural strategies with severely depressed people.

Longmore and Worrell (2007) raised another concern in a review of component studies by asking, "Do we need to challenge thoughts in CBT?" They concluded that "there is little empirical support for the role of cognitive change as causal in the symptomatic improvements achieved in CBT" (p. 173).

Suffice to say at this point that both cognitive and behavioural factors can be important foci of intervention. For example, in a randomized controlled trial of people with major depression, Dobson et al. (2008) reported that clients previously exposed to CT were significantly less likely to relapse following the termination of treatment than clients withdrawn from medication. The authors further concluded that both cognitive therapy and behavioural activation are less expensive and more enduring (observed at a two-year follow-up) alternatives to medication in the treatment of depression. More generally, the cognitive-behavioural approach has had a vital impact on psychiatry and clinical psychology. Evidence continues to accumulate for the efficacy and effectiveness of CBT to reduce clinical symptoms and improve quality of life for people with a variety of psychological disorders and clinical problems.

We now turn to a discussion of the psychoanalytic paradigm followed by the humanistic-existential paradigms. While

the classic psychoanalytic paradigm has diminished in its influence, some approaches reflecting this paradigm are growing in impact (e.g., interpersonal therapy). Also, as the psychoanalytic approach reminds us, it is important not to lose sight of the potential influence that early life experiences can have on subsequent manifestations of abnormal behaviour.

2.4   The Psychoanalytic Paradigm

The central assumption of the **psychoanalytic** or **psychodynamic paradigm**, originally developed by Sigmund Freud (1856–1939; see photo), is that psychopathology results from unconscious conflicts in the individual. We will look at the significant impact of Freud in the development of this paradigm, but we will also examine the ways in which the focus of this paradigm has shifted.

Classical Psychoanalytic Theory

Classical psychoanalytic theory refers to the original views of Freud. His theories encompassed both the structure of the mind itself and the development and dynamics of personality.

National Library of Medicine/Science Source

Sigmund Freud was the founder of the psychoanalytic paradigm, both proposing a theory of the causes of mental disorder and devising a new method of therapy.

Structure of the Mind

Freud divided the mind, or the psyche, into three principal parts: id, ego, and superego. These are metaphors for specific functions or energies. According to Freud, the **id** is present at birth and is the part of the mind that accounts for all the energy needed to run the psyche. It comprises the basic urges for food, water, elimination, warmth, affection, and sex. Trained as a neurologist, Freud saw the source of all the id's energy as biological. Only later, as the infant develops, is this energy, which Freud called **libido**, converted into psychic energy, all of it **unconscious**, below the level of awareness.

The id seeks immediate gratification and operates according to the **pleasure principle**. When the id is not satisfied, tension is produced, and the id strives to eliminate this tension. For example, the infant feels hunger, an aversive drive, and is impelled to move about, sucking, to reduce the tension. Another means of obtaining gratification is **primary process thinking**, generating images—in essence, fantasies—of what is desired. The infant who wants the mother's milk imagines sucking at the mother's breast and thereby obtains some short-term satisfaction.

The ego is the next aspect of the psyche to develop. Unlike the id, the **ego** is primarily conscious and begins to develop from the id during the second six months of life. Its task is to deal with reality. Through its planning and decision-making functions, called **secondary process thinking**, the ego realizes that operating on the pleasure principle at all times is not the most effective way of maintaining life. The ego thus operates on the **reality principle** as it mediates between the demands of reality and the immediate gratification desired by the id.

The final part of the psyche to emerge is the **super-ego**, which operates roughly as the conscience and develops throughout childhood. Freud believed that the superego developed from the ego much as the ego developed from the id. As children discover that many of their impulses, such as biting or bedwetting, are not acceptable to their parents, they begin to incorporate, or introject, parental values as their own to enjoy parental approval and avoid disapproval.

The behaviour of the human being, as conceptualized by Freud, is thus a complex interplay of these three parts of the psyche. The interplay of these forces is referred to as the **psychodynamics** of the personality.

The id's instincts as well as many of the superego's activities are not known to the conscious mind. While the ego is primarily conscious and is involved in thinking and planning, it, too, has important unconscious aspects (the defence mechanisms) that protect it from anxiety. Freud considered most of the important determinants of behaviour to be unconscious.

Neurotic Anxiety

When one's life is in jeopardy, one feels **objective (realistic) anxiety**—the ego's reaction, according to Freud, to danger in the external world. The person whose personality has not developed fully, perhaps because he or she is fixated at one or another stage, may experience **neurotic anxiety**, a feeling of fear that is not connected to reality or to

Jennie Woodcock; Reflections Photolibrary/Getty Images

In classical psychoanalytic theory, too much or too little gratification during one of the psychosexual stages is hypothesized to lead to regression to this stage during stress.

any real threat. **Moral anxiety** arises when the impulses of the superego punish an individual for not meeting expectations and thereby satisfying the principle that drives the superego—namely, the perfection principle.

Defence Mechanisms: Coping with Anxiety

According to Freud and elaborated by his daughter Anna (A. Freud, 1966), the discomfort experienced by the anxious ego can be reduced in several ways. Objective anxiety, rooted in reality, can often be handled by removing or avoiding the danger in the external world or by dealing with it in a rational way. Neurotic anxiety can be handled by means of a defence mechanism. A **defence mechanism** is a strategy, unconsciously used, to protect the ego from anxiety. Perhaps the most important is **repression**, which pushes unacceptable impulses and thoughts into the unconscious. By remaining repressed, these infantile memories and desires cannot be corrected by adult experience and therefore retain their original intensity and immaturity. **Denial**, another important defence mechanism, entails disavowing a traumatic experience, such as being raped, and pushing it into the unconscious. **Projection** attributes to external agents characteristics or desires that an individual possesses but cannot accept in his or her conscious awareness. For example, a woman who unconsciously is averse to regarding herself as angry at others may instead see others as angry with her. Other defence mechanisms are **displacement**, redirecting emotional responses from a perhaps dangerous object to a substitute (e.g., yelling at one's spouse instead of at one's boss); **reaction formation**, converting one feeling (e.g., hate) into its opposite (in this case, love); **regression**, retreating to the behavioural patterns of an earlier age (see photo); **rationalization**, inventing a reason for an unreasonable action or attitude; and **sublimation**, converting sexual or aggressive impulses into socially valued behaviours, especially creative activity.

Focus on Discovery 2.2

What is Psychotherapy?

Shorn of its theoretical complexities, any **psychotherapy** is a social interaction in which a trained professional tries to help another person, the client or patient, behave and feel differently. The therapist follows procedures that are to a greater or lesser extent prescribed by a certain theory or school of thought. The basic assumption is that particular kinds of verbal and nonverbal exchanges in a trusting relationship can achieve goals, such as reducing anxiety and eliminating self-defeating or dangerous behaviour.

Basic as this definition may seem, there is little general agreement about what really constitutes psychotherapy. A person's next-door neighbour might utter the same words of comfort as a clinical psychologist, but should we regard this as psychotherapy? In what way is psychotherapy different from such non-professional reassurance? Is the distinction made on the straightforward basis of whether the dispenser of reassurance has a particular academic degree? Does it relate to whether the giver of information has a theory that dictates what he or she says? These are difficult questions.

Generally, people who seek or are sent for professional help have first tried non-professional avenues to feeling better. They have confided in friends or a spouse, perhaps spoken to the family doctor or a member of the clergy, and maybe tried several of the many self-help books and programs that are so popular. For most people in psychological distress, one or more of these options provide enough relief, and they seek no further help. But for others, these attempts fall short. These are the people who go to mental health clinics, university counselling centres, and the private offices of independent practitioners.

London (1986) categorized psychotherapies as **insight therapies** or **action (behavioural) therapies**. Insight therapies, such as psychoanalysis, assume that behaviour, emotions, and thoughts become disordered because people do not understand what motivates them, especially when their needs and drives conflict. Insight therapies try to help people discover why they behave, feel, and think as they do. The premise is that greater awareness of motivations will yield greater control over and subsequent improvement in thought, emotion, and behaviour. However, more recent findings imply that attaining insight is not necessarily the sole or prime factor in determining the therapeutic effect of dynamic psychotherapy (e.g., Messer & Abbass, 2010; see Chapter 17).

Of course, insight is not exclusive to the insight therapies. The action, or behavioural, therapies bring insight to the individual as well, and the newer cognitive therapies can be seen as a blend of insight and behavioural therapies. It is a matter of emphasis, of focus. In the behavioural therapies, the focus is on changing behaviour; insight is often a peripheral benefit. In the insight therapies, the focus is less on changing people's behaviour directly than on enhancing their understanding of their motives, fears, and conflicts. To facilitate such insights, therapists of different theoretical persuasions employ a variety of techniques. There are scores of theories and psychotherapies, each with its enthusiastic supporters. We present in this chapter a detailed description of the more prominent theories and methods of intervention. We hope to provide you with the means to evaluate critically new therapies that arise or, at the very least, to know what questions to ask in order to evaluate them effectively.

All these defence mechanisms allow the ego to discharge some id energy while not facing frankly the true nature of the motivation. Because defence mechanisms are more readily observed than other symptoms of a disordered personality, they often make people aware of their troubled natures and provide the impetus for consulting a therapist. It should be noted that contemporary psychoanalytic theorists consider some use of defence mechanisms to be adaptive and healthy. A period of denial after the death of a loved one, for example, can help in adjusting to the loss. For the most part, however, defence mechanisms are maladaptive.

Psychoanalytic Therapy

Since Freud's time, the body of psychoanalytic thinking has changed in important ways, but all treatments purporting to be psychoanalytic have some basic tenets in common. (See Focus on Discovery 2.2 for a discussion about psychotherapy.) Classical psychoanalysis is based on Freud's second theory of neurotic anxiety, that neurotic anxiety is the reaction of the ego when a previously punished and repressed id impulse presses for expression. When the unconscious part of the ego encounters a situation that reminds it of a repressed conflict from childhood—one usually having to do with sexual or aggressive impulses—it is overcome by debilitating tension. Psychoanalytic therapy is an insight therapy. It attempts to remove the earlier repression and help the client face the childhood conflict, gain insight into it, and resolve it in the light of adult reality. The repression, occurring so long ago, has prevented the ego from growing in an adult fashion; the lifting of the repression is supposed to enable this relearning to take place.

Analysts employ a number of techniques in their efforts to lift repressions. Perhaps the best known is **free association**. The client reclines on a couch, facing away from the analyst, and is encouraged to give free rein to his or her thoughts, verbalizing whatever comes to mind without the censoring done in everyday life. It is assumed that the client can learn this skill, gradually overcoming defences built up over many years, but there often arise blocks to free association. The client may suddenly become silent or change the topic. These **resistances** are noted by the analyst as they are assumed to signal a sensitive, or ego-threatening, area. These sensitive areas are precisely what the analyst will want to probe further.

Dream analysis is another analytic technique. Psychoanalytic theory holds that, in sleep, ego defences are relaxed, allowing normally repressed material to enter the sleeper's consciousness. Since this material is extremely threatening, it is rarely allowed into consciousness in its actual form; rather, the repressed material is disguised and dreams take on heavily symbolic content (referred to as the **latent content** of the dream). For example, a woman who fears sexual advances from men may dream of being attacked by warriors with spears; the spears are considered phallic symbols, substituting for an explicit sexual advance.

Another key component of psychoanalytic therapy is **transference**. Here, the client's responses to the analyst are not in keeping with the analyst–client relationship but seem instead to reflect relationships with important people in the client's past. For example, a client may feel that the analyst is bored by what he or she is saying (as a parent might have seemed) and, as a result, might struggle to be entertaining (as he or she had done in the past to gain parental attention). Analysts encourage the development of transference by intentionally remaining shadowy figures, sitting behind their clients and divulging little of their personal lives or feelings during a session. Through careful observation of these transferred attitudes, analysts can gain insight into the childhood origin of repressed conflicts. It is precisely when analysts notice transference developing that they begin to hope that an important repressed conflict is getting closer to the surface.

Countertransference is the analyst's feelings toward the client. Analysts must be aware of their own feelings so that they can see the client clearly. Thus, psychoanalysis of the analyst-in-training is typically part of their training.

As previously repressed material begins to appear in therapy, **interpretation** comes into play. The analyst points out to the client the meaning of certain behaviours. Defence mechanisms, the ego's unconscious tools for warding off anxiety, are a principal focus of interpretation. For instance, a man might change the subject whenever anything touches on closeness during the course of a session. The analyst will at some point interpret the client's behaviour, pointing out its defensive nature in the hope of stimulating the client to acknowledge that he has trouble with intimacy.

Modifications in Psychoanalytic Therapy

As happens with all paradigms, psychoanalytic therapy has evolved substantially over time. One innovation was to apply it to groups of people rather than only to individuals. Some therapists focus on the psychodynamics of individuals in the group, using typical techniques, such as free association, interpretation, and dream analysis (Wolf & Kutash, 1990). Others conceive of the group itself as having a collective set of psychodynamics, manifested by such things as group transference to the therapist. Within psychoanalytic circles, there has been controversy about the value of a group approach. The key issue is whether the group format dilutes the transference to the therapist and thus makes the therapy ineffective.

Other current analytic therapies include ego analysis, brief psychodynamic therapy, and interpersonal psychodynamic therapy.

Ego analysis   After Freud's death, a group of practitioners, generally referred to as ego analysts, introduced important modifications to psychoanalytic therapy. Their approach is sometimes described as psychodynamic rather than psychoanalytic. The major figures in this loosely formed movement include Karen Horney, Anna Freud, Erik Erikson, David Rapaport, and Heinz Hartmann. Although Freud did not ignore people's interactions with the environment, he essentially believed that they are driven by intrapsychic urges. Those who subscribe to **ego analysis** place greater emphasis on a person's ability to control the environment and to select the time and the means for satisfying instinctual drives, contending that the individual is as much ego as id. In addition, they focus more on the person's current living conditions than did Freud.

Ego analysts believe in a set of ego functions that are primarily conscious, capable of controlling both id instincts and the external environment, and that, significantly, do not depend on the id for their energy. They assume that these ego functions and capabilities are present at birth and develop through experience.

Brief psychodynamic therapy   Freud originally conceived of psychoanalysis as a relatively short-term process. He thought that the analyst should focus on specific problems, make it clear to the client that therapy would not exceed a certain number of sessions, and structure sessions in a directive fashion. Freud thus envisioned a more active and briefer psychoanalysis than what eventually developed.

Doidge and associates investigated the nature of psychodynamic therapy in an Ontario survey (see Doidge, 1999; Doidge, Simon, Gillies, & Ruskin, 1994). They found that 59% of those receiving psychoanalysis were women and that the mean number of current diagnoses was four. On average, each client had one diagnosable personality disorder. Overall, 82% of the clients had tried other forms of therapy, including drug treatment. Most clients had received psychoanalytic treatment for many years. A follow-up study found that the average length of time in treatment was 4.8 years (see Doidge et al., 2002).

Time-limited psychotherapy is available as an alternative to the many years sometimes required for classic psychodynamic treatment. The early pioneers in time-limited psychotherapy, called **brief therapy**, were the psychoanalysts Ferenczi (1952) and Alexander and French (1946). This shorter form was developed to meet the expectations of the many clients who prefer therapy to be fairly short term and targeted to specific problems in their everyday lives.

The growth of brief therapy also evolved from the need to respond to psychological emergencies (Koss & Shiang, 1994). Cases of shell shock during the Second World War led to Grinker and Spiegel's (1945) classic short-term analytic treatment of what is now called post-traumatic stress disorder. A related contribution came from Lindemann's (1944) crisis intervention with the survivors of Boston's famous Cocoanut Grove nightclub fire in 1942 (see photo).

Insurance companies and government health plans have played a role in shortening the duration of treatment by

Over 400 lives were lost in the fire at the Cocoanut Grove nightclub in 1942. The crisis intervention work that followed influenced the development of brief psychodynamic therapy.

encouraging therapists to adapt their ideas to brief therapy. They have become increasingly reluctant to cover more than a limited number of psychotherapy sessions in a given calendar year and have set limits on reimbursement amounts.

All these factors, combined with the growing acceptability of psychotherapy in the population at large, have set the stage for a stronger focus on time-limited psychodynamic therapy. Brief therapies share several common elements (Koss & Shiang, 1994):

- Assessment tends to be rapid and early.
- It is made clear right away that therapy will be limited and that improvement is expected within a small number of sessions (from 6 to 25).
- Goals are concrete and focused on improving the client's worst symptoms, helping the client understand what is going on in his or her life, and enabling the client to cope better in the future.
- Interpretations are directed more toward present life circumstances and client behaviour than on the historical significance of feelings.
- Development of transference is not encouraged.
- There is a general understanding that psychotherapy does not cure, but that it can help individuals learn to deal better with life's inevitable stressors.

Contemporary psychoanalytic thought Lerner (2008) has provided a contemporary assessment of psychoanalysis and current psychodynamic perspectives. He concluded that "psychoanalysis since Freud has undergone enormous revisions and transformations that have altered many fundamental aspects of Freud's original ideas. Profound shifts in the psychoanalytic understanding of female sexuality, infant and child development, and severe psychopathology are crucial examples of the psychoanalytic landscape" (Lerner,

2008, p. 129). Lerner identified five conceptual approaches that are predominant in contemporary psychoanalytic thought: (1) modern structural theory; (2) self-psychology; (3) object relations theory; (4) interpersonal-relational; and (5) attachment theory. We now discuss interpersonal therapy as an illustration of how this conceptual approach has been incorporated into contemporary forms of treatment.

Interpersonal therapy Interpersonal therapy is a contemporary variation of brief psychodynamic therapy that has grown in popularity and impact. This relational approach emphasizes the interactions between a client and his or her social environment. The American psychiatrist Harry Stack Sullivan pioneered the interpersonal approach. Other key figures, including attachment theorist John Bowlby, and more recent versions of interpersonal therapy incorporate a more extensive focus on attachment needs (for a historical overview, see Weissman, 2006). According to Sullivan, our needs are interpersonal in that whether they are met depends on the complementary needs of other people. A key turning point for the infant is when he or she realizes that survival depends on the mother's co-operation in satisfying the infant's basic needs. Sometimes called a neo-Freudian, Sullivan held that a client's basic difficulty is a misperception of reality stemming from disorganization in the interpersonal relationships of childhood, primarily the relationship between child and parents. He conceived of the analyst as a "participant observer" in the therapy process (not as a blank screen for transference), arguing that the therapist, like the scientist, is a part of the process that he or she is studying—an analyst does not see clients without at the same time affecting them. While interpersonal therapy focuses on past relationships, an important goal is to examine these past influences in terms of how they have an impact on and contribute to current relationships.

Particularly prominent is the **interpersonal therapy (IPT)** of Klerman and Weissman (Klerman et al., 1984). The IPT therapist concentrates on the client's current interpersonal difficulties and discusses with the client better ways of relating to others. Although IPT incorporates some psychodynamic ideas, it is distinct in several ways from traditional forms of psychoanalysis. *Mastering Depression: The Patient's Guide to Therapy* contains the following section in the description of IPT:

> *"The IPT therapist will not: 1) Interpret your dreams; 2) Have treatment go on indefinitely; 3) Delve into your early childhood; 4) Encourage you to free associate; 5) Make you feel very dependent on the treatment or the therapist."*
>
> (Weissman, 1995, pp. 11–12)

IPT's techniques combine empathic listening with suggestions for behavioural changes, as well as how to implement them. The IPT therapist might explore with the client the complexities of present-day problems, with an emphasis on the client's relationships with others. The therapist might then encourage the client to make specific behavioural changes, sometimes facilitating these shifts by having the client practise new behaviours in the consulting room (role-playing).

According to Weissman (2006), IPT has been used successfully in many cultures and it is equally effective for clients of diverse backgrounds. Weissman has observed that it is somewhat remarkable that only minor adaptations are needed when modifying IPT for use in various cultures.

The potential benefits of IPT have been demonstrated in many studies. IPT is used most commonly to treat depression. For instance, a study led by Queen's University researcher Kate Harkness (Harkness et al., 2002) found that the usual link between stressful events and bouts of depression is weakened considerably among women who received IPT and then two years of maintenance IPT. IPT has been applied to various forms of depression, including postpartum depression and depression in the elderly. It was also used as a potential treatment for heart patients recovering from cardiac difficulties, but was not found to be particularly effective relative to other interventions (Lespérance et al., 2007). This finding is somewhat surprising given that interpersonal hostility is a key factor that seems to put people at risk for heart disease and poorer recoveries (see Chida & Steptoe, 2009). The effectiveness of IPT appears to depend on client attributes; the results from one study of the treatment of depression suggests that IPT is comparable to CBT or antidepressant treatment, but it is less effective relative to other forms of treatment for people who have experienced maltreatment (Harkness, Bagby, & Kennedy, 2012). Perhaps when maltreatment is involved, a more intensive intervention over a longer period is required.

Evaluating the Psychoanalytic Paradigm

Perhaps no investigator of human behaviour has been so honoured and so criticized as Freud. Freud was vilified when he proposed his theory of infantile sexuality (i.e., the notion that infants and children are motivated by sexual drives). In turn-of-the-century Vienna, sexuality was rarely discussed. One criticism levelled against Freud's theory applies to other psychoanalytic theories as well: theories based on anecdotal evidence gathered during therapy sessions are not grounded in objectivity and therefore are not scientific. Unlike those who work within the biological paradigm or within the learning and cognitive paradigms (which entail conducting formal research on the causes and treatments of abnormal behaviour), Freud believed that the information obtained from therapy sessions was enough to validate his theory and demonstrate the effectiveness of the therapy. His clients, however, were not merely a small sample. They were also atypical, being largely affluent, educated, and Viennese. In Chapter 4, we will discuss the severe limitations of such data.

It is also important to keep in mind that psychodynamic concepts, such as id, ego, and the unconscious, though meant to be used as metaphors to describe psychic functions, sometimes were described as though they had an existence of their own, with the power to act and think. Freud (1937) spoke of their attempts to ensure their own survival and the attempts of the id and superego to overthrow the ego.

Even with these substantial criticisms, however, Freud's contribution to the field of abnormal psychology remains enormous. His ongoing influence is most evident in the following three commonly held assumptions:

1. *Childhood experiences help shape adult personality.* Contemporary clinicians and researchers still view childhood experiences as crucial, and this is largely due to Freud's influence. Indeed, more recent longitudinal research demonstrates that childhood predictors of psychopathology can be manifested 40 years later (see Pine, 2007).

2. *There are unconscious influences on behaviour.* Research shows that people can be unaware of the causes of their behaviour. While unconscious factors and processes may influence us, it is doubtful that the unconscious is a repository of id instincts.

3. *People use defence mechanisms to control anxiety or stress.* There is a great deal of research on coping with stress (see Chapter 9), and defence mechanisms are included in an appendix of the *DSM-IV-TR* (the catalogue of mental disorders published by the American Psychiatric Association and reviewed in Chapter 3).

Although there are many legitimate concerns about the validity and usefulness of Freud's work, it is impossible to acquire a good grasp of the field of abnormal psychology without some familiarity with his writings. Further, as noted by Tryon (2008), "the psychodynamic model of psychopathology . . . continues to be widely taught and to broadly inform clinical practice" (p. 963).

An important development in recent years that contrasts with the criticism that certain aspects of psychoanalytic theory are vague or too abstract to test is that contemporary research on psychoanalytic interventions seems to attest to their effectiveness. Saskia de Maat and colleagues (de Maat, de Jonghe, Schoevers, & Dekker, 2009) conducted a systematic review of 27 studies dealing with the effectiveness of long-term psychoanalytic therapy published since 1970. They concluded that psychotherapy resulted in high mean overall success rates (64% at termination; 55% at follow-up). A meta-analysis (see Chapter 4) of 17 studies on the effectiveness of short-term psychodynamic therapy showed that it yielded significant improvements that were maintained at follow-up and were comparable in magnitude with the gains achieved through other forms of treatment (Leichsenring, Rabung, & Leibing, 2004). A follow-up investigation of 23 treatment studies found once again that short-term psychodynamic therapy led to significant improvements relative to control conditions and it yielded comparable benefits relative to other forms of therapy, including CBT (Leichsenring & Leibing, 2007). These data have contributed to an influential and spirited defence of contemporary short-term psychodynamic psychotherapy by authors such as Shedler (2010), who maintain that this approach is just as effective or is more effective than CBT. Shedler's (2010) seminal paper in the *American Psychologist* generated a storm of critical responses in the same journal that Shedler (2011) later replied to with the question "Science or ideology?" In other words, he dismissed claims that other theoretical orientations are superior by suggesting that this conclusion is not supported by extant data. More recently, Shelder (2015) has maintained that the evidence base in favour of other therapies is really quite weak; moreover, he suggests that these therapies are weak and have yielded trivial benefits. Do you agree with this provocative position? This important issue is revisited in Chapter 17.

2.5 The Humanistic Paradigm

Humanistic therapies, like psychoanalytic therapies, are insight-focused, based on the assumption that disordered behaviour results from a lack of insight, and can best be treated by increasing the individual's awareness of motivations and needs. There are, however, useful contrasts between psychoanalysis and its offshoots on the one hand and humanistic and existential approaches on the other. The psychoanalytic paradigm assumes that human nature, the id, is something in need of restraint; that effective socialization requires the ego to mediate between the environment and the basically antisocial, at best asocial, impulses stemming from biological urges. The humanistic paradigm places greater emphasis on the person's freedom of choice, regarding free will as the person's most important characteristic. Yet, free will is a double-edged sword, for it can bring not only fulfillment and pleasure, but also acute pain and suffering. Its exercise, therefore, requires special courage. Not everyone can meet this challenge. Those who cannot are regarded as candidates for client-centred and existential therapies. Humanistic paradigms, also referred to as experiential or phenomenological, seldom focus on how psychological problems develop. Their main influence is on intervention, and so our discussion deals primarily with therapy.

Carl Rogers' Client-Centred Therapy

Carl Rogers (see photo) was an American psychologist of enormous influence whose theorizing about psychotherapy grew slowly out of years of intensive clinical experience. After teaching at the university level in the 1940s and 1950s, he helped organize the Center for Studies of the Person in La Jolla, California. How influential is Rogers? A survey was conducted of 2,400 North American psychotherapists and Rogers was identified as the most influential psychotherapist figure (Cook, Biyanova, & Coyne, 2009). Beck and Ellis finished second and sixth, respectively.

Rogers' **client-centred therapy** (also referred to as person-centred therapy) is based on several assumptions about human nature and the way we can try to understand it (Rogers, 1951, 1961):

- People can be understood only from the vantage point of their own perceptions and feelings; that is, from their phenomenological world. We must look at the way they experience events because this is the major determinant of behaviour and makes each person unique.

- Healthy people are aware of their behaviour. In this sense, Rogers' system is similar to psychoanalysis and ego analysis, for it emphasizes the desirability of being aware of motives. People with a high level of self-awareness and a sense of personal agency are said to be thoughtful, and this is a primary goal of counselling (Rennie, 1998).

- Healthy people are innately good and effective. They become ineffective and disturbed only when faulty learning intervenes.

- Healthy people are purposive and goal-directed. They do not respond passively to the influence of their environment or to their inner drives. They are self-directed.

- Therapists should not attempt to manipulate events for the individual. Rather, they should create conditions that will facilitate independent decision-making by the client. When people are not concerned with the evaluations, demands, and preferences of others, their lives are guided by an innate tendency toward **self-actualization**.

This emphasis on self-actualization and maximizing potential and the belief that people are innately good are in keeping with the current movement toward *positive psychology*. Positive psychology promotes a focus on attributes and personal characteristics (e.g., resilience, optimism, hope) that emphasizes "wellness" and being able to function, as opposed to psychology's seeming preoccupation with negative outcomes and dysfunction. Thus, rather than focusing on vulnerability factors, positive psychology focuses on protective factors.

Rogers' Therapeutic Intervention   Consistent with his view of human nature, Rogers avoided imposing goals on the client during therapy. The client is to take the lead and direct the course of the conversation and the session. The therapist's job is to create the conditions that, during the session, help the client return to his or her basic nature and judge which course of life

Roger Ressmeyer/Corbis/VCG/Getty Images

Carl Rogers, a humanistic therapist, proposed that the key ingredient in therapy is the attitude and style of the therapist rather than specific techniques.

is intrinsically gratifying. Because of his positive view of people, Rogers assumed that their decisions would not only make them happy with themselves but also turn them into good, civilized people. The road to these good decisions is not easy, however.

According to Rogers and other humanistic and existential therapists, people must take responsibility for themselves, even when they are troubled. It is often difficult for a therapist to refrain from giving advice, from taking charge of a client's life, especially when the client appears incapable of making decisions. But Rogerians hold steadfastly to the rule that a person's innate capacity for growth and self-direction will assert itself if the therapeutic atmosphere is warm, attentive, and receptive, and especially if the therapist accepts the person for who he or she is, providing what he called **unconditional positive regard**.

Other people set what Rogers called "conditions of worth" (e.g., "I will love you if. . ."). In contrast, unconditional positive regard is reflected by the client-centred therapist valuing clients as they are, whatever their behaviour. People have value merely for being people, and the therapist must care deeply for and respect a client for the simple reason that he or she is another human being engaged in the struggle of growing and being alive.

Although client-centred therapy is not technique-oriented, one strategy is central to this approach: empathy. Because empathy is so important in Rogerian therapy and in all other kinds of therapy (not to mention ordinary social intercourse), let us examine it more closely.

It is useful to distinguish the following two types of empathy (Egan, 1975):

- *Primary empathy* is the therapist's understanding, accepting, and communicating to the client what the client is thinking or feeling. The therapist conveys primary empathy by restating the client's thoughts and feelings, pretty much in the client's own words.

- *Advanced empathy* entails an inference by the therapist of the thoughts and feelings that lie behind what the client is saying, and of which the client may only be dimly, if at all, aware. Advanced empathy essentially involves an interpretation by the therapist of the meaning of what the client is thinking and feeling.

At the primary empathic level, the therapist accepts the client's view, understands it, and communicates to the client that it is appreciated. At the advanced or interpretive level, however, the therapist offers something new, a perspective that he or she hopes is better, more productive, and that implies new modes of action. Advanced empathizing builds on the information provided over a number of sessions in which the therapist concentrates on making primary-level empathic statements.

The client-centred therapist, operating within a phenomenological philosophy, must have as the goal the movement of a client from his or her present phenomenological world to another one—hence the importance of the advanced-empathy stage. Since people's emotions and actions are determined by how they construe themselves and their surroundings—by their phenomenology—those who are dysfunctional or otherwise dissatisfied with their present mode of living are in need of a new phenomenology. From the very outset then, client-centred therapy—and all other phenomenological therapies—concentrates on clients adopting frameworks different from those they had upon beginning treatment. Merely reflecting back to clients their current phenomenology cannot in itself bring therapeutic change. A new phenomenology must be acquired.

In our view, advanced empathy represents theory building on the part of the therapist. After considering over a number of sessions what the client has been saying and how he or she has been saying it, the therapist generates a hypothesis about what may be the true source of distress hidden from the client.

Exposure to an empathetic therapist can have a powerful, positive effect, as shown initially in studies conducted by Coons and associates with clients diagnosed with schizophrenia from Ontario psychiatric hospitals (see Coons, 1967; Coons & Peacock, 1970). Participation in groups led by an empathetic therapist led to substantial improvements in personality and intellectual functioning, improvements greater than those from insight-based psychotherapy.

How much role does empathy play? A meta-analysis of 59 independent studies with 3,599 clients concluded that empathy is a moderately strong predictor of therapy outcomes for different theoretical orientations. This study also found that the positive effects for empathy were stronger among less experienced therapists and were only found when empathy was assessed by clients and observers and not when empathy was assessed by the therapists themselves (see Elliott, Bohart, Watson, & Greenberg, 2011). These researchers also distinguished three forms of empathy: (1) empathetic rapport with the client; (2) communication attunement to the messages and signals expressed by the client; and (3) person empathy (i.e., showing an understanding of the client's world and experiences).

Evaluating the Humanistic Paradigm

A recent review concluded that the humanistic paradigm and the psychotherapy research testing it have yielded many contributions, including the development of practice-informed research measures and coding systems. These authors also maintained that evidence supports a humanistic treatment orientation and the volume of research conducted points to greater emphasis on the humanistic paradigm in university-based training programs (Angus et al., 2015).

As for Carl Rogers himself, clearly he should be credited with originating the field of psychotherapy research. He insisted that therapy outcomes be empirically evaluated, and he pioneered the use of tape recordings so that therapists' behaviour could be related to therapeutic outcomes. The major prediction of Rogerian therapy, of course, is that therapists' empathy should relate to outcomes, and as noted above, there is substantial support for this contention. It clearly makes sense to continue to emphasize empathy in the training of therapists, because this quality is likely to make it easier for clients to reveal highly personal and sometimes unpleasant facts about themselves.

2.6 Consequences of Adopting a Paradigm

The student who adopts a particular paradigm necessarily makes a prior decision concerning what kinds of data will be collected and how they will be interpreted. Thus, he or she may very well ignore possibilities and overlook other information in advancing what seems to be the most probable explanation. A behaviourist is prone to attribute the high prevalence of schizophrenia in lower-class groups to the paucity of social rewards that these people received, based on the assumption that normal development requires a certain amount of reinforcement patterning. A biologically oriented theorist will be quick to remind the behaviourist of the many deprived people who do not become schizophrenic. The behaviourist will undoubtedly counter with the argument that those who do not become schizophrenic had different reinforcement histories. The biologically oriented theorist will reply that such post hoc statements can always be made.

Different Perspectives on a Clinical Problem: Cathy—A Case of Trichotillomania

The disorders described in subsequent sections of the book can usually be interpreted from the perspective of several paradigms. For instance, consider the following case excerpt of a Canadian university student with trichotillomania (TTM), an impulse control disorder involving chronic hair pulling.

> "She wanted to work on her problem of hair pulling because it made her both depressed and angry. The problem kept her from being able to study and perform in school because, according to her, she could spend a mean of 4 hours pulling her hair in a 7-hour study period. Cathy had already been in therapy with psychoanalytic treatment for almost 2 years . . . without any effect on the severity and frequency of her pulling behavior. She also had been treated with medication (Prozac) for 5 months, which according to her made her problem worse because 'she was feeling so happy she didn't care if she was pulling at all anymore' . . . She complained of pulling her own hair, every day, up to a maximum of 100 hairs on the worst days. She also had two other habit disorders— biting her cheeks and nail biting—that she considered less disruptive. She experienced tension prior to pulling and was most at risk to pull during academic performances. Ideas about failing preoccupied her . . . Cathy believed her TTM had started when she was 12 years old, after her parents' divorce. At the time, her grades in school were falling and consequently, she felt very anxious about failing her school year."

> (Pelissier & O'Connor, 2004, p. 59–60).

How can Cathy's behaviour be interpreted? A behavioural theorist would focus on the reinforcement of the relief of tension provided by the chronic hair pulling. A psychoanalytic theorist would focus on the interpersonal dynamics and early life experiences. The trichotillomania could be attributed to a sense of anxiety reflecting the unconscious interplay of the id and the superego, with this conflict distracting the ego from the conscious need to study and do well in school. Finally, if viewed from a cognitive perspective, which was the main perspective adopted by the authors, the theorist would focus on irrational fears about failure. As it turned out, Cathy suffered from extreme levels of perfectionism and concern over mistakes, and this became a central focus of treatment.

Eclecticism in Psychotherapy: Practice Makes Imperfect

A word is needed about paradigms and the activities of therapists. The treatment approaches, as described so far, may appear to be separate, non-overlapping schools of therapy. You may have the impression that a behaviour therapist would never listen to a client's report of a dream, nor would a psychoanalyst be caught dead prescribing **assertion training** to a client. Such suppositions could not be further from the truth. Many therapists subscribe to **eclecticism**, employing ideas and therapeutic techniques from a variety of schools (Hunsley & Lefebvre, 1990). A trend toward integrating psychotherapies has culminated in a combined approach known as *prescriptive eclectic therapy* (see Norcross & Beutler, 2000) and a survey of therapists treating eating disorder clients suggests that an eclectic approach may be the norm rather than the exception (von Ranson & Robinson, 2006). This survey of clinicians in Calgary found that eclectic therapy was the main approach employed by half of the clinicians. CBT was the second most popular option and was used by one-third of the clinicians. Those who engage in eclectic therapy prefer the term "integrative" rather than "eclectic," and the most common integration is cognitive therapy (Norcross, Karpiak, & Lister, 2005; also see Fruzzetti & Erikson, 2010; Harwood, Beutler, & Charvat, 2010; and Martin & Young, 2010).

Therapists often behave in ways not entirely consistent with the theories they hold. For years, practising behaviour therapists have been listening empathically to clients, trying to make out their perspectives on events, on the assumption that this understanding would help them plan a better program for changing troublesome behaviour. Behavioural theories do not prescribe such a procedure, but on the basis of clinical experience, and perhaps through their own humanity, behaviour therapists have realized that empathic listening helps them establish rapport, determine what is really bothering the client, and plan a sensible therapy program. Freud himself is said to have been more directive and to have done far more to change immediate behaviour than would be concluded from his writings alone.

Treatment is a complex and ultimately highly individual process, and these are weighty issues. In Chapter 17, we will return to these and other issues and give them the attention they deserve. You should be aware of this complexity at the beginning, however, to better appreciate the intricacies and realities of psychotherapy.

2.7 Psychosocial Influences on Mental Health

The paradigms just described allow room for external influences that have an impact on a person; indeed, our discussion of the biological paradigm included an emphasis on research focused on gene–environment interactions. However, overall, the main focus of these paradigms is on factors inside the person that contribute to whether a person remains relatively well-adjusted or is at risk of some form of mental illness. In reality, in addition to the growing body of research on gene–environment interactions, there is now overwhelming evidence of the role that external factors, especially psychosocial influences, have in contributing to mental health versus mental illness. This next segment of Chapter 2 will examine factors located outside the self, but will do so with one important caveat: people are not simply shaped by their environments, because each person can also be an agent of change. That is, people can make decisions and engage in behaviours that alter their environments. One basic way this can occur is in terms of the company we keep. Consider, for instance, a woman who falls in love with a man who is physically attractive and quite charming yet this prospective partner also has very dubious interpersonal tendencies and a track record of causing trouble for himself and for those around them. If this man is selected over a less engaging but more prosocial, agreeable, and dependable man, then the nature of the psychosocial environment has been qualitatively changed. We will return to this theme later in this book when discussing the concept of self-generated stress (see Hammen, 1991) and the notion that some people make their lives much more stressful than would otherwise be the case.

Several factors that influence mental health are now described below. These descriptions are then followed by overviews of two paradigms that seek to integrate the factors that are based both inside and outside the self.

Familial Factors

As noted earlier, classic psychoanalytic theory places great importance on a child's early experiences with her or his parents. There are several parent-related factors that contribute to risk or resilience. For instance, how do parents interact with their child? Are they warm and responsive or harsh and controlling? Does one or more parents have a history of mental illness? Are the parents getting along with each other? And does the family have enough money and other resources? We will see that each of these factors can make a big difference.

Parenting Styles   In her classic work, Diana Baumrind (1971) identified three parenting styles: **authoritarian parenting**, **permissive parenting**, and **authoritative parenting**. The authoritarian and permissive styles lead to negative outcomes in children, but for different reasons. Authoritarian parents tend to be restrictive, punitive, and overcontrolling. Children respond to the perceived harshness of their parents with externalizing problems or internalizing problems (Hetherington & Martin, 1986; Patterson & Stouthamer-Loeber, 1984). Exposure to authoritarian parenting also leads to poorer intellectual and social development (see Clarke-Stewart & Apfel, 1979). Whereas authoritarian parents are overinvolved with their children, permissive parents show little involvement and may seem disinterested in their children. This type of parenting style is also associated with internalizing and externalizing symptoms in children. An authoritative approach is most adaptive. Authoritative parents use discipline in conjunction with reason and warmth. That is, guidelines are set out for the child but the rationale is communicated in a matter that signifies a warm, caring attitude.

Research from Soniya Luthar and her colleagues has helped us to understand that coming from an affluent home is not necessarily protective when it is accompanied by a destructive parental orientation. Her work on adolescents described as "privileged but pressured" shows that mental health issues and behavioural problems among youth are linked with a parenting style characterized by high expectations and parental criticism yet the parents also are neglectful and show a lack of involvement with their sons or daughters (see Luthar & Becker, 2002). The media has referred to this phenomenon as "affluenza." This research program has identified parental criticism as particularly destructive in terms of its link with non-suicidal self-injury among privileged youth (Yates, Tracy, & Luthar, 2008). Another recent study of three school areas in the United States where there are heavy concentrations of privileged youth found that one school area was linked with elevated rates of substance abuse, while the two other areas had elevated levels of internalizing problems (e.g., anxiety, depression) and externalizing problems (e.g., acting out behavioural problems).

Affluenza was used successfully in 2012 by the defence lawyer for Texas adolescent Ethan Couch. It was argued by a psychologist at the original trial that Couch was raised by wealthy, noninvolved parents who never set limits for him; thus, he never learned right from wrong. Initially, Couch was found guilty but received probation for killing four people while driving drunk. However, Couch was later sentenced to about two years in jail when he violated his probation terms by travelling to Mexico with his mother Tonya Couch.

Parental Marital Discord   Conflict in the family is also implicated in poor mental health. Family situations can play a role in terms of all of the stressors associated with living with a single parent who is trying to cope with a marital breakup, but in some ways, it is more damaging if a couple stays together when perhaps they shouldn't be together. When conflict is taken to the extreme, children may grow up in an atmosphere where they frequently witness family violence. The children themselves may experience emotional or physical abuse. Here the role of multiple exposures must be taken into account. One investigation found that it was the joint exposure to domestic violence and child abuse that was linked with adolescent internalizing and externalizing problems and there was much less impact when either domestic violence or child abuse occurred in isolation (Moylan et al., 2010).

When multiple factors might be operating, it is sometimes difficult to ascertain which factors are playing the greatest role in contributing to maladjustment. This challenge was addressed in a study with 867 twin pairs that sought to examine the impact of family conflict independent of the role of genetic factors that contributed to family adjustment (see Schermerhorn et al., 2011). This study used sophisticated analyses to establish that family conflict had a direct impact on child maladjustment, independent of genetic factors and other environmental factors. While genetic factors were linked with differences in marital quality, the investigators were able to establish that low marital quality and lack of parental agreement about parenting styles were both implicated in internalizing and externalizing problems.

Parental Mental Illness

One of the most pernicious risk factors is exposure to mental illness in one or both parents. Analyses of the Canadian Community Health Survey-Mental Health Cycle 1.2 estimate that in Canada, 570,000 children under the age of 12 live in households where there is one or more of parental mood, anxiety, or substance use disorders. This situation applies to 12.2% or about 1 in 8 children in Canada. Moreover, 17% of the time, there is only one parent in the home (Bassani, Padoin, Philipp, & Veldhuizen, 2009; Bassani, Padoin, & Veldhuizen, 2008).

What is it like to grow up in a family where there is a parent with a severe mental illness? A summary of 10 qualitative studies involving accounts from the children compiled by a team of Canadian researchers paints a very troubling picture (see Gladstone, Boydell, Seeman, & McKeever, 2011). We will describe the main themes here and encourage you to read the detailed descriptions in this compelling article. Overall, children with a mentally ill parent described their delicate balancing act of trying to cope with the parental mental health problems while trying to maintain their own relationships. They spoke of finding ways to remain physically and psychologically detached at times to try to foster a sense of their own independence and autonomy. Major themes the studies uncovered were as follows:

- Good days and bad days: Their parents' good days were contrasted with extremely bad days in which parents would withdraw and be physically and psychologically absent or engage in behaviours that the children described as upsetting, embarrassing, and frightening.

- Caregiving activities: All studies indicated that children would have to engage extensively in taking care of their parent or their siblings in an attempt to compensate for parental unavailability.

- Bottled-up emotions: A consistent theme is that children mourned a lack of opportunity to be able to express their negative feelings and get emotional support from their psychologically unavailable parents.

- Pervasive fear: Another theme in most studies is that children had a highly anxious existence involving chronic fears of either violence or parental suicide.

- School as a refuge: Children identified school as a place of escape where they could stop thinking about their home situation.

- Trying to save the situation: Children reported taking it upon themselves to save the situation by regulating their own behaviours and trying to influence others in order to maintain some sense of family stability. These efforts often involved going to extreme lengths to be helpful, coming up with ways to avoid conflict, and cancelling their activities when they were needed at home.

- Lack of public interaction due to stigma: Public situations are largely avoided due to the possibility of embarrassment because of the parent's behaviours, but more so because of children being very cognizant of stigma.

This last finding, concerning the stigma surrounding mental illness, brings us back to our examination of this topic in Chapter 1. It reminds us that the family members of people suffering from mental illness are not immune to the impact of hostile public opinions and beliefs of less informed people.

Qualitative accounts are accompanied by empirical studies that have quantified the impact of parental psychological problems on children. For instance, Goodman et al. (2010) conducted a meta-analysis of 193 studies examining maternal depression and child psychopathology. They found small but significant associations between maternal depression and higher levels of internalizing symptoms, externalizing symptoms, and general psychopathology among their children. Analyses of mediating factors showed that the associations were stronger among younger as opposed to older children and among girls versus boys. The obtained associations were also stronger among families living in poverty.

Before discussing factors outside the family, we close this section by reiterating that it is important to take into account cumulative risk; that is, the effects of being exposed to multiple risk factors. An impressive study by Kessler et al. (2010), using data from World Health Organization surveys, examined 51,945 adults from 21 countries. The researchers focused on the association of 12 childhood adversities with 20 different disorders experienced during adulthood. Overall, it was deemed that childhood adversities played a substantial role and accounted for about 30% of the variance in these disorders. Most notably, childhood adversities had strong associations with all disorders at all stages of the life courses and their additive effects associated with having multiple co-occurring adversities. The strongest predictors were the ones associated with maladaptive family functioning (i.e., parental mental illness, child abuse, and neglect).

Peers and the Broader Social Environment

Research on the role of peer influences on psychopathology tends to emphasize two elements: peer status and peer victimization. In both instances, it is difficult to disentangle whether mental health difficulties and behavioural tendencies were precursors or consequences. As we see below, what is clear is that both types of factors are important.

Not surprisingly, children who are popular tend to be better adjusted than children who are less popular. One of the most widely cited studies is a Canadian study that examined Grade 4 and 5 students over a two-year period. This investigation, by Boivin, Hymel, and Bukowski (1995) found that negative peer status led to loneliness, which in turn predicted depression. While this study focused on childhood and early adolescence, peer status during childhood can have long-term consequence. Analyses of data from the Stockholm Birth Cohort Study followed over 10,000 participants for 30 years (see Modin, Ostberg, & Almquist, 2011). It was found that sixth-grade peer status predicted anxiety and depression 30 years later but for women, not for men. These associations held after taking into account socio-economic status, family status, school performance, and cognitive decline.

Contemporary research on peer status is focusing on the feeling of social exclusion and how it relates to a personality style known as rejection sensitivity, with some people being hypersensitive to whether they are accepted or rejected by others. Peer influences are not independent of parental factors; for instance, rejection sensitivity is linked with a reported history of low parental acceptance and perceived parental rejection (McLachlan, Zimmer-Gembeck, & McGregor, 2010).

Peer victimization can take many forms, including extreme acts of bullying. Boivin et al. (1995) found that peer victimization was similar to negative peer status in that victimization was also linked with loneliness and depression. But as was noted earlier, it is difficult to ascertain whether victimization precedes or results from abnormal behaviours. A more recent investigation emphasizes the cycle that seems to take place. Examination of over 1,500 Canadian children between the ages of 6 to 8 in the Quebec Longitudinal Study of Child Development found that externalizing problems led to academic underachievement and peer victimization, but that underachievement and victimization, in turn, predicted increases in internalizing and externalizing problems (see van Lier et al., 2012). Other Canadian research indicates that children who have been victimized are more likely to perceive that students and their teachers have poor relationships and these relationships worsen over time (Leadbeater, Sukhawathanakul, Smith, & Bowen, 2015).

Clearly, overt acts of peer victimization can have a profound influence on children and adolescents, as illustrated by tragic cases resulting in suicides due to being bullied. People will long remember the tragic case of Amanda Todd, the 15-year-old from British Columbia who made a YouTube video begging for the victimization to stop but later took her own life

THE CANADIAN PRESS/Andrew Vaughan

Debra Pepler is a pioneer in Canadian prevention efforts focused on bullying and childhood aggression. She is a member and former Director of the LaMarsh Centre for Child and Youth Research at York University. In 2015, she received the Canadian Psychological Association Donald O. Hebb Award for Distinguished Contribution to Psychology as a Science.

in 2012 due to being bullied and humiliated, including cyber-bullying. Amanda's story is yet another example of how far mistreatment can go and how tragedy ensues.

While these cases are exceedingly sad, they continue to provide a catalyst for essential changes, as illustrated by renewed calls for a national bullying strategy. The establishment of a national strategy to reduce bullying and victimization throughout Canada is the mission of PREVNet, the Promoting Relationships and Eliminating Violence Network (see www.prevnet.ca). PREVNet was established over a decade ago by Debra Pepler (see photo) from York University and Wendy Craig from Queen's University when they received a Network of Centres of Excellence grant. The tireless efforts of the members of PREVnet have resulted in substantial improvements focused on four themes: education, assessment, intervention, and policy. A key feature of PREVNet is its annual international conference on bullying, which provides a forum for the latest research on bullying and victimization.

2.8 The Cultural Context

One of the broadest and most pervasive sources of external influences is the culture in which we live. We will now consider cultural considerations and the important issue of cultural diversity, especially as it pertains to Canada. The role of cultural factors is a theme that appears in several chapters of this book, including the assessment and diagnostic issues in Chapter 3.

Cultural diversity is important to highly heterogeneous countries such as Canada, since most of our discussion of psychopathology is presented within the context and constraints of Western European society. Studies of the influences of culture on psychopathology have proliferated in recent years. A caveat: our discussion runs the risk of stereotyping because we are going to review generalizations that experts make about groups of people from different cultures. People from minority groups are, however, individuals who can differ as much from each other as their cultural or racial group differs from another cultural or racial group (cf. Weizmann, Weiner, Wiesenthal, & Ziegler, 1991). It is critical to keep this point in mind as cultural differences are discussed in this and subsequent chapters. Nonetheless, a consideration of group characteristics is important and is part of a specialty called *minority mental health* (see Sue & Sue, 2003). The major paradigms have on occasion been revised to assist clinicians in their work with people from different cultural backgrounds. For example, cultural differences in internal dialogue and beliefs about adaptive coping have been incorporated into cognitive-behavioural paradigms (e.g., Ivey, Ivey, & Simek-Morgan, 1997). Theories of **multicultural counselling and therapy** (e.g., Sue & Sue, 2003) attempt to incorporate these revisions into an integrated perspective. Hwang, Myers, Abe-Kim, and Ting (2008) developed an integrative, conceptual paradigm for understanding how culture influences different mental health domains (prevalence, etiology, phenomenology, diagnostic and assessment issues, coping styles and help-seeking pathways, and treatment and intervention issues). The Cultural Influences on Mental Health model is an important framework for understanding the complexities of interrelationships among the different domains of mental health.

While our focus in this section is on cultural, ethnic, and racial factors related to people suffering from psychological disorders in Canada, relatively little controlled research has been conducted in Canada. Therefore, we sometimes must extrapolate from relevant research conducted in the United States. Unfortunately, a majority of investigations with American minorities fail to provide information relevant to the assessment and treatment of people in Canada (for a discussion, see Bowman, 2000).

Canada is a pluralistic society that has a history and policy of multiculturalism (Esses & Gardner, 1996). If clinicians in Canada are to do more than pay lip service to cultural considerations, it is important that they understand the cultural fabric of the country and the mental implications of our cultural diversity. These implications are explored in the next section.

Mental Health Implications of Cultural Diversity in Canada

Our analysis of cultural diversity in Canada has implications for clinical practice. Mental health practitioners, including psychologists, need to be aware of Canada's unique cultural diversity. Clinicians must respect the dignity and worth of each individual, regardless of cultural background. Should members of minority groups be recruited into the mental health professions? Greater availability of clinicians from different cultures would possibly better meet the needs of clients with values different from those of the majority culture.

Psychiatric Problems in Minority Groups

The issue of whether psychiatric problems are more or less frequent in minority groups, relative to other groups, is complex because the answer depends on which minority group is being investigated. Do French Canadians differ from Anglo Canadians in the extent of their mental health problems? Probably they do not, at least not in any major way. Romano, Tremblay, Vitaro, Zoccolillo, and Pagani (2001) assessed a community sample of French-speaking 14- to 17-year-olds in Quebec and noted that the prevalence of psychiatric disorders fell within the range reported in research with English-speaking teenagers.

There are marked differences, however, between the prevalence of mental health problems among the general Canadian population and among Aboriginal people, who constitute 4% of the Canadian population. Studies report proportionally higher levels of mental health problems in many Canadian Aboriginal communities. We will examine the problem of suicide among young Native people in Chapter 8 (Canadian Perspectives 8.3) and highlight other issues throughout this book. Canadian Perspectives 2.1 provides an overview of these problems and discusses historical and current social factors that can contribute to psychological distress and disorder in Aboriginal people, at both the individual and community levels.

Canadian Perspectives 2.1

Origins of Mental Health Problems among Aboriginal People

"The last time Marcia Martel saw her mother at home, it was late summer and she was a chubby little Indian kid of 4. She doesn't remember much because she was crying and clutching the tall grass as strange people pulled her away."

—from *Nation of Lost Souls*, Diebel, March 16, 2009, p. A1.

"Mr. Speaker, I stand before you today to offer an apology to former students of Indian residential schools. The treatment of children in Indian residential schools is a sad chapter in our history. . . . The government now recognizes that the consequences of the Indian residential schools policy were profoundly negative and that this policy has had a lasting and damaging impact on aboriginal culture, heritage and language."

—from the text of then-Prime Minister Stephen Harper's statement of apology, June 11, 2008.

Laurence Kirmayer and his colleagues (Kirmayer, Brass, & Tait, 2000) reviewed research on the mental health of the First Nations, Inuit, and Métis of Canada. Depression, drug abuse, suicide, low self-esteem, symptoms of post-traumatic stress, and violence are widespread problems in many communities, especially among children and youth. Drug abuse frequently leads to child abuse, including child sexual abuse, an issue that also needs to be considered when there is family conflict. Kirmayer et al. (2000) attribute these mental health problems to cultural discontinuity and oppression, noting that Aboriginal Canadians have experienced institutional discrimination for more than 300 years. In many cases, they have been forbidden to speak their own language, prohibited from engaging in religious and cultural practices, driven from the land they had inhabited for hundreds of years, and forced onto reserves in undesirable locations without regard for the special sanctity that land has for them. In one disastrous "experiment," Inuit people were relocated to the Far North to protect Canadian sovereignty (Tester & Kulchyski, 1994). Poverty and economic marginalization are endemic in many Aboriginal communities. Disproportionately high rates of obesity, diabetes, and other physical diseases are also a problem.

The federal and provincial governments systematically sought the cultural assimilation of Aboriginal children through forced attendance at residential schools, followed by out-of-community adoption by non-Aboriginal families (Kirmayer et al., 2000). The residential schools were a 100-year failed experiment (e.g., Miller, 1996). Between 1879 and 1973, more than 100,000 Aboriginal children were taken from their families and sent to church-run and government-administered boarding schools mandated to educate the children (see photo). Aboriginal parents were considered to be incapable of educating their children and passing on "proper" European values.

The last federally run residential school closed in Saskatchewan in 1996. Kirmayer et al. (2000) noted:

> *"Beyond the impact on individuals of abrupt separation from their families, multiple losses, deprivation, and brutality, the residential school system denied Aboriginal communities the basic human right to transmit their traditions and maintain their cultural identity." (p. 608)*

Thousands of Aboriginal people have been involved in lawsuits against the federal government and the Anglican, United, and Roman Catholic churches for the abuses they suffered. On December 15, 2006, an historic settlement was reached in favour of the abused former students. It's estimated that over 80,000 people in total were entitled to benefits at an estimated cost to the federal government of $2 billion in restitution (Canadian Press, 2006). Implementation of the Indian Residential Schools Settlement Agreement began on September 19, 2007. On June 1, 2008, the government formed the Truth and Reconciliation Commission as part of the court-approved agreement (negotiated between legal counsel for former students, legal counsel for the churches, the Government of Canada, the Assembly of First Nations, and other Aboriginal organizations). The truth and reconciliation approach is a form of "restorative justice" that, in contrast to the customary adversarial or retributive justice, focuses on healing relationships between offenders, victims, and the community in which an offence takes place. The Truth and Reconciliation Commission completed its work at the end of 2015 under the direction of Commission Chair Chief Justice Murray Sinclair. It gathered statements from

Library and Archives Canada /PA-042122

Fort Resolution, N.W.T. Bishop Breynat and Aboriginal pupils of the Roman Catholic Mission.

over 7,000 residential school survivors and located and gathered together over four million documents. This information is housed at the National Centre for Truth and Reconciliation at the University of Manitoba. The Commission's final report was issued in July 2015 and it calls for a national plan for memorializing past wrongs and for a greater integration of indigenous perspectives into curricula at all levels of school.

In 2009, another class-action lawsuit was filed against the Attorney General of Canada over the treatment of thousands of Aboriginal children from 1965 to 1985 (see Diebel, 2009). Marcia Martel was one of those children.

When the provinces took over responsibility for Aboriginal health, welfare, and educational services in the 1960s, child and welfare services focused on "child neglect," and social workers chose adoption and long-term foster care for many Aboriginal children. By the end of the 1960s, between 30 and 40% of children who were legal wards of the provinces were Aboriginal children (Kirmayer et al., 2000). In 1959 the rate had been only 1%!

Kirmayer et al. (2000) believe that it was short-sighted policies such as these (and many others) that produced the "collective trauma, loss, and grief" that, in conjunction with poverty and the sense of deprivation created by "the values of consumer capitalism," led to the high rates of physical health problems and psychiatric disorders found in many Aboriginal communities (p. 609). Conflicts about identification can be severe. Young Aboriginal people in particular can be torn between traditional values and those of the more privileged majority culture, and this in part may underlie the high rates of psychological and social problems among Aboriginal young people. For many of them, there is little hope of wage-earning jobs, and the pursuit of higher education is fraught with obstacles. Is it any wonder that so many Aboriginal youth have no clear sense of identity or life direction?

Aboriginal communities do differ, of course, in their political structure, religious activities, and social and psychological problems. Some communities have experienced cultural revitalization and political empowerment. The Cree of James Bay, for example, are particularly politically active. In 1975 they won significant rights and major concessions (including monetary compensation; land-claims settlement; provisions for environmental and traditional activity protection; and some control over health, social, and education services). Within communities, potential protective factors may be associated with less psychological distress in individuals. In one study of the Cree of James Bay, Kirmayer and his colleagues (Kirmayer, Boothroyd, Tanner, Adelson, & Robinson, 2000) found that having a good relationship with other people in the community and "spending more time in the bush" predicted less distress. The Cree are noted for the degree to which extended families go to the bush to hunt and trap. Why should living in the bush be related to reduced distress?

> *"A large part of bush life involves contact with nature, spiritual relations with animals, consumption of valued foods and participation in other traditional activities. Increased time in the bush may confer mental health benefits by increasing family solidarity and social support, reinforcing cultural identity, improving physical health with nutritious bush foods and exercise, or providing respite from the pressures of settlement life."* (Kirmayer et al., 2000, p. 48)

The Cree suicide rate is not any higher than the rate among non-Aboriginal Canadians.

Just as there are community success stories, we can cite many examples at the individual level where Aboriginal people have risen above the circumstances we have outlined. Paul Okalik is one success story. His story was eloquently told over a decade ago in *Maclean's* magazine.

> *"At 17, Okalik went through an all-too-common rite of passage for troubled Inuit teenagers: he was thrown in jail. Okalik was drinking heavily, got kicked out of school, and then was caught trying to break into a post office to steal liquor. The three-month sentence he was given might have marked the start of a dissolute life."* (Geddes, 2001, p.16)

In 1999, at the age of 34, Paul Okalik (see photo) became premier of Canada's newest territory in the central and eastern Arctic—Nunavut, Canada's first public government with a majority of Aboriginal lawmakers. Okalik made the news in 2016 when he resigned as Nunavut's Minister of Health and Justice to protest the continuing sale of beer and wine in the community while there were insufficient services to treat addiction and related problems.

Nunavut celebrated its tenth birthday on April 1, 2009. Unfortunately, today, it has continuing socio-economic problems,

THE CANADIAN PRESS/Jonathan Hayward

Paul Okalik, who "wrestled personal demons to the ground" (Geddes, 2001, p. 17), became the first premier of the Territory of Nunavut. He later resigned as the territory's Minister of Health and Justice, saying he could not continue in his post when the government sells beer and wine but does not provide adequate treatment options for addiction.

including overcrowded housing, a tuberculosis epidemic, high unemployment, and only a 25% high school graduation rate. Sadly, it currently has a suicide epidemic that is grave enough to be deemed a public health emergency.

Thinking Critically

1. How can you account for Paul Okalik's success at such a young age? Did he experience fewer risk factors than his peers, or did certain protective factors make it possible for him to take the harder path to success? Speculate about possible risk and protective factors.

2. Would you agree that solutions to mental health problems among Canada's Aboriginal people require societal and economic strategies, in addition to psychological interventions?

Some cultural and religious groups receive attention not for elevated rates of mental disorder, but for atypically low rates of mental disorder. The Hutterites in Manitoba, who live in isolated, religious communities that are relatively free from outside influences, have remarkably low levels of mental illness. This German-speaking, Anabaptist sect emigrated in the 1870s from central Europe to Manitoba. Research conducted in 1953 (Eaton & Weil, 1953) found that they had the lowest lifetime prevalence of schizophrenia (1.1 per 1,000) of any group studied thus far in North America. A reanalysis of the original data (Torrey, 1995) and another study (Nimgaonkar et al., 2000) confirmed this finding. Genetic and lifestyle factors probably play a role in contributing to these low rates.

Research on the mental health of immigrants to Canada has found additional evidence for what is known as the **healthy immigrant effect**, and this has been attributed in part to pre-screening processes that limit entry to potential immigrants with health problems (Government of Canada,

2006). A Statistics Canada report indicated that immigrants had comparatively lower rates of depression and alcohol dependence than Canadian-born members of the population (Ali, 2002), unrelated to language proficiency in English or French, employment status, or sense of belonging. Recent analyses have confirmed a clear survival advantage for immigrants, but it was also found that the situation is more complex than first realized. Indeed, the healthy immigrant effect is more evident among adults, and less detectable among children and adolescents, as well as elderly adults (Vang, Sigouin, Flenon, & Gagnon, 2015). Moreover, Canadian survey data indicate that children who immigrated at a relatively early age had a comparatively higher risk for mood disorders (Islam, 2015). More generally, the recent Syrian refugee crisis underscores that a person's prior life context and severe challenges before immigration make it unlikely that newcomers will necessarily fit the description of the healthy immigrant effect.

Poor language proficiency is one factor that undermines the healthy immigrant effect. Limited language proficiency is a robust predictor of poor health status (also see Fuller-Thomson, Noack, & George, 2011). Other predictors were limited friendliness of neighbours and problems accessing health care (Ng, Pottie, & Spitzer, 2011). About 1 in 4 immigrants who experienced a health decline reported serious problems in accessing care (Fuller-Thomson et al., 2011). Another vulnerability factor is living in an area of Canada where there is a lower percentage of immigrants; not surprisingly, lower depression is reported by those who reside where there are other recent immigrants coping with similar challenges (Stafford, Newbold, & Ross, 2011).

Reitmanova and Gustafson (2009) conducted a qualitative study of the mental health needs of visible minority immigrants to St. John's, Newfoundland, considered a small urban centre. They examined facilitators and barriers to maintaining mental health. Numerous factors interacted in dynamic ways as stressors of immigrant mental health, including lack of family and social support, unemployment and low socio-economic status, inhospitable social and physical environments (e.g., racial and ethnic inequality and discrimination), lack of freedom to practise religious beliefs and cultural traditions, limited autonomy of some immigrant women, and inadequate coping skills. Reitmanova and Gustafson (2009) offered 18 recommendations directed toward decision-makers in government, health agencies, and social services. A major recommendation was that mental health authorities and policy makers recognize immigrants as a unique population that should qualify for special services.

Cultural diversity has implications for the assessment and diagnosis (see Chapter 3) of psychological disorders. In terms of clinical assessment, it is problematic that clinicians often interact with clients who have difficulty conversing in one of the official languages of Canada. Imagine a distressed Portuguese-speaking mother having to take her 10-year-old daughter along to act as the interpreter when she talks to her therapist about her profound depression and suicidal thoughts! Further, few major standardized clinical tests have norms for Canada or norms for its major minority groups, including French Canadians.

Paradigms that attempt to integrate factors and influences that are both inside and outside the self are presented below. As the description of these models unfold, it is important to remain cognizant of cultural differences and how many factors are altered in small or large ways as a result of the cultural context experienced by an individual.

2.9 Diathesis–Stress and Biopsychosocial: Integrative Paradigms

"Rather than adopting a single explanatory perspective, as is often advocated in traditional theories of science, etiological models for

psychiatric disorders need to be pluralistic or multilevel. . . . A range of compelling evidence indicates that these disorders involve causal processes that act within and outside of the individual, and that involve processes best understood from biological, psychological, and sociocultural perspectives."

—*Kenneth S. Kendler, 2008, p. 695*

Clearly, abnormal behaviour is much too diverse to be explained or treated adequately by any one of the current paradigms. It is probably advantageous that psychologists do not agree on which paradigm is the best. We know far too little to make hard and fast decisions on the exclusive superiority of any one paradigm. The best approach is often to assume multiple causation. A particular disorder is likely to be quite complex and develop through an interaction of factors. Two integrative paradigms are now explored.

The Diathesis–Stress Paradigm

A paradigm that is more broad and inclusive than the ones discussed earlier in this chapter, called the **diathesis–stress paradigm**, links biological, psychological, and environmental factors. It is not limited to one particular school of thought, such as learning, cognitive, or psychodynamic, but focuses on the interaction between a predisposition toward disease—the diathesis—and environmental, or life, disturbances—the stress (see photo). Diathesis refers most precisely to a constitutional predisposition toward illness, but the term may be extended to any characteristic or set of characteristics that increases a person's chance of developing a disorder.

In the realm of biology, a number of disorders appear to have a genetically transmitted diathesis; that is, having a close relative with the disorder increases a person's risk for the disorder since there is a sharing of genetic endowment to some degree. Although the precise nature of these genetic diatheses is currently unknown (e.g., we don't know exactly what is inherited that increases susceptibility to schizophrenia), it is clear that a genetic predisposition is an important component of many psychopathologies. Other biological diatheses include oxygen deprivation at birth, poor nutrition, a maternal viral infection, or maternal smoking during pregnancy. Each of these conditions may lead to changes in the brain that predispose toward psychopathology.

In the psychological realm, a diathesis for depression may be the cognitive set already mentioned: the chronic feeling of hopelessness sometimes found in depressed people. Or, taking a psychodynamic view, it may be an extreme sense of dependency on others, perhaps because of frustrations during one of the psychosexual stages. Another psychological diathesis is the ability to be easily hypnotized, which may be a diathesis for dissociative identity disorder (formerly called multiple personality disorder).

© iStock.com/Vetta Collection/Andrew Rich

Life stress, such as being overwhelmed at work or living in a war zone, is an important component of the diathesis–stress paradigm.

These psychological diatheses can arise for a variety of reasons. Some, such as hypnotizability, are personality characteristics that are, in part, genetically determined. Others, such as a sense of hopelessness, may result from adverse life experiences. The diathesis–stress paradigm is integrative because it draws on all these diverse sources of information about the causes of diatheses.

Possessing the diathesis for a disorder increases a person's risk of developing it but does not guarantee that the disorder will develop. It is the stress part of diathesis–stress that accounts for how a diathesis may be translated into an actual disorder. In this context, stress generally refers to some noxious or unpleasant environmental stimulus that triggers psychopathology. Psychological stressors include both major traumatic events (e.g., losing one's job, divorce, death of a spouse) and more mundane happenings (e.g., being stuck in traffic). The diathesis–stress model goes beyond the major paradigms we have already discussed by including these environmental events.

The key point of the diathesis–stress model is that both diathesis and stress are necessary in the development of disorders (see Figure 2.6). Some people, for example, inherit a biological predisposition that places them at high risk for schizophrenia (see Chapter 11); given a certain amount of stress, they stand a good chance of developing schizophrenia. Other people, at low genetic risk, are not likely to develop schizophrenia, regardless of how difficult their lives are.

In one illustrative study, Keller and colleagues (Keller, Neale, & Kendler, 2007) reported that different types of life events are linked to specific patterns of depressive symptoms, suggesting that even if a person carries a genetic diathesis for depression, the clinical manifestations of that diathesis might be strongly influenced by specific types of life experiences. A further implication is that the development of new drug treatments for depression should possibly consider not only the underlying genetic and molecular neurobiology of the disorder, but also the ways in which that neurobiology might be differentially shaped by stressful life events.

Another feature of the diathesis–stress paradigm is that psychopathology is unlikely to result from any single factor. As seen in our earlier discussion of gene–environment interactions, a genetically transmitted diathesis may be necessary for some disorders, but it is embedded in a network of other factors that also play a part; for example, genetically transmitted diatheses for other personality characteristics, childhood experiences that shape personality, the development of behavioural competencies and coping strategies, stressors encountered in adulthood, and cultural influences. We illustrate this point by returning to our earlier discussion of temperament-based personality types. The three types (resilient, undercontrolled, and overcontrolled) are styles that represent qualitatively different diatheses or vulnerabilities. These styles become intertwined with different environmental experiences very early in life. Consider, for instance, how the same parent or teacher might react to one child who is easygoing and adapts well to challenge versus the child who is quiet, unassuming, and relatively disengaged and the child who is always getting into trouble and generating conflict with other children.

One illustration of how these personality types as diatheses interact with environmental factors was provided by Oshri, Rogosch, and Cicchetti (2013), who longitudinally examined the life experiences and adjustment profiles of children who were first studied when they were 10 to 12 years old. They confirmed that there were differences in adjustment difficulties (e.g., greater marijuana use and externalizing problems) in the undercontrolled children but these differences were mediated by different levels and types of experiences of childhood

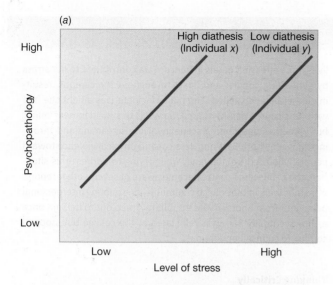

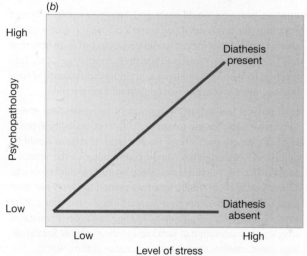

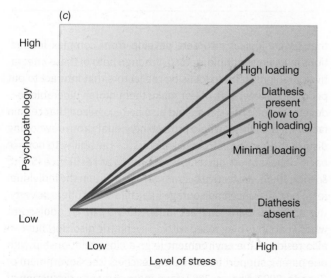

FIGURE 2.6 Three depictions of diathesis–stress models. (a) An individual with a large dose of the diathesis requires only a moderate amount of stress to develop psychopathology, whereas an individual with a small dose of the diathesis requires a large amount of stress to precipitate a breakdown. (b) The diathesis is dichotomous; stress level has no effect on those without the diathesis. (c) The diathesis is continuous; increasing stress increases psychopathology for all people with at least a minimal amount of the diathesis. After Monroe and Simons (1991).

maltreatment. Oshri et al. (2013) concluded that childhood maltreatment is a potent stressor to be considered in diathesis–stress models.

Another intriguing example of the diathesis–stress model was provided recently by researchers from Quebec (see Brendgen et al., 2015). They reported evidence suggesting that being victimized by a close friend seemed to activate a genetic predisposition to anxiety; however, it was specific to close friends because victimization by peers in general did not activate the diathesis.

One final caveat must be noted here. An intriguing paper on diathesis–stress models by Belsky and Pluess (2009) introduced the notion of **differential susceptibility**. They suggested and showed that some factors that are considered diatheses should actually be considered differential susceptibility factors because they involved the expected adverse reaction to negative experiences but also positive reactions to positive experiences. For example, it would actually be a situation of differential susceptibility if a vulnerable child reacted poorly to parental criticism but also tended to react quite positively to parental praise and support.

Student Perspectives 2.1 illustrates how a vulnerability interacts with significant stress to exacerbate adjustment problems. Much of the work in the stress field focuses on how people cope with life transitions and one key transition that is challenging for all students is moving from high school to college or university. Some students have a particularly difficult time, as illustrated in the box.

The Biopsychosocial Paradigm

Many clinical scientists describe an integrative paradigm that is quite similar to and overlaps with the diathesis–stress perspective: the **biopsychosocial paradigm**. Biological, psychological, and social factors are conceptualized as different levels of analysis or subsystems within the paradigm (Engel, 1980). Like the diathesis–stress paradigm, the biopsychosocial paradigm is not limited to a particular school of thought. Figure 2.7 illustrates the biopsychosocial paradigm. The figure incorporates an array of the possible causal factors, including some of those described in connection with the discussion of the diathesis–stress paradigm. The key point about the biopsychosocial paradigm is that explanations for the causes of disorders typically involve complex interactions among many biological, psychological, and socio-environmental and socio-cultural factors. The actual variables and the degree of influence of the variables from the different domains typically differ from disorder to disorder. Thus, similar to the diathesis–stress paradigm, the biopsychosocial paradigm is integrative because it accepts the interplay of many factors and draws on diverse sources of information about the causes of psychological disorders.

Many scholarly articles and research papers are based on the diathesis–stress and biopsychosocial paradigms (e.g., Kendler, 2008), a reflection of the now widely accepted view

Student Perspectives 2.1

Diathesis and Stress in a Student with Borderline Personality Disorder

Draper and Faulkner (2009) provided a compelling case study with their detailed account of Sara, a 19-year-old first-year university student who attended a small Catholic college in the United States. Sara came for counselling as a result of anxiety and obsessive thoughts and preoccupations over Jessica, her resident hall roommate who broke off their romantic relationship. In fact, Sara indicated that her main reason for counselling was to get Jessica back. Sara was diagnosed with borderline personality disorder as a result of her pattern of uncontrollable rage, emotional outbursts, and difficulties with others. Additional symptoms included an extensive history of self-harm and threats of suicide.

The diathesis for Sara involved exposure to her mother, who was described as rigidly controlling but emotionally unavailable to Sara. Sara described herself as pampered but she also experienced great inconsistencies in her mother's behaviour. Sara was dictated to and told what emotions she could experience at some points but then was emotionally neglected and ignored at other points. Draper and Faulkner (2009) applied an objects relation approach focused on the theme of the search for the "all good mother" who was emotionally unavailable in early childhood. This created an interpersonal vulnerability in Sara that was triggered by the general stress of being away from home and then having an intense interpersonal conflict that ended in rejection. The stressors are important in terms of bringing the vulnerability to the fore.

One danger with diathesis–stress models is that stress is often conceptualized as something that happens to us. Later in this book we will consider the work of Hammen (1991), who focused on stress generation and the notion that people can make their own lives more stressful. In this instance, Sara contributed to her stress by generating conflict and upset throughout the campus, resulting in her being expelled. The major incident was a fight she had with Jessica in a common area. Sara felt this incident was minor but witnesses described a scene involving screaming and throwing things (by both Sara and Jessica) and physical violence toward people who tried to intervene. While trying to address this situation, the counselling centre became aware of several other reports from members in the college community of troubling interpersonal behaviour from another student, but it turned out to be Sara once again. Eventually Sara was reinstated at the college but stopped coming to counselling sessions.

Thinking Critically

1. Imagine how you would react and how you would interpret Sara and her problems if you were a behaviourist or a cognitive therapist. What factors would you focus on? Note here that one factor that was implicated was the secondary gain that Sara received by getting campus-wide attention and a sense of having the power to provoke reactions from other people.

2. How do you feel about the concept of self-generated stress? Should we allow for the role of personal responsibility in terms of adding to our own stress? Do you think that Sara would be able to acknowledge her role in contributing to the interpersonal difficulties? Perhaps not, since one of the chief problems turned out to be that Sara's mother tended to shield her from developing a sense of personal responsibility. In fact, her mother responded to Sara's expulsion by fighting to have her reinstated with little consideration of Sara's role in the matter or Sara's feelings about whether she wished to continue at the college.

Psychological factors

personality
unconscious determinants
cognitive set or style
psychological stressors
coping strategies
social skills

Biological factors

genetic predisposition
brain structure
neurochemistry
hormones
autonomic nervous system functions
maternal viral infection

Social factors

(including socio-environmental and socio-cultural factors)

major traumatic events
marital conflict
family dysfunction
peer relationships
cultural standards
poverty

that psychological disorders develop from complex interactions involving multiple factors. Although both of these integrative paradigms tend to focus on the factors that interact to put people at greater **risk** of—or make them more vulnerable to—developing disorders, it should also be recognized that certain factors, if present, can help protect individuals from developing disorders. Protection from risk factors, or the ability to bounce back in the face of adversity, is referred to as **resilience** (Smith & Prior, 1995). Protective factors can occur within the individual (e.g., perseverance and courage in a child who suffers poverty; the ability to think and act independently in an adolescent whose parent is diagnosed with a psychiatric disorder) but can also reside in the environment (e.g., a close relationship with one parent; support from a caring teacher) (see Government of Canada, 2006; Phares, 2003, for a more complete discussion of protective factors and resiliency).

FIGURE 2.7 The biopsychosocial paradigm. Although disturbances in each area can contribute to the development of psychological disorders, the causes cannot be neatly divided and there is usually interaction among the three domains of influence.

TABLE 2.1	Risk Factors Potentially Influencing the Development of Mental Health Problems and Mental Disorders In individuals			
Individual Factors	**Family/Social Factors**	**School Context**	**Life Events and Situations**	**Community and Cultural Factors**
• Prenatal brain damage • Prematurity • Birth injury • Low birth weight, birth complications • Physical and intellectual disability • Poor health in infancy • Insecure attachment in infant/child • Low intelligence • Difficult temperament • Chronic illness • Poor social skills • Low self-esteem • Alienation • Impulsivity	• Having a teenage mother • Having a single parent • Absence of father in childhood • Large family size • Anti-social role models (in childhood) • Family violence; marital disorder • Harsh or inconsistent discipline • Poor supervision and monitoring of child • Parent mental disorder • Social isolation	• Lack of warmth and affection • Bullying • Peer rejection • Poor attachment to school • Inadequate behaviour management • Deviant peer group • School failure	• Physical, sexual, and emotional abuse • School transitions • Divorce and family breakup • Death of family member • Physical illness or impairment • Unemployment, homelessness • Incarceration • Poverty or economic insecurity • Job insecurity • Unsatisfactory work-place relationships • Natural disasters	• Socio-economic disadvantage • Social or cultural discrimination • Isolation • Neighbourhood violence and crime • Population density and housing conditions • Lack of support services including transport, shopping, recreational facilities

*Many of these factors are specific to particular stages of the lifespan, particularly childhood. Others have an impact across the lifespan; for example, socio-economic disadvantage.

Source: Promotion, Prevention and Early Intervention for Mental Health, Table 2, p. 16. Department of Health, Australia Government, 2000 © Commonwealth of Australia. Used with permission of the Australian Government.

Table 2.1 summarizes risk factors that potentially influence the development of mental health problems and mental disorders in people. This table, adapted from the report *The Human Face of Mental Health and Mental Illness in Canada 2006* (Government of Canada, 2006), illustrates the complexity and variety of risk factors that can be considered from a diathesis–stress or biopsychosocial perspective.

There are some important caveats about these risk factors. First, the occurrence of many risk factors is specific to particular stages of the lifespan, particularly childhood. Contemporary biopsychosocial models of psychopathology in children are described in Chapter 15. These models typically incorporate a developmental psychopathology focus (see Cicchetti, 1984); i.e., a general framework for understanding disordered behaviour in relation to normal development. Second, it is often the case that disorders reflect a complex interplay of multiple risk factors.

Earlier, we discussed maltreatment as a severe stressor. Clearly, maltreatment or abuse is a powerful risk factor: a history of maltreatment in childhood is acknowledged as a consistent and strong predictor of subsequent emotional difficulties. According to the World Health Organization (2004), tens of millions of children are abused and neglected each year, and 20% of females and 10% of males are victims of childhood sexual abuse. Canadian data suggest that levels of maltreatment may be on the rise! The 2003 Canadian Incidence Study of Reported Child Abuse and Neglect, led by Nico Trocmé, found that in the nine provinces surveyed (all but Quebec), there was a 125% increase over five years, with 9.64 substantiated cases per thousand children in 1998 versus 21.71 in 2003 (see Trocmé et al., 2005).

A horrific case of physical, emotional, and sexual abuse drew revulsion worldwide in 2008 when a woman, then 42 years old, escaped from a squalid, rat-infested cellar built beneath the family's home near Vienna, Austria. Her father had locked her in this dungeon when she was 18. Over the next 24 years, he raped her more than 3,000 times, fathered her seven children, and let one die in captivity as a newborn (Oleksyn & Kole, 2009).

On March 19, 2009, Josef Fritzl, 73, pleaded guilty to homicide, enslavement, rape, incest, forced imprisonment, and coercion (see photo). He was sentenced to life in a secure

AFP/Getty Images

Josef Fritzl locked his daughter in a dungeon for 24 years and subjected her to continuous physical, emotional, and sexual abuse.

psychiatric ward. One can hardly imagine the terrible psychological consequences to his daughter Elizabeth, who was described by prosecutors as a "broken" woman, and her six surviving children, three of whom had never seen daylight until the crime was exposed. She and the children, who ranged in age from 6 to 20, spent months recovering in a psychiatric clinic.

We will explore this important risk factor and its often tragic consequences in greater detail in Chapter 5, Canadian Perspectives 5.1, and examine it in relation to other psychosocial risk and protective factors, since maltreatment often operates as part of a complex set of psychosocial factors (e.g., family disruption and poverty; Bagley & Mallick, 2000). However, despite our focus on psychosocial factors, note that a biological vulnerability also seems to play a role in influencing the impact of maltreatment. Some people show remarkable resilience and overcome a history of maltreatment, while others do not. A provocative study of maltreatment and subsequent aggression found that maltreated children with a genotype conferring high levels of monoamine oxidase A (MAO-A) were substantially less likely to display anti-social behaviour as adults (Caspi et al., 2002). This is a classic example of a gene–environment interaction. This finding was qualified by the results of a newer study that found that lifetime levels of maltreatment and conduct disorder were associated robustly but there was no evidence of a gene–environment interaction (Young et al., 2006). That is, there was no support for the hypothesis that polymorphism in the gene encoding MAO-A confers risk for conduct disorder. Additional research is needed to examine this possibility.

Some factors, such as socio-economic disadvantage, can occur and have an impact across the lifespan. However, as you will see in the following section, the link to psychological disorders is complex. Even our relatively brief discussion highlights the complex interplay of factors in the biopsychosocial model.

An Example: Socio-Economic Status and Poverty

It is generally accepted that extreme poverty and low socio-economic status (SES) confer risk for increased rates of mental illness. This is a tricky issue to some extent because profound mental illness can limit socio-economic opportunities, so it is important, wherever possible, to examine the role of SES in longitudinal research that can establish that low socio-economic status preceded the onset of mental health problems. Further, socio-economic status might be closely related to relevant "third variables" (see Chapter 4), including job status, education, perceived stress, neighbourhood violence and crime, social support, physical health, marital and family functioning, parental psychopathology, and so forth. This situation is further complicated by evidence from the Canadian Community Health Survey indicating that Canadians with lower income levels, relative to people with higher income levels, tend to report greater barriers to mental health care (Slaunwhite, 2015). Women from lower-income homes were particularly likely to report availability and accessibility issues due to pragmatic concerns such as a lack of transportation.

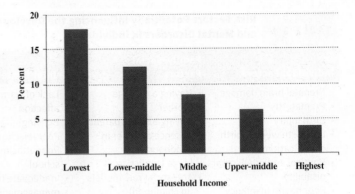

FIGURE 2.8 Mental health perceived as fair or poor among adults aged 15+ years, by household income, Canada, 2002.
Source: Statistics Canada, Canadian Community Health Survey, 2002, Mental Health and Well-being Cycle 1.2.

Existing data do support a link between SES and mental health. The Canadian Community Mental Health Survey's Mental Health and Well-being Cycle documented an apparent steady decline in mental health as a function of lower levels of household income (see Government of Canada, 2006). This effect is illustrated in Figure 2.8.

Given these associations, we can only hope that campaigns to end poverty throughout the world will some day be successful. In Canada, in 1989, politicians in the House of Commons pledged to eradicate child poverty by the year 2000. This goal is still not close to being achieved, underscored by a 2006 report that almost 1 out of every 6 (almost 1.2 million) children in Canada live in poverty; 1 in 4 Aboriginal children live in poverty (see Campaign 2000, 2006). Indeed, Canada still lacks a national, comprehensive strategy to end poverty, although specific plans have been proposed (National Council of Welfare, 2007). Quebec passed anti-poverty legislation in 2002 and has since cut child poverty in half (see Monsebraaten & Talaga, 2009). In 2009, Ontario passed legislation that committed the province to become a leading jurisdiction in the battle against poverty. The Poverty Reduction Act was hailed by advocates as "historic." More than 350 groups pushed the government to adopt the goal of cutting child poverty by 25% in five years. The act requires successive governments to draft poverty-fighting strategies with specific goals every five years and to report annually to the legislature on progress. All parties supported the legislation.

How might SES combine with other factors in the biopsychosocial model? Essex et al. (2006) confirmed in longitudinal research that children with higher SES have less severe internalizing and externalizing mental health symptoms. Different etiologic pathways were identified for those with low versus high SES backgrounds. The key factor for those with low SES was chronic maternal stress during the child's infancy. The key factor for those from a high SES background was a parental history of depression along with a family history of psychopathology. For all children, an absence of social and academic impairment during the transition to school was a mediator or buffer of possible mental health problems.

An important caveat about SES is that many of its effects are actually due to living in an impoverished neighbourhood.

The negative impact of being poor is amplified when the person lives in a poor neighbourhood, which is defined as poor-quality housing, few available resources, and unsafe conditions (Cutrona, Wallace, & Wesner, 2006). Cutrona et al. (2006) focused on how a poor neighbourhood escalates levels of depression. They identified three specific processes associated with poor neighbourhoods that increase depression: (1) increased daily stress; (2) greater vulnerability to negative events; and (3) disrupted social ties (i.e., less chance to develop positive affiliations). The message is clear: not only do people need a certain level of money, they also need to live in a better location.

Throughout this book, you will discover elaborate explanations of disorders in which numerous variables, both risk and protective, work together to bring about maladaptive or adaptive outcomes. While our focus tends to be on factors and outcomes in general, it is important to realize that research tends to promote broad generalizations but life for the individual person is quite complex and it is important to consider what matters to each person. The case studies located throughout this book serve as an effective reminder of the need to focus on the unique circumstances of each person.

Summary

2.1 Scientific inquiry is a special way in which human beings acquire knowledge about their world. People may see only what they are prepared to see, and certain phenomena may go undetected because scientists can discover only the things about which they already have some general idea. One is better able to keep track of subjective influences by making explicit one's paradigm, or scientific perspective. The paradigm that is operating will guide the hypotheses that are tested and how the results and their implications are interpreted.

2.2 Several major paradigms, or points of view, are current in the study of psychopathology and therapy. The biological paradigm assumes that psychopathology is caused by an organic defect. Two biological factors relevant to psychopathology are genetics and neurochemistry. Biological therapies attempt to rectify the specific biological defects underlying disorders or to alleviate symptoms of disorders, often using drugs to do so.

2.3 At present, the most influential psychological paradigm is the cognitive-behavioural paradigm, which is a blend of the cognitive and behavioural approaches. Behavioural, or learning, paradigms suggest that aberrant behaviour has developed through classical conditioning, operant conditioning, or modelling. Investigators who believe that abnormal behaviour may have been learned examine all situations affecting behaviour and define concepts carefully. Behaviour therapists try to apply learning principles to bring about change in overt behaviour, thought, and emotion. Cognitive theorists have argued that certain schemas and irrational interpretations are major factors in abnormality. Theorists such as Ellis focus on irrational beliefs while Beck focuses on negative thoughts and dysfunctional attitudes about the self, other people, and the future.

2.4 Another paradigm derives from the work of Sigmund Freud. The psychoanalytic, or psychodynamic, point of view directs our attention to repressions and other unconscious processes traceable to early-childhood conflicts that have set in motion certain psychodynamics. Whereas present-day ego analysts, who are part of this tradition, place greater emphasis on conscious ego functions, the psychoanalytic paradigm has generally searched the unconscious and early life of the client for the causes of abnormality. Therapeutic interventions based on psychoanalytic theory usually attempt to lift repressions so that the client can examine the infantile and unfounded nature of his or her fears.

2.5 The humanistic paradigm and the therapy approach that reflects it are insight-oriented, like psychoanalysis, and regard freedom to choose and personal responsibility as key human characteristics. Rogers' client-centred therapy entails complete acceptance of and empathy for the client, restating the client's thoughts and feelings and sometimes offering new perspectives on the client's problem. This paradigm has identified general processes such as treating the person with empathy and positive regard that have become accepted elements of the general therapeutic process.

2.6 The most important implication of paradigms is that they determine where and how investigators look for answers. Paradigms necessarily limit perceptions of the world, for investigators will interpret data differently according to their points of view. In our opinion, it is fortunate that mental health workers are not all operating within the same paradigm, for at this point too little is known about psychopathology and its treatment to settle on any one of them.

2.7 A consideration of paradigms that focus primarily on vulnerabilities inside the individual must be balanced by a consideration of external factors in the immediate and broader environment that confer risk for mental health problems. Familial factors and peer factors play a role as well as the broader cultural factors.

2.8 Studies of the influences of culture on psychopathology have proliferated in recent years. The cultural and racial backgrounds of clients present a variety of challenges. Particular issues in Canada surround the assessment and treatment of French Canadians, Aboriginal Canadians, Asian Canadians, and foreign-born Canadians whose first language is not English or French, including the kinds of problems these groups may have and the kinds of sensitivities clinicians should possess to deal respectfully and effectively with people from minority groups. It is critical to keep in mind that there are typically more differences within cultural groups than there are between them. Remembering this important point can help avoid the dangers of stereotyping members of a culture.

2.9 Because each of these paradigms seems to have something to offer to our understanding of mental disorders, there has been a movement to develop more integrative paradigms. The diathesis–stress paradigm assumes that people are predisposed to react adversely to environmental stressors. The diathesis or vulnerability may be biological, as appears to be the case in schizophrenia, or psychological, such as the chronic sense of hopelessness that seems to contribute to depression. Diatheses may be caused by early-childhood experiences, genetically determined personality traits, or socio-cultural influences. Similarly, the biopsychosocial paradigm presumes that disorders are a function of multifactorial interactions involving biological, psychological, and social variables. This model truly reflects the theme that dysfunction reflects the interplay of multiple causes.

Key Terms

action (behavioural) therapies
adoptees method
assertion training
authoritarian parenting
authoritative parenting
aversive conditioning
behaviour genetics
behaviour modification
behaviour therapy
behavioural (learning)
   paradigm
behaviourism
biological paradigm
biopsychosocial paradigm
brief therapy
classical conditioning
client-centred therapy
cognition
cognitive-behavioural therapy
   (CBT)
cognitive paradigm
cognitive restructuring
concordance
conditioned response
conditioned stimulus
counterconditioning
countertransference
cultural diversity
cumulative risk
deep brain stimulation

defence mechanism
denial
diathesis–stress paradigm
differential susceptibility
discriminative stimulus
disease model
displacement
dizygotic (DZ) twins
dream analysis
eclecticism
ego
ego analysis
extinction
family method
free association
genes
genotype
healthy immigrant effect
humanistic therapies
id
index cases (probands)
insight therapies
interpersonal therapy (IPT)
interpretation
introspection
irrational beliefs
latent content
law of effect
libido
linkage analysis

medical model
modelling
monozygotic (MZ) twins
moral anxiety
multicultural counselling and
   therapy
negative reinforcement
nerve impulse
neuron
neurotic anxiety
neurotransmitters
objective (realistic) anxiety
operant conditioning
overcontrolling type
paradigm
permissive parenting
phenotype
pleasure principle
positive reinforcement
primary process thinking
projection
psychoanalytic
   (psychodynamic) paradigm
psychodynamics
psychotherapy
rational-emotive behaviour
   therapy (REBT)
rationalization
reaction formation
reality principle

reductionism
regression
repression
resilience
resilient type
resistances
reuptake
risk
role-playing
schema
secondary process thinking
self-actualization
self-efficacy
sublimation
successive approximations
superego
sympathetic nervous system
synapse
systematic desensitization
temperament
transference
twin method
unconditional positive regard
unconditioned response
unconditioned stimulus
unconscious
undercontrolling type

Reflections: Past, Present, and Future

1. A "single cause" approach has been abandoned by most clinicians and psychopathologists, who now believe that psychological disorders arise from multiple causes. Assume that you are asked to name 10 major causes or risk factors for a mental disorder. Based on your understanding of the different paradigms, which factors would you nominate?

2. Our integrative paradigms focus on the interaction between a predisposition toward disease (the diathesis) and environmental, or life, disturbances (the stress), and the interaction among biological, psychological, and social factors. How would you incorporate your 10 causes into a diathesis–stress paradigm or the biopsychosocial paradigm? Using a diagram, illustrate your application of the biopsychosocial paradigm.

3. Why and how do some people succumb to biopsychosocial risk factors while others react in adaptive ways, sometimes in the face of overwhelming adversity? We need to better understand the complexities of protective factors (resiliency) and the mechanisms underlying the consequences of such factors. Do various resiliency factors interact to produce protection from diatheses or multiple risk factors? What are the mechanisms or underlying processes that provide protection? Are there critical times in a person's life (e.g., childhood) when resiliency factors can play a vital role in the development of psychological outcomes?

4. How would you develop and evaluate a specialized treatment program for depression or substance abuse among the Innu of Labrador (see Chapters 8 and 12)? Do you think it will ever be possible to develop valid treatments that are specific to other minority groups in Canada, such as Asian Canadians? What factors would need to be incorporated into the treatments described in this chapter?

CHAPTER 3

Clinical Assessment, Classification, and Diagnosis

LEARNING OBJECTIVES

1. Differentiate between reliability and validity in assessment.

2. Describe psychological assessment.

3. Compare and contrast different types of biological assessment.

4. Explain why diagnosis matters.

5. Describe the history of classification.

6. Discuss issues in the classification of abnormal behaviour.

7. Describe the diagnostic system of the American Psychiatric Association (*DSM-5*).

Susan's friends are concerned about her so they bring her to the university counselling centre for help. Susan is an extreme perfectionist who is relentlessly pursuing As or A+s because she wants to get into medical school. Her friends are alarmed because Susan is always on edge and sleeps only three hours a night at most, but they are especially concerned about the fact that she has become a workaholic who never has any fun and doesn't seem to get any satisfaction when she gets superb grades. In fact, when she does succeed, Susan criticizes herself and says that it should have come easier because other students seem to be effortlessly perfect. Imagine you are the chief psychologist for the centre. Your job is to determine the extent of Susan's adjustment problems using a variety of assessment techniques and then use therapeutic techniques to foster a healthier approach. You use a variety of assessment techniques, including having Susan complete personality measures and undergo a structured interview. You conclude that Susan suffers from clinical anhedonia (an inability to experience pleasure) but this is just the symptom manifestation. While she clearly has a sleep disorder as well, Susan's behaviours stem from a sense of inferiority and feeling like an imposter, and she is compensating for these feelings by trying to perfect. You then establish that this pattern seemed to emerge when Susan was in Grade 3 and in a classroom with peers who were preoccupied with social comparisons.

This chapter initially focuses on the various types of clinical assessment that are used to evaluate psychological and behavioural problems and the factors contributing to them. Many of the assessment tools we describe here are used to help determine a diagnosis. After reviewing psychological assessment, we then turn to the classification of abnormal behaviour, in particular the *Diagnostic and Statistical Manual of Mental Disorders, Fifth Edition* (*DSM-5*), published by the American Psychiatric Association.

The assessment procedures used and the decisions that follow are a product of many influences, including pragmatic concerns (i.e., the cost of assessment in time and money) but also the theoretical orientation and paradigm endorsed by the clinician. The approach taken with Susan would likely vary largely as a function of the theoretical orientation of the centre's psychologist. The most recent survey of practising clinical psychologists suggests that Susan is most likely to encounter a psychologist who endorses the cognitive paradigm. Figure 3.1 summarizes the results of a 2010 survey and earlier surveys conducted over 50 years with members of the Society of Clinical Psychologists (see Norcross & Karpiak, 2012). The most predominant theoretical orientation was cognitive (31%), followed by eclectic-integrative (22%) and then psychodynamic (18%) and behavioural (15%). Humanistic orientation (including Rogerian therapy) was followed by only 4% of clinical psychologists and

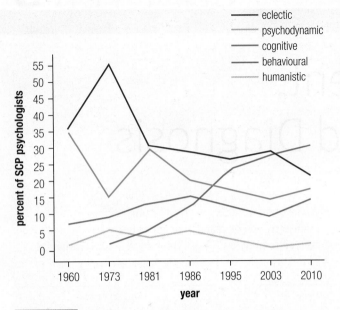

FIGURE 3.1 Primary theoretical orientations endorsed by psychologists in the Society of Clinical Psychology (SCP) over five decades. *Source:* Norcross & Karpiak, 2012, p. 5.

was outnumbered by interpersonal approaches. These survey results are similar to those described in Chapter 2 regarding theoretical orientations of psychologists in Quebec. Figure 3.1 shows the rise of the cognitive approach. A psychologist trained in the cognitive tradition would focus on Susan's thinking patterns and use assessment tools described later in the cognitive assessment section. A psychologist trained in the psychodynamic tradition would perhaps use some of the projective techniques described later in this chapter but then focus on some of the interpersonal themes that come up when it is indicated that Susan's perfectionism actually reflects being exposed repeatedly to parental criticism after making mistakes.

We review many assessment tools in this chapter. The most popular tools currently emphasized in psychological assessment training are intelligence tests and objective personality tests, with neuropsychological assessment and tests focused on treatment effectiveness (e.g., depression, anxiety symptom measures) increasing in popularity over the past decade (Ready & Veague, 2014). There is greater interest in determining if treatment is effective; to this end, clients are often asked to complete symptom measures weekly as they progress in therapy. (For example, a client being treated for depression would complete a measure of depression each week.) Before getting into the tools themselves, it is important to review reliability and validity.

3.1 Reliability and Validity in Assessment

The concepts of reliability and validity are extremely complex. There are several kinds of each, and an entire subfield of psychology—psychometrics—exists primarily for their study.

We provide here a general overview of what reliability and validity mean in the context of clinical assessments.

Reliability

In the most general sense, **reliability** is consistency of measurement. There are several types of reliability, some of which we discuss here.

- **Inter-rater reliability** measures the degree to which two independent observers or judges agree. To take an example from baseball, the third-base umpire may or may not agree with the home-plate umpire as to whether a line drive down the left-field line is fair or foul.

- **Test–retest reliability** measures the extent to which people being observed twice or taking the same test twice, perhaps several weeks or months apart, score in generally the same way. This kind of reliability makes sense only when the theory assumes that people will not change appreciably between testings on the variable being measured. A prime example of a situation in which this type of reliability makes sense is in evaluating intelligence tests.

- Sometimes psychologists use two forms of a test rather than giving the same test twice, perhaps when there is concern that people will remember their answers from the first test and aim merely to be consistent. This approach enables the tester to determine **alternate-form reliability**, the extent to which scores on the two forms of the test are consistent.

- Finally, **internal consistency reliability** assesses whether the items on a test are related to one another. For example, with an anxiety questionnaire containing 20 items we would expect the items to be interrelated, or to correlate with one another, if they truly tap anxiety. A person who reports a dry mouth in a threatening situation would be expected to report increases in muscle tension, as well.

In each of these types of reliability, a correlation—a measure of how closely two variables are related—is calculated between raters or sets of items. The higher the correlation, the better the reliability.

Validity

Validity is the extent to which a measure fulfills its intended purpose. For example, if a questionnaire is intended to measure a person's hostility, does it in fact do so? Before we describe several types of validity, it is important to note that validity is related to reliability: unreliable measures will not have good validity. Because an unreliable measure does not yield consistent results, an unreliable measure will not relate very strongly to other measures. For example, an unreliable measure of coping is not likely to relate well to how a person adjusts to a stressful life experience.

Content validity is the extent to which a measure adequately samples the domain of interest. For example, in

Chapter 9, we describe a measure of life stress that consists of a list of 43 life experiences. Respondents indicate which of these experiences—for example, losing one's job—they have had in some time period, such as the past year. Content validity would be high if most stressful events that people experience are captured by this list. However, content validity is only modest if events that actually occur are not represented.

Criterion validity is evaluated by determining whether a measure is associated in an expected way with some other measure (the criterion). Sometimes these relationships may be concurrent: both variables are measured at the same point in time, and the resulting validity is sometimes referred to as *concurrent validity*. For example, we will describe later a measure of the distorted thoughts believed to play an important role in depression. Criterion validity for this test could be established by showing that the test is actually related to depression; that is, depressed people score higher on the test than do non-depressed people. Alternatively, criterion validity can be assessed by evaluating the measure's ability to predict some other variable that is measured in the future; this kind of criterion validity is often referred to as *predictive validity*. For example, IQ tests were originally developed to predict future school performance. Similarly, a measure of distorted thinking could be used to predict the development of episodes of depression in the future.

Construct validity is relevant when we want to interpret a test as a measure of some characteristic or construct that is not simply defined (Cronbach & Meehl, 1955). A construct is an inferred attribute, such as anxiousness or distorted cognition, that a test is trying to measure. Consider an anxiety-proneness questionnaire as an example. The construct validity question is whether the variation we observe between people on a self-report test of anxiety proneness is really due to individual differences in anxiety proneness. Just because we call our test a measure of anxiety proneness and the items seem to be about the tendency to become anxious ("I find that I become anxious in many situations"), it is not certain that the test is a valid measure of anxiety proneness. People's responses to a questionnaire are determined by more variables than simply the construct being measured. For example, people vary in their willingness to admit to undesirable characteristics such as anxiety proneness; thus, scores on the questionnaire will be partly determined by this characteristic as well as by anxiety proneness itself.

Construct validity is evaluated by looking at a wide variety of data from multiple sources. For example, people diagnosed as having an anxiety disorder and people without such a diagnosis could be compared on their scores on the self-report measure of anxiety proneness. The self-report measure would achieve some construct validity if the people with anxiety disorders scored higher than a control group. Similarly, the self-report measure could be related to other measures thought to suggest anxiety, such as observations of fidgeting, trembling, or excessive sweating. When the self-report measure is associated with the observational one, its construct validity is increased. Studies may also examine change on the self-report measure. For example, if the measure has good construct validity, we would expect scores of clients with anxiety disorders to become lower after a course of a therapy that is effective in reducing anxiety.

More broadly, the question of construct validity is related to a particular theory of anxiety proneness. For example, we might hypothesize that a proneness to anxiety is caused by certain childhood experiences. We could then obtain further evidence for the construct validity of our questionnaire by showing that it relates to these childhood experiences. At the same time, we would have also gathered support for our theory of anxiety proneness. Thus, construct validation is an important part of the process of theory testing.

Another type of validity known as **case validity** has been suggested recently by Teglasi, Nebbergall, and Newman (2012). Case validity is unique because the focus here is on validity of the interpretations and decisions made with respect to a particular person. They recommended the need for another type of validity because information about multiple constructs as they apply to an individual "is not fully captured by the principles of construct validity" (p. 467). Case validity would be demonstrated when the person is accurately assessed in their life context in a way that takes into account interactions between the person and situations as well as interactions of the person's schemas (e.g., the combination of a need to be perfect in a person who also tends to be a procrastinator). Teglasi et al. (2012) noted that case validity requires considering the person in typical situations versus maximal situations (i.e., the difference between how a person usually is versus what they are capable of in atypical or extreme situations). The concept of case validity is revisited later in our discussion of case conceptualization in Focus on Discovery 3.1.

3.2 Psychological Assessment

Psychological assessment techniques are designed to determine cognitive, emotional, personality, and behavioural factors in psychopathological functioning. We will see that beyond the basic interview, which is used in various guises almost universally, many of the assessment techniques stem from the paradigms presented in Chapter 2. We discuss here clinical interviews, psychological tests (including personality and intelligence tests), and behavioural and cognitive assessment techniques.

Clinical Interviews

Most of us have probably been interviewed at one time or another, although the conversation may have been so informal that we did not regard it as an interview. To the layperson, the word "interview" connotes a formal, highly structured conversation, but we find it useful to construe the term as any interpersonal encounter, conversational in style, in which one person, the interviewer, uses language as the principal means of finding out about another person, the interviewee. Thus, a pollster who asks a college student which party he or she will vote for in an upcoming election is interviewing with the restricted goal of learning which party the student prefers. A clinical psychologist who asks a client about the circumstances of his or her most recent hospitalization is similarly conducting an interview.

One way in which a **clinical interview** is perhaps different from a casual conversation or a poll is the attention the interviewer pays to how the respondent answers—or does not answer—questions. For example, if a client is recounting marital conflicts, the clinician will generally be attentive to any emotion accompanying the comments. If the person does not seem upset about a difficult situation, the answers will probably be understood differently than they would be if the person were crying or agitated while relating the story.

The paradigm within which an interviewer operates influences the type of information sought, how it is obtained, and how it is interpreted. A psychoanalytically trained clinician can be expected to inquire about the person's childhood. He or she is also likely to remain sceptical of verbal reports because the analytic paradigm holds that the most significant aspects of a disturbed or normal person's developmental history are repressed into the unconscious. Of course, how the data are interpreted is influenced by the paradigm. The behaviourally oriented clinician is likely to focus on current environmental conditions that can be related to changes in the person's behaviour; for example, the circumstances under which the person becomes anxious. Thus, the clinical interview varies with the paradigm adopted by the interviewer. Like scientists, clinical interviewers in some measure find only the information for which they are looking.

Great skill is necessary to carry out good clinical interviews, for they are usually conducted with people who are under considerable stress. Clinicians, regardless of their theoretical orientation, recognize the importance of establishing rapport with the client. The interviewer must obtain the trust of the person; it is naive to assume that a client will easily reveal information to another, even to an authority figure with the title "Doctor." Even a client who sincerely, perhaps desperately, wants to recount intensely personal problems to a professional may not be able to do so without assistance. Psychodynamic clinicians assume that people entering therapy usually are not even aware of what is truly bothering them. Behavioural clinicians, although they concentrate more on what can be observed, also appreciate the difficulties people have in sorting out the factors responsible for their distress.

Most clinicians empathize with their clients in an effort to draw them out, to encourage them to elaborate on their concerns, and to examine different facets of a problem. Humanistic therapists employ specific empathy techniques to accomplish these goals. A simple summary statement of what the client has been saying can help sustain the momentum of talk about painful and possibly embarrassing events and feelings, and an accepting attitude toward personal disclosures dispels the fear that revealing "secrets of the heart" (London, 1964) to another human being will have disastrous consequences.

The interview can be a source of considerable information to the clinician. Its importance in abnormal psychology and psychiatry is unquestionable. Whether the information gleaned can always be depended on is not so clear, however. Clinicians often tend to overlook situational factors of the interview that may exert strong influences on what the client says or does. Consider for a moment how a teenager is likely to respond to the question, "How often have you used illegal drugs?" when it is asked by a young, informally dressed psychologist as opposed to a 60-year-old psychologist in a business suit.

Interviews vary in the degree to which they are structured. In practice, most clinicians operate from only the vaguest outlines. Exactly *how* information is collected is left largely up to the particular interviewer and depends, too, on the responsiveness and responses of the interviewee. Through years of clinical experience and both teaching and learning from students and colleagues, each clinician develops ways of asking questions with which he or she is comfortable and that seem to draw out the information that will be of maximum benefit to the client. Thus, to the extent that an interview is unstructured, the interviewer must rely on intuition and general experience. As a consequence, reliability for initial clinical interviews is probably low; that is, two interviewers may well reach different conclusions about the same client. And because the overwhelming majority of clinical interviews are conducted within confidential relationships, it has not been possible to establish either their reliability or their validity through systematic research.

We need to look at the broader picture here to avoid a judgement that may be too harsh. Both reliability and validity may indeed be low for a single clinical interview that is conducted in an unstructured fashion. But clinicians usually do more than one interview with a given client, and hence a self-corrective process is probably at work. The clinician may regard as valid what a client said in the first interview, but then at the sixth recognize it to have been incorrect or only partially correct.

Structured Interviews

At times, mental health professionals need to collect standardized information, particularly for making diagnostic judgements based on the *DSM*. Investigators have developed structured interviews, such as the Structured Clinical Interview for *DSM-5* Disorders (SCID) (First, Williams, Karg, & Spitzer, 2016), which assists researchers and clinicians in making diagnostic decisions regarding the most common disorders. A **structured interview** is one in which the questions are set out in a prescribed fashion for the interviewer.

The SCID is a branching interview; that is, the client's response to one question determines the next question that is asked. It also contains detailed instructions to the interviewer concerning when and how to probe in detail and when to go on to questions bearing on another diagnosis. Most symptoms are rated on a three-point scale of severity, with instructions in the interview schedule for directly translating the symptom ratings into diagnoses. The initial questions pertaining to obsessive-compulsive disorder (OCD; discussed in Chapter 6) from the SCID for DSM-IV are presented in Figure 3.2. A sample

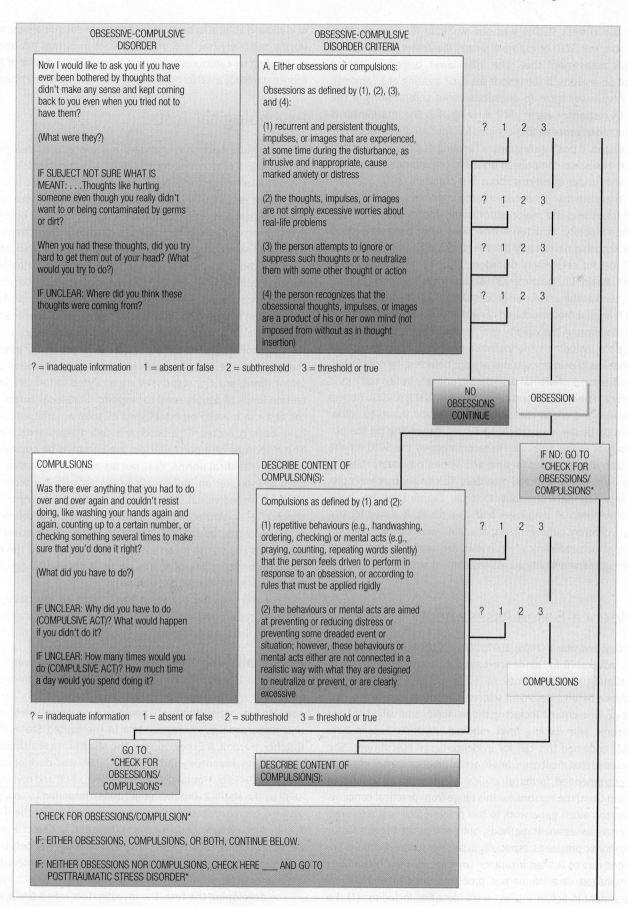

FIGURE 3.2 Sample item from the SCID. Reprinted with permission from First, M.B., Spitzer, R.I., Gibbon, M., Williams, J.B.W.: *Structured Clinical Interview for DSM-IV Axis I Disorders-Clinician Version (SCID-CV)*, Washington, DC, American Psychiatric Press, 1997. Copyright © 1997.

from the current SCID-5 was not available for reproduction; however, the SCID-IV example clearly illustrates the structure of this assessment tool. The interviewer begins by asking about obsessions. If the responses elicit a rating of 1 (absent), the interviewer turns to questions about compulsions. If the client's responses again elicit a rating of 1, the interviewer is instructed to proceed to questions for another disorder. On the other hand, if positive responses (a rating of 2 or 3) are elicited about obsessive-compulsive disorder, the interviewer continues with further questions about that problem.

There are many other structured interviews and the use of such interviews is a major factor in the improvement of diagnostic reliability. Structured interviews have been developed for diagnosing personality disorders, including a version of the SCID just for personality disorders (SCID-5-PD; First, Williams, Smith, Benjamin, & Spitzer, 2016), and for more specific disorders, such as the anxiety disorders (DiNardo et al., 1993). Rogers (2003) argued that structured clinical interviews are essential in order to improve the validity of diagnoses. On the basis of available data, including evidence that more than half of the cases of depression in primary settings are not detected, he concluded, "The diagnosis of mental disorders in primary health settings is clearly a hit-or-miss proposition" (Rogers, 2003, p. 220). Rogers then analyzed which clinical interview is best suited to actual use in particular assessment situations depending on the primary goal of the assessor. He recommended the SCID for the clinician who is pressed for time and wishes to evaluate the possible existence of selected disorders. To cite another example, the International Personality Disorder Examination has been translated into 10 languages and, as a result, is suited for use across different cultures. The main point made by Rogers is that many structured clinical interviews are available and should have high clinical utility across assessment situations.

Evidence-Based Assessment

Hunsley and Mash (2005, 2007, 2008, 2010) are pioneers who have advocated for evidence-based assessment as a way of paralleling developments in evidence-based treatments. Evidence-based assessment selects assessment measures based on extensive criteria including the reliability and validity of the measures and reading level required. Amanda Jensen-Doss (2011) endorsed this call for evidence-based assessment. She concluded that most clinicians in actual practice are not engaged in recommended forms of clinical assessment. According to Jensen-Doss, the reasons for this range from practical concerns about too much paperwork to low perceived clinical relevance of certain assessment methods, but perhaps the biggest factor is economic pressures, especially in settings where shortcuts are needed due to limited insurance coverage and the restrictions of managed care. Numerous problems undermining clinical assessment in actual settings were identified including: (1) the continuing proliferation and predominance of the unstructured clinical interview; (2) the low reliability and validity of unstructured clinical interviews; (3) suggestions that very low numbers of clinicians adhere to best practice assessment guidelines; and (4) the relatively rare use of assessment in formal treatment monitoring by clinicians (see Jensen-Doss, 2011). Some of the more commonly used forms of assessment are now described.

Psychological Tests

Psychological tests are standardized procedures designed to measure a person's performance on a particular task or to assess his or her personality, or thoughts, feelings, and behaviour. If the results of a diagnostic interview are inconclusive, psychological tests can provide information that can be used in a supplementary way to arrive at a diagnosis. For example, a client with schizophrenia may be very guarded during an interview and choose not to reveal information regarding delusional beliefs. Psychological tests may alert the clinician to the possible presence of schizophrenia. These tests also yield important information in their own right, such as personality characteristics or situational determinants of a person's problems.

Psychological tests further structure the process of assessment. The same test is administered to many people at different times, and the responses are analyzed to indicate how certain kinds of people tend to respond. Statistical norms for the test can thereby be established as soon as sufficient data have been collected. This process is called standardization. The responses of a particular person can then be compared with the statistical norms. Test norms are standards that are used to interpret an individual's score because the score by itself for an individual is meaningless without a comparison context. Test norms are usually expressed in terms of the mean scores obtained by specific groups (e.g., the mean score for Canadians versus the mean score for Americans) and the distribution or variability of scores within a population (usually expressed as the standard deviation).

We will examine the three basic types of psychological tests: self-report personality inventories, projective personality tests, and tests of intelligence.

Personality Inventories

In a personality inventory, the person is asked to complete a self-report questionnaire indicating whether statements assessing habitual tendencies apply to him or her. The best-known and most frequently used and researched psychological test in the United States (see Butcher, Nezami, & Exner, 1998) is the Minnesota Multiphasic Personality Inventory (MMPI). The MMPI was developed in the early 1940s by Hathaway and McKinley (1943) and revised in 1989 as the MMPI-2 (Butcher et al., 1989). Intended to serve as an inexpensive means of detecting psychopathology, the MMPI is called *multiphasic* because it was designed to detect a number of psychological problems. The MMPI has been widely used to screen large groups of people for whom clinical interviews are not feasible.

In developing the test, the investigators relied on factual information. First, many clinicians provided statements that they considered indicative of various mental problems. Second, these items were rated as self-descriptive or not by clients already diagnosed as having particular disorders and by a large group of individuals considered normal. Items that "discriminated" among the clients were retained; that is, items were selected if clients in one clinical group responded to them more often in a certain way than did those in other groups.

With additional refinements, sets of these items were established as scales for determining whether a respondent should be diagnosed in a particular way. If an individual answered a large number of the items in a scale in the same way as had a certain diagnostic group, his or her behaviour was expected to resemble that of the particular diagnostic group. The 10 scales are described in Table 3.1.

The MMPI-2 (Butcher et al., 1989) has several noteworthy changes designed to improve its validity and acceptability. The original sample of 70 years ago lacked representation of racial minorities, including African Americans and Native Americans;

its standardization sample was restricted to white men and women—essentially to Minnesotans.

The new version was standardized using a sample that was much larger and more representative of 1980 U.S. census figures. Several items containing allusions to sexual adjustment, bowel and bladder functions, and excessive religiosity were removed because they were judged in some testing contexts to be needlessly intrusive and objectionable. Sexist wording was eliminated, along with outmoded idioms. Several new scales deal with substance abuse, Type A behaviour, and marital problems.

Aside from these differences, the MMPI-2 is quite similar to the original, having the same format, yielding the same scale scores and profiles, and providing continuity with the vast literature already existing on the original MMPI. Items similar to those on the various scales are presented in Table 3.1. The extensive research literature shows that the MMPI is reliable

TABLE 3.1   Typical Clinical Interpretations of Items Similar to Those on The MMPI-2

Scale	Sample Item	Interpretation
? (cannot say)	This is merely the number of reading items left unanswered or marked both true and false.	A high score indicates evasiveness, difficulties, or other problems that could invalidate the results of the test. A very high score could also suggest severe depression or obsessional tendencies.
L (Lie)	Don't like everyone I know. (False)	Person is trying to look good, to present self as someone with an ideal personality.
F (Infrequency)	Everything tastes alike. (True)	Person is trying to look abnormal, perhaps to ensure getting special attention from the clinician.
K (Correction)	Feel best ever. (True)	Person is guarded, defensive in taking test, wishes to avoid appearing incompetent or poorly adjusted.
1. Hs (Hypochondriasis)	Body tingles. (True)	Person is overly sensitive to and concerned about bodily sensations as signs of possible physical illness.
2. D (Depression)	Life usually feels worthwhile to me. (False)	Person is discouraged, pessimistic, sad, self-deprecating, feeling inadequate.
3. Hy (Hysteria)	Often feel very weak. (True)	Person has somatic complaints unlikely to be due to physical problems; also tends to be demanding and histrionic.
4. Pd (Psychopathy)	Don't care what others think of me. (True)	Person expresses little concern for social mores; is irresponsible; has only superficial relationships.
5. Mf (Masculinity-femininity)	Like collecting plants. (True, female)	Person shows non-traditional gender characteristics, e.g., men with high scores tend to be artistic and sensitive; women with high scores tend to be rebellious and assertive.
6. Pa (Paranoia)	If not afraid of being caught, most people would lie and cheat. (True)	Person tends to misinterpret the motives of others; is suspicious and jealous, vengeful, and brooding.
7. Pt (Psychasthenia)	Not self confident. (True)	Person is overanxious, full of self-doubts, moralistic, and generally obsessive-compulsive.
8. Sc (Schizophrenia)	Smell peculiar odors. (True)	Person has bizarre sensory experiences and beliefs; is socially reclusive.
9. Ma (Hypomania)	Want to do shocking things. (True)	Person has overly ambitious aspirations and can be hyperactive, impatient, and irritable.
0. Si (Social introversion)	Like parties. (False)	Person is very modest and shy, preferring solitary activities.

Note: The first four scales assess the validity of the test; the numbered scales are the clinical or content scales.

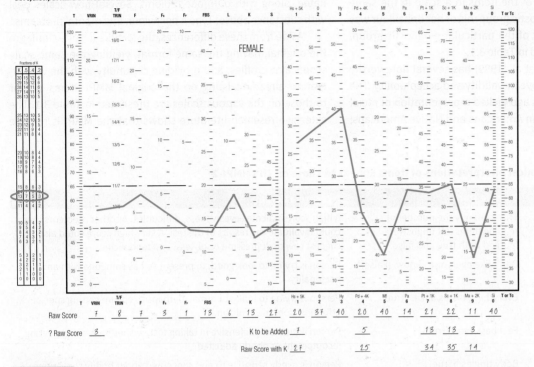

FIGURE 3.3   Hypothetical MMPI-2 profile. Profile excerpted from the MMPI®-2 (Minnesota Multiphasic Personality Inventory®-2) Manual for Administration, Scoring, and Interpretation, Revised Edition. Copyright © 2001 by the Regents of the University of Minnesota. Used by permission of the University of Minnesota Press. All rights reserved. "MMPI" and "Minnesota Multiphasic Personality Inventory" are trademarks owned by the Regents of the University of Minnesota.

and has adequate criterion validity when it is related to ratings made by spouses or clinicians (Graham, 1990).

Like many other personality inventories, the MMPI can now be administered by computer, and there are several commercial MMPI services that score the test and provide narratives about the respondent. Of course, the validity and usefulness of the printouts are only as good as the program, which in turn is only as good as the competency and experience of the psychologist who wrote it. Figure 3.3 shows a hypothetical profile. Such profiles can be used in conjunction with a therapist's evaluation to help diagnose a client, assess personality functioning and coping style, and identify likely obstacles to treatment.

We may well wonder whether answers that would designate a person as normal might not be easy to fake. A superficial knowledge of contemporary abnormal psychology, for example, would alert even a seriously disturbed person that in order to be regarded as normal, he or she must not admit to worrying a great deal about germs on doorknobs. There is evidence that these tests *can* be "psyched out." In most testing circumstances, however, people do not want to falsify their responses, because they *want* to be helped.

Moreover, as shown in Table 3.1, the test designers have included as part of the MMPI several so-called validity scales designed to detect deliberately faked responses. In one of these, the lie scale, a series of statements sets a trap for the person who is trying to look too good. An item on the lie scale might be, "I read the newspaper editorials every night." The assumption is that few people would be able to endorse such a statement honestly. Individuals who endorse a large number of the statements in the lie scale might well be attempting to present themselves in a particularly good light. Their scores on other scales are generally viewed with more than the usual scepticism. Being aware of these validity scales, however, does allow people to effectively fake a normal profile (Baer & Sekirnjak, 1997).

The MMPI-2 has been a lightning rod for controversy on several levels since 2003. Butcher (2010) provided an overview of the controversial changes as part of his claim that "The MMPI-2 community of researchers is sharply divided according to these changes" (p. 12). The most dramatic change was the release of a shortened version (338 items, 40% shorter) that did away with the classic clinical scales and instead introduced the

MMPI-2 Restructured Clinical (RC) scales (see Tellegen et al., 2003). These dimensions were derived from theoretical conceptualizations and confirmed via statistical analyses. The nine RC scales are demoralization, somatic complaints, low positive emotions, dysfunctional negative emotions, cynicism, ideas of persecution, anti-social behaviours, aberrant experiences, and hypomanic activation. Ben-Porath and Tellegen (2008) subsequently published the MMPI-2 Restructured Form (RF), which has the RC scales at its core, but there are 42 scales in total. The chief doubt regarding the RC and RF scales is whether they have sufficient construct validity and actually represent the conceptualizations they were intended for. In fact, many argue that the MMPI-2-RF is so different from the MMPI-2 that it is not a revision, but a new test altogether that requires much more extensive psychometric testing (Butcher, Hass, Greene, & Nelson, 2015).

Another highly contentious change is the introduction of the MMPI-2 Lees-Haley Fake Bad Scale. This scale was created to primarily identify people in personal litigation lawsuits who claim to have been injured but who are actually malingering and **faking bad** (i.e., accentuating deficits that don't really exist, such as the child who pretends to have a stomach ache to get out of going to school). What is the problem with the Fake Bad Scale? Analyses indicate that it tends to misclassify an unacceptably high proportion of people as fakers who are not actually faking (see Butcher, Arbisi, Atlis, & McNulty, 2008; Nelson, Sweet, & Demakis, 2006). It has since been renamed the Symptom Validity Scale, and is not acceptable for use in court (Butcher et al., 2015).

Projective Personality Tests

A **projective test** is a psychological assessment device in which a set of standard stimuli—inkblots or drawings—ambiguous enough to allow variation in responses is presented to the individual. The assumption is that because the stimulus materials are unstructured, the client's responses will be determined primarily by unconscious processes and will reveal his or her true attitudes, motivations, and modes of behaviour. This notion is referred to as the **projective hypothesis**. If a client reports seeing eyes in an ambiguous inkblot, for example, the projective hypothesis might be that the client tends toward paranoia.

The **Rorschach Ink Blot Test** is perhaps the best-known projective technique (see photo for more about Rorschach). In the Rorschach test, a person is shown 10 inkblots, one at a time, and asked to tell what figures or objects he or she sees in each of them. Half the inkblots are in black, white, and shades of grey, two also have red splotches, and three are in pastel colours. This test has been a matter of controversy and public debate, including in 2009, when the test was posted on Wikipedia along with recommended answers when the copyright lapsed and the measure was deemed to be in the public domain (for a discussion, see Butcher, 2010).

The **Thematic Apperception Test (TAT)** is another well-known projective test. In this test, a person is shown a series of black-and-white pictures one by one and asked to tell a story related to each. For example, a client seeing a picture of a pre-pubescent girl looking at fashionably attired mannequins in a store window may tell a story that contains angry references to the girl's parents. The clinician may, through the projective hypothesis, infer that the client harbours resentment toward his or her parents.

As you might guess, projective techniques are derived from the psychoanalytic paradigm. The use of projective tests assumes that the respondent would be either unable or unwilling to express his or her true feelings if asked directly. Psychoanalytically oriented clinicians often favour such tests, a tendency consistent with the psychoanalytic assumption that people protect themselves from unpleasant thoughts and feelings by repressing them into the unconscious. Thus, the real purposes of a test are best left unclear so as to bypass the defence mechanism of repression and get to the basic causes of distress.

Our discussion of projective tests has focused on how they were conceptualized and used originally—as a stimulus to fantasy that was assumed to bypass ego defences. The content of the person's responses was viewed as *symbolic* of internal dynamics; for example, a man might be judged to have homosexual interests on the basis of his seeing buttocks in the Rorschach inkblots (Chapman & Chapman, 1969).

Other uses of the Rorschach test, however, concentrate more on the *form* of the person's responses. The test is considered more as a perceptual-cognitive task, and the person's responses are viewed as a sample of how he or she perceptually

Public Domain

During a ride in the country with his two children, Hermann Rorschach (1884–1922), a Swiss psychiatrist, noticed that what they saw in the clouds reflected their personalities. From this observation came the famous inkblot test.

and cognitively organizes real-life situations (Exner, 1986). Erdberg and Exner (1984), for example, concluded from the research literature that respondents who see a great deal of human movement in the Rorschach inkblots (e.g., "The man is running to catch a plane") tend to use inner resources when coping with their needs, whereas those whose Rorschach responses involve colour ("The red spot is a kidney") are more likely to seek interaction with the environment. Rorschach suggested this approach in his original manual, *Psychodiagnostics: A Diagnostic Test Based on Perception* (1921), but he died only eight months after publishing his 10 inkblots and his immediate followers devised other methods of interpreting the test.

Though many clinical practitioners still rely on the projective hypothesis in analyzing Rorschach responses, academic researchers have been paying a good deal of attention to Exner's work, although the scoring system is labour intensive. Regarding its reliability and validity, this work has enthusiastic supporters, as well as harsh critics (e.g., Garb, Wood, Lilienfeld, & Nezworski, 2005). Attempting to make a blanket statement about the validity of the Exner system for scoring the Rorschach is perhaps not the right approach, for the system may have more validity in some cases than in others. It appears, for instance, to have considerable validity in identifying people with schizophrenia or at risk of developing schizophrenia (Viglione, 1999). The utility of the Rorschach in this case can most likely be attributed to the fact that a person's responses on the test are highly related to the communication disturbances that are an important symptom of schizophrenia. However, as argued by Hunsley and Bailey (2001), even in this case it is possible that the information provided by the Rorschach could have been obtained more simply and directly through, for example, an interview.

Critics of projective testing have been and remain particularly concerned about its use as part of assessment and testimony in the courtroom. For example, Wood, Nezworski, Lilienfeld, and Garb (2009) stated that the Rorschach, TAT, and other projective tests are used in a substantial number of legal cases and about one-third of forensic psychologists indicate that they continue to use these measures. The authors suggested that these measures continue to be used because they "overpathologize" respondents, suggesting that they are psychologically sick or dangerous in a way that might fit the agendas of certain lawyers. That is, a parent seeking custody of a child may be portrayed as psychologically unfit, or a dismissed employee who is seeking damages for wrongful dismissal will be asked to take the Rorschach and then be deemed to be unreliable and delusional. Another common use is to establish symptoms of post-traumatic stress disorder in personal injury cases. Thus, these measures are often used regardless of concerns about their reliability and validity. A recent meta-analytic review of Exner's system found support for many variables, primarily those that assess cognitive and perceptual processes (Mihura, Meyer, Dumitrascu, & Bombel, 2013). In fact, a group, including Howard Garb, who previously called for a

Universal History Archive/Getty Images

The French psychologist Alfred Binet developed the first IQ test to predict how well children would do in school.

moratorium on the use of the Rorschach, was influenced by this review and stated, "the time has come to withdraw this recommendation so far as it applies to the Cognitive Quartet of Rorschach scores" (Wood, Garb, Nezworski, Lilienfeld, & Duke, 2015, p. 243).

How often are projective tests actually used in current practice? Clearly, they are still used extensively, but their use is in decline. Norcross and Karpiak's (2012) survey found that there has been a sharp decline in use over the past two decades. Specifically, 72% of members reported using projective tests in 1986 versus 23% in 2010.

Intelligence Tests
Alfred Binet, a French psychologist (see photo), originally constructed mental tests to help the Parisian school board predict which children were in need of special schooling. Intelligence testing has since developed into one of the largest psychological industries. An **intelligence test**, often referred as an IQ (intelligence quotient) test, is a standardized means of assessing a person's current mental ability. Individually administered tests, such as the Wechsler Adult Intelligence Scale (WAIS), the Wechsler Intelligence Scale for Children (WISC), and the Stanford-Binet, are all based on the assumption that a detailed sample of an individual's current intellectual functioning can predict how well he or she will perform in school. Intelligence tests are also used

- in conjunction with achievement tests, to diagnose learning disabilities, and to identify areas of strengths and weaknesses for academic planning;

- to help determine whether a person has an intellectual disability;

- to identify intellectually gifted children so that appropriate instruction can be provided to them in school; and

- as part of neuropsychological evaluations, for example, the periodic testing of a person believed to be suffering from a degenerative dementia, so that deterioration of mental ability can be followed over time.

IQ tests tap several functions asserted to constitute intelligence, including language skills, abstract thinking, non-verbal reasoning, visual-spatial skills, attention and concentration, and speed of processing. Scores on most IQ tests are standardized so that 100 is the mean and 15 or 16 is the standard deviation (a measure of how scores are dispersed above and below the average). Approximately 65% of the population receives scores between 85 and 115. Those with a score below 70 are two standard deviations below the mean of the population and are considered to have "significant subaverage general intellectual functioning." Those with scores above 130 (two standard deviations above the mean) are considered "intellectually gifted." Approximately 2.5% of the population falls at each of these extremes. In Chapter 15, we discuss people whose IQ falls at the low end of the distribution.

IQ tests are highly reliable (e.g., Carnivez & Watkins, 1998) and have good criterion validity. For example, they distinguish between individuals who are intellectually gifted and individuals with an intellectual disability and between people with different occupations or levels of educational attainment (Reynolds et al., 1997). They also predict later educational attainment and occupational success (e.g., Damian et al., 2015).

Given the widespread use of IQ tests and other measures of cognitive ability, it is important that test-takers are evaluated according to norms that are applicable to their geographical, cultural, and racial backgrounds. Canadian scholar Don Saklofske and his colleagues (e.g., Saklofske & Hildebrand, 1999) have been involved in efforts to "renorm" the Wechsler tests of intelligence downward, since Canadian raw score means actually appear to be *higher* than the equivalent scores in the United States. These higher scores have been consistently found over the last two decades, on performance, verbal, and total scores, for children and adults (Miller, Weiss, Beal, Saklofske, Zhu, & Holdnack, 2015). As such, Saklofske and colleagues strongly advise that Canadian norms be used whenever Canadians are being tested.

While Saklofske and his colleagues have identified the need for Canadian norms, other psychometric characteristics tend to be similar when U.S. and Canadian standardization samples are compared (see Saklofske, Hildebrand, & Gorsuch, 2000). For instance, Bowden, Lange, Weiss, and Saklofske (2008) found evidence of the invariance of the "measurement model" (a description of the numerical and theoretical relation between "observed" scores and the corresponding "latent" variables or constructs) underlying WAIS third edition scores in the U.S. and Canadian standardization samples.

Intelligence tests and other measures of cognitive ability have been the source of extensive controversy over the years as a result of apparent racial and cultural differences. Historically, according to Reynolds and Suzuki (2012), differences between Black and White populations have been assessed for over 50 years and it is typically the case that Blacks have scores that are lower by 15 points (or one standard deviation). There are some indications that this gap is narrowing, with it now being about 10 points (see Nisbett et al., 2012). This difference has been highly controversial because authors such as Jensen and Rushton have attributed the difference to genetic factors, despite the fact that research has yielded no evidence of genetic polymorphisms (Nisbett et al., 2012). What is the current perspective? Clearly, environmental factors play a role in light of evidence that there is a substantial increase in IQ scores when children are adopted and move from working-class homes to middle-class homes (Nisbett et al., 2012). Reynolds and Suzuki (2012) favour an interactionist perspective that is in keeping with a biopsychosocial approach. They repudiate more extreme positions and concluded that "over time, exclusively genetic and environmental explanations have so little credibility that they can hardly be called current" (p. 91). How do social factors come into play? There is now extensive data indicating that test scores reflect **stereotype threat** or differential diagnostic threat (see Gasquoine, 2009). That is, scores fluctuate out of concerns about how the information will be used according to stereotypical preconceptions about members of a particular group.

The issue of **cultural bias** or racial bias in assessment is not simple, nor is it clear that such biases make the assessment instruments useless. Some studies of bias in testing conducted in the United States have demonstrated that mainstream procedures, such as the Wechsler Intelligence Scale for Children—Revised, have equivalent predictive validity for minority and non-minority children (Sattler, 1992); IQ tests predict academic achievement equally well for both groups. Similarly, MMPI profiles relate equally well to clinician ratings among African Americans and Caucasians (McNulty et al., 1997). However, evidence that similar results are obtained when examining predicted outcomes does not lessen the possibility that an individual child or adult will be mistreated or misclassified due to erroneous conclusions being drawn about their cognitive capacities. Indeed, there seems to be significant problems in using standardized intelligence testing with Aboriginal clients, especially children. Canadian Perspectives 3.1 discusses this issue.

One solution that has been used is to rely on **race norms** (i.e., revised norms for various racial or cultural groups). Gasquoine (2009) suggested an alternative, more individualized approach that involves establishing "individual comparison standards" that operate on a case-by-case basis and take personal life circumstances into account. For example, some adjustment must be made for a child who is new to Canada and has been moved repeatedly from one school district to another during his or her brief time in Canada.

Interest in recent years has also focused extensively on "emotional intelligence," reflected in such abilities as delaying gratification and being sensitive to the needs of others (Goleman, 1995). This aspect of human functioning may be as important to future success as the strictly intellectual achievements measured by traditional IQ tests. Emotional intelligence may also be

Canadian Perspectives 3.1

IQ Testing and Aboriginal Canadians

"Apparently, many well-meaning but misinformed members of our profession are using intelligence testing in a completely inappropriate and even harmful manner. The clients involved may not have the power or may not believe they have the power to do anything about it. With such a power imbalance, it is all the more important that counsellors be absolutely scrupulous about the ethics of testing."

—Wes G. Darrow of the Canadian International Development Agency, on the use of intelligence testing with Aboriginal Canadians (1986, p. 98)

Is bias in assessment present when the norms of the majority population are applied to culturally different minority group children and adults? More specifically, are there problems in the assessment of intelligence using standardized IQ tests with culturally different Canadian Aboriginal people?

This possibility was addressed in a study by Wilgosh, Mulcahy, and Watters (1986) for a sample of Canadian Inuit children whose WISC-R scores, using the original norms, would fall below a scaled score of 70 (see the section on intellectual disability in Chapter 15). Past studies with Aboriginal Canadian children had typically reported below average verbal scores and average or above average performance scores for the WISC (e.g., St. John, Krichev, & Bauman, 1976) and the WISC-R (e.g., Seyfort, Spreen, & Lahmer, 1980). Seyfort et al. (1980) identified an apparent lack of internal consistency for many of the WISC-R subtests for their Aboriginal sample. They suggested that the children had difficulty understanding numerous items and/or that many WISC-R items tapped different abilities and skills in the Aboriginal sample relative to the majority population. The participants in the Wilgosh et al. (1986) Inuit Norming Study were a randomly selected representative sample of girls and boys between the ages of 7 years 0 months and 14 years 11 months from the Kitikmeot and Keewatin districts of the Northwest Territories. The full WISC-R was administered by skilled psychometrists with special training related to the assessment of northern Aboriginal children. The children were assessed individually and an effort was made to optimize the testing conditions. Five items in the information subtest, one in the similarities subtest, and one in the comprehension subtest were modified to reflect Canadian content. In addition, one similarities item and two arithmetic items were reworded to facilitate understanding.

What did Wilgosh et al. (1986) find? Over three-quarters of the children (77%) attained a verbal IQ scaled score less than 70, but only 5.7% of them had a performance scaled score less than 70. The respective percentage for full scale IQ was about 32. What do these results imply? Approximately 75% of Inuit children in the norming group would be classified as having an intellectual disability *on the basis of their verbal IQ scores alone.* If the group had reflected the theoretical normal curve and the Wechsler normative group, the proportion would actually have approximated only 2.2% (Wilgosh et al., 1986). The authors concluded that "using the Wechsler Verbal and Full Scale norms for the WISC-R would result in misclassification of great numbers of Inuit children" (Wilgosh et al., 1986,

p. 273). Further, a major factor resulting in the misclassification was presumed to be verbal comprehension of the English language, the second language for all of the Inuit children. The information and vocabulary subtests accounted for the majority of unanswered or incorrectly answered items.

Wilgosh et al. (1986) noted that "in actual educational programming for the Inuit children . . . sole reliance is certainly not placed on the WISC-R scores" (p. 275). Nonetheless, Darou (1992) argued that many Aboriginal children are, in fact, streamed into special education programs based on their IQ test results and that some Aboriginal administrative bodies perceive intelligence testing to be "just another tool of white domination" (p. 97). He believes that IQ tests are biased both *against* and *for* Aboriginals in unusual and complicated ways, as illustrated in this anecdote about Zachary, a hunter from a remote area near James Bay who was administered the Kohs Blocks subtest:

"The test involves showing the subject a square drawing on a small card. The subject recreates the design with four or nine red and white cubes. The subject is assigned certain points depending upon how quickly he or she completes the task. This test has the highest validity of all the WISC sub-tests. When Zachary did it, he appeared to be in no hurry, he placed the blocks by an "S" pattern instead of by rows as most people do (the "S" saving two arm movements), and at the end he would frame the blocks with his fingers for a few seconds, and sometimes adjust the blocks a little. He did the test so fast that he went off-scale on all seven examples. The test goes off scale at an I.Q. equivalent of 180." (Darou, 1992, p. 97)

In discussions afterwards, Zachary explained that he believed the test was biased in his favour. He pointed out that, when he was young, his family ate or starved depending on his ability to recognize patterns. Despite anecdotes such as these, the weight of the available evidence indicates that Aboriginal people often perform poorly on standardized tests of intelligence, especially on measures developed to assess verbal intelligence, in comparison with the original normative group.

Thinking Critically

1. Is it possible that the low-scaled scores for verbal intelligence of the Inuit children, relative to the normative data, reflect not a test bias, but differences in educational opportunities that have resulted in "real" differences in educational achievement?

2. Do you think that the findings reported by Wilgosh et al. (1986) are unique to the Inuit or do you think that they could apply to any minority group in Canada that has English as a second language, especially if that group lives in an isolated cultural and educational context?

3. What do you think should be the "culturally meaningful educational priorities" (Wilgosh et al., 1986, p. 275) for Aboriginal children in Canada? Should increased emphasis on comprehension of the English language be a high priority in the local cultural context? Or, as appeared to be the case with Zachary, should the focus be on adaptability within their own culture?

an important protective factor in terms of levels of adjustment. High levels of emotional intelligence are associated negatively with alexithymia (see Saklofske, Austin, & Minski, 2003), a condition of reduced emotional awareness that is a risk factor for a variety of adjustment problems. Moreover, high levels of emotional intelligence are associated with greater levels of subjective well-being and reduced proneness to depression (Saklofske et al., 2003). Research continues to focus on demonstrating that the relationship between emotional intelligence and these other outcomes (e.g., depression, well-being) is not simply due to some other factor (e.g., general intelligence or personality). For example, in Canadian university students, emotional intelligence was found to predict anxiety, depression, and life satisfaction, among other variables, above and beyond traditional measures of personality and coping (Siegling, Vesely, Petrides, & Saklofske, 2015). Evidence is building for the role of emotional intelligence on psychological well-being and other outcomes.

Behavioural and Cognitive Assessment and Case Formulation

Traditional assessment concentrates on measuring underlying personality structures and traits, such as obsessiveness, paranoia, coldness, and aggressiveness. In addition to a focus on specific cognitive and behavioural assessment instruments, cognitive-behavioural clinicians develop a specific case formulation for each client, known as a **cognitive-behavioural case formulation**, as described in Focus on Discovery 3.1. It is "a provisional map of a person's presenting problems that describes the territory of the problems and explains the processes that caused and maintain the problem" (Bieling & Kuyken, 2003, p. 53). It includes a clinician's inferences about underlying processes that can be tested as hypotheses. It is used as the basis for planning interventions and evolves over time as further information is discovered.

Focus on Discovery 3.1

Cognitive-Behavioural Case Formulation

"[Jacqueline] Persons. . . tells us quite correctly that the best way to administer empirically supported treatments in clinical settings is to modify them based on the needs of the individual client."

—*Heimberg, 2009, p. 136*

Jacqueline Persons and her colleagues (e.g., Persons & Davidson, 2001, 2010; Persons, 2005; Persons, Beckner, & Tompkins, 2013) have described an approach that formulates an individualized cognitive-behavioural "theory" about a particular case with a view to helping a therapist develop an effective and efficient plan for treatment. The formulation is, of course, based on a general cognitive-behavioural theory (e.g., Beck's cognitive theory of psychological disorders). A key purpose of the formulation is to explain how a client's problems relate to one another in order to help the therapist select treatment "targets," since it is usually appropriate to first focus on issues that seem to play a causal role in other problems (e.g., depression causes marital problems, which contribute to behaviour problems in a child).

Different formulations imply different intervention strategies. Persons and Davidson (2001) described the case of a person complaining of severe fatigue. Two formulations appeared possible: abuse of sleep medication or negative thinking in reaction to a stressor. Either one of them could explain the fatigue, and each would lead to different treatments. As Persons and Davidson (2001) noted, "All formulations are considered hypotheses, and the therapist is constantly revising and sharpening the formulations as the therapy proceeds" (p. 89).

Persons and Davidson (2001) use the case of "Judy," a 35-year-old single woman who lived alone and worked as a teacher, to illustrate the five components of their approach: problem list, diagnosis, working hypothesis, strengths and assets, and treatment plan.

Problem List

A problem list includes difficulties the client is having in various domains: psychological, interpersonal, occupational, medical, financial, housing, legal, and leisure. A comprehensive list helps ensure that significant problems are not missed and facilitates the search for themes and speculation about causal relations. Psychological problems, in particular, are described in terms of cognitive, behavioural, and mood components (consistent with Beck's cognitive theory). Judy's problem list included the following: depressed, dissatisfied, passive; disorganized, unfocused, and unproductive; job dissatisfaction; social isolation; no relationship; and unassertive.

Diagnosis

Although a psychiatric diagnosis is not a required part of cognitive-behavioural case formulations, Persons and Davidson include it because a diagnosis can lead to initial hypotheses about how to formulate the case and provide information about possible interventions. Judy received a diagnosis of dysthymic disorder (i.e., persistent and chronic depression that is milder in intensity than the depression in major depressive disorders).

Working Hypothesis

The working hypothesis is the "heart" of Persons and Davidson's formulation. The mini-theory of the case develops through adaptation of a general theory and describes relations among the problems. For example, according to Beck's theory, stressful events activate schemas (core beliefs) to produce problems and symptoms. Therefore, the working hypothesis would describe the hypotheses about the negative schemas (e.g., beliefs about self, others, the world, and the future) that appear to cause the problems—external precipitants (e.g., a poor work evaluation) or activating situations (e.g., attending meetings with the boss) that activate internal structures (schemas)—and the origins or historical incidents or circumstances that contributed to the development of the schemas or functional relationships among the problems. In a summary of the working hypothesis, the clinician "tells a story" that describes the relations among the components of the working

(continued)

hypothesis and integrates them with the problems on the list. Persons and Davidson (2001) summarized Judy's working hypothesis as follows:

> "When she was faced with taking actions to further her goals, her schemata that she was incapable and damaged were activated. She had learned from her mother's passive behaviors and from her father's abusive ones that she was damaged and incapable of taking action. When these schemata were activated, she became passive and inactive, with the result that she did not achieve her goals and felt dissatisfied and discouraged. This pattern occurred repeatedly in both work and social situations, and led to the difficulties she experienced in both those settings." (p. 97)

Figure 3.4 illustrates this "working hypothesis" for Judy in the form of a flow chart.

Strengths and Assets

Information about strengths and assets (e.g., social skills, sense of humour, financial resources, social support, stable lifestyle) can help the therapist to develop the working hypothesis, enhance the treatment plan, and determine realistic treatment goals. Judy had several strengths and assets, including a stable lifestyle, intelligence, excellent social skills, and a strong support network.

Treatment Plan

According to Persons and Davidson, the treatment plan is based directly on the cognitive-behavioural case formulation and has six components: goals, modality, frequency, initial interventions, adjunct therapies, and obstacles. The "goals" and "obstacles" components are especially crucial. Judy's treatment plan had six goals, including reducing dysphoria and procrastination, improving her ability to prioritize and organize, finding a more satisfying job, spending more time with friends, beginning to date in order to find a partner, and being more assertive. Obstacles to treatment included her procrastination, unassertiveness, and belief that she cannot be successful.

The possible clinical uses of the case formulation are multiple. Persons and Davidson noted that here it helped clarify treatment goals, helped the therapist to maintain a "clear focus" and address multiple problems, facilitated the client's taking an active and collaborative role, and assisted the therapist to cope with negative emotional reactions to working with the client.

Persons, Beckner, and Tompkins (2013) highlight another benefit of the case formulation approach: it fosters early identification of non-responsiveness to treatment. The clinician can then work with the patient to examine hypotheses about what has gone wrong, ideally leading to a better formulation, which in turn should lead to improved treatment and outcome.

Do you believe that individual cognitive-behavioural therapy (CBT) is appropriate in Judy's case, and if so, how often should she meet with her therapist? What initial interventions would you propose? Under what circumstances would you employ adjunct treatments, such as pharmacotherapy?

How useful are these case formulations? Are they reliable and valid? Initially, Bieling and Kuyken (2003) evaluated the available data and concluded that the evidence for the reliability of the cognitive case formulation method is modest and there is a need for research to examine the validity of case formulations and to determine their impact on treatment outcome. More recently, Flinn, Braham, and das Nair (2015) conducted a review of 18 case formulation studies and indicated that reliability estimates are quite variable and range from slight to substantial evidence of reliability. Not surprisingly, a key factor that tends to increase reliability is the training and experience level of those conducting the case formulation. Current conclusions are based on studies of inter-rater reliability because only one study has assessed the test–retest reliability of case formulations.

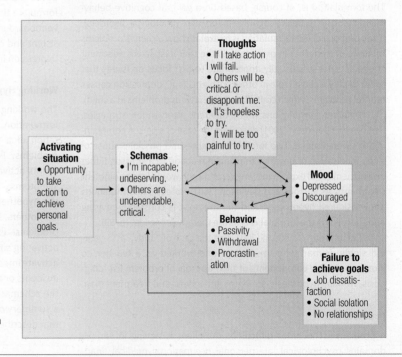

FIGURE 3.4   The working hypothesis for the client "Judy." From Persons and Davidson, Cognitive-behavioral case formulation, *Handbook of cognitive-behavioral therapies,* 2001. Reprinted with permission of the Guilford Press.

David Sacks/PhotoDisc/Getty Images, Inc.

Cognitive assessment focuses on the person's perception of a situation, since the same event can be perceived differently by different people or at different times. For example, moving could be regarded as very stressful or seen in a positive light.

The information necessary for a behavioural or cognitive assessment and case formulation is gathered by several methods, including direct observation of behaviour, interviews, and self-report measures, which are described next.

Cognitive and behavioural therapists make extensive use of self-report inventories. Some of these questionnaires are similar to the personality tests we have already described. But others have a much greater situational focus than traditional questionnaires. They tap a wide range of cognitions, such as fear of negative evaluation, a tendency to think irrationally, and a tendency to make negative inferences about life

experiences. New cognitive-behavioural self-report measures are regularly constructed and they must be subjected to psychometric evaluation.

Some measures assess specific aspects of anxiety. For example, Carleton, Collimore, and Asmundson (2007) from the University of Regina reported on the construct validity of a brief measure of the fear of negative evaluation (BFNE-II), a characteristic of social anxiety disorder. Similarly, Carleton, Norton, and Asmundson (2007) developed a brief Intolerance of Uncertainty Scale (IUS) to assess anxious and avoidance components of the tendency to consider the possibility of a negative event occurring to be unacceptable, irrespective of the probability of occurrence. Intolerance of uncertainty is a key component of worry.

Another example concerns depression. A psychological theory of depression (Beck, 1967), which we will examine in greater detail in Chapter 8, holds that it is caused primarily by negative ideas people have about themselves, their world, and their future. People may believe, for instance, that they are not worth much and that things are never going to get better. Researchers employing cognitive assessment set themselves the task of trying to identify these different kinds of cognitions. One assessment device used in this context is the Dysfunctional Attitude Scale (DAS). The DAS contains items such as "People will probably think less of me if I make a mistake" (Weissman & Beck, 1978). Supporting the theory of construct validity, researchers have shown that they can differentiate between depressed and non-depressed people on the basis of their scores on this scale and that scores decrease (i.e., improve) after interventions that relieve depression.

Summary of Psychological Assessment Methods

The psychological assessments we have described in this section are summarized in Table 3.2. It is important to achieve integration within psychological assessment and with other approaches, including neurobiological perspectives.

TABLE 3.2   Major Psychological Assessment Methods

Interviews	Clinical interviews	Conversational technique in which the clinician attempts to learn about the client's problems. Content of the interview varies depending on the paradigm of the interviewer.
	Structured interviews	Questions to be asked are spelled out in detail in a booklet; most often used for gathering information to make a diagnosis.
Psychological tests	Personality tests	Self-report questionnaires, used to assess a broad range of characteristics, as in the MMPI.
	Projective personality tests	Ambiguous stimuli, such as inkblots (Rorschach test), are presented and responses are thought to be determined by unconscious processes.
	Tests of cognition	Self-report questionnaires that typically focus on a single cognitive characteristic, such as dysfunctional attitudes or fear of negative evaluation.
	Intelligence tests	Assessments of current mental functioning. Used to predict school performance and diagnose intellectual disability.

3.3 Biological Assessment

Recall from Chapter 2 that some people interested in psychopathology have assumed, quite reasonably, that some malfunctions of the psyche are likely to be due to or at least reflected in malfunctions of the soma. We turn now to contemporary work in biological assessment.

Brain Imaging: "Seeing" The Brain

Because many behavioural problems can be brought on by brain abnormalities, neurological tests, such as checking the reflexes, examining the retina for any indication of blood vessel damage, and evaluating motor coordination and perception, have been used for many years to diagnose brain dysfunction. More recently, devices have become available that allow clinicians and researchers a much more direct look at both the structure and functioning of the brain.

Types of Brain Imaging Computerized axial tomography, the **CT scan**, helps to assess structural brain abnormalities (and is able to image other parts of the body for medical purposes). A moving beam of X-rays passes into a horizontal cross-section of the client's brain, scanning it through 360 degrees; the moving X-ray detector on the other side measures the amount of radioactivity that penetrates, thus detecting subtle differences in tissue density. A computer uses the information to construct a two-dimensional, detailed image of the cross-section, giving it optimal contrasts. Then the client's head is moved, and the machine scans another cross-section of the brain. The resulting images can show the enlargement of ventricles, which signals degeneration of tissue and the locations of tumours (see photo) and blood clots. Indeed, CT scans were used in a study in London, Ontario, to confirm that clients with a first episode of schizophrenia had a mild degree of enlargement of ventricles and cortical sulci (Malla et al., 2002). Single photon emission computerized tomography (SPECT)

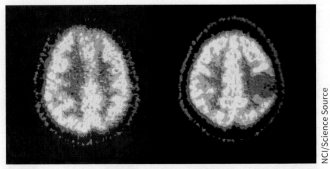

These two CT scans show a horizontal slice through the brain. The one on the left is normal; the one on the right has a tumour on the right side.

NCI/Science Source

allows assessment of cerebral blood flow and is used increasingly in neuropsychiatry.

Newer computer-based devices for seeing the living brain include **magnetic resonance imaging**, also known as **MRI**, which is superior to the CT scan because it produces pictures of higher quality and does not rely on even the small amount of radiation required by a CT scan. In MRI, the person is placed inside a large, circular magnet, which causes the hydrogen atoms in the body to move. When the magnetic force is turned off, the atoms return to their original positions and thereby produce an electromagnetic signal. These signals are then read by the computer and translated into pictures of brain tissue. The implications of this technique are enormous. For example, it has allowed physicians to locate and remove delicate brain tumours that would have been considered inoperable without such sophisticated methods of viewing brain structures.

More recently, a modification, called **functional magnetic resonance imaging (fMRI)**, has been developed that allows researchers to take MRI pictures so quickly that metabolic changes can be measured, providing a picture of the brain at work rather than of its structure alone (see photo). It enables investigators to map cognitive, affective, and experiential processes onto brain substrates. Using this technique, one study found that there was less activation in the frontal lobes of clients with schizophrenia than in the frontal lobes of people with normal-functioning brains as they performed a cognitive task (Yurgelun-Todd et al., 1996; see photo).

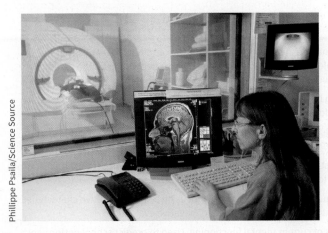

Phillippe Psaila/Science Source

Functional magnetic resonance imaging (fMRI) technology allows researchers to see images of the brain at work.

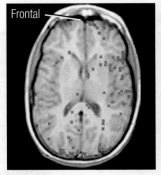
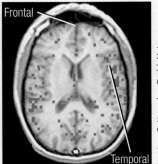

Courtesy D. Yurgelun-Todd, McLean Hospital

Functional magnetic resonance images (fMRI) of a client diagnosed with schizophrenia (right) and a healthy individual (left). The red squares represent activation of the brain during a verbal task compared with the baseline. The client shows less frontal and more temporal activation. (Yurgelun-Todd et al., 1996)

One interesting case demonstrates the type of information that can emerge using fMRI. Scott Routley was a Canadian man in a vegetative state for over a decade following a car accident. His parents saw signs of a conscious mind (e.g., communication by blinking), but medical staff members were not in agreement until fMRI scans were completed in 2012. Scott was able to tell researchers at the University of Western Ontario via his fMRI responses that he was not in pain. Unfortunately, Scott has since died (in 2013) but research on the use of fMRI with patients in vegetative states continues.

A case study from Montreal further illustrates the types of information that can emerge from fMRI assessments (Bentaleb, Beauregard, Liddle, & Stip, 2002). This research focused on a woman with schizophrenia who experienced auditory hallucinations that went away when she listened to loud external speech. She had learned to stop her hallucinations by turning up the volume of her radio or television. Comparisons using fMRI were made between her brain activity during the hallucinations and while listening to external speech, and these results were compared with the results for a matched control participant. The researchers found that auditory verbal hallucinations were linked with increased metabolic activity in the left primary auditory cortex and the right middle temporal gyrus. Overall, this case study clarified the mechanisms involved in auditory hallucinations by showing that they stem jointly from aberrant activation of the auditory cortex and the misinterpreted inner speech of the client with schizophrenia. Previous theorists did not consider the possibility that both factors might simultaneously play a role in auditory hallucinations.

Another study conducted in British Columbia used fMRI procedures to compare eight criminal psychopaths and eight criminals without psychopathy (Kiehl et al., 2001). The main focus was on affective processing while completing a memory task. The researchers were able to obtain evidence consistent with the view that "criminal psychopathy is associated with abnormalities in the function of structures in the limbic system and frontal cortex while engaged in processing of affective stimuli" (Kiehl et al., 2001, p. 682). More recent data continue to implicate abnormalities in the ventromedial prefrontal cortex when psychopaths are required to make moral judgments (Harenski, Harenski, Shane, & Kiehl, 2010).

Since the fMRI can be used to determine where in the brain activity occurs during cognitive tasks, it may prove useful in determining the mechanisms related to changes that occur during cognitive-behavioural therapy. In an early example of such a study, Schwartz (1998) reported fMRI data indicating that obsessive-compulsive disorder (OCD) appears to be characterized by abnormal activation in the orbital-frontal complex and that cognitive-behavioural treatment produced changes in left orbital-frontal activation, but only in treatment responders. Thus treatment may influence directly the parts of the brain affected by the disorder.

Positron emission tomography, the **PET scan**, a more expensive and invasive procedure, allows measurement of brain function. A substance used by the brain is labelled with a short-lived

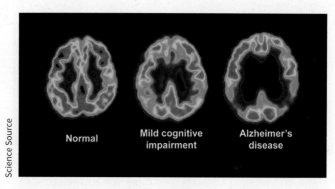

The PET scan on the left shows a normal brain; the one in the middle shows mild cognitive impairment; the one on the right shows the brain of a client with Alzheimer's disease.

radioactive isotope and injected into the bloodstream. The radioactive molecules of the substance emit a particle called a positron, which quickly collides with an electron. A pair of high-energy light particles shoot out from the skull in opposite directions and are detected by the scanner. The computer analyzes millions of such recordings and converts them into a picture of the functioning brain. The images are in colour; fuzzy spots of lighter and warmer colours are areas in which metabolic rates for the substance are higher.

Visual images of the working brain can indicate sites of epileptic seizures, brain cancers, Alzheimer's disease (see photo), strokes, and trauma from head injuries, as well as the distribution of psychoactive drugs in the brain. The PET scanner is also being used to study possible abnormal biological processes that underlie disorders, such as the failure of the frontal cortex of clients with schizophrenia to become activated while they attempt to perform a cognitive task. PET images are often overlaid on averaged MRI images to allow for the articulation of both function and structure.

Clinical Utility of Biological Assessment Measures of Brain Structure and Function

An important question is "What evidence is there that sophisticated biological assessment measures actually contribute meaningfully to the assessment, clinical management, and treatment of individual clients?" Do they make a real difference, and, if so, in what ways? Fortunately, evidence of the usefulness of these measures is accumulating. Velakoulis and Lloyd (1998) described the utility of SPECT scanning in clients with neuropsychiatric disorders involving early onset dementia. SPECT scanning confirmed the presence of abnormalities in 88% of the 56 clients tested; the authors noted that while in no cases were the SPECT scanning assessments the sole piece of evidence used to make diagnoses, they played a vital role in establishing the diagnosis. SPECT scans had to be interpreted within the context of other information because the scans reveal abnormalities that are common across various neurological conditions (i.e., they are non-specific).

Perhaps the ultimate test of the clinical utility of these measures is the extent to which the information gleaned actually changes diagnoses and makes them more accurate. One study compared the conclusions reached about clinical

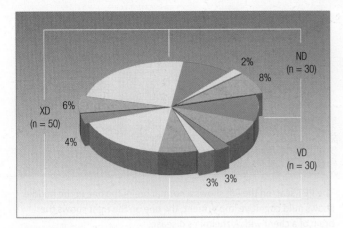

FIGURE 3.5 Changes in the diagnostic groups due to information from MRI and neuropsychology in a sample of clients investigated for cognitive disturbances in a memory clinic (*n* = 100). The location in the diagram indicates the final comprehensive clinical diagnosis (XD = no dementia, ND = neurodegenerative dementia, VD = vascular dementia); the colour indicates the initial clinical diagnosis (beige: XD; green: ND; grey: VD). The sectors within each of the final diagnostic groups represent the changes from the initial diagnostic groups. The overall frequency of change in diagnosis (26%) is significantly different from chance level (CI: 0.260.09). *Source:* Hentschel et al. (2005).

decisions by two physicians who were either provided or not provided CT scan data (see Condefer, Haworth, & Wilcock, 2004). The clients were being assessed for memory disorders and dementia. The study showed that the CT scan data had an influence on diagnosis and treatment planning in 10 to 15% of the cases.

The clinical utility of biological assessment measures was clearly illustrated in a study by Hentschel et al. (2005) that was conducted with clients referred to a university clinic because of memory difficulties. This study showed that magnetic resonance imaging (MRI), along with the final comprehensive clinical diagnosis of neuropsychology status, led to a change in the diagnosis of over one-quarter of the clients assessed. The initial diagnoses and final diagnoses are shown in Figure 3.5. This figure illustrates the changes in diagnostic status for those who were thought initially to have no dementia, neurodegenerative dementia, or vascular dementia. You will learn more about these age-related disorders in Chapter 16.

Martin Paulus (2008) conducted a review to address the question of whether neuroimaging can contribute to the diagnosis and treatment of anxiety disorders. He concluded that fMRI has potential as a clinical tool, "but neuroimaging groups will need to better develop its specificity and sensitivity so that fMRI results can be meaningful for an individual patient not just for groups of individuals" (Paulus, 2008, p. 348). Similarly, Serene, Ashtari, Szeszko, and Kumra (2007) reviewed MRI studies of four childhood psychiatric disorders: attention deficit hyperactivity disorder (ADHD), major depressive disorder, bipolar disorder, and schizophrenia. The results revealed abnormalities in the developmental trajectories seen in healthy children,

thereby potentially increasing our understanding of the pathophysiology of childhood psychiatric disorders. For example, frontostriatal abnormalities are reported consistently in ADHD, possibly a reflection of abnormalities in the development of cognitive control. However, Serene et al. (2007) concluded that "routine neuroimaging for children with severe emotional disturbances is not indicated for diagnostic purposes" (p. 135). On the other hand, the authors noted that a better understanding of the neurobiology of such childhood disorders can possibly lead to the development of new therapies and predictors of treatment response.

Although the preceding studies demonstrating the potential clinical utility of neuroimaging are promising, Paulus (2015) concludes that there has been "almost no impact" on actual practice (p. 631). He advocates for a focus on identifying predictors of treatment outcome that might more substantially influence practice, rather than the current focus by many groups on identifying mechanisms of change.

Neuropsychological Assessment

"With such a wide array of eminent researchers and institutions, human neuropsychology in Canada should continue to thrive well into the foreseeable future, and Canadian investigators can be expected to remain respected leaders in this scientific endeavour."

—*Hayman-Abello, Hayman-Abello, and Rourke, 2003, p. 120*

The past decade has witnessed many advances in neuropsychological assessment. What exactly is neuropsychological assessment? It is important at this point to note a distinction between neurologists and neuropsychologists, even though both specialists are concerned with the study of the central nervous system. A **neurologist** is a physician who specializes in medical diseases that affect the nervous system, such as muscular dystrophy, cerebral palsy, or Alzheimer's disease. A **neuropsychologist** is a psychologist who studies how dysfunctions of the brain affect the way we think, feel, and behave. A neuropsychologist is trained as a psychologist—and as such is interested in thought, emotion, and behaviour—but one with a focus on how abnormalities of the brain affect behaviour in deleterious ways. Both kinds of specialists contribute much to each other as they work in different ways, often collaboratively, to learn how the nervous system functions and how to ameliorate problems caused by disease or injury to the brain.

Seidman and Bruder (2003) summarized the goals of neuropsychological testing as follows:

1. to measure as reliably, validly, and completely as possible the behavioural correlates of brain functions

2. to identify the characteristic profile associated with a neurobehavioural syndrome (differential diagnosis)

3. to establish possible localization, lateralization, and etiology of a brain lesion

4. to determine whether neuropsychological deficits are present (i.e., cognitive, perceptual, or motor) regardless of diagnosis

5. to describe neuropsychological strengths, weaknesses, and strategy of problem solving

6. to assess the patient's feelings about his or her syndrome

7. to provide treatment recommendations (i.e., to client, family, school)

(Source: Adapted with permission from John Wiley & Sons, Inc.)

One might reasonably assume that neurologists and physicians, with the help of such procedures and technological devices as PET, CT, and MRI scans, can observe the brain and its functions more or less directly and thus assess all brain abnormalities. Many brain abnormalities and injuries, however, involve alterations in structure so subtle or slight in extent that they have thus far eluded direct physical examination.

Neuropsychologists have developed tests to assess behavioural disturbances caused by brain dysfunctions. The literature on these tests is extensive, and as with most areas of psychology, so, too, is disagreement about them. The weight of the evidence does indicate that psychological tests have some validity in the assessment of brain damage, however, and they are often used in conjunction with the brain-scanning techniques just described. They are accordingly called **neuropsychological tests**. All are based on the idea that different psychological functions (e.g., motor speed, memory, language) are localized in different areas of the brain. Thus, finding a deficit on a particular test can provide clues about where in the brain some damage may exist.

One neuropsychological test is Reitan's modification of a battery or group of tests previously developed by Halstead. The concept of using a battery of tests, each tapping a different function, is critical, for only by studying a person's pattern of performance can an investigator adequately judge whether the person is brain damaged and where the damage is located. The following are four of the tests included in the Halstead-Reitan battery:

1. *Tactile Performance Test—Time.* While blindfolded, the client tries to fit variously shaped blocks into spaces of a form board, first using the preferred hand, then the other, and finally both (see photo).

2. *Tactile Performance Test—Memory.* After completing the timed test, the participant is asked to draw the form board from memory, showing the blocks in their proper location. Both this and the timed test are sensitive to damage in the right parietal lobe.

3. *Category Test.* The client, seeing an image on a screen that suggests one of the numbers from one to four, presses a button to show which number he or she thinks it is. A bell indicates that the choice is correct, a buzzer that it is incorrect. The client must keep track of these images and signals in order to figure out the rules for making the correct choices. This test measures problem solving, in particular the ability to abstract a principle from a non-verbal array of events. Impaired performance on this test is the best overall indicator of brain damage.

4. *Speech Sounds Perception Test.* Participants listen to a series of nonsense words, each comprising two consonants with a long "e" sound in the middle. They then select the "word" they heard from a set of alternatives. This test measures left-hemisphere function, especially temporal and parietal areas.

Extensive research has demonstrated that the battery is valid for detecting brain damage resulting from a variety of conditions, such as tumours, stroke, and head injury. Furthermore, this battery of tests can play an important role in making difficult diagnostic decisions, helping the clinician discriminate, for example, between dementia due to depression and dementia due to a degenerative brain disease (Reed & Reed, 1997).

The Luria-Nebraska battery (Golden, Hammeke, & Purisch, 1978), based on the work of the Russian psychologist Aleksandr Luria (1902–77), is also in widespread use (Moses & Purisch, 1997). A battery of 269 items makes up 11 sections to determine basic and complex motor skills, rhythm and pitch abilities, tactile and kinesthetic skills, verbal and spatial skills, receptive speech ability, expressive speech ability, writing skills, reading skills, arithmetic skills, memory, and intellectual processes. The pattern of scores on these sections, as well as on the 32 items found to be the most discriminating and indicative of overall impairment, helps reveal damage to the frontal, temporal, sensorimotor, or parietal-occipital area of the right or left hemisphere.

The Luria-Nebraska battery can be administered in two and a half hours, and can be scored in a highly reliable manner (e.g., Kashden & Franzen, 1996). Criterion validity has been established by findings such as a correct classification rate

Richard T. Nowitz/Science Source

Neuropsychological tests assess various performance deficits in the hope of detecting a specific area of brain malfunction. Shown here is the Tactile Performance Test—Time.

of over 86% when used with a sample of neurological clients and control groups (Moses et al., 1992). The Luria-Nebraska is also believed to pick up effects of brain damage that are not (yet) detectable by neurological examination; such deficits are in the cognitive domain rather than in the motor or sensory domains on which neurological assessments focus (e.g., assessing reflexes). A particular advantage of the Luria-Nebraska tests is that one can control for educational level so that a less-educated person will not receive a lower score solely because of limited educational experience (Brickman et al., 1984). Finally, a version for children ages 8 to 12 has been found useful in diagnosing brain damage and in evaluating the educational strengths and weaknesses of children (Sweet et al., 1986).

Canadian research in human neuropsychology has a long legacy of eminent contributions, starting with the publication of Donald Hebb's *Organization of Behavior* (1949), which described a theory of biological psychology that emphasized the role of behaviour. Canadian research in the various sub-specialties of neuropsychology is in the vanguard of the field (e.g., Costa, 1996; Fuerst & Rourke, 1995; Hayman-Abello, Hayman-Abello, & Rourke, 2003). Indeed, Fuerst and Rourke (1995) noted that, "In proportion to respective populations, Canada harbours more eminent researchers in the field than any other country, including the United States" (p. 12). Much of this current Canadian research is in the area of neuropsychological assessment. For example, Donald T. Stuss, director of the Rotman Research Institute of the Baycrest Centre of Geriatric Care in Toronto, conducted neurobehavioural research with a focus on memory and frontal-lobe functions and on forms of dementia, including patterns of neuropsychological functioning in people with Alzheimer's disease. In one interesting early series of studies, he and his colleagues assessed the long-term residual effects of prefrontal leucotomies on neuropsychological functions (e.g., Stuss & Benson, 1983). The contributions of Byron P. Rourke (see photo) and his colleagues from the University of Windsor include extensive work on the development of non-verbal methods for the neuropsychological assessment of children and adults with learning disabilities, research on subtypes of psychosocial functioning in children with learning disabilities, and work on subgroups of people with Alzheimer's disease (see Hayman-Abello et al., 2003). Rourke (2008) discussed the implications of brain–behaviour relationships in humans and asked whether forms of psychosocial functioning are predictable from neuropsychological analysis in the individual case. He concluded that they often are.

> "We have demonstrated that patterns of neuropsychological assets and deficits (involving auditory-perceptual, visual-perceptual, somatosensory, motor, psychomotor, and linguistic skills) are consistently related to particular forms and levels of severity of psychosocial functioning in children with LD (learning disabilities)."
>
> *(Rourke, 2008, p. 38).*

In the late 1980s, the federal department Health and Welfare Canada allocated significant funding for a comprehensive, longitudinal study of the effects of dementia on Canadian society. This major research project involved the participation of over 10,000 Canadians at centres across Canada (Canadian Study of Health and Aging Working Group, 1994a; Costa, 1996) and is referred to as the Canadian Study of Health and Aging (CSHA). The study is described in some detail in Canadian Perspectives 16.1. The full neuropsychological test battery administered to many of the participants was developed by a team of Canadian neuropsychologists charged with the task of producing a comprehensive neuropsychological battery that could be administered in approximately one hour. Details of the test battery and neuropsychological investigation are described by Holly Tuokko, from the University of Victoria, and her colleagues (Tuokko, Kristjansson, & Miller, 1995) and by Steenhuis and Ostbye (1995). According to Costa (1996), the CSHA is the largest epidemiological study of dementia to include a formal neuropsychological assessment.

At the University of Toronto, Konstantine Zakzanis and his colleagues (Zakzanis, Leach, & Kaplan, 1999) put together a compendium of neuropsychological profiles in which test sensitivities were compiled for several dementia (see Chapter 16) and neuropsychiatric disorders. The profiles were designed to help clinicians and researchers select neuropsychological tests on the basis of sensitivities of the tests to specific syndromes (as opposed to choosing tests on the basis of clinical lore, availability, history of use, and so forth). The work by Zakzanis et al. (1999) and other Canadian neuroscientists promises to place the selection and use of neuropsychological tests on firmer scientific ground.

A survey of neuropsychologists in the United States and Canada revealed that "ethnic/racial minorities are underrepresented in the field of neuropsychology" (Elbulak-Charcape et al., 2014, p. 359). A lack of appropriate norms and tests were identified as challenges, and some respondents even reported doing assessments in a foreign language that they are not proficient in. Not surprisingly, a call was issued for greater multicultural training among neuropsychologists.

Photo courtesy Byron P. Rourke

Byron P. Rourke, an eminent neuropsychologist at the University of Windsor, has conducted groundbreaking research on the neuropsychological assessment of people with learning disabilities.

Given the length of administration of these test batteries (several hours), a current research direction in the neuropsychology field is the use of computerized testing. For instance, Zakzanis and Azarbehi (2014) described an intriguing web-based real-time examination of cognitive functioning called Brainscreen. Despite significant enthusiasm related to saving time and money, along with greater standardization, actual utilization rates of computerized tests are very low at this time (Rabin et al., 2014), but greater use is anticipated in the future as new innovations continue to emerge.

Psychophysiological Assessment

Psychophysiology is concerned with the bodily changes that accompany psychological events or that are associated with a person's psychological characteristics. Experimenters have used measures such as heart rate, tension in the muscles, blood flow in various parts of the body, and brain waves to study the physiological changes that occur when people are afraid, depressed, asleep, imagining, solving problems, and so on. The assessments we describe here are not sensitive enough to be used for diagnosis; they can, however, provide important information. For example, in using exposure to treat a client with an anxiety disorder, it would be useful to know the extent to which the client shows physiological arousal when exposed to the stimuli that create anxiety. Clients who show higher levels of physiological arousal may be experiencing higher levels of fear, which predict more benefit from the therapy (e.g., Foa et al., 1995).

The activities of the autonomic nervous system are frequently assessed by electrical and chemical measurements in an attempt to understand the nature of emotion. One important measure is heart rate. Each heartbeat generates spreading changes in electrical potential, which can be recorded by an electrocardiograph (see photo), or on a suitably tuned polygraph, and graphically depicted in an **electrocardiogram**. Electrodes are usually placed on the chest and lead to an instrument for measuring electric currents. The deflections of this instrument may be seen as waves on a computer screen, or a pen recorder may register the waves on a continuously moving roll of graph paper. Both types of recordings are called electrocardiograms.

A second measure of autonomic nervous system activity is **electrodermal responding**, or skin conductance. Anxiety, fear, anger, and other emotions increase activity in the sympathetic nervous system, which then boosts sweat-gland activity. Increased sweat-gland activity increases the electrical conductance of the skin. Conductance is typically measured by determining the current that flows through the skin when a known small voltage derived from an external source is passed between two electrodes on the hand. This current shows a pronounced increase after activation of the sweat glands. Since the sweat glands are activated by the sympathetic nervous system, increased sweat-gland activity indicates sympathetic

autonomic excitation and is often taken as a measure of emotional arousal. These measures are used widely in research in psychopathology.

Advances in technology allow researchers to track changes in physiological processes such as blood pressure in vivo, as people go about their normal business. Participants wear a portable device that automatically records blood pressure many times during the day. A team of researchers from the University of British Columbia gathered measures of ambulatory blood pressure from a sample of undergraduate women and showed that higher mean levels of arterial blood pressure were associated significantly with more extreme beliefs about needing to diet and negative appraisals of body shape (Bedford, Linden, & Barr, 2011). Presumably, if untreated, this elevated blood pressure will take quite a toll over time in contributing to subsequent health problems.

Brain activity can be measured by an **electroencephalogram, or EEG**. Electrodes placed on the scalp record electrical activity in the underlying brain area. Abnormal patterns of electrical activity can indicate epilepsy or can help in locating brain lesions or tumours.

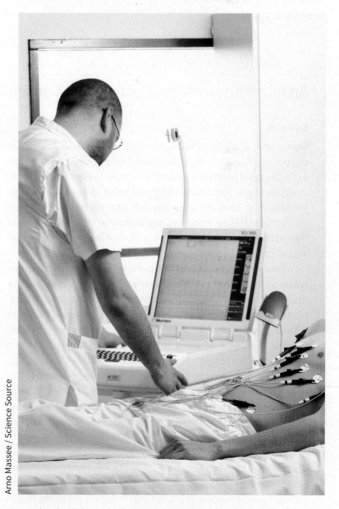

Arno Massee / Science Source

In psychophysiological assessment, physical changes in the body are measured. The electrocardiograph is one such assessment.

TABLE 3.3	Biological Assessment Methods
Brain imaging	CT and MRI scans reveal the structure of the brain. PET and fMRI are used to study brain function.
Neuropsychological assessment	Behavioural tests such as the Halstead-Reitan and Luria-Nebraska assess abilities such as motor speed, memory, and spatial ability. Deficits on particular tests help localize an area of brain dysfunction.
Psychophysiological assessment	This method includes measures of electrical activity in the autonomic nervous system, such as skin conductance, or in the central nervous system, such as the EEG.

As with the brain-imaging techniques reviewed earlier, a more complete picture of a human being is obtained when physiological functioning is assessed while the person is engaging in some form of behaviour or cognitive activity. If experimenters are interested in the psychophysiological responses of clients with OCD, for example, they would likely study the clients while presenting stimuli, such as dirt, that would elicit the problematic behaviours.

The biological assessment methods we have described are summarized in Table 3.3.

We have reviewed the main forms of clinical assessment. A combination of clinical interviews, psychological testing, and/or biological test results are often used in the determination of a diagnosis.

3.4 Diagnosis: Why It Matters

We now turn our attention to the diagnosis and classification of psychopathology, starting with Ernest H., a case example. In general, when evaluating someone, the information from various types of assessment is gathered together and then the task is to determine whether the person meets criteria for one or more disorders. People who do not meet clinical criteria for a disorder may still have a level of impairment or subjective distress that warrants clinical intervention. Here it is important to acknowledge that people can differ substantially in their experience and expression of symptoms and the fit with existing clinical descriptions needs to allow for uniqueness.

An Illustration of the Psychosocial Consequences of Maladjustment

Ernest H.

Slumping in a comfortable leather chair, Ernest H., a 35-year-old city police officer from Winnipeg, looked sceptically at his therapist as he struggled to relate a series of problems. His recent inability to maintain an erection when making love to his wife was the immediate reason for his seeking therapy but, after gentle prodding from the therapist, Ernest recounted a host of other difficulties, some of them dating from his childhood, but most of them originating during the previous several years.

Ernest's childhood had not been a happy one. His mother, whom he loved dearly, died suddenly when he was only six and, for the next 10 years, he lived either with his father or a maternal aunt. His father drank heavily, seldom managing to get through any day without some alcohol. Moreover, the man's moods were extremely variable—he had even spent several months in a hospital with a diagnosis of manic-depressive psychosis. His father's income was so irregular that he could seldom pay bills on time or afford to live in any but the most run-down neighbourhoods. At times, Ernest's father was totally incapable of caring for himself, let alone his son. Ernest would then spend weeks, sometimes months, with his aunt in a nearby suburb of Winnipeg.

Despite these challenging early life experiences, Ernest completed high school and entered university. He earned his miscellaneous living expenses by waiting tables at a small restaurant. During these university years, his psychological problems began to concern him. He often became profoundly depressed for no apparent reason, and these bouts of sadness were sometimes followed by periods of manic elation. His lack of control over these mood swings troubled him greatly, for he had observed the same pattern in his father. He also felt an acute self-consciousness with people whom he felt had authority over him—his boss, his professors, and even some of his classmates, with whom he unfavourably compared himself. Ernest was especially sensitive about his cheap cell phone and clothes, which were old and worn compared with his peers—their families had more money than his.

It was on the opening day of classes in his junior year that he first saw his future wife, Judy. When the tall, slender young woman moved to her seat with grace and self-assurance, his were not the only eyes that followed her. Ernest spent the rest of that semester watching Judy from afar, taking care to sit where he could glance over at her without being conspicuous. Then one day, they bumped into each other quite by accident while leaving class, and her warmth and charm emboldened him to ask her to join him for some coffee. When Judy said yes, Ernest almost wished she had not.

Amazingly enough, as he saw it, they soon fell in love and they were married before the end of his senior year. Ernest could never quite believe that his wife, as intelligent as she was beautiful, really cared for him. As the years wore on, his doubts about himself and about Judy's feelings toward him would continue to grow.

He hoped to enter law school, and both his grades and his score on the law-school boards made these plans a possibility, but he decided instead to enter the police academy. He later told his therapist that the decision reflected his doubts about his intellectual abilities as well as his increasing uneasiness in situations in which he felt himself being evaluated. Seminars had become unbearable for Ernest in his last year of university, and he had hopes that the badge and uniform of a police officer would give him the instant recognition and respect that he seemed incapable of earning on his own.

To help him get through the academy, his wife quit university at the end of her third year, against Ernest's pleas, and sought a secretarial job. He felt Judy was far brighter than he and saw no reason why she should sacrifice her potential to help him make his way in life. But at the same time he recognized the fiscal realities and grudgingly accepted her financial support.

The police academy proved to be even more stressful than university. Ernest's mood swings, although less frequent, still troubled him. And like his father, who was now confined to a psychiatric hospital, he drank to ease his psychological pain. He felt that his instructors considered him a fool when he had difficulty standing up in front of the class to give an answer that he himself knew was correct. But he made it through the physical, intellectual, and social rigours of the academy, and he was assigned to foot patrol in one of the wealthier sections of the city.

Several years later, when it seemed that life should be getting easier, he found himself in even greater turmoil. Now 32 years old, with a fairly secure job that paid reasonably well, he began to think of starting a family. Judy wanted this as well, and it was at this time that his problems with impotence began. He thought at first it was the alcohol; he was drinking at least six ounces of rye whisky every night, except when on the swing shift. Soon, though, he began to wonder whether he was actually avoiding the responsibility of having a child, and later he began to doubt that his wife really found him attractive and desirable. The more

understanding and patient Judy was about his sometimes frantic efforts to consummate sex with her, the less "manly" he felt himself to be. He was unable to accept help from his wife, for he did not believe that this was the "right" way to maintain a sexual relationship. The problem in bed spread to other areas of their lives. The less often they made love, the more suspicious he was of Judy, for she had become even more beautiful and vibrant as she entered her thirties.

The impetus for his contacting the therapist was an ugly argument with his wife one evening when she came home late from work. Ernest had been agitated for several days and was now consuming almost a full bottle of rye each night. Ernest, already drunk, attacked Judy both verbally and physically about her alleged infidelity. In her own anger and fear, Judy now questioned his masculinity for striking her and taunted him about his sexual problems. Ernest stormed out of their home, spent the night at a local bar, and somehow pulled himself together enough the next day to seek professional help from a psychologist available to assist, assess, and provide therapy to members of the police force.

DSM-5 DIAGNOSIS OF ERNEST H.
Alcohol use disorder
Substance-induced/medication-induced sexual dysfunction
Bipolar I disorder, most recent episode manic, in full remission
Avoidant personality disorder
V61.10* Relationship distress with spouse or intimate partner (other problems related to primary support group)

DSM-5 V codes are explained in a later section.

Ernest's case illustrates how current problems in functioning are typically the long-term product of personal vulnerabilities and life experiences. Imagine that you are the psychologist assigned to Ernest. Your role would be to assess Ernest and establish what diagnoses apply. You would then incorporate this information into a case formulation that would guide the course of treatment and treatment options.

Diagnosis is a critical aspect of the field of abnormal psychology. It is essential for professionals to be able to communicate accurately with one another about the types of cases they are treating or studying. Furthermore, a disorder must be classified correctly before its causes or best treatments can be found. For example, if one research group has found a successful treatment for depression but has defined the treatment in an unconventional manner, the finding is not likely to be replicated by another group of investigators. Only in recent decades, however, has diagnosis been accorded the attention it deserves.

To beginning students of abnormal psychology, description of diagnosis could seem overwhelming at times because it sometimes relies on fine distinctions and many elements are involved. But arriving at the correct diagnosis is fundamentally important and a key first step in deciding the appropriate course of treatment. This process can be quite complex when

it becomes evident that a person has multiple problems and several disorders may apply.

In our review of diagnosis, we focus on the official diagnostic system widely employed by mental health professionals, the *Diagnostic and Statistical Manual of Mental Disorders (DSM)*, now in its fifth edition, commonly referred to as the *DSM-5* (American Psychiatric Association, 2013). The *DSM* is published by the American Psychiatric Association and has an interesting history, including the many recent controversies and unprecedented public scrutiny that accompanied the May 2013 publication of *DSM-5* and the process leading up to its arrival. We will examine the issues involved here in detail after considering the history of classification in general and the various stages in the development of the *DSM*.

It is important to set an overall context before beginning our historical overview. Why does diagnosis matter and who does it matter to the most? What is at stake? Montreal psychiatrist Joel Paris has outlined the various realms impacted by the *DSM-5* (see Paris, 2013). He identified five "constituencies" of the *DSM-5*. These constituencies (i.e., involved parties) are shown in Table 3.4 and they provide a clear sense of the various ways that it matters in terms of how disorders are classified and diagnosed. This analysis includes key questions related to the diagnostic system.

TABLE 3.4 The Constituencies of the *DSM-5*

Constituency	Related Question(s)
Research	To what extent does the classification system advance research? Do the people in clinical trials who meet prescribed criteria have clinical problems representative of typical clinical problems?
Clinical practice	Does the system advance clinical practice in terms of guiding treatment and understanding of the disorder?
The pharmaceutical industry	To what extent does the pharmaceutical industry influence how disorders are defined? Is the recognition of new disorders guided by a profit-driven goal of providing more drugs to more people?
The legal system	Do biases and inadequacies in how disorder is determined get reflected in skewed legal decisions?
The general public	How does the classification and description of disorders relate to general beliefs about mental disorder among people in general?

The questions listed in Table 3.4 underscore the fact that despite its substantial imperfections, the diagnostic system has a direct bearing on many real-world issues and it can have a substantial impact on the lives of people. Consider, for instance, the plight of a person with a particular form of dysfunction who needs access to therapy and does not have the personal resources needed (i.e., broad insurance coverage or sufficient personal monetary funds) and the disorder itself is not recognized in the *DSM-5*. This series of roadblocks makes it unlikely that this person will receive professional treatment and they will instead have to rely on informal sources of support.

Below we provide an overview of the history of classification. It is clear that advances have been made over the years but there is still plenty of room for improvement.

3.5 | A Brief History of Classification

By the end of the nineteenth century, medicine had progressed far beyond its practice during the Middle Ages, when bloodletting was at least part of the treatment of virtually all physical problems. Gradually, people recognized that different illnesses required different treatments. Diagnostic procedures were improved, diseases classified, and applicable remedies administered. Impressed by the successes that new diagnostic procedures had achieved in the field of medicine, investigators of abnormal behaviour also sought to develop classification schemes. Advances in other sciences, such as botany and chemistry, had followed the development of classification

systems, reinforcing hope that similar efforts in the field of abnormal behaviour might bring progress. Unfortunately, progress in classifying mental disorders was not to be easily gained.

Early Efforts at Classification

During the nineteenth and early twentieth centuries, there was great inconsistency in the classification of abnormal behaviour. By the end of the nineteenth century, the diversity of classifications was recognized as a serious problem that impeded communication among people in the field, and several attempts were made to produce a widely adopted system of classification. In the United Kingdom in 1882, for example, the Statistical Committee of the Royal Medico-Psychological Association produced a classification scheme; however, even though it was revised several times, it was never adopted by the association's members. In Paris in 1889, the Congress of Mental Science adopted a single classification system, but it was never widely used. In the United States, the Association of Medical Superintendents of American Institutions for the Insane, a forerunner of the American Psychiatric Association, adopted a somewhat revised version of the British system in 1886. Then, in 1913, this group accepted a new classification scheme that incorporated some of Emil Kraepelin's ideas. Again, consistency was lacking. The New York State Commission on Lunacy, for example, insisted on retaining its own system (Kendell, 1975).

Development of the WHO and *DSM* Systems

More recent efforts at achieving uniformity of classification have not been totally successful either. In 1939, the World Health Organization (WHO) added mental disorders to the *International List of Causes of Death*. In 1948, the list was expanded to become the *International Statistical Classification of Diseases, Injuries, and Causes of Death (ICD)*, a comprehensive listing of all diseases, including a classification of abnormal behaviour. Although this nomenclature was unanimously adopted at a WHO conference, the mental disorders section was not widely accepted. Even though American psychiatrists had played a prominent role in the WHO effort, the American Psychiatric Association published its own *Diagnostic and Statistical Manual (DSM)* in 1952.

In 1969, the WHO published a new classification system that was more widely accepted. A second version of the American Psychiatric Association's *DSM, DSM-II* (1968), was similar to the WHO system, and, in the United Kingdom, a glossary of definitions was produced to accompany it (General Register Office, 1968). But true consensus still eluded the field. The WHO classifications were simply a listing of diagnostic categories; the actual behaviours or symptoms that were the bases for the diagnoses were not specified. *DSM-II* and the British *Glossary of Mental Disorders* provided some of this crucial information but did not specify the same symptoms for a given disorder. Thus, actual diagnostic practices still varied widely.

In 1980, the American Psychiatric Association published an extensively revised diagnostic manual *(DSM-III);* a somewhat revised version, *DSM-III-R,* appeared in 1987. Several major innovations distinguish the third edition and subsequent versions of the *DSM.* Perhaps the most sweeping change was the use of **multiaxial classification**, whereby each individual is rated on five separate dimensions, or axes. The multiaxial classification prevailed until it was removed recently in the *DSM-5.* The axes are nevertheless worth considering in some detail because they highlight some important diagnostic considerations. The five axes were:

- *Axis I.* All diagnostic categories except personality disorders and mental retardation
- *Axis II.* Personality disorders and mental retardation
- *Axis III.* General medical conditions
- *Axis IV.* Psychosocial and environmental problems
- *Axis V.* Current level of functioning

The multiaxial system, by requiring judgements on each of the five axes, forced the diagnostician to consider a broad range of information.

Axis I included all diagnostic categories except personality disorders and mental retardation (now known as intellectual disability), which made up Axis II. Thus, axes I and II composed the classification of abnormal behaviour. On Axis III the clinician indicated any general medical conditions believed to be relevant to the mental disorder in question. For example, the existence of a heart condition in a person who has also been diagnosed with depression would have important implications for treatment; some antidepressant drugs could worsen the heart condition.

Axis IV was created to code psychosocial and environmental problems that the person has been experiencing and that may be contributing to the disorder. These included occupational problems, economic problems, interpersonal difficulties with family members, and a variety of problems in other life areas that may influence psychological functioning. Finally, on Axis V, the clinician had to indicate the person's current level of adaptive functioning. Life areas considered included social relationships, occupational functioning, and use of leisure time. Ratings of current functioning are supposed to give information about the need for treatment.

In 1988, the American Psychiatric Association task force, chaired by psychiatrist Allen Frances, began work on *DSM-IV.* Working groups that included many psychologists were established to review sections of *DSM-III-R,* prepare literature reviews, analyze previously collected data, and collect new data if needed. An important change in the process for this edition was the adoption of a highly conservative approach to making changes in the diagnostic criteria—the reasons for changes in diagnoses would be explicitly stated and clearly supported by data. In previous versions, the reasons for diagnostic changes had not always been explicit.

DSM-IV was published in 1994 and the American Psychiatric Association subsequently completed a "text revision" (*DSM-IV-TR*; American Psychiatric Association, 2000). The revised version contained very few substantive changes to the different diagnostic categories and criteria, although some sections were rewritten to enhance clarity and incorporate recent research findings related to issues such as the prevalence, course, and etiology of disorders. Canadian psychologist Paula Caplan (1995) was outspoken in her criticism of various versions of the *DSM,* especially of the fact that many people with divergent viewpoints are not given the opportunity to participate in the decision-making process. Among those who are critical of the *DSM,* one group asserts that classification per se is irrelevant to the field of abnormal behaviour, and a second group finds specific deficiencies in the manner in which diagnoses are made in the *DSM.*

It is important to highlight that the *DSM* is controversial and, as noted earlier, this is certainly the case with the *DSM-5.* To many clinical scientists and practitioners, it is not "the book of truth" about psychological problems, nor is it universally embraced by psychiatrists, psychologists, and others in the field. It was developed originally by physicians who applied a medical model to the diagnosis of presumed psychiatric illnesses and who assumed that categorical diagnoses correspond to actual underlying disease entities with specific symptoms, treatments, and prognoses. Some question whether the majority of *DSM* categories correspond to real, underlying entities; they argue that the categories refer to hypothetical constructs that may or may not exist in reality, unlike medical diagnoses where the basic cause is frequently known and the presence of the disease can usually be objectively determined (for example, by a blood or urine test). There are also "concerns that financial decisions have driven the DSM process" (Blashfield et al., 2014, p. 44).

Others take issue with the fact that certain disorders seem to exist in reality but are not recognized in the *DSM-5.* This is hard to understand from any reasonable perspective; shouldn't the *DSM-5* capture disorders that people actually experience? The failure to include certain disorders that have become more prominent in certain years, such as Internet addiction disorder (see Student Perspectives 3.1), seems very puzzling, but could be a reflection of simply needing more scientific evidence.

How does the *DSM* define the subject matter of this textbook? Recognizing that the term **mental disorder** is problematic and that "no definition adequately specifies precise boundaries for the concept," *DSM-5* provides the following definition:

> *"A syndrome characterized by clinically significant disturbance in individual's cognition, emotion regulation, or behavior that reflects a dysfunction in the psychological, biological, or developmental processes underlying mental functioning. Mental disorders are usually associated with significant distress or disability in social, occupational, or other important activities."*

> *(American Psychiatric Association, 2013, p. 20)*

Student Perspectives 3.1

Internet Addiction Disorder on Campus: Why isn't it in *DSM-5*?

The Internet can be a boon to many. Post-secondary students are heavy users when compared with the general population and report that the Internet can be a tool to support and enhance their academic pursuits (Douglas et al., 2008). Further, its networking capabilities can be socially enabling. However, there has been increasing criticism that it can be just as socially isolating. The term "Internet addiction disorder" (IAD), sometimes referred to as cyber disorder, Internet overuse, problematic computer use, or pathological computer use or video game playing, typically applies to excessive and out-of-control use that interferes with daily living (academic, occupational, social, financial, and physical functional impairment).

In 1995, when the Internet was in its infancy, physician Ivan Goldberg proposed IAD as a disorder using *DSM-IV* pathological gambling as his model—in a satirical hoax! Subsequently, Kimberly Young, also using pathological gambling as her model, in 1998 published the results of a serious investigation of (1) the existence of Internet addiction, and (2) the extent of problems caused by potential misuse. She compared 396 "dependent" Internet users with 100 "nondependent" users and found significant behavioural (e.g., difficulty controlling usage) and functional (e.g., severity of problems) differences between the two groups. IAD has been researched extensively over the past decade or more and its classification as a psychological disorder has been and continues to be debated—sometimes hotly (see Douglas et al., 2008).

There is a growing body of research on IAD in students, including extensive research in Asia and in Europe. A recent study of 2,257 British students who were screened with a diagnostic measure adapted for detecting IAD found that 71 students (3.2%) had IAD symptoms (Kuss, Griffiths, & Binder, 2013). Personality factors that predicted IAD status were higher levels of neuroticism and lower levels of agreeableness. Other recent research suggests that there are two types of students with problematic Internet use. One group is characterized by impulsivity and tends to use illicit drugs and tobacco. The other group consists of students who tend to be socially anxious, depressed, and have family conflict (De Leo & Wulfert, 2013).

Should IAD be included as a disorder in *DSM-5*? Jerald Block (2008) made a strong case for inclusion of IAD. He described the diagnosis as a "compulsive-impulsive spectrum disorder that involves on-line and/or offline computer usage" (p. 306). In addition to excessive gaming, he includes sexual preoccupation and email/text messaging subtypes in this common disorder. According to Block, the variants share four components:

- excessive use (associated with loss of the sense of time);
- withdrawal symptoms (e.g., anger, tension, feeling "blue" when access is denied);
- tolerance (including the need for better equipment, more software, or more hours of use); and
- negative repercussions (e.g., fatigue, arguments, lying, poor achievement, and social isolation).

Block (2008) noted that diagnosis is complicated by the fact that about 86% of IAD cases have another *DSM* diagnosis; that in the United States (and presumably in Canada), people generally present for only the comorbid condition(s); and that, "unless the therapist is specifically looking for Internet addiction, it is unlikely to be detected" (p. 306).

Unfortunately, *DSM-5* did not include IAD, despite including a diagnostic category in the "conditions for further study" section called Internet gaming disorder. Although IAD was considered for the proposed "behavioural addictions" diagnostic category, work group members concluded that there was insufficient research evidence for a new disorder but recommended that it be included in the *DSM-5* appendix with a goal of encouraging further research. This recommendation was not accepted, though the more finite condition of Internet gaming disorder was included.

In Asia, therapists are trained to screen for IAD. Why? One reason is because the problem is more visible there! Much of the activity occurs publicly in Internet cafes, whereas in Western countries it is often more private and engaged in at home. Nonetheless, a study of Internet addiction among Norwegian adults (Bakken et al., 2009) reported the highest prevalence among young males (among those 16–29 years, 4.1% were addicted and 19.0% were at risk; among those 30–39 years, the rates were 3.3% and 10.7%, respectively). Male gender, young age, university-level education, and an unsatisfactory financial situation were positively associated with problematic Internet use. In a meta-synthesis of qualitative research over a decade, Douglas et al. (2008) concluded, "the Internet provides an entertaining and interactive environment where those susceptible to its allure can find escape by coping with negative emotions such as loneliness, isolation and boredom, release stress, discharge anger and frustration, and feel a sense of belonging and recognition. . . . The Internet addict tends to neglect almost everything in their lives in an effort to satisfy their desire of being online" (p. 304).

Fortunately, both psychological and pharmacological treatments seem promising in treating IAD. Initial results indicate that they are "highly effective" (Winkler et al., 2013, p. 317). Results like these suggest that researchers and clinicians such as Young, Block, and others might be correct to lobby for the recognition of Internet addiction as a recognized clinical disorder in *DSM-5*. Indeed, others have proposed a litany of serious consequences of IAD, including family conflict, marital discord, academic failure, job loss, excessive financial debt, fatigue and sleep problems, and poor eating and exercise patterns.

Nonetheless, others argue that IAD is neither an addiction nor a specific disorder. Indeed, various organizations, including the American Medical Association, recommended against including IAD as a formal diagnosis in the revised *DSM*. Is it a true addiction or simply symptomatic of existing disorders?

What is your own position on this issue? Do you think IAD should have been included as a new clinical disorder in *DSM-5*? Do you know a fellow student with IAD? Were the professionals involved in developing the *DSM-5* simply lagging behind the times in not recognizing a relatively new condition? There is a subjective element, it seems, in determining when there is enough evidence to warrant including a new condition in the *DSM*.

A number of other conditions were excluded from consideration in *DSM-5*. Social deviant behaviour that reflects a conflict between the person and society is not a disorder unless it reflects dysfunction in the person. Also excluded are culturally sanctioned responses. This caveat underscores the need to consider the situational or cultural context.

3.6 Issues in the Classification of Abnormal Behaviour

We will examine here the usefulness of classification. Although there is significant value in classifying abnormal behaviour, there are many criticisms.

The Value of Classification and Diagnoses

The various types of abnormal behaviour differ from one another in many ways, and thus classifying them is essential, for these differences may constitute keys to the causes and treatments of various deviant behaviours. Forming categories furthers knowledge, for once a category is formed, additional information may be ascertained about it. Even though the category is only an asserted, and not a proven, entity, it may still be heuristically useful in that it facilitates the acquisition of new information. Only after a diagnostic category has been formed can we study people who fit its definition in the hope of uncovering factors responsible for the development of their problems and of devising treatments that may help them. For example, bipolar disorder was once not typically distinguished from depression. If this distinction had not been made, it is unlikely that lithium would have been recognized as an effective treatment for bipolar disorder.

Criticisms of Classification

Some critics of classification argue that to classify someone as depressed or anxious results in a loss of information about that person, thereby reducing some of the uniqueness of the individual being studied. In evaluating this claim, recall our earlier discussions of paradigms and their effect on how we glean information about our world. It appears to be in the nature of humankind to categorize whenever we perceive and think about anything. Those who argue against classification per se are overlooking the inevitability of classification and categorization in human thought.

In classification, some information must inevitably be lost. What matters is whether the information lost is relevant, and relevance depends on the purposes of the classification system. Any classification is designed to group together objects sharing a common property and to ignore differences in the objects that are not relevant to the purposes at hand. If our intention is merely to count odd and even rolls of a die, it is irrelevant whether a die comes up one, three, or five, or two, four, or six. In judging abnormal behaviour, however, we cannot so easily decide what is wheat and what is chaff, for the relevant and irrelevant dimensions of abnormal behaviour are uncertain. Thus, when we do classify, we may be grouping people together on rather trivial bases while ignoring their extremely important differences.

In Chapter 1, we discussed issues related to attitudes toward people with psychological disorders. We must revisit the topic in the current context to reinforce the fact that classification can have negative effects on a person. Consider how your life might be changed after being diagnosed as having schizophrenia. You might become guarded and suspicious lest someone recognize your disorder. Or you might be chronically on edge, fearing the onset of another episode. The fact that you are a "former mental patient" could have a stigmatizing effect. Friends and loved ones might treat you differently, and you might have difficulty obtaining employment. There is little doubt that diagnosis can have such negative consequences. We must recognize and continually be on guard against the possible social stigma of a diagnosis.

Categorical vs. Dimensional Classification

The *DSM* represents a **categorical classification**, a yes-no approach to classification. Does the client have schizophrenia or not? It may be argued that this type of classification, because it postulates discrete (separate) diagnostic entities, does not allow continuity between normal and abnormal behaviour to be taken into consideration. Those who advance the continuity argument hold that abnormal and normal behaviours differ only in intensity or degree, not in kind; therefore, discrete diagnostic categories foster a false impression of discontinuity.

In contrast, in **dimensional classification**, the entities or objects being classified must be ranked on a quantitative dimension (e.g., a 1-to-10 scale of anxiety, where 1 represents minimal and 10 extreme). Classification would be accomplished by assessing clients on the relevant dimensions and perhaps plotting the location of the client in a system of coordinates defined by his or her score on each dimension. (See Figure 3.6 for an illustration of the difference between categorical and dimensional classification.) A dimensional system can subsume a categorical system by specifying a cutting point, or threshold, on one of the quantitative dimensions. This capability is a potential advantage of the dimensional approach.

A dimensional approach also allows for the possibility that certain individuals may experience a number of troubling symptoms of a disorder but not meet the number of symptoms required for an actual diagnosis. Contemporary research on disorders such as depression shows that there is substantial evidence for continuity and that people who experience symptoms of depression but do not meet the criteria for a

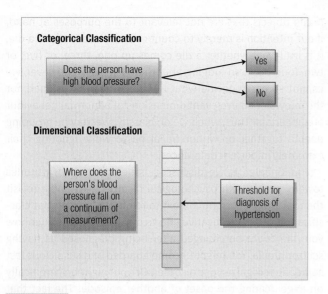

FIGURE 3.6 | Categorical vs. dimensional classification

diagnosis nevertheless experience significant levels of distress and impairment and appear to warrant treatment (see Flett, Vredenburg, & Krames, 1997; Maser et al., 2009).

Clearly, a dimensional system can be applied to most of the symptoms that constitute the diagnoses of the *DSM*. Anxiety, depression, and the many personality traits that are included in the personality disorders are found in different people to varying degrees and thus do not seem to fit well with the *DSM* categorical model.

The choice between a categorical and a dimensional system of classification, however, is not as simple as it might seem initially. Consider hypertension (high blood pressure), a topic discussed at length in Chapter 9. Blood-pressure measurements form a continuum, which clearly fits a dimensional approach; yet researchers have found it useful to categorize certain people as having high blood pressure in order to research the causes and possible treatments for the condition. A similar situation could exist for the *DSM* categories. Even though anxiety clearly exists in differing degrees in different people and thus is a dimensional variable, it could prove useful to create a diagnostic category for those people whose anxiety is extreme. There is a certain inevitable arbitrariness to such a categorization (where exactly should the cut-off be?), but it could be fruitful nonetheless. We will return to this issue in our discussion of personality disorders in Chapter 13. *DSM-5* has been modified to include more dimensional ratings in general. This change was signalled in a 2009 commentary on the conceptual development of *DSM-5* when the chairpersons and coordinators of the revision process (Regier, Narrow, Kuhl, & Kupfer, 2009) stated:

> "The single most important precondition for moving forward to improve the clinical and scientific utility of DSM-5 will be the incorporation of simple dimensional measures for assessing syndromes within broad diagnostic categories and supraordinate dimensions that cross current diagnostic boundaries.

> *Thus, we have decided that one, if not the major difference between DSM-IV and DSM-5 will be the more prominent use of dimensional measures in DSM-5." (p. 649)*

Reliability: The Cornerstone of a Diagnostic System

We defined inter-rater reliability at the start of the chapter as the extent to which two judges agree about an event. For example, suppose you wanted to know whether a child suspected of having attention-deficit/hyperactivity disorder did indeed have difficulty paying attention and staying seated in the classroom. You could decide to observe the child during a day at school. To determine whether the observational data were reliable, you would want to have at least two people watch the child and make independent judgements about the child's attention and activity. The extent to which the raters agreed would be an index of inter-rater reliability. (See Figure 3.7 for an illustration.)

Reliability is a primary criterion for judging any classification system because those applying it must be able to agree on what is and what is not an instance of a particular category. A person diagnosed as having an anxiety disorder by one clinician should be given the same diagnosis by another clinician, as well. After all, if someone is not diagnosed correctly, he or she may not receive the best treatment available. Prior to *DSM-III*, diagnostic reliability was not acceptable, mainly because the criteria for making a diagnosis were not presented clearly and methods of assessing a client's symptoms were not standardized (Ward et al., 1962).

The two components of reliability—agreeing on who is a member of a class and who is not—are *sensitivity* and *specificity*. **Sensitivity** is agreement regarding the presence of a specific diagnosis; **specificity** is agreement concerning the absence of a diagnosis. As we will see, reliability for most current diagnostic categories is relatively good.

DSM-5 field trials conducted in Canada and in the United States show that there is substantial variability in inter-rater

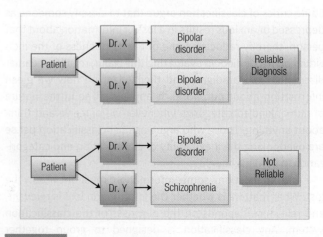

FIGURE 3.7 | Inter-rater reliability

reliability (see Regier et al., 2013). Overall, 23 diagnoses were evaluated by assessing the agreement of two independent clinicians. The study used a statistic called "kappa." **Kappa** measures the proportion of agreement over and above what would be expected by chance. Generally, kappas over .70 are considered good. It was found that 14 diagnoses were in the good or very good range in terms of agreement, but six were in the questionable range, and three were in the unacceptable range. Examples of disorders in the good to very good range included PTSD, autism spectrum disorder, and borderline personality disorder. Disorders in the questionable or unacceptable range included major depressive disorder and generalized anxiety disorder; their reduced reliability was attributed, in part, to their substantial heterogeneity in the symptom expression across people and being disorders with a high level of comorbidity. Importantly, given our earlier discussion of the dimensional versus categorical approach, Regier et al. (2013) noted that the results tended to be more favourable for disorders that more easily lent themselves to dimensional assessments. Also, the authors made the point that clinicians tend to think dimensionally and this is the essence of adjusting treatment when there are changes in someone's symptom expression.

How Valid are Diagnostic Categories?

Validity is a complex topic. We described the several types of validity at the start of this chapter, but here we will focus on the type of validity that is most important for diagnosis—construct validity. As noted previously, the diagnoses of the *DSM* are referred to as hypothetical constructs because they are inferred, not proven, entities. A diagnosis of schizophrenia, for instance, does not have the same status as a diagnosis of diabetes. In the case of diabetes, we know the symptoms, the

biological malfunction that produces them, and some of the causes. For schizophrenia, we have a proposed set of symptoms but only very tentative information regarding mechanisms that may produce the symptoms.

Construct validity is determined by evaluating the extent to which accurate statements and predictions can be made about a category once it has been formed. In other words, to what extent does the construct enter into a network of lawful relationships? Some of these relationships may be about possible causes of the disorder; for example, a genetic predisposition or a biochemical imbalance. Others could be about characteristics of the disorder that are not symptoms but that occur frequently in association with it; for example, poor social skills in people with schizophrenia. Other relationships could refer to predictions about the course of the disorder or the probable response to particular treatments. The greater the number and strength of relationships into which a diagnosis enters, the greater the construct validity (see Figure 3.8).

The *DSM* and Criticisms of Diagnosis

Beginning with *DSM-III,* an effort was made to create more reliable and valid diagnostic categories. Major improvements include the following:

1. The characteristics and symptoms of each diagnostic category were described much more extensively than they were in *DSM-II.*

2. Much more attention was paid to how the symptoms of a given disorder may differ depending on the culture in which it appears. Focus on Discovery 3.2 describes efforts by the *DSM* to be more sensitive to the effects of culture and explores cultural factors from an assessment perspective.

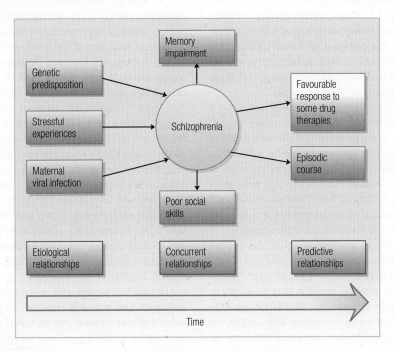

FIGURE 3.8 Construct validity. Some lawful relationships of the construct of schizophrenia.

Focus on Discovery 3.2

Ethnic and Cultural Considerations in *DSM-5*

Below we describe a clinical vignette taken from Kirmayer, Rousseau, Jarvis, and Guzder (2003). This example illustrates the need for a complex and sensitive approach to diagnosis and clinical assessment that recognizes differences in cultural backgrounds. We then outline changes in *DSM-5* that place greater emphasis on cultural considerations.

A 16-year-old girl from Haiti presents with disorganized schizophrenia, which began around age 14. Her family has not been compliant with treatment and this has led to several hospitalizations of the patient in a dehydrated state. During the third hospitalization, the clinical team decide to explore the family's interpretation of the illness. A grand-aunt insists on sending the girl to Haiti for a traditional diagnosis. The traditional healer indicates that the problem is due to an ancestor's spirit in the mother's family and that for this reason it will be a prolonged illness. This explanation helps to restore cohesion in the extended family by rallying people around the patient, and her family receives much support. The traditional interpretation and treatment has broken the family's sense of shame and isolation and promoted an alliance with the medical team and the acceptance of anti-psychotic medication (Kirmayer et al., 2003, p. 25).

Previous editions of the *DSM* were criticized for their lack of attention to cultural and ethnic variations in psychopathology. *DSM-IV-TR* was modified to enhance its cultural sensitivity in three ways: (1) by including in the main body of the manual a discussion of cultural and ethnic factors for each disorder; (2) by providing in the appendix a general framework for evaluating the role of culture and ethnicity; and (3) by describing culture-bound syndromes in an appendix.

Significant revisions were made in *DSM-5*. La Roche and colleagues (2015) differentiate between two types of cultural revisions present in *DSM-5*: those that are an extension of previous revisions and those that are related to the overall restructuring of *DSM-5*. Included in the latter category are the dimensional elements present in *DSM-5*, which may have a significant cultural impact (e.g., normative data could be collected for different cultural groups). Included in the former category are expanded descriptions of culture, including a cultural element in the definition of mental disorder; the removal of Axis IV, which represented a spot to specify psychosocial stressors (e.g., racism could have been included there); and changes in language and cultural assessment (detailed below).

The term "culture-bound syndrome" has been replaced in *DSM-5* for various reasons, including the sense that the term "culture-bound" places too much emphasis on the particularity and limited nature of culturally distinct syndromes (see American Psychiatric Association, 2013). In other words, the term was seen as minimizing the reality of these adjustment problems. Instead, the *DSM-5* favours three terms ("cultural syndromes," "cultural idioms," and "cultural explanations") because they are more relevant to clinical practice and accurate descriptions of cultural concepts of distress and dysfunction.

Among the cultural issues of which clinicians need to be aware are language differences between the therapist and the client and the way in which the client's culture talks about emotional distress. Many cultures, for example, describe grief or anxiety in physical terms—"I am sick in my heart" or "My heart is heavy"—rather than in psychological terms. Individuals also vary in the degree to which they identify with their cultural or ethnic group. Some value assimilation into the majority culture, whereas others

wish to maintain close ties to their ethnic background. In general, clinicians are advised to be constantly mindful of how culture and ethnicity influence diagnosis and treatment.

Here is an example of one of the 25 culture-bound syndromes listed in *DSM-IV-TR*: koro—reported in south and east Asia, an episode of intense anxiety about the possibility that the penis or nipples will recede into the body, possibly leading to death. In *DSM-5*, *koro* is defined very similarly, but placed in the OCD section, and then also referred to in the glossary of cultural concepts of distress.

Although *DSM-IV* introduced an **Outline for Cultural Formulation** designed to guide treatment planning from a perspective sensitive to differences in ethnocultural backgrounds and context, in practice, this outline had little impact; indeed, 57% of consultants working at the McGill Cultural Consultation Service in Montreal indicated that they had little or no familiarity with it. Upon using it, however, 61% found it to be very useful or extremely useful in organizing their assessments and consultation reports (Kirmayer et al., 2008).

DSM-5 introduced two key changes that should result in much greater consideration of cultural issues. First, the revised Outline for Cultural Formulation now calls for five specific assessments. In addition to an overall cultural assessment, the four other specific themes considered are: (1) the cultural identity of the individual; (2) the cultural consideration of distress; (3) psychosocial stressors and cultural features of both vulnerability and resilience; and (4) cultural features of the relationship between the individual and the clinician. Attempts have been made to refine the Outline for Cultural Formulation based on qualitative analyses of feedback provided by patients and clinicians (see Aggarwal et al., 2013). Potential barriers mentioned by patients included ambiguity of design, over-standardization, and lack of buy-in. Perceived barriers mentioned by clinicians included lack of clinician buy-in, being overly repetitive, and the need for sensitivity to differences in the severity of patient illness.

In addition, the American Psychiatric Association has now developed the **Cultural Formulation Interview (CFI)**. The CFI is described as a semi-structured interview tapping four themes: (1) cultural definition of the problem; (2) cultural perceptions of cause, context, and support; (3) cultural factors affecting self-coping and past help-seeking; and (4) cultural factors affecting current help-seeking (see American Psychiatric Association, 2013).

The CFI relies heavily on input from the person being interviewed. While it seems like an obvious step forward, the use of the CFI will still be constrained by language abilities and by the extent to which the person can communicate and is able to share insights and observations. A sensitive approach is clearly required. A reasonable suggestion was made several years ago by Kirmayer, Rousseau, and Santhanam (2003): to work in multidisciplinary teams that are culturally diverse and reflective of the client population. This strategy could involve working closely with interpreters and "culture brokers" who would assist with the clarification of the cultural context. The use of a team approach could also help address another problem. Aggarwal et al. (2013) illustrated how the cultural formulation also reflects the clinician conducting the evaluation and a second clinician can provide a cultural formulation that is at variance with the initial assessment. He pointed to the need for practical guidelines for making cultural formulations across varying treatment settings.

3. Specific *diagnostic criteria*—the symptoms and other facts that must be present to justify the diagnosis—were spelled out more precisely, and the clinical symptoms that constitute a diagnosis were defined in a glossary.

The improved explicitness of the *DSM* criteria has reduced the descriptive inadequacies that were the major source of diagnostic unreliability and thus has led to improved reliability. However, as the study by Regier et al. (2013) indicates, this has not entirely eliminated the problem. Another factor in improved reliability is the use of standardized, reliably scored interviews for collecting the information needed for a diagnosis. Clearly, despite some obvious advances, there is still room for improvement because the reliability of some specific diagnoses is well below expectations and acceptable standards. We will now take a closer look at *DSM-5*.

3.7 The Diagnostic System of the American Psychiatric Association (*DSM-5*)

"In all, [DSM-5] is a combination of suspense, mystery and prepublication controversy that many publishers would die for. The psychiatric association knows it has a corner on the market and a blockbuster series."

—Benedict Carey, The New York Times,
December 18, 2008

Table 3.5 summarizes the main diagnostic categories in *DSM-5*. We list them here to give you a broad overview of what's inside *DSM-5*. We save our descriptions of these diagnoses for subsequent chapters.

As previously noted, the multiaxial system, including a designated spot to indicate psychosocial stressors (i.e., Axis IV), was not retained in *DSM-5*; however, *DSM-5* contains "V codes." Recall that the diagnostic description of Ernest H. included a V code referring to relationship problems. **DSM-5 V codes** are conditions or significant factors that are not disorders per se but can have a strong influence on treatment. Examples include homelessness, child maltreatment, and divorce. A person might be eligible for insurance coverage for treatment even if they did not have a diagnosable disorder but had significant impairment due to a V code condition being present. For instance, sex addiction might not be covered since it is not in the *DSM-5*, but it could be covered if the clinician focused on the consequences of the abnormal behaviour and generously identified a V code condition (e.g., relationship distress with spouse or intimate partner).

TABLE 3.5 *DSM-5* Diagnostic Categories

Category	Sample Disorder(s)
Neurodevelopmental	Intellectual disability, autism spectrum disorder
Psychotic	Schizophrenia
Bipolar	Bipolar I disorder
Depressive	Major depressive disorder
Anxiety	Panic disorder, social anxiety disorder
Obsessive-Compulsive	Obsessive-compulsive disorder, hoarding disorder
Trauma/Stressor-Related	Post-traumatic stress disorder
Dissociative	Dissociative identity disorder
Somatic	Somatic symptom disorder, illness anxiety disorder
Feeding and Eating	Anorexia nervosa
Elimination	Enuresis (bedwetting)
Sleep-Wake	Insomnia disorder, nightmare disorder
Sexual Dysfunctions	Erectile disorder
Gender Dysphoria	Gender dysphoria
Disruptive, Impulse Control, Conduct	Conduct disorder
Substance	Alcohol use disorder
Neurocognitive	Delirium
Personality	Borderline personality disorder
Paraphilic	Voyeuristic disorder, transvestic disorder

Development of the *DSM-5*

Planning for the *DSM-5* began in 1999 with collaboration between the American Psychiatric Association and the U.S. National Institute of Mental Health (NIMH) designed to stimulate research to address key issues in psychiatric nosology (the classification of disorders). A major objective was to initiate a renewed focus on the validity of diagnosis. Another objective was to eliminate disparities between the *DSM* and the World Health Organization's ICD (whose version 11 was slated for publication around 2018). The resulting publications are intended to serve as resources for the *DSM* task force and disorder-specific work groups. The *DSM-5* task force was announced in July 2007. It had 27 members, with David Kupfer as chair. The 120 members of the 13 work groups charged with reviewing scientific advances and research-based information to develop the fifth edition of the manual were announced on May 1, 2008.

In addition to the goals outlined above, what other stated goals and objectives guided the *DSM-5* committee? Additional aims were outlined by Kupfer, Kuhl, and Wulsin (2013). They stated that revisions were designed to address gaps in the diagnostic and classification system and update the system based on research developments, including new developments in the neuroscience field.

Another clear goal was to reduce the proportion of diagnoses falling in the "not otherwise specified" diagnostic category by making changes to symptom criteria where necessary. As one illustration of why this is necessary, it has typically been the case that the generic "not otherwise specified" category is the most frequent eating disorder diagnosis. A related change in *DSM-5* is worth mentioning here: the terms "other specified" and "unspecified" (rather than "not otherwise specified") are now being used. For example, if a client presents with eating disorder symptoms causing significant distress and/or impairment, but full criteria are not met for any of the eating disorders, the clinician can diagnose "other specified feeding or eating disorder" and then specify the reason (e.g., bulimia nervosa of limited duration). Alternatively, the clinician can diagnose "unspecified feeding or eating disorder" and in so doing, the reason is not given. The latter situation would most likely arise in an emergency room or similar setting due to a lack of information. The existence of these categories highlights that people can experience significant distress and/or impairment despite not meeting full criteria for a disorder.

Another stated goal of the *DSM-5* committee was to supplement the categorical approach with a greater number of dimensional ratings. This issue of the validity of a categorical vs. dimensional approach was discussed earlier in this chapter.

Finally, according to Kupfer et al. (2013), a key overarching goal was to streamline and simplify the *DSM-5* in order to increase its clinical usefulness when used by doctors in primary care. This is a key objective since the family doctor is often the first point of contact (indeed sometimes the only point of contact) for people needing psychological help.

In a news release on February 10, 2010, the American Psychiatric Association posted the proposed draft disorders and draft diagnostic criteria for *DSM-5* and invited comment until almost the end of April 2010. It was noted that the criteria would be reviewed and refined over the subsequent two years, during which the association would conduct three phases of field trials to test proposed diagnostic criteria "in real-world clinical settings." New diagnostic categories were proposed, other categories were eliminated or subsumed under other new or old categories, and categories were proposed for future consideration.

The DSM-5 was published in May 2013 (see American Psychiatric Association, 2013) but only after Kupfer and his colleagues withstood a barrage of criticism and commentary prior to its publication. This onslaught only intensified following the actual publication of the manual. Kupfer et al. (2013) described the *DSM-5* as "a living document" in order to convey that the *DSM-5* will be updated sooner than later when gaps or issues are identified.

In retrospect, the process of developing the *DSM-5* in today's society was quite intriguing. While our focus must remain on the diagnostic issues and the implications for understanding, assessing, and diagnosing disorders, we would be remiss if we failed to briefly comment on the role of the Internet and various media in the information age. Virtually anyone can have their own blog and this enabled experts and members of the general public to weigh in on proposed *DSM-5* changes in an unprecedented manner, and to do so sometimes after selective consideration and portrayal of the issues. Without a doubt, this served to heighten public awareness of issues involving mental illness and its diagnosis and classification. Substantial misinformation was also circulated.

Overview of Changes in *DSM-5*

Table 3.6 lists the various ways of tracking what is new in the *DSM-5*. The table illustrates that the changes in *DSM-5* take many forms, such as the introduction of new disorders and the rolling of various disorders into one overarching category (e.g., autism spectrum disorder). Changes in symptoms' descriptions have also occurred, usually in response to new empirical findings that help with the fine-tuning process. The manual itself has been reformulated in various chapters, with the order of chapters representing the life cycle: disorders for children are at the beginning and disorders primarily for older adults are toward the back of the manual. Also, where possible, dimensional ratings have been added to allow for ratings of the severity of a disorder. Also, as noted by Kupfer (2013), an important addition is a greater focus on heightening awareness

TABLE 3.6	Overview of Revisions in *DSM-5*: A Summary of Broad Additions

1. New disorders (e.g., binge eating disorder; hoarding disorder)

2. New criteria for existing disorders (e.g., PTSD criteria more clearly spell out what qualifies as a "traumatic experience")

3. New superordinate categories combining previous categories (e.g., autism spectrum disorder; substance abuse and substance dependence combined into substance use disorder)

4. New conceptualizations of current disorders (e.g., gender dysphoria viewed as a gender incongruence instead of cross-gender identification; obsessive-compulsive disorder no longer considered an anxiety disorder—now listed in stand-alone chapter; separation anxiety disorder now listed as an anxiety disorder and not grouped with disorders occurring among children to reflect separation anxiety disorder in adults)

5. New names for existing disorders (e.g., depersonalization disorder becomes depersonalization/derealization disorder; somatoform disorders become somatic symptom and related disorders)

6. New dimensional ratings within disorders (e.g., schizophrenia subtypes have been replaced with a dimensional rating of the severity of core symptoms known as the symptom severity scale [SS-*DSM-5*], a measure that seems useful in clinical practice and seems to facilitate clinical diagnoses [see Ritsner, Mar, Arbitman, & Grinshpoon, 2013])

7. New emphasis on suicidality (i.e., suicide risk associated with many disorders now discussed and highlighted)

8. New manual format reflecting the age span with chapters for childhood disorders at the beginning and chapters for disorders found more often among older adults appearing later in the manual

in diagnosing suicidal tendencies. Suicidal tendencies, while typically linked with depression, often co-occur with various disorders and it is important to emphasize it since the potential for harm is a key element of case formulations.

Controversial Changes in *DSM-5*

The biggest controversies stemming from the creation of the *DSM-5* are listed in Table 3.7. As seen in the table, one controversial development is the creation of the autism spectrum disorder category, which combines various disorders and does away with disorders such as **Asperger's syndrome**, which is a milder form of autism. A key reason for the change is that in clinical settings, the specific diagnosis assigned (autism vs. Asperger's) was more related to the setting than to the actual child being assessed. People diagnosed with Asperger's disorder could not be differentiated from those with high functioning autism (Lord & Bishop, 2015). Although this change was research-based, in particular informed by clinical psychology research, the public remains concerned about the change if it means that children who would otherwise be diagnosed with Asperger's syndrome are no longer deemed to meet the criteria outlined in autism spectrum disorder. The new criteria are outlined in Chapter 15.

The second contentious issue is the inclusion of a new disorder for children called **disruptive mood dysregulation disorder (DMDD)**. The criteria for this new disorder involve displays three or more times a week of severe temper tantrums that are out of proportion with the situation and not in keeping with the child's developmental level. It is grouped among the depressive disorders. This disorder has been mocked as "the temper tantrum disorder" but was motivated by desires to limit the number of children and adolescents with mood swings who were seen as having hypomanic symptoms found typically in bipolar disorder (see American Psychiatric Association, 2013). Opponents of this disorder argue that normal behaviour is being treated as a disorder, and this artificially inflates the number of children with disorders and also places a potentially pejorative label on them. Proponents of this disorder point to empirical evidence that distinguishes DMDD from bipolar disorder and mania (Towbin, Axelson, Leibenluft, & Birmaher, 2013), but overall empirical support for this disorder has been deemed to be quite weak (see Widiger, Crego, & Oltmanns, 2015).

Other evidence comes from research involving epidemiology. **Epidemiology** is the study of the frequency and distribution of a disorder in a population. In epidemiological research, data are gathered about the rates of a disorder and its possible correlates in a large sample or population. One focus of epidemiology is to determine the proportion of a population that has a disorder at a given time. This determination is known as **prevalence**. For example, "12-month prevalence" is the proportion of a sample that had experienced a disorder in the year preceding an interview. **Lifetime prevalence** is the proportion of the sample that had ever experienced the disorder up to the time of the interview. Regarding DMDD, there are new epidemiological data showing that DMDD is distinguishable and has a prevalence of only about 1% when the frequency and duration criteria are used to distinguish children who chronically have mood dysregulation from those who have occasional outbursts of temperamental behaviour (Copeland, Angold, Costello, & Egger, 2013). However, there appears to be a problem with comorbidity. **Comorbidity**, or co-occurrence of different disorders, has been called "the premier challenge facing mental health professionals" (Kendall & Clarkin, 1992, p. 833). It can be a major problem because it makes treatment planning more difficult, affects treatment compliance, and complicates the coordination of the delivery of services (Nathan & Langenbucher, 1999). A major criticism of the evidence-based treatment literature is that it usually excludes cases with co-occurring conditions despite the fact that high rates of comorbidity are common in clinical samples (e.g., Westen, Novotny, & Thompson-Brenner, 2004). In this particular instance, DMDD had high levels of comorbidity with both depressive disorders and oppositional defiant disorder, and more than one-third of the children and adolescents diagnosed with DMDD also had co-occurring emotional and behavioural disorders (Copeland et al., 2013). This raises a concern about how distinct DMDD is in reality from these other disorders. It will be intriguing to see whether subsequent research supports this distinct diagnostic category.

The third contentious issue with *DSM-5* is the removal of the bereavement exclusion from the diagnostic criteria for major depressive disorder. Is it depression when someone is suffering from grief? Previously, depression was not diagnosed if the person was bereaved for up to two months as a result of major loss. This posed a practical problem in the sense that someone diagnosed as depressed prior to a loss would technically no longer qualify as depressed following the death. However, many people do experience major depression following the loss of a loved one. This exclusion has been removed with the caveat that clinicians remain aware of situations in which the depression is really still a by-product of bereavement. This decision has been highly criticized; for instance, in an editorial in the journal *The Lancet,* concerns were expressed that grief will be pathologized and a time limit should not be placed on the grief associated with the loss of a loved one (The Lancet, 2013).

The fourth issue is the last-minute decision of the *DSM-5* group examining personality disorders to revert to a categorical approach when it appeared that a dimensional approach was about to be implemented. Indeed, the new dimensional

TABLE 3.7	Controversial *DSM-5* Changes and Decisions
1.	Autism spectrum disorder is a new overarching category.
2.	Disruptive mood dysregulation disorder was created.
3.	Bereavement was excluded from the diagnostic criteria for major depressive disorder.
4.	Personality disorders are considered categories, not dimensions.
5.	Some disorders (e.g., non-suicidal self-injury) were omitted.

approach was announced in the draft version and then quickly amended. The existing categorical approach was retained but included key dimensions that can also be rated to supplement the categorical approach. This issue is revisited in Chapter 13 when we consider personality disorders.

The end result is that the old approach to personality disorders has been retained but the *DSM-5* also contains a description of the alternative model and listed it as needing further study. According to this proposal, there is a new category called "personality disorder—trait specified." With this diagnostic category, level of personality impairment is assessed in four categories that emphasize how the self and interpersonal issues are involved in personality dysfunction. The four categories are identity, self-direction, empathy, and intimacy. Five personality trait domains are evaluated: (1) negative affectivity vs. emotional stability; (2) detachment vs. extroversion; (3) antagonism vs. agreeableness; (4) disinhibition vs. conscientiousness; and (5) psychoticism vs. lucidity. These five trait domains closely resemble the domains in the five-factor personality model, with the trait dimension of openness being replaced with the dimension of psychoticism.

Many argue that the dimensional approach is more appropriate. Samuel's (2015) review noted low inter-rater reliabilities for the personality disorder categories, as well as limited agreement between personality disorder diagnoses and other methods, including questionnaires and semi-structured interviews. Initial work on the dimensional model shows promise for improved reliability but it is too early for any firm conclusions. Other methods aimed at increasing the reliability and validity of personality disorder diagnoses include the combination of self and informant reports (Miller & Lynam, 2015).

The fifth controversial issue is the failure to include non-suicidal self-injury as a new disorder and instead relegate it to a condition for further study. It appeared initially that non-suicidal self-injury disorder would form the basis of a new disorder but its status was changed to a disorder for further study. These issues are discussed in Student Perspectives 3.2.

In addition to these specific concerns with *DSM-5,* particularly harsh were the damning criticisms from *DSM-IV* Chair Allen Frances, who during his time as chair had set the bar for revisions at a very high level and made conservative changes only after the accumulation of a great deal of evidence. It is exceptionally rare for the previous leader of a process to be so opposed to the next iteration of the process. Frances has written extensively on his blog and has been interviewed by several leading media outlets around the world. His campaign against certain changes introduced in the *DSM-5,* while well-intentioned, also served as an effective platform for the publication of his own book titled *Saving Normal: An Insider's Revolt Against Out-of-Control Psychiatric Diagnosis, DSM-5, Big Pharma, and the Medicalization of Ordinary Life* (Frances, 2013). Some of his main challenges are outlined below. His book was published the same month that *DSM-5* was released.

Frances (2013) has argued for a return to the cautious approach used in *DSM-IV,* and he contends that proposed changes will result in many conditions being classified as

Allen Frances chaired the process of creating the *DSM-IV* and has argued that the changes in *DSM-5* will medicalize and pathologize normal behaviours.

abnormal when they merely reflect normal or typical behaviour. He sees this as being a disservice to the people being diagnosed but a great service to one of the constituencies in Table 3.4: the pharmaceutical industry, which stands to make money by developing new drugs for newly identified disorders.

Frances (2013) also alleged in his book that the increased prevalence of three disorders (autism, attention-deficit/hyperactive disorder, and childhood bipolar depression) is more illusory than real and there are profound problems with "diagnostic inflation," which he attributes largely to how the medical insurance system works in the United States. In short, "to get paid, the doctor must make an approved diagnosis. . . . A premature rush to a reimbursable psychiatric diagnosis often results in unnecessary, potentially harmful, and often costly treatment for problems that would have disappeared on their own" (p. 85).

Frances (2013) argued that the dramatic increase in prevalence in disorders such as autism is due to changes in diagnostic habits and not because more children are developing autism. Is Frances correct? Rates of autism are being closely monitored in Canada and while some of the increase could reflect diagnostic changes, the researcher leading this analysis, Hélène Ouellette-Kuntz from Queen's University, has stated that perhaps two-thirds of the increase may reflect either increased awareness or diagnostic changes, but one-third of the increase in cases remains to be explained and it is not simply due to increased diagnoses. She oversees the National Epidemiologic Database for the Study of Autism in Canada (NEDSAC). Ouellette-Kuntz and colleagues (2014) reported that the prevalence of autism spectrum disorders has increased dramatically in Canada across all regions studied and across all three age groups (2–4 years old, 5–9 years old, and 10–14 years old). After reviewing diagnostic and other possible causes of the increase in cases, they state "we cannot rule out the possibility of a true increase in incidence" (p. 134). However, they also speculate that the *DSM-5* criteria may result in a decrease in diagnosis.

Extensive news coverage followed the publication of *DSM-5* not only because of its historic appearance, but also because of the controversies that arose when, just as the *DSM-5* was

Student Perspectives 3.2

"Non-Suicidal Self-Injury" in Young People: Should it be in the *DSM-5*?

The *DSM-5* should be praised for its greater focus on suicidality throughout the diagnostic manual (though there are some concerns that are described below). In a commentary in August 2012, Kupfer (2013) discussed how the manual shines the spotlight on suicidal tendencies. He described how suicidal behaviour disorder and non-suicidal self-injury have been described as conditions for further study and acknowledged that non-suicidal self-injury "is regarded as a major problem on college campuses and a public health issue that needs to be better understood" (Kupfer, 2013). The *DSM-5* considers non-suicidal self-injury (NSSI) to potentially be a disorder when on five days or more in a year an individual has intentionally inflicted damage on herself or himself and it is not a socially sanctioned act.

When a condition is identified as a public health issue, should it not be recognized as a disorder in the regular sense? Generic reasons typically given for not including this disorder is that more evidence is needed and it overlaps too much with borderline personality disorder, yet it is now acknowledged widely that there is a discernible subset of people with extensive non-suicidal self-injury who do not have borderline personality disorder (for a discussion, see Plener & Fegert, 2012). Regarding the lack of evidence, this too is debatable; indeed, Muehlenkamp, Claes, Havertape, and Plener (2012) noted that on the topic of the prevalence of NSSI in adolescents, they located 52 studies between 2005 and 2011 that met inclusion criteria. Parenthetically, they reported that the lifetime prevalence of NSSI was 18.0%.

Kupfer (2013) was correct in noting NSSI among college and university students, and it is also a problem among adolescents. It is for this reason that the topic of non-suicidal self-injury was the focus of a special issue in 2012 of the journal *Child and Adolescent Psychiatry and Mental Health* (see Plener & Fegert, 2012).

What does the recent research literature indicate about NSSI among university and college students? A multi-campus Internet study based on a probability sample of 5,689 undergraduate and graduate students found that the past-year prevalence of NSSI was 14.3%. NSSI was more common among undergraduates than graduate students and among those students with higher levels of depression, cigarette smoking, gambling, and frequent binge drinking (Serras, Saules, Cranford, & Eisenberg, 2010). University of British Columbia researcher David Klonsky found that across four samples, including a sample of university students, NSSI had a robust link with attempted suicide that was much stronger than the link between borderline personality disorder

and attempted suicide and that was only rivalled by the strong link between suicide ideation and attempted suicide (Klonsky, May, & Glenn, 2013).

Research conducted at Brock University in Ontario found that 439 out of 1,090 first-year undergraduate students indicated that they had engaged in at least one act of NSSI. Supplementary analyses indicated that students with NSSI can be differentiated by whether there is or is not high risk for suicidal behaviour. About 1 in 5 with a history of NSSI were in the high frequency of NSSI but low suicidal risk. Overall, about 1 in 8 with a history of NSSI were in the high suicidal risk group. Those with heightened risk had higher levels of suicidal ideation and a more extensive history of suicide attempts. They also had a higher degree of psychosocial impairment (see Hamza & Willoughby, 2013). Longitudinal research over one year with 666 participants at Brock University found that "persistent injurers" who continued to engage in NSSI were differentiated by greater levels of psychosocial impairment. Moreover, those who continued, resumed, or started engaging in NSSI while at university also had concomitant increases in problem behaviours, problems with parents (i.e., greater parental psychological control and parental criticism), internalizing symptoms, and suicide ideation (Hamza & Willoughby, 2014). Overall, 27 students began engaging in NSSI while at university, while 42 were "relapsers" and 68 were deemed "persistent." There were also 195 students in the "recovered" category, meaning that they had seemingly eliminated their self-injury tendencies.

Do you think that NSSI should have been included in *DSM-5*? Further information about this possible disorder and the reasons why NSSI often takes place is provided in Chapter 10 on eating disorders.

One other concern about the *DSM-5* approach to suicide should be noted in closing. In some respects, was the increased focus on suicidality in the *DSM-5* too zealous? This question refers to the decision to include a new condition, "suicidal behaviour disorder," as one for further study. This proposed disorder would apply to anyone who has attempted suicide within the past 24 months and it is not a case of non-suicidal intentional self-injury. While the goal here is to promote more research on the causes, correlates, and consequences of suicidal behaviour, should having engaged in a suicidal act result in being diagnosed with a disorder? Is this legitimate or did the *DSM-5* creators go too far in a manner that fits with the criticism that they have overpathologized people? Should a behavioural act and a disorder be equated? Perhaps your view on this depends on whether you know someone who has attempted suicide. If so, do you think the proposed creation of this disorder would ultimately help them or make life more difficult for them?

---

being released, the Director of the National Institute of Mental Health (NIMH), Thomas Insel, used his blog to criticize the *DSM* and its categories as "the gold standard" and suggested that the NIMH may no longer support research based on assigning people to *DSM-5* categories! Instead, consistent with the development of the NIMH's Research Domain Criteria (RDoC) project, he emphasized that the goal is to create new criteria that reflect new developments in genetics and neuroscience.

The problem with this stance, however, is that much more information is needed across the spectrum of disorders before the criteria envisioned by Insel are available. Insel later softened his position and released a joint press release on May 13, 2013, with the president-elect of the American Psychiatric Association, Jeffrey Lieberman. Here it was affirmed that the *DSM-5* and the international system, the *ICD-10,* remain the best choices at present.

Edward Shorter, esteemed scholar from the University of Toronto, also renewed his criticisms of the *DSM* following the release of the *DSM-5*. The chief problems with *DSM-5,* in his estimation, are a lack of clarity because "these operational criteria . . . don't give you a clear overview of what the thing is" (Brean, 2013, p. A3) and an overarching concern about the validity of proposed disorders. Specifically, Shorter stated that, "What psychiatry has problems with now is with verification of the diseases it has proposed. Do these really exist in nature or not? And this has been a very vexatious stumbling block indeed" (Brean, 2013, A3).

It is perhaps for all of these reasons that the *DSM* is apparently not used by some clinicians. First and his colleagues (2014) issued a call for a study of how and to what extent the *DSM* is actually used and they then conducted a survey of 894 clinicians, counsellors, and nurse practitioners who volunteered to complete an online survey. First, Koh, and Adler (2015) yielded evidence indicating that a substantial minority (about 3 in 10 respondents) did not see the *DSM* as useful and were not using it. Reasons for using it by those who did use it included communicating diagnostic information to other professionals and needing to refer to it for administrative purposes, including billing.

We encourage you to keep all of these issues in mind as you consider the information presented on the various disorders in the chapters to come.

Summary

3.1 Clinicians rely on several modes of assessment in trying to find out how best to describe a client, search for the reasons a person is troubled, and design effective preventive or remedial treatments. Regardless of how unstructured an assessment method may appear, it inevitably reflects the paradigm of the investigator. However clinicians and researchers go about gathering assessment information, they must be concerned with both reliability—whether measurement is consistent and replicable—and validity—whether our assessments are tapping into what we want to be measuring. The many assessment procedures described in this chapter vary greatly in their reliability and validity.

3.2 The two main approaches to assessment are psychological and biological. Psychological assessments include clinical interviews, structured or relatively unstructured conversations in which the clinician probes the client for information about his or her problems; psychological tests, which range from the presentation of ambiguous stimuli, as in the Rorschach Ink Blot Test, to empirically derived self-report questionnaires, such as the Minnesota Multiphasic Personality Inventory; and intelligence tests, which evaluate a person's intellectual ability and predict how well he or she will do in future academic situations. Whereas traditional assessment seeks to understand people in terms of general traits or personality structure, specificity is the hallmark of cognitive and behavioural assessment, the assumption being that assessing psychological variables such as anxiety or distorted cognitions as they occur in specific situations will yield more useful information about people.

3.3 Biological assessments include sophisticated, computer-controlled imaging techniques, such as CT scans, that allow us to actually see various structures of the living brain; neuropsychological tests, such as the Halstead-Reitan, that base inferences of brain defects on variations in responses to psychological tests; and psychophysiological measurements, such as heart rate and skin conductance.

3.4 Diagnosis is a critical aspect of the field of abnormal psychology. Having an agreed-upon system of classification makes it possible for clinicians to communicate effectively with one another and facilitates the search for causes and treatments for the various disorders.

3.5 Early attempts at a classification system were not widely adopted, perpetuating great inconsistency in the classification of abnormal behaviour. The recent editions of the *Diagnostic and Statistical Manual of Mental Disorders,* published by the American Psychiatric Association, reflect the continuing efforts by mental health professionals to classify the various psychopathologies.

3.6 Several issues must be considered in evaluating the classification of abnormality. An important one is whether the categorical approach of the *DSM,* as opposed to a dimensional classification system, is best for the field. Because recent versions of the *DSM* are far more concrete and descriptive than was *DSM-II*, diagnoses based on these versions are more reliable; that is, independent diagnosticians are now more likely to agree on the diagnosis they make of a particular case. Construct validity—how well the diagnosis relates to other aspects of the disorder, such as prognosis and response to treatment—remains more of an open question. In chapters dealing with specific disorders, we will see that validity varies with the diagnostic category being considered.

3.7 *The DSM-5* was published in May 2013 and there were many significant changes, including the elimination of the multiaxial organization of the previous version of the manual. The *DSM-5* was designed with the goals of increasing the validity of category descriptions, adding more focus on dimensional ratings, and decreasing the number of diagnoses in the "not otherwise specified" category. It has been plagued by several controversies, including the creation of an overall category for autism spectrum disorders, the addition of the diagnosis of disruptive mood dysregulation disorder, and the deletion of the bereavement exclusion in the diagnosis of depression.

Key Terms

alternate-form reliability
Asperger's syndrome
case validity

categorical classification
clinical interview
cognitive-behavioural case formulation

comorbidity
construct validity
content validity

criterion validity
CT scan
cultural bias
Cultural Formulation Interview (CFI)
Diagnostic and Statistical Manual of Mental Disorders (DSM)
dimensional classification
disruptive mood dysregulation disorder (DMDD)
DSM-5
DSM-5 V codes
DSM-IV
DSM-IV-TR
electrocardiogram
electrodermal responding
electroencephalogram (EEG)
epidemiology
evidence-based assessment

faking bad
functional magnetic resonance imaging (fMRI)
intelligence test
inter-rater reliability
internal consistency reliability
kappa
lifetime prevalence
magnetic resonance imaging (MRI)
mental disorder
Minnesota Multiphasic Personality Inventory (MMPI)
multiaxial classification
neurologist
neuropsychological tests
neuropsychologist
Outline for Cultural Formulation
personality inventory

PET scan
prevalence
projective hypothesis
projective test
psychological tests
psychophysiology
race norms
reliability
Rorschach Ink Blot Test
sensitivity
specificity
standardization
stereotype threat
structured interview
test norms
test–retest reliability
Thematic Apperception Test (TAT)

Reflections: Past, Present, and Future

1. In Chapter 2, we examined contemporary paradigms of abnormal psychology, summarized the consequences of adopting a particular paradigm, and introduced integrative paradigms. Assume that you are a practising clinical psychologist. Do you think your choice of assessment devices will be guided mostly by your orientation or by your initial sense of the specific psychological disorders presented by your clients?

2. What is your own position on issues of classification and diagnosis of psychological disorders? Is the *DSM-5* really a major improvement over past versions? Do you think it will lead to more effective and efficient treatment? How would you refine and improve upon it? Do you agree with critics such as Allen Frances?

3. In reaction to critics of the participation process in the development of the *DSM,* Sadler (2004) proposed previously that final decisions be based on a democratic voting process. Would you agree? Could a scientifically valid decision be "politically incorrect" and thereby voted against?

4. *DSM-5* and its predecessor *DSM-IV-TR* seem more culturally sensitive than previous versions. However, do you think that any system can ever have the sensitivity required to capture the issues and concerns of a diverse population? *DSM-5* is currently being translated into 18 languages. Why do you think that a diagnostic system published by the American Psychiatric Association draws such widespread attention in the world?

CHAPTER 4

Research Methods in the Study of Abnormal Behaviour

LEARNING OBJECTIVES

1. Define science, and describe scientific methods, including testability, replicability, and the role of theory.

2. Describe research methods using small samples (case studies, qualitative research), as well as population-based epidemiological research methods.

3. Explain correlational research methods and the limitations of this approach.

4. Compare and contrast experimental research methods, including experiments with groups of participants, single-subject experiments, and mixed designs.

Given the different ways of conceptualizing and treating abnormal behaviour and the problems in its classification and assessment, it follows that there is also less than total agreement about how abnormal behaviour ought to be studied and what the facts of the field are. Yet it is precisely because facts about mental disorders are hard to come by that it is important to pursue them using the scientific research methods that are applied in contemporary psychopathology. This chapter discusses these methods and provides a sense of the strengths and limitations of each.

4.1 Science and Scientific Methods

Science is the pursuit of systematized knowledge through observation. Thus, the term, which comes from the Latin *scire*, "to know," refers both to a method (the systematic acquisition and evaluation of information) and to a goal (the development of general theories that explain the information). It is always important for scientific observations and explanations to be testable (open to systematic probes) and reliable (replicable).

Testability and Replicability

A scientific approach requires first that propositions and ideas be stated in a clear and precise way. Only then can scientific claims be exposed to systematic probes and tests, any one of which could negate the scientist's expectations about what will be found. Statements, theories, and assertions, regardless of how plausible they may seem, must be testable in the public arena and subject to disproof. It is not enough to assert, for example, that traumatic experiences during childhood may cause psychological maladjustment in adulthood. Such a hypothesis must be amenable to systematic testing that could show it to be false. Closely related to testability is the requirement that each observation that contributes to a scientific body of knowledge be replicable or reliable. Whatever is observed must be replicable; that is, it must occur under prescribed circumstances not once, but repeatedly. If the event cannot be reproduced, scientists become wary of the legitimacy of the original observation.

The Role of Theory

"In sum, a theory is corroborated to the extent that we have subjected it to risky tests; the more dangerous the tests it has survived, the better corroborated it is."

—Kenneth N. Levy, 2008, p. 558

A **theory** is a set of propositions meant to explain a class of phenomena. A primary goal of science is to advance theories to account for data, often by proposing cause–effect relationships. The results of empirical research allow the adequacy of theories to be evaluated. Theories themselves can also play an important role in guiding research by suggesting that certain additional data be collected. More specifically, a theory permits the generation of **hypotheses**—expectations about what should occur if a theory is true—to be tested in research. For example, suppose you want to test a classical-conditioning theory of phobias. As a researcher, you begin by developing a specific hypothesis based on the theory. For example, if the classical-conditioning theory is valid, people with phobias should be more likely than those in the general population to have had traumatic experiences with the situations they fear, such as flying. By collecting data on the frequency of traumatic experiences with phobic stimuli among people with phobias, and comparing this information with corresponding data from people without phobias, you could determine whether your hypothesis was confirmed, thus supporting the theory, or was discontinued, thus invalidating the theory.

The generation of a theory is perhaps the most challenging part of the scientific enterprise. It is sometimes asserted that a scientist formulates a theory simply by considering data that have been previously collected and then deciding, in a rather straightforward fashion, that a given way of thinking about the data is the most economical and useful. Although some theory-building follows this course, not all does. Aspects too seldom mentioned are the *creativity* of the act and the *excitement* of finding a novel way to conceptualize things. A theory sometimes seems to leap from the scientist's head in a wonderful moment of insight. New ideas suddenly occur, and connections previously overlooked are suddenly grasped. What formerly seemed obscure or meaningless makes a new kind of sense within the framework of the new theory.

Theories are *constructions* put together by scientists. In formulating a theory, scientists must often make use of theoretical concepts: unobservable states or processes that are inferred from observable data. Repression is a theoretical concept. Theoretical concepts are inferred from observable data. For example, an analyst might infer the presence of a repressed conflict from a client's continual avoidance of discussing his or her relationship with authority figures.

Several advantages can be gained by using theoretical terms. For example, in abnormal psychology, we may want to bridge temporal gaps with theoretical concepts. If a child has had a particularly frightening experience and his or her behaviour changes for a lengthy period of time, we need to explain how the earlier event exerted an influence over subsequent behaviour (see photo). The unobservable and inferred concept of *acquired fear* has been very helpful in this regard. Theoretical concepts can also summarize already observed relationships. We may observe that whether people are taking an examination, are expecting a momentary electric shock, or are arguing with a companion, they all have sweaty palms, trembling hands, and a fast heartbeat. If we ask them how they feel, they

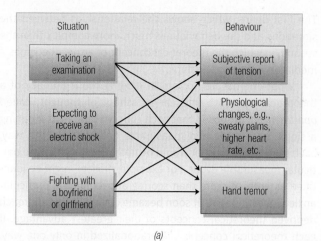

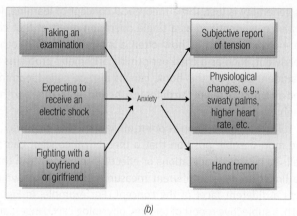

FIGURE 4.1 An illustration of the advantages of using anxiety as a theoretical concept. The arrows in (b) are fewer and more readily understood.

all report that they are tense. The relationships can be depicted as shown in Figure 4.1a. We could also say that all the situations have made these individuals anxious and that anxiety has in turn caused the reported tension, the sweaty palms, the faster heartbeat, and the trembling hands. Figure 4.1b shows anxiety as a theoretical concept explaining what has been observed.

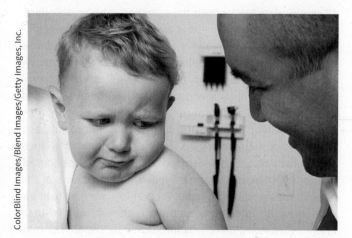

A theoretical concept, such as acquired fear, is useful in accounting for the fact that some earlier experience can have an effect on current behaviour.

The first figure, which shows the relationships between the situations and the behaviour, is much more complex than the second, in which the theoretical concept of anxiety becomes a mediator of the relationships.

What criteria are applied in judging the legitimacy of a theoretical concept? One earlier school of thought, called *operationism,* proposed that each concept take as its meaning a single observable and measurable operation. In this way, each theoretical concept would be *nothing more* than one particular measurable event. For example, anxiety might be identified as nothing more than scoring above 50 on a particular anxiety questionnaire. It soon became clear that this approach deprived theoretical concepts of their greatest advantage. If each theoretical concept is operationalized in only one way, its generality is lost. If the theoretical concept of learning, for instance, is identified as a single operation or effect that can be measured, such as how often a rat presses a bar, other behaviour, such as a child performing arithmetic problems or a student studying this book, cannot also be called learning, and attempts to relate the different phenomena to one another might be discouraged.

The early operationist point of view quickly gave way to the more flexible position that a theoretical concept can be defined by sets of operations or effects. The concept can thus be linked to several different measurements, each of which taps a different facet of the concept. For example, in Figure 4.1b, a subjective report of tension, physiological changes, and hand trembling form a set of operations defining anxiety. Theoretical concepts are better defined by sets of operations than by a single operation.

4.2 Case Study, Qualitative, and Epidemiological Research Methods

All empirical research entails the collection of observable data. Sometimes research remains at a purely descriptive level, but often researchers observe several events and try to determine how they are associated or related. In the field of abnormal psychology, there is a large body of descriptive literature concerning the typical symptoms of people who have been diagnosed as having particular disorders. These symptoms can then be related to other characteristics, such as gender or social class. For example, eating disorders are more common in women than in men. But science demands more than descriptions of relationships. We often want to understand the causes of the relationships we have observed. For example, we want to know why eating disorders are found more often in women than in men. (Discussed more fully in Chapter 10, the answer may lie in social pressures for women to be thin.) In this chapter, we describe the most commonly used research methods in the study of abnormal behaviour. The methods vary in the extent

to which they allow researchers to infer causal relationships. In this section we describe the research methods that employ few research participants (case study, qualitative research) as well as epidemiological research, which is at the other extreme, studying disorders at the population level.

The Case Study

The most familiar and time-honoured method of observing others is to study them one at a time and record detailed information about them. Clinicians prepare a **case study** by collecting historical and biographical information on a single individual, often including experiences during therapy sessions. A comprehensive case study would cover family history and background, medical history, educational background, jobs held, marital history, and details concerning development, adjustment, personality, life course, and current situation. Important to bear in mind, though, is the role of the clinician's paradigm in determining the kinds of information actually collected and reported in a case study. To take but one example, case studies of psychoanalytically oriented clinicians contain more information about the client's early childhood and conflicts with parents than do reports made by behaviourally oriented practitioners.

Case studies from practising clinicians may lack the degree of control and objectivity of research using other methods, but these descriptive accounts have played an important role in the study of abnormal behaviour.

Providing Detailed Description Because it deals with a single individual, the case study can include much more detail than is typically included with other research methods. In a famous case history of multiple personality reported in 1954, psychiatrists Thigpen and Cleckley described a client, known as Eve White, who assumed at various times three very distinct personalities. Their description of the case required an entire book, *The Three Faces of Eve.* The following brief case example

Chris Costner Sizemore was the subject of the famous "Three Faces of Eve" case. She subsequently claimed to have had 21 separate personalities but indicated that they emerge three at a time.

Gerald Martineau/The Washington Post/Getty Images

Brief Case Example

The Three Faces of Eve

Eve White had been seen in psychotherapy for several months because she was experiencing severe headaches accompanied by blackouts. Her therapist (Dr. Thigpen) described her as a retiring and gently conventional figure. One day during the course of an interview, however, she changed abruptly and in a surprising way.

> *As if seized by sudden pain, she put both hands to her head. After a tense moment of silence, both hands dropped. There was a quick, reckless smile, and, in a bright voice that sparkled, she said, "Hi there, Doc!" The demure and constrained posture of Eve White had melted into buoyant repose. . . . This new and apparently carefree girl spoke casually of Eve White and her problems, always using she or her in every reference, always respecting the strict bounds of a separate identity . . . When asked her name, she immediately replied, "Oh, I'm Eve Black."*
>
> (Thigpen & Cleckley, 1954, p. 137)

After this rather startling revelation, Eve was observed over a period of 14 months in a series of interviews that ran to almost 100 hours. A very important part of Eve White's therapy was to help her learn about Eve Black, her other, infectiously exuberant self, who added seductive and expensive clothing to her wardrobe and lived unremembered episodes of her life. During this period, a third personality, Jane, emerged while Eve White was recollecting an early incident in which she had been painfully scalded by water from a wash pot.

Jane, who from then on knew all that happened to the two Eves, although they did not share knowledge of her existence, was "far more mature, more vivid, more boldly capable, and more interesting than Eve White" (Thigpen & Cleckley, 1954, p. 137).

Jane developed a deep and revering affection for the first Eve, who was considered somewhat a ninny by Eve Black. Jane knew nothing of Eve White's earlier life except what she learned through Eve's memories.

Some 11 months later, in a calamitous session with all three personalities present at different times, Eve Black emerged and reminisced for a moment about the many good times she had had in the past but then remarked that she did not seem to have real fun anymore. She began to sob, the only time Dr. Thigpen had seen her in tears. She told him that she wanted him to have her red dress to remember her by. All expression left her face and her eyes closed. Eve White opened them. When Jane was summoned a few minutes later, she soon realized that there was no longer any Eve Black or White and she began to experience a terrifying lost event. "No, no! . . . Oh no, Mother . . . I can't . . . Don't make me do it," she cried. Jane, who earlier had known nothing of Eve's childhood, was five years old and at her grandmother's funeral. Her mother was holding her high off the floor and above the coffin and saying that she must touch her grandmother's face. As she felt her hand leave the clammy cheek, the young woman screamed so piercingly that Dr. Cleckley, Dr. Thigpen's associate, came running from his office across the hall.

The two physicians were not certain who confronted them. In the searing intensity of the remembered moment, a new personality had been welded. Their transformed client did not at first feel herself as apart and as sharply distinct a person as had the two Eves and Jane, although she knew a great deal about all of them. When her initial bewilderment lessened, she tended to identify herself with Jane. But the identification was not sure or complete, and she mourned the absence of the two Eves as though they were lost sisters. This new person decided to call herself Mrs. Evelyn White.

---

emphasizes the moments in which new personalities emerged and what the separate selves knew of one another.

The case of Eve White, Eve Black, Jane, and eventually Evelyn constitutes a valuable classic in the literature because it is one of only a few detailed accounts of a rare phenomenon, multiple personality, now known as *dissociative identity disorder,* a controversial disorder discussed in Chapter 7. In addition to illustrating the disorder itself, the original report of Thigpen and Cleckley provides valuable details about the interview procedures they followed and how the treatment progressed in this specific case.

However, the validity of the information gathered in a case study is sometimes questionable. Indeed, the real Eve, a woman named Chris Sizemore (see photo), wrote a book that challenged Thigpen and Cleckley's account of her case (Sizemore & Pittillo, 1977). She claimed that, following her period of therapy with them, her personality continued to fragment. In all, 21 separate and distinct strangers inhabited her body at one time or another. And, contrary to Thigpen and Cleckley's report, Sizemore maintains that nine of the personalities existed before Eve Black

ever appeared. One set of personalities—they usually came in threes—would weaken and fade, to be replaced by others. Eventually, her personality changes were so constant and numerous that she might become her three persons in rapid switches resembling the flipping of television channels. The debilitating roundrobin of transformations and the fierce battle for dominance among her selves filled her entire day. After resolving what she hoped was her last trio, by realizing finally that her alternate personalities were true aspects of herself rather than strangers from without, Chris Sizemore decided to reveal her story as a means of coping with past ordeals. In a BBC interview (the "Hard Talk" program's March 25, 2009, episode), Sizemore stated that she is now a well person who has not experienced any symptoms over the last 30 years. She perceives her previous multiple personalities as a coping mechanism used to deal with having experienced multiple traumas (primarily witnessing deaths of adults) during her early childhood. Sizemore also recounted in the BBC interview that her two children have different mothers because one was raised by Eve White and the other child was raised by another one of her personalities.

The Case Study as Evidence   Case histories are especially useful when they negate an assumed universal relationship or law. Consider, for example, the proposition that episodes of depression are always preceded by an increase in life stress. Finding even a single case in which this is not true would negate the theory or at least force it to be changed to assert that only some episodes of depression are triggered by stress.

The case study fares less well as evidence in support of a particular theory or proposition. Case studies do not provide the means for ruling out alternative hypotheses. To illustrate this problem, let us consider a clinician who has developed a new treatment for depression, tries it out on a client, and observes that the depression lifts after 10 weeks of therapy. Although it would be tempting to conclude that the therapy worked, such a conclusion cannot legitimately be drawn because any of several other factors could also have produced the change. A stressful situation in the client's life may have resolved itself, or perhaps episodes of depression are naturally time-limited. Thus, several plausible rival hypotheses could account for the clinical improvement. The data yielded by the case study do not allow us to determine the true cause of the change.

Generating Hypotheses

The case study plays a unique and important role in generating hypotheses. Through exposure to the life histories of a great number of clients, clinicians gain experience in understanding and interpreting them. Eventually, they may notice similarities of circumstances and outcomes and formulate important hypotheses that could not have been uncovered in a more controlled investigation. For example, in his clinical work with disturbed children, Kanner (1943) noticed that some children showed a similar constellation of symptoms, including failure to develop language and extreme isolation from other people. He proposed a new diagnosis—infantile autism—which was subsequently confirmed by larger-scale research (see Chapter 15).

Stiles (2010) has advocated for **theory-building case studies** and the notion that an adequate theory must be able to account for commonalities across case studies as well as the distinct and unique elements of a particular case. He suggested that there should be a close match between theoretical and case descriptions.

Some case studies are so unique that it seems impossible to generalize to other individuals, including other people with the same disorder. A fascinating Canadian example is a case study of preferential bestiality (zoophilia) reported by Earls and Lalumière (2002). A 54-year-old white male was serving a five-year prison sentence for cruelty to animals—a cruelty that had been exhibited in sexual activity with horses. He reported that his sexual attraction to animals developed while he grew up on a farm. The most distinguishing aspect of this case is reflected in the following excerpt:

> "He also reported that his involvement with horses was not limited to sexual acts, but also included a strong emotional component. In his most recent offense, he inserted his arm to its full length into the vagina of a mare and punctured its vaginal wall. The horse subsequently died. The subject reported that the mare had shown interest in a stallion, and he had killed the mare as a result of jealousy."

> (Earls & Lalumière, 2002, p. 86)

Case studies such as these are primarily informative in terms of the specific and unique manifestations of a disorder. However, when similar case studies begin to surface, it may result in the authors getting new insights into the nature of the phenomenon being considered and point to necessary changes in theoretical understanding. In this instance, Earls and Lalumière (2009) have reported another extreme case of zoophilia. The new case of a 47-year-old man named "Possum" is fascinating because it recounts his passion for horses. Equally important, though, is the authors' revised conclusion that zoophilia may not be as rare as first believed. In their earlier paper, the authors characterized zoophilia as being extremely rare, but they have since modified this view. This modified conclusion was based, in part, on the many responses they received from the public about other cases of zoophilia when the media reported their original case study (see Earls & Lalumière, 2009). This sequence of events illustrates the potential information value of case study accounts.

To sum up, the case study is an excellent way of examining the behaviour of a single individual in great detail and of generating hypotheses that can later be evaluated by controlled research. It is useful in clinical settings, where the focus is on just one person. Historically, it has been concluded that the case study is of limited scientific use because it may not reveal principles characteristic of people in general and is unable to provide satisfactory evidence concerning cause–effect relationships.

The Case Study for Psychotherapy Training

Despite their limited scientific use, there is growing interest in case studies in recent years, primarily for psychotherapy training. Over the past 15 years, there has been an increase in the number of case studies published, and there are even two journals devoted to publishing case studies (McLeod, 2015). Mackrill and Iwakabe (2013) present a strong case for the usefulness of case studies for training novice psychotherapists. McLeod and Elliott (2011) observed that there is increasing recognition that systematic case studies can play a vital role in adding to the evidence base for psychotherapy and counselling policy, practice, and training. They contend that case studies are now more useful as research evidence due to the advent of sophisticated methods of data collection and recording. The ability to record sessions removes one of the longstanding criticisms, because the conclusions of case studies can be evaluated objectively by people other than the therapist or counsellor who was initially involved. And valuable insights can be obtained about what works and does not work. We know, for instance, that case studies can help highlight what makes for good vs. poor therapy outcomes as illustrated by Watson, Goldman, and Greenberg's (2007) intriguing book on case studies of successes vs. failures in emotion-focused therapy.

Although a single case study may not suffice as evidence in support of a theory, there is a place for case studies for practitioners who are new to psychotherapy or new to a particular therapeutic orientation. The use of multiple research methods, with the case study approach as one method, has gained popularity (McLeod, 2015). For example, a large-scale randomized controlled trial may demonstrate that a new form of psychotherapy is effective for treating depression. This information guides the choice to use this new psychotherapy; however, a published case study detailing the delivery of that new psychotherapy is likely to be more useful to a practitioner who wants to learn the new intervention.

The Rise of Qualitative Research

As the field of psychology continues to grow, there is a proliferation of qualitative research, and this is also evident in clinical and counselling psychology. Qualitative research is similar to case study research in that the focus is on the unique and rich experiences of a small group of people who are studied in depth. Descriptive accounts with a subjective emphasis on the individual are the focus rather than quantitative research (i.e., numerical counts of large groups of people studied with an emphasis on general and broadly applicable associations and principles).

Qualitative research is subject to some of the same criticisms that apply to case study accounts, but well-done qualitative research can illuminate important phenomena that seem to reflect issues and themes that matter to people and are central to understanding them. Three examples of qualitative research conducted in Canada help illustrate this point. First, Lafrance and Stoppard (2006) used a feminist perspective to analyze the accounts provided by 15 women who had recovered from depression. One consistent theme that emerged was of personal transformation and developing a new identity to the point of no longer being who they were previously. Former selves emphasized three overlapping themes that were chronic sources of distress: (1) "the good woman," who is overly focused on being pleasing, obedient, and quiet; (2) "the control freak," who is striving for perfection; and (3) "the victim," who is non-assertive and too selfless.

Second, a qualitative study led by Christine Kurtz Landy from the School of Nursing at York University examines the life experiences of socio-economically disadvantaged post-partum women (see Landy, Sword, & Valaitis, 2009). Themes that emerged were: (1) the significant struggles associated with becoming a mother and feeling out of control during the intense period right after giving birth; and (2) the sense of burden superimposed on this life transition due to the context of living a life of poverty. Landy et al. (2009) illuminated a stark reality for many new mothers living in poverty; namely, that emotional social support was simply not available to them and there is a paucity of help at home. Also, two sources of stigma were identified: the stigma of being on welfare and the stigma felt by teenage mothers because people "judged them to be bad mothers, stupid, and sexually promiscuous" (p. 198).

Finally, an equally compelling study by Marcus et al. (2012) involved a grounded theory analysis of eight young adults who are Internet bloggers who provided ongoing accounts of their mental health issues online in 2008 and 2009. A grounded theory analysis is an extensive and systematic approach that involves beginning "from the ground up" without hypotheses. Hypotheses emerge eventually as categories come into focus. Two compelling themes emerged: (1) "I am powerless" and (2) "I am utterly alone." These feelings of being powerless and feeling entirely isolated will resonate with many people who have had their own adjustment difficulties. It may provide comfort for those of you who have felt this way to learn that other people have similar experiences and that sharing these feelings with others can help to establish some common bonds.

Epidemiological Research

As described in Chapter 3, epidemiology is the study of the frequency and distribution of a disorder in a population. In epidemiological research, data are gathered about the rates of a disorder and its possible correlates in a large sample or population. This information can then be used to give a general picture of a disorder, how many people it affects, whether it is more common in men than in women, and whether its occurrence also varies according to social and cultural factors.

Epidemiological research focuses on determining three features of a disorder:

1. **prevalence**—the proportion of a population that has the disorder at a given point or period of time (often lifetime)
2. **incidence**—the number of new cases of the disorder that occur in some period, usually a year
3. **risk factors**—conditions or variables that, if present, increase the likelihood of developing the disorder

Knowing the prevalence and incidence rates of various mental disorders and the risk factors associated with these disorders is important for planning health care facilities and services and for allocating provincial and federal grants for the study of disorders. Canadian Perspectives 4.1 presents additional information on how epidemiological research and other types of research often combine to clarify the role of risk factors in mental disorder.

Clearly, knowledge about risk factors can give clues to the causes of disorders. For example, the Ontario study revealed that depression is about twice as common in women as in men. Thus, gender is a risk factor for depression. In Chapter 8, we will see that knowledge of this risk factor has led to a theory of depression that suggests that it is due to a particular style of coping with stress that is more common in women than in men. Thus, the results of epidemiological research may provide hypotheses that can be more thoroughly investigated using other research methods. The study of risk factors in epidemiological research examines relationships among variables, and is actually an example of the correlational method, which we will look at next.

Canadian Perspectives 4.1

Early Risk Factors and Psychological Disorders in a Canadian Setting: The Role of Abuse

The 1990 Ontario *Mental Health Supplement* study (Lin et al., 1996; Ontario Ministry of Health, 1994) examined the relation between selected risk factors and mental disorders in people living in the community. Risk factors included the experience of severe physical or sexual abuse as a child, a history of parental mental disorder, and failure to graduate from high school. The study also assessed the relation between selected socio-demographic features (unemployment, public assistance, and low income) and mental disorders. People with a disorder ("disordered group") were compared with those without a disorder ("healthy group"). Figure 4.2 provides information on two groups with mental disorders: those with only one disorder and those with two or more disorders. Clearly, those with two or more disorders are especially disadvantaged, relative to both the healthy group and the single-disorder group, on all of the theorized risk and socio-demographic factors.

Parental mental disorder and **severe abuse** are the strongest risk factors from among all of the variables examined. For example, 61% of participants with two or more disorders and 41% of those with one disorder reported that their parents had a mental disorder, whereas only 21% of the healthy group reported evidence of mental disorder in a parent. These results are consistent with the findings from the U.S. National Comorbidity Study (Kessler, Davis, & Kendler, 1997). A long history of research findings supports an association between mental disorder in parents and psychological problems in their offspring. Evidence for the link between abuse and mental disorders is relatively more recent.

Parenthetically, recent Canadian data also highlight the role of parental influence on child physical abuse and illustrate the importance of considering the presence of multiple risk factors as a cluster variable. Analyses conducted by researchers at the

University of Toronto focused on data from Statistics Canada surveys, including CCHS 3.1 data gathered in 2005 from respondents in Manitoba and Saskatchewan (see Fuller-Thomson & Sawyer, 2012). The focus was on three risk factors: parental divorce, parental unemployment, and parental addiction. Physical abuse was reported by 3.0% of the participants who did not experience any of these factors. Each factor by itself was associated with increased physical abuse, with parental addiction being the greatest individual risk factor (18.0% to 19.5% reporting physical abuse). However, when all three factors were present, rates of physical abuse varied from 36.0% to 41.0%, which amounts to a 15-times increase in risk! How is this information useful in a practical sense? Fuller-Thomson and Sawyer (2012) noted that health care professionals should be particularly attuned to signs of physical abuse when they encounter families characterized by two or more of these factors. Also, prevention efforts can be directed at people most likely to become physically abused. This is valuable information but it is important to caution that the surveys were cross-sectional and we cannot conclude that the risk factors caused physical abuse.

Abuse has a clear role in contributing to comorbid disorders. The Ontario epidemiological study found that 38% of people with two or more disorders reported experiencing severe sexual or physical abuse as a child and that the comparable figures for the one-disorder and healthy groups were 21% and 10%, respectively. Sexual abuse ranged from repeated indecent exposure to being sexually attacked, while physical abuse included being pushed, grabbed, shoved, and physically attacked.

Harriet MacMillan of McMaster University and Tracie Afifi of the University of Manitoba have published some of the most recent data and reviews on the relationship between different forms of child abuse and mental disorders, as well as protective factors. Harriet MacMillan was appointed to the Order of Canada in 2016, one of Canada's highest honours.

MacMillan et al. (2001) conducted further analyses on the Ontario study and found that 13% of women and 4% of men in the general population had been sexually abused during childhood or adolescence. This history of abuse confers increased likelihood of lifetime psychopathology in various forms, an association that is stronger for women than men (MacMillan et al., 2001). A third wave of Ontario data was collected in 2000–2001; MacMillan et al. (2013) found higher rates of sexual abuse using these data (22% for women, 8% for men), possibly because the question was framed so as to allow for adolescent perpetrators, unlike the previous survey, which specified that the perpetrator was an adult. They also reported that the co-occurrence of abuse is very high among siblings and represents a risk factor. They suggest all children in a family should be assessed for abuse if one child has been suspected.

The most comprehensive report on the state of child abuse in Canada used the 2012 Canadian Community Health Survey-Mental Health (CCHS), a nationally representative sample consisting of 23,395 respondents aged 18 and older from all 10 provinces (Afifi et al., 2014). They were asked to report whether they were physically abused (e.g., slapped on the face, spanked with a hard object, pushed, kicked, burned), sexually abused, or witnessed intimate partner violence (i.e., saw their caregivers hit each other). Results are striking. Almost one-third of Canadians reported a history of

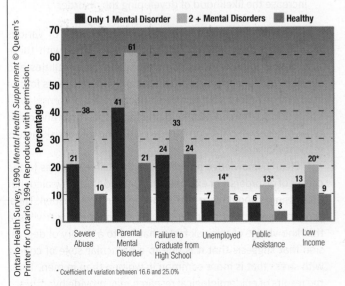

Ontario Health Survey, 1990, *Mental Health Supplement* © Queen's Printer for Ontario, 1994. Reproduced with permission.

* Coefficient of variation between 16.6 and 25.0%

FIGURE 4.2 Early risk factors and associated socio-demographic features for people age 15 to 64 with one or with two or more mental disorders. Y-axis measures percentage of people within a category who were categorized by the risk factor.

some form of child abuse. All three types of abuse were associated with all mental health problems assessed. Further, similar to the Ontario study, greater abuse was associated with greater psychopathology. People who experienced all three types of abuse were more than 5 times more likely to report depression, almost 11 times more likely to report drug abuse or dependence, and 27 times more likely to have attempted suicide. There were some gender differences: a history of child abuse in women was more strongly related to attention deficit disorder and suicidality than it was in men.

These data on the relationship between child abuse and mental disorders are quite compelling. However, not all children with a history of abuse go on to develop psychopathology, leading to the question of what factors are associated with resilience. Afifi and MacMillan (2011) reviewed protective factors and concluded that stable family environment and supportive relationships were associated with greater resilience, as were certain personality traits, but to a lesser extent. They make several suggestions for future research, including that these findings on protective factors be used in the development of interventions for maltreated children. They also recommend the use of qualitative research for the identification of additional protective factors that could subsequently be studied quantitatively. Finally, a relatively new focus is on resilience among sexually abused males. Harriet MacMillan of McMaster University is part of a newly funded team led by Christine Wekerle, also at McMaster, to examine this population. Their project is entitled, "Understanding Health Risks and Promoting Resilience in Male Youth with Sexual Violence Experience."

Other outcomes of abuse have also been studied. Tanaka, Georgiades, Boyle, and MacMillan (2015) examined the relationship between various forms of child abuse and educational attainment using the Ontario Child Health Study. Child maltreatment, in particular physical abuse, was generally associated with lower levels of educational attainment. As might be expected, a history of maltreatment also contributes to greater disability (i.e., limitations or restrictions in work or school performance or everyday activities). Tonmyr, Jamieson, Mery, and MacMillan (2005) reported that both child sexual abuse and physical abuse were important correlates of disability. Some cases of abuse are so appalling and disturbing as to defy credibility. Can these cases, even though rare, really happen in contemporary Canadian society? A high-profile case in the village of Blackstock, Ontario, that was revealed in June 2001 was described by police officers as the worst case of child abuse they had ever seen. The parents of two teenaged boys, 14 and 15 years old, were charged with forcible confinement, assault, assault with a weapon, aggravated assault, and failing to provide the necessities of life. The mother was also charged with administering a noxious substance. Police alleged that the boys were locked in separate covered cribs for long periods over the preceding 10 years. They were apparently forced to wear diapers, physically punished, and denied sufficient food. Can you imagine the possible long-term psychological consequences of abuse such as this? Although the parents were initially given a sentence of only nine months, the Ontario Court of Appeal sentenced the mother and father to five and four years, respectively, in federal penitentiaries (Tyler, 2004).

What role should governments and individuals play in protecting children from abuse? Canada has had child protection legislation since 1893 (Walters, 1995). Since 1980, the provinces and territories have enacted "duty-to-report" legislation in order to further protect those children whose safety and needs are at risk. It is mandatory to report children who need "protection" using a "best interests of the child" test. In the case of the two teens described above, a local child welfare agency reported the suspicion of abuse to the police. One major incentive behind Canada's duty-to-report legislation is to reduce the long-term negative consequences of abuse and neglect. Organizers of Capital Health's Child and Adolescent Protection Centre, an Edmonton program for investigating alleged child abuse, reported that they saw 50% more children than expected during the first year of operation (CMAJ, 2000). More than half of the 450 cases involved allegations of child sexual abuse and 236 cases involved children younger than five years old. Unfortunately, most Canadian children who are being abused are not being presented to such organizations. Only 7.6% of respondents who reported a history of child abuse in the 2012 CCHS (described above) reported having contact with any child protection organizations (Afifi et al., 2015).

Rates of abuse, including sexual abuse and parental neglect, are particularly high among First Nations communities. According to the Government of Canada (2006) report summary, in excess of 30% of First Nations and Inuit adults probably experienced child sexual abuse. Among Ontario's First Nations communities, 14% of boys and 28% of girls aged 12–17 years old reported some form of sexual abuse. These are much higher rates than for non-Aboriginal children. The 2003 Canadian Incidence Study of Reported Child Abuse and Neglect (Trocmé et al., 2005), found that the proportion of on-reserve First Nations children who have been investigated for alleged maltreatment is significantly higher than is the case for other Canadian children, and the most important reason why First Nations children come to the attention of child welfare personnel is parental physical neglect (due to poverty, poor housing, and addictions). Fluke et al. (2010) analyzed the factors that contribute to a decision to place a Canadian child in out-of-home care. Aboriginal ethnicity was not a significant predictor; however, agencies that had 20% or more Aboriginal cases were three times more likely to place Aboriginal children in out-of-home care, compared with agencies that had fewer than 20% Aboriginal cases. They concluded that a lack of resources in such communities is likely responsible for these findings.

In summary, the results of the major epidemiological study conducted in Ontario and other recent Canadian and international studies suggest that severe physical and sexual abuse and even spanking and slapping are risk factors for the onset and/or persistence of adult psychiatric disorders. The authors of the initial Ontario report (Ontario Ministry of Health, 1994) acknowledged that it is unclear how mistreatment in childhood leads to adult mental disorder but argued that research into the issue deserves government priority and that "there is an urgent need for effective programs both to prevent child abuse and to minimize its harmful after-effects" (p. 15). While this call was issued many years ago, Canada still has a long way to go in addressing maltreatment, in terms of both preventive interventions and in research developments. Afifi et al. (2014) concluded that child maltreatment is a major public health problem in Canada (and around the world), and given that 32% of Canadians have experienced child abuse, and abuse is strongly linked to psychopathology and other negative outcomes, prevention needs to be a priority.

We will assess the link between child abuse and specific disorders in more detail in subsequent chapters. Issues related to intervention and prevention of child sexual abuse are also discussed in Chapter 14, and elder abuse in Canada is covered in Chapter 16.

(continued)

Thinking Critically

1. Not everyone who experiences severe child abuse develops a mental disorder. What other factors can play a role in determining how abuse affects a child? Is severe child abuse a necessary or sufficient condition for adult psychological disorders? Why or why not? What other risk or protective variables increase or decrease the likelihood that an abused child will develop a psychological disorder?

2. Based on your understanding of the cultural and contextual factors surrounding child abuse in Canada's Aboriginal population,

how would you attempt to reduce the prevalence of abuse? Design a multi-faceted intervention program. Should Native healing and spiritual activities play a role?

3. Given that a history of childhood maltreatment is associated with lower levels of educational attainment, and in particular severe physical abuse is associated with fewer years of education (Tanaka et al., 2015), what steps could be taken to improve the retention rates for students with a history of abuse?

4.3   The Correlational Method

A great deal of research in psychopathology relies on the **correlational method**. This method establishes whether there is a relationship between or among two or more variables. It is often employed in epidemiological research, as well as in other studies. In correlational research, the variables being studied are measured as they exist in nature. This feature distinguishes the method from experimental research, in which variables are actually manipulated and controlled by the researcher. To understand this difference, consider that the possible role of stress in a disorder such as hypertension can be addressed with either a correlational or an experimental design. In a correlational study, we would measure stress levels by having people fill out a questionnaire or by interviewing them about their recent stressful experiences. Stress would then be correlated with blood pressure measurements collected from these same people. In an experimental study, in contrast, the experimenter would create or manipulate stress in the laboratory; for example, while their blood pressure was being monitored, some participants might be asked to give a speech to an audience about the aspect of their personal appearance they find least appealing (see Figure 4.3).

Correlational studies, then, address questions of the form "Are variable *X* and variable *Y* associated in some way so that they vary together (co-relate)?" For example, a national study of Canadian preschoolers showed that behavioural problems were higher among children from less affluent neighbourhoods (Kohen, Brooks-Gunn, Leventhal, & Hertzman, 2002).

Measuring Correlation

The first step in determining a correlation is to obtain pairs of observations of the variables in question, such as height and weight, for each member of a group of participants. Once such pairs of measurements are obtained, the strength of the relationship between the two sets of observations can be calculated to determine the **correlation coefficient**, denoted by the symbol *r*. This statistic may take any value between −1.00 and +1.00, and it measures both the magnitude and the direction of a relationship. The higher the absolute value of *r*, the larger

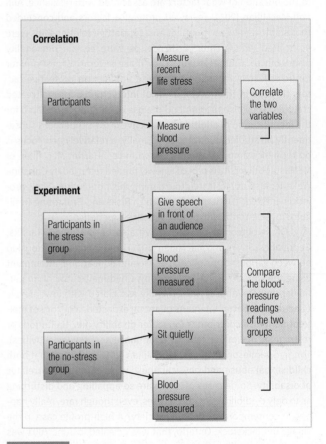

FIGURE 4.3   Correlational vs. experimental studies.

or stronger the relationship between the two variables. An *r* of either +1.00 or −1.00 indicates the highest possible, or perfect, relationship, whereas an *r* of 0.00 indicates that the variables are unrelated. If the sign of *r* is positive, the two variables are said to be *positively related;* in other words, as the values for variable *X* increase, those for variable *Y* also tend to increase. For example, assume that the correlation between height and weight is +.88. This correlation would indicate a very strong positive relationship: as height increases, so does weight. Conversely, when the sign of *r* is negative, variables are said to be *negatively related;* as scores on one variable increase, those for the other tend to decrease. For example, the number of hours spent watching television is negatively correlated with grade point average (GPA); as the number of hours of television increases, GPA decreases.

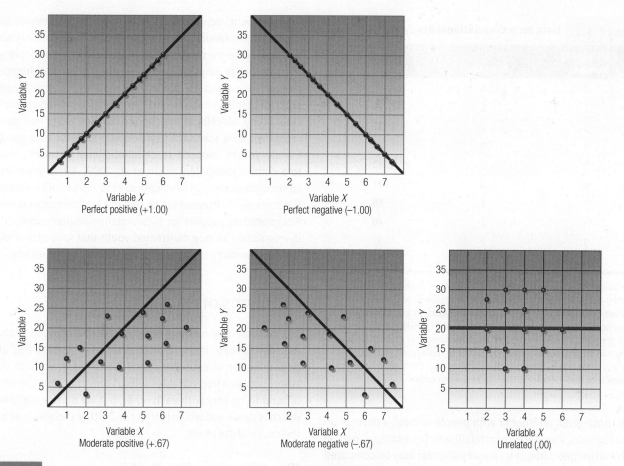

Scatter diagrams showing various degrees of correlational relationships.

Plotting a relationship graphically often helps make it clearer. Figure 4.4 presents what are called scatter diagrams of positive and negative correlations, as well as unrelated variables. In the diagrams, each point corresponds to two values determined for a given person, the value of variable X and that of variable Y. In perfect relationships, all the points fall on a straight line; if we know the value of only one of the variables for an individual, we can state with certainty the value of the other variable. Similarly, when the correlation is relatively large, there is only a small degree of scatter about the line of perfect correlation. The values tend to scatter increasingly and become dispersed as the correlations become lower. When the correlation reaches 0.00, knowledge of a person's score on one variable tells us nothing about his or her score on the other.

Statistical Significance

Thus far we have established that the magnitude of a correlation coefficient tells us the strength of a relationship between two variables. But scientists demand a more rigorous evaluation of the importance of correlations and use the concept of statistical significance for this purpose. Essentially, **statistical significance** refers to the likelihood that the results of an investigation are due to chance. A statistically significant correlation is one that is not likely to have occurred by chance.

Traditionally, in psychological research, a correlation is considered statistically significant if the likelihood or probability that it is a chance finding is 5 or less in 100. This level of significance is called the .05 level, commonly written as $p = .05$ (the p stands for probability). In general, as the size of the correlation coefficient increases, the result is more and more likely to be statistically significant. For example, a correlation of .80 is more likely to be significant than a correlation of .40. Whether a correlation attains statistical significance also depends on the number of observations made. The greater the number of observations, the smaller r (the correlation) needs to be to reach statistical significance. For example, a correlation of $r = .30$ is statistically significant when the number of observations is large—say, 300—but it would not be significant if only 20 observations were made. Thus, if alcohol consumption and depressed mood were assessed in a sample of 20 men and the correlation between depression and drinking was found to be .32, the correlation would not be statistically significant. However, the same correlation would be significant if 150 men were studied.

Applications to Psychopathology

The correlational method is widely used in the field of abnormal psychology. Whenever we compare people given one diagnosis

TABLE 4.1 Data for a Correlational Study

Participant Number	Diagnosis	Stress Score
1	1	65
2	1	72
3	2	40
4	1	86
5	2	72
6	2	21
7	1	65
8	2	40
9	1	37
10	2	28

Note: Diagnosis—having an anxiety disorder or not (with having an anxiety disorder designated as 1 and not having an anxiety disorder as 2)—is correlated with an assessment of recent life stress on a 0–100 scale. Higher scores indicate greater recent stress. As in previous examples, to make the point clearly, we present a smaller sample of cases than would be used in an actual research study. Notice that diagnosis is associated with recent life stress. Clients with an anxiety disorder tend to have higher stress scores than people without an anxiety disorder.

with those given another or with people without a psychological diagnosis, the study is correlational. For example, people with and people without an anxiety disorder may be compared on their physiological reactivity with a stressor administered in the laboratory.

When the correlational method is used in research on psychopathology, one of the variables is typically diagnosis; for example, whether the participant is diagnosed as having an anxiety disorder or not. To calculate a correlation between this variable and another one, diagnosis is quantified so that having an anxiety disorder is designated by a score of 1 and not having a disorder by a score of 2. (It does not matter what numbers are actually used.) The diagnosis variable can then be correlated with another variable, such as the amount of stress that has been recently experienced. An illustration of the data from such a study is presented in Table 4.1.

Often such investigations are not recognized as correlational, perhaps because participants come to a laboratory for testing. But the logic of such studies is correlational; the correlation between two variables—having an anxiety disorder or not and scores on the measure of recent life stress—is what is being examined. Variables such as having an anxiety disorder or not are called **classificatory variables**. The anxiety disorders were already present and were simply measured by the researcher. Other examples of classificatory variables are age, sex, social class, and body build. These variables are naturally occurring patterns and are not manipulated by the researcher, an important requirement for the experimental method discussed later. Thus, most research on the causes of psychopathology is correlational.

As an example, a U.S. study (Powers, Ressler, & Bradley, 2009) examined relations between reported childhood maltreatment, depression in adulthood, and perceived social support from family and friends. Childhood emotional abuse and neglect were shown to be more predictive of depression than sexual or physical abuse. Further, perceived friendship support appeared to protect (or "buffer") women against adult depression despite childhood maltreatment. In another 2009 study, MacMillan and her colleagues examined cortisol responses to a standard psychosocial stressor in a group of female youths exposed to childhood maltreatment, relative to a control group (MacMillan et al., 2009). While youth in the control group showed a typical increase in cortisol in reaction to the stressor, maltreated youth showed an attenuated response interpreted as support for hypothalamic-pituitary-adrenal axis dysregulation among maltreated youth that may play a role in their vulnerability to physical and psychological problems.

Problems of Causality

The correlational method, although often employed in abnormal psychology, has a critical drawback: it does not allow determination of cause–effect relationships. A sizeable correlation between two variables tells us only that they are related or tend to co-vary with each other, but we do not really know which is cause and which is effect or if either variable is actually the cause of the other.

The Directionality Problem When two variables are correlated, how can we tell which is the cause and which is the effect? For example, a correlation has been found between the diagnosis of schizophrenia and social class: lower-class people are more frequently diagnosed as having schizophrenia than are middle- and upper-class people. One possible explanation is that the stresses of living in the lowest social class cause an increase in the prevalence of schizophrenia. But a second and perhaps equally plausible hypothesis has been advanced. It may be that the disorganized behaviour patterns of individuals with schizophrenia cause them to perform poorly in their educational and occupational endeavours and thus to become impoverished. The **directionality problem**, as it is sometimes called, is present in many correlational research designs, hence the often-cited dictum, "Correlation does not imply causation."

Although correlation does not imply causation, determining whether two variables correlate may serve to disconfirm certain causal hypotheses; that is, causation does imply correlation. For example, if an investigator asserts that cigarette smoking causes lung cancer, he or she is implying that lung cancer and smoking will be correlated. Studies of these two variables must show this positive correlation or the theory will be discontinued.

One way of overcoming the directionality problem is based on the idea that causes must precede effects. According to this idea, studies investigating the hypothesized causes of psychopathology would use a prospective, longitudinal design in which the hypothesized causes are studied before a disorder has developed. In this way, the hypothesized causes could be measured before the effect. The most desirable way of collecting information about the development of schizophrenia, for example, would be to select a large sample of babies and follow them, measuring certain hypothesized causes, for the 20 to 45 years that are the period of risk for the onset of schizophrenia. But such a method would be prohibitively expensive, for only about 1 individual in 100 eventually develops schizophrenia. The yield of data from such a simple longitudinal study would be small indeed.

The **high-risk method** overcomes this problem. With this approach, only individuals with greater than average risk of developing schizophrenia in adulthood would be selected for study. Most current research using this methodology studies individuals who have a parent diagnosed with schizophrenia. (Having a parent with schizophrenia increases a person's risk for developing schizophrenia.) The high-risk method is also used to study several other disorders, and we will examine these findings in subsequent chapters.

We can illustrate the longitudinal approach with an example in the area of maltreatment and depression. Prospective studies in this area are few. However, Liu, Alloy, Abramson, Iacoviella, and Whitehouse (2009) examined whether experiences of current emotional maltreatment predicted the development of new episodes of depression in vulnerable young adults followed prospectively for 2.5 years. Greater overall emotional maltreatment predicted shorter time to onset of new major and minor depression, and episodes of the subtype of hopelessness depression (see Chapter 8). Further, current emotional maltreatment from peers and from authority figures separately predicted shorter time to development of new hopelessness depression episodes.

The Third-Variable Problem

Another difficulty in interpreting correlational findings is called the **third-variable problem**; that is, the correlation may have been produced by a third, unforeseen factor. In the following example, an obvious third variable is identified.

> "One regularly finds a high positive correlation between the number of churches in a city and the number of crimes committed in that city. That is, the more churches a city has, the more crimes are committed in it. Does this mean that religion fosters crime, or does it mean that crime fosters religion? It means neither. The relationship is due to a particular third variable—population. The higher the population of a particular community, the greater . . . the number of churches and . . . the frequency of criminal activity."
>
> (Neale & Liebert, 1980, p. 109)

Another example is the aforementioned study of Canadian preschoolers (see Kohen et al., 2002). Low neighbourhood income may be associated with child behaviour problems because of a third variable: children may be imitating frustrated parents who more frequently engage in behavioural dyscontrol.

Unfortunately, the psychopathologist is forced to make heavy use of the correlational method because diagnosis, a classificatory variable, is best suited to this strategy. But the relationships discovered between diagnosis and other variables are then clouded by the third-variable and directionality problems. Searching for the causes of the various psychopathologies will continue to be a challenge.

Longitudinal Modelling and Group Trajectories

Any convincing attempt to shed light on possible causal factors requires that researchers conduct longitudinal research, preferably with multiple waves of data being provided by multiple informants and being collected over several time periods. But even when such efforts are undertaken, attempts to establish causality are further complicated by the fact that there is substantial heterogeneity within a sample and we must get rid of a "one size fits all" mentality.

We should distinguish between **nomothetic research** (from the Greek word "*nomos*" meaning law) and **idiographic research** (from the Greek word "*idios*" meaning private) research. The correlational research we have reviewed thus far has been nomothetic in nature. It typically involves measuring a group of people on a number of variables (e.g., anxiety, depression) and then focuses on the relationships among those variables with the goal of making generalizations that apply to the population. It is also known as variable-centred research. But there is substantial variability within any sample. We may find that anxiety and depression are correlated. However, this does not mean that every person we assess will have high levels of both; thus, there are limitations to the nomothetic approach. Idiographic research, on the other hand, focuses on the individual. Case studies and qualitative approaches are examples of idiographic research methods; they result in a detailed understanding of the individual, but as noted earlier, they have been criticized as unrepresentative and unreliable. In summary, nomothetic research concerns itself with what we have in common with others (relationships between individuals) whereas idiographic research focuses on what is unique about an individual (relationships within individuals). Taking idiographic research one step further, Castro-Schilo and Ferrer (2013) refer to "idiographic-oriented" research when the pattern examined is within groups of individuals, rather than within just one individual. This type of research is person-centred and, as outlined below, can focus on identifying distinct clusters of people.

An important trend over the past two decades is an increasing focus in clinical research on **developmental trajectories** and on **group-based trajectory models** (see Nagin & Odgers, 2010). Developmental trajectories are the levels of a particular behaviour over time. Does the behaviour increase, decrease, or stay at about the same level over time? Over time, does a child show increasing levels of anti-social behaviour, declining levels, or stable levels? What other differences can be found among the adolescent who is depressed but has more moderate symptoms over time vs. the adolescent who has persistently elevated depression?

The notion of group-based trajectory is based on evidence that it is impossible to distinguish clear subgroups of participants in a sample and it is important to distinguish these groups both when considering the contribution of developmental factors and the best treatment options for these people (Nagin & Odgers, 2010). Groups are identified through a complicated procedure known as latent class growth analysis and they are known as latent classes. Multivariate statistical techniques are used to establish growth curves. Researchers using this approach can examine predictors of class membership as well as predictors of growth within a particular class.

This is a complicated topic that we will discuss only briefly. It is easiest to illustrate it with a research example from the depression field. Young men in the Oregon Youth Study were followed from the ages of 15 to 24 years old (see Stoolmiller, Kim, & Capaldi, 2005). Their parents also participated. Four latent trajectory classes were identified among the young men based on yearly assessments of depression: very low depression, moderate-decreasing depression, high-decreasing depression, and high persistent depression. Not surprisingly, the high persistent group seemed to differ qualitatively from the other three groups based on analyses of associated factors and outcomes. To the surprise of the researchers, almost 1 in 4 young men had persistently high depression, suggesting that persistent high depression is underdiagnosed in young men. They differed from participants in the other three groups in terms of childhood parental, contextual, and individual risk factors. The four key factors that distinguished the high persistent depression class were a greater number of parental transitions, childhood academic achievement problems, parental depressive symptoms, and negative life events (see Stoolmiller et al., 2005). Parental transitions is the number of changes involving parents (e.g., separation, divorce, remarriage, repartnering with estranged partner).

These data are illustrative in several respects. Most notably, research that focuses only on one point in time provides us with a very limited view and there are huge differences among people who may seem similar in levels of depression, but differences between them are likely to emerge as time goes by. We would not be able to discern from one point in time the changes in terms of which people became more depressed vs. the people who maintained their level of depression or actually got better.

4.4   The Experiment

The factors causing the associations and relationships revealed by correlational research cannot be determined with absolute certainty. The experiment is generally considered the most powerful tool for determining causal relationships between events. It involves the random assignment of participants to the different conditions being investigated, the manipulation of an independent variable, and the measurement of a dependent variable. In the field of psychopathology, the experiment is most often used to evaluate the effects of therapies.

As an introduction to the basic components of experimental research, let us consider here the major aspects of the design and results of a study of how expressing emotions about past traumatic events is related to health (Pennebaker, Kiecolt-Glaser, & Glaser, 1988). In this experiment, 50 undergraduates participated in a six-week study, one part of which required them to come to a laboratory for four consecutive days. On each of the four days, half the students wrote a short essay about a past traumatic event. They were instructed as follows:

> "During each of the four writing days, I want you to write about the most traumatic and upsetting experiences of your entire life. You can write on different topics each day or on the same topic for all four days. The important thing is that you write about your deepest thoughts and feelings. Ideally, whatever you write about should deal with an event or experience that you have not talked with others about in detail."

> (Pennebaker et al., 1988, p. 240)

The remaining students also came to the laboratory each day, but they wrote essays describing such things as their daily activities, a recent social event, the shoes they were wearing, and their plans for the rest of the day.

Information about how often the participating undergraduates used the university health centre was obtained for the 15-week period before the study began and for the 6 weeks after it had begun. These data are shown in Figure 4.5. Members of the two groups had visited the health centre about equally prior to the experiment. After writing the essays, however, the number of visits declined for students who wrote about traumas and increased for the remaining students. (This increase may have been due to seasonal variation in rates of visits to the health centre, for the second measure of number of visits was

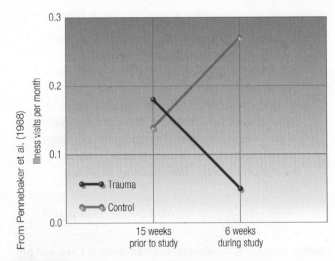

FIGURE 4.5   Visits to a health centre on account of illness for the periods before and during the experiment.

taken in February, just before mid-term exams.) From these data the investigators concluded that expressing emotions has a beneficial effect on physical health.

Basic Features of Experimental Design for Groups of Participants

The foregoing example illustrates many of the basic features of an experiment. Most of the discussion in this section refers to experiments conducted with groups of participants.

1. The researcher typically begins with an **experimental hypothesis**; that is, what he or she assumes will happen when a particular variable is manipulated. Pennebaker and his colleagues hypothesized that expressing emotion about a past event would improve health.

2. The investigator chooses an **independent variable** that can be manipulated; that is, some factor that will be under the experimenter's control. In the case of the Pennebaker study, some students wrote about past traumatic events and others about mundane happenings.

3. Participants are assigned to the two conditions by **random assignment** so that each participant has an equal chance of being in each condition.

4. The researcher arranges for the measurement of a **dependent variable**, something that is expected to depend on or vary with manipulations of the independent variable. The dependent variable in this study was the number of visits to the health centre.

5. When differences between groups are found to be a function of variations in the independent variable, the researcher is said to have produced an **experimental effect**.

An experiment led by Martin Zack from the Centre for Addiction and Mental Health involved manipulating mood by exposing University of Toronto introductory psychology students to either negative words, positive words, or neutral words (Zack et al., 2006). This experiment examined the effects of mood state on beer drinking. Thus, mood state was the independent variable and amount of beer drunk was the dependent variable. As expected, exposure to a negative mood state, relative to a positive or neutral mood state, resulted in drinking more beer.

Experiments are often conducted in clinical research to evaluate the effectiveness of treatments. Studies focusing on drug treatments typically involve assigning participants randomly to either the drug treatment group or a non-intervention group in which the person receives a placebo. The **placebo effect** is an improvement in a physical or psychological condition that is attributable to a client's expectations of help rather than to any specific active ingredient in a treatment. A substantial number of people may improve even though they did not actually receive a drug and instead received a placebo (e.g., a sugar pill). Bridge et al. (2009) conducted a meta-analysis of "second generation" antidepressant trials conducted since

1995 involving children and adolescents with major depression. They reported that the average response to placebo was 48%, but the mean response to active medication was only slightly higher at 59%. Placebo effects should be evaluated according to double-blind procedures. When neither the researchers nor the clients are aware of who has been placed in the treatment and placebo control groups, the design is referred to as a **double-blind procedure**.

The second type of experiment involves randomly assigning participants to one of two or more therapy treatments. A typical study involves comparing a group of participants who receive an intervention with those in a non-intervention control group.

To illustrate, consider a hypothetical study of the effectiveness of cognitive therapy in reducing depression among 20 depressed clients. In brief, the independent variable is cognitive therapy vs. no treatment; 10 clients are randomly assigned to receive cognitive therapy and 10 are randomly assigned to a no-treatment control group. The dependent variable is scores on a standardized measure of the severity of depression, assessed after 12 weeks of treatment or no treatment; higher scores reflect more severe depression.

Data for each of the clients in each group are presented in Table 4.2. Note that the average scores of the two groups differ considerably (8.3 for the cognitive-therapy group and 21.8 for the no-treatment group). This difference between groups, also called *between-group variance,* is the experimental effect; it has been caused by the independent variable. Note also from the table that the scores of individual participants within each group vary considerably; this is called *within-group variance.* Within the cognitive-therapy group, for example, most participants have low scores, but participant number 7 has a high score (18). Cognitive therapy did not seem to be of much help to this individual, but we don't know why. Similarly, most people in the no-treatment group have high scores, but participant

TABLE 4.2	**Results of a Hypothetical Study Comparing Cognitive Therapy with no Treatment for Depression**		
	Cognitive Therapy		**No Treatment**
Participant 1	8	Participant 11	22
Participant 2	6	Participant 12	14
Participant 3	12	Participant 13	26
Participant 4	4	Participant 14	28
Participant 5	3	Participant 15	19
Participant 6	6	Participant 16	27
Participant 7	18	Participant 17	6
Participant 8	14	Participant 18	32
Participant 9	7	Participant 19	21
Participant 10	5	Participant 20	23
Group average	8.3		21.8

Note: Scores for each participant after treatment are shown.

number 17 has a low score (6). The cause of this within-group variability is unknown.

Statistical significance is tested by dividing the between-group variance (the difference between the average scores of the two groups—in this example 21.8 – 8.3 = 13.5) by a measure of the within-group variance. When the average difference between the two groups is large relative to the within-group variance, the result is more likely to be statistically significant. From the results of this hypothetical experiment, we would conclude that cognitive therapy is more effective in decreasing depression than no treatment at all.

Internal Validity

As noted above, an important feature of any experimental design is the inclusion of at least one **control group** that does not receive the experimental treatment (the independent variable). A control group is necessary for comparative purposes if the effects in an experiment are to be attributed to the manipulation of the independent variable. The data from a control group provide a standard against which the effects of an independent variable (in this case, expressing emotion or cognitive therapy) can be compared.

To illustrate this point with another example, consider a study of the effectiveness of a particular therapy in modifying some form of abnormal behaviour. An experiment conducted in Quebec examined the efficacy of cognitive-behavioural therapy in the treatment of generalized anxiety disorder (see Chapter 5). Laberge, Dugas, and Ladouceur (2000) found that the treatment was successful in reducing dysfunctional beliefs about worry. If there had been no control group, then it would not have been an experiment. However, the study did include a group of people with generalized anxiety disorder who were assigned randomly to a waiting list and had not yet received the therapeutic treatment. These individuals represented an effective comparison group because they were presumably similar in every respect to those who experienced the experimental treatment. If there had been no control group against which to compare the improvement, valid conclusions could not have been drawn. The reduction in dysfunctional beliefs from the beginning of the treatment to the end could have been brought about by several factors in addition to or instead of the treatment employed, such as the passage of time.

Variables such as the passage of time are often called **confounds**. Their effects are intermixed with those of the independent variable, and like the third variables in correlational studies, they make the results difficult or impossible to interpret. These confounds, as well as others, are widespread in research on the effects of psychotherapy, as is documented throughout this book. Studies in which the effect obtained cannot be attributed with confidence to the independent variable are called *internally invalid* studies. In contrast, research has **internal validity** when the effect can be confidently attributed to the manipulation of the independent variable.

In the study by Laberge et al. (2000), internal validity was improved by the inclusion of a control group. The changes in anxiety experienced by these control participants constituted a standard against which the effects of the independent variable could be assessed. If a change in anxiety is brought about by particular environmental events, quite beyond any therapeutic intervention, the experimental group receiving the treatment and the control group receiving no treatment are likely to be affected equally. On the other hand, if after six months the anxiety level of the treated group has lessened more than that of the untreated control group, we can be relatively confident that this difference is attributable to the treatment.

The inclusion of a control group does not always ensure internal validity, however. Consider yet another study of therapy: the treatment of two hospital wards of psychiatric clients. An investigator may decide to select one ward to receive an experimental treatment and another ward to be a control group. When the researcher later compares the frequencies of deviant behaviour in these two groups, he or she will want to attribute any differences between them to the fact that clients in one ward received treatment and those in the other did not. But the researcher cannot legitimately draw this inference, for there is a competing hypothesis that cannot be disproved. Even before treatment, the clients who happened to receive therapy might have had a lower level of deviant behaviour than the clients who became the control group. The principle of experimental design that was disregarded in this defective study is that of *random assignment.* This principle would be at work in a two-group experiment if a coin were tossed for each participant. If the coin turns up heads, the participant is assigned to one group; if tails, he or she is assigned to the other. This procedure minimizes the likelihood that differences between the groups after treatment will reflect pre-treatment differences in the samples rather than true experimental effects.

Furthermore, using both a control group and random assignment handles the type of confounds we described in our earlier example of treatment for high anxiety. When groups are formed by random assignment, confounds such as the resolution of a stressful life situation are equally likely to occur in both the treated group and the control group. There is no reason to believe that life stress would be resolved more often in one group than the other. Random assignment was employed in the experiments described earlier.

External Validity

External validity is the extent to which results can be generalized beyond the immediate study. If investigators have demonstrated that a particular treatment helps a group of clients, they will undoubtedly want to conclude that this treatment will be effective in administering to other clients, at other times, and in other places.

Determining the external validity of the results of a psychological experiment is difficult. Merely knowing that one is a participant in an experiment can alter behaviour, and thus the results produced in the laboratory might not automatically be produced in the natural environment. Researchers must be alert to the extent to which they claim generalization for findings, for there is no entirely adequate way of dealing with the questions of external validity. The best that can be done is to perform similar studies in new settings with new participants so that the limitations, or the generality, of a finding can be determined.

Analogue Experiments

Suppose that a researcher has hypothesized that a child's emotionally charged, overdependent relationship with his or her mother causes generalized anxiety disorder. An experimental test of this hypothesis would require assigning infants randomly to either of two groups of mothers. The mothers in one group would undergo an extensive training program to ensure that they would be able to create a highly emotional atmosphere and foster overdependence in children. The mothers in the second group would be trained not to create such a relationship with the children under their care. The researcher would wait until the participants in each group reached adulthood and then determine how many of them had developed generalized anxiety disorder.

Obviously, such an experimental design contains insurmountable practical problems. But practical issues are hardly the principal ones that must concern us. Consider the ethics of such an experiment. Would the potential scientific gain of proving that an overdependent relationship with a person's mother brings on generalized anxiety disorder outweigh the suffering that would be imposed on some of the participants? In almost any person's view, it would not. Ethical issues are considered in detail in Chapter 18.

Before we leave the topic of research ethics for now, it is worth mentioning one other issue that researchers must carefully consider. It is important in experimental treatment studies to include participants who are in the control group and who do not receive the intervention. But how does a researcher weigh the interests of science and the need for comparison vs. the well-being of an individual person? If something works and it is important to alleviate suffering of someone in distress in a timely manner, should a person who is assigned randomly to a control group be deprived of the intervention? A common practice is for control group participants to also receive the intervention after the study is completed so that they may benefit as well. What if we already know that a treatment helps, but we want to find out whether a new treatment helps even more? Should we still randomly assign people to a control group and make them wait for treatment? Often times, once a treatment is established as significantly more effective than a control condition, future treatment studies may omit the control group and simply test whether a new treatment is significantly better than an already established treatment.

In an effort to take advantage of the benefits of the experimental method, researchers seeking the causes of abnormal behaviour have sometimes used a format known as an analogue experiment. Investigators attempt to bring a related phenomenon—that is, an analogue—into the laboratory for more intensive study. Because a true experiment is now being conducted, results can be obtained that may be interpreted in cause–effect terms. However, the problem of external validity may be accentuated because the actual phenomenon of interest is not being studied.

In one type of analogue study, behaviour is rendered temporarily abnormal through experimental manipulations. For example, lactate infusion can elicit a panic attack, hypnotic suggestion can produce blindness similar to that seen in conversion disorder, and threats to self-esteem can increase anxiety and depression. If pathology can be experimentally induced by any one of these manipulations, the same process existing in the natural environment might well be a cause of the disorder.

The key to interpreting such studies lies in the validity of the independent variable as a reflection of some experience one might actually have in real life and of the dependent variable as an analogue of a clinical problem. Is a stressor encountered in the laboratory fundamentally similar to one that occurs in the natural environment? Are transient increases in anxiety or depression reasonable analogues of their clinical counterparts? Results of such experiments must be interpreted with great caution and generalized with care, although they can provide valuable information about the origins of psychopathology.

Single-Subject Experimental Research

We have been discussing experimental research as it is conducted on groups of participants, but experiments do not always have to be conducted on groups. In single-subject experimental designs, participants are studied one at a time and experience a manipulated variable. The strategy appears to violate many principles of research design. There is no control group to act as a check on a single subject. Moreover, generalization is difficult because the findings may relate to a unique aspect of the one individual whose behaviour has been explored. Hence, the study of a single individual would appear unlikely to yield any findings that could possess the slightest degree of internal or external validity. Nevertheless, the experimental study of a single subject can be an effective research technique for certain purposes.

A case study reported by Hendricks and Thompson (2005) serves as an example. They illustrated the integration of both cognitive-behavioural therapy (CBT) and interpersonal therapy (IPT) for the treatment of bulimia nervosa complicated by depression and alcohol abuse. Their approach was based on the case formulation method introduced in Chapter 3.

> *"Rebecca, a 25-year-old Hispanic female, referred herself for treatment of eating difficulties and depressed mood. At intake, she was 6 ft tall and weighed 150 lb (body mass index [BMI] = 20.3). She reported binging and inducing vomiting approximately once per week, and dated the onset of this behavior at 3 months before coming to therapy. She recalled that she had never had any concerns about her physical appearance until the time of her first romantic relationship at age 21. Apparently, her first boyfriend criticized her 175-lb (BMI = 23.7) physique and pressured her to lose weight, substantially affecting the way she viewed her body. At the end of this relationship, Rebecca felt disgusted with her appearance and decided that the only way to ensure success in her future relationships was to lose weight. An additional precipitating factor for her eating disturbance appeared to be graduation*

from college at age 22. Feeling that she had little control over the direction of her life, Rebecca restricted her eating behavior in an attempt to "have control over something" in her life. At one point, her body weight dropped to 135 lb (BMI = 18.3). Alarmed at her behavior, Rebecca moved to her hometown to be closer to her family and friends. She slightly increased her food intake and gradually gained weight, however, she remained unhappy and was determined to restrict her diet and modify her appearance. According to her report, Rebecca began to binge and vomit as a way to cope with her depression. To further manage her negative affect, she began drinking to intoxication two to three times per week. These binge drinking episodes often coincided with her episodes of binging/purging." (pp. 171–172)

Specific CBT and IPT strategies were selected and implemented by Hendricks and Thompson based on the conceptualization of the specific factors pertinent to Rebecca's difficulties. Figure 4.6 summarizes treatment outcomes for behavioural measures recorded throughout the treatment and follow-up. Stage 1 focused on reduction of restrictive eating behaviour and binge drinking through specific CBT techniques. Stage 2 focused on negative thoughts regarding shape and body appearance using other CBT techniques. Stage 3 additionally employed CBT relapse prevention strategies. Stage 4 employed IPT since Rebecca continued to purge in response to interpersonal crises. Rebecca was no longer experiencing clinically significant symptoms of bulimia, alcohol abuse, or depression at the end of treatment (12 months) or follow-up (18 months post-treatment onset).

Hendricks and Thompson (2005) concluded that CBT is possibly more effective in the elimination of binge eating and binge drinking, whereas IPT may be more effective in reducing purging. Not shown in Figure 4.6 is the reduction in depression, which is possibly due to either or both interventions. According

to the authors, the findings have important implications because the results support (1) the possible effectiveness of the case formulation approach relative to a standard, manualized treatment; (2) the integration of CBT and IPT for the treatment of bulimia; and (3) theories that ascribe a critical role for interpersonal difficulties in the "core eating disorder pathology" (Hendricks & Thompson, 2005, p. 174).

In another form of single-subject design, usually referred to as a **reversal** or **ABAB design**, some aspect of the participant's behaviour is carefully measured in a specific sequence: (1) during an initial time period, the baseline (A); (2) during a period when a treatment is introduced (B); (3) during a reinstatement of the conditions that prevailed in the baseline period (A); and (4) finally, during a reintroduction of the experimental manipulation (B). If behaviour in the experimental period is different from that in the baseline period, reverses when the experimentally manipulated conditions are reversed, and re-reverses when the treatment is again introduced, there is little doubt that the manipulation, rather than chance or uncontrolled factors, has produced the change. The reversal technique cannot always be employed, however, for a participant's initial state may not be recoverable. Treatment aims to produce enduring change—the goal of all therapeutic interventions. Further, reinstating the client's original condition would generally be considered unethical. The ABAB design is most appropriate when it is assumed that the effects of manipulations are temporary. Sometimes an AB time series design is informative. For example, Wragg and Whitehead (2004) investigated CBT with a 15-year-old girl with first episode psychosis. After a baseline assessment (A) she received a 16-week CBT intervention for psychosis (B). Previous work had not focused on CBT for adolescents with psychosis. Although there were improvements in symptoms of psychosis, anxiety, and depression, the results were inconclusive for other measures, including self-esteem and an integrative recovery style (related to relapse). The authors hypothesized that the girl's negative self-evaluations were responsible for the negative results and concluded that a further series of single-subject studies should be conducted to target negative evaluations before initiating a randomized control trial.

The fact that a treatment works for a single subject does not necessarily imply that it will be universally effective. If the search for more widely applicable treatment is a major focus, the single-subject design may help investigators decide whether large-scale research with groups is warranted. Hendricks and Thompson (2005) suggested that future research should explore the efficacy of integrative CBT-IPT treatments with large samples of people with bulimia nervosa. This strategy was actually used successfully by Robert Ladouceur and his colleagues at Université Laval in Quebec City in the development of their cognitive-behavioural treatment of pathological gamblers. Bujold, Ladouceur, Sylvain, and Boisvert (1994) employed a single-subject design to test a treatment program that had four components: cognitive correction of erroneous perceptions about gambling, problem-solving training, social skills training, and relapse prevention. Following the combined treatment, participants

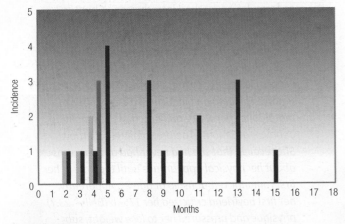

FIGURE 4.6 Self-reported incidence of binge eating (pink bars), vomiting (blue bars), and binge drinking (green bars). Stage 1 = 0 – 1 months; Stage 2 = 1 – 2 months; Stage 3 = 2 – 5 months; Stage 4 = 5 – 18 months.

Source: Hendricks & Thompson, 2005, pp. 171–174. Reprinted with permission of John Wiley & Sons, Inc.

no longer met the criteria for pathological gambling and the positive outcome was maintained at a nine-month follow-up. This success led to evaluation of the efficacy of the treatment package in a controlled group study (see the next section on mixed designs). Sylvain, Ladouceur, and Boisvert (1997) reported significant changes in the treatment group, relative to a waitlist control group, on various outcome measures. The therapeutic gains were maintained at 6- and 12-month follow-ups.

However, wouldn't it be useful to know more precisely what the active components of the program are? Ladouceur and his associates hypothesized that the key factor in the development and maintenance of pathological gambling is the erroneous perceptions that gamblers have. According to their theory (Ladouceur & Walker, 1998), the core cognitive error relates to the gambler's misconception about randomness. Gamblers develop a set of false beliefs, thinking that they can control events governed by chance. They develop superstitious behaviours that they believe can increase the likelihood of winning (e.g., wearing a lucky tie while gambling). But, in fact, the "house" ultimately wins in all legalized forms of gambling! Ladouceur et al. (1998), therefore, evaluated the efficacy of an exclusively cognitive intervention to correct the pathological gambler's dysfunctional schema. Five pathological gamblers were treated in a single-subject multiple-baseline design. The treatment was successful for four of the participants, suggesting that a cognitive intervention that focuses on the gambler's misconception about the notion of randomness holds promise as a treatment for pathological gambling. Of course, the fact that the treatment was unsuccessful with one participant is an indication that other factors must also be considered. Boutin, Tremblay, and Ladouceur (2009) later showed that it is possible to modify beliefs related to randomness, using a larger sample of participants at an on-site casino information centre. Compared with a control group, those who visited the centre had more accurate perceptions about randomness (but actual gambling behaviour did not differ across groups). The experimental group more readily understood that a slot machine that had not paid out in a long time was not about to pay out. This gambling example demonstrates how different methodologies can be used sequentially to build support for a particular theory.

Mixed Designs

Experimental and correlational research techniques can be combined in what is called a **mixed design**. Participants from two or more discrete and typically non-overlapping populations are assigned to each experimental condition. The two different types of populations—for example, clients with either schizophrenia or a phobia—constitute a classificatory variable; that is, the variables of schizophrenia and phobia were neither manipulated nor created by the investigator, and they can only be correlated with the manipulated conditions, which are true experimental variables.

As an example of how a mixed design is applied, consider an investigation of the effectiveness of three types of therapy

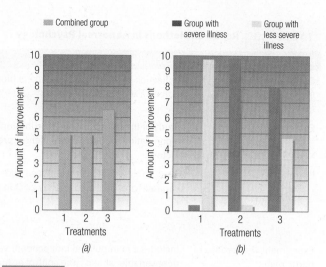

FIGURE 4.7 Effects of three treatments on clients whose symptoms vary in degree of severity. (*a*) When the severity of the illness is not known and the clients are grouped together, treatment number 3 appears to be the best. (*b*) The same data as in (*a*) are reanalyzed, dividing clients by severity. Now treatment 3 is no longer best for any clients.

(the experimental variable) on clients divided into two groups on the basis of the severity of their illnesses (the classificatory or correlational variable). The question is whether the effectiveness of the treatments varies with the severity of illness. The hypothetical outcome of such a study is presented in Figure 4.7. Figure 4.7a illustrates the unfortunate conclusions that would be drawn were the clients not divided into those with severe and those with less severe illnesses. When all clients are grouped together, treatment 3 produces the greatest amount of improvement. Therefore, if no information about differential characteristics of the clients is available, treatment 3 would be preferred. When the severity of the clients' difficulties is considered, however, treatment 3 is no longer the therapy of choice for any of the clients. Rather, as seen in Figure 4.7b, treatment 1 would be selected for those with less severe illness and treatment 2 for clients with more severe illness. Thus, a mixed design can identify which treatment applies best to which group of clients.

In interpreting the results of mixed designs, we must always be aware of the fact that one of the variables (severity of illness in our example) is not manipulated but is instead a classificatory or correlational variable. Therefore, the problems in interpreting correlations, especially the possible operation of third variables, arise in interpreting the results of mixed designs as well.

Although not strictly a mixed design, the previously cited study by Bridge et al. (2009) focused on placebo response and the researchers concluded that lower baseline depression severity and younger age are associated with higher placebo response. The strongest predictor of the placebo response was the number of study sites. Bridge et al. suggested that the methodology of clinical trials can be improved by carefully recruiting from fewer sites children and adolescents with moderate to severe depression. In an editorial comment, Emslie (2009) stated that "including only moderately to severely depressed youths will increase the probability of identifying a signal of

TABLE 4.3   **Research Methods in Abnormal Psychology**

Method	Description	Evaluation
Case study	Collection of detailed historical and biographical information on a single individual	Excellent source of hypotheses but cannot determine causal relationships because cannot rule out alternative hypotheses
Epidemiology	Study of the frequency and distribution of a disorder in a population; determines incidence, prevalence, and risk factors	Knowledge of risk factors provides clues regarding causes of disorders
Correlation	Study of the relationship between two or more variables; variables are measured as they exist in nature	Cannot determine causality because of the directionality and third-variable problems; used extensively in research on the causes of psychopathology because diagnosis is a correlational or classificatory variable
Experiment with groups of participants	Includes a manipulated independent variable, a dependent variable, at least one control group, and random assignment	Most powerful method for determining causal relationships; used mainly in studies of the effectiveness of therapies
Experiment with single subjects	Includes a manipulated variable and contrasts behaviour during the time the manipulation is occurring with behaviour during a period when the manipulation is not occurring (as in the ABAB design)	Can demonstrate causal relationships, although generalization can be a problem
Mixed design	Includes both an experimental (manipulated) variable and a classificatory (correlational) variable	Can demonstrate that an experimental condition (e.g., a type of therapy) has different effects depending on the variable (e.g., severity of illness)
Meta-analysis	Summarizes effect sizes across many studies	Can provide a useful summary but not free of bias, as described in Focus on Discovery 4.1

whether a particular compound has antidepressant properties in the pediatric age group by decreasing the number of subjects who respond to placebo" (p. 2).

A summary of the major research methods of abnormal psychology, and their strengths and weaknesses, appears in Table 4.3. You have probably concluded that there is no perfect method that will easily reveal the secrets of psychopathology and therapy. You are correct! Scientific knowledge is based on integrating or synthesizing a body of evidence yielded by investigations conducted with varying methodologies, not on merely considering individual studies one at a time.

How does a researcher or clinician go about drawing conclusions from a series of published or otherwise available investigations? A simple strategy is to read individual studies, mull them over, and decide what they mean overall. The disadvantage with this approach is that the researcher's biases and subjective impressions can play a significant role in determining what conclusion is drawn. It is fairly common for two scientists to read the same studies and reach very different conclusions. Is there a solution to this problem? Focus on Discovery 4.1 discusses how scientists synthesize information using a method called *meta-analysis*.

Focus on Discovery 4.1

Meta-Analysis: The Effects of Psychotherapy and Beyond

"The reality is that, despite the claims of true believers, meta-analysis is neither a purely objective, mechanical process nor a panacea for answering all questions."

—Streiner (2005, p. 829)

Smith, Glass, and Miller (1980) originally devised **meta-analysis** as a new way to evaluate the effects of psychotherapy. The first step is a thorough literature search to identify all relevant studies.

Because these studies have typically reported their findings in different formats and used different statistical tests, meta-analysis then puts all the results into a common format, using a statistic called the *effect size*. In the case of treatment, the effect size offers a way of standardizing the differences in improvement between, for example, a therapy group and a control group, or between groups receiving two different types of therapy, so that the results of many different studies can be averaged. The independent variables can be any factors considered influential in the outcome.

In their oft-cited report, Smith et al. (1980) meta-analyzed 475 psychotherapy outcome studies involving more than 25,000 clients and 1,700 effect sizes. They came to two conclusions that have attracted considerable attention and controversy. First, they concluded that a wide range of therapies produce more improvement than does no treatment. Specifically, treated clients were found to be better off than almost 80% of untreated clients. Subsequent meta-analyses by other authors have confirmed these early findings (e.g., Lambert & Ogles, 2004). Second, Smith et al. contended that effect sizes across diverse modes of intervention do not differ from one another; that is, different therapies are about equally effective. This second conclusion has been especially contentious. Some subsequent meta-analytic studies compared insight therapy with cognitive and behavioural interventions and concluded that there is a slight but consistent advantage for the latter, although some proponents of insight therapy contend that behavioural and cognitive therapies focus on milder disorders (see Lambert & Ogles, 2004).

Since the pioneering work by Smith et al. (1980), there has been an exponential explosion of meta-analytic reports in the psychological and medical research literature. Indeed, David Streiner (2005) of the Baycrest Centre for Geriatric Care in Toronto noted that while there were only 3 published meta-analyses in 1981, in 2003, there were 1,712. Some topics have been the subject of more than one meta-analysis and researchers have collated the results of several meta-analyses into a **meta-meta-analysis**. Meta-analysis has been applied to forms of intervention other than psychotherapy, including biological treatments. For example, numerous meta-analyses have evaluated the efficacy of antidepressants. In an evaluation of these meta-analyses, Moncrieff and Kirsch (2005) concluded that selective serotonin reuptake inhibitors (SSRIs) "have no clinically meaningful advantage over placebo" (p. 157). They further argued that any statistical superiority over placebos is due to "methodological artifacts." Needless to say, these conclusions were controversial, especially since at least four other meta-analyses previously supported the use of this class of drugs for the treatment of depression, including one co-authored by Moncrieff himself! Although there have been numerous analyses of the problems and pitfalls of meta-analysis, Streiner (2005) attempted to explain once again "why different people with honourable intentions can come to different conclusions regarding meta-analyses" (p. 829). Why are such debates ongoing after more than 30 years? Why doesn't meta-analysis provide definitive answers?

First, meta-analysis is a complicated process that requires decisions at each of numerous phases or steps based on a degree of judgement, and equally competent researchers can make different decisions that affect the ultimate conclusions (see also Butler, Chapman, Forman, & Beck, 2006). These outcomes can be influenced right from the initial step of posing the question. For example, if we ask the question, "Are SSRIs more effective than CBT in treating depression?" we raise a long list of issues, including whether we should focus on all types of depression or limit our analyses to a specific form of depression, and so forth. Streiner notes that there are no correct answers to the myriad questions and that different investigators can make different but equally plausible decisions. When researchers conduct a meta-analysis, they must rely on past studies and these studies may have key limitations and differ in quality. Indeed, Streiner claims that the majority of published studies are missing critical information, and it is necessary to choose to fill in the information somehow or reject the study. Meta-analyses conducted on studies that used, for example, measures with poor reliability and validity can result in misleading conclusions. Johnson, Low, and MacDonald (2015) reviewed 200 meta-analyses related to health promotion and found that many had ratings of methodological quality; however, very few incorporated these quality ratings into their analyses. Johnson et al. recommend analyzing quality in interaction with possible moderator variables, reviewed next, so that these differences in methodological quality are firmly taken into account in any study conclusions.

Butler et al. (2006) consider meta-analyses to be more informative if the results also take into account **moderator variables** (i.e., other factors such as gender that may influence or qualify the results in some meaningful way). For example, Malouff, Thorsteinsson, and Schutte (2007) described a meta-analysis of 31 studies that examined the efficacy of problem-solving therapy in reducing mental and physical health problems. Problem-solving therapy involves teaching clients how to use a step-by-step process to solve life problems (see D'Zurilla & Nezu, 2010). Malouff et al. (2007) concluded that problem-solving therapy was as effective as other bona fide treatment. Significant moderators included whether the problem-solving therapy involved training in applying a problem-solving orientation to life, whether homework was assigned, and whether a developer of problem-solving therapy helped conduct the study!

Second, how do we interpret the results of the meta-analysis? There is still room for subjective interpretation. Streiner considers this issue to be the heart of the Moncrieff and Kirsch (2005) controversy. Consistent with previous meta-analyses, they concluded that there is a statistically significant effect of SSRIs on depression relative to placebos, but argue that it is a trivial difference that is not of clinical importance—a clinical judgement. As noted by Streiner (2005), "This is not an issue that can be resolved through statistical argument or recourse to picking nits about methodology" (p. 830).

Despite limitations, quantitative synthesis has been used to aid meaningful evaluation of other areas of evidence in abnormal psychology where a large number of studies in the literature vary considerably in the nature of the samples examined, methodological and reporting quality, operationalization of variables, and the statistical significance of findings. For example, recall our discussion of the experiment by Pennebaker et al. (1988) with university students who wrote essays about past traumatic events. The authors concluded that written emotional expression has beneficial health effects. However, research on the effects of written expression of stressful experiences has increased dramatically over the years. Is Pennebaker et al.'s original conclusion valid today? The answer is yes and no! Harris (2006) conducted a meta-analysis that examined whether writing about stressful experiences affects health care utilization (HCU) compared with writing on neutral topics or no-writing control groups. Harris examined effect sizes for healthy samples (13 studies), samples with pre-existing medical conditions (6 studies), and samples pre-screened for psychological criteria (10 studies). He concluded that, "Writing about stressful experiences reduces HCU in healthy samples but not in samples defined by medical diagnoses or exposure to stress or other psychological factors" (Harris, 2006, p. 243).

Will a meta-analysis related to an important issue in abnormal psychology ever lead to the definitive conclusion? It will probably not. The judgements of clinicians and even your own interpretation will inevitably play a role.

Summary

4.1 Science represents an agreed-upon problem-solving enterprise, with specific procedures for gathering and interpreting data to build a systematic body of knowledge. Scientists generate theories, most often by considering available data, but creativity also plays a role. Scientific statements must have the following characteristics: they must be testable in the public arena; they must be exposed to tests that could disconfirm them; they must derive from reliable, replicable observations; and inferred concepts must be linked to observable and measurable events or outcomes. A science is only as good as its methodology. As a student of abnormal psychology, you must appreciate the strengths and limitations of the research methods of the field if you are to adequately evaluate research and theories.

4.2 Clinical case studies serve unique and important functions in psychopathology, such as allowing rare phenomena to be studied intensively in all their complexity. Case studies also encourage the formulation of hypotheses that can be tested later through controlled research. They are also valuable for psychotherapy training. However, the data they yield may not be valid, and they are of limited value in providing evidence to favour a theory. However, as is the case with qualitative research in general, getting to know people in detail is a rich source of hypotheses and theorizations. Case studies and qualitative research rely on few participants whereas epidemiological research relies on a large sample or population. Epidemiological research gathers information about the prevalence and incidence of disorders and about risk factors that increase the probability of a disorder. Prevalence is the proportion of a population that has a disorder at a given point or period of time, whereas incidence is the number of new cases of the disorder that occur in some period.

4.3 Correlational methods are the most important means of conducting research on the causes of abnormal behaviour, for diagnoses are classificatory and are not experimentally manipulated variables. In correlational studies, statistical procedures allow us to determine the extent to which two or more variables correlate, or co-vary. However, conclusions drawn from nearly all correlational studies cannot legitimately be interpreted in cause–effect terms. The directionality and third-variable problems are the source of this difficulty. The limitations of correlational methods are particularly evident as developmental research on trajectories of symptoms that do or do not change over time highlights the need for sophisticated approaches that allow for the heterogeneity that exists among people with comparable symptoms.

4.4 The experimental method entails the manipulation of independent variables and the careful measurement of their effects on dependent variables. An experiment begins with a hypothesis to be tested. In the case of experiments with groups of participants, they are generally randomly assigned to one of at least two groups: an experimental group, which experiences the manipulation of the independent variable; and a control group, which does not. If differences between the experimental and control groups are observed on the dependent variable, researchers can conclude that the independent variable did have an effect. If all these conditions are met, the experiment has strong internal validity. Placebo control groups are often used in psychotherapy research. Clients in such groups receive support and encouragement, but not what is hypothesized to be the active ingredient in the therapy administered to the group with which the placebo group is being compared. The external validity of research findings—whether they can be generalized to situations and people not studied within the experiment—can be assessed only by performing similar experiments in the actual domain of interest with new participants. Single-subject experimental designs that expose one person to different treatments over a period of time can provide internally valid results, although the generality of conclusions is typically limited. Mixed designs are combinations of experimental and correlational methods. For example, two different kinds of clients (the classificatory variable) may be exposed to various treatments (the experimental variable). Meta-analysis puts statistical comparisons from single studies into a common format (the effect size) in order to average the results of a group of studies.

Key Terms

analogue experiment
case study
classificatory variables
confounds
control group
correlation coefficient
correlational method
dependent variable
developmental trajectories
directionality problem
double-blind procedure
epidemiology
experiment
experimental effect
experimental hypothesis

external validity
group-based trajectory models
high-risk method
hypotheses
idiographic research
incidence
independent variable
internal validity
latent class growth analysis
meta-analysis
meta-meta-analysis
mixed design
moderator variables
nomothetic research
parental mental disorder

placebo effect
prevalence
qualitative research
quantitative research
random assignment
reversal (ABAB) design
risk factors
science
severe abuse
single-subject experimental design
statistical significance
theory
theory-building case studies
third-variable problem

Reflections: Past, Present, and Future

1. In Chapter 1, we discussed the issue of reform of our health care system and management of costs of health care services, including services for the mentally ill. Although it is vitally important that we maximize the efficient use of our psychological health care dollars, academics and policy-makers in Canada are starting to reconsider the cost of failing to prevent or treat psychological disorders (e.g., Hunsley et al., 1999). What are the long-term costs of failing to invest in services for people with mental disorders? Can we develop effective prevention programs? Outline your vision for the development of a long-term, comprehensive prevention and treatment strategy for Canada.

2. In the next chapter, we will examine the anxiety disorders. Assume that the Government of Canada has hired you to head a team that will conduct a long-term longitudinal study of risk factors for the development of anxiety disorders. You will track a sample of infants, starting with the mother's pregnancy and continuing until the children reach the age of 30. Assume that you are able to hire any experts that you desire as members of your team. What would be the composition of your team? What biopsychosocial risk and protective factors would you assess and why?

CHAPTER 5

Anxiety Disorders

LEARNING OBJECTIVES

1. Describe the symptom components of anxiety and distinguish between normal and clinical levels of anxiety.

2. Define various specific phobias.

3. Describe social anxiety disorder (SAD).

4. Explain the theories of etiology of specific phobias and SAD.

5. Describe panic disorder and agoraphobia.

6. Explain the theories of etiology of panic disorder and agoraphobia.

7. Describe generalized anxiety disorder (GAD) and its etiology.

8. Compare and contrast the components and effectiveness of therapies for anxiety disorders.

"I had been struggling with severe anxiety for a while, but I didn't really want to get help because I was embarrassed to admit that I had a problem, especially since I didn't know anyone else who felt the way I did and I didn't really . . . well, I didn't know if it was even 'a thing', really . . . And there's such a stigma there. There was no way I could ask about it."

—*Kate Waddingham, a third-year student at the University of Ottawa, in DeClerq, 2012*

This brave account from Kate Waddingham is something that is relevant to many students because problems with anxiety are quite common, as campus life can be fraught with stress and uncertainty—both real and perceived. What distinguishes Kate is her willingness to go public and her equally brave decision to seek help from health services at the University of Ottawa after a close friend committed suicide.

Allan Rock, president and vice-chancellor of the University of Ottawa (and former Minister of Health from 1997 to 2002) has written columns (e.g., *The Globe and Mail*, September 24, 2015) encouraging students who are struggling with mental health problems to reach out to the counselling centres that are much more present on university campuses in Canada now compared with when he was a student. He suffered from anxiety, including panic attacks, as well as depression during

his time as an undergraduate at the University of Ottawa. He described the difficulty of seeking help at that time, not knowing where to turn.

5.1 | Anxiety and Anxiety Disorders

There is perhaps no single topic in abnormal psychology that touches as many of us as anxiety, that unpleasant feeling of fear and apprehension. This chapter will focus on anxiety that has escalated to the point of becoming an anxiety disorder. We will discuss anxiety in general before describing various anxious disorders, including specific phobias, social anxiety disorder (SAD), panic disorder, agoraphobia, and generalized anxiety disorder (GAD). Note that post-traumatic stress disorder (PTSD) and obsessive-compulsive disorder (OCD) were formerly classified as anxiety disorders, but are now considered in separate chapters of the *DSM-5* manual (and this text). These changes are not simply symbolic and reflect arguments put forth for many years that OCD and PTSD are distinct from the other major anxiety disorders. Also note that separation anxiety disorder is only briefly discussed in this chapter and is more thoroughly examined in Chapter 15 because it primarily applies to children, but emerging research on adult separation anxiety has resulted in separation anxiety disorder now being included in the *DSM-5* anxiety disorders chapter. Selective mutism is another disorder that mostly applies to children that is now included in the anxiety disorders chapter in *DSM-5*. We will also save our detailed discussion of selective mutism for Chapter 15.

Typically, anxiety is regarded as having two distinguishable components: the physiological and the cognitive. The physiological component is the heightened level of arousal and physiological activation, as reflected by symptoms such as a higher heart rate, shortness of breath, and dry mouth. The cognitive component is the subjective perception of the anxious arousal and the associated cognitive processes: worry and rumination. Oftentimes clinicians also refer to a third component: a behavioural component of anxiety involving avoidance and other safety behaviours, such as using alcohol to manage anxiety at a party or bringing a safe person (a close friend or family member that the individual can cling to at the party). Another characteristic is that anxiety tends to be future-focused; that is, the emphasis is on things that could happen. Because many of the things that people worry about actually never happen, anxiety and worry can be reinforced by the avoidance of feared outcomes and possible experiences that never happen. Persistent uncontrollable worry about many themes is the main component of generalized anxiety disorder.

The different elements of anxiety are reflected in conceptualizations of a form of anxiety that most students can relate to: **test anxiety**. Sarason's (1984) Reactions to Tests Scale has two subscales tapping the physiological component (i.e., tension and bodily symptoms) and two subscales tapping the cognitive component (i.e., worry and **test-irrelevant thinking**, which is the tendency for the mind to wander when it is difficult to concentrate).

Extensive research on the underlying roots of test anxiety has yielded a number of important insights that can be applied broadly to other types of anxiety. It has been established, for instance, that test anxiety can be highly debilitating if it gets out of control (see Flett & Blankstein, 1994). Similarly, at the root of generalized anxiety disorder is the sense that anxiety pervades many aspects of life and the person feels totally unable to do anything to control it. Also, what seems to be at the root of much test anxiety, as well as several other types of anxiety, is a sense of the self as deficient and powerless. Students with test anxiety tend to be very self-critical and have negative thoughts about themselves, often during the test itself (Flett & Blankstein, 1994). A sense of the self as deficient is also viewed by some as the core of social anxiety disorder (Moscovitch, 2009). In fact, in extreme cases of test anxiety, when the primary fear is that of being negatively evaluated by others, a diagnosis of social anxiety disorder may be applied.

It is normal and perhaps even adaptive to experience some degree of anxiety, especially when in potentially life-threatening situations that jeopardize someone's survival. Anxiety can also motivate us to start studying or work on an upcoming presentation. But when does anxiety become a problem that requires intervention? Here we return to our earlier discussions of what constitutes abnormality and dysfunction that requires clinical intervention. The anxiety must be chronic, relatively intense, associated with role impairment, and cause significant distress for self or others. But there is clearly a subjective element here. The role of subjectivity is shown with the debate that took place about proposed *DSM-5* changes to generalized anxiety disorder that were not implemented. While the core element remains uncontrollable worry, a key change considered for the diagnostic criteria was a substantial reduction in the number of associated symptoms needed to qualify for a diagnosis. Some authors (e.g., Starcevic, Portman, & Beck, 2012) argued vociferously that this change would have artificially inflated the number of people with an anxiety disorder because people with normal, everyday worries could qualify for a diagnosis of generalized anxiety disorder. Similarly, prevalence rates for social anxiety disorder can vary widely from one study to the next. This variability is at least in part due to the subjectivity regarding the degree of impairment. How impairing does the anxiety have to be to warrant a clinical diagnosis?

Situational factors must also be taken into account. It is normal to feel highly anxious in a situation that is upsetting and a threat to personal survival. But what tends to distinguish chronically anxious people is their propensity to perceive threat and to be concerned and worried when there is no objective threat or the situation is ambiguous. This element was illustrated clearly in a recent longitudinal study by Craske et al. (2012). They showed in an experimental situation involving the presentation of various stimuli that were neutral or aversive that those adolescents who reacted with a strong startle response even when presented with a safety cue (connoting no threat) were the most likely to go on to develop an anxiety disorder. The tendency to perceive threat in neutral or ambiguous life situations predicts elevated anxiety (for a discussion, see Flett, Endler, & Fairlie, 1997).

Anxiety disorders are diagnosed when subjectively experienced feelings of anxiety are clearly present. The key defining features of the major anxiety disorders discussed later in this chapter are summarized in Table 5.1. We will see in our broader descriptions of the various anxiety disorders that they have many factors in common but also have some key distinguishing features.

As a group, the anxiety disorders are the most common psychological disorders and a majority of Canadians who met criteria for an anxiety disorder report that it interfered with their home, school, work, and social life (Government of Canada, 2006). Indeed, a survey of physicians in Alberta found that among people with symptoms warranting a diagnosis, anxiety disorders were most common, with about 1 in 5 having some form of anxiety disorder (Slomp, Bland, Patterson, & Whittaker, 2009). According to the Ontario *Mental Health Supplement* study (Ontario Ministry of Health, 1994), a clear gender difference exists, with 16% of women and 9% of men having suffered from anxiety disorders in the preceding year. The highest one-year prevalence rates (i.e., almost 1 in 5) were found in women 15 to 24 years of age. Anxiety disorders were more common

TABLE 5.1   Summary of Major Anxiety Disorders

Disorder	Description
Specific phobia	Fear and avoidance of objects or situations that do not present any real danger.
Social anxiety disorder	Fear and avoidance of social situations due to possible negative evaluation from others.
Panic disorder	Recurrent unexpected panic attacks involving a sudden onset of physiological symptoms, such as dizziness, rapid heart rate, and trembling, accompanied by terror and feelings of impending doom.
Agoraphobia	Fear of being in public places.
Generalized anxiety disorder	Persistent, uncontrollable worry, often about minor things.
Separation anxiety disorder	The anxious arousal and worry about losing contact with and proximity to other people, typically significant others.
Selective mutism	Failure to speak in one situation (usually school) when able to speak in other situations (usually home).

AP Photo/Gene J. Puskar

In 2009, Toronto-born Joey Votto, star baseball player with the Cincinnati Reds, disclosed that he suffered from anxiety and depression following the death of his father. Another famous baseball player, pitcher Zack Greinke of the Arizona Diamondbacks, almost left a career in baseball due to social anxiety disorder.

in women than in men across all age groups. Similar results were found in 15 countries around the world (see Seedat et al., 2009). However, men from all walks of life also suffer from these disorders. For example, baseball player Joey Votto (see photo) has suffered from anxiety.

Somers, Goldner, Waraich, and Hsu (2006) pooled the results of 41 international epidemiological studies and reported one-year and lifetime prevalence rates for total anxiety disorders of 10.6% and 16.6%, respectively, and noted that, "The prevalence of anxiety disorders eclipses the capacity of specialized mental health services" (p. 100). Kessler et al. (2012) surveyed existing U.S. data in an attempt to provide the clearest picture possible of lifetime morbid risk (LMR) and one-year prevalence of various disorders. The survey found that estimates of LMR were highest for a major depressive episode (29.9%), followed by six disorders: specific phobia (18.4%), social anxiety disorder (13.0%), post-traumatic stress disorder (10.1%), generalized anxiety disorder (9.0%), separation anxiety disorder (8.7%), and panic disorder (6.8%). The 12-month prevalence data indicated that the three most prevalent disorders were specific phobia (12.1%), major depressive episode (8.6%), and social anxiety disorder (7.4%). The disorders with the earliest median age of onset (15–17 years old) were the phobias (including specific phobia, agoraphobia, and social phobia) and separation anxiety. The disorders with the latest median age of onset (23–30 years old) included two anxiety disorders (panic and generalized anxiety disorder), as well as major depression. Given these median ages of onset, it is not surprising that university students are often coping with the onset of anxiety disorders. See Student Perspectives 5.1 for a discussion of anxiety disorders among university and college students.

The earlier onset of separation anxiety may be one reason why it was limited to being diagnosed in childhood, until the recent *DSM-5*. **Separation anxiety** is the anxiety that results from not having contact or the possibility of losing contact with attachment figures. It is seen generally as a type of anxiety that is prevalent among children of various ages but not relevant among older people. However, there is increasing focus on an adult form of separation anxiety disorder that would apply to those adults who cannot stand to be alone and are cognitively preoccupied with losing contact with loved ones. It is intriguing that in a study conducted with 520 clients from an anxiety disorders clinic in Australia, the separation anxiety disorder diagnosis was the most prevalent when all anxiety disorder diagnoses were considered; in fact, almost 1 in 4 adult clients were diagnosed with an adult form of separation anxiety disorder (Silove et al., 2010). These data suggest that the separation anxiety disorder diagnosis in adults deserves much more consideration than it currently receives.

We began this chapter with a quotation from a student suffering from problems with anxiety; we presented this excerpt because anxiety disorders are quite prevalent among students. Indeed, you may be thinking about your own experiences with anxiety because almost everyone is anxious at one time or another.

It is also important to acknowledge the significant impact an anxiety disorder diagnosis can have on a person's life. Recent research from the University of Regina suggests that anxiety disorders are associated with suicide ideation and suicide

Student Perspectives 5.1

Anxiety Disorders in University and College Students

"Sandra B. was a 20-year-old college student who presented to a student health clinic reporting recurrent panic attacks. Her first attack occurred seven months earlier while smoking marijuana at an end-of-term party. At the time she felt depersonalized, dizzy, short of breath, and her heart was beating wildly. Sandra had an overwhelming fear that she was going crazy . . . In the following months, Sandra continued to experience unexpected panic attacks and became increasingly convinced that she was losing control of her mind. Most of her panics occurred unexpectedly during the day, although they sometimes also occurred at night, wrenching her out of a deep sleep. Sandra began avoiding a variety of substances (e.g., alcohol, marijuana, coffee) and activities (e.g., aerobics classes) because they produced bodily sensations, such as palpitations and dizziness, that she feared. She believed that if these sensations became too intense then she might "tip over the edge" into insanity. Increasingly, Sandra also began to avoid shopping malls, lecture halls, and other public places for fear that she would have a panic attack and lose control . . . As a result of avoiding lectures, her grades began to fall and she was at risk for failing her courses."

(Asmundson & Taylor, 2003, p. 1281)

This student suffers from panic disorder. Given that anxiety disorders are the most prevalent disorders found in surveys of adolescents, it should not be too surprising that data indicate that anxiety disorders continue to be quite common among students. For instance, a large and nationally representative epidemiological study in the United States conducted by Blanco et al. (2008) found a 12-month prevalence rate of almost 12% in college students aged 19 to 25.

Panic attacks that meet clinical criteria are particularly well-documented. Norton et al. (2008) reported that 4.3% (or about 1 in 25 students) actually met *DSM-IV* criteria for a panic attack. Among those who met the criteria, the average number of panic attacks over the previous year was four and the typical panicker had experienced attacks for over four years. Panic is a common occurrence among students. Norton, Harrison, Hauch, and Rhodes (1985) administered a self-report measure known as the Panic Attack Questionnaire and found that 34% of undergraduates reported experiencing at least one panic attack in the previous year. Another Canadian study found that more than half of the students surveyed reported histories of panic (Wilson, Sandler, Asmundson, Larsen, & Ediger, 1991).

Thinking Critically

1. Would you count yourself among the many students who have experienced a subclinical panic attack in the past year? If so, did something trigger the attack, or did it seem to "come out of the blue"?

2. Is there continuity between clinical and subclinical anxiety? What do you think helps distinguish students with a clinically diagnosable problem vs. those with a milder form? Consider incorporating the finding that people with a diagnosed disorder appear to experience greater effects on their daily lives (e.g., lifestyle impairment, lifestyle restriction) relative to students with non-clinical panic (see Cox, Endler, & Swinson, 1991).

3. Given the extensive anxiety among students, do you think it is fair to compare students on tests such as the Graduate Record Exam? Do differences in test anxiety undermine the validity of test results?

---

attempts (Thibodeau, Welch, Sareen, & Asmundson, 2013). Past research had attributed suicidality among people with anxiety disorders to comorbid depression or other factors. This was the first study to show that anxiety disorders themselves are related to suicidality.

We turn now to an examination of the defining characteristics and theories of etiology for each of the anxiety disorders. Each specific disorder is described in more detail. Each disorder is discussed in terms of not only its features, but also cognitive-behavioural and biological theories that have been postulated and received some empirical support. A common theme reiterated across the disorders is that dysfunctional levels of anxiety reflect cognitive appraisal processes contributing to the perception of anxiety, as well as physiological factors that render particular people more vulnerable to anxiety.

5.2 | Specific Phobias

Specific Phobia Definition

Specific phobias are unwarranted fears caused by the presence or anticipation of a specific object or situation. The fear and avoidance are out of proportion to the danger actually posed and are recognized by the sufferer as groundless. Extreme fear of heights, closed spaces, snakes, or spiders—provided that there is no objective danger—accompanied by sufficient distress to disrupt one's life is likely to be diagnosed as a specific phobia.

Many specific fears do not cause enough hardship to compel an individual to seek treatment. For example, an urban dweller with an intense fear of snakes will probably have little direct contact with the feared object and may therefore not believe that anything is seriously wrong, and a specific phobia would not be diagnosed. The term "specific phobia" implies that the person suffers intense distress and social or occupational impairment because of the anxiety. A study of the fears and phobias of women in Calgary (Costello, 1982) found that about 5% of women with a phobia were "incapacitated" by it.

Over the years, complex terms have been formulated to name these unwarranted fear and avoidance patterns. In each instance, the suffix -phobia is preceded by a Greek word for the feared object or situation. The suffix is derived from the name of the Greek god Phobos, who frightened his enemies. Some of the more familiar terms are claustrophobia, fear of closed spaces; arachnophobia, fear of spiders; and acrophobia, fear of heights. More exotic fears have also been given Greek-derived names, such as ergasiophobia, fear of working; pnigophobia, fear of choking; and taphephobia, fear of being buried alive (McNally, 1997). A 2015 encyclopedia on phobias, edited in Canada by Irena Milosevic and Randi McCabe (2015) at McMaster University, details hundreds of them, including erythrophobia, fear of blushing (Kocovski, Abbott, & Fleming, 2015), and triskaideka-phobia, fear of the number 13 (Ashbaugh, 2015). These authoritative terms convey the impression that we understand how a particular problem originated and how it can be treated. Nothing could be further from the truth. As with so much in the field of abnormal psychology, there are more theories and jargon pertaining to phobias than there are firm findings.

New phobias tend to emerge in keeping with societal changes. One of the newest phobias is **nomophobia**. Nomophobia—meaning no mobile phone phobia—is a reflection of our increasing reliance on technology. It is a pathological fear of remaining out of touch with technology that is experienced by people who have become overly dependent on using their mobile phones or personal computers. Case studies suggest that nomophobia arises as a way of compensating for other types of anxiety. For example, one man with panic disorder and agoraphobia needed cellphone access due to his chronic need to feel safe; the phone represented a connection to other people, including emergency services (King, Valenca, & Nardi, 2010). A recent study focused on the development of a questionnaire to assess this new fear and found that it consists of the following four dimensions: inability to communicate, being disconnected, inability to access information, and inconvenience (Yildrim & Correia, 2015).

Psychologists tend to focus on different aspects of phobias according to the paradigm they have adopted. This is particularly evident in Freud's celebrated case of Little Hans, who was afraid of horses. Freud's analysis has been reinterpreted by other classic psychoanalytic theorists such as Bowlby and Klein from their own theoretical perspectives (see Midgley, 2006). Psychoanalysts focus on the content of the phobia and see the phobic object as a symbol of an important unconscious fear. Freud paid particular attention to Hans's reference to the "black things around horses' mouths and the things in front of their eyes." The horse was regarded as representing the father, who had a moustache and wore eyeglasses. Freud theorized that fear of the father had become transformed into fear of horses, which

Hans then avoided. Thus, psychoanalysts believe that the content of phobias has important symbolic value. Behaviourists, on the other hand, tend to ignore the content of the phobia and focus instead on its function. For them, fear of snakes and fear of heights are equivalent in the means by which they are acquired, in how they might be reduced, and so on.

Specific Phobia Subtypes

In DSM-5, specific phobias are subdivided according to the source of the fear: blood, injuries, and injections; situations (e.g., planes, elevators, enclosed spaces); animals (e.g., snakes, spiders, dogs); the natural environment (e.g., heights, water); and other (for all other phobias). These subtypes are summarized in Table 5.2.

These categories can be further subdivided. For example, dental phobia (fear of the dentist) is considered part of the blood-injection-injury category; however, recent research supports that dental phobia may be best considered a specific phobia category of its own (van Houtem et al., 2014). Unlike the majority of people with phobias from the blood-injection-injury category, most people with dental phobia do not have a tendency to faint in response to their feared stimulus. Not surprisingly, people with dental phobia avoid going to the dentist, which could result in detrimental effects on their dental health.

Research is lacking on many specific phobias, in large part due to the avoidance associated with them (i.e., people find ways to avoid the situations they fear, rather than seek treatment). Also adults are often embarrassed to admit such strong fears of situations and objects. For example, children are often afraid of storms

TABLE 5.2 Summary of Specific Phobia Subtypes

DSM-5 Subtype	Examples
Blood-injection-injury	Getting a shot
	Seeing blood
	Going to the dentist
Situations	Enclosed spaces
	Elevators
	Planes
Animals	Insects (spiders)
	Dogs
	Snakes
Natural environment	Storms
	Water
	Heights
Other	Choking
	Vomiting
	Clown

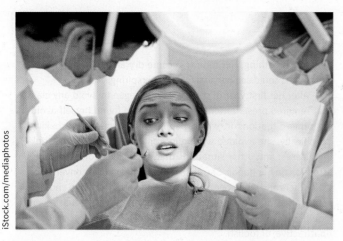

iStock.com/mediaphotos

People with dental phobia often avoid going to the dentist, which can significantly impact their health.

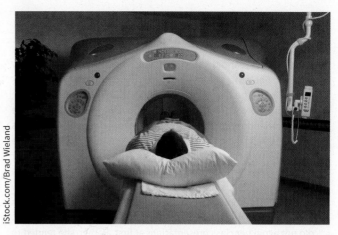

iStock.com/Brad Wieland

Claustrophobia, a fear of closed spaces, is a significant problem for people who must undergo MRI tests, since MRIs involve spending a prolonged amount of time in an enclosed chamber. Mock MRI studies have been conducted with university students to assess levels of claustrophobia (see McGlynn, Karg, & Lawyer, 2003).

but adults rarely admit such a fear. There has been research on the effect of major weather events as traumas, but very little research on storm phobias, part of the natural environment category, despite a lifetime prevalence rate of 2%. Researchers at Ryerson University in Toronto have developed a questionnaire to assess a fear of storms, including items about monitoring weather, anxious physical symptoms during storms, and avoidance behaviours (Nelson, Vorstenbosch, & Antony, 2014), which should spur more research on this particular phobia.

We referred earlier to the high prevalence of specific phobia reported by Kessler et al. (2012). Specific phobias of clinical significance also seem to persist. A U.S. study conducted by Stinson et al. (2007) found that specific phobias tend to be long-lasting, with a mean duration of 20 years, and only 8% of people with a specific phobia received treatment. The most common specific phobia subtypes in order were: (1) animal phobias (including insects, snakes, and birds); (2) heights;

(3) being in closed spaces; (4) flying; (5) being in or on water; (6) going to the dentist; (7) seeing blood or getting an injection; and (8) storms, thunder, or lightning.

Specific phobias are often discussed as if they occur by themselves, but in reality, people often have two or more specific phobias. This has resulted in proposals for a generalized subtype of specific phobia for people with multiple phobias. A recent survey of adolescents found that adolescents with multiple phobias, relative to those with only one phobia, have an earlier onset, with elevated severity and associated levels of impairment (Burstein et al., 2012).

The specific fear focused on in a phobia can vary cross-culturally. In China, for example, a person with *Pa-leng* (a fear of the cold) worries that loss of body heat may be life-threatening. This fear appears to be related to the Chinese philosophy of yin and yang: yin is the cold, windy, energy-sapping, and passive aspects of life, while yang is the hot, powerful, and active aspects.

Nic Leister/Getty Images, Inc.

A fear of storms is relatively common but adults are typically embarrassed to admit such a fear.

5.3 Social Anxiety Disorder (Social Phobia)

Ms. K. (see "Social Anxiety Disorder and College Life") appears to suffer from a prototypical form of social anxiety disorder (SAD) in the *DSM-5,* formerly known as social phobia. **Social anxiety disorder** is characterized by persistent, irrational fears of being judged by other people. It can be extremely debilitating. Individuals with social anxiety disorder try to avoid particular situations in which they might be evaluated, fearing that they will reveal signs of anxiousness or behave in an embarrassing way. They are particularly concerned about blushing, shaking, and sweating—the physiological symptoms of anxiety that are observable to others. Speaking or performing in public, eating

Social Anxiety Disorder and College Life

Ms. K. is a 29-year-old student who presented with social anxiety disorder. She reported being shy as a child and could remember pretending to be ill to stay home from school. As she got older, she met more children and by high school was quite comfortable with her friends at school. Meeting new people was still difficult, as was public speaking in class. Fortunately, neither situation came up often. In college, Ms. K.'s problem became worse. Several of her classes required her to make presentations. In addition, because she lived off campus, she found it particularly difficult to meet new friends. The few times she tried to talk to people in class, she felt as though she had nothing to say. Before long, she stopped trying. Ms. K. did not avoid her class presentations at first. Rather, she tended to overprepare for them and used slides when possible because the dark room helped to decrease her anxiety. Still during presentations she could feel her heart pounding and she tended to have

difficulty breathing. Her mouth became dry and she was sure her classmates could see her shaking and perspiring.

After her first year of college, Ms. K. began to avoid any class that required presentations. In addition, she found herself avoiding other situations in which people might notice her shaking. Specifically, she avoided writing in front of others, holding drinking glasses, and other situations that might focus other people's attention on her hands. She also avoided engaging in conversation with others and when people approached her, she tried to end conversation as quickly as possible. In addition to fearing that others would notice her anxiety, Ms. K. felt others might see her as weak, unattractive, or foolish.

Source: Antony & McCabe, 2003, p. 1047. In A. Tasman, J. Kay, J. A. Lieberman, M. B. First, & M. Riba (Eds.), *Psychiatry* (4th ed.), Reproduced with permission from John Wiley & Sons, Ltd.

---

in public, using public lavatories (for fear of judgement, not germs), and other activities carried out in the presence of others can elicit extreme anxiety.

The types of situations feared and avoided can be roughly broken into three types: public speaking or other types of performances (e.g., piano recital), social interactions (e.g., initiating or maintaining conversations at a party, talking with a group of friends, asking a store clerk for help, stopping a stranger to ask for directions), and being observed in public (walking down a busy street, sitting on a bus in rush hour, working with others in the vicinity, filling out a form with others watching).

Cox, Clara, Sareen, and Stein (2008) examined the structure of feared situations among people with a lifetime diagnosis of SAD in the National Comorbidity Survey—Replication (NCS-R) and the Canadian Community Health Survey (CCHS) and found strong support for this three-factor model (see photos).

Most people with SAD rate public speaking situations as the most anxiety-provoking situations. However, surprisingly, some clients describe having reduced anxiety when delivering a presentation or performance compared with socializing, stating that they can put on an "act" or a different "face," and not have to be themselves. Oscar-winning actress Jennifer

There are three main types of situations feared and avoided by those with social anxiety disorder: public speaking (or other performance), social interactions, and being observed in public. The core fear across all of these situations is that of being judged negatively by other people.

Lawrence has revealed being (unsuccessfully) treated for social anxiety as a child, anxiety that started when she began attending school. She describes having felt "not good enough" and "stupid" in school, and did not like the usual social activities enjoyed by most students (e.g., field trips, recess, parties). She credits acting with having helped her regain her confidence.

One extreme but true example illustrates how social anxiety can have a strong impact on the lives of college and university students. A fourth-year seminar class taught by one of the authors included a student who admitted to having social anxiety disorder. She indicated bravely that she would still make a required presentation to the seminar group, but only on the condition that no one looked at her, especially the professor. Everyone was instructed to keep their eyes trained forward at the student's slide presentation while she talked at the back of the class. The presentation went off without a hitch and the students developed a better understanding of abnormal behaviour.

Prior to *DSM-5*, SAD could be classified as either generalized or specific, depending on the range of situations that were feared and avoided. Generalized SAD would be diagnosed for clients who feared many different interpersonal situations, while specific social phobia would be diagnosed if there was an intense fear of one particular situation (usually public speaking). People with generalized social phobia were found to have an earlier age of onset, more comorbidity with other disorders, such as depression and alcohol abuse, and more severe impairment (e.g., Stein & Kessler, 1999). In *DSM-5*, the qualifier "generalized" was dropped with the recognition that people with SAD can have a range of social fears and it is a quantitative rather than a qualitative distinction. However, public speaking anxiety seems to be qualitatively and quantitatively distinct from other subtypes (Blote, Kint, Miers, & Westenberg, 2009). That is, it is not simply a lesser or milder form of SAD. Accordingly, following recommendations from the *DSM-5* work group about the utility of a specifier indicating "performance only" (if the fear is restricted to speaking or performing in public) (see Bögels et al., 2010), the *DSM-5* SAD criteria were modified to allow for a performance-only specifier.

Social anxiety disorder has a high comorbidity rate with other disorders and often occurs in conjunction with generalized anxiety disorder, specific phobias, panic disorder, avoidant personality disorder, and mood disorders (Chartier, Walker, & Stein, 2003). Social anxiety disorder also has high levels of comorbidity with heavy drinking and alcohol dependence, perhaps due to self-medication with alcohol (see Stansfeld et al., 2008). People diagnosed with SAD seem also to be especially vulnerable to marijuana-related problems (Buckner & Schmidt, 2009). Similar to alcohol, the marijuana use typically develops after the onset of SAD; the cannabis is used to cope with social anxiety. One of the authors has had several clients over the years express a desire to use cannabis before attending an initial group therapy session for SAD, all referring to the desire to reduce their anticipatory anxiety. Retired football player Ricky Williams has been diagnosed with SAD and also used cannabis (see photo).

In children, social anxiety disorder is often comorbid with other forms of anxiety. Most children diagnosed with selective mutism are also diagnosed with SAD. **Selective mutism** is

Jay Gula/Getty Images, Inc.

Ricky Williams is now retired as an NFL player. He won the Heisman Trophy in college and, in 2006, he was a member of the Toronto Argonauts while suspended from the NFL for marijuana use. Williams has acknowledged suffering from extreme shyness and has been diagnosed with social anxiety disorder. Williams has been treated successfully with a combination of cognitive-behaviour therapy and the drug Paxil, but has since discontinued his use of the drug because it did not agree with his eating habits.

most often characterized by the failure to speak at school when a child is able to speak at home, and recent research supports the classification of selective mutism as an anxiety disorder in *DSM-5* (for a recent review, see Muris & Ollendick, 2015). We will take a closer look at selective mutism in Chapter 15, with the other disorders that are most often first diagnosed in childhood.

Although onset of SAD can occur in childhood, it generally takes place during adolescence, when social awareness and interaction with others become much more important in a person's life. The lifetime prevalence of social anxiety disorder in the CCHS 1.2 was 7.5% in men and 8.7% in women. The average age of onset was 13 years and average duration of symptoms was 20 years (see Stansfeld et al., 2008). The prevalence of social anxiety disorder was higher among people who had never married or were divorced, had not completed secondary education, had lower income or were unemployed, reported lacking adequate social support, reported low quality of life, or had a chronic physical condition (see Stansfeld et al., 2008).

Analyses of data from Ontario's *Mental Health Supplement* study (see Stein & Kean, 2000) found that diagnosed social anxiety disorder was associated with marked dissatisfaction and low functioning in terms of quality of life, and it was actually linked with dropping out of school! This finding should not come as a surprise given that many components of school are social in nature, including sitting in a classroom surrounded by other people, walking down a busy hallway, interacting with educators and other students (e.g., with the expectation to socialize and do group projects), giving presentations, and so on. A recent form of social anxiety that is mostly relevant for young people is social media anxiety—the fear of being judged by others related to social media use, such as misinterpreting communication from others via text, having too few or not enough "likes" on Facebook, or fear of missing out.

A large Finnish study (Ranta et al., 2009) of 12- to 17-year-old adolescents in the general population found a 12-month prevalence of 3.2% for social anxiety disorder and 4.6% for sub-clinical social anxiety disorder. As age increased, prevalence increased and the gender ratio shifted to primarily females. Social anxiety disorder was associated with educational impairment, depression and anxiety in parents, and peer victimization. Only 1 in 5 of these adolescents had been in contact with a mental health professional. One of the most vexing aspects of social anxiety disorder is that it tends to mitigate against help-seeking for both mental and physical health problems, likely due to concerns about social evaluation from health care professionals, as well as fellow clients in the waiting room.

Recent data from a 10-year longitudinal study indicate that social anxiety disorder tends to persist. This study of over 3,000 clients who were initially between the ages of 14 to 24 years old found that social anxiety was present for at least 5 years and only about 1 in 7 people had complete remission of their social anxiety. Predictors of persistent social anxiety included having a parent with diagnosed social anxiety, experiencing depression, having a temperament style of elevated behavioural inhibition, having symptoms of panic disorder, and having more extreme symptoms to begin with (see Beesdo-Baum et al., 2012).

There were a number of changes in *DSM-5*, including the performance-only specifier described above, and the change in name from social phobia to social anxiety disorder. As we have seen, SAD can be quite impairing, but the former name of social phobia was often confused with specific phobia and did not connote this level of impairment (Heimberg et al., 2014). Also new to *DSM-5*, the clinician evaluates whether the degree of fear is excessive and takes into account the socio-cultural context when doing so. For example, reticence may be a sign of respect rather than social anxiety.

Like specific phobias, SAD varies cross-culturally. A Japanese syndrome called *taijin kyofusho* (TKS) is an extreme fear of embarrassing others—for example, by blushing in their presence, glancing at their genital areas, or making odd faces. In SAD, the core fear is of being judged negatively. In TKS, the core fear is causing others to feel anxious. It is believed that TKS arises from elements of traditional Japanese culture, which encourages extreme concern for the feelings of others yet discourages direct communication of feelings (McNally, 1997). Contemporary research suggests that this syndrome may be more widespread than first believed. The symptoms of one subtype of TKS were detected in social anxiety disorder clients both from Korea and the United States and it was associated in both samples with social anxiety, depression, and disability (Choy et al., 2008).

5.4   Etiology of Specific Phobias and SAD

We consider the etiology of specific phobias and social anxiety disorder together, as they have a history of being grouped together in some of the relevant research. Proposals about the causes of specific phobias and SAD have been made by adherents of the behavioural, cognitive, biological, and psychoanalytic paradigms. We now look at the ideas of each of these paradigms.

Behavioural Theories

Behavioural theories focus on learning as the way in which phobias are acquired. Several types of learning may be involved.

Avoidance Conditioning   The main behavioural account of phobias is that such reactions are learned avoidance responses. Historically, the model of how a phobia is acquired is considered to be Watson and Rayner's (1920) demonstration of the apparent conditioning of a fear or phobia in Little Albert (see photo). The avoidance-conditioning formulation, which is based on the two-factor theory originally proposed by Mowrer (1947), holds that phobias develop from two related sets of learning:

1. Via classical conditioning, a person can learn to fear a neutral stimulus (the CS) if it is paired with an intrinsically painful or frightening event (the UCS).

2. The person can learn to reduce this conditioned fear by escaping from or avoiding the CS. This second kind of learning is assumed to be operant conditioning; the response is maintained by its reinforcing consequence of reducing fear.

An important issue exists in the application of the avoidance-conditioning model to phobias. The fact that Little Albert's fear of white rats was acquired through conditioning cannot be taken as evidence that all fears and phobias are acquired by this means. Rather, the evidence demonstrates only the *possibility* that some fears may be acquired in this particular way. Furthermore, attempts to replicate Watson and Rayner's

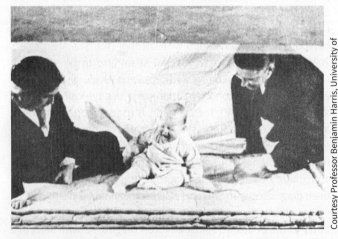

Little Albert, shown here with Watson and Rayner, was classically conditioned to develop a fear of a white rat.

Courtesy Professor Benjamin Harris, University of New Hampshire experiment were not successful for the most part (e.g., English, 1929). Nevertheless, data attest to the possibility that people can learn to fear certain stimuli.

Ethical considerations have restrained most researchers from employing highly aversive stimuli with human beings, but considerable evidence indicates that fear is extinguished rather quickly when the CS is presented a few times without the reinforcement of moderate levels of shock (Bridger & Mandel, 1965). Outside the laboratory, the evidence for the avoidance-conditioning theory is mixed. Some clinical phobias fit the model rather well. A phobia of a specific object or situation has sometimes been reported after a particularly painful experience with that object. Some people become intensely afraid of heights after a bad fall, others develop a phobia of driving after experiencing a panic attack in their car, and people with SAD often report traumatic social experiences. Other clinical reports suggest that phobias may develop without a prior frightening experience. Many individuals with severe fears of snakes, germs, and airplanes tell clinicians that they have had no particularly unpleasant experiences with these objects or situations. Can this problem with the avoidance-conditioning model be solved? One attempt to do so involves modelling.

Modelling
In addition to learning to fear something as a result of an unpleasant experience with it, a person can also learn fears through imitating the reactions of others. Thus, some phobias may be acquired by modelling. The learning of fear by observing others is generally referred to as **vicarious learning**.

In one study, Bandura and Rosenthal (1966) arranged for participants to watch another person, the model (a confederate of the experimenter), in an aversive-conditioning situation. The model was hooked up to an impressive-looking array of electrical apparatuses. On hearing a buzzer, the model withdrew his hand rapidly from the arm of the chair and feigned pain. The physiological responses of the participants witnessing this behaviour were recorded. After the participants had watched the model "suffer" a number of times, they showed an increased frequency of emotional responses when the buzzer sounded. Thus, they reacted emotionally to a harmless stimulus even though they had had no direct contact with a noxious event.

Research by Olsson and Phelps (2004) demonstrated that Pavlovian conditioning and observational learning via imitation can both play a role; in fact, they showed that observing another person's fear response and not having explicit, conscious awareness of this conditioned stimulus can still contribute to the apparent learning of a fear response. Vicarious learning may also be accomplished through verbal instructions. Thus, phobic reactions can be learned through another's description of what could happen. For example, a child may come to fear an activity after a parent has repeatedly warned him or her not to engage in it lest dire consequences ensue. Indeed, the *anxious-rearing model* is based on the premise that anxiety disorders in children are due to constant parental warnings that increase anxiety in the child.

Prepared Learning
Another issue that the original avoidance-learning model fails to address is that people tend to fear only certain objects and events, such as spiders, snakes, and heights, but not others, such as lambs. The fact that certain neutral stimuli, called *prepared stimuli,* are more likely than others to become classically conditioned stimuli may account for this tendency. For example, rats readily learn to associate taste with nausea but not with shock when the two are paired (Garcia, McGowan, & Green, 1972). Some fears may well reflect classical conditioning, but only to stimuli to which an organism is physiologically prepared to be sensitive (Ohman & Mineka, 2001). Conditioning experiments that show quick extinction of fear may have used CSs that the organism was not prepared to associate with UCSs. Prepared learning is also relevant to learning fear by modelling. Cook and Mineka (1989) studied four groups of rhesus monkeys, each of which saw a different videotape showing a monkey seemingly react with fear to different stimuli: a toy snake, a toy crocodile, flowers, or a toy rabbit. Only the monkeys exposed to the tapes showing the toy snake or toy crocodile acquired fear of the object shown, again demonstrating that not every stimulus is capable of becoming a source of acquired fear. There is considerable evidence in support of the preparedness theory of phobias (see Ohman & Mineka, 2001, for review). Evidence that college students have much stronger and distinct reactions to spiders vs. bees, wasps, beetles, and moths has also been interpreted as an indication of biological preparedness shaped evolutionarily by natural selection (see Gerdes, Pauli, & Alpers, 2009).

The Role of Diathesis
One question to consider is why some people who have traumatic experiences do not develop enduring fears. For example, 50% of people with a severe fear of dogs reported a prior traumatic experience, yet 50% of people who were not afraid of dogs reported a similar experience (DiNardo et al., 1988; see photo). Why did only some people develop this fear? A cognitive diathesis (predisposition)—a tendency to believe that similar traumatic experiences

DiNardo's study (1988) showed that after a traumatic experience with a dog, those who developed a persistent fear of dogs were anxious about having similar future experiences.

will occur in the future—may be important in developing a phobia. Another possible psychological diathesis is a history of not being able to control the environment (Mineka & Zinbarg, 1996). Aversive conditioning experiences, such as severe teasing, have been proposed to play a role in the development of SAD. McCabe et al. (2003) found a significant link between perceptions of teasing and bullying in childhood and SAD.

In sum, the data suggest that while some phobias are learned through avoidance conditioning, avoidance conditioning should not be regarded as a totally validated theory; many people with phobias do not report either direct exposure to a traumatic event or exposure to fearful models (Merckelbach et al., 1989).

Social Skills Deficits in Social Anxiety Disorder

A behavioural model of social anxiety disorder considers inappropriate behaviour or a lack of social skills as the cause of social anxiety. According to this view, the individual has not learned how to behave so that he or she feels comfortable with others, or the person repeatedly commits faux pas, is awkward and socially inept, and is often criticized by social companions. Support for this model comes from findings that socially anxious people are often rated as being low in social skills (e.g., Twentyman & McFall, 1975).

Of course, social skill deficits may have arisen over time because the person was fearful of interacting with others for other reasons, such as classical conditioning, and therefore had little experience doing so. Also, extreme anxiety may be impairing the person's ability to use appropriate social skills. In fact, recent data supports that the use of safety behaviours during a speech performance may be responsible for poorer performance ratings (Rowa et al., 2015). The lack of interpersonal skills in an adult who has SAD may therefore reveal little of etiological significance, though the information may be very important in planning effective therapeutic interventions. Social skills deficits may be more pronounced and problematic in children with SAD than adults, but even then, findings are not consistent. Parent and child reports of social skills did not differ comparing children with SAD and those with GAD, but the two groups did differ on some observable behaviours (e.g., anxious speech patterns) (Scharfstein & Beidel, 2015).

Cognitive Theories

Cognitive views focus on how thought processes can serve as a diathesis and on how thoughts can maintain a phobia or anxiety. Anxiety is related to being more likely to attend to negative stimuli, to interpret ambiguous information as threatening, and to believe that negative events are more likely than positive ones to occur in the future (Mathews & MacLeod, 1994). For instance, spider phobia involves automatic thought processes and implicit cognitive associations involving themes of disgust and threat that occur without conscious introspection or awareness (Teachman & Woody, 2003).

Cognitive processes are strongly implicated in the etiology and maintenance of SAD. Socially anxious people are more concerned about evaluation than are people who are not socially

anxious (Goldfried, Padawer, & Robins, 1984) and they are highly aware of the image they present to others (Bates, 1990). They are high in public self-consciousness and are preoccupied with a need to seem perfect and not make mistakes in front of other people (Flett, Coulter, & Hewitt, 2012). Socially anxious people's hypersensitivity to social cues is reflected by a tendency to be cognitively preoccupied with situations in which they were treated negatively by others (Nepon, Flett, Hewitt, & Molnar, 2011). SAD is also linked with excessive self-criticism (Cox, Walker, Enns, & Karpinski, 2002). David Moscovitch (2009) at the University of Waterloo concluded that the fundamental core thematic fear in SAD is "the self is deficient." He maintains that the key situational triggers are those situations and circumstances that will publicly reveal the self as inadequate. Unfortunately, socially anxious people tend to view themselves negatively even when they have actually performed well in a social interaction (Wallace & Alden, 1997) and they are less certain about their positive self-views, and, relative to people without SAD, they see their positive attributes as being less important (Moscovitch et al., 2009). Experimental data suggest that people with SAD have a cognitive bias toward being more attentive visually to negative faces than to positive faces, but no such bias is evident among people with OCD or in control participants (Eastwood et al., 2005). People with other anxiety disorders have also been shown to have attentional biases toward disorder-relevant threat; interestingly, the bias starts in childhood and increases with age (Dudeney, Sharpe, & Hunt, 2015). Socially anxious people also seem to fear having a negative impact on other people; that is, they are worried about causing discomfort in other people (Rector, Kocovski, & Ryder, 2006), in some ways similar to the concerns present in TKS.

Cognitive models of SAD (e.g., Clark & Wells, 1995; Rapee & Heimberg, 1997) link social anxiety with the following key characteristics: (1) an attentional bias to focus on negative social information (e.g., perceived criticism and hostile reactions from others) and interpret ambiguous situations as negative; (2) perfectionistic standards for accepted social performances; and (3) a high degree of public self-consciousness. Not only do people with SAD have a tendency to interpret ambiguous social situations as negative and a reflection of their personal shortcomings, they also have a memory bias linked to this interpretation bias (Hertel, Brozovich, Joormann, & Gotlib, 2008). In other words, people with SAD tend to falsely recall events they have interpreted as having emotionally negative features.

David Clark's model of SAD has clear treatment implications; in fact, Clark (2001) advises against exposure as usual, but instead advocates for the use of behavioural experiments and role plays. The key problem according to Clark (2001) is that people with SAD have an excessive self-focus that amplifies their mistaken and rigid beliefs that they will be rejected by others if they do not engage in appropriate behaviour. Clark (2001) emphasized the importance of facilitating an external focus on other people along with developing the realization that other people are not typically judgemental and will not automatically be punitive and reject the person with SAD. One technique that follows from this approach is called "widening the bandwidth." Clients are instructed to act in ways that they feel are totally unacceptable and then objectively watch for the lack of a negative reaction from other people. At times when there is no reaction, the clients see that they can widen the scope of their behaviours without fear of negative consequences. People with SAD are particularly concerned about committing social blunders. They believe that the cost of such mistakes is much greater than do individuals with other anxiety disorders or healthy controls (Moscovitch et al., 2015), so challenging these interpretations is an important therapeutic goal.

Rachman, Gruter-Andrew, and Shafran (2000) reported that socially anxious students not only anticipate negative social experiences, they also engage in extensive **post-event processing (PEP)** of the negative social experiences. Post-event processing is a form of rumination (dwelling) about previous experiences and responses to these situations, especially experiences involving other people that did not turn out well. Subsequent research confirmed a link between social anxiety and PEP. Kocovski, Endler, Rector, and Flett (2005) reported that those high in social anxiety are more likely to ruminate and less likely to distract themselves as a way of coping with a threatening social event (i.e., making a mistake in public). Experimental data have confirmed that children with SAD show a pattern of fewer positive thoughts and a greater number of negative thoughts following a social evaluation experience (Schmitz et al., 2010). There are also indications that negative PEP contributes to subsequent performance declines in social situations among socially anxious children (Schmitz et al., 2011). Finally, experimental data with university students indicates that socially anxious students who are induced into a state of high self-focus, compared with those instructed to focus on the other person during a conversation, report the next day a higher level of negative PEP thoughts but not a lower level of positive thoughts (Gaydukevych & Kocovski, 2012).

Overall, then, there are many cognitive elements that are seen to play an important causal role in the development and maintenance of social anxiety disorder. We have examined behavioural and cognitive paradigms in the development of specific phobias and SAD, and now we turn to biological factors.

Biological Theories

Why do some people acquire unrealistic fears when others do not, given similar opportunities for learning? Perhaps those who are adversely affected by stress have a biological malfunction (a diathesis) that somehow predisposes them to develop a phobia following a particular stressful event.

Much of the current biological work examines brain structures and associated neurobiological processes. Current work is focused extensively on the role of the amygdala, which is a cerebral structure of the brain's temporal lobe. Functional MRI and PET studies of specific phobia and SAD have examined responses across three conditions: negative emotion, positive emotion, and neutral conditions. Results of meta-analyses show conclusively that people with these disorders, relative to comparison participants, have greater activity in two areas associated with negative emotional responses: the amygdala and the insula (Etkin & Wager, 2007; Ipser, Singh, & Stein, 2013). Interestingly, exposure-based therapy for clients with specific phobias leads to decreased activation in some of the same areas of the brain (Ipser et al., 2013). More generally, the various anxiety disorders may reflect a complex array of biological factors and processes. Research in two areas seems promising: the autonomic nervous system (ANS) and genetic factors.

Autonomic Nervous System   One way people differ in their reaction to certain environmental situations is the ease with which their autonomic nervous systems become aroused. Lacey (1967) identified a dimension of autonomic activity that he called stability-lability. Labile, or jumpy, individuals are those whose autonomic systems are readily aroused by a wide range of stimuli. Because of the extent to which the autonomic nervous system is involved in fear and hence in phobic behaviour, a dimension such as **autonomic lability** assumes considerable importance. Since there is reason to believe that autonomic lability is to some degree genetically determined (Gabbay, 1992), heredity may very well have a significant role in the development of phobias.

Genetic Factors   Several studies have examined whether a genetic factor is involved in phobias. Temperament differences among newborns are influenced largely by genetic factors. Jerome Kagan has focused on the trait of behavioural inhibition or shyness (Kagan, 1997). Some infants as young as four months become agitated and cry when they are shown toys or other stimuli. This behaviour pattern, which may be inherited, may set the stage for the later development of phobias.

The data we have described do not unequivocally implicate genetic factors. Smoller, Gardner-Schuster, and Covino (2008) reviewed the role of genetic factors in phobic and panic disorders and concluded that these disorders are familial and moderately heritable but no specific susceptibility genes have been found thus far. Linkage analyses seek to identify the specific genes implicated in these disorders.

Psychoanalytic Theories

Freud was the first to attempt to account systematically for the development of phobic behaviour. According to Freud, phobias are a defence against the anxiety produced by repressed id impulses. This anxiety is displaced from the feared id impulse and moved to an object or situation that has some symbolic connection to it. These objects or situations—for example, elevators or closed spaces—then become the phobic stimuli. By avoiding them the person is able to avoid dealing with repressed conflicts. The phobia is the ego's way of warding off a confrontation with the real problem, a repressed childhood conflict. Arieti (1979) proposed that the repression stems from a particular interpersonal problem of childhood rather than from an id impulse. As with most psychoanalytic theorizing, most of the supporting evidence is restricted to conclusions drawn from clinical case reports.

We have described two anxiety disorders (specific phobia and social anxiety disorder) and will now turn our attention to the remaining three anxiety disorders in this chapter (panic disorder, agoraphobia, and generalized anxiety disorder) before we consider treatment options.

5.5 Panic Disorder and Agoraphobia

In *DSM-IV-TR*, panic disorder was diagnosed as being with or without agoraphobia, but this distinction was dropped in *DSM-5*. Panic disorder and agoraphobia are now two separate disorders, although, as you will see, they are still linked in many ways.

Panic Disorder

In **panic disorder**, a person suffers a sudden and often inexplicable attack of a host of jarring symptoms: laboured breathing, heart palpitations, nausea, and chest pain; feelings of choking and smothering; dizziness, sweating, and trembling; and intense apprehension, terror, and feelings of impending doom. **Depersonalization**, a feeling of being outside one's body, and **derealization**, a feeling of the world's not being real, as well as fears of losing control, of going crazy, or even of dying, may beset and overwhelm the person.

Given the variety of symptoms that can be present during a panic attack, there have been several attempts to classify clients with panic disorder based on the symptoms they experience the most. Only four symptoms are required to meet criteria for a panic attack (out of a possible 13), therefore three people can each have panic attacks without sharing a single symptom. A recent study found that about a third of people have both cognitive (e.g., fear of losing control) and autonomic (e.g., feeling hot) symptoms, and another third have primarily autonomic symptoms, but the largest group (40%) was aspecific (Pattyn et al., 2015). Future research is warranted to see if this classification can be replicated and to determine how useful it actually is.

Panic attacks may occur frequently, perhaps once a week or more often; they usually last for minutes, rarely for hours; and they are sometimes linked to specific situations, such as driving a car. They are referred to as cued or expected panic attacks when they are associated strongly with situational triggers. The exclusive presence of cued attacks most likely reflects the presence of a specific phobia. For example, a person with a specific phobia of dogs may always have a panic attack when in the presence of dogs. When their relationship with stimuli is present but not as strong, they are referred to as situationally predisposed attacks. Situationally predisposed panic attacks often

TABLE 5.3	Summary of Types of Panic Attacks
Type of Panic Attack	**Description**
Uncued/unexpected	Out of the blue; the type required for a diagnosis of panic disorder
Cued/expected	Strongly associated with trigger
Situationally predisposed	Some association with trigger
Nocturnal	Waking from sleep in a panic (unexpected)

occur in SAD. Panic attacks can also occur in seemingly benign states, such as relaxation or sleep, and in unexpected situations; in these cases, they are referred to as uncued attacks. Waking in a state of panic is referred to as a nocturnal panic attack. Table 5.3 outlines the different types of panic attacks.

Recurrent unexpected attacks and either worry about having attacks in the future or a change in behaviour as a result of the attacks are required for the diagnosis of panic disorder. Panic attacks can be a part of many anxiety disorders; they are not sufficient for a diagnosis of panic disorder. Also, a person with panic disorder can have both unexpected and expected panic attacks; the important point is that unexpected attacks are required for a diagnosis of panic disorder.

When people are worried about future attacks, it is usually because they are concerned that the symptoms really mean they are having a heart attack or that they have some other physical health condition. They may also be concerned that others will notice the panic symptoms and judge them. Finally, if they have cognitive symptoms such as a fear of "going crazy" as part of their panic attack experience, this particular fear may extend beyond the actual panic attack; their worry about future attacks may be because they view the panic attacks as a sign of "going crazy."

The change in behaviour that often occurs as a result of the panic attacks usually involves avoidance. People commonly avoid the situations in which they have endured panic attacks in the past. They may avoid going out of the house alone in case they have a panic attack. They may also avoid exercise (or other activities like going on roller coasters) in an attempt to avoid the physical sensations they fear.

Panic disorder has been linked with a wide range of conditions, including depression, generalized anxiety disorder, alcohol and drug use, and personality disorders. Panic disorder is also linked with physical conditions such as asthma, and in people suffering from both, it is believed that the panic exacerbates the asthma and vice versa (Lehrer et al., 2008). As with many disorders, comorbidity in panic disorder is associated with greater severity and poorer outcomes (Newman et al., 1998).

More than 80% of people diagnosed as having one of the other anxiety disorders also experience panic attacks (Barlow et al., 1985). Kinley et al. (2009) analyzed the CCHS data set to determine the prevalence rates and correlates of panic attacks among Canadians. The 12-month prevalence of panic attacks was 6.4%. Panic attacks were related to numerous psychological and physical function variables, including poor overall functioning, suicidal ideation, psychological distress, activity restriction, chronic physical conditions, and self-rated physical and mental health (Kinley et al., 2009). The authors concluded that panic attacks may be a marker of severe psychopathology independent of a diagnosis of panic disorder. Research such as this study has led to a panic attack specifier in *DSM-5*. For example, if a person with social anxiety disorder meets criteria for panic attacks, then the diagnosis would be "social anxiety disorder with panic attacks." This specifier is not limited to anxiety disorders, and can also apply to certain medical conditions.

Disorders that bear some relationship to panic disorder occur in other cultures. Among the Inuit of Northern Canada and west Greenland, *kayak-angst* occurs among seal hunters who are alone at sea (see photo). Attacks involve intense fear, disorientation, and concerns about drowning. *DSM-5* also lists possible culture-specific symptoms, like headaches and crying, that may be reported by clients as they are describing panic attacks, but they are not officially included as part of the four required symptoms.

Agoraphobia

Agoraphobia (from the Greek *agora,* meaning "marketplace") is a cluster of fears centring on public places and being unable to escape or find help should one become incapacitated. Fears of shopping, crowds, and travelling are often present. Many people with agoraphobia are unable to leave the house or do so only with great distress. To be diagnosed with agoraphobia,

Disorders similar to panic attacks occur cross-culturally. Among the Inuit, *kayak-angst* is defined as intense fear in lone hunters.

a person would have to be anxious about at least two types of situations out of the following five: public transportation, open spaces, enclosed spaces, lines/crowds (see photo), and being out of the house alone. Usually the primary concern is about having panic-like symptoms and not being able to escape the situation, but it could also be a fear of incontinence (loss of bladder control) or other embarrassing symptoms.

People who have panic disorder typically avoid the situations in which a panic attack could be dangerous or embarrassing. If the avoidance is limited to one type of situation, then that would be captured in the panic disorder diagnosis. If the avoidance is more widespread and covers two agoraphobic situations, then an additional diagnosis of agoraphobia would be warranted. Many people with panic disorder go on to develop agoraphobia, but not everyone with panic disorder

---

A Life Debilitated by Panic Disorder

Margot Paul answers the door slowly, with her head held down. "Come in quickly," she says, "before you let the cats out." Margot has four cats and they are often her only company. She lives alone and rarely goes outside, afraid she'll get hit by a car, fall and break her bones, or suffer a stroke. Margot suffers from agoraphobia, an anxiety condition that causes her extreme panic, or even terror, when she's subjected to any situation outside of her "safety zone." Like many people with agoraphobia, Margot's safety zone is her home. Margot, now in her 80s, traces her anxiety back to the age of 11 when a man in her First Nations community on Lennox Island, P.E.I., assaulted her. "He chased me and knocked me down," she says. "He tried to tear my clothes off, but I fought him off. I was terrified. He told me he'd kill me if I opened my mouth, so I didn't tell anybody." Margot remembers that after the incident she started making excuses for not leaving the house. "When I thought about that man, I was taken over with fear and trembling," she says. "I hid for a long, long time. I really believed he would kill me." At the age of 15, Margot ran away, but she couldn't run away from the fear. "When I saw people fighting, like a man and his girlfriend, panic would come on me," she says. Working for a travelling fair, Margot saw the man who assaulted her one more time. She says seeing him produced terror in her—"sheer terror." But she says the assault wasn't the only thing that contributed to her condition. "Kids used

to tell me how ugly I was," she says. "I was so afraid of being seen, I would always wear a hat to hide my face." Margot says she was also insecure because she grew up speaking only Mi'kmaq and her English was poor. She moved to Halifax when she was 18 years old and worked in restaurants, in bars, and for bootleggers. She says she would often suffer from anxiety and go into hiding, but then the symptoms would lift and she would be able to work again. Margot married and had five children. One of her sons comes over once or twice a week to take her grocery shopping or to the doctor. She calls him her "safe person," meaning he is one of the few people she trusts. Except for these trips, Margot hasn't been outside for over a year.... One of her daughters, who also suffers from agoraphobia, lives upstairs from her. Margot's doctor tells her that her thought patterns fuel her fears. "What I think really does have an effect on how I feel," she says. "The mind is the computer of the body and what you feed it, it will produce. By changing the way I think, I've found a big difference." But Margot is still reluctant to join a self-help group. "I don't think I could even join a group," she says. "I feel like I don't fit in. . . . It seems like all my life I've been hiding," she says. "My life is a sad, sad story." Margot died of a heart attack on April 27, 2001. Documents indicated that she was older than realized—92 years old at the time of her death.

Scott Barbour/Stringer/Getty Images, Inc.

A crowd is likely to be very distressing to a person with agoraphobia, who is often afraid of having panic-like symptoms in a public place and not being able to escape.

has agoraphobia. Similarly, not everyone with agoraphobia meets criteria for panic disorder or even has a history of panic attacks (Asmundson, Taylor, & Smits, 2014).

Gordon Asmundson at the University of Regina and his colleagues (2014) reviewed the decision to split panic disorder and agoraphobia into separate diagnoses. One issue they raised is that symptoms of panic disorder can count toward a diagnosis of agoraphobia and that symptoms of agoraphobia can count toward a diagnosis of panic disorder. This overlap in symptoms may negatively affect diagnostic reliability.

When panic disorder or other anxiety disorders are present, they most often precede the development of agoraphobia. However, depressive and substance use disorders often develop after the onset of agoraphobia (American Psychiatric Association, 2013). Agoraphobia is much more common among women than among men.

The preceding case in Canada described by Ananda Duquette (2001) illustrates what it is like to live with panic disorder and agoraphobia and provides some insight into possible causes (see "A Life Debilitated by Panic Disorder").

5.6 Etiology of Panic Disorder and Agoraphobia

Similar to specific phobias and SAD, both biological and psychological theories have been proposed to explain panic disorder and agoraphobia.

Biological Theories

In a minority of cases, physical sensations caused by an illness lead some people to develop panic disorder. Mitral valve prolapse syndrome causes heart palpitations, and inner ear disease causes dizziness; both can be terrifying, leading to the development of panic disorder (Asmundson, Larsen, & Stein, 1998).

Panic disorder runs in families and has greater concordance in identical-twin pairs than in fraternal twins (Smoller et al., 2008). Smoller et al. (2008) summarized the results of six controlled family studies. These studies have established an increased risk of 5–16% among relatives of those with panic disorder. Early onset of panic disorder is associated with increased risk for family members. Thus, a genetic diathesis may be involved, and specific chromosomes are being investigated. For example, an investigation of Canadian samples (Rothe et al., 2006) builds on evidence for the influence of the Val158Met COMT polymorphism or other loci within or near the COMT gene (on chromosome 22) on susceptibility to panic disorder. Rothe et al. (2006) concluded that, "If COMT is further proven to be involved then new targets for drug development may be uncovered leading to enhanced pharmacological treatment of panic disorder" (p. 2241). In a review of linkage and association studies of anxiety disorders, Hamilton (2009) identified 96 studies that focused primarily on genetic association between one or a small number of genes and panic disorder. There were 76 discrete genes being studied that represented many aspects of fear circuit biology (e.g., receptors for neuropeptides, monoamines, and gamma-aminobutyric acid). Other studies took a more comprehensive approach and involved 340 genes of neurobiological interest (e.g., related to serotonin, dopamine, or cholecystokinin systems). However, most of the findings have not been replicated. Hamilton (2009) concluded that COMT appears to be one of the few consistent findings in anxiety disorder genetics. However, the link is not only to panic disorder; disorders such as schizophrenia, major depression, and anxiety-related personality traits are also implicated. Further, the lack of replication continues. Savage and colleagues (2015) investigated 26 polymorphisms on 11 genes and found only one significant relationship: ASIC1 was significantly associated with respiratory rate (but not subjective anxiety). They failed to replicate the COMT finding, among other previously supported gene-anxiety associations.

Noradrenergic Activity Another biological theory suggests that panic is caused by overactivity in the noradrenergic system (neurons that use norepinephrine as a neurotransmitter). One version of this theory focuses on a nucleus in the pons called the locus ceruleus. Stimulation of the locus ceruleus causes monkeys to have what appears to be a panic attack, suggesting that naturally occurring attacks involve noradrenergic overactivation (Redmond, 1977). Subsequent research with humans has found that yohimbine, a drug that stimulates activity in the locus ceruleus, can elicit panic attacks in people with panic disorder (Charney et al., 1987). However, other research is not consistent with this position. Importantly, drugs that block firing in the locus ceruleus have not been found to be very effective in treating panic attacks (McNally, 1994).

One idea about noradrenergic overactivity that has received strong support is that it results from a problem in gamma-aminobutyric acid (GABA) neurons that generally inhibit noradrenergic activity. For instance, a PET (positron emission tomography) study found fewer GABA-receptor binding sites in clients with panic disorder than in members of the control group (Malizia et al., 1998). Evidence has now accumulated to indicate that GABA interneurons play important roles in the acquisition, cognitive storage, and extinction of fear (see Mohler, 2012). These data also suggest that therapeutic improvement involves changes in GABA receptors, but this applies to both anxiety and depression (Mohler, 2012).

Cholecystokinin   Canadian psychiatrist Jacques Bradwejn and his colleagues in Toronto, Ottawa, and Montreal initiated another stimulating line of research in the attempt to understand the neurobiology of panic disorder (e.g., Bradwejn, Koszycki, & Meterissian, 1990). They discovered that cholecystokinin (CCK), a peptide that occurs in the cerebral cortex, amygdala, hippocampus, and brain stem, induces anxiety-like symptoms in rats and that the effect can be blocked with benzodiazepines, suggesting that changes in CCK produce changes in the development or expression of panic (e.g., Koszycki, Torres, Swain, & Bradwejn, 2005). Bradwejn hypothesized that panic disorder is, at least in part, due to hypersensitivity to CCK. The mechanism of this sensitivity is not clear: CCK sensitivity may affect the action of other neurotransmitters or neurons in the noradrenergic system, or people may be reacting psychologically to the strong physical sensations caused by CCK.

Subsequent work has explored how healthy adult volunteers respond to CCK-4 injections (Eser et al., 2009). Initial results indicated that following the injection, overall brain activation patterns are not associated with the subjective anxiety response, but amygdala activation is seemingly involved in the subjective perception of anxiety. Figure 5.1 illustrates how one participant responded to the injection.

More contemporary work continues to implicate CCK in panic disorder. Zwanzger, Domschke, and Bradwejn (2012) concluded that the neuronal network of CCK is such that CCK is a key modulator of the fear network. In addition, exposure to CCK-4 induces panic attacks and clients with panic disorder have a clear sensitivity to CCK-4. Finally, Zwanzger et al. (2012) also noted that there is a genetic basis to CCK-4 and its role in panic disorder.

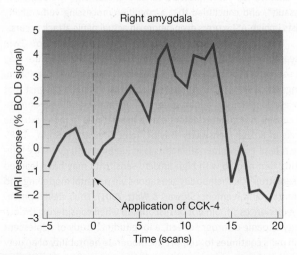

Right amygdala

Application of CCK-4

FIGURE 5.1   Time course of activity in the right amygdala of a participant with high amygdala activation in the first minute after CCK-4 injection. Reprinted with permission of John Wiley & Sons, Ltd.

Psychological Theories

The principal psychological theory of agoraphobia is the fear-of-fear hypothesis (e.g., Goldstein & Chambless, 1978), which suggests that agoraphobia is not a fear of public places per se, but a fear of having panic-like symptoms in public.

As for panic attacks themselves, the foundation for their development may be an ANS that is predisposed to be overly active (Barlow, 1988) coupled with a psychological tendency to become very upset by these sensations. When high physiological arousal occurs, some people construe these unusual autonomic reactions (such as rapid heart rate) as a sign of great danger or even as a sign that they are dying. After repeated occurrences, the person comes to fear having these internal sensations and, by worrying excessively, makes them worse and panic attacks more likely. Thus, the psychology of the person takes over from where the biology began. The person becomes more vigilant about even subtle signs of an impending panic attack, and this, too, makes an attack more probable. The result is a vicious circle: fearing another panic attack leads to increased autonomic activity; symptoms of this activity are interpreted in catastrophic ways; and these interpretations in turn raise the anxiety level, which eventually blossoms into a full-blown panic attack (Craske & Barlow, 1993).

Telch and colleagues (Telch, Harrington, Smits, & Powers, 2011) studied students with no history of panic attacks who were divided into two groups (high and low scorers) based on their test scores on the Anxiety Sensitivity Index (ASI; Peterson & Reiss, 1987). The 16-item ASI measures the extent to which people respond fearfully to bodily sensations that could reflect a fear response. High scorers believe that these sensations have harmful somatic, psychological, or social consequences. Sample ASI items are shown in Table 5.4. All participants experienced two trials. In one trial they breathed room air, and in the other they breathed air with a higher than usual concentration of carbon dioxide. Half the participants were told that the carbon dioxide would be relaxing, and half were told that it would produce symptoms of high arousal. Panic attacks did not occur in participants when they breathed room air, confirming previous findings. Also, the frequency of panic attacks was higher in participants who were high in fear of their own bodily

TABLE 5.4	**Sample Items from the Anxiety Sensitivity Index**
Unusual body sensations scare me.	
When I notice that my heart is beating I worry that I might have a heart attack.	
It scares me when I feel faint.	
It scares me when I feel "shaky" (trembling).	

Note: People respond to each item on a 0 (very little) to 4 (very much) scale.

Source: Peterson, R. A., & Reiss, R. L. (1987). The Anxiety Sensitivity Index: Construct validity and factor analytic structure. *Journal of Anxiety Disorders,* 1(3), 265–277. Reprinted with permission from Elsevier.

sensations. Finally, and most important, the frequency of panic attacks was strikingly high in participants who feared their bodily sensations, breathed air containing a high concentration of carbon dioxide, and did not expect it to be arousing. This result is exactly what the theory predicts: unexplained physiological arousal in someone who is highly fearful of such sensations leads to panic attacks. Thus, a heightened tendency to be afraid of fear sensations appears to play an important role.

In contrast to many conceptualizations of anxiety, anxiety sensitivity is presumed to be a dispositional characteristic that precedes the development of anxiety disorders. There is, in fact, converging evidence that anxiety sensitivity acts as a risk factor for anxiety psychopathology (see Schmidt, Zvolensky, & Maner, 2006, for review). Schmidt et al. (2007) prospectively followed more than 400 non-clinical participants over a two-year period. Anxiety sensitivity predicted the development of spontaneous panic attacks. More importantly, independent of a history of anxiety problems and baseline trait anxiety, anxiety sensitivity predicted the development of anxiety diagnoses as well as other clinical diagnoses, including mood and alcohol-use disorders. Thus, there is strong evidence for anxiety sensitivity as a risk factor in the development of numerous clinical syndromes.

Extensive research is continuing on anxiety sensitivity. An important meta-analysis of 117 studies concluded that anxiety sensitivity is most closely related to panic disorder, but it is also related to other anxiety disorders (GAD, SAD), as well as post-traumatic stress disorder (Naragon-Gainey, 2010). Interestingly, the neural underpinnings of anxiety sensitivity have been a focus of recent research (Poletti et al., 2015). Clients with *DSM-IV* panic disorder with agoraphobia were presented with emotional faces or shapes while undergoing functional magnetic resonance imaging. Anxiety sensitivity was correlated with greater activity in the following brain regions while processing the emotional faces: anterior cingulate cortex and insula. These areas of the brain are involved in the processing of threat and these results are consistent with previous anxiety findings. Canadian contributions to research on anxiety sensitivity and the "fear of fear" are described in Canadian Perspectives 5.1. Research activities have focused on assessing the anxiety sensitivity construct as well as its correlates.

Fortunately, high anxiety sensitivity appears amenable to CBT. A meta-analysis of 24 randomized controlled trials (RCTs) found large treatment effect sizes for treatment-seeking samples and moderate to large effect sizes for at-risk participants who did not seek treatment (Smits, Berry, Tart, & Powers, 2008). For instance, a longitudinal investigation in which participants underwent a CBT-based anxiety sensitivity amelioration training as a form of primary prevention yielded significant reductions in anxiety sensitivity. These reductions were specific to anxiety sensitivity, as opposed to other cognitive risk factors for anxiety (Schmidt et al., 2007). Also, changes in anxiety sensitivity preceded changes in panic symptoms for a sample of clients with panic disorder who underwent 11 sessions of CBT, as did changes in self-efficacy (Gallagher et al., 2013).

Canadian Perspectives 5.1

Research on the Psychometric Properties and Applications of the Anxiety Sensitivity Index

Several Canadian research groups have examined the psychometric properties and research applications of the Anxiety Sensitivity Index (ASI) as a way of finding out more about "the fear of fear," or the tendency to catastrophize the meaning of bodily symptoms. One question that has been asked is whether anxiety sensitivity is a unitary construct. While some research indicates that the ASI consists of only one factor, Canadian work with a modified ASI, the ASI-3, suggests three factors reflecting physical, cognitive, and social concerns (see Taylor et al., 2007). Whereas generalized anxiety disorder seems to implicate all three ASI factors, meta-analytic results implicate the physical and cognitive factors primarily in panic disorder, while social concerns, as might be expected, had their greatest associations with social anxiety disorder (Naragon-Gainey, 2010).

Research conducted at the University of Regina showed that students with high anxiety sensitivity, relative to those with low anxiety sensitivity, had greater subcortical startle responses when exposed to trials of white noise (McMillan, Asmundson, Zvolensky, & Carleton, 2012). Other research applications of the ASI include work on the cognitive aspects of anxiety sensitivity. For instance, Canadian researchers have used cognitive tasks to establish that high scorers on the ASI have a cognitive bias that involves an orientation toward the selective processing of threat cues. However, the pattern varies for women and men (Stewart, Conrod, Gignac, & Pihl, 1998); high-anxiety-sensitive men tended to selectively process word cues reflecting social and psychological threats (e.g., "embarrassment"), while high-anxiety-sensitive women tended to selectively process cues involving physical threat (e.g., "hospitalization"). McCabe (1999) compared high- and low-ASI participants in terms of their memory for neutral words, positive words, anxiety words, and threatening words. She found that those with high ASI scores were more likely to recall words that connoted a sense of threat (e.g., "harassment," "assault") and concluded that a cognitive processing vulnerability exists in high-ASI scorers even before an actual panic attack occurs.

How do differences in anxiety sensitivity develop? Twin research shows that ASI scores are heritable, so this measure may be the source of the genetic diathesis for panic disorder (Stein, Jang, & Livesley, 1999). Additional data from Canada suggest that anxiety sensitivity is a joint reflection of genetic and environmental causes, but genetic factors play a greater role in more extreme levels of anxiety sensitivity (Taylor, Jang, Stewart, & Stein, 2008). The role of environmental factors is in keeping with evidence indicating that people with high anxiety sensitivity may have learned to catastrophize their bodily sensations via parental modelling and parental reinforcement (Stewart & Watt, 2001). Thus, developmental experiences should not be discounted when considering the etiology of panic disorder. Indeed, a longitudinal study of adolescent twin pairs continues to support the moderate heritability of anxiety sensitivity but there is also a clear role for nonspecific environmental events (Zavos, Gregory, & Eley, 2012).

5.7 Generalized Anxiety Disorder (GAD)

GAD Definition

All-encompassing worry often is a reflection of **generalized anxiety disorder (GAD)**. The individual with GAD is persistently anxious, often about minor items. Chronic, uncontrollable worry about all manner of things is the hallmark of GAD; the most frequent worries of people with GAD concern their health and the hassles of daily life, such as being late for appointments or having too much work to do. The uncontrollable nature of the worries associated with GAD has been confirmed by both self-reports and laboratory data (e.g., Becker et al., 1998). Other features of GAD include difficulty concentrating, tiring easily, restlessness, irritability, and a high level of muscle tension. See "Generalized Anxiety Disorder and Sleep Problems" for information on how GAD affects sleep.

Although people with GAD do not typically seek psychological treatment, the lifetime prevalence of the disorder is fairly high; prevalence in the NCS-R was 4.2% for men and 7.1% for women (Kessler et al., 2005). GAD typically begins in the person's mid-teens, though many people report having had the problem all their lives (Barlow et al., 1986). Stressful life events appear to play some role in its onset (Blazer, Hughes, & George, 1987). It has a high level of comorbidity with other anxiety disorders and with mood disorders (Brown, Barlow, & Liebowitz, 1994). It is difficult to treat GAD successfully. In one five-year follow-up study, only 18% of clients had achieved a full remission of symptoms (Woodman et al., 1999).

More recent findings illustrate how prevalence rates vary when certain diagnostic criteria are relaxed. Ruscio et al. (2005) analyzed data from the NCS-R and found that lifetime prevalence of GAD increases by 40% when the "excessive and uncontrollable worry" requirement is removed. Although excessive GAD begins earlier in life, is more chronic, and is associated with greater severity and comorbidity, the non-excessive cases showed persistence and impairment, high rates of treatment-seeking, and elevated comorbidity relative to non-GAD people. In a further broadening of the definition, Ruscio et al. (2007) reported that relaxing the excessive worry, three associated symptoms, and the 6-month duration criteria more than doubles the estimated prevalence (13.7% lifetime and 6.6% 12-month). Further, the subthreshold manifestations were still predictive of elevated risk of subsequent secondary disorders. These results contributed to considering relaxing the excessive and uncontrollable worry symptom so that persistent everyday worries could signify GAD. It was further proposed by the *DSM-5* work group that GAD be changed to "generalized anxiety and worry disorder" to reflect the predominant or "hallmark" feature of the disorder (see Andrews et al., 2010), but this suggestion was rejected. Recent research has continued to question whether both "excessive" and "uncontrollable" are necessary criteria for a diagnosis of GAD (Rutter & Brown, 2015). Excessiveness and uncontrollability have been found to correlate with each other very highly, which should not be surprising. If you are having trouble controlling worry, then of course it would become excessive. Despite this overlap, these two criteria seem to relate somewhat differently to other outcomes: excessiveness was more strongly related to measures of stress and anxiety whereas uncontrollability was a better predictor of the number of other diagnoses the client had (Rutter & Brown, 2015).

Etiology of Generalized Anxiety Disorder

Cognitive-Behavioural Views

In attempting to account for generalized anxiety, learning theorists (e.g., Wolpe, 1958) look to the environment. For example, a person anxious most of his or her waking hours might well be fearful of social contacts. If that individual spends a good deal of time with other people, it may be more useful to regard the anxiety as tied to these circumstances rather than to any internal factors. This behavioural model of GAD is identical to one of the learning views of phobias. The anxiety is regarded as having been classically conditioned to external stimuli, but with a broader range of conditioned stimuli.

The focus of other cognitive and behavioural views of GAD mesh so closely that we will discuss them in tandem. Anxiety results when people are confronted with painful stimuli over which they have no control. Cognitive theory emphasizes the perception of not being in control as a central characteristic of all forms of anxiety (Mandler, 1966). Thus, a CBT model of

---

Generalized Anxiety Disorder and Sleep Problems

LS IS A 36-YEAR-OLD woman, who presented to a primary care physician complaining that she has difficulty falling and staying asleep. During the evaluation the patient described herself as a nervous and anxious person. She had married for the second time approximately 10 months earlier and started a new job as a director of a child care center shortly thereafter. With further prompting, she described recurrent worries that she may be fired from her new job and "plunge" into financial difficulties. This worry, although completely unfounded, occupied her much of the time, making it difficult for her to concentrate and preventing her from falling asleep at night. She stated that she wakes up often in the middle of the night worrying about her numerous obligations.

Reproduced from Monnier, Lydiard, & Brawman-Mintzer, 2003, p. 1399. In A. Tasman, J. Kay, & J. A. Lieberman (Eds.), *Psychiatry* (2nd ed.), New York: Wiley.

generalized anxiety focuses on control and helplessness. Studies of humans have shown that stressful events over which people can exert some control are less anxiety-provoking than are events over which they can exercise no control. Research also suggests that, in certain circumstances, it is sufficient for the subject to only perceive control; control need not actually exist (e.g., Geer, Davison, & Gatchel, 1970). Linking these findings to GAD, Barlow (1988) has shown that these people perceive threatening events as out of their control.

Related to this idea of control is the fact that predictable events produce less anxiety than do unpredictable events (see Mineka, 1992). For example, animals prefer a signalled, predictable shock to one that is not signalled (Seligman & Binik, 1977). The absence of the signal can serve as a sign of safety, indicating that there is no shock and no need to worry. Unsignalled and therefore unpredictable aversive stimuli may lead to chronic vigilance and fear—in humans, what we would call worry (Borkovec & Inz, 1990).

A perceived lack of control contributes to a sense of uncertainty. Extensive research has shown the role of an **intolerance of uncertainty** in the experience of chronic worry and GAD (e.g., Ladouceur, Gosselin, & Dugas, 2000). Researchers at Université Laval and Concordia University have shown that manipulations designed to increase uncertainty intolerance lead to heightened levels of worry (Ladouceur et al., 2000). Uncertainty intolerance is particularly relevant when assessing ambiguous situations, and appraisals of ambiguous situations mediate the association between uncertainty intolerance and worry (Koerner & Dugas, 2008). Accordingly, CBT interventions with individuals with GAD are effective to the extent that they focus on removing uncertainty intolerance (Dugas & Koerner, 2005). Clinical improvement is associated with significant reductions in levels of uncertainty intolerance.

Recent meta-analytic findings revealed that intolerance of uncertainty is associated not only with GAD but also with OCD and depression. The respective mean correlations were .57 for GAD, .50 for OCD, and .53 for major depressive disorder. The correlation was significantly stronger for GAD vs. OCD (Gentes & Ruscio, 2011).

Canadian researchers Koerner and Dugas (2006) proposed a two-factor model that links GAD with a classic approach-avoidance conflict. The two factors are intolerance of uncertainty and a fear of anxiety. According to this formulation, GAD-prone people with an intolerance of uncertainty have a desire to engage in approach behaviours to reduce their feelings of uncertainty. However, they are also characterized simultaneously by a fear of anxiety that promotes the use of avoidance strategies designed to limit the experience of anxious arousal. Initial support for this model was provided by an experimental study showing that being intolerant of anxiety and also fearful of anxiety results in greater worry than either factor by itself (Buhr & Dugas, 2009).

One notion that has been applied to anxiety disorders in general and people with GAD in particular is that they are at risk, at least in part, because they are highly sensitive to and cognitively preoccupied with threat cues. Technological advances have resulted in more refined tests of this possibility. Whereas previous research has been dominated by the use of the Stroop

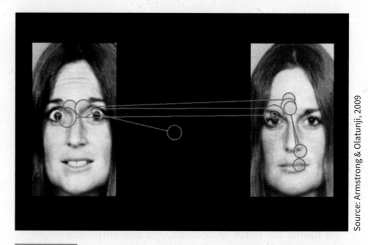

Source: Armstrong & Olatunji, 2009

FIGURE 5.2   Scanpath from an eye tracking experiment that presented participants with these two photos. (Blue lines show where a participant looked when presented with these photos; circles represent fixation points, and area of circles represents duration of fixation on each point.)

test, more contemporary research makes use of eye tracking technology that affords a continual measure of visual attention processes across a range of behaviours, including eye blinks (for an overview, see Armstrong & Olatunji, 2009). Figure 5.2 illustrates how eye tracking responses can vary depending on the presence vs. absence of a threat cue that has been detected.

The attention of people with GAD is easily drawn to stimuli that suggest possible physical harm or social misfortune, such as criticism, embarrassment, or rejection (MacLeod, Mathews, & Tata, 1986). People with GAD, for example, may be quick to notice when the person they are speaking with looks around the room from time to time, and they thus begin to worry about being rejected. Further, people with GAD are more inclined to interpret ambiguous stimuli as threatening and to believe that ominous events are more likely to happen to them (Butler & Mathews, 1983). The heightened sensitivity to threatening stimuli occurs even when the stimuli cannot be consciously perceived (Bradley et al., 1995).

Another cognitive view has been offered by Borkovec and his colleagues (e.g., Borkovec & Newman, 1998). Their focus is on the main symptom of uncontrollable worry. From a punishment perspective, why would anyone worry a lot? Since worry is thought to be a negative state, its repetition, one would think, should be avoided. Borkovec has shown that worry is actually negatively reinforcing. Why? Worry distracts people from negative emotions. Borkovec's theory is reflected in work on cognitive avoidance conducted at Concordia University in Montreal. Sexton and Dugas (2009) found that measures of cognitive avoidance were linked with measures of generalized worry and pathological worry. Supplementary analyses found that two key worry-related processes that contributed to cognitive avoidance were negative beliefs about worry and fear of the somatic symptoms of anxiety.

The key to understanding this position is to realize that worry does not produce much emotional arousal. It does not produce the physiological changes that usually accompany emotion, and it actually blocks the processing of emotional stimuli. Therefore, by worrying, people with GAD are avoiding certain unpleasant images and so their anxiety about these images does not extinguish.

There is one final cognitive element that may be linked to the etiology of GAD: metacognitive beliefs about worry, which can be positive or negative (Wells, 2010). Positive beliefs about worry, such as that worrying helps to solve a problem, and negative beliefs about worry, such as that worrying is dangerous, can increase worry and anxiety levels. A recent study had German students track their beliefs and their worry several times a day for a week (Thielsch, Andor, & Ehring, 2015). Negative metacognitive beliefs as well as an intolerance of uncertainty both predicted levels of worry but positive metacognitive beliefs did not. Their study was an initial attempt to look at how these factors relate to one another on a daily basis, but needs to be replicated in a sample of clients with GAD.

Biological Perspectives

Growing evidence indicates that GAD may have a genetic component. Researchers conducting an analysis of the data from the Virginia Adult Twin Study of Psychiatric and Substance Use Disorders examined the heritability of six anxiety disorders in terms of the presence or absence of lifetime disorder (Hettema, Prescott, Myers, Neale, & Kendler, 2005). GAD had both a heritable and an environmental component and the genetic influence was comparable for men and women.

Biological work has been informed greatly by a breakthrough study by Nitschke et al. (2009), which involved presenting GAD clients and control participants with neutral and aversive pictures while in an fMRI set-up. It was found that GAD clients had greater anticipatory reactions in response to the warning signal that pictures were about to be presented and this was reflected in greater activation in the bilateral dorsal amygdala! In addition, longitudinal testing indicated that higher pre-treatment activation in the anterior cingulate cortex while in the fMRI set-up was associated with greater subsequent reductions in anxiety and worry following treatment with venlafaxine. Recent follow-up work has confirmed white matter abnormalities in the amygdala and cingulated cortex in GAD clients (Zhang et al., 2013).

The most prevalent neurobiological model for GAD is based on knowledge of the operation of the benzodiazepines, a group of drugs that are often effective in treating anxiety. Researchers have discovered a receptor in the brain for benzodiazepines that is linked to the inhibitory neurotransmitter GABA (see Schienle, Hettema, Caceda, & Nemeroff, 2011). In normal fear reactions, neurons throughout the brain fire and create the experience of anxiety. This neural firing also stimulates the GABA system, which inhibits this activity and thus reduces anxiety. GAD may result from some defect in the GABA system, so that anxiety is not brought under control. The benzodiazepines may reduce anxiety by enhancing the release of GABA. Similarly, drugs that block or inhibit the GABA system lead to increases in anxiety (Insell, 1986). This approach seems destined to enhance our understanding of anxiety.

Psychoanalytic View

Psychoanalytic theory regards the source of generalized anxiety as an unconscious conflict between the ego and id impulses. The impulses, usually sexual or aggressive in nature, are struggling for expression, but the ego cannot allow their expression because it unconsciously fears that punishment will follow. Since the source of the anxiety is unconscious, the person experiences apprehension and distress without knowing why. The true source of anxiety—namely, desires associated with previously punished id impulses seeking expression—is ever-present. The person with a phobia may be regarded as more fortunate, since, according to psychoanalytic theory, his or her anxiety is displaced onto a specific object or situation, which can then be avoided. The person with GAD has not developed this type of defence and is constantly anxious.

5.8 Therapies for Anxiety Disorders

This final section of Chapter 5 focuses on therapies for the anxiety disorders. We consider therapies for anxiety disorders as a whole because many treatment strategies can be applied broadly to the various anxiety disorders. We also note some strategies that are specific to a particular anxiety disorder.

It was noted earlier in our discussion of phobias that most people suffer with their phobias and do not seek treatment (see Stinson et al., 2007) and indeed, a recent survey of over 3,000 people found that those with an anxiety disorder were much less likely than people with other disorders (including depression) to seek treatment (Johnson & Coles, 2013). A lack of information about anxiety was cited as a reason for non–treatment-seeking behaviour. In fact, Coles et al. (2014) conducted a national survey and found that less than 20% of respondents recognized symptoms of anxiety disorders, but 50% recognized depression. Further, SAD was recognized significantly less often (8.8%) than the other anxiety disorders. Being able to identify symptoms may be a precursor to help-seeking behaviour.

Behavioural Approaches to Treatment

Systematic desensitization was the first major behavioural treatment to be used widely in treating phobias (Wolpe, 1958). The individual with a phobia imagines a series of increasingly frightening scenes while in a state of deep relaxation. Clinical and experimental evidence indicates that this technique is effective in eliminating, or at least reducing, phobias. Many behaviour therapists, however, came to recognize the critical importance of exposure to real-life phobic situations, sometimes during the period in which a client is being desensitized in imagination and sometimes instead of the imagery-based procedure (Craske, Rapee, & Barlow, 1992).

Historically, clinical researchers have regarded such **in vivo exposure** as superior to techniques using imagination, not a surprising finding given that imaginary stimuli are by definition not the real thing! In a meta-analytic review of 33 RCTs of the treatment of specific phobias, Wolitzky-Taylor, Horowitz, Powers, and Telch (2008) concluded that exposure-based treatment produced large effect sizes relative to no treatment and outperformed both placebo conditions and other psychotherapeutic approaches. In vivo exposure outperformed other modes of exposure (e.g., imaginal exposure and virtual reality) at post-treatment (but not at follow-up). However, in a comprehensive review, Choy, Fyer, and Lipsitz (2007) concluded that while most phobias do respond well to in vivo exposure, it is associated with a high dropout rate and low treatment acceptance.

A more recent type of exposure involving the use of virtual reality has now been used successfully across many anxiety disorders, including specific phobia, social anxiety disorder, panic disorder, and agoraphobia (Malbos, 2015). **Virtual reality (VR) exposure** involves exposure to stimuli that come in the form of computer-generated graphics. Head-mounted displays and/or VR glasses are often used (see photos). Malbos (2015) reviewed two critical elements of VR: it occurs in real time and there is a feeling of actually being there. VR exposure for social anxiety disorder, for instance, involved exposure to four scenes that include performing in the presence of others and being scrutinized by others (Klinger et al., 2005). VR exposure can be tailored to involve graded exposures to threatening stimuli in a hierarchy similar to the increasingly anxiety-provoking situations used for in vivo exposure (see Table 5.5). The sequence would begin with a situation that is associated with the lowest fear (i.e., asking for directions at the gas station).

Early research used case studies or very small samples to evaluate the usefulness of VR exposure and there has been a push for better methodologies (Opris et al., 2012). There are now methodologically rigorous studies comparing VR exposure to adequate controls. For example, Anderson et al. (2013)

completed a randomized controlled trial comparing VR exposure with exposure group therapy and a wait-list control group for clients with social anxiety disorder who had public speaking as their primary fear. For the VR exposures, they had a virtual conference room, classroom, and auditorium to allow for different sizes of audiences. The amount of control for doing exposures tailored to a client's idiosyncratic fears is impressive. The researchers could make the audience members seem interested, bored, or even hostile! They found VR exposure to be just as effective as exposure group therapy after eight weeks of treatment, and also at a one-year follow-up.

A meta-analysis of 23 studies comparing in vivo exposure with virtual reality exposure treatments found VR exposure to be just as effective as in vivo exposure (Opris et al., 2012). This review concluded that VR exposure therapy has a powerful real-life impact and yields stable outcomes comparable to other treatment interventions. In addition, VR exposure treatment has comparatively better efficacy for the fear of flying. Given the high cost associated with in vivo exposure for fear of flying, there has been great interest in the use of VR exposure

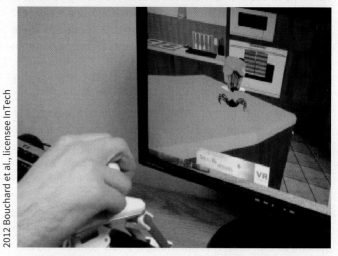

2012 Bouchard et al., licensee InTech

TABLE 5.5	Exposure Hierarchy for Social Anxiety Disorder
Item	**Fear Rating (0 to 100)**
Have a party and invite everyone from work	99
Go to Christmas party for one hour without drinking	90
Invite Cindy to have dinner and see a movie	85
Go for a job interview	80
Ask boss for a day off work	65
Ask questions in a meeting at work	65
Eat lunch with co-workers	60
Talk to a stranger on a bus	50
Talk to a cousin on the telephone for 10 minutes	40
Ask for directions at the gas station	35

Adapted with permission from Antony & McCabe, 2003, p. 1319. In A. Tasman, J. Kay, & J. A. Lieberman (Eds.), *Psychiatry* (2nd ed.). New York: Wiley.

In the first photo, a man is using an iPad to take part in a VR exposure for dog phobia while in the second photo, a person with a spider phobia is using a touch-sensitive haptic device to crush and kill spiders.

for this specific phobia (Malbos, 2015). The focus of a second meta-analysis was on the use of VR across a variety of psychological interventions and disorders, but over half of the 30 studies included in the meta-analysis actually targeted anxiety (Turner & Casey, 2014). They found significant effects for VR psychological treatment, even when taking into account the methodological rigour of the studies.

Finally, there is a move by some researchers from VR exposure to **augmented reality (AR) exposure** (see Baus & Bouchard, 2014 for a review). AR combines VR and the physical world, making it less expensive to develop given that a complete virtual environment does not have to be programmed. Thus far, AR has been used exclusively in the treatment of small animal phobias (Baus & Bouchard, 2014).

Treatment approaches are often tailored to the specific anxiety disorder under consideration. An example of the tailored approach can be seen with blood-injection-injury phobias. These phobias have been distinguished from other specific phobias because of the distinctive reactions such clients have to the usual behavioural approach of relaxation paired with exposure (Page, 1994). Relaxation tends to make matters worse for people with blood-and-injection phobias. Why? Consider the typical reaction. After the initial fright, accompanied by dramatic increases in heart rate and blood pressure, a person with a blood-injection-injury phobia often experiences a sudden drop in blood pressure and heart rate and faints. By trying to relax, clients with these phobias may well contribute to the tendency to faint, increasing their already high levels of fear and avoidance, as well as their embarrassment (Öst, 1992). Clients with blood-injection-injury phobias are now encouraged to tense rather than relax their muscles when confronting the fearsome situation (see photo). Indeed, Choy et al. (2007) concluded that blood-injection-injury phobia is uniquely responsive to applied tension. McMurty et al. (2015) reviewed 11 studies focused on the treatment of needle phobia, and similarly concluded that the applied muscle tension was helpful in the reduction of fainting. Also, exposure led to a reduced fear of needles in both children and adults.

There are three key challenges for exposure-based treatments that need to be addressed in future research. First, more information is needed on the specific mechanisms of change, consistent with a general need for more insight about why interventions work when they do indeed work. Second, there are still challenges in terms of incorporating the research knowledge on exposure into actual clinical practice. Some useful suggestions have been summarized by Abramowitz (2013). A final challenge relates to the decision on the part of therapists to actually deliver exposure-based interventions. Exposures are generally underused in community settings, possibly due to being viewed as an unpleasant treatment strategy for both clients and therapists (Peterman, Read, Wei, & Kendall, 2015). Peterman et al. describe ways to promote flexibility and adapt exposure exercises to engage clients. They focus on youth and children and recommend the use of creativity to turn exposures into a game, such as making up a bingo card with the exposure exercises detailed on squares.

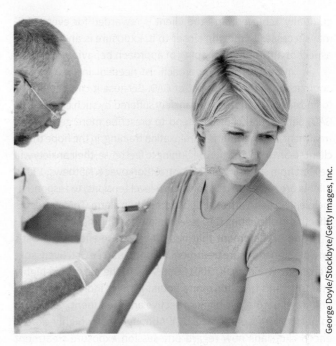

Blood-and-injection phobias are different from other specific phobias. Clients with this type of phobia are encouraged not to relax, but to tense their muscles when they encounter the feared situation.

A wide range of behavioural principles have been incorporated into various forms of treatment. Learning social skills can help people with SAD who may not know what to do or say in social situations. Some CBT therapists encourage clients to role-play interpersonal encounters in the consulting room or in therapy groups and several studies attest to the long-term effectiveness of this approach (e.g., Garcia-Lopez et al., 2006). A recent study compared social effectiveness therapy, an approach that combines exposure therapy and social skills training, with exposure therapy alone (Beidel et al., 2014). Both treatments were found to be more effective than the wait-list control group. Although the two treatment groups did not differ on most outcomes, the social effectiveness therapy group did have some superior outcomes, but future research is necessary to make firm conclusions about the benefits of social skills training for SAD.

Modelling is another technique that uses exposure to feared situations. In modelling therapy, fearful clients are exposed to filmed or live demonstrations of other people interacting fearlessly with the phobic object (e.g., handling snakes). **Flooding** is a therapeutic technique in which the client is exposed to the source of the phobia at full intensity. The extreme discomfort that is inevitable discourages therapists from using this technique, except perhaps as a last resort when graduated exposure has not worked.

Therapists who favour operant techniques ignore the fear assumed to underlie phobias and attend instead to the overt avoidance of phobic objects and to the approach behaviour that must replace it. They treat approach to the feared situation as any other operant and shape it via the principle of successive approximations. Real-life exposures to the phobic object are gradually achieved, and the client is rewarded for even minimal successes in moving closer to it. Exposure is an inevitable aspect of any operant shaping of approach behaviours.

A more nuanced approach is needed in behavioural approaches to the treatment of GAD. Because it can be difficult to find specific causes of the anxiety suffered by such clients with GAD, behavioural clinicians tend to prescribe more generalized treatment, such as intensive relaxation training, in the hope that if clients learn to relax when beginning to feel tense, their anxiety will be kept from spiralling out of control (Borkovec & Mathews, 1988). Clients are taught to relax away low-level tensions, to respond to incipient anxiety with relaxation rather than alarm. This strategy is effective in alleviating GAD (see Borkovec & Whisman, 1996).

One development that has proven quite effective is Öst's one-session exposure treatment for phobias (see Öst, Svensson, Hellstrom, & Lindwall, 2001; Öst, 2012). The session is highly intensive and lasts for many hours! Results indicate that this one-day treatment is highly effective and treatment gains tend to persist over time (Öst, 2012). Although many highly experienced clinicians now regard one-session exposure treatment for specific phobias as the treatment of choice, Wolitzky-Taylor et al. (2008) concluded that multi-session exposure treatments outperformed single-session treatments on various measures of phobic dysfunction, and more sessions predicted more favourable outcomes.

Cognitive Approaches

Cognitive treatments for specific phobias have been viewed with scepticism because the phobic fear is often recognized by the individual as excessive or unreasonable. *DSM-IV* required that the person recognize the fear as such. In *DSM-5*, the anxiety has to be judged by the clinician as out of proportion to the actual danger present, given that people with anxiety disorders commonly overestimate the degree of danger. However, people diagnosed with a specific phobia will typically readily admit that they are more anxious than they should be. If the person already acknowledges that the fear is of something harmless, what use can it be to alter the person's thoughts about it? Indeed, there is no evidence that the elimination of irrational beliefs alone, without exposure to the fearsome situations, reduces phobic avoidance (e.g., Turner et al., 1992). Exposure appears to be the primary treatment technique for specific phobias (see photo).

With social anxiety disorder, on the other hand, such cognitive methods—typically combined with exposure and possibly social skills training—are more promising. People with social anxiety disorder benefit from treatment strategies derived from Aaron Beck and Albert Ellis. They may be persuaded by the therapist to more accurately appraise people's reactions to them (e.g., the teacher's frown may reflect a bad mood rather than disapproval), but also to rely less on the approval of others for a sense of self-worth. Cognitive approaches have been used more often since it was recognized that many people with social anxiety disorder have adequate social skills but do not use them because of self-defeating thoughts.

An RCT (Clark et al., 2006) reported that cognitive therapy appears to be superior to a combination of exposure plus applied relaxation in the treatment of social anxiety disorder. As noted earlier when we described the cognitive factors involved in the etiology and maintenance of SAD, Clark's approach to treating SAD focuses on behavioural experiments aimed at changing beliefs rather than traditional exposure. Another commonly used approach for treating SAD is Heimberg's cognitive behavioural group therapy (CBGT), which is a combination of cognitive restructuring and situational exposure typically delivered in groups of six to eight clients (Heimberg & Becker, 2002). Prospective group members are typically anxious to face the prospect of attending group sessions and are surprised to discover that this form of treatment is actually recommended, given this is the type of situation they often fear the most! However, the group format allows for excellent opportunities for in vivo exposures (presentations, job interviews, cocktail parties) and there is significant support for the efficacy of this group approach (Heimberg & Becker, 2002).

One well-validated therapy, panic-control therapy, developed by Barlow and his associates (e.g., Barlow & Craske, 1994), has three principal components: (1) relaxation training; (2) a combination of Ellis- and Beck-type CBT interventions, including cognitive restructuring; and (3) exposure to the internal cues that trigger panic, known as interoceptive exposure. Regarding the second component, Sanderson and Rego (2000) emphasize the need for clients to self-monitor the cognitions that occur during the actual panic episode. For the third component, **interoceptive exposure**, the client practises behaviours in the consulting room that can elicit feelings associated with panic. For example, a client may be asked to breathe through a straw, spin in a chair, or run on the spot. When sensations such as dizziness, increased heart rate, and other signs of panic begin to be felt, the client (1) experiences them under safe conditions and (2) applies previously learned cognitive strategies so that the sensations become less threatening.

Pierre Perrin/Getty Images Inc.

In the most frequent treatment for phobias, clients are exposed to what they fear most; here, an enclosed space.

With practice and with encouragement or persuasion from the therapist, the client learns to reinterpret internal sensations, no longer seeing them as signals of loss of control and panic, but rather as cues that are intrinsically harmless and can be controlled with certain skills. The intentional creation of these sensations by the client, coupled with success in coping with them, reduces their unpredictability and changes their meaning for the client (Craske, Maidenberg, & Bystritsky, 1995).

A multi-site study indicates that Barlow's panic-control therapy is superior to imipramine in reducing panic attacks. Furthermore, adding the drug to this psychological therapy does not bestow an advantage. These findings show up both immediately after the end of treatment and at a 15-month follow-up (Barlow, 1999). Landon and Barlow (2004) reviewed CBT treatment for panic disorder and concluded that it is well-tolerated, cost-effective, and produces treatment gains in 40 to 90% of clients, with most studies reporting high rates. Importantly, there is support for the effectiveness of panic-control treatment when it is delivered in private practice (Strand & Warren, 2014). Although clients did not see themselves as completely cured, they were satisfied with treatment and felt that panic was no longer significantly interfering in their lives. Finally, Kenardy, Robinson, and Dob (2005) conducted a long-term follow-up of clients who received CBT for panic disorder within an RCT. Outcomes after six to eight years were significantly better than baseline measures of panic, avoidance, and depression.

In sum, CBT interventions have been used extensively to treat anxiety disorders and meta-analyses support their usefulness (e.g., Deacon & Abramowitz, 2004). Hollon, Stewart, and Strunk (2006) concluded that CBT interventions are generally more successful than drug treatments because they create lasting change, while the benefits of drug treatments (i.e., psychoactive medications) are less permanent and "appear to be largely palliative in nature" (p. 285). Now that CBT interventions have been found to be effective, two key questions follow: (1) What specific factors or processes account for improvement? and (2) Do tightly controlled laboratory studies translate into effective treatments in actual clinical practice? Regarding the key processes involved in change, research is increasingly supporting the role of threat reappraisal in symptom improvement, but the definitive study is still needed to establish threat reappraisal as the main factor vs. other mechanisms (see Smits, Julian, Rosenfield, & Powers, 2012).

But are the benefits documented in tightly controlled randomized trial intervention studies realized when treatment occurs in clinical practice? That is, do the treatment gains generalize to the real world? We already indicated this seems to be true for panic-control treatment (Strand & Warren, 2014). Hunsley and Lee's (2007) examination of 35 effectiveness studies led them to conclude that improvement rates as a result of CBT were comparable in clinical practice settings with the improvement rates obtained in RCTs. For instance, in terms of CBT as a form of treatment for SAD, the moderate to large effects of treatment found in previous studies were replicated. Follow-up

meta-analytic studies that focused specifically on effectiveness studies conducted thus far on the treatment of anxiety disorders concluded that CBT interventions are effective in clinically representative conditions and tend to generalize to real-world clinical practice (Stewart & Chambless, 2009; van Ingen, Freiheit, & Vye, 2009). Nonetheless, follow-up studies longer than one year are needed to better understand and prevent relapse (Choy et al., 2007).

All the behavioural and cognitive therapies for phobias have a recurrent theme—namely, the need for the client to begin exposing himself or herself to what has been deemed too terrifying to face. It should be noted that homework or between-session learning is considered to be an essential component of CBT. Glenn et al. (2013) examined the impact of homework completion and client engagement on various outcomes for clients who had undergone CBT for anxiety disorders. They found that completing exposures, attending therapy, and having better homework adherence were all related to greater improvements. When clients start therapy for an anxiety disorder, they often ask what the evidence is for the effectiveness of the approach and also whether doing homework really matters. Research such as Glenn et al.'s study helps to answer these practical questions.

Finally, mindfulness and acceptance-based approaches have become more and more popular for treating anxiety disorders. There is evidence for the efficacy of these approaches for GAD (Hayes-Skelton, Roemer, & Orsillo, 2013), SAD (Kocovski et al., 2013), and treatment-resistant panic disorder and agoraphobia (Gloster et al., 2015). The goal is to become more open and accepting of anxious thoughts and feelings, rather than trying to avoid or change them. Recent research aimed at understanding how GAD treatment works focused on a possible mechanism of action called decentering, which is the ability to view thoughts and emotions objectively, without getting caught up in them. Clients with GAD who improved on decentering while undergoing applied relaxation training or acceptance-based behavioural therapy became less anxious (Hayes-Skelton, Calloway, Orsillo, & Roemer, 2015).

One type of mindfulness meditation often used in these programs, *lovingkindness*, involves being kind to oneself and then extending that kindness to others. Researchers in British Columbia have taken kindness one step further in the treatment of SAD (Trew & Alden, 2015). They had one group of socially anxious students performing kind acts toward others, another group doing social interaction exposures, and a third group simply recording daily thoughts. Those doing acts of kindness had greater reductions in their desire to avoid social situations. We will say more about mindfulness when we look at depression in Chapter 8 and stress in Chapter 9.

Biological Approaches

Drugs that reduce anxiety are referred to as sedatives, tranquilizers, or **anxiolytics**. (The suffix *-lytic* comes from the Greek word meaning to loosen or dissolve.) Barbiturates

TABLE 5.6 **Summary of Drugs Used to Treat Anxiety Disorders**

Drug Category	Generic Names	Trade Names	Uses
Benzodiazepines	Diazepam, alprazolam, lorazepam, clonazepam	Valium, Xanax, Ativan, Clonapam	Anxiety disorders
Monoamine oxidase inhibitors	Phenelzine	Nardil	SAD
Selective serotonin reuptake inhibitors	Paroxetine, sertraline	Paxil, Zoloft	SAD, GAD, panic disorder
Serotonin norepinephrine reuptake inhibitors	Venlafaxine	Effexor	SAD, GAD, panic disorder
Azapirones	Buspirone	BuSpar	GAD

were the first major category of drugs used to treat anxiety disorders, but because they are highly addictive and present great risk of a lethal overdose, they were supplanted in the 1950s by two other classes of drugs: propanediols (e.g., Miltown) and benzodiazepines (e.g., Valium and Xanax). Valium and Xanax are still used today, although they have been largely supplanted by newer benzodiazepines, such as Ativan and Clonapam. These drugs are of demonstrated benefit with some anxiety disorders; however, they are not used extensively with the specific phobias. Although the risk of lethal overdose is not as great as with barbiturates, benzodiazepines are addictive and can produce a severe withdrawal syndrome (Schweizer et al., 1990). Canadian clinical practice guidelines continue to include the benzodiazepines as a possible pharmacotherapy option for the anxiety disorders as a whole, with the recommendation that they be used short-term, perhaps early in treatment or for managing crises (Katzman et al., 2014). Table 5.6 summarizes Health Canada-approved medications for the anxiety disorders.

Drugs originally developed to treat depression (antidepressants) have become popular in treating many anxiety disorders. One class of these drugs, the monoamine oxidase (MAO) inhibitors, fared better in treating SAD than did a benzodiazepine (Gelernter et al., 1991) and, in another study, was as effective as CBGT at a 12-week follow-up (Heimberg et al., 1998). But MAO inhibitors, such as phenelzine (Nardil), are often not used because of dietary restrictions (e.g., certain meats and cheeses need to be avoided) and secondary side effects; they can lead to weight gain, insomnia, sexual dysfunction, and hypertension. These side effects led to the development of reversible inhibitors of MAOI-A (RIMAs), which have less restrictive or non-existent dietary restrictions as well as fewer other side effects, but unfortunately they are not as effective in the treatment of SAD (see Blanco et al., 2013 for a review).

The selective serotonin reuptake inhibitors (SSRIs), such as fluoxetine (Prozac), were also originally developed to treat depression. They, too, have been found to reduce social anxiety (in particular paroxetine/Paxil) and considering the side effects noted above for the MAOs (e.g., phenelzine), the SSRIs are a preferred drug treatment option for SAD (Blanco et al., 2013; Katzman et al., 2014). SSRIs are also the drug treatment of choice for GAD as well as panic disorder. The

effectiveness of SSRIs accords with the results of a PET study with MRI scanning illustrating the role of serotonin Type 1A receptor binding in people with panic disorder (Neumeister et al., 2005).

The SSRIs may be the most popular and well known, but there are also other medications that are considered first-line agents for several anxiety disorders. For example, venlafaxine, a serotonin-norepinephrine reuptake inhibitor (SNRI), is another possible first-line agent for use with GAD, SAD, and panic disorder. For GAD and SAD, pregabalin, an anti-convulsant, is also listed as a possible first-line agent in the Canadian practice guidelines (Katzman et al., 2014). Further, although panic disorder and agoraphobia are now two separate diagnoses, the research leading to these guidelines was based on *DSM-IV* and therefore, the recommendations are mostly related to panic disorder. Finally, there is limited research on pharmacotherapy for specific phobia, possibly due to the efficacy of exposure therapy, and as such, it is generally not indicated (Katzman et al., 2014).

With the exception of specific phobias, the SSRIs are indicated for all anxiety disorders (Katzman et al., 2014). But what problems can arise? Most notably, a very substantial problem is lack of treatment response. Koen and Stein (2011) noted that up to 50% of people with social anxiety disorder do not respond to SRI treatment. They highlighted particular gaps in knowledge in GAD. Specifically, there is little information about what to do for the client with GAD who fails to respond to drug treatment. Another problem is a limited research base because the effectiveness of GAD treatments in real-world settings is largely unknown. Clinical studies in academic settings do not tend to recruit the typical person with GAD who has multiple comorbid disorders and a wide range of associated problems. And even less is known about GAD in children and in the elderly (see Koen & Stein, 2011).

Another key problem in treating anxiety disorders with drugs is that many drugs have undesirable side effects, ranging from nausea, dizziness, drowsiness, memory loss, and depression to physical addiction and damage to body organs (see Ryan et al., 2008). Unfortunately, in their efforts to reduce anxiety, many people use anxiolytics or alcohol on their own; the use and abuse of drugs is common in anxiety-ridden people. A Canadian survey indicates that rates of self-medication range from 8% (for SAD) to 36% (for GAD) and self-medication among those with an anxiety disorder is linked with suicidal ideation and suicide attempts (Bolton, Cox, Clara, & Sareen, 2006). A follow-up study by this group of Winnipeg researchers confirmed that self-medication with alcohol was highest for GAD (Robinson, Sareen, Cox, & Bolton, 2009) and was particularly likely among those with a concurrent mood or personality disorder.

Farach et al. (2012) made a number of compelling observations about the current state of drug treatment. Most notably, they concluded that innovative drug treatments in the lab have not resulted in available drugs "despite billions of research dollars invested in drug development" (p. 833). Parenthetically, the fact that billions have been invested highlights the worldwide problem in the prevalence of anxiety disorders. Farach et al. (2012) also note two important emerging themes: (1) drugs are being developed due to their impact on specific neuroreceptors; and (2) there is growing evidence of how drugs impact on fear-related memory. A recent study by Frick and colleagues (2015) highlights the need for additional research on drug treatments. They found support that people with SAD actually have too much of the neurotransmitter serotonin, which leads to increased anxiety, whereas past research and treatment is based on the theory that they actually have abnormally low levels of serotonin.

We will conclude the biological treatment section by taking a closer look at drugs that affect fear-related memory. Recently, d-cycloserine (DCS) emerged as a medication that could enhance exposure-based treatment by facilitating extinction of fear. It is administered close in time to the exposure (1–2 hours before) and on a limited number of occasions (3–5 times)—aspects that are critical to the effective use of this agent (Hofmann, 2014). Rodrigues et al. (2014) completed a review and meta-analysis of all randomized double-blind, placebo-controlled trials of DCS; 13 studies were included, 9 on anxiety disorders and 4 on OCD. Overall they found strong effects. Another review was also supportive of the use of DCS in conjunction with exposure but with one important caveat: if the exposure does not go well, this drug can enhance fear memory reconsolidation (Hofmann, 2014). Hofmann had a catchy way to summarize these effects in the title of his paper: "making good exposures better and bad exposures worse." Hofmann suggested the possibility of administering this drug after the exposure, only for successful exposures, and there is limited support at this time for the efficacy of DCS when administered post-exposure. There are a number of other pharmacological agents that are currently being investigated for their ability to enhance extinction (see Fitzgerald, Seemann, & Maren, 2014 for a review).

Psychoanalytic Approaches

Classical psychoanalytic treatments of phobias attempted to uncover the repressed conflicts believed to underlie the extreme fear and avoidance characteristic of these disorders. Because the phobia itself was regarded as symptomatic of underlying conflicts, it was usually not dealt with directly. Indeed, direct attempts to reduce phobic avoidance were contraindicated because the phobia is assumed to protect the person from repressed conflicts that are too painful to confront. Contemporary ego analysts focus less on gaining historical insights and more on encouraging the client to confront the phobia. However, they do view the phobia as an outgrowth of an earlier problem. Many analytically oriented clinicians recognize the importance of exposure to what is feared, although they often regard any subsequent improvement as merely symptomatic and not as a resolution of the underlying conflict that was assumed to have produced the phobia (Wolitzky & Eagle, 1990).

Milrod et al. (2007) demonstrated preliminary efficacy of a manualized psychodynamic psychotherapy for panic disorder. The RCT compared the specific psychodynamic treatment with applied relaxation training in twice-weekly sessions for 12 weeks. Participants in the psychodynamic group had significantly greater reductions in panic symptom severity. Roth (2010) compared psychological therapies of different kinds for panic attacks (e.g., CBT, muscle relaxation, breathing training, psychoanalytic psychotherapy) to make inferences about "common effective mechanisms" and concluded that "the likely common element of all these therapies is that they reduce the immediate expectancy of a panic attack, disrupting the vicious circle of fearing fear" (p. 1).

It should be noted that panic treatment studies of all modalities report substantial proportions of clients who do not respond to efficacious treatments or who prematurely terminate treatment (see Milrod et al., 2007, for review). For example, Landon and Barlow (2004) concluded that about 40% of CBT clients do not have a satisfactory response. Thus, it is important to discover predictors of success. One exciting development is the use of neuroimaging to predict who will fare well in CBT for panic disorder and agoraphobia. In Germany, Hahn et al. (2015) were able to predict treatment response based on data collected using functional magnetic resonance imaging *prior* to CBT. The implications of being able to match clients to treatments we know will help them are significant.

Canadian clinical practice guidelines, including recommendations for both psychotherapy and pharmacotherapy, highlight the lack of research on combined treatments (Katzman et al., 2014). For many of the anxiety disorders they note that very few studies have evaluated CBT and medication in combination compared with each alone, and most often the combination does not yield better results than either treatment alone. There are some exceptions. For example, an RCT comparing phenelzine, CBGT, and their combination for SAD found that the combined treatment was superior to either treatment alone on a number of outcomes (Blanco et al., 2010). However, phenelzine (a MAO inhibitor) is not currently a first-line medication for SAD. Despite the paucity of evidence in favour of combined treatments, in clinical practice, clients are often receiving medication and CBT simultaneously.

Summary

5.1 Anxiety disorders are among the most prevalent mental health problems. People with anxiety disorders feel an overwhelming apprehension that seems unwarranted. Anxiety consists of both physiological arousal and cognitive worry. Everyone can relate to the experience of anxiety, but to be diagnosed with an anxiety disorder, the anxious symptoms have to cause clinically significant distress or impairment. Some common themes can be found across anxiety disorders, including a sense of the self as deficient or ineffective.

5.2 Specific phobias are intense, unreasonable fears that cause distress or impairment. They occur related to many different situations or objects, including needles, elevators, snakes, spiders, and storms. *DSM-5* classifies the various situations and objects according to the following subtypes: blood, injuries, and injections; situations; animals; the natural environment; and other.

5.3 Social anxiety disorder is the fear of social situations in which a person may be scrutinized by other people. There are three types of situations: interacting with others, presentations, and being observed by others. If the fear is limited to speaking or performing in public, a performance-only specifier is indicated. People with SAD often avoid the situations they are afraid of, causing significant interference in quality of life.

5.4 There are many theories about the etiology of specific phobias and social anxiety disorder. Behavioural theorists have several ideas of how phobias are acquired: through classical conditioning, the pairing of an innocuous object or situation with an innately painful event; through operant conditioning, whereby a person is rewarded for avoidance; through modelling, imitating the fear and avoidance of others; and through cognition, by making a catastrophe of a social mishap that could be construed in a less negative fashion. Cognitive theories are more strongly implicated in the etiology of social anxiety disorder. Not all people who have such experiences develop a phobia. Biological theories state that it may be that a genetically transmitted physiological diathesis—lability of the autonomic nervous system—predisposes certain people to acquire phobias. The psychoanalytic view of phobias is that they are a defence against repressed conflicts.

5.5 A person with panic disorder has sudden, inexplicable, and periodic attacks of intense anxiety. The panic attacks often lead to worry about having future attacks and the person may even avoid certain situations (like exercise) in an attempt to avoid having more panic attacks. A number of laboratory manipulations (e.g., having the client

hyperventilate or breathe air with a high concentration of carbon dioxide) can induce panic attacks in those with the disorder. Individuals with panic disorder fear their own physical sensations and then amplify them until they are overwhelmed. In agoraphobia, people fear certain situations outside of the home (e.g., public transportation, standing in lines, shopping malls) because they may not be able to escape or they may develop panic-like symptoms (e.g., dizziness, racing heart).

5.6 Biological (e.g., genetics, overactive noradrenergic system, hypersensitivity to cholecystokinin) and psychological (e.g., anxiety sensitivity) factors play a role in the etiology of panic disorder and agoraphobia. Many people with agoraphobia first have panic attacks or panic disorder (but not all). They subsequently fear having panic attacks or panic-like symptoms in public, leading them to avoid many situations.

5.7 In generalized anxiety disorder, the individual's life is beset with virtually constant tension, apprehension, and worry. Some behavioural theorists assume that with adequate assessment, this pervasive anxiety can be pinned down to a finite set of anxiety-provoking circumstances, thereby likening it to a phobia and making it more treatable. A sense of helplessness can also cause people to be anxious in a wide range of situations. Cognitive factors implicated in the etiology and maintenance of worry include intolerance of uncertainty and metacognitive beliefs about worry. Biological approaches focus on the therapeutic effects of the benzodiazepines and how they might enhance the activity of the neurotransmitter GABA. Psychoanalytic theory regards the source as an unconscious conflict between the ego and id impulses.

5.8 There are many therapies for anxiety disorders. Cognitive behavioural interventions seem to be quite effective overall and limited research suggests that CBT works in actual clinical settings. The search is now on for why CBT works; in the case of anxiety, evidence is accumulating for the role of threat appraisals. Perhaps the most widely employed treatments are anxiolytic and other drugs dispensed by medical practitioners. However, with many disorders, up to 50% of people do not respond to drug treatment and other treatments must be considered, either alone or in combination with drug treatment. There are several problems inherent in drug treatment, including side effects and limited information about what should be considered when drug treatment does not work. Classical psychoanalysis focused almost exclusively on uncovering repressed conflicts, but more contemporary psychodynamic approaches directly target the anxiety or phobia.

Key Terms

agoraphobia	flooding	separation anxiety
anxiety	generalized anxiety disorder (GAD)	social anxiety disorder
anxiety disorders	interoceptive exposure	specific phobias
anxiety sensitivity	intolerance of uncertainty	test anxiety
anxiolytics	in vivo exposure	test-irrelevant thinking
augmented reality (AR) exposure	nomophobia	vicarious learning
autonomic lability	panic disorder	virtual reality (VR) exposure
depersonalization	post-event processing (PEP)	
derealization	selective mutism	

Reflections: Past, Present, and Future

1. In the previous chapter, you were asked to design a longitudinal study of risk factors for the development of anxiety disorders. Now that you have learned more about factors supported by empirical research, how would you redesign your long-term study? What risk factors would you retain? What risk factors would you add to the design?

2. Anxiety is relevant to our understanding of many of the other disorders discussed in this book (e.g., obsessive compulsive disorder, post-traumatic stress disorder, somatoform and dissociative disorders, psychophysiological disorders, mood disorders, and schizophrenia). As you read about the different disorders, think about how you would adapt the treatment strategies outlined in this chapter for use with other disorders.

3. By now you will have discovered that adolescents and young adults, including college and university students, are not immune from psychological difficulties, and in the ensuing chapters you will read about other psychological problems that are, unfortunately, relatively common in young people. A mental health author headlined a newspaper article, "Stress takes troubling toll on students in university" (Crawford, 2009, September 3). It can be very difficult to be young and at school trying to deal with what may be perceived as overwhelming stress—perhaps away from home for the first time and feeling homesick, handling finances and social and academic pressures on your own, maybe feeling lonely or upset by a relationship separation or breakup. It's no wonder that many students feel anxious or blue or turn to alcohol or other drugs to ease the psychological pain. However, Canadian colleges and universities take these and other mental health issues very seriously and help is available on campus for every student. Indeed, resources have improved significantly over recent decades and professional counsellors are available who are skilled at helping students with their psychological and other difficulties. Review all of the mental health resources and programs at your college or university. For example, how are students helped to ease the transition from high school to campus life? Is there a focus on early intervention? Are there enough competent professionals to meet the needs of students? Is there a role for fellow students to play? What changes would you recommend to the administration of your college or university in terms of the services and opportunities that should be made available to students?

CHAPTER 6

Obsessive-Compulsive and Related Disorders

LEARNING OBJECTIVES

1. Describe the new diagnostic category of obsessive-compulsive and related disorders.

2. Describe the diagnostic features of OCD.

3. Outline the etiology of OCD.

4. Describe psychological and biological therapies for OCD.

5. Describe hoarding disorder.

6. Describe body dysmorphic disorder.

7. Describe trichotillomania (hair-pulling disorder) and excoriation (skin-picking disorder).

6.1 Obsessive-Compulsive and Related Disorders (OCRDs)

In this chapter we focus primarily on obsessive-compulsive disorder (OCD). OCD is less common than many of the anxiety disorders we examined in Chapter 5, with a 12-month prevalence of about 1% and a lifetime prevalence of about 2% (Ruscio et al., 2010), but it causes a high degree of impairment. In fact, the World Health Organization listed OCD as one of the top 10 most impairing conditions based on lost income and decreased quality of life (Veale & Roberts, 2014). There is also a high degree of comorbidity: the majority of people with OCD (as high as 90%; Ruscio et al., 2010) are diagnosed with other conditions, including anxiety disorders, mood disorders, impulse-control disorders, and substance use disorders, contributing to the high degree of impairment and difficulty in treating this disorder that we describe later in this chapter.

Further evidence of the high level of chronicity, impairment, and distress associated with OCD can be gleaned from research examining links to suicidality and mortality. A recent meta-analysis concluded there is a moderate to high link between OCD and suicidal ideation as well as suicide attempts (Ange-lakis et al., 2015). About a third of people with OCD reported suicidal ideation and about 10% had histories of suicide attempts. A variety of factors strengthened the relationship between OCD and suicidality, including being diagnosed with a comorbid disorder and having more severe anxious and depressive symptoms. Severe obsessions were more relevant for predicting suicide risk than compulsions. Overall, the authors of this meta-analysis concluded that their findings should help to change past views that clients with OCD are at low risk for suicide. The meta-analysis also points clinicians to consider comorbid diagnoses and severe obsessions as risk factors for suicidality.

People with OCD also have higher rates of mortality than the general population for both natural and unnatural causes of death (Meier et al., 2016). Other factors that are related to mortality were taken into account (e.g., somatic comorbidities, age), leading to the conclusion that a diagnosis of OCD is uniquely associated with increased mortality risk. As with suicidality, comorbidity increases the likelihood of mortality. Being diagnosed with a comorbid anxiety disorder, depression, or a substance use disorder is associated with higher mortality rates than OCD alone.

Prior to *DSM-5*, OCD was considered an anxiety disorder and that is why some of the research on OCD that we review in this chapter was conducted in conjunction with some or all of the anxiety disorders. However, OCD differs in key respects from anxiety disorders, such as in the domains of repetitive thoughts and behaviours and inability to resist impulses and urges. The Research Planning Agenda for *DSM-5* Work Group was successful in creating a new *DSM-5* category entitled **obsessive-compulsive and related disorders (OCRDs)**. Similarly, the World Health Organization (WHO) has been preparing the 11th revision of the International Classification of Diseases and Related Health Problems (*ICD-11*, which was to be presented in 2018), and plans were for it too to have an OCRD grouping (Stein et al., 2016). Similar to the *DSM-5*, those working on the *ICD-11* also point to the repetitive thoughts and behaviours as the common link among disorders classified as OCRDs.

In *DSM-5*, the OCRD "related disorders" are hoarding disorder, which was formerly considered a subtype of OCD; body dysmorphic disorder, which was formerly considered a somatoform disorder; trichotillomania (hair-pulling disorder), which was formerly categorized as an impulse control disorder; and excoriation (skin-picking disorder), which did not appear in previous versions of the *DSM*. Trichotillomania and excoriation are often grouped together as body-focused repetitive behaviours.

The OCRDs share some features (e.g., preoccupations, repetitive behaviours) and tend to co-occur. If a clinician diagnoses one of these conditions, it is prudent to screen for the others. Although OCD was removed from the anxiety disorders category, it is acknowledged that OCD co-occurs at a high rate with many of the anxiety disorders. Over 75% of people with OCD were found to meet criteria for an anxiety disorder (Ruscio et al., 2010).

Why was OCD taken out of the anxiety disorders grouping? Many clinicians still view OCD as an anxiety disorder and many anxiety disorder clinics are set up to treat OCD. Anxiety plays a prominent role in OCD: obsessions typically trigger an anxious response that is relieved with the compulsions. However, the repetitive behaviours seen in OCD are not typically present in the anxiety disorders, but are present among the other OCRDs.

Still, not everyone agrees with combining these particular disorders into an OCRD category simply because they involve repetitive behaviours (and thoughts). Abramowitz and Jacoby (2015) presented a critical review, rejecting this categorization. They cite research showing that while OCD and body dysmorphic disorder may share enough features to belong in the same category, the others (hoarding disorder, trichotillomania, excoriation) do not. In particular they focus on how the function of the repetitive behaviour is different in OCD (to reduce obsessional fear) compared with hair-pulling or skin-picking (no obsessional fear, but rather the trigger is often general tension or boredom). In fact, people diagnosed with body-focused repetitive behaviours may pull hair or pick skin out of habit, without conscious awareness.

The controversy with *DSM-5* continues to present itself. As you read through the descriptions of the various OCRDs, consider for yourself how similar they are and whether they belong as part of the same grouping.

6.2 Obsessive-Compulsive Disorder (OCD)

Obsessive-compulsive disorder (OCD) is a chronic disorder in which the mind is flooded with persistent and uncontrollable thoughts (obsessions) and the individual is compelled to repeat certain acts again and again (compulsions), suffering significant distress and interference with everyday functioning. OCD affects men and women equally, and although it can occur in children, the typical age of onset is around 20 years of age, and developing OCD later in life (beyond early 30s) is very rare (Ruscio et al., 2010).

Obsessions are intrusive and recurring thoughts, impulses, and images that come unbidden to the mind and appear irrational and uncontrollable to the individual experiencing them. Whereas many of us may have similar fleeting experiences, the obsessive individual, as we see in the case of Bernice, has them with such force and frequency that they interfere with normal functioning. Clinically, the most frequent obsessions concern

---

When Grief Triggered Persistent OCD

BERNICE was 46 years old when she entered treatment. This was the fourth time she had been in outpatient therapy, and she had previously been hospitalized twice. Her obsessive-compulsive disorder had begun 12 years earlier, shortly after the death of her father. Since then, it had waxed and waned and currently was as severe as it had ever been.

Bernice was obsessed with a fear of contamination, a fear she vaguely linked to her father's death from pneumonia. Although she reported that she was afraid of nearly everything, because germs could be anywhere, she was particularly upset by touching wood, "scratchy objects," mail, canned goods, and "silver flecks." By silver flecks, Bernice meant silver embossing on a greeting card, eyeglass frames, shiny appliances, and silverware. She was unable to state why these particular objects were sources of possible contamination.

Bernice tried to reduce her discomfort by engaging in compulsive rituals that took up almost all her waking hours. She spent three to four hours in the morning in the bathroom, washing and rewashing herself. Between baths, she scraped away the outside layer of her bar of soap so that it would be totally free of germs. Mealtimes also lasted for hours because Bernice performed time-consuming rituals, eating three bites of food at a time, chewing each mouthful 300 times. These steps were meant magically to decontaminate her food. Even Bernice's husband was sometimes involved in these mealtime ceremonies, shaking a tea kettle and frozen vegetables over her head to remove the germs. Bernice's rituals and fear of contamination had reduced her life to doing almost nothing else. She would not leave the house, do housework, or even talk on the telephone.

fears of contamination, fears of expressing some sexual or aggressive impulse, and hypochondriacal fears of bodily dysfunction (Jenike, Baer, & Minichiello, 1986). Contamination obsessions may include a fear of germs from other people or using public toilets. A violent obsession might be a thought or image of using a steak knife while eating dinner at a restaurant to stab someone at a nearby table. Other obsessions involve a concern about unintentionally causing harm to others (e.g., thought of dropping a ball from a tennis bag causing a car to swerve and hit a pedestrian). An example of a sexual obsession is an unwanted impulse to grab a woman's breast while riding the subway. Religious obsessions can often have sexual content (e.g., "Images of Jesus with an erection on the cross," Abramowitz & Jacoby, 2015, p. 167). Some obsessions involve symmetry; for example, a client wanting the box of tissues to be parallel to the edge of the table. Obsessions are ego-dystonic (foreign to their personality) and the obsessional themes vary across individuals and, according to O'Connor, Aardema, and Pélissier (2005), the themes often have great personal relevance. Most people with OCD keep the content and frequency of their obsessions secret for many years (Newth & Rachman, 2001). The severity of obsessions has been identified as a factor that contributes to poorer quality of life (Masellis, Rector, & Richter, 2003).

A **compulsion** is a repetitive behaviour or mental act that the person feels driven to perform to reduce the distress caused by obsessive thoughts or to prevent some calamity from occurring. The activity is not realistically connected with its apparent purpose and is clearly excessive. Bernice did not need to chew each morsel of food 300 times, for example. Often an individual who continually repeats some action fears dire consequences if the act is not performed. The sheer frequency of repetition may be staggering. Some examples of commonly reported compulsions include:

- checking, going back many times to verify that already performed acts were actually carried out—for example:

  "A 36-year-old single man had checking compulsions that focused on excrement, and he engaged in prolonged and meticulous inspection of any speck of brown, particularly on his clothes and shoes."

  "A 40-year-old nursery school teacher checked that all rugs and carpets were absolutely flat, lest someone trip over them, and spent long periods looking for needles and pins on the floor and in furniture."

  "A 19-year-old clerk carried out 4 hours of checking after other members of the family retired at night. He checked all the electrical appliances, doors, taps, and so on and was not able to get to bed before 3 or 4 o'clock in the morning" (Rachman, 2003a, pp. 142–143).

- pursuing cleanliness (e.g., handwashing, cleaning the house) and orderliness (e.g., arranging objects until they are "just right"), sometimes through elaborate ceremonies that take hours and even most of the day.

- mental rituals (e.g., repeating prayers in response to "bad" thoughts). This example highlights that compulsions are not always behaviours; they can be mental acts.

VCG/VCG via Getty Images, Inc.

Soccer superstar David Beckham has described several instances in which his teammates, aware of his OCD, rearranged objects to get him upset.

- performing repetitive, magical, protective practices, such as counting, saying certain numbers, or touching a talisman or a particular part of the body. Soccer star David Beckham (see photo) is one celebrity who has acknowledged OCD and a problem with repetitive counting, such as counting and re-counting the soft drinks in his refrigerator. Beckham has indicated that he has come to accept his OCD but also said that it is "tiring."

- performing a particular act, such as eating extremely slowly.

rune hellestad/Corbis via Getty Images

Lena Dunham, star and creator of the hit HBO TV show *Girls,* has acknowledged battling OCD since the age of 9. Her character on the show, Hannah, has also displayed symptoms of OCD, including counting compulsions. In a 2013 episode of the show, she goes for treatment accompanied by her parents. Dunham has described the usefulness of meditation instead of medication for addressing her personal symptoms.

With respect to the last point, when the slowness is the central problem and is not secondary to other OCD symptoms, such as checking, then it is a related condition known as *primary obsessional slowness.* How slow is slow? Rachman (2003b) described the case of a 38-year-old man who would take three hours each morning to get ready for work, including 45 minutes for teeth-brushing. A bath would take between three to five hours.

According to Rachman (2002), three "multipliers" that increase the intensity and frequency of compulsive checking are a sense of personal responsibility, the probability of harm if checking does not take place, and the predicted seriousness of harm.

We often hear people described as compulsive gamblers, compulsive eaters, and compulsive drinkers. Even though individuals may report an irresistible urge to gamble, eat, and drink, such behaviour is not clinically regarded as a compulsion because it is often engaged in with pleasure. A true compulsion is viewed by most OCD sufferers as ego-dystonic. Stern and Cobb (1978) found that 78% of a sample of compulsive individuals viewed their rituals as "rather silly or absurd" but were still unable to stop them.

Compulsions are most often viewed as a consequence of obsessions. As noted earlier, they are typically done to decrease the anxiety associated with an obsession. For example, a teenage boy who has the unwanted thought that he is going to cause harm to his baby sister may spend hours ensuring he has not left any small objects on the floor that could lead to her choking. However, some researchers are questioning the idea that compulsions are simply a consequence of obsessions, and are instead suggesting that the tendency to develop avoidance habits may be a key feature of OCD (Gillan et al., 2014).

OCD often has a negative effect on the individual's relations with other people, especially family members. People saddled with the irresistible need to wash their hands every 10 minutes, or to touch every doorknob they pass, or to count every tile in a bathroom floor, are likely to cause concern and even resentment in spouses, children, friends, or co-workers. Overt conflict may indicate the need for family therapy as a supplement to individual therapies. Also, families often go along with the compulsions, following rigid rules or even helping with rituals, so as not to upset the person with OCD (Cherian et al., 2014). These "helping" behaviours are associated with poorer outcomes for the person with OCD, but it is currently unclear whether it is more severe OCD symptoms that pull for such behaviours among family members, or whether the helping behaviours themselves are contributing to more severe presentations of OCD. Regardless, family involvement in therapy may prove helpful.

Often people with OCD are misdiagnosed. Over a thousand New York physicians were emailed a survey describing a patient with OCD (Glazier, Swing, & McGinn, 2015). The patient described in the vignette had one of the following eight symptom presentations: "obsessions regarding aggression, contamination, fear of saying things, homosexuality, pedophilia, religion, somatic concerns, or symmetry" (p.e761). The physicians were asked to diagnose the patient and provide treatment recommendations. Surprisingly, half of the cases were misdiagnosed! Moreover, compared with properly diagnosed clients, those who were misdiagnosed were less likely to be recommended for appropriate treatments, and more likely to be recommended inappropriate treatments. Not surprising was that the type of symptom presentation strongly affected the rate of misdiagnosis. Physicians were good at identifying symmetry obsessions as OCD (only a 3.7% misidentification rate). Rates of misidentification were high (over 70%) for obsessions involving homosexuality, aggression, saying certain things, and pedophilia. The authors made recommendations on the need for greater training on OCD.

6.3 Etiology of Obsessive-Compulsive Disorder

Behavioural and Cognitive Theories

Behavioural accounts of compulsions consider them learned behaviours reinforced by fear reduction. Compulsive handwashing, for example, is viewed as an operant escape-response that reduces an obsessional preoccupation with and fear of contamination by dirt or germs. Similarly, compulsive checking may reduce anxiety about whatever disaster the person anticipates if the checking ritual is not completed. Anxiety, as measured by self-reports, and psychophysiological responses can indeed be reduced by such compulsive behaviour. The very high frequency of compulsive acts occurs in order to give the person reassurance because the stimuli that elicit anxiety are hard to discriminate. For example, it is hard to know when germs are present and when they have been eliminated by a cleaning ritual (Mineka & Zinbarg, 1996).

It has also been proposed that compulsive checking results from a memory deficit. An inability to remember some action accurately (such as turning off the stove) or to distinguish between an actual behaviour and an imagined behaviour ("Maybe I just thought I turned off the stove") could cause someone to check repeatedly. General research on OCD suggests inconsistent evidence of memory deficits for verbal information, but there is stronger evidence for impairments in memory for non-verbal information (Muller & Roberts, 2005). A review by Cuttler and Graf (2009) from the University of British Columbia yielded new insights into whether memory deficits exist. They compared the results of research with OCD checkers and non-checkers and found that deficits in retrospective memory are found among checkers and non-checkers, so the deficits do not seem to have a special role in checking compulsions. However, some evidence suggests that checkers have unique deficits in prospective memory (see Cuttler & Graf, 2009). One caveat is that this research was conducted with student samples (i.e., subclinical checkers) and the generalization to individuals with OCD requires further work. While **retrospective memory** is the ability to remember recent events and experiences, **prospective memory** is defined and measured by these authors as "the ability to look forward and to remember at the right place or time to perform an intended action"

TABLE 6.1 Faulty Appraisals Implicated in the Etiology and Persistence of Obsessions by Cognitive-Behavioural Therapists

Faulty Appraisal	Explanation	Example
Overestimation of threat and negative consequences	The obsession is viewed as highly threatening and possibly resulting in very undesirable negative outcomes.	I have touched this doorknob. It is contaminated with germs that may now invade my body and cause cancer.
Inflated responsibility	The obsession is considered an indication that one has the power to bring about, or prevent, the occurrence of harm or other negative outcomes to self or others.	I notice a piece of glass on the road and think that it could cause a tire to blow and result in a fatal accident. Knowing this, I am responsible to ensure the glass is removed.
Over importance of thoughts	The obsession is considered highly significant because of its prominence within the stream of consciousness.	The very fact that I am thinking unwanted intrusive thoughts of harming others means that these thoughts must be highly significant.
Over importance of thought control	The obsession must be successfully dismissed from consciousness, and failure to do so represents a serious threat of possible negative consequences.	It is important that I suppress any intrusive thought of inappropriately touching a child because failure to control the thought means that I might lose control and actually commit such a horrible offence.
Thought–action fusion	The presence of the obsession increases the likelihood that the unwanted event will occur, and even thinking such a repugnant thought is morally equivalent to engaging in the forbidden act.	If I think about my father dying in a plane crash, this increases the probability that the event will actually happen; having unwanted intrusive thoughts of inappropriately touching a child is as morally reprehensible as actually doing it.
Catastrophic misinterpretation of significance	The obsession is interpreted as a sign or indication of something meaningful about the individual.	If I have unwanted intrusive thoughts of harming other people, this may mean that I am a latent psychopath.
Perfectionism	The best way to deal with the obsession is to achieve a perfect, complete, or just right state.	If I keep saying this phrase over and over until I can repeat it perfectly, then I will feel better and can get on with my daily activities.
Intolerance of uncertainty	It is intolerable to have any doubt or uncertainty associated with the obsession.	I cannot be certain that I understand this sentence, so I will reread it several times until I know that I understand what I have read.
Ego-dystonicity	The obsession is considered inconsistent, alien, and even threatening to one's self-definition.	A young man avoids public washrooms because of the obsessional doubt of whether he just molested a child in the washroom. Such a thought is completely contrary to his high moral standards and conscientiousness.

Adapted with kind permission from Springer Science and Business Media: Clark, D.A. (2000) "Cognitive Behavior Therapy for Obsessions and Compulsions: New Applications and Emerging Trends," *Journal of Contemporary Psychotherapy.* Volume 30, Number 2.

(p. 814) when the action is expected and required. Radomsky and colleagues (2014) at Concordia University examined another distinction in the quest to determine whether there is a memory deficit among people with OCD who have checking compulsions. They compared relevant and irrelevant checking in samples of clients with OCD and non-clinical students. Relevant checking was found to affect memory confidence, vividness, and detail for both groups, whereas irrelevant checking did not.

Overall evaluation of cognitive biases in OCD initially concluded that there is only weak evidence for the existence of cognitive biases overall and that cognitive biases may only exist among the subset of people with contamination concerns (Summerfeldt & Endler, 1998). However, more recent data indicate that individuals with OCD may have a processing abnormality for threatening visual material (Moritz et al., 2009).

So, how can we account for obsessive thoughts? The obsessions of diagnosed people usually make them anxious,

as do the somewhat similar intrusive thoughts of normal people after exposure to stressful stimuli, such as a scary movie. Most people occasionally experience unwanted ideas that are similar in content to obsessions and unpleasant thoughts increase during times of stress. An international study involving many researchers (including Adam Radomsky from Concordia University) surveyed participants from 15 cities across six continents on whether they experienced intrusive (unwanted) thoughts (Moulding et al., 2014). The vast majority of people (94%) reported experiencing unwanted thoughts. The most popular unwanted thoughts were related to contamination, aggression, and doubting. Results like these suggest that it may not be the intrusive thoughts themselves that are most problematic, but rather the interpretation of those thoughts and the compulsions used to counteract the unwanted thoughts. Normal individuals can tolerate or dismiss these cognitions, but for individuals with OCD, the thoughts may be particularly vivid and elicit great concern, perhaps because childhood experiences taught them that some thoughts are dangerous or unacceptable.

Rachman advanced a cognitive theory of obsessions in OCD (see Rachman, 1998). He posited that unwanted intrusive thoughts are the roots of obsessions and that obsessions often involve catastrophic misinterpretations of the importance and significance of negative intrusive thoughts. Rachman and Shafran (1998) identified a range of cognitive factors involved in OCD in addition to the obsessions themselves, including an inflated sense of personal responsibility for outcomes and a cognitive bias involving thought–action fusion. Thought–action fusion involves two beliefs: (1) the mere act of thinking about unpleasant events increases the perceived likelihood that they will actually happen and (2) at a moral level, thinking something unpleasant (e.g., imagining hurting others) is the same as actually having carried it out. Thus, thought–action fusion involves a blurring of the distinction between thinking about something and reacting as if the behaviour has actually happened.

Table 6.1 lists faulty cognitive appraisals, as summarized by David Clark (2001, 2005) from the University of New Brunswick. Themes represented here include a sense of being responsible for events that may or may not occur, the overimportance of thought control, an inability to tolerate uncertainty, and thought–action fusion. Many of these thoughts are represented on a measure known as the Meta-Cognitive Beliefs Questionnaire (Clark, Purdon, & Wang, 2003). Beliefs about thought control and the negative consequences of uncontrolled thoughts are highly predictive of obsessions (Clark et al., 2003). Other Canadian research suggests that there are metacognitive differences in OCD—specifically, that people with OCD have such highly developed cognitive self-consciousness that they reflect excessively on their cognitive processes (Janeck, Calamari, Riemann, & Heffelfinger, 2003). In other words, they engage in too much thinking about thinking itself!

What is distressing about intrusive thoughts? Studies conducted in Ontario suggest that thoughts are especially upsetting if they are inconsistent with valued aspects of the self (Rowa & Purdon, 2003) and they are perceived as personally meaningful and significant (Rowa, Purdon, Summerfeldt, & Antony, 2005). Thus, people who pride themselves on their altruism would be highly distressed by repetitive, intrusive thoughts reflecting an urge to hurt other people.

Biological Factors

There is some evidence for a genetic side to OCD. Initial evidence supporting the role of genetics was gleaned from prevalence rates. The prevalence of OCD is higher among the first-degree relatives of OCD clients (10.3%) than in control relatives (1.9%) (Pauls et al., 1995). More recent research has focused on the identification of genetic markers. The authors of a genome-wide association study said that they "identified interesting candidate genes for OCD, but failed to detect any genome-wide significant findings" (Mattheisen et al., 2015). The researchers went on to state that with larger samples, significance may be reached. Thus, biological factors may predispose some people to OCD. Another study further highlights the complexity of the role of genetics in OCD, as well as the importance of examining comorbidity. In a collaboration involving more than 100 research centres around the world, including Canadian ones, Yu and colleagues (2015) found that genetic risks may be different for OCD co-occurring with Tourette's syndrome, compared with OCD alone. Tourette's syndrome is marked by both motor and vocal tics and has been linked to basal ganglia dysfunction (as has OCD, see below). People with Tourette's often have OCD as well (Sheppard et al., 1999).

Encephalitis, head injuries, and brain tumours have all also been associated with the development of OCD (Jenike, 1986). Interest has focused on two areas of the brain that could be affected by such trauma: the frontal lobes and the basal ganglia, a set of subcortical nuclei including the caudate, putamen, globus pallidus, and amygdala (see Figure 6.1). PET scan studies have shown increased activation in the frontal lobes of OCD

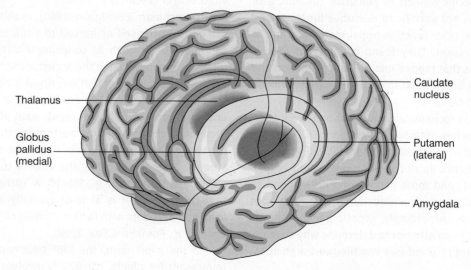

Thalamus

Globus pallidus (medial)

Caudate nucleus

Putamen (lateral)

Amygdala

FIGURE 6.1 The basal ganglia. Enhanced activation in the basal ganglia has been found among clients with OCD.

clients, perhaps a reflection of the person's overconcern with their own thoughts. The focus on the basal ganglia, a system linked to the control of motor behaviour, is due to its relevance to compulsions as well as to the relationship between OCD and Tourette's syndrome. Like the frontal lobes, the evidence is for increased activation in the basal ganglia, but it is not clear whether this enhanced activation is a cause or consequence of OCD. Rauch et al. (1994) provided evidence in support of the importance to OCD of both brain regions mentioned above. They presented participants with stimuli selected for them, such as a glove contaminated with garbage or an unlocked door, and found that blood flow in the brain increased in the frontal area and to some of the basal ganglia. People with OCD also have smaller putamen than people in the control group (Rosenberg et al., 1997). Nakao et al. (2009) examined the cognitive function of OCD clients and "healthy" volunteers by neuropsychological tests and fMRI while participants performed tasks to assess attention and non-verbal memory. The clients were divided into a short-term disorder group (duration average of 5.5 years) and a long-term group (duration over 20 years). The long-term group showed attention and memory deficits. The authors concluded that "abnormal brain activation occurs in the early phase of OCD and that the long-term persistence of OCD might involve a decline in cognitive function" (p. 814).

Snyder et al. (2015) conducted a meta-analysis of 110 studies that compared clients with OCD with healthy controls on executive function. "Executive functions are a set of general-purpose cognitive control abilities, mainly supported by the prefrontal cortex (PFC), which allow individuals to regulate their thoughts and behaviors" (Snyder et al., 2015, p. 301). Executive function deficits result in various impairments in daily living, such as difficulties making decisions and prioritizing, engaging in goal-directed behaviour, and planning for the future. Each study in the meta-analysis included at least one neuropsychological measure of executive function. They evaluated four hypotheses, namely that there is broad impairment in executive function, more limited impairments in specific aspects of executive function, general slowing that is not specific to executive function, and lastly, that any executive function impairments are due to co-occurring depression. They found evidence of impairment on most tasks that tapped into executive function and concluded there is broad impairment in executive function among clients with OCD.

Research on neurochemical factors has focused on serotonin. As noted below, pharmacotherapy for OCD focuses on selective serotonin reuptake inhibitors (SSRIs). However, 40–60% of OCD clients do not show improvement following SSRI treatment, and most people who do respond to these medications only show a reduction in symptoms, not a complete recovery. Accordingly, genetic polymorphisms are being explored in an attempt to determine why so many OCD sufferers do not respond (see Van Nieuwerburgh et al., 2009).

Psychoanalytic Theory

In classical psychoanalytic theory, obsessions and compulsions are viewed as similar, resulting from instinctual forces, sexual or aggressive, that are not under control because of overly harsh toilet training. The person is thus fixated at the anal stage. The symptoms observed represent the outcome of the struggle between the id and the defence mechanisms; sometimes the aggressive instincts of the id predominate, sometimes the defence mechanisms. For example, when obsessive thoughts of killing intrude, the forces of the id are dominant. More often, however, the observed symptoms reflect the partially successful operation of one of the defence mechanisms. For example, an individual fixated at the anal stage may, by reaction formation, resist the urge to soil and become compulsively neat, clean, and orderly.

Alfred Adler (1930) viewed OCD as a result of feelings of incompetence. He believed that when children are kept from developing a sense of competence by doting or excessively dominating parents, they develop an inferiority complex and may unconsciously adopt compulsive rituals in order to carve out a domain in which they exert control and can feel proficient. Adler proposed that the compulsive act allows a person mastery of something, even if only the positioning of writing implements on a desk. There is little empirical support for these theories.

6.4 Therapies for OCD

Behavioural Approaches to Treatment

When someone suffers from OCD, the overarching goal is to stop the compulsive acts from occurring. Accordingly, the most widely used and generally accepted behavioural approach to compulsive rituals, pioneered in England by Victor Meyer (1966), is **exposure and response prevention (ERP)** (Rachman & Hodgson, 1980). In this method the person exposes himself or herself to situations that elicit the compulsive act—such as touching a dirty dish—and then refrains from performing the accustomed ritual—handwashing. The assumption is that the ritual is negatively reinforcing because it reduces the anxiety that is aroused by some environmental stimulus or event, such as dust on a chair. Preventing the person from performing the ritual (response prevention) will expose him or her to the anxiety-provoking stimulus, thereby allowing the anxiety to be extinguished. Controlled research (e.g., Stanley & Turner, 1995) suggests that this treatment is at least partially effective for more than half of clients with OCD, including children and adolescents (e.g., Franklin & Foa, 1998).

In the short term, the ERP treatment is arduous and unpleasant for clients. It typically involves exposures lasting upwards of 90 minutes for 15 to 20 sessions within a three-week period, with instructions to practise between sessions, as well. It is estimated that 17 to 19% of clients refuse treatment (for a review, see Clark, 2005), and refusal to enter treatment and dropping out are generally recognized problems for many interventions for OCD. People with OCD tend to procrastinate, fear changes, and be overly concerned about others controlling them—traits that can create special problems for manipulative approaches such as behaviour therapy. In a more recent meta-analytic review of the effectiveness of psychological treatments for OCD, Rosa-Alcazar et al. (2008) concluded that therapist-guided exposure is better than therapist-assisted self-guided exposure and in vivo exposure combined, with exposure via imagination being superior to exposure in vivo alone.

Cognitive Approaches to Treatment

A combined cognitive behavioural therapy (CBT) approach is clearly required when treating OCD rather than just a cognitive approach because an inherent part of any cognitive therapy is exposure and response prevention. To evaluate whether or not performing a compulsive ritual will have catastrophic consequences, the client must stop performing that ritual.

Salkovskis and Warwick (1985) provided one of the earliest demonstrations of the usefulness of a CBT approach when they showed that cognitive restructuring helped an OCD client who relapsed following ERP. This client had developed the belief that her hand creams would cause cancer. Salkovskis (1998) has gone on to outline how cognitive procedures can eliminate the dysfunctional beliefs that contribute to the OCD clients' faulty appraisals. His model focuses on the notion of perceived responsibility, which is defined as "the belief that one has power which is pivotal to bring about or prevent subjectively crucial outcomes" (Salkovskis, 1998, p. 40). Cognitive and behavioural techniques focus on the modification of dysfunctional beliefs involving this sense of personal responsibility. This can involve having the client actually test whether something bad happens as a result of being prevented from performing the ritual (see Van Oppen et al., 1995).

Several investigators based in Canada have extended the CBT interventions used to treat OCD. Freeston and Ladouceur and associates outlined a five-step treatment program, with the fifth step being relapse prevention (see Freeston et al., 1997; Ladouceur et al., 1995). Another extension has been proposed by O'Connor and Robillard (2000) from Montreal. They focus on the OCD client's conviction that imaginary events may actually come true. Their modification, known as the "inference-based approach," is geared toward identifying and ameliorating the obsessional inference, which has become embedded within a fictional account constructed by the client. Over time, this imaginary account may be treated as if it were real. O'Connor and Robillard advocate a mixed approach that combines CBT with their inference-based approach (also see O'Connor et al., 2005). They investigated processes of change for inference-based therapy and found that targeting doubt led to decreases in OCD symptoms, providing support for their therapeutic approach (Perreault & O'Connor, 2014).

How effective is CBT for treating OCD? As noted above, OCD is difficult to treat. However, CBT conducted in clinical settings with well-trained clinicians has proven effective (see Hunsley & Lee, 2007; van Ingen et al., 2009). Jonsson and Hougaard (2009) conducted a meta-analysis of 13 trials of group CBT/ERP for OCD and concluded that the group treatments are effective. In two studies, better results were achieved by group CBT relative to pharmacological treatment. Rosa-Alcazar and colleagues (2008) concluded that ERP, cognitive restructuring, and the combination of the two were effective in reducing obsessions and compulsions and appeared to show a similar effectiveness. They suggested that both techniques actually employ similar treatment strategies (i.e., they both use behavioural and cognitive strategies).

More recently, Öst and colleagues (2015) completed a meta-analysis of all randomized controlled trials of different forms of CBT for OCD published between 1993 and 2014. They found no differences between group and individual approaches, and also no differences between ERP treatments and other forms of CBT. CBT was significantly better than pharmacotherapy. However, the combination of CBT and medication was not superior to the combination of CBT and placebo.

Interestingly, there is support that CBT affects volumes of brain regions that are abnormal in clients with OCD (Atmaca et al., 2016). This CBT study followed a pharmacotherapy study that found similar volume changes (Atmaca et al., 2015), suggesting that CBT and pharmacotherapy lead to similar effects on the brain.

While CBT is effective in treating OCD, Foa (2010) observed that about 20% of clients drop out and another 20% are not treated successfully. Clearly, there is substantial room for improvement when 2 out of 5 people with OCD are not helped. In addition, Foa (2010) pointed to the continuing need to tailor treatment to the specific symptoms and needs of individuals with OCD. That is, mostly due to sample size restrictions, we know very little about what might work best for someone who has OCD with primarily checking compulsions vs. counting or compulsive washing.

Other researchers are focused on using technology to deliver CBT for OCD. Internet-based CBT has shown promise and in fact had results similar to face-to-face CBT (Mewton et al., 2014). Stubbings and colleagues (2015) report the value of using videoconferencing and textchat with a client with severe OCD. They credit the technology with reducing the client's anxiety and allowing for greater disclosure of symptom content that was embarrassing for the client to share.

There may be other methods of improving the efficacy of CBT. Canadian Perspectives 6.1 looks at the possible benefits of physical exercise in the treatment of OCD.

Canadian Perspectives **6.1**

Can Physical Exercise Help People with OCD?

We all know that exercise is good for us. Given the well-documented benefits associated with physical exercise, it is no wonder that researchers are now taking a closer look at the use of physical exercise for various forms of psychopathology. Gordon Asmundson at the University of Regina, along with American colleagues (Powers, Asmundson, & Smits, 2015), edited a special issue of the journal *Cognitive Behaviour Therapy* that included nine papers evaluating the use of exercise in the treatment of OCD, PTSD, mood, and anxiety disorders. In their opening comments, the editors noted that unlike CBT, exercise is free, widely available, and lacks stigma. The focus of the special issue was on documenting the "state of the science" and spurring further research on such issues as the amount of exercise required "to make the most of exercise interventions as a means of symptom reduction" (p. 237).

One of the papers was by a Canadian group at Sunnybrook Health Sciences Centre in Toronto, led by psychologist Neil Rector. They completed a pilot study to investigate the possible benefits of physical exercise in the treatment of OCD (Rector, Richter, Lerman, & Regev, 2015). Rector and colleagues did not suggest exercise be used instead of CBT. Rather, they were interested in determining whether adding exercise to a CBT protocol would enhance outcomes.

They added structured physical activity to CBT for the treatment of 11 clients with OCD. The clients completed group CBT for 15 weeks at the clinic, focusing on exposure and response prevention early on, and shifting emphasis to cognitive approaches in later sessions. The physical exercise took place at a gym for three days per week for 12 weeks. They were asked to do 15 to 30 minutes of aerobic exercise during the first four weeks, and to increase it to 30 to 45 minutes during the last eight weeks. Heart rates were monitored and the intensity of exercise was customized for each client. Forms of exercise varied (e.g., elliptical, treadmill, bicycle, and swimming).

Importantly, participants' adherence was over 80%; most people did most of their exercise. And their OCD symptoms improved, even more than is commonly seen for clients undergoing CBT. The authors concluded that exercise may have helped. Of course there were limitations to this small pilot study (e.g., the lack of a control group). With these pilot results, the authors "are now proceeding with a large-scale, multi-site randomized controlled trial" in which they will compare the following four groups: exercise, CBT, combination of exercise and CBT, and a no-treatment control group (Rector et al., 2015, p. 338). They will address many other questions, including how physical exercise is helpful.

Biological Approaches to Treatment

According to Ravindran and Stein (2010), similar to the anxiety disorders you read about in Chapter 5, selective serotonin reuptake inhibitors (SSRIs) are useful first-line treatments for OCD. It is also known that serotonin-based treatments are more easily tolerated by clients with OCD, but a very substantial problem is lack of treatment response. Koen and Stein (2011) noted that up to 50% of people with OCD do not respond to SSRI treatment. As noted in Chapter 5, side effects are also an issue.

The desperation of mental health workers, surpassed only by that of the clients, explains the occasional use of psychosurgery in treating OCD. The procedure in current use, cingulotomy, involves destroying two to three centimetres of white matter in the cingulum, an area near the corpus callosum. Although Jung and colleagues (2006) found that 8 of 17 clients with refractory OCD showed some clinical improvement following the procedure, this intervention is viewed as a treatment of last resort, given its permanence, the risks of psychosurgery, and the poor understanding of how it works.

The U.S. Food and Drug Administration granted a "humanitarian device exemption" to the manufacturers of a "deep brain stimulation system" as a therapy for severe OCD (Graham, 2009). The agency based the decision on research with 26 clients with severe OCD who had tried and failed numerous other therapies. Clients showed a 40% reduction in symptoms following a year of deep brain stimulation. Current guidelines for the use of deep brain stimulation in the treatment of OCD were outlined in a paper led by Clement Hamani, a researcher

at the Toronto Western Hospital and the Centre for Addiction and Mental Health. The guidelines support the use of bilateral (but not unilateral) subthalamic nucleus deep brain stimulation for OCD treatment non-responders (Hamani et al., 2014). Deep brain stimulation is only offered to a small subset of OCD clients and it is not a cure-all. Only severe clients who have not been successfully treated with conventional approaches can be offered it, and they are expected to see a reduction in symptoms, making them more like average (rather than severe) OCD clients. We will discuss this treatment in more detail in Chapter 8 on mood disorders.

Psychoanalytic Approaches to Treatment

Psychoanalytic treatment for obsessions and compulsions resembles that for phobias and generalized anxiety—namely, lifting repression and allowing the client to confront what he or she (presumably) truly fears. The intrusive thoughts and compulsive behaviour protect the ego from the repressed conflict; however, they are difficult targets for therapeutic intervention, and psychoanalytic procedures have thus not been effective in treating this disorder.

Such shortcomings have prompted some analytic clinicians to take a more active, behavioural approach, using analytic understanding more as a way to increase compliance with behavioural procedures (Jenike, 1990). One view hypothesizes that the indecision one sees in most people with OCD derives from a need for guaranteed correctness before any action can be taken (Salzman, 1985). Thus, clients must learn to tolerate the uncertainty and anxiety that all people feel as they confront the reality that nothing is certain or absolutely controllable in life. The ultimate focus of the treatment remains gaining insight into the unconscious determinants of the symptoms.

Next we move on to the obsessive-compulsive related disorders, starting with hoarding disorder. There are many features in common across these conditions. A recent review highlights the role of shame in hoarding (related to living with clutter), hair-pulling and skin-picking (related to visible damage), and body dysmorphic disorder (body-related shame) (Weingarden & Renshaw, 2015). As you read the rest of this chapter, consider the high degree of shame experienced by people with these disorders, and the difficulty they face in disclosing their symptoms.

6.5 Hoarding Disorder

The general public is well aware of **hoarding disorder** as a result of TV shows like *Hoarders* and *Hoarding: Buried Alive* and some poignant case studies. An intriguing case that received international attention, involving a man from Burnaby, British Columbia, with hoarding disorder is presented below.

Hoarding disorder is diagnosed when the person has difficulty discarding objects and the clutter has come to dominate his or her life. Hoarding disorder was added to *DSM*-5; people with significant hoarding were previously diagnosed with OCD, but recent research described below clearly supports that there are important differences between hoarding and other OCD symptom presentations. The Burnaby man described below clearly fits the *DSM-5* criteria for hoarding disorder shown in Table 6.2.

Note that the *DSM* criteria focus on the difficulty of parting with possessions, but not acquiring possessions. There is a specifier for a clinician to indicate if excessive acquisition is part of the client's presentation. In fact, 80–90% of people with hoarding disorder also have excessive acquisition (APA, 2013). They buy many items they do not have room for or acquire free items (e.g., garbage from others, flyers). Therefore, for most people with hoarding disorder, parting with items and acquiring items are both problematic.

Also note that criterion D in Table 6.2 regarding clinically significant distress or impairment includes an element of safety; whether the hoarding behaviour results in an unsafe environment for self or others is taken into account in the diagnosis of hoarding disorder. For example, a renter with excessive clutter may put him- or herself and others in jeopardy if fire safety is compromised. Similarly, a neighbour's car-related collection that includes many gasoline bottles may put people's lives at risk, on top of the unsightly clutter that may hurt surrounding property values. It may sound insensitive to be concerned about property values and appearances, but there are well-documented cases of frustrated neighbours living near hoarders. Only if there is a safety risk or a bylaw violation do neighbours have any recourse.

So how and why is hoarding disorder now distinct from OCD in the *DSM-5?* First and foremost, evidence clearly indicates that hoarding disorder is distinguishable from OCD. Analyses of physiological data clearly indicate differences between people with hoarding disorder and people with OCD (see Frost, Steketee, & Tolin, 2012). There are also differences in neural activity between the two groups (Tolin, Witt, & Stevens, 2014). With respect to genetics, Monzani and colleagues (2014) found unique genetic factors for OCD, hoarding disorder, and body dysmorphic disorder (described in the section "Etiology of Hoarding Disorder"). Finally, people with hoarding are excited by their orientation toward objects, especially new possessions, while people with OCD are distressed when they have an obsession with objects.

Hoarding Disorder: A Case of Life or Death

A 2013 story originating from Burnaby, British Columbia, drew significant attention in Canada and around the world. A 70-year-old man had to be rescued in his home by firefighters when a friend of the man alerted the RCMP to his apparent disappearance. Eyewitness accounts say that firefighters found the man trapped under clutter after cutting through the clutter in the front hallway with chainsaws in order to create a path to reach him (see Chow, 2013). Corporal Dave Reid said, "We made verbal contact with the guy but he basically told us he was trapped underneath a whole pile of debris, couldn't get out, couldn't move, hadn't moved in a couple of days. . . [the clutter] was floor to ceiling, in every room, on both floors. So it was bad" (Chow, 2013). It was also reported that city staff had tried more than 10 times between 2003 and 2006 to get the man to comply with anti-clutter bylaws. The city finally cleaned it up and added the cost to his tax bill. Particularly ironic was that this man was characterized by city staff as believing previously that "his property has been arranged for his best personal health and safety" yet he would have died if the firefighters had not come along.

Alex Garcia/Chicago Tribune/MCT/Getty Images

The difference between being a hoarder and a collector is illustrated in this photo. Emergency personnel had to come to the rescue of the Burnaby man living here.

TABLE 6.2	*DSM-5* Criteria for Hoarding Disorder

A. Persistent difficulty discarding or parting with possessions, regardless of their actual value.

B. This difficulty is due to a perceived need to save the items and to distress associated with discarding them.

C. The difficulty discarding possessions results in the accumulation of possessions that congest and clutter active living areas and subsequently compromises their intended use. If living areas are uncluttered, it is only because of the interventions of third parties (i.e., family members, cleaners, authorities).

D. The hoarding causes clinically significant distress or impairment in social, occupational, or other important areas of functioning (including maintaining a safe environment for self and others).

E. The hoarding is not attributable to another medical condition (e.g., brain injury, cerebrovascular disease, Prader-Willi syndrome).

F. The hoarding is not better explained by the symptoms of another mental disorder (e.g., obsessions in obsessive-compulsive disorder, decreased energy in major depressive disorder, delusions in schizophrenia or another psychotic disorder, cognitive deficits in major neurocognitive disorder, restricted interests in autism spectrum disorder).

Reprinted with permission from the Diagnostic and Statistical Manual of Mental Disorders, Fifth Edition, (Copyright 2013). American Psychiatric Association.

There is a great deal of interest in hoarding disorder and new findings are accumulating rapidly. One of the exceptional leaders in this field is Randy Frost from Smith College in Massachusetts (see photo). Frost and his colleagues have been highly influential in advancing hoarding disorder to a recognized clinical disorder.

The current status of the burgeoning literature was summarized impressively by Frost et al. (2012) in a paper in the influential *Annual Review of Clinical Psychology*. They noted that there was no systematic description of hoarding disorder prior to the 1990s and the first systematic study was provided by Frost and Gross (1993), who defined hoarding as "the acquisition of and the failure to discard" (p. 367). Key findings summarized in their review included evidence that hoarding is associated with older age and that there are cases of older people becoming hoarders. Also, problems with hoarding seem to be detectable worldwide, and evidence of sex differences is inconsistent and equivocal. It was indicated that the prevalence of hoarding ranges anywhere from 2% to 5% and it is twice as prevalent as obsessive-compulsive disorder (also see Iervolino et al., 2009; Mueller et al., 2009).

Other recent data relate to the issue of the categorical vs. dimensional view of psychopathology that was discussed in Chapter 3; evidence across three samples suggests that hoarding is dimensional rather than categorical. Thus, when talking about an individual person, we really should not be discussing hoarders per se. Instead, we should be discussing how much this person engages in hoarding along a continuous dimension (see Timpano et al., 2013). Also, new research

shows the importance of obtaining informant ratings: when comparisons are made with reports from friends and family members, people high in hoarding symptoms consistently under-report the extent of their hoarding symptoms and hoarding behaviours (DiMauro, Tolin, Frost, & Steketee, 2013).

What distinguishes those with hoarding disorder from normative collecting behaviour? Collectors are more selective, collecting a narrower range of items (Nordsletten, Fernández de la Cruz, Billotti, & Mataix-Cols, 2013). They were also more likely to organize their collections, and not have the significant clutter associated with hoarding disorder. However, they did report attachment to and difficulty discarding items, similar to people with hoarding disorder. Most importantly, clutter did not significantly impair the lives of those who collect. With the inclusion of hoarding disorder in *DSM-5*, the possible over-pathologization of normal collecting has been raised. However, results such as these are helpful in noting that normal collecting will not be diagnosed as hoarding disorder.

Hoarding disorder can be diagnosed reliably and with adequate validity, as shown by a recent field trial that examined the diagnostic criteria (see Mataix-Cols et al., 2013). This investigation involved evaluating 50 unselected people with hoarding behaviours and 20 unselected self-defined "collectors." Psychiatric assessments that included a semi-structured interview found that 29 of the 50 people met diagnostic criteria for hoarding disorder and, as should be the case, none of the 20 collectors were deemed to have hoarding disorder.

One key issue is the extent to which hoarding disorder is comorbid with other disorders. A detailed investigation of a large Internet sample of 363 people who self-identified as having problems with hoarding resulted in the identification of three types of hoarders (Hall, Tolin, Frost, & Steketee, 2013). One group was described as non-comorbid hoarding and this applied to 42% of the people in the sample. Another 42% had hoarding and comorbid depression. These people had elevated levels of perfectionism, impulsivity, lower self-control, and poor

Randy Frost from Smith College is a leading expert on hoarding disorder. Frost also is a leader in the perfectionism field and has published an authoritative book with his colleague Gail Steketee called *Stuff: Compulsive Hoarding and the Meaning of Things.*

emotion regulation strategies. The third group accounted for the other 16% and these people had a combined form of hoarding and inattention. The relatively low number of people in this category was not in keeping with suggestions that hoarding is a form of behaviour potentiated by attention deficit symptoms. Finally, the researchers noted the inability to detect a group of hoarders with comorbid hoarding and obsessive-compulsive tendencies. These results further illustrate how hoarding and obsessive-compulsive disorder are distinguishable. In fact, they bring us back to an earlier point on whether hoarding disorder should even be classified as an OCRD (Abramowitz & Jacoby, 2015).

Perhaps the most salient point noted by Frost et al. (2012) in their review is that hoarding disorder remained "under the mental health radar for many years" (p. 220). A clinician faced with someone with hoarding disorder in the 1970s and 1980s would have had little information to formulate a diagnosis or recommend treatment options. Clearly, a disorder that is now recognized and that influences many people would, on a technical basis, not have existed several decades ago based on its exclusion from the *DSM*. This raises reasonable questions about what other conditions that are not currently recognized are also "flying under the radar."

Although hoarding disorder remained under the radar for many years, clearly things have changed. For example, an article in the Winnipeg press recently reported a hoarding "epidemic," noting that OCD Centre Manitoba receives over 300 calls a year related to hoarding (Baxter, 2015). Another organization in Winnipeg called This Full House offers resources to support older adults (age 55 and older) struggling with hoarding to live a safe life. The organization notes how hoarding can lead to fires, eviction, and injury from falls, which is particularly relevant for this older age group. We will return to hoarding disorder among older adults when we consider treatment for this condition.

Etiology of Hoarding Disorder

What causes people to live in a cluttered, unsafe environment? As noted earlier, there is evidence for a genetic contribution to hoarding disorder (Monzani et al., 2014). Further, the question has arisen whether difficulty parting with items and excessive acquisition of items have a common etiology. Nordsletten, Monzani, and colleagues (2013) found strong genetic and moderate non-shared environmental correlations between these two aspects of hoarding disorder.

Cognitive factors also play a role. Frost and Hartl (1996) advanced an initial cognitive model in which hoarding was conceptualized as reflecting several influences, including faulty information processing (i.e., distractibility and difficulty thinking about categories), erroneous cognitions about the importance and meaning of possessions, and misguided attachments with objects to seemingly compensate for emotional deficits in attachment to people. Other cognitive processes play a role, including rumination, which was shown to predict severity of

hoarding behaviour (Portero et al., 2015). Finally, researchers from the University of British Columbia's Centre for Collaborative Research on Hoarding conducted a review on cognitive performance among people with hoarding disorder (Woody et al., 2014) and found performance deficits in many areas. For example, people with hoarding disorder perceive more categories, take longer to sort objects, and are more anxious while doing so, compared to control participants.

There has been a research focus on hoarding behaviours in adults and even more so in older adults. However, recently, researchers have been advocating for more studies on hoarding among children and adolescents (Burton, Arnold, & Soreni, 2015; Morris et al., in press). They point out that hoarding symptoms often have their onset in childhood and adolescence. However, there is a need for assessment tools that are appropriate for these younger age groups. There is currently no evidence-based intervention for hoarding in children, other than case studies following CBT methods. We turn next to the treatment of hoarding disorder in adults and older adults.

Treatment of Hoarding Disorder

Pharmacotherapy is often used in the treatment of hoarding disorder, including venlafaxine, a selective serotonin and norepinephrine reuptake inhibitor (SSNRI) (Saxena & Summer, 2014). A meta-analysis identified seven studies that have assessed the efficacy of pharmacotherapy for pathological hoarding: more than half of participants were treatment responders (Brakoulias, Eslick, & Starcevic, 2015).

Hoarding disorder is often treated using OCD protocols, given it was a subtype of OCD until becoming its own diagnostic category in *DSM*-5. Unfortunately the presence of hoarding symptoms has been related to poorer treatment outcome. Bloch and colleagues (2014) conducted a meta-analysis comparing how well people with OCD without hoarding symptoms responded to treatment vs. how well people with OCD with hoarding symptoms responded to treatment. Those without hoarding symptoms benefitted more from various treatments than those with hoarding symptoms. People with hoarding symptoms may require more specific treatment plans.

CBT for hoarding involves many strategies that are similar to treatment with OCD and the anxiety disorders (Steketee et al., 2010). Starting with a case formulation, as well as using exposure and cognitive restructuring, are typical CBT strategies used across many disorders. However, these elements are tailored to hoarding. The case formulation focuses on the problem behaviour of hoarding, the exposure is aimed at not acquiring items as well as discarding items, and the cognitive restructuring targets beliefs that are problematic for hoarding. Unique to CBT for hoarding is skills training, which focuses on organizing, problem solving, and decision-making. Motivational interviewing techniques are also used when clients present with ambivalence about working on the reduction of hoarding in therapy. Finally, the therapist often travels to the client's home for more intensive exposure, lasting hours for some clients with severe hoarding.

Is CBT for hoarding effective? Randy Frost's model (Frost & Hartl, 1996) was tested in a collaboration with Gail Steketee, another main researcher in this area (Steketee et al., 2010; Muroff et al., 2014). They randomly assigned participants with clinically significant hoarding to a 26-session CBT protocol or wait-list. Those in the CBT condition had significant decreases in hoarding symptoms at post-treatment, which were maintained at a follow-up assessment that was up to 12 months long. Most clients who received CBT were rated as improved. Higher severity of hoarding and perfectionism at pretreatment and gender (being male) were all related to worse outcomes. Overall, there was significant change that was sustained at follow-up, but the outcomes were still not as good as those seen with CBT for many other conditions (OCD, anxiety disorders). They highlight that the older age of people with hoarding disorder in treatment studies may contribute to the lack of treatment response seen (i.e., they have long-standing symptoms). Participants in this study were an average age of 55 years, which is considerably higher than those in many non-hoarding CBT studies.

Hoarding may be particularly problematic to treat among older adults. Andersen and colleagues (2008) completed a qualitative study of eight older Canadian adults (ranging in age from 71 to 90 years). Items hoarded included food (e.g., canned food, half-eaten meals, stale bread, empty food containers), books, newspapers, junk mail, old clothes, pill bottles, and other people's garbage. Among the clinical implications outlined, the researchers reported a lack of trust of caregivers, suspiciousness that caregivers with large purses and coats would covertly take their belongings during a home visit, and a preoccupation with control, making it difficult for anyone to help them.

A case study more fully describing one of the eight adults (Raymond, a pseudonym) highlights how hoarding took up all of his time, with Raymond stating: "I don't have time for myself" (Andersen, Raffin-Bouchal, & Marcy-Edwards, 2013, p. 444). The picture shows the amount of material in his living room, leaving only a pathway to access his bedroom. Raymond hoarded a binder on cancer and stated, "Why should I keep it when it takes up space and room?," yet he kept it since 1960, despite not having cancer. The detailed narrative of Raymond's case also highlighted how difficult it is to treat an older person

with hoarding: "Over a period of 4 months of weekly visits, Raymond was only able to send 17 books and 6 articles for recycling" (p. 449). Of note, hoarding severity has been found to predict functional disability among older adults, highlighting the need for its treatment in this population (Ayers et al., 2014). Additionally, hoarding severity assessed by clinicians, rather than clients themselves filling out self-report questionnaires, was a better predictor of disability. Clinical implications include the importance of accurate, objective assessment of hoarding symptoms among older adults.

Novel treatments are currently being developed for the treatment of hoarding disorder, including a treatment specifically for use with older adults (Ayers et al., 2014). Twenty-four sessions of cognitive rehabilitation aimed at improving executive functioning combined with behaviour therapy were delivered to 11 clients who were at least 60 years of age. The focus of the behaviour therapy was on exposure to discarding and not acquiring. Clients were assessed before, during, and after treatment on symptoms of hoarding. They found improvement at twice the rate of their past experience of delivering CBT alone. Although promising, this evaluation was an open trial, meaning there was no control group. Nonetheless, for a geriatric population with hoarding symptoms, an approach involving more than CBT may be necessary. Another novel approach, inference-based therapy, discussed above in the OCD treatment section, was successfully used to treat a woman with hoarding disorder by researchers in Quebec (see St-Pierre-Delorme et al., 2011 for the case study).

6.6 Body Dysmorphic Disorder

With **body dysmorphic disorder (BDD)**, a person is preoccupied with an imagined or exaggerated defect in appearance, frequently in the face; for example, facial wrinkles, excess facial hair, or the shape or size of the nose. Women tend also to focus on the skin, hips, breasts, and legs, whereas men are more inclined to believe they are too short, that their penises are too small, or that they have too much body hair. Some clients with the disorder may spend hours each day checking on their defect, looking at themselves in mirrors. Others take steps to avoid being reminded of the defect by eliminating mirrors from their homes or camouflaging the defect, for example by wearing very loose clothing (Phillips, 2009). These concerns are distressing and may lead to frequent consultations with plastic surgeons because some people with BDD are never satisfied with the results of cosmetic surgery. About a third of people with BDD have very poor insight regarding their symptoms, to the point of being delusional (APA, 2013). Others have good insight in that they can recognize that their appearance concerns may not be true. On average, however, insight is poor, which can explain why these clients are not satisfied with any attempts at plastic surgery.

Andersen, E., Raffin-Bouchal, S., & Marcy-Edwards, D. (2013)

Raymond's living room

BDD occurs mostly among women, typically begins in late adolescence, and is frequently comorbid with depression, social anxiety disorder, eating disorders, thoughts of suicide, substance use and personality disorders (Altamura et al., 2001; Buhlmann, Reese, Renaud, & Wilhelm, 2008; Phillips, 2009). BDD is usually chronic; recently, the first long-term study of the course of BDD found over a four-year period that only 1 in 5 clients with BDD experienced full remission but even among these people there was a moderate to high probability of full or partial relapse (Phillips et al., 2013). People were less likely to achieve remission of their symptoms as a function of three factors: having more severe symptoms at intake, a longer lifetime duration of BDD, and being an adult when assessed.

Should BDD be a separate diagnostic category? It is unclear whether BDD's status as a specific diagnosis is warranted. For example, people who are excessively preoccupied with their appearance and frequently check their looks might be diagnosed with OCD, and some experts believe that BDD should be subsumed as a subtype of OCD (Kroenke, Sharpe, & Sykes, 2007). This is further supported by recent evidence showing a strong role for shared genetic factors in BDD and OCD (Monzani et al., 2012, 2014). Other people may hold a belief about a defect so unrelated to reality as to suggest a delusional disorder. Others have suggested that BDD would be better classified as a variation of social anxiety disorder, a mood disorder, or even an eating disorder (see Buhlmann et al., 2008).

What has changed with the new *DSM-5* criteria? The first major change was moving BDD to the obsessive-compulsive and related disorders category. The second change involved the addition of the following criterion, which requires "the individual has performed repetitive behaviors (e.g., mirror checking, excessive grooming…..) or mental acts (e.g., comparing his or her appearance with that of others)…" (APA, 2013, p. 242). The revised set of criteria has led to increased precision: the criteria

Actor Reid Ewing, star of *Modern Family*, revealed that he suffers from body dysmorphic disorder and has undergone numerous plastic surgeries on his face, starting at age 19, which he regrets.

are more in line with how people with BDD present. However, there has been no real change in prevalence rates (Schieber et al., 2015). Note that these repetitive behaviours link BDD to the other disorders in this chapter; that is, the OCRDs all involve repetitive behaviours.

Etiology of Body Dysmorphic Disorder

As noted above, there is a genetic component implicated in the etiology of BDD (Monzani et al., 2012, 2014). Further, recent research has evaluated brain volumes and found differences comparing individuals with BDD and healthy controls, specifically lower volumes in the right orbitofrontal cortex and left anterior cingulate cortex for the BDD group (Buchanan et al., 2014). Even more, a greater duration of BDD illness was associated with lower right orbitofrontal cortex volumes.

Fang and Wilhelm (2015) reviewed cognitive and emotional processing mechanisms of BDD. Figure 6.2 presents a cognitive behavioural model of BDD. According to this model, it is assumed that everyone has appearance-related thoughts, but what differentiates those with BDD from a healthy population is that they strongly attend to these thoughts and make catastrophic interpretations, leading to negative emotions (e.g., anxiety, depression, and shame). Note the similarity to OCD; just like people with OCD, people with BDD are focused on unwanted thoughts. Efforts to regulate the resulting emotions are not adaptive: they avoid social situations, engage in mirror checking, and apply makeup to hide any real or perceived imperfections. These strategies may lead to temporary relief—for example, avoiding a social situation may reduce anxiety temporarily—but serve to negatively reinforce the maladaptive beliefs. It is also acknowledged in this model

Actress Uma Thurman, star of *Kill Bill Volumes 1 & 2,* revealed that she suffers from body dysmorphic disorder. Other women celebrities who have indicated that they have body dysmorphic disorder include singer Lily Allen and actress Sarah Michelle Gellar.

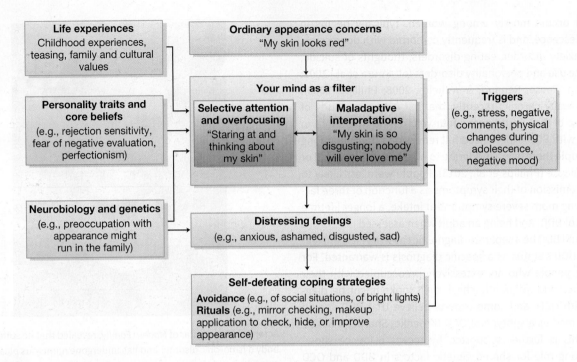

FIGURE 6.2 Cognitive behavioural model of body dysmorphic disorder. Figure adapted with permission from S. Wilhelm, *Feeling Good About the Way You Look: A Program for Overcoming Body Image Problems*. New York: Guilford, 2006.

that certain life experiences (e.g., bullying), personality traits (e.g., having a high fear of negative evaluation), and genetic factors can influence the extent to which a person will excessively focus on appearance concerns and make maladaptive interpretations. Finally, the role of triggers is also taken into account. For example, changes during adolescence may result in greater selective attention and maladaptive interpretations. This model has heavily influenced CBT for BDD, outlined in the next section.

Treatment of Body Dysmorphic Disorder

Psychological and pharmacological treatments for BDD have received increased attention in recent years. Psychological interventions have focused primarily on short-term (7 to 30) sessions of CBT or behavioural or cognitive therapy alone. Similar to OCD, behavioural interventions typically focus on exposure and response prevention. For example, a client might be gradually confronted with anxiety-provoking situations, such as going to a movie theatre, and staying in the situation without engaging in rituals (e.g., mirror checking) or avoidance behaviours (e.g., avoiding eye contact with others), until anxiety decreases. Cognitive strategies would focus on identifying maladaptive, self-defeating thoughts and core beliefs, such as "If I don't look perfect, it's impossible to be happy," or "I'm unlovable," that seem to maintain body-dysmorphic thoughts and behaviours; evaluating the accuracy of these negative thoughts and irrational beliefs; and assisting the development of more realistic thoughts and beliefs. Final sessions typically focus on relapse prevention.

Medication trials have primarily investigated SSRIs. A meta-analysis (Williams, Hadjistavropoulos, & Sharpe, 2006) concluded that both CBT and medication are effective in treating BDD, although CBT was associated with significantly higher effect sizes. Further, CBT appeared to be highly acceptable to clients, and recent research attests to the long-term outcomes (Veale, Miles, & Anson, 2015), although a significant number of participants still had chronic symptoms. Buhlmann et al. (2008) noted that clinicians still face numerous challenges in the CBT treatment of BDD. Issues include comorbid depression, suicidality, substance use disorders, personality disorders, the role of early life experiences, delusional intensity of beliefs, and motivation to change. One study found that both CBT and exposure with response prevention were quite effective overall, but this may be questioned in that BDD clients still expressed significant dissatisfaction with body parts following eight weeks of treatment (Khemlani-Patel, Neziroglu, & Mancusi, 2011). CBT was shown to be more effective than anxiety management, even for people with depression and those with delusional appearance beliefs (Veale et al., 2014). Another CBT approach uses optional modules: Wilhelm and colleagues (2014) reported on a modular CBT intervention containing core elements applicable to all clients with BDD, as well as extra optional modules covering specific symptoms that may only be relevant to a subset of clients (e.g., a module on mood management). They found positive results and suggest further evaluation of this modular approach. Finally, an open trial in Canada evaluated the efficacy of inference-based therapy in the treatment of BDD (Taillon et al., 2013). Ten of 13 participants completed the therapy and improved on BDD symptoms. Note that we already reported on the use of inference-based therapy for OCD and hoarding disorder.

6.7 Body-Focused Repetitive Behaviours: Trichotillomania (Hair-Pulling) and Excoriation (Skin-Picking)

There are two **body-focused repetitive behaviours** in *DSM-5*. **Trichotillomania (hair-pulling disorder)** has a longer history of being in the *DSM*. **Excoriation (skin-picking disorder)** is new in *DSM-5*, although symptoms may have previously been diagnosed as impulse control disorder—not otherwise specified. Given that much of the current research has grouped these two disorders together, after reviewing the diagnostic features of each disorder, we will consider etiology and treatment together.

Trichotillomania (Hair-Pulling Disorder)

The main feature of trichotillomania is hair pulling. Hair can be pulled from any part of the body, but usually people with this disorder pull hair from their scalp, eyebrows, or eyelids (see photo). Trichotillomania is diagnosed when the person cannot resist the urge to pluck out his or her hair, often resulting in significant hair loss. They want to stop pulling out their hair, but have great difficulty doing so. They may pull hair intermittently throughout the day, or engage in long sessions of hair pulling. People with trichotillomania often experience intense shame following a hair-pulling episode, and try to hide it by wearing hats, scarves, and/or using makeup. For example, if eyebrow hair is pulled, eyeliner may be used to fill in any visible skin, to make it less apparent. They may also avoid interacting with other people during times of obvious hair loss.

Getting a hair cut can be challenging for people with trichotillomania, due to the shame associated with having to explain the source of hair loss to a stylist. In fact, the Canadian Body-Focused Repetitive Behaviour Support Network includes a list on their website of Canadian hairdressers who are knowledgeable and considered "safe" spaces. Founded in 2013, this organization aims to reduce the stigma associated with these disorders.

Trichotillomania typically has its onset in adolescence and is related to body image (Altenburger, Tung, & Keuthen, 2014). In children, boys and girls are equally represented, but in adults trichotillomania is much more common in women, and prevalence is estimated at 1–2% (APA, 2013). Comorbidity is high with major depression and excoriation disorder, which we consider next.

Excoriation (Skin-Picking Disorder)

The main feature of excoriation is skin-picking. The skin-picking can take place at any part of the body, but most commonly people with excoriation pick their faces, hands, and/or arms. Fingernails are usually used for skin-picking, but some people also use implements (e.g., tweezers, needles). For a diagnosis of excoriation, the skin-picking behaviour must be chronic such that it leads to lesions on the skin. People with excoriation experience significant shame and want to stop, but have great difficulty doing so.

There can be medical complications. Chronic skin picking can lead to significant scarring and infection, which may require antibiotic treatment.

Skin-picking disorder was examined in a group of university students (Odlaug et al., 2013). Women were found to have higher depressive symptoms, and men perceived themselves as less attractive. Overall, excoriation was found to be associated with an increased prevalence of mood, anxiety, eating, substance, and impulse control disorders. Impulsivity has been examined in other research (Oliveira et al., 2015). Adults with excoriation who were classified as high on impulsivity reported higher urges to pick and higher psychological distress (anxiety and depression) compared with those low in impulsivity.

Skin-picking often co-occurs with body dysmorphic disorder, and when it does, the skin-picking symptoms are worse (Grant et al., 2015). Also, as noted earlier, excoriation often co-occurs with trichotillomania, and like trichotillomania, excoriation is often comorbid with major depression.

Etiology of Body-Focused Repetitive Behaviours

We described the role of genetics in the etiology of the other disorders in this chapter. Body-focused repetitive behaviours also have a genetic component. Of interest, trichotillomania and excoriation were found to be influenced by the same genetic factor, which was different than OCD, hoarding disorder, and BDD (Monzani et al., 2014)—another reason to group these two disorders together in our discussion of etiology and treatment.

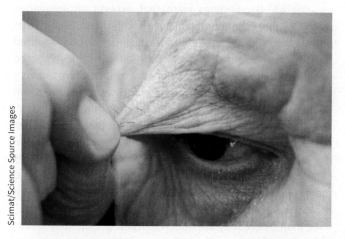

Scimat/Science Source Images

An elderly man pulls hair from his eyelids; hair pulling is the hallmark of trichotillomania. Other common areas for hair pulling are the scalp and eyebrows.

Excess cortical thickness in areas related to inhibitory control has been implicated in trichotillomania (Odlaug, Chamberlain, Derbyshire, Leppink, & Grant, 2014). Roos and colleagues (2015) compared brain volumes and cortical thickness in trichotillomania and excoriation, and their findings suggest some differences across the two conditions. For example, clients with excoriation had greater volume of the ventral striatum bilaterally, compared with clients with trichotillomania and control participants. They suggest these results point to greater involvement of the reward system with skin-picking disorder. They also found that clients with trichotillomania had reduced thickness of the right parahippocampal gyrus compared with those with excoriation disorder and control participants. They suggest this result may be related to dissociative symptoms seen among clients with trichotillomania.

Neurocognitive risk factors were evaluated in a group of young adults with body-focused repetitive behaviours compared with a control sample (Flessner et al., 2015). Poorer cognitive flexibility differentiated those in the clinical and control samples. Other aspects tested (planning and organization) were not different across groups, but were significantly associated with symptom severity.

Two models focus on what triggers the hair-pulling and skin-picking behaviours among people with these disorders. First, the emotion regulation model states that hair-pulling and skin-picking behaviours are triggered by negative emotions. The hair-pulling and skin-picking behaviours serve to decrease the negative emotions, which in turn make it more likely that the individual will engage in these behaviours (i.e., it is negatively reinforcing). Second, the frustrated action model states that hair-pulling and skin-picking behaviours are triggered by frustration and boredom. Engaging in the behaviours alleviates these states, and similar to the emotion regulation model, the individual is therefore more likely to engage in these behaviours.

Roberts and colleagues (2015), in Quebec, tested these two models, comparing a group with body-focused repetitive behaviours and a control group. They placed participants in conditions of boredom/frustration, stress, and relaxation. The clinical group reported a stronger urge to engage in skin-picking or hair-pulling when in the boredom/frustration condition than in the relaxation condition, but not the stress condition, providing support for the frustrated action model.

Therapy for Body-Focused Repetitive Behaviours

Habit reversal training, originally developed in the 1970s, has been the behavioural treatment most often used for body-focused repetitive behaviour disorders and other impulse control disorders (Azrin & Nunn, 1973), although it has since been simplified and is often combined with cognitive techniques (Odlaug & Grant, 2012). One focus of habit reversal is awareness training, which involves the identification of triggers or high-risk situations that often lead a person with one or both of these conditions to engage in hair-pulling and/or skin-picking. For example, having a fight with a friend may lead to anger, which may be a trigger. Another trigger may be boredom, so having a lot of free time may be a high-risk situation. Another key component of habit reversal involves identifying competing responses—other things people can do, like hold an ice pack or rubber ball, or sit on their hands—to allow time for the urge (to pull hair or to pick skin) to pass. The original habit reversal training protocol included many other elements (e.g., relaxation training, social support) that are still used by some clinicians. Self-monitoring, awareness training, and the identification of competing responses are the most commonly used components of habit reversal training (Flessner et al., 2010).

A systematic review and meta-analysis on the treatment of trichotillomania was conducted for both pharmacological treatments as well as psychological treatments (Slikboer et al., in press). Some forms of medication showed promise in the treatment of trichotillomania (e.g., N-acetyl cysteine, clomipramine, and olanzapine, but not fluoxetine). With respect to behaviour therapy, when it was compared with a non-treatment control group, it appeared effective. However, when compared with an active control condition such as supportive therapy, results were similar across conditions, calling into question behavioural models of this condition.

As noted above, there is a tendency to combine habit reversal with other strategies. Capriotti et al. (2015) reported on the treatment of four clients with excoriation using habit reversal combined with acceptance strategies, which they called acceptance-enhanced behaviour therapy. Three of their four clients responded to this treatment.

Other research in the area of treatment for the body-focused repetitive behaviours has focused on identifying which therapies are actively being delivered by clinicians and whether there should be more effort made to disseminate treatments. Of 67 clinicians who responded to a survey on how to best treat trichotillomania, most recommended some form of CBT for both children and adults (Flessner et al., 2010). Of the various strategies under the CBT umbrella, self-monitoring, awareness training, competing response training, habit reversal, and stimulus control were the most commonly listed techniques.

Overall, the findings were that experts recommended using CBT for trichotillomania, but are clinicians aware of that and are they accepting referrals from clients with body-focused repetitive behaviour disorders? The Canadian Body-Focused Repetitive Behaviour Support Network reports there are very few experts in Canada and finding appropriate treatment can be difficult. Active efforts aimed at the dissemination of effective therapies may be an important step. To that end, Keuthen and colleagues (2015) evaluated the role of professional training for body-focused repetitive behaviours. They found that clinicians who participated in their intensive training accepted more clients with body-focused repetitive behaviours into their practices and were more likely to use CBT skills with those clients, than before they attended the training. Hopefully results like these will lead more clinicians to obtain advanced training in the delivery of evidence-based treatments for body-focused repetitive behaviour disorders.

Summary

6.1 Obsessive-compulsive and related disorders (OCRDs) is a new category in *DSM-5*. Included in this category are the following disorders: Obsessive-compulsive disorder (OCD), hoarding disorder, body dysmorphic disorder, trichotillomania, and excoriation disorder.

6.2 People with OCD have intrusive, unwanted thoughts and feel pressured to engage in stereotyped rituals lest they be overcome by frightening levels of anxiety. This disorder can become disabling, interfering not only with the life of the person who experiences the difficulties but also with the lives of those close to that person.

6.3 Many factors are implicated in the etiology of OCD, including genetics and other biological factors. In behavioural accounts, compulsions are considered learned avoidance responses. Cognitive factors include faulty appraisals, such as overimportance of thoughts and intolerance of uncertainty.

6.4 There are psychological and biological therapies for OCD, although it is one of the most difficult disorders to treat. Exposure and response prevention (ERP) is the most common psychological approach used for treating OCD. ERP involves exposure to the obsession (e.g., germs) and refraining from the compulsion (e.g., handwashing).

6.5 Hoarding disorder used to be considered a subtype of OCD but is a new diagnostic category in *DSM-5*. People with hoarding disorder have a hard time discarding material and typically acquire a lot of new material as well. Hoarding disorder is more common among older adults. Treatment is usually some form of CBT, potentially involving long home visits, but many people with hoarding disorder are not trusting of treatment providers.

6.6 People with body dysmorphic disorder (BDD) are preoccupied with an imagined or exaggerated defect. They spend considerable time trying to hide the defect or even resort to plastic surgery. Of the obsessive-compulsive related disorders, BDD is most like OCD.

6.7 Trichotillomania (hair-pulling disorder) and excoriation (skin-picking disorder) are two types of body-focused repetitive behaviour disorders. They are highly comorbid with one another and with major depressive disorder. Like OCD, they are characterized by repetitive thoughts and behaviours, but there is controversy over whether they truly are disorders related to OCD. Habit reversal training, during which clients identify triggers and alternate behaviours, is commonly used to treat trichotillomania and excoriation.

Key Terms

body dysmorphic disorder (BDD)
body-focused repetitive behaviours
compulsion
excoriation (skin-picking disorder)
exposure and response prevention (ERP)

habit reversal training
hoarding disorder
obsessions
obsessive-compulsive and related disorders (OCRDs)

obsessive-compulsive disorder (OCD)
prospective memory
retrospective memory
trichotillomania (hair-pulling disorder)

Reflections: Past, Present, and Future

1. In the previous chapter, you were asked to revisit your design for a longitudinal study of risk factors for the development of anxiety disorders. Now that you have learned about OCD and related disorders, how would you redesign your long-term study? What risk factors would you retain? What new risk factors would you add to the design?

2. We have discussed a dimensional vs. categorical approach to psychopathology several times. In terms of the diagnostic criteria for hoarding disorder, what do you think is most important in distinguishing between people with hoarding disorder and collectors? In your estimation, does a show like *Hoarders* serve an important public service by heightening awareness or does it tend to stigmatize and stereotype people with mental disorders in general?

CHAPTER 7

Somatic Symptom Disorders and Dissociative Disorders

LEARNING OBJECTIVES

1. Describe somatic symptom disorders.

2. Describe conversion disorder.

3. Compare and contrast psychological, behavioural, and social-cultural factors in conversion disorder.

4. Differentiate among the dissociative disorders: dissociative amnesia, dissociative fugue, depersonalization/derealization disorder, and dissociative identity disorder.

5. Summarize the etiology of and treatment approaches and options for dissociative disorders.

Somatoform disorder was in the news in 2012 due to an apparent group outbreak of symptoms of conversion disorder in Le Roy, in upper New York state (see photo). In total, 18 people (16 girls, 1 boy, and 1 adult woman) developed uncontrollable tics, twitching, and jerking similar to Tourette's syndrome. This unique situation received worldwide media attention. Similar outbreaks in the past have been referred to as examples of "psychogenic illness" or "mass hysteria" and are usually attributed to prolonged exposure to stress. It was decided that the Le Roy residents suffered from conversion disorder, a type of somatoform disorder (i.e., a physical condition that is medically unexplained and instead reflects psychological factors) and the conversion disorder was exacerbated by all the media attention, including attention via social media. But was this really the case? Could an environmental cause be responsible? The parents of the adolescents turned to activist Erin Brockovich, whose team pointed to the possible role of a 1971 train derailment that took place just outside Le Roy. The derailment resulted in the spilling of the chemical TCE (trichloroethylene), which has not been fully cleaned up. TCE exposure has been known to cause neurological symptoms in keeping with those experienced in Le Roy. However, subsequent tests failed to identify an environmental cause, supporting the conversion disorder explanation.

Seven years earlier, public attention on conversion disorder increased when it was reported that a cluster of five Amish girls between the ages of 9 and 13 experienced an "outbreak" of diagnosable cases of conversion disorder (see Cassady et al., 2005). The girls knew each other and had shared symptoms. Common symptoms included motor deficits, life-threatening anorexia, and neck weakness that made them unable to hold up their heads. Possible environmental and organic causes were discounted; instead, in this instance, the symptoms were deemed to be a stress reaction to psychosocial pressures and expectations common among adolescent Amish girls.

What do you believe happened in Le Roy? The ability to accept the conversion disorder diagnosis seems easier when the focus is on the general group situation rather than on individual cases. Several parents objected to the diagnosis and remarked that their daughters were under no undue stress. One father indicated that his daughter had a happy, normal life and had not experienced trauma of any sort (see Dominus, 2012). But in the absence of a physical or medical cause, a somatoform disorder is considered.

The first part of this chapter focuses on physical problems that seem to reflect psychological adjustment problems. One of the biggest challenges for physicians and for mental health personnel is to determine whether physical symptoms are due to medical explanations or psychological problems. Individual cases are often not clear, but the diagnostic situation has not been made any easier by a set of diagnostic criteria that have undergone substantial change. Until the most recent *DSM* revision, a somatoform disorder was ruled out if it could not be determined conclusively that there was no medical explanation. This criterion has been removed from the *DSM-5* requirements. Another change is that the term "somatoform disorder" has now been changed to "somatic symptom disorder."

Chapter 7 examines disorders such as conversion disorder as well as dissociative disorders. The disorders in this chapter are related to anxiety disorders in that, in early versions of the *DSM,* all these disorders were subsumed under the heading of neuroses because anxiety was considered the predominant underlying factor in each case. Starting with *DSM-III,* classification came to be based on observable behaviour, not on presumed etiology. Anxiety is not necessarily observable in the somatoform and dissociative disorders. In somatic symptom and related disorders, the individual complains of bodily symptoms that suggest a physical defect or dysfunction—sometimes rather dramatic in nature—but for which no physiological basis can be found. As suggested above, somatoform disorders reflect the mind–body connection and the growing realization that psychological and physical functioning interact with each other. Recent data from a sample of over 3,000 students continued to highlight the overlap between physical and psychological functioning. This study found that 9.5% of students had a somatic syndrome and almost one-quarter of these students also had an anxiety syndrome. Other predictors of somatic syndromes included depression and impairment in daily activities (Fischer, Gaab, Ehlert, & Nater, 2013).

In **dissociative disorders**, the individual experiences disruptions of consciousness, memory, and identity. The onset of both classes of disorders is assumed by many to be related to some stressful experience, and the two classes sometimes co-occur. We will examine the somatoform and dissociative disorders, focusing in more depth on those disorders about which more is known. Less is known about these disorders relative to many others and there is controversy about their causes and treatment.

Gillian Laub for the New York Times

Lydia Parker from Le Roy, New York, is shown here with her younger sister. Lydia experienced the symptoms of conversion disorder and has bruises on her face as a result of hitting herself with her cellphone when she experienced uncontrollable tics. Lydia and her family reject the conversion disorder diagnosis.

7.1 Somatic Symptom and Related Disorders

As noted in Chapter 1, *soma* means "body." In these disorders, psychological problems take a physical form. The physical symptoms have no known physiological explanation and are not under voluntary control. They are thought to be linked to psychological factors, presumably anxiety, and are assumed to be psychologically caused (see Merskey & Mai, 2005). In this section, we look at two somatoform disorders: conversion disorder and somatization disorder. This is preceded by brief discussions of two *DSM-IV-TR* categories of somatoform disorders about which less information is available: **pain disorder** and hypochondriasis. Pain disorder and *hypochondriasis* are no longer distinct disorders in the *DSM-5*.

A summary of the somatoform disorders that were included previously in *DSM-IV-TR* appears in Table 7.1. This category has been controversial ever since the release of *DSM-IV*. Indeed, a group of prominent researchers presented the radical argument that somatoform disorders should be removed from the *DSM-5* (Mayou et al., 2005). They listed seven concerns that did indeed result in some major changes in the new *DSM-5*. Key concerns included the fact that the terminology is often unacceptable to clients and the distinction between disease-based symptoms and those that are psychogenic may be more apparent than real.

In 2010, the *DSM-5* Somatic Symptom Disorders Work Group noted that the *DSM-IV* terminology was quite confusing. Further, because somatoform disorders, psychological factors affecting medical condition, and factitious disorders (see Focus on Discovery 7.1) all involve presentation of physical symptoms and/or concern about medical illness, the work group suggested renaming this group of disorders **somatic symptom disorders**. The grouping of these disorders into a single section, a recommendation that was subsequently accepted, was based on clinical utility—these individuals are primarily seen in general medical settings—rather than due to possible shared etiology

TABLE 7.1	Summary of the Somatoform Disorders in the *DSM-IV-TR*
Disorder	**Description**
Pain disorder	The onset and maintenance of pain, caused largely by psychological factors.
Body dysmorphic disorder	Preoccupation with imagined or exaggerated defects in physical appearance.
Hypochondriasis	Preoccupation with fears of having a serious illness.
Conversion disorder	Sensory or motor symptoms without any physiological cause.
Somatization	Recurrent, multiple physical complaints that have no biological basis.

Focus on Discovery 7.1

Malingering and Factitious Disorder

Conversion disorder is difficult to distinguish from **malingering**. In malingering, an individual fakes an incapacity in order to avoid a responsibility, such as work or military duty, or to achieve some goal, such as being awarded a large insurance settlement. Malingering is diagnosed when the conversion-like symptoms are determined to be under voluntary control, which is not thought to be the case in true conversion disorders.

In trying to discriminate conversion reactions from malingering, clinicians may attempt to determine whether the symptoms have been consciously or unconsciously adopted. However, how can anyone know with any degree of certainty whether behaviour is consciously or unconsciously motivated? One aspect of behaviour that can sometimes help distinguish the two disorders is known as **la belle indifférence**, characterized by a relative lack of concern or a blasé attitude toward the symptoms. Clients with conversion disorder sometimes demonstrate this behaviour; they also appear willing and eager to talk endlessly and dramatically about their symptoms, but often without the concern one might expect. In contrast, malingerers are likely to be more guarded and cautious, perhaps because they consider interviews a challenge or threat to the success of the lie. But this distinction is not foolproof, for only about one-third of people with conversion disorders show *la belle indifférence*. Furthermore, a stoic attitude is sometimes found among clients with verified medical diseases.

Case Illustration: The Difficulty of Detecting Malingering

Drob, Meehan, and Waxman (2009) described numerous clinical and conceptual errors that contribute to false attributions of malingering in forensic evaluations, including the use of assessment tools that can detect feigning but can't reliably determine incentive and volition or consciousness (defining characteristics of malingering). They also noted that evaluators might overlook the possibility that feigning is a function of true pathology. A case study reported by Ladowsky-Brooks and Fischer (2003) illustrates the need for multiple forms of assessment. The case is of a 50-year-old man who was assessed in Canada and had apparent symptoms of diminished cognitive functioning, but his pattern of errors on a memory test was highly consistent with deliberate malingering. However, further physiological testing (MRI and SPECT scan) revealed that the man was actually suffering from frontal-temporal lobe dementia and was not malingering.

Also related to the disorders we have been discussing is another *DSM-5* category, **factitious disorder**. In this disorder, people intentionally produce physical symptoms (or sometimes psychological ones). They may make up symptoms—for example, reporting acute pain—or inflict injuries on themselves. In contrast to malingering, the symptoms in factitious disorder are less obviously linked to a recognizable goal; the motivation for adopting the

Kathleen Bush is taken into custody and charged with child abuse and fraud for deliberately causing her child's illnesses.

physical or psychological symptoms is much less clear. The individual, for some unknown reason, wants to assume the role of client.

Factitious disorder may also involve a parent creating physical illnesses in a child; in this case, it is called *factitious disorder by proxy* or *Munchausen syndrome by proxy*. A Canadian case of apparent Munchausen syndrome by proxy considered by the courts took place in Saskatchewan in 2010. In this instance, a mother (initials RW) was accused of trying to smother her two-year-old daughter (EW) and administered harmful medication and tobacco during bottle-feeding as a way of seeking attention and help for herself without any apparent external incentive (see EW (Re), 2012 SKQB 1 (CanLII)).

In one particularly extreme case, a seven-year-old girl was hospitalized over 150 times and experienced 40 surgeries at a cost of over $2 million. Her mother, Kathleen Bush (see photo), caused her illnesses by using drugs and even contaminating her feeding tube with faecal material (Toufexis, 1996). The motivation in a case such as this appears to be the need to be regarded as an excellent parent and tireless in seeing to the child's needs. This disorder has received more public attention in recent years, in part due to claims by rap artist Eminem. He has stated that he was made ill during his childhood by his mother, who he alleges suffers from Munchausen syndrome by proxy.

If someone is making themselves ill, then the disorder is simply referred to as Munchausen syndrome. Two Canadian cases involved nurses who presented with urinary tract infections, flank pain, and gross hematuria (blood in the urine). Evidence in both cases suggested that these women had infused blood into their own bladders (Chew, Pace, & Honey, 2002).

or mechanism. In addition, as alluded to earlier, because of the implicit "mind–body dualism" and the difficulties with reliably assessing "medically unexplained symptoms," the work group proposed that these symptoms be de-emphasized as core features of many of these disorders. Accordingly, the focus is now

on the extent to which such symptoms result in "subjective distress and impairment" (American Psychiatric Association, 2013).

Because somatization disorder, hypochondriasis, pain disorder, and undifferentiated somatoform disorder (which is now described as somatic symptom disorder) share certain common features—somatic symptoms and cognitive distortions—the work group proposed that these disorders be grouped under a common rubric named "complex somatic symptom disorder," which was later modified to "somatic symptom disorder."

In the following sections, we explore in more detail the manifestations of disorders that reflect themes involving the body. One such disorder, body dysmorphic disorder, was discussed in Chapter 6. It was introduced earlier to reflect the change in how it is now considered and classified according to the *DSM-5*.

In **hypochondriasis**, which is now diagnosed as somatic symptom disorder in *DSM-5*, individuals are preoccupied with persistent fears of having a serious disease, despite medical reassurance to the contrary. The disorder typically begins in early adulthood and has a chronic course. In one study, over 60% of diagnosed cases still had the disorder when followed up five years later (Barsky et al., 1998). Clients with this little-used diagnosis are frequent consumers of medical services and are likely to have mood or anxiety disorders (Noyes et al., 2006). The theory is that they overreact to ordinary physical sensations and minor abnormalities, such as irregular heartbeat, occasional coughing, or a stomach ache, seeing these as evidence for their beliefs, and, indeed, people with high scores on a measure of hypochondriasis are more likely than others to attribute physical sensations to an illness (MacLeod, Haynes, & Sensky, 1998). Similarly, people with hypochondriasis make catastrophic interpretations of symptoms, such as believing that a red blotch on the skin is skin cancer (Rief, Hiller, & Margraf, 1998). Asmundson, Taylor, Wright, and Cox (2001) cited a *Globe and Mail* newspaper account of the compelling case study of James V to illustrate that people who actually experience abnormally intense sensations may be particularly vulnerable to hypochondriasis.

> "For reasons no one understood, Mr. V felt as if a million bugs crawled over him. To quiet his torment, he scratched himself so tenaciously that he ripped open his skin, even though he fell within the range of what is considered average intelligence and he was aware of the damage he was inflicting. . . . Heavily scarred from his assaults . . . [he] had a high tolerance for pain and would break his bones and tear off his fingernails as well as scratch himself."

> (As cited by Asmundson et al., 2001, pp. 368–369)

Sadly, Mr. V died at the young age of 25 from infections of the blood and spine.

In a review of prevalence studies, Asmundson, Taylor, Sevgur, and Cox (2001) concluded that hypochondriasis is evident in about 5% of the general population. Prevalence rates are higher in studies that selectively restrict their sample to individuals presenting at medical clinics.

Hypochondriasis is not well differentiated from somatization disorder, which is also characterized by a long history of complaints of medical illnesses (Noyes et al., 2006). As indicated above, given the overlap and ambiguity, hypochondriasis has been dropped from *DSM-5* and this symptom expression is now incorporated into the somatic symptom disorder category.

However, there are some cases, typically a minority of cases, in which the person being diagnosed is seemingly obsessed with having or having acquired a serious medical illness that has not been diagnosed. This symptom expression was recognized by inclusion in the *DSM-5* of **illness anxiety disorder**. Other symptoms include a high degree of anxiety about health but somatic symptoms are not present or are only mild in intensity.

At the research level, most contemporary researchers do focus on health anxiety rather than hypochondriasis per se. Health anxiety has been defined as "health-related fears and beliefs, based on interpretations, or perhaps more often, *misinterpretations* of bodily signs and symptoms as being indicative of serious illness" (Asmundson, Taylor, Sevgur, & Cox, 2001, p. 4). Health anxiety is not limited to hypochondriasis but can also be linked with anxiety and mood disorders. According to Asmundson, Taylor, Sevgur, and Cox (2001), health anxiety would be present in both hypochondriasis and an illness phobia. Whereas hypochondriasis is a fear of *having* an illness, an illness phobia is a fear of *contracting* an illness.

A taxometric study established that health anxiety is best conceptualized on a continuum along a dimension rather than as an all-or-none category (Ferguson, 2009). That is, health anxiety is something that someone has more or less of rather than an all-or-none category. This is consistent with continuous measures used to assess health anxiety. A related study of hypochondriasis also supported a dimensional rather than a categorical model (Longley et al., 2010).

The Illness Attitudes Scale (IAS) is used to assess health anxiety. Stewart and Watt (2001) suggest that it consists reliably of four factors: (1) worry about illness and pain (i.e., illness fears); (2) disease conviction (i.e., illness beliefs); (3) health habits (i.e., safety-seeking behaviours); and (4) symptom interference with lifestyle (i.e., disruptive effects).

A general neurotic syndrome is regarded as a contributing factor in the etiology of health anxiety along with more specific factors such as cognitive mechanisms (Asmundson, Taylor, Wright, & Cox, 2001). A twin study conducted in Canada found that after controlling for medical morbidity, health anxiety was moderately heritable, but most of the variance was due to environmental factors (Taylor, Thordarson, Jang, & Asmundson, 2006). This finding supports past interpretations that health anxiety is mostly learned.

According to Rachman (2012), cognitive factors are central to an understanding of health anxiety and at the root of these disorders are "catastrophic misinterpretations" (p. 502) of bodily sensations or bodily changes. In essence, people overreact to physical sensations. This emphasis on cognitive factors is reflected in the model of health anxiety outlined by Salkovskis and Warwick (2001) presented in Figure 7.1. This model has four contributing factors: (1) a critical precipitating incident; (2) a previous experience of illness and related medical factors; (3) the presence of inflexible or negative cognitive assumptions (i.e., believing strongly that unexplained bodily changes are always a sign of serious illness); and (4) the severity of anxiety. The latter, the severity of anxiety, is a function of two factors that

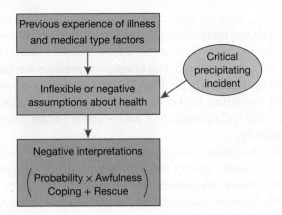

FIGURE 7.1 Cognitive model of the development of health anxiety.
Source: "Making Sense of Hypochondriasis: A Cognitive Model of Health Activity," Paul M. Salkovskis and Hilary M. C. Warwick, in *Health Anxiety*, G. J. G. Asmundson, S. Taylor, & B. J. Cox, eds., 2001. © John Wiley & Sons Limited. Reproduced with Permission.

will increase anxiety and two that will decrease it. Health anxiety will increase multiplicatively as a function of related increases in (1) the perceived likelihood or probability of illness and (2) the perceived cost, awfulness, and burden of illness. Health anxiety will decrease as a function of (1) the perceived ability to cope and (2) the perceived presence of rescue factors (i.e., the availability and perceived effectiveness of medical help).

Support for the role of catastrophizing of bodily sensations in health anxiety comes from a 14-day daily diary study with a 14-day follow-up conducted by a team of Canadian researchers (see Gautreau et al., 2015). This study found that catastrophizing bodily symptoms maintained health anxiety for both men and women. Evidence was also uncovered for a cyclical self-perpetuating pattern, with health anxiety and catastrophization contributing dynamically to each other.

We turn now to a discussion of the symptoms of conversion disorder and somatization disorder and then to theories of etiology and therapies.

7.2　Conversion Disorder

"Conversion disorder requires a decision regarding the role of psychological factors, a criterion that is hard to verify, not required for other somatoform disorders, and divergent from the largely theoretical, phenomenological nature of DSM-IV."

—Kroenke et al., 2007, p. 283

Conversion disorder was illustrated at the beginning of this chapter. As indicated earlier, in **conversion disorder**, physiologically normal people experience sensory or motor symptoms, such as a sudden loss of vision or paralysis, suggesting an illness related to neurological damage of some sort, although the body organs and nervous system are found to be fine. Suf-

ferers may experience paralysis of arms or legs; seizures and coordination disturbances; a sensation of prickling, tingling, or creeping on the skin; insensitivity to pain; or the loss or impairment of sensations, called **anaesthesias**. Vision may be seriously impaired; the person may become partially or completely blind or have tunnel vision. *Aphonia,* loss of the voice and all but whispered speech, and *anosmia,* loss or impairment of the sense of smell, are other conversion disorders.

Note that in *DSM-5* conversion disorder is also called "functional neurological symptom disorder." This change was made to connote abnormal central nervous system functioning (see APA, 2013).

The term "conversion" was derived originally from Freud, who thought that the energy of a repressed instinct was diverted into sensory-motor channels and blocked functioning. Thus, anxiety and psychological conflict were believed to be *converted* into physical symptoms.

George Fraser (1994), while at the Royal Ottawa Hospital, reported two cases of conversion disorder that involved an apparent loss of eyesight:

> *"Both were young male military recruits who had been 'strongly encouraged' to join the military by relatives. One of the cases was referred to psychiatry with a 2-week history of 'blindness'. He had been fully investigated neurologically and ophthalmologically. No pathology was found. All eye reflexes were normal, yet despite efforts to catch him in an unguarded moment, suggesting malingering, he persisted with his blindness. He had even sustained bruising by bumping into objects. History revealed his loss of vision occurred suddenly while doing combat manoeuvres on the bayonet range. Interestingly, he stated, 'I just couldn't see myself killing people.' He feared telling his parents that he was terrified to be in military life. After confirming the diagnosis and the cause, I told him that he would be released from military services, but it was only with hypnosis (one session, as was the case with the other soldier) that he immediately regained his vision. Also, he was able to visually describe accurately all the locations he had been to during the 2 weeks of conversion blindness."*
>
> (Fraser, 1994, p. 138)

The men described by Fraser suffered from a form of conversion disorder involving "hysterical" blindness and illustrate the role that stress plays in the development of conversion disorders. **Hysteria**, the term originally used to describe what are now known as conversion disorders, has a long history, dating back to the earliest writings on abnormal behaviour. Hippocrates considered it an affliction limited solely to women and due to the wandering of the uterus through the body. (The Greek word *hystera* means "womb.")

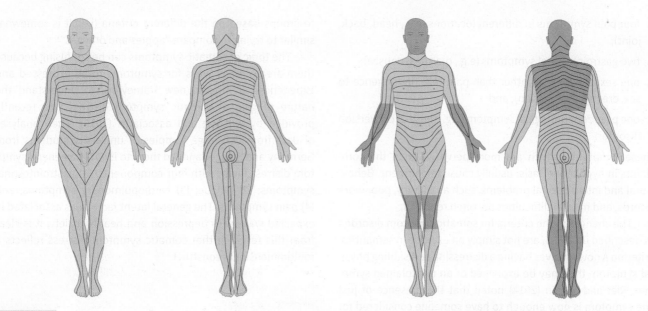

FIGURE 7.2 Hysterical anaesthesias can be distinguished from neurological dysfunctions. The patterns of neural innervation are shown on the left. Typical areas of anaesthesias in hysterical patients are superimposed on the right. The hysterical anaesthesias do not make anatomical sense. Based on an illustration by Frank H. Netter, from *The CIBA Collection of Medical Illustrations,* 1975. CIBA Pharmaceutical Company, Division of CIBA-GEIGY Corporation.

Presumably, the wandering uterus symbolized the longing to produce a child.

Conversion symptoms usually develop in adolescence or early adulthood, typically after undergoing life stress. An episode may end abruptly, but sooner or later the disorder is likely to return, either in its original form or with a symptom of a different nature and site. Prevalence of conversion disorder is less than 1%, and more women than men are given the diagnosis (Singh & Lee, 1997). It is frequently comorbid with other Axis I diagnoses, such as depression, substance abuse, anxiety, and dissociative disorders, and with personality disorders, notably borderline and histrionic personality disorders (Rechlin, Loew, & Joraschky, 1997; Stonnington, Barry, & Fisher, 2006). People with conversion symptoms frequently report a history of physical or sexual abuse (see Stonnington et al., 2006).

It is important to distinguish a conversion paralysis or sensory dysfunction from similar problems that have a true neurological basis (see Figure 7.2). Sometimes this task is easy, as when the paralysis does not make anatomical sense. A classic example is *glove anaesthesia,* a rare syndrome in which the individual experiences little or no sensation in the part of the hand that would be covered by a glove (see Figure 7.2). For years this was the textbook illustration of anatomical nonsense because the nerves here run continuously from the hand up the arm. Yet, even in this case, it now appears that misdiagnosis can occur. A currently recognized disease, *carpal tunnel syndrome,* can produce symptoms similar to those of glove anaesthesia. Nerves in the wrist run through a tunnel formed by the wrist bones and membranes. The tunnel can become swollen and may pinch the nerves, leading to tingling, numbness, and pain in the hand.

Since the majority of paralyses, analgesias, and sensory failures do have biological causes, true neurological problems may sometimes be misdiagnosed as conversion disorders. Studies conducted during the 1960s indicated that on follow-up, many clients diagnosed with conversion disorder may have been misdiagnosed. One study found that nine years after diagnosis, an alarming number—60%—of these individuals had either died or developed symptoms of physical disease! A high proportion had diseases of the central nervous system (Slater & Glithero, 1965). Fortunately, with technological advances in detecting illness and disease (such as the MRI), the rate of misdiagnosis appears on the decline. A survey by Stone et al. (2005) of studies conducted in the 1950s to present day found a dramatic decline in misdiagnoses (from 29% down to about 4%) and this pattern was evident across age and held for males and females.

Somatization Disorder

In 1859, the French physician Pierre Briquet described a syndrome that first bore his name, Briquet's syndrome, and in *DSM-IV-TR,* it was referred to as **somatization disorder**. As indicated above, somatization disorder has been dropped from the *DSM-5,* but as noted in the manual, those who would have previously had this diagnosis will meet the criteria for somatic symptom disorder if they have the maladaptive thoughts, feelings, and behaviours of people with this diagnosis (see APA, 2013). The form of the disorder is characterized by recurrent, multiple somatic complaints, with no apparent physical cause, for which medical attention is sought. To meet the previous diagnostic criteria, the person needed to have:

1. four pain symptoms in different locations (e.g., head, back, joint);

2. two gastrointestinal symptoms (e.g., diarrhea, nausea);

3. one sexual symptom other than pain (e.g., indifference to sex, erectile dysfunction); and

4. one pseudoneurological symptom (e.g., those of conversion disorder).

These symptoms, which are more pervasive than the complaints in hypochondriasis, usually cause impairment. Behavioural and interpersonal problems, such as truancy, poor work records, and marital difficulties are often reported.

The changes in the criteria for somatic symptom disorder, as described in *DSM-5*, are not simply an exercise in semantics. Criterion A now involves having a distressing or disabling physical symptom that may be explained or an unexplained symptom. Rief and Martin (2014) noted that the presence of just one symptom is now enough to have someone considered for a somatic symptom disorder, but there is clinical utility in distinguishing people who have a greater number of total symptoms. This is a point of contention for Ross (2015). He noted that *DSM-III* required a person to have 13 symptoms in order to meet diagnostic criteria for somatization disorder, and it is no small change when the *DSM-5* requires the presence of only one symptom in order to diagnose somatic symptom disorder. He then reanalyzed his own data for samples of people from Winnipeg, Manitoba, and from Shanghai, China. Ross (2015) reported that no one in either sample met the old criteria for somatization disorder but about 5% of the people in each sample met the new *DSM-5* criteria for somatic symptom disorder. He concludes that the more than 10-fold increase in the prevalence of this disorder suggests that the new criteria need to be re-examined. Ross (2015) noted that this change in prevalence due to changing criteria is unprecedented.

Criterion B used to involve the number of somatic symptoms but now involves determining the presence or absence of psychological features such as health anxiety, disproportionate and repetitive thoughts about symptoms, and devoting too much time or energy to the symptoms. The disorder now requires the presence of one or more of these psychological symptoms. Rief and Martin (2014) suggested that these criteria may need some refinement but make sense because they were identified on the basis of prior research investigations.

What is the impact of these changing criteria? A new study of 325 clients with medically unexplained symptoms found that 93% met criteria for a somatoform disorder according to the old criteria but only 45.5% met the new criteria for a somatic symptom disorder (van Dessel, van der Wouden, Dekker, & van der Horst, 2016). These people had more severe symptoms and their levels of physical functioning were considerably lower than those clients who met the old criteria. This qualitative difference has important ramifications. For instance, people with more severe symptoms are typically less likely to respond positively to interventions. Moreover, it is difficult to compare the results of research for people assigned to groups based on the different criteria (i.e., it is somewhat similar to trying to compare "apples and oranges").

The topic of somatic symptoms can be confusing because there are so many ways for symptoms to be expressed and experienced. A helpful new framework to understand the nature of general somatic symptom distress was recently provided by Witthoft and associates (2016). Their analyses of data from two large samples of university students from Germany and Switzerland led them to identify a general symptom distress factor with four components: (1) gastrointestinal symptoms; (2) fatigue; (3) cardiopulmonary symptoms; and (4) pain symptoms. The general latent factor was associated in expected ways with depression and health anxiety. It is clear from this research that somatic symptom distress reflects a multidimensional construct.

7.3 Etiology of Somatoform Disorders

Much of the theorizing in the area of somatoform disorders has been directed solely toward understanding hysteria as originally conceptualized by Freud. Consequently, it has focused on explanations of conversion disorder. Later in this section, we examine psychoanalytic views of conversion disorder and then look at what behavioural, cognitive, and biological theorists have to offer. First, we briefly discuss ideas about the etiology of somatization disorder.

Etiology of Somatoform Disorders

It has been proposed that people with this form of disorder are more sensitive to physical sensations, overattend to them, or interpret them catastrophically (e.g., Kirmayer, Robbins, & Paris, 1994). People may also have a memory bias for information that connotes physical threat. The results of one experiment showed that somatoform clients had greater supraliminal interferences for physical threat words presented as part of a Stroop task. An explicit memory test also indicated that somatoform clients had a memory bias for physical threat words (Lim & Kim, 2005).

A behavioural view holds that the various aches, discomforts, and dysfunctions are the manifestation of unrealistic anxiety about bodily systems. In keeping with the possible role of anxiety, clients have high levels of cortisol, an indication that they are under stress (Rief et al., 1998). Perhaps the extreme tension of an individual localizes in stomach muscles, resulting in feelings of nausea or vomiting. Once normal functioning is disrupted, the maladaptive pattern may strengthen because of the attention it receives or the excuses it provides. In a related vein, the reporting of physical symptoms has been seen as a strategy to explain poor performance in evaluative situations. Attributing poor performance to illness is psychologically less threatening than attributing it to some personal failing (Smith, Snyder, & Perkins, 1983).

Bialas and Craig (2007) explored the hypothesis that the illness behaviours might be learned responses acquired via exposure to parental illness and health anxiety in childhood. They examined patterns of interaction in mothers (mothers with somatization disorder, organically ill mothers, and healthy mothers) and their school-age children in semi-structured play tasks and during a meal. Mothers with this type of disorder and their children interacted differently relative to other mother–child pairs. For example, during play, children of somatizing mothers expressed more health and safety needs than children of other mothers. The findings are consistent with theories of environmental influence in the development of somatization.

Psychoanalytic Theory of Conversion Disorder

Conversion disorder occupies a central place in psychoanalytic theory, for it offered Freud a clear opportunity to explore the concept of the unconscious. In *Studies in Hysteria* (1895; 1982), Breuer and Freud proposed that a conversion disorder is caused when a person experiences an event that creates great emotional arousal, but the effect is not expressed and the memory of the event is cut off from conscious experience. The specific conversion symptoms were said to be related causally to the traumatic event that preceded them.

Anna O., for example, while watching at the bedside of her seriously ill father, had dropped off into a waking dream with her right arm over the back of her chair. She saw a black snake emerge from the wall and come toward her sick father to bite him. She tried to ward it off, but her right arm had gone to sleep. When she looked at her hand, her fingers turned into little snakes with death's heads. The next day, a bent branch recalled her hallucination of the snake, and at once her right arm became rigidly extended. After that, her arm responded in the same way whenever some object revived her hallucination. Later, when Anna O. fell into her "absences" and took to her own bed, the contracture of her right arm became chronic and extended to paralysis and anaesthesia of her right side.

In his later writings, Freud hypothesized that conversion disorder in women is rooted in an unresolved Electra complex. The young female child becomes sexually attached to her father, but these unacceptable impulses are repressed. The result is both a preoccupation with sex and at the same time an avoidance of it. Sexual excitement or some event reawakens these repressed impulses as an adolescent or adult, creating anxiety. The anxiety is then transformed or converted into physical symptoms.

A more recent psychodynamic interpretation of one form of conversion disorder, hysterical blindness, is based on experimental studies of hysterically blind people whose behaviour on visual tests showed that they were influenced by the stimuli even though they explicitly denied seeing them (Sackeim, Nordlie, & Gur, 1979). Two studies involved teenaged women. The first case concerned a 16-year-old who had experienced sudden loss of peripheral vision and reported that her visual field had become tubular and constricted. On a special visual test she had performed significantly worse than would a person who was indeed blind! The clinicians reasoned that she had some awareness of the illuminated stimulus and she wanted, consciously or unconsciously, to preserve her blindness by performing poorly on the test. The second case was seemingly contradictory in that Celia, a hysterically blind adolescent girl, showed almost perfect visual performance. Her initial symptom was a sudden loss of sight in both eyes, followed by severe blurring of vision. When three triangles were projected on three display windows of a console, two of the triangles inverted, one of them upright, in 599 trials of 600 she pressed the switch under the upright triangle, the correct response.

Sackeim et al. (1979) proposed a two-stage defensive reaction to account for these conflicting findings: (1) perceptual representations of visual stimuli are blocked from awareness and, on this basis, people report themselves blind; and (2) information is nonetheless extracted from the perceptual representations. If clients feel that they must deny being privy to this information, they perform more poorly than they would by chance on perceptual tasks. If clients do not need to deny having such information, they perform the task well but still maintain that they are blind. Whether or not hysterically blind people unconsciously need to deny receiving perceptual information is viewed as dependent on personality factors and motivation.

Are the people who claim that they are blind and yet on another level respond to visual stimuli being truthful? Sackeim and his colleagues reported that some patients with lesions in the visual cortex, rather than damage to the eye, said that they were blind yet performed well on visual tasks. Such individuals have vision (sometimes called "blindsight"), but they do not *know* that they can see. Therefore, it is possible for people to claim truthfully that they cannot see but give evidence that they can.

Behavioural Theory of Conversion Disorder and Cognitive Factors

An early behavioural account of conversion disorder was proposed by Ullmann and Krasner (1975). They viewed conversion disorder as similar to malingering in that the person adopts the symptom to secure some end. In their opinion, the person with a conversion disorder attempts to behave according to his or her conception of how a person with a disease affecting the motor or sensory abilities would act. This theory raises two questions: (1) Are people capable of such behaviour? and (2) Under what conditions would such behaviour be most likely to occur?

Considerable evidence indicates that the answer to the first question is yes: people can adopt patterns of behaviour that match many of the classic conversion symptoms. For example, paralyses, analgesias, and blindness can be induced in people under hypnosis. As a partial answer to the second question, Ullmann and Krasner specify two conditions that increase the likelihood that motor and sensory disabilities will be imitated. First, the individual must have had some experience with the role to be adopted; he or she may have had similar physical problems or may have observed them in others. Second, the enactment of a role must be *rewarded;* an individual will assume a disability only if it can be expected either to reduce stress or to reap other positive consequences.

Although this behavioural interpretation might seem to make sense, the literature does not support it completely. Celia, for example, did not act in accordance with Ullmann and Krasner's theory. The very intelligent Celia performed perfectly in the visual discrimination task while still claiming severely blurred vision. Such a pattern of behaviour seems a rather clumsy enactment of a role. If you wanted to convince someone that you could not see, why answer correctly?

Celia's actions seem more consistent with Sackeim's theory. On the level of conscious awareness, Celia probably saw only blurred images, as she claimed. But during the test the triangles were distinguished on an unconscious level, and she could pick out the upright one wherever it appeared. It is interesting to note that Celia's visual problems gained her crucial attention and help from her parents. Three years after the onset of her visual difficulties, Celia dramatically recovered clear sight while on a trip with her parents. Earlier in the summer, Celia had graduated from high school with grades well above average. The need to receive reinforcement for poor vision had perhaps passed, and her eyesight returned.

Numerous cognitive factors shown to be prevalent in people with conversion disorders are consistent with cognitive interpretations, including the tendency to discount the importance of psychological factors contributing to the presenting complaints, illness beliefs, denial of external stressors, suppression of the expression of distress, and avoidance behaviours (see Stonnington et al., 2006 for review). Cognitive behavioural therapy (CBT) lends itself well to addressing such issues. Research is also evaluating the role of specific cognitive mechanisms. Recently, the first ever study of neurocognitive functioning of children and adolescents with conversion symptoms yielded some promising insights. This study found that when children and adolescents were evaluated with a test battery of neurocognitive functioning, conversion symptoms were linked with deficits in attention, executive functioning, and working memory (see Kozlowska et al., 2015). The authors suggested that there are problems in cognitive integrative processing and that initial treatment interventions should focus on automatic processes rather than the effortful processes that pose problems.

Social and Cultural Factors in Conversion disorder

A possible role for social and cultural factors is suggested by the apparent decrease in the incidence of conversion disorder over the last century. Contemporary clinicians rarely see anyone with such problems. Several hypotheses have been proposed to explain this apparent decrease. Therapists with a psychoanalytic bent point out that in the second half of the nineteenth century, when the incidence of conversion reactions was apparently high in France and Austria, repressive sexual attitudes may have contributed to the increased prevalence of the disorder (see artwork). The decrease in its incidence, then, may be attributed to a general relaxing of sexual mores and to the greater sophistication of contemporary culture,

The Novel, A Lady in a Garden reading a book, Dicey, Frank (fl.1880–88)/Private Collection/ © Christopher Wood Gallery, London, UK/The Bridgeman Art Library

Some psychoanalysts believe that the high frequency of conversion disorder in 19th-century Europe was due to the repressive sexual attitudes of the time. This period is known as the Victorian era and it is equated with behaving in a restrained manner according to "sensibilities."

which is more tolerant of anxiety than it is of dysfunctions that do not make physiological sense.

Support for the role of social and cultural factors also comes from studies showing that conversion disorder is more common among people with lower socio-economic status and from rural areas (Folks, Ford, & Regan, 1984), who may be less knowledgeable about medical and psychological concepts. Further evidence derives from studies showing that the diagnosis of hysteria has declined in industrialized societies such as England (Hare, 1969) but has remained common in undeveloped countries such as Libya (Pu et al., 1986). These data, although consistent, are difficult to interpret. They could mean that increasing sophistication about medical diseases leads to decreased prevalence of conversion disorder. Alternatively, diagnostic practices may vary from country to country, producing different rates. A large-scale study conducted by diagnosticians trained to follow the same procedures is needed.

Biological Factors in Conversion Disorder

Although genetic factors have been proposed as being important in the development of conversion disorder, this topic has not received extensive testing. The little research that does exist does not support this proposal. For example, Torgersen (1986) examined 10 cases of conversion disorder, 12 of somatization disorder, and 7 of pain disorder. No co-twin had the same diagnosis as his or her proband!

A growing number of studies point to links between brain structures and conversion disorder. A possible role for the brain was suggested initially by the fact that conversion symptoms are more likely to occur on the left side than on the right side of the body; left-side functioning is controlled by the right hemisphere of the brain. Thus, the majority of conversion symptoms may be related to the functioning of the right hemisphere. Consistent with this idea, research has shown that in people with left-sided conversion symptoms, stimulation of the right hemisphere yields smaller muscle responses than does stimulation of the left hemisphere (Foong et al., 1997). More recent fMRI research suggests that when processing stressful events, people with conversion disorder have a failure to activate the right inferior frontal cortex and the connectivity between the amygdala and motor areas of the brain are enhanced in these people (Aybek et al., 2014). Further evidence of abnormal cerebral activation in 10 distinct areas of the brain was found in another recent study (Burke et al., 2014). We are now in an era of extensive research on the neural elements of conversion disorder. According to one contemporary review, while no one etiological model has been developed thus far, we at least know for certain based on this scientific evidence that it is possible to distinguish actual conversion disorder from feigning (see Dar & Kanaan, 2016).

Various case studies have also implicated brain structures. A study conducted in Toronto on three women with a sensory form of conversion disorder used fMRI to implicate brain structure (Ghaffar, Staines, & Feinstein, 2006) and found that stimulating a numb hand or foot did not activate the somatosensory region of the brain; however, stimulating each client's other hand or foot (which was not numb) did result in activation of the somatosensory region. Stonnington et al. (2006) argue that these and other recent neuroimaging studies implicate neurological circuits that link volition, movement, and perception in conversions triggered by psychological processes. A more recent case study examined conversion disorder in a client with a four-year history of hysterical mutism (i.e., nonvocalization). Analyses of fMRI data taken before and after recovery pointed to impaired connectivity between speech-related brain networks and brain networks that regulate anxiety (Bryant & Das, 2012).

While case examples and controlled studies are clearly informative, these pieces of evidence may be more useful in telling us *how* the conversion disorder occurs rather than *why* it occurs. Models such as the one outlined in Figure 7.3 are needed to account for onset and differential vulnerability. Also, because there is little longitudinal research in this area focusing on people prior to the onset of their conversion disorder, we cannot discount the possibility that differences in the brain are a consequence rather than a cause.

Stonnington et al. (2006) proposed a comprehensive biopsychosocial model of conversion disorder that integrates empirical findings and different causal models (see Figure 7.3). The model takes into account the risk factors, perpetuating factors, and triggering events. Although the model was developed specifically for conversion disorder, it can serve as a useful framework for other somatoform disorders.

Therapies for Somatoform Disorders

"Hard-to-treat clients may engender feelings of powerlessness, frustration, and mistrust in their treaters, which, if unprocessed, may lead to a poor relationship and excessive use of medication, tests, and procedures."

—Stonnington et al., 2006, p. 1515, on treating conversion disorder

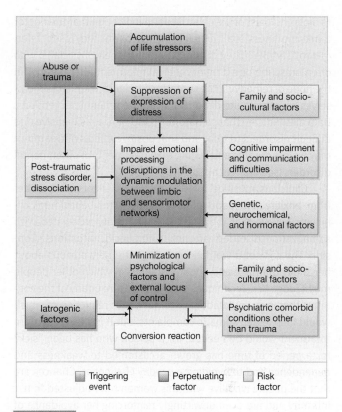

FIGURE 7.3 Biopsychosocial conceptualization of conversion disorder.

Source: C. M. Stonnington, J. J. Barry, & R. S. Fisher, "Conversion disorder: Clinical case conference," *The American Journal of Psychiatry,* 163, 1510–1517. Reprinted with permission from *The American Journal of Psychiatry* (© 2006) American Psychiatric Association.

Because somatoform disorders are rarer than most other disorders seen by mental health professionals, less controlled research exists on the efficacy of different treatments relative to many other disorders. Historically, case reports and clinical speculation were the main sources of information on how to help people with these disorders. However, in recent years a number of randomized controlled trials (RCTs) have focused on the treatment of people with diagnosed disorders.

Kroenke's (2007) review of 23 RCT studies showed that the results vary depending on whether the focus was generically on medically unexplained symptoms or a more severe and clinically delineated somatoform disorder. The benefits of treatment were less evident in studies with people suffering from medically unexplained symptoms, perhaps because this involved lower levels of dysfunction. The studies of people with somatoform disorder found that CBT was effective across various conditions and it was the most effective form of treatment. This tendency for lower treatment efficacy for people with medically unexplained symptoms was confirmed in a subsequent meta-analysis of studies that utilized short-term psychotherapy (Kleinstauber, Witthoft, & Hiller, 2011). These authors also noted that the primary treatment goal in these studies is improving the ability to cope with symptoms rather than removing the symptoms.

People with somatoform disorders define their problems in physical terms. They interpret a referral from their physician to a psychologist or psychiatrist as an indication that the doctor thinks the illness is "all in their head"; therefore, they resent referrals to "shrinks." They try the patience of their physicians, who often prescribe one drug or medical treatment after another in the hope of remedying the somatic complaint. The clients themselves are often quite dissatisfied with treatment interventions. Data also indicate that somatoform disorders are expensive and difficult disorders to treat and that positive effects of treatment may be less durable and lasting than treatments of other mental disorders (see Crane et al., 2012).

Clinicians must be mindful that such clients often suffer from anxiety and depression. Cognitive and behavioural clinicians believe that the high levels of anxiety associated with somatization disorders are linked to specific situations. Consider the case of a woman who was extremely anxious about her shaky marriage and about situations in which other people might judge her. Techniques such as exposure or any of the cognitive therapies could address her fears, the reduction of which would help lessen somatic complaints. But it is likely that more treatment would be needed, for a person who has been "sick" for a period of time has grown accustomed to weakness and dependency and to avoiding everyday challenges. Chances are that the people who live with this woman have adjusted to her infirmity and are even unwittingly reinforcing her avoidance of normal adult responsibilities. Family therapy might help her and her family members change the web of relationships to support her movement toward greater autonomy. Assertion training and social skills training might be used to provide more adaptive ways of interacting with people and challenge the core belief that "I am a poor, weak, sick person." CBT therapists have applied a wide range of techniques intended to make it worthwhile for the client to give up the symptoms. For example, a reinforcement approach attempts to provide the client with greater incentives for improvement than for remaining incapacitated.

In general, cognitive-behavioural approaches have also proved effective in reducing hypochondriacal concerns. Treatment may entail such strategies as pointing out the client's selective attention to bodily symptoms and discouraging the client from seeking medical reassurance that he or she is not ill. Taylor, Asmundson, and Coons (2005) noted that hypochondriasis was regarded historically as treatment resistant, but a contemporary meta-analysis of 13 studies with an RCT design found that CBT was effective and outperformed comparison conditions at both post-test and follow-up (Olatunji et al., 2014). There was a large effect size at post-test but a small effect size at follow-up. This conclusion is qualified somewhat by a subsequent study that compared CBT and exposure therapy. It was found that both treatment approaches were effective in treating primary and secondary symptoms among people with hypochondriasis/health anxiety. It is worth noting that the people in the exposure treatment condition had a higher rate of completion and CBT was not superior to exposure treatment in terms of degree of improvement on cognitive measures (see Weck et al., 2015).

Finally, given psychoanalytic interpretations of various disorders, does psychodynamic therapy work with these disorders? It does according to a meta-analysis of 14 studies conducted on short-term psychodynamic psychotherapy (see Abbass, Kisely, & Kroenke, 2009). It was concluded that short-term psychodynamic psychotherapy resulted in significant reductions to physical symptoms, psychological symptoms, and health-care utilization. Moreover, these improvements were maintained in follow-up assessments.

7.4 Dissociative Disorders

"The dissociative disorders have been mired in controversy for a number of years but empirical investigation has been gradually replacing uninformed speculation, and the onus is now on the critics of the dissociative disorders to provide data supporting their position."

— *Cardena and Gleaves, 2007, p. 495*

In this section, we examine three dissociative disorders—dissociative amnesia, depersonalization/derealization disorder, and dissociative identity disorder or DID (formerly known as multiple personality disorder)—all of which are characterized by changes in a person's sense of identity, memory, or consciousness. The dissociative disorders are summarized in Table 7.2. Also included is a general diagnostic category—other specified dissociative disorder—that includes dissociative trance (i.e., a narrowing or loss of awareness showing unresponsiveness or insensitivity to environmental cues). Individuals with these disorders may be unable to recall important personal events or may temporarily forget their identity or even assume a new identity. They may even wander far from their usual surroundings. We all have everyday dissociative experiences of one kind or another. (See Canadian Perspectives 7.1.)

TABLE 7.2 **Summary of the *DSM-5* Dissociative Disorders**

Disorder	Description
Dissociative amnesia	Memory loss following a stressful experience.
Depersonalization/ Derealization disorder	Altered experience of the self.
Dissociative identity disorder	Having at least two distinct ego states—alters—that act independently of each other.
Other specified dissociative disorder	Symptoms that cause clinically significant distress or impairment but do not meet the full criteria for the disorders listed above. Four specific manifestations are chronic and recurrent syndromes of mixed dissociative symptoms, identity disturbance due to prolonged and intense coercive persuasion, acute dissociative reactions to stressful events, and dissociative trance.

Few sources of high-quality data concerning the prevalence of the various dissociative disorders are available. Perhaps the best study to date was conducted by Colin Ross (1991). This study found prevalence rates of 7.0%, 2.4%, and 0.2% for amnesia, depersonalization, and fugue, respectively.

Our examination of the four major dissociative disorders will first cover symptoms and then theories of etiology and therapies.

Dissociative Amnesia

A person with **dissociative amnesia** is unable to recall important personal information, usually after some stressful episode. The information is not permanently lost, but it cannot be retrieved during the episode of amnesia. The holes in memory are too extensive to be explained by ordinary forgetfulness.

Canadian Perspectives 7.1

Everyday Dissociative Experiences in Winnipeg

Colin Ross, a Canadian psychiatrist now based in Texas, did most of his extensive research on multiple personality disorder in Canada. In Winnipeg, he and his associates investigated whether typical Canadians living in the community have everyday occurrences of dissociation.

Have you ever sat at your desk studying, lapsed into daydreaming about the upcoming weekend, and become unaware of what was happening around you? Have you ever been so engrossed in imagining a "story" or engaged in a personal narrative with yourself that it actually seemed real? Have you ever had an impression that you were viewing yourself from outside your body? These are all dissociative experiences.

How did Colin Ross determine the frequency of dissociative experiences in a community sample? Ross, Joshi, and Currie (1990) tapped a representative sample of 1,055 adults, having them complete a reliable and validated self-report measure of dissociative experiences: the Dissociative Experiences Scale (DES). The distribution of the respondents' total scores (which can range between 0 and 100) is shown in Figure 7.4. The figure indicates that (1) a majority of people in the general population report having had at least a few dissociative experiences, although only a small number have had many; and (2) most people report never having experienced the most "pathological" items, although some have. Fewer than 75 people reported having had no dissociative experiences at all. Ross reanalyzed the data and concluded that 3.3% of the sample had had pathological dissociative experiences, "and therefore presumptively had a dissociative disorder" (Ross, 1997, p. 105). Ross considers 3% to be a "conservative estimate," which, when extrapolated to all of North America, suggests that about 10 million North Americans have a dissociative disorder. However, note that the majority of DES items are not inherently pathological.

The results of the Winnipeg study indicate that the most common dissociative experiences include being able to ignore pain, missing part of a conversation, and being uncertain about whether you actually did something or only thought about it. Relatively few people endorsed very unusual, even bizarre experiences, such as not recognizing your own reflection in a mirror, finding yourself dressed in clothes you don't remember putting on, finding yourself in a place but unaware of how you got there, or feeling as though your body is not your own.

Before we conclude that over 3% of the general community population has DID, we should replicate the study using trained interviewers who employ a structured interview, such as the Structured Clinical Interview for various *DSM* disorders (SCID) (Spitzer, Gibbon, & Williams, 1996), to confirm actual diagnoses. Further, certain DES items, when taken in isolation, seem dubious examples

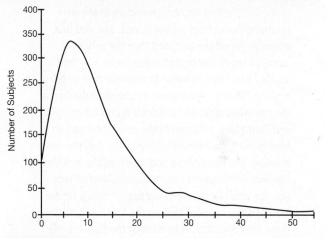

FIGURE 7.4 Distribution of dissociative experience scale scores in the general population ($n = 1,055$).

of dissociation (e.g., absorption in a television program or movie; staring into space), and this highlights discrepancies between self-report measures and what can be learned using the clinical interview. Indeed, follow-up work on the DES indicated that scores are not continuous and, in fact, represent a "taxon" or discrete category. A subset of eight items is now used to identify the presence or absence of dissociation (e.g., Seedat, Stein, & Forde, 2003). The eight items used to distinguish a more pathological form of dissociation primarily reflect themes of depersonalization and derealization (i.e., things, people, and the environment are unreal).

What factors can cause dissociation? Stress and fatigue are key factors. It is likely that these factors contributed to the high rates of dissociation that Laposa and Alden (2003) found in their study of post-traumatic stress disorder (PTSD) in hospital emergency room workers. Almost half of their participants had "clinically meaningful dissociation," according to their self-reports. Moreover, more than half reported periods of blanking out, going on "automatic pilot," and feeling unreal, like being in a movie or dream. Other general triggers for dissociation would include binge drinking or the use of various psychoactive drugs. The hypnotic induction can also elicit dissociative symptoms, especially in suggestible people.

Finally, we remind you that dissociative experiences in the general population and among students are non-pathological, typically transient, and are rarely a sign of serious psychological problems. However, extensive episodes of depersonalization and derealization that interfere with daily functioning signal the need for intervention.

(continued)

Thinking Critically

1. Which of the dissociative experiences described above have you experienced? Remember that dissociative experiences, even if recurrent, should not be considered problematic if they do not cause distress or impairment.

2. There can be numerous triggers for dissociative experiences other than traumatic life events. How do you explain the dissociative experiences that you had in the past? What do you think triggered these experiences? Could boredom also cause dissociative symptoms?

Fraser (1994) used case studies to illustrate the symptoms of the various dissociative disorders. Fraser described dissociative amnesia by outlining the case of a 17-year-old female student

> *". . . who was referred because of two episodes of amnesia. The first had happened while she was returning home from school by bus. She was just about to get off the bus, and then the very next moment she found herself in her home. She had no idea how she got home but did not dare to tell anyone. Several nights later, as she disembarked at the same bus stop, she suddenly found herself lying in a field alone, stripped to the waist. She had no idea of the time interval lost but felt it was the same evening. She went home and reported the incident. She was investigated neurologically, and all was normal, and she was referred to psychiatry. Under hypnosis she recalled that on the first incident, there were four boys who were at the bus stop. As they started to make sexual advances, she bolted away and ran home. It was assumed that she did this in a dissociated state. On the second incident, the same group of boys was waiting at the bus stop. This time they grabbed her and hauled her into a nearby field. They pulled off her brassiere and appeared to be intending to do more when somehow they were frightened off."*

> *(Fraser, 1994, pp. 144–145)*

Most often the memory loss involves all events during a limited period of time following some traumatic experience, such as the one described above or witnessing the death of a loved one. More rarely the amnesia is for only selected events during a circumscribed period of distress, is continuous from a traumatic event to the present (see photo of "Mr. Nobody"), or is total, covering the person's entire life (Coons & Milstein, 1992). The person's behaviour during the period of amnesia is otherwise unremarkable, except that the memory loss may bring some disorientation and purposeless wandering (see photo from *Finding Nemo*). With total amnesia, the client does not recognize relatives and friends, but retains the ability to talk, read, and reason and also retains talents and previously acquired knowledge of the world and of how to function in it. The amnesic episode may last several hours or as long as several years. It usually disappears as suddenly as it came on, with complete recovery and only a small chance of recurrence.

Memory loss is common in many brain disorders, as well as in substance abuse, but amnesia and memory loss caused by brain disorders or substance abuse can be fairly easily distinguished. In degenerative brain diseases, memory fails more slowly over time, is not linked to life stress, and is accompanied by other cognitive deficits, such as the inability to learn new information. Memory loss following a brain injury caused

Disney Enterprises/Album Photo Archive/Newscom

Though Disney Pixar's *Finding Nemo* may be an animated film meant for children, it has been touted as one of the few films to accurately portray amnesia. Blue tangfish Dory (right) suffers from "short-term memory loss," a symptom consistent with amnesic syndrome. This accurate portrayal continues in the 2016 sequel, *Finding Dory*, in which Dory tries to reunite with her family.

The Canadian Press/Andrew Vaughan

"Mr. Nobody" became Canada's most famous case of faked amnesia. For many years, he alleged that a mugging caused memory loss, including his identity, and he sought Canadian citizenship. Mr. Nobody (who went by the name Philip Staufen) married his lawyer's daughter in 2001. In 2007, he admitted that he was a Romanian impostor whose birth name is Ciprian Skeid. He said he hated his homeland and his true identity and wanted a new life in Canada. "I'd rather be a fake nobody than the real me."

by some trauma (e.g., an automobile accident) or substance abuse can be easily linked to the trauma or the substance being abused.

There can be significant cultural differences in the expression of dissociative amnesia. This point is illustrated in the following case of an Inuit adolescent who apparently suffered from dissociative amnesia in the context of spirit possession.

> "D.N. is a 19-year-old Inuit male student who is the eldest in his family. He described his father as teaching him the traditional skills; his mother he viewed as a scolding rejecting figure. He complained of several years of depression and suicidal ideation related to a confused sexual identity. While alone, hunting on the tundra, he felt a presence touch his shoulder and saying 'Don't look back.' He did nevertheless and saw a faceless apparition wearing a caribou parka. . . . The latter named Nanonalok (Big Bear) said 'Don't be afraid, I'm your grandfather.' Initially friendly the spirit informed D.N. that he would leave him alone if he married 'E,' a young woman in whom D.N. had an ambivalent interest. He refused to obey and so began nightly battles associated with amnesia, from which he emerged with torn clothes, bruises, and a gunshot wound 'caused' by the spirit."

(Seltzer, 1983, pp. 53–54)

According to Seltzer (1983), this young man received treatment for dissociative disorder, since further assessment yielded no evidence of depression or thought disorder. D. N. received only some of this treatment away from home because he insisted that the spirits would lose their energy if he were away from his Arctic environment.

More recent research has sought to identify the regions of the brain that are involved in dissociative amnesia. A brain imaging study comparing 14 people with dissociative amnesia and 19 control participants found reduced glucose utilization in the right inferolateral prefrontal cortex, which is in keeping with other evidence linking this region with autobiographical memory (Brand et al., 2009). The investigators suggested that dissociative amnesia is likely associated with hypometabolism in this brain region.

Dissociative Fugue

Dissociative fugue was previously considered a *DSM* disorder, but it is no longer considered to be a separate disorder; it is now considered a "specifier" or subtype of dissociative amnesia (for a discussion, see Spiegel et al., 2011). That is, people can have dissociative amnesia with or without dissociative fugue. If you are a fan of the television series *Breaking Bad*, you may recall that in the show's second season, Walter White, played by Bryan Cranston, faked a dissociative fugue state to cover up his kidnapping. The difficulty here is, how do we know when

dissociative fugue is real? Dissociative fugue played a key role in the actual case of Rita Graveline, a woman from Quebec who was charged with shooting and killing her abusive husband, Michael. According to testimony, he had a severe drinking problem and he had been severely abusive for many years. Rita and Michael were married for 31 years. She had been pushed and shoved many times and had a bottle smashed over her head. She also endured many death threats from her husband. Rita Graveline was acquitted in 2001 by a Quebec jury. The key part of her defence was that she was in a dissociative fugue state and had total amnesia for the events leading up to the killing, as well as for the act itself. An appeal was granted due to procedural problems and a new trial took place, and the Supreme Court of Canada found Rita Graveline not guilty in 2006. It was noted at the time that it is rare for a person to be found not guilty based on a defence of dissociative amnesia. The amnesia was believed to have been triggered by Rita's drinking and history of depression, as well as the trauma of the events that took place on the night of the event.

Memory loss is more extensive in dissociative fugue and that is why it is a specifier of dissociative amnesia in *DSM-5*. The person not only becomes totally amnesic but suddenly leaves home and work and assumes a new identity. Sometimes the person takes a new name, a new home, a new job, and even a new set of personality characteristics. The person may even succeed in establishing a fairly complex social life. More often, however, the new life does not crystallize to this extent, and the fugue is of briefer duration. It consists for the most part of limited, but apparently purposeful, travel, during which social contacts are minimal or absent.

Fugues typically occur after a person has experienced some severe stress, such as marital quarrels, personal rejection, financial or occupational difficulties, war service, or a natural disaster. Recovery, although it takes varying amounts of time, is usually complete, and the individual does not recollect what took place during the flight from his or her usual haunts.

Fraser (1994) described another case in which a young man had engaged in three violent acts, including breaking a person's jaw in a fight, yet had total amnesia for these events. Further analysis focused on the time that this young man spent in prison. Fraser found that

> ". . . hypnosis helped him recall being gang-raped by a group of prison inmates who had singled him out because he was mild-mannered and of different racial origin. He had been sexually abused by these men on numerous occasions. Apparently, attempts to tell the prison guards only resulted in laughter by the guards, who told him the prison 'was not the Holiday Inn and didn't cater to room change requests.' When some of the more sadistic events were being recalled in hypnosis, a state that called itself 'Empty' stated that it had taken over and accepted the severe episodes of anal intercourse."

(Fraser, 1994, p. 143)

According to Fraser, the young man committed the three assaults because "Empty" had overreacted and responded with rage to minimal touching.

Depersonalization/Derealization Disorder

In **depersonalization/derealization disorder**, the person's perception or experience of the self is disconcertingly and disruptively altered. Its inclusion in diagnostic frameworks is controversial because depersonalization/derealization disorder, unlike other dissociative disorders, involves no disturbance of memory. In a depersonalization episode, which is typically triggered by stress, individuals rather suddenly lose their sense of self. They have unusual sensory experiences; for example, their limbs may seem drastically changed in size or their voices may sound strange to them. They may have the impression that they are outside their bodies, viewing themselves from a distance. Sometimes they feel mechanical, as though they and others are robots, or they move as though in a world that has lost its reality. Similar episodes sometimes occur in several other disorders: schizophrenia (see Chapter 11), post-traumatic stress disorder (Chapter 9), and borderline personality disorder (Chapter 13) (Maldonado, Butler, & Spiegel, 1998).

DSM-5 retains this disorder but changed the criteria to include **derealization**, which is essentially a fogginess or sense of detachment from the situational context or things in the situation (see Spiegel et al., 2011). Previously, derealization was seen as an indicator of dissociative disorders not otherwise specified.

This disorder usually begins in adolescence and has a chronic course. Comorbid personality disorders are frequent, as are anxiety disorders and depression (Simeon et al., 1997). In one study (Baker et al., 2007), 80 participants with depersonalization disorder were assessed using the Revised Illness Perception Questionnaire. Illness perceptions were generally negative. Greater depersonalization disorder severity was associated with a strong illness identity, psychological illness causal attributions, and high levels of depression. The authors concluded that, "The findings offer some support for a cognitive model of understanding depersonalization disorder, namely that attribution processes are linked to perceived symptom severity and a wide range of experiences come to be seen as part of the disorder" (Baker et al., 2007, p. 105).

The following case illustrates the symptoms of depersonalization/derealization disorder, as well as the fact that sufferers often report childhood trauma.

> *"Mrs. A was a 43-year-old woman who was living with her mother and son and worked at a clerical job. She had felt depersonalized as far back as she could remember. 'It's as if the real me is taken out and put on a shelf or stored somewhere inside*

of me. Whatever makes me me is not there. It is like an opaque curtain . . . like going through the motions and having to exert discipline to keep the unit together.' She had suffered several episodes of depersonalization annually and found them extremely distressing. She had experienced panic attacks for 1 year when she was 35 and had been diagnosed with self-defeating personality disorder. Her childhood trauma history included nightly genital fondling and frequent enemas by her mother from earliest memory to age 10."

(Simeon et al., 1997, p. 1109)

Some people experience symptoms of depersonalization but not the significant distress that is needed for a diagnosis. However, these individuals have depersonalization experiences that seem similar in many respects to those reported by people with the disorder. Charbonneau and O'Connor (1999) analyzed the depersonalization experiences of 20 people from Montreal and found that onset was associated with traumatic life events in general or specific events involving sexual abuse. The most common reaction was a sense of derealization, with statements such as "I feel as if I am floating away from reality" endorsed by 90% or more of the participants. Desomatization was also reported, with 80% or more of the participants agreeing with statements such as "My body does not feel like it belongs." The most common thought or sensation accompanying the depersonalization experience involved worries about feeling isolated and detached from other people (reported by 60%), followed by a feeling of being vulnerable and embarrassed about the situation (reported by 45%). No single diagnosis was associated consistently with depersonalization. The depersonalization group had elevated levels of depression and trait anxiety relative to a community control group.

Dissociative Identity Disorder

Consider what it would be like to have dissociative identity disorder. This was what afflicted Chris Sizemore, the woman with the famous three faces of Eve who was described in Chapter 4. People tell you about things you have done that seem out of character, events of which you have no memory. You have been waking up each morning with the remains of a cup of tea by your bedside—and you do not like tea. How can you explain these happenings? If you think about seeking treatment, do you not worry whether the psychiatrist or psychologist will believe you?

We all have days when we are not quite ourselves. This is assumed to be normal and is not what is meant by multiple personality. According to *DSM-IV-TR*, a proper diagnosis of **dissociative identity disorder (DID)** requires that a person have at least two separate ego states, or *alters*—different modes of being and feeling and acting that exist independently of each other and that come forth and are in control at different times.

There is usually one primary personality, and treatment is typically sought by the primary alter. There are typically two to four alters at the time a diagnosis is made, but over the course of treatment several more often emerge. Gaps in memory occur in all cases and are produced because at least one alter has no contact with the others; that is, alter A has no memory for what alter B is like or even any knowledge of having this alternate state of being. The existence of different alters must also be long-lasting and cause considerable disruption in one's life; it cannot be a temporary change resulting from the ingestion of a drug, for example.

Each alter may be quite complex, with its own behaviour patterns, memories, and relationships; each determines the nature and acts of the individual when it is in command (see photo of Herschel Walker). Usually, the personalities are quite different, even opposites of one another. They may have different handedness, wear glasses with different prescriptions, and have allergies to different substances. The original and subordinate alters are all aware of lost periods of time, and the voices of the others may sometimes echo into an alter's consciousness, even though the alter may not know to whom these voices belong.

DID presumably begins in childhood, but it is rarely diagnosed until adulthood. The diagnosis is much more common in women than in men. The presence of other diagnoses—in particular, depression, borderline personality disorder, and somatization disorder—is frequent (Boon & Draijer, 1993; Oeztuerk & Sar, 2008). DID is often accompanied by headaches, substance abuse, phobias, hallucinations, suicide ideation and attempts, sexual dysfunction, and self-abusive behaviour, as well as by other dissociative symptoms such as amnesia and depersonalization (Scroppo et al., 1998). A study by Ross et al. (1990) of 102 multiple personality disorder clients, including a subset from Winnipeg and Ottawa, used a structured interview to determine that about 90% had a history of suicidal tendencies, depression, recurring headaches, and sexual abuse.

A related possibility is that individuals suffering from dissociative symptoms have a disorganized or insecure attachment style because they were exposed as young children to the frightening and chaotic behaviour of their caregiver (Liotti, 1992; Oeztuerk & Sar, 2008). Indeed, a study of clinically treated adolescents from three Canadian cities confirmed that attachment-related trauma was linked significantly with self-reported symptoms of dissociation (West, Adam, Spreng, & Rose, 2001).

Cases of DID are often mislabelled as schizophrenia in the media. This diagnostic category derives part of its name from the Greek root schizo, which means "splitting away from," hence the confusion. A split in the personality, wherein two or more fairly separate and coherent systems of being exist alternately in the same person, is very different from any recognized symptoms of schizophrenia, which involves a splitting away from reality.

Controversies in the Diagnosis of DID
Although DID is recognized formally as a diagnosis by its inclusion in DSM-IV-TR, its inclusion in the DSM is controversial. Montreal psychiatrist Joel Paris has dismissed DID diagnoses as a fad that started with the publication of the book and movie Sybil and has expressed outrage that DID is retained in DSM-5 because he views it as unscientific in theory and practice (see Paris, 2012). Indeed, a previous survey of American psychiatrists found that two-thirds of the participants had reservations about the inclusion of DID in DSM-IV (Pope et al., 1999). A follow-up study of 550 Canadian psychiatrists found that more than two-thirds had reservations about including DID in DSM-IV-TR (Lalonde, Hudson, Gigante, & Pope, 2001). Compared with the American sample, the Canadian respondents were significantly more skeptical about the scientific validity and diagnostic legitimacy of DID. There were no significant differences between the views of English-speaking and French-speaking respondents, a finding inconsistent with the hypothesis that French-speaking Canadian psychiatrists would be less accepting of DID diagnoses because there is little support for the diagnosis in the French-language research literature. However, consistent with the findings of the earlier study, psychoanalytically oriented psychiatrists were significantly more accepting of the validity of DID than were biologically oriented psychiatrists.

Pope, Barry, Bodkin, and Hudson (2006) tracked scientific interest in the dissociative disorders over a 20-year period from 1984 to 2003. They reported that annual publications rose from low levels in the 1980s to a peak in the mid-1990s, followed by a sharp decline by 2003, whereas 25 comparison diagnoses showed constant or rising publication rates. About a third of the most recent papers were skeptical of the validity of dissociative amnesia and/or recovered-memory therapy. They concluded that dissociative amnesia and DID "presently do not command widespread scientific acceptance" (Pope et al., 2006, p. 19). Moreover, several DID treatment units in Canada and the United States were closed down (see Piper & Merskey, 2004a). Piper and Merskey (2004a) concluded that DID cannot be reliably diagnosed and that "consistent evidence of blatant iatrogenesis appears in the practices of some of the disorder's proponents" (p. 592). Iatrogenesis involves inducing a change in a client (in this case a different identity state) inadvertently by a therapist or by his or her treatment. Various letters to the editor of the Canadian Journal of Psychiatry, including one from George Fraser, took issue with these conclusions. In 2009, Colin Ross finally responded to the Piper and Mersky critique and argued that DID "has established diagnostic reliability and concurrent validity, the trauma histories of affected individuals can be corroborated, and the existing prospective treatment literature demonstrates improvement in individuals receiving psychotherapy for the disorder" (Ross, 2009, p. 221). As for the recent views expressed by Paris (2012), David Spiegel, a psychiatrist from Stanford University, took exception and concluded that "he is both wrong and is intellectually sloppy" (Blackwell, 2012). Spiegel chaired the DID DSM-5 subcommittee and maintains that an even-handed assessment of the evidence supports the validity of DID and its inclusion in DSM-5 (see Spiegel et al., 2011, 2013). He also expressed concern that people suffering from DID may not come forward for help as a result of the controversy.

DID was first mentioned in the nineteenth century. In a review of the literature, Sutcliffe and Jones (1962) identified a total of 77 cases, most of which were reported between 1890 and 1920. After that, reports of DID declined until the 1970s, when they increased markedly. More formal data on the prevalence of DID were collected on samples of adults in Winnipeg (Ross, 1991) and in Turkey (Akyuz et al., 1999). Prevalence was 1.3% in Winnipeg and 0.4% in Turkey. Although these prevalence figures may not seem high, they are—previously, prevalence was thought to be about 1 in 1 million. Spiegel et al. (2011) suggest that DID may be found in about 1 out of 100 people.

What caused the re-emergence of the DID diagnosis in the past 30 years? One possible explanation is that in *DSM-III*, published in 1980, diagnostic criteria were spelled out clearly for the first time (Putnam, 1997). But it is also possible that more people began to adopt the role of a client with DID or that clinicians had always seen a similar number of cases but chose to report them only when interest in DID grew. We can also speculate that the earlier decline in the number of diagnoses of DID resulted from the increasing popularity of the concept of schizophrenia; that is, cases of DID may have been mistakenly diagnosed as cases of schizophrenia (Rosenbaum, 1980). However, the symptoms of the two disorders

Esther Lin/Forza LLC/Forza LLC/Getty Images

Famous NFL football star Herschel Walker revealed in his autobiography, *Breaking Free: My Life with Dissociative Identity Disorder*, that he has at least 12 "alters" (see Christian, 2008, May 19).

are actually not very similar. Although the voices of the alters may be experienced as auditory hallucinations, clients with DID do not show the thought disorder and behavioural disorganization of schizophrenia. As noted earlier, another factor of possible relevance was the 1973 publication of *Sybil,* which presented a dramatic case with 16 personalities (Schreiber, 1973). This case, featured in a movie starring Sally Field, attracted a great deal of attention and spawned much interest in the disorder. Some critics have hypothesized that this heightened interest led some therapists to suggest strongly to clients that they had DID, sometimes using hypnosis to probe for alters. Ironically, it has been claimed that Sybil's alters were created during therapy by a therapist who gave substance to the client's different emotional states by giving them names (Rieger, 1998).

There is little doubt that the validity of DIDs will continue to be a highly controversial topic. While debate rages, research findings will continue to stir the debate. One intriguing line of investigation is focused on the physiological underpinnings of DID. A study from the Netherlands (Reinders et al., 2006) suggested that different identity states show different psychobiological reactions to trauma-related memory, including subjective reactions, cardiovascular responses, and cerebral activation patterns determined by a PET scan. The hypothesis is that DID clients have a traumatic identity state that can access repressed memories and emotions and a neutral identity state or states that is protective, inhibiting access to traumatic memories and allowing the client to concentrate on daily life functioning. Another Dutch study (Hermans et al., 2006) reported that an attentional bias for social threat cues was identity state-dependent (a claimed strong awareness of trauma) in DID clients and deviated from patterns observed in controls. In another study (Huntjens et al., 2007), the authors failed to find evidence of inter-identity amnesia for emotionally toned stimuli. It was argued that dissociative amnesia in DID reflects a disturbance in meta-memory functioning (knowledge, beliefs, and feelings about memory) rather than an actual retrieval inability. It should be pointed out that there was overlap among some of the authors in these studies and that some of the same participants were used in the different studies. Kong, Allen, and Glisky (2008) also showed that self-reported inter-identity amnesia is not corroborated by objective explicit memory transfer tests.

More recently, a fascinating case study published in the journal *Cognitive Neuroscience* points to brain structures that may be involved in DID. This study, by Savoy, Frederick, Keuroghlian, and Wolk (2012), details the results of two fMRI sessions months apart with a client referred to as RV ("research volunteer"). RV is a middle-aged woman who has been receiving treatment for 20 years. She has three personalities referred to as ABC (A for her adult personality, B for a 2-year-old baby personality, and C for a 4-to 6-year-old child). While past studies have examined the physiological correlates of multiple personalities, this case is different because RV can switch

Dissociative Disorders in Students

Given that maltreatment and trauma are quite prevalent among students, is it possible to identify students who are trying to cope with dissociative disorders? While this topic has not been the subject of extensive research and it is clear that the research conducted thus far could be improved in some substantial ways, the existing evidence suggests that the answer is "yes." This topic first became a central focus in a study conducted by Sandberg and Lynn (1992) published in the *Journal of Abnormal Psychology*. The Dissociative Experiences Scale (DES; Bernstein & Putnam, 1986), the same measure described earlier in Canadian Perspectives 7.1, was administered to 650 undergraduate students at Ohio University and 35 students were identified for a high dissociation group based on their responses. They were compared with a control group of 32 students with moderate to low DES scores. The students in the high DES group reported greater physical and psychological maltreatment from both their mothers and fathers. They also reported greater psychopathology and lower university adjustment. The two groups did not differ in levels of social desirability. Each student also underwent a dissociation clinical interview and 2 of the 35 students in the high dissociation group were deemed to have a diagnosable disorder (one student with multiple personality disorder and one with psychogenic amnesia) versus no students in the other group. These data suggest that only a small proportion of students with dissociative tendencies actually meet diagnostic thresholds for dissociative disorder but that dissociative disorder does exist.

However, a different conclusion follows from a more recent study conducted with university students from the Philippines. This study by Gingrich (2009) evaluated 459 first-year students and again identified 30 with elevated self-reported dissociative symptoms and 30 students with low levels of symptoms in the control group. Diagnostic SCID interviews found that 19 students had a dissociative disorder (7 with dissociative identity disorder, 2 with dissociative amnesia, and 10 with dissociative disorder not otherwise specified). Interestingly, while 11 students with high dissociative self-reports were found to not meet diagnostic thresholds according to the SCID, another self-report inventory tapping dissociation and the self-report measure overestimated clinical dysfunction, with all but one student deemed to have a disorder. These 19 students with diagnosable conditions according to the SCID were then compared with the other 41 students and were found to have significantly higher levels of amnesia, depersonalization, derealization, identity confusion, and identity alteration.

If these data are accepted, on the surface, it does indeed seem that large student populations will include some students who have diagnosable dissociative disorders. The stress inherent in being a student is a challenge for all students but this should especially be the case for students coping with dissociative disorders.

Thinking Critically

1. Is it possible or even likely that some college and university students will have a type of diagnosable form of dissociative disorder? How do you think Paris (2012) would account for this possibility?

2. Why do you think it was the case that the Gingrich (2009) study found all but 29 students in the high dissociation group had a diagnosable condition when evaluated with the self-report measure, but only 19 students did so when evaluated with the SCID? What factors might account for this discrepancy?

---

quickly from one personality to another and was requested to do so several times by the researchers because their initial focus was on brain activation during switches. Savoy et al. (2012) reported that none of the personalities enjoyed going in the fMRI machine and the baby personality could not keep her head still, so they focused on comparisons between the adult and child personalities. Several intriguing findings emerged. Most notably, there were consistent cortical and subcortical activations recorded during the switching trials. Also, the nucleus accumbens area of the brain was continually activated, in keeping with suggestions that this is a reward activation centre for the brain with the reward in this case being escaping traumatic pain. Finally, there was consistent activation of several areas of the prefrontal cortex, which the authors interpreted as consistent with these areas being involved in attentional shifts known to take place during multi-tasking as well as episodic memory retrievals and engagement in self-referent evaluations. The authors cautioned appropriately that this case may be low in generalizability even among people with DID because RV is unique in her abilities to rapidly switch personalities when cued.

Is it possible to detect dissociative disorders in students? This issue is the topic addressed in Student Perspectives 7.1.

7.5 Etiology of and Therapies for Dissociative Disorders

Etiology of Dissociative Disorders

The term "dissociative disorders" refers to the mechanism, dissociation, that is thought to cause the disorders. Historically, the concept comes from the writings of Pierre Janet, the French neurologist. The basic idea is that consciousness is usually a unified experience, including cognition, emotion, and motivation. But under stress, memories of a trauma may be stored in such a way that they are not accessible to awareness when the person has returned to a more normal state (Kihlstrom, Tataryn, & Hoyt, 1993). Possible outcomes are amnesia or fugue.

The behavioural view of dissociative disorders is somewhat similar to these early speculations. Behavioural theorists consider dissociation as an avoidance response that protects the person from stressful events and memories of these events. Because the person does not consciously confront these painful memories, the fear elicited has no opportunity to be extinguished.

There are two major theories of DID and associated models. One assumes that DID begins in childhood as a result of severe physical or sexual abuse. This is known as the *trauma model of dissociation*. The abuse causes dissociation and the formation of alters as a way of escaping the trauma (Gleaves, 1996). However, since not everyone who experiences child abuse develops DID, it is further proposed that a diathesis is present among those who do. Similarly, other forms of trauma that create overwhelming distress could lead to the development of DID (see photo).

Another proposed diathesis is that people who develop DID are very prone to engage in fantasy (Lynn & Rhue, 1988). This is known as the *fantasy model of dissociation*. A comprehensive analysis conducted by Dalenberg and associates (2012) led the authors to conclude that there is strong empirical support for the trauma model and little support for the fantasy model of dissociation. Another contemporary study conducted in England again concluded that it is traumatic experiences rather than fantasy processes that are implicated in dissociation (Vissia et al., 2016).

Trauma is believed to cause distress and the inability to tolerate and regulate distress (i.e., affective dysregulation), which is then believed to contribute to dissociation. One

Severe trauma in childhood is regarded as a major cause of dissociative disorders.

caveat, however, is that recent work suggests that affective dysregulation in the absence of trauma is still associated with dissociation (Briere & Runtz, 2015).

The other DID theory considers the disorder to be an enactment of learned social roles. The alters appear in adulthood, typically due to suggestions by a therapist (Lilienfeld et al., 1999; Spanos, 1994). DID is not viewed as a conscious deception (or malingering) in this theory; the issue is not whether DID is real but how it developed and is maintained. Canadian Contributions 7.1 provides a more complete description of the views and contributions of Nicholas Spanos in this area.

A critical piece of evidence regarding the two theories is whether or not DID actually develops in childhood as a result of abuse. When clients with DID enter therapy, they are usually unaware of their alters, but as therapy progresses, alters emerge and clients report that their alters did begin in childhood. Typically, however, there has been no corroborating evidence

Canadian Contributions 7.1

Nicholas P. Spanos and a Socio-Cognitive Perspective on DID

"Despite its current popularity, the notion that MPD [multiple personality disorder] is a naturally occurring disorder that results from severe child abuse is fraught with difficulties."

—*Nicholas Spanos, Multiple Identities and False Memories: A Sociocognitive Perspective (1996, p. 2)*

Nicholas Spanos (see photo) was a professor of psychology and director of the Laboratory for Experimental Hypnosis at Carleton University in Ottawa from 1975 to 1994. Spanos was also a pilot of small airplanes, and unfortunately, he died tragically in a plane

crash while taking off from Martha's Vineyard in the Cape Cod area of Massachusetts in 1994. However, Spanos left a research legacy that continues to generate controversy and interest to this day. Spanos had more than 250 publications. Published posthumously was a major book submitted before his death (Spanos, 1996). In this book, he challenged the validity of DID as a distinct psychiatric disorder. Spanos developed a cognitive-behavioural model of hypnosis that has become the most influential in the field. Although he made important contributions in several other areas, including demonic possession and the Salem witchcraft trials, in the area of dissociative disorders, he is known primarily for three things.

First, Spanos (1994) had been a leading advocate of the idea that DID basically involves role-playing. He pointed out that a small number of clinicians contribute most of the diagnoses of DID. A survey conducted in Switzerland, for example, found that 66% of

Nicholas Spanos believed that DID is essentially a socially constructed form of role-playing.

the diagnoses of DID were made by fewer than 10% of the psychiatrists who responded. Perhaps these clinicians have very liberal criteria for making the diagnosis. Alternatively, though, cases of DID may be referred to clinicians who have acquired a reputation for specializing in this condition (Gleaves, 1996). Therefore, the data are inconclusive.

Second, Spanos used role-playing studies with students to provide a unique perspective on the trial of an infamous serial murderer in California who came to be known as the Hillside Strangler (Spanos, Weekes, & Bertrand, 1985). The accused murderer, Ken Bianchi, unsuccessfully pled not guilty by reason of insanity, claiming that the murders had been committed by his alter, Steve. Bianchi was supposedly under hypnosis during a pre-trial meeting with a mental health professional to determine his legal responsibility for his crimes. The interviewer (I) asked for a second personality to come forward.

> *"I. I've talked a bit to Ken but I think that perhaps there might be another part of Ken that I haven't talked to. And I would like to communicate with that other part. And I would like that other part to come to talk with me . . . . And when you're here, lift the left hand off the chair to signal to me that you are here. Would you please come, Part, so I can talk to you? . . .Part, would you come and lift Ken's hand to indicate to me that you are here? Would you talk to me, Part, by saying 'I'm here'?"*

(Schwarz, 1981, pp. 142–143)

Bianchi (B) answered yes to the last question, and then he and the interviewer had the following conversation.

> "I. Part, are you the same as Ken or are you different in any way . . .
> B. I'm not him.
> I. You're not him. Who are you? Do you have a name?
> B. I'm not Ken.
> I. You're not him? Okay. Who are you? Tell me about yourself. Do you have a name I can call you by?
> B. Steve. You can call me Steve." (Schwarz, 1981, pp. 139–140)

In the Spanos et al. (1985) study, undergraduate students were told that they would play the role of an accused murderer and that, despite much evidence of guilt, a plea of not guilty had been entered. They were also told that they were to participate in a

Ken Bianchi, the Hillside Strangler, attempted an insanity defence for his serial killings, but the court decided that he had merely tried to fake a multiple personality.

simulated psychiatric interview that might involve hypnosis. Then the students were taken to another room and introduced to the psychiatrist, actually an experimental assistant. After a number of standard questions, the interviews diverged depending on which of three experimental conditions the students were assigned to. In the most important of these, the Bianchi condition, students were given a rudimentary hypnotic induction and were instructed to let a second personality come forward, just as in the actual Bianchi case.

After the experimental manipulations, the possible existence of a second personality was probed directly by the "psychiatrist." In addition, students were asked questions about the facts of the murders. Finally, in a second session, those who had acknowledged the presence of another personality were asked to take two personality tests twice—once each for their two personalities. Eighty-one percent of the students in the Bianchi condition adopted a new name, and many of these admitted guilt for the murders. Even the personality test scores of the two personalities differed considerably.

Clearly, when the situation demands, people can adopt a second personality. Spanos et al. (1985) suggested that some people who present as multiple personalities may have a rich fantasy life and considerable practice imagining that they are other people, especially when, like Bianchi, they find themselves in a situation in which there are inducements and cues to behave as though a previous bad act had been committed by another personality. We should remember, however, that this demonstration illustrates only that such role-playing is possible; it in no way determines that cases of multiple personality have such origins. Furthermore, the impact of such role-playing studies depends on how compelling the role-playing is as an analogue of DID. Critics have pointed out that DID is a complex disorder involving many symptoms, including auditory hallucinations, time loss, and depersonalization. None

(continued)

Courtesy Nicholas P. Spanos

AP/Wide World Photos

of these symptoms has been produced in role-playing studies (Gleaves, 1996).

In the actual trial of Bianchi, his insanity plea did not hold up, in part because of evidence from Martin Orne, a well-known expert on hypnosis. Orne subsequently interviewed Bianchi and demonstrated that his role enactment differed in important ways from how true multiple personalities and deeply hypnotized people act (Orne, Dinges, & Orne, 1984).

Finally, the third thing that Spanos is known for is his research on people who reported seeing UFOs (unidentified flying objects) (Spanos, Cross, Dickson, & DuBreuil, 1993). These 49 people were recruited via an advertisement placed in an Ottawa newspaper, and then their psychological characteristics were compared with samples of students and community members who did not report seeing a UFO. Spanos et al. (1993) found that

there was no evidence indicating that the UFO group had higher levels of psychopathology, higher levels of fantasy-proneness, or lower levels of intelligence relative to the other two groups. The factor that best distinguished the groups was the tendency for members of the UFO group to believe wholeheartedly in UFOs and alien life forms. Spanos et al. (1993) concluded that "with respect to UFO experiences, these ideas suggest that beliefs in alien visitation and flying saucers serve as templates against which people shape ambiguous external information, diffuse physical sensations, and vivid imaginings into alien encounters that are experienced as real events" (p. 631). According to Spanos, the alleged UFO incidents are by-products of cognitive constructions that largely operate when people are asleep. They are complex false memories. These same cognitive constructions could operate in other false memories.

this, and we have previously cautioned about the uncritical acceptance of self-reports. The situation is similar regarding physical or sexual abuse: very high rates have been reported (e.g., Ross et al., 1990), but they have not been corroborated.

One study, however, has come close to providing clearer data regarding both childhood onset and abuse in cases of DID, although it has been criticized by proponents of the role-enactment theory (Lilienfeld et al., 1999). The study, which was conducted over a period of two decades, examined 150 convicted murderers in detail (Lewis et al., 1997). Fourteen cases of DID were found. That the study was conducted on convicted murderers is important because in this situation, adopting the role of a person with DID involves an obvious payoff. But the evidence indicated that 12 of the 14 cases had long-standing DID symptoms that preceded their incarceration: 8 had experienced trances during childhood, 9 had had auditory hallucinations, and 10 had had imaginary companions (a frequent report among DID clients). Each of these symptoms was corroborated by at least three outside sources (e.g., interviews with family members, teachers, parole officers). Furthermore, several participants showed distinctly different handwriting styles well before committing their crimes (see Figure 7.5).

Focus on Discovery 7.2 examines the validity of recovered memories among people in general, but especially among people with DID who come to recall certain memories. We will see that opinions differ greatly in terms of whether recovered memories are seen as true or false.

Also important in this study was the documentation of physical or sexual abuse during childhood for 11 cases. Again, this was apparently confirmed by outside sources and physical evidence such as scars. Indeed, the authors noted that "the term 'abuse' does not do justice to the quality of maltreatment these individuals endured. A more accurate term would be 'torture'!" (Lewis et al., 1997, p. 1707). One boy was allegedly set on fire, another was circumcised by his father at age 3, and another was forced to sit on a hot stove. These data, then, seem to lend support to the proposition that DID does begin in childhood and that it is related to extreme stress. Nonetheless, in

a two-part critical review entitled, "The Persistence of Folly," published in the *Canadian Journal of Psychiatry,* Piper and Mersky (2004 a, b) concluded that there really isn't any proof for the claim that DID is caused by childhood trauma and that DID cases in children are rarely reported, implying that there are few actual cases.

Therapies for Dissociative Disorders

Dissociative disorders suggest, perhaps better than any other disorders, the possible relevance of psychoanalytic theorizing. In three disorders—amnesia, fugue, and DID—people behave in ways that seem to indicate that they cannot access forgotten earlier parts of their lives. And since these people may at the same time be unaware of having forgotten something, the hypothesis that they have repressed or dissociated massive portions of their lives is compelling (MacGregor, 1996). Consequently, a psychoanalytic approach is perhaps more widespread as a choice of treatment for dissociative disorders than for any other psychological problems. The goal of lifting repressions is the order of the day, pursued via the use of basic psychoanalytic techniques.

Because dissociative disorders are widely believed to arise from traumatic events that the person is trying to block from consciousness, there are links between therapies for these disorders and therapies for PTSD. Indeed, PTSD is the most commonly diagnosed comorbid disorder with DID (Loewenstein, 1991). It is therefore no surprise that some mental health specialists propose strategies for these problems that are reminiscent of treatments for PTSD, such as encouraging the clients to think back to the traumatic events that are believed to have triggered the problem and to view them in a context of safety and support and with the expectation that they can come to terms with the horrible things that happened to them. Indeed, in a critical review, Lev-Wiesel (2008) acknowledged that about 80% of adult childhood sexual abuse survivors diagnosed with PTSD actually suffer from dissociative disorders.

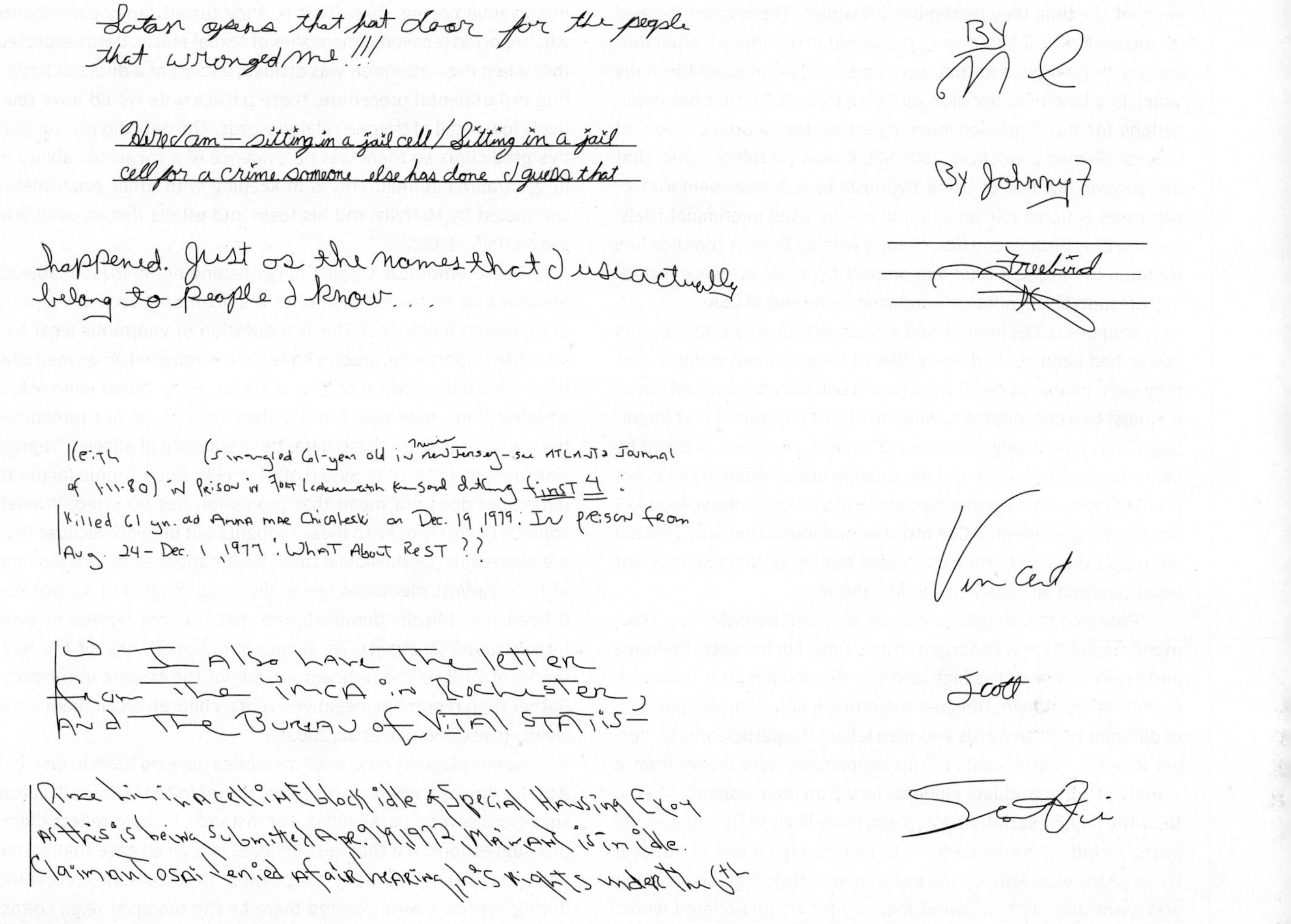

FIGURE 7.5 Handwriting samples from DID cases.

Source: Lewis et al., 1997, "Objective documentation of child abuse and dissociation on 12 murderers with dissociative identity disorder," *American Journal of Psychiatry,* 154, 1703–1710. Reprinted with permission from The American Journal of Psychiatry. © 2007 American Psychiatric Association.

Focus on Discovery 7.2

Repressed Memories of Childhood Sexual Abuse

"The movement to help survivors recall these allegedly repressed memories resulted in the worst catastrophe to befall the mental health field since the lobotomy era."

—Richard J. McNally, a leading authority on trauma and memory, in a guest editorial in the Canadian Journal of Psychiatry (2005a, p. 815)

Here we focus on the special instance of *recovered memories* of childhood sexual abuse (CSA). In these cases, the client had no memory of abuse until it was recovered, typically during psychotherapy. Few issues are more hotly debated in psychology and in the courts than whether these recovered memories are valid. Memory and some hypnosis researchers caution against a blanket acceptance of memories of sexual or physical abuse recovered during therapy (e.g., Laney & Loftus, 2005; Spanos, 1996). It is important to raise such questions; good science requires it, and the issue is key for court cases where recovered memories may play a major role in convicting a parent or other person of sexual abuse (Pope,

1995). However, from a feminist perspective, Connie Kristiansen at Carleton University and her associates (Kristiansen et al., 1999) outlined concerns about ideologies prevailing over scientific research and the possibility that women who have indeed been abused will remain silent because the validity of recovered memories in general has been called into question. And more recently, Brewin (2012) has suggested that the phenomenon of recovered memories is very much in keeping with what we know about how memory works. Specifically, he observed that events are better encoded and recalled when they relate to a sense of personal identity, but people with DID should have memory issues as a result of early trauma that causes identity disturbance. Brewin (2012) also noted that high levels of overwhelming emotion can undermine the encoding and recall of memory.

Recovered memories of CSA assumed great importance in a series of court cases (Earleywine & Gann, 1995). In a typical scenario, a woman accuses one or both of her parents of having abused her during childhood and brings charges against them. Courts in several U.S. states allow plaintiffs to sue for damages within three

(continued)

years of the time they remember the abuse. These cases depend on memories of CSA that were recovered in adulthood, often during psychotherapy, and that were apparently repressed for many years. In a landmark decision on February 1, 2007, that has implications for the repressed memory issue, the Supreme Court of Canada (*Regina v. Trochym*, 2007 SCC 6) in a 6-3 ruling stated that the 30-year practice of using hypnosis to enhance memories of witnesses is unreliable and should not be used in criminal trials. Canada thus became the first country with an English common law tradition to impose a total ban on post-hypnotic evidence including, presumably, hypnotically induced memories of CSA.

Williams (1995) interviewed women whose sexual abuse years earlier had been verified. Fully 38% of these women claimed that they were unable to recall the abuse when they were asked about it almost two decades later. Williams (1995) concluded that forgetting CSA is a relatively common occurrence. However, as noted by Laney and Loftus (2005), not mentioning abuse when asked is not proof of repression. Further, Goodman et al. (2003) interviewed 175 adults with documented CSA histories and found that only 19% did *not* report the abuse. They concluded that forgetting CSA may not be as common an experience as first thought.

Research has sought to explain why and describe how traumatic memories may be forgotten over time. For instance, DePrince and Freyd (2004) tested high and low dissociators in a "directed-forgetting" paradigm. Directed forgetting involves presenting lists of different types of words and then telling the participants to "forget about it." Participants in this experiment were drawn from a sample of undergraduate students based on their responses to the DES. The high dissociation group was more likely to have traumatic pasts, including events deemed to involve high levels of betrayal by someone else. Also, on the experimental task, high dissociation was associated with impaired memory for trauma-related words (e.g., "incest"). The data are in keeping with the notion that dissociation is linked with the forgetting of traumatic information from one's past, and this has significant implications for the recovered memory debate.

However, a subsequent experiment by McNally, Ristuccia, and Perlman (2005) that compared adults who reported continuous memories or recovered memories of CSA and those who had never been abused yielded data seemingly inconsistent with the DePrince and Freyd (2004) findings. Specifically, McNally et al. (2005) found that all groups of participants had enhanced memory for trauma words (as opposed to neutral words), including those without CSA. The main purpose was to try to find evidence of a dissociative coping style. That is, they tested those participants who reported recovered memories of sexual abuse. It was expected that when their attention was divided, as part of a directed forgetting experimental procedure, these participants would have relatively low recall of trauma-related words. The data did not support this prediction, so there was no evidence of a conscious ability to forget trauma stimuli. This is in keeping with other experiments conducted by McNally and his team and others (for an overview, see McNally, 2005b).

These empirical studies notwithstanding, is it justifiable to assume that recovered memories are *invariably* accurate reports of repressed memories? This is a question of enormous legal and scientific importance. Studies have been conducted on women who have reported a history of sexual abuse. The women were asked whether there ever was a time when they could not remember the abuse. Based on these data, the frequency of alleged "repression" ranges from 18 to 59% (Loftus, 1993). But a simple failure to remember does not mean that repression has occurred. Women could actively try to keep these thoughts out of mind because they are distressing. Or the abuse could have happened before the time of their earliest memories (generally around age 3 or 4). Nor has it been scientifically demonstrated that children repress or even forget traumatic events. As already mentioned, one of the hallmarks of PTSD is the frequent reliving of the trauma in memory. Rather than repressing negative events, children recall them quite vividly (see Goodman et al., 2003).

Some allegedly recovered memories have no basis in fact, but if that is the case, where do they come from? In 1993 Elizabeth Loftus suggested several possibilities. For instance, it could reflect therapist suggestions. If a therapist believes in a given case that sexual abuse has been repressed, it is possible that memories recovered during hypnosis were planted there by the therapist (e.g., Loftus, 1997). Also, cognitive psychologists have shown that it is possible for people to construct recollections of events that did not happen.

There is little doubt that CSA exists. But we must be wary of uncritical acceptance of reports of abuse. Social scientists, lawyers, and the courts share a heavy responsibility in deciding whether a given recovered memory is a reflection of an actual (and criminal) event. Erring in either direction creates an injustice. Prout and Dobson (1998) suggested that the best approach is a "middle ground perspective," one that recognizes that while child abuse claims can be quite legitimate, there is also the possibility that certain clinicians have facilitated false reports, and each case should be evaluated individually without preconceptions.

Psychoanalysis had its beginnings in hypnosis. Through the years, practitioners have continued to use hypnosis with clients diagnosed with dissociative disorders as a means of helping them gain access to hidden portions of their personality—to a lost identity or to a set of events precipitating or flowing from a trauma.

Clients are unusually hypnotizable, and it is believed that they cope with stress by using their hypnotizability (unconsciously) to enter a dissociative, trancelike state (Butler et al., 1996). For these reasons, hypnosis is used commonly in treatment. The general idea is that the recovery of repressed painful memories will be facilitated by recreating the state entered into during the original abuse, a hypothesis consistent with classic research on state-dependent learning (e.g., Eich, 1995). Typically, the person is hypnotized (sometimes with the aid of drugs such as sodium amytal) and encouraged to go back in his or her mind to events in childhood—a technique called age regression. The hope is that accessing these traumatic memories will allow the adult to realize that the dangers from childhood are not now present and that his or her current life need not be governed by these ghosts from the past (Loewenstein, 1991).

The usual primary goal in therapy for DID is integration of the several personalities. Practitioners attempt to convince the person that forgetting or splitting into different personalities is no longer necessary to deal with traumas, either those in the past that triggered the original dissociation or those in the present or yet to be confronted in the future. In addition, assuming that DID and the other dissociative disorders are in some measure an escape response to high levels of stress, treatment can be enhanced by teaching the client to cope better with present-day challenges.

Because of the rarity of DID, there are no controlled outcome studies and researchers continue to call for rigorous and tightly controlled clinical trials (see Lynn et al., 2015). It was the case for several years that nearly all the well-reported outcome data came from the clinical observations of one highly experienced therapist, Richard Kluft (e.g., 2001). Over a 10-year period, Kluft had contact with 123 cases. Of these, 68% apparently achieved integration of their alters that was stable for at least three months (33 remained stable for almost two and a half years). The greater the number of personalities, the longer the treatment lasted; in general, therapy took almost two years and upwards of 500 hours per client. In a follow-up, Kluft reported that 84% of the original 123 clients had achieved stable integration of their multiple personalities and another 10% were at least functioning better (Kluft, 1994). Sometimes complete integration of personalities cannot be achieved, and the most realistic outcome is some manner of "conflict-free collaboration" among the person's various personalities (Kluft, 1988, p. 578). A long-term study of DID clients from Canada and the United States who received this treatment revealed that they showed significant improvements on a number of indicators, including dissociative symptoms and symptoms of borderline personality disorder (Ellason & Ross, 1997). This study suggests that DID clients may respond well to treatment, with the caveat that the results must be interpreted with caution owing to the lack of control groups for comparison purposes.

At a meeting in Vancouver in 1994, the Executive Council of the International Society for the Study of Dissociation (ISSD; now the International Society for the Study of Trauma and Dissociation) formulated a series of agreed-upon treatment guidelines (ISSD, 2004). A Guidelines Revision Task Force developed new guidelines in 2005 (see Chu, 2006). They recommended a three-phase or stage-oriented treatment approach that focuses on (1) safety, stabilization, and symptom reduction; (2) working directly and in depth with traumatic memories; and (3) identity integration and rehabilitation. Separate guidelines for children were published in 2004 (ISSD, 2004). The third revision of the guidelines for adults was released seven years later and is still in place (ISSD, 2011). This document provides a good overview of existing knowledge and Brown (2011) concluded that it provides an even-handed overview of evidence on the validity of DID. DID is conceptualized as a failure of normal developmental integration that is primarily due to early traumatic experiences. The most recent guidelines continue to support the three-phase approach to treatment. The treatment guidelines also stipulate that therapists should take a respectful neutral stance regarding clients' recalled memories.

While there are few recent studies of actual treatment for DID, a large collaborative study conducted by researchers in the United States and Canada has provided a wealth of useful treatment and outcome data. This study is based on self-reports from 280 clients and their therapists who are described as "community clinicians" (see Brand et al., 2009, 2012). Longitudinal research has followed 119 of the 226 clients for 30 months (Brand et al., 2013). Collectively, the findings indicate that most therapists surveyed follow the three-stage process but treatment in the final phase is more individualized. It also is apparent from these studies that people with dissociative disorders can have severe and long-lasting problems (with an average of 8.1 prior hospitalizations) but very significant improvements are typically achieved over time; this was found with self-reports and clinician ratings, which indicated less self-injury and fewer hospitalizations as treatment progresses. However, Brand and her colleagues cautioned that even with improvement, long-term intervention is required because clients are not "cured" after 30 months; that is, even though levels of functioning improved significantly and symptoms became less prominent, the improved participants still had clinically elevated levels of dissociation and associated adjustment problems.

Summary

7.1 There are some physical problems that are actually better seen as psychological problems. Specific somatoform disorders fall under the somatic symptoms disorder according to changes in *DSM-5*. Changes in diagnostic criteria now reflected in the description of somatic symptom disorder have affected how many people warrant a diagnosis and the levels of dysfunction and impairment associated with these disorders. In some versions of the disorder, there are physical symptoms for which no biological basis can be found. The sensory and motor dysfunctions of conversion disorder suggest neurological impairments, but ones that do not always make anatomical sense. Somatic symptom disorders lead to frequent visits to physicians, hospitalization, and even unnecessary surgery.

7.2 Someone with conversion disorder is experiencing sensory or motor symptoms such as seeming to partially or fully lose their vision or becoming paralyzed but no physiological problems can be identified. The term "conversion" is traced back to Freud and his notions that unacceptable impulses get expressed in an anxiety that is redirected and aimed at sensory-motor systems and mechanisms.

7.3 Psychoanalytic theory proposes that in conversion disorder, repressed impulses are converted into physical symptoms. Behavioural theories focus on the conscious and deliberate adoption of the symptoms as a means of obtaining a desired goal. Numerous cognitive, social, and cultural factors are also prevalent in people with conversion disorders. A biopsychosocial model of conversion disorder integrates empirical findings and different causal models.

7.4 An inability to recall important personal information, usually after some traumatic experience, is diagnosed as dissociative amnesia. In dissociative fugue, a specific form of dissociative amnesia, the person moves away, assumes a new identity, and is amnesic for his or her previous life. In depersonalization/derealization disorder, the person's perception of the self is altered; he or she may experience being outside the body or changes in the size of body parts. The person with dissociative identity disorder has two or more distinct and fully developed personalities, each with unique memories, behaviour patterns, and relationships.

7.5 Clinicians typically focus their treatment efforts for dissociative identity disorder on understanding the anxiety associated with

the forgotten memories, since it is viewed as etiologically significant. Specific theories of the origins of dissociative identity disorder implicate either early exposure during childhood to physical or sexual abuse or the enactment of a learned social role without necessarily suggesting that DID is not real. The usual primary goal in therapy for dissociative identity disorder is integration of the several personalities.

Key Terms

anaesthesias
conversion disorder
depersonalization/derealization disorder
derealization
dissociative amnesia
dissociative disorders

dissociative fugue
dissociative identity disorder (DID)
factitious disorder
hypochondriasis
hysteria
illness anxiety disorder

la belle indifférence
malingering
pain disorder
somatic symptom disorders
somatization disorder

Reflections: Past, Present, and Future

1. In Chapter 2, we pointed out that in some cultures, such as the Chinese, people tend to describe psychological problems as somatic or physical illnesses, perhaps in part because they can feel less shame if they have a physical illness rather than a psychological disorder. Do you think that their belief system increases the likelihood that diagnosable somatic disorders will be more prevalent in people from these cultures?

2. The somatic symptom disorders are typically more prevalent in women than in men. Do you think that the prevalence of somatoform disorders in Chinese males will be as high as or higher than the prevalence of these disorders in Chinese women?

3. Conversion disorder is often comorbid with other disorders. Assume that you are a psychologist who is conducting CBT with a client who has a conversion disorder as well as depression and a personality disorder such as a dependent personality disorder (i.e., someone who needs to always be with others to compensate for a weak sense of self). How would this information influence your case conceptualization and the development of your treatment plan?

4. What are your thoughts on Nick Spanos's socio-cognitive perspective on DID? Do you think that he is right in the following claim?

   "Expectations transmitted to clients, and the selective reinforcement of increasingly dramatic displays in MPD [multiple personality disorder] clients, frequently translate into an increase in the number of alters and an increase in the extent of abuse 'remembered' by those alters" (Spanos, 1996, p. 233).

5. Do you believe that some cases of DID are therapist produced? Why or why not?

6. Should DID be allowed as an excusing condition for a criminal act? In the United States, Billy Milligan, a 23-year-old drifter, was acquitted of rape as a result of being diagnosed with multiple personality disorder. Psychologists believed that Billy had 10 personalities (eight male and two female). His 19-year-old lesbian personality, Adelena, was held responsible for committing the rapes. We will return to this issue in Chapter 18. In the meantime, reflect on whether or not DID should be allowed as a defence against criminal charges in Canada.

Mood Disorders and Suicide

LEARNING OBJECTIVES

1. Describe the general characteristics of mood disorders.

2. Explain psychological theories of mood disorders.

3. Explain biological theories of mood disorders.

4. Compare and contrast the components and effectiveness of therapies for mood disorders.

5. Describe various perspectives on suicide, suicide prevention efforts, and related ethical issues.

Billy, a Student with Major Depressive Disorder

BILLY is a 20-year-old white male ". . . . presenting for counselling with depressive symptoms, feelings of being 'overwhelmed' with anxiety about school performance and value conflicts pertaining to his choice of major. Billy is a first-generation college student who was awarded a teaching fellowship to attend the university in recognition of his achievements as a high school student and his interest in becoming a teacher in the rural community in which he was reared" (Mobley, 2008, p. 87).

Billy was referred for counselling by his family physician, who diagnosed him provisionally with major depressive disorder. His main symptoms were depressed mood and low self-esteem but no suicide ideation. Billy completed the most well-known self-report measure of depression, the Beck Depression Inventory—II (BDI-II;

Beck, Steer, & Brown, 1996). The BDI-II consists of 21 sets of statements representing symptoms of depression and the respondent indicates which statements apply to them. Billy received a BDI-II score of 35, which exceeds the cut-off point for severe depression, and his counsellor confirmed that he met diagnostic criteria for major depressive disorder. His symptoms included depressed mood, significant weight gain, sleep disturbance, loss of energy, inappropriate guilt, and a diminished ability to concentrate.

We will return to Billy in other segments of this chapter. The good news is that as a result of the counsellor using a wide range of techniques (cognitive-behavioural therapy, Adlerian lifestyle assessment, and the Gestalt empty chair technique) across 20 sessions, Billy was no longer depressed, as reflected by his final BDI-II score of 5.

Chapter 8 examines mood disorders. Billy experienced many symptoms of major depressive disorder. We begin with a further description of depression followed by bipolar disorder and chronic mood disorders. We then present research on biological and psychological factors relevant to these disorders and discuss their treatment. In the final section we examine suicide.

problems, such as panic attacks, substance abuse, sexual dysfunction, and personality disorders. The presence of other disorders can increase severity and result in poorer prognosis (Government of Canada, 2006). Throughout history, while they may not have been formally diagnosed, many famous artists, composers, and writers, such as Paul Gauguin (see painting) and Pyotr Tchaikovsky (see photo), probably had a mood disorder.

8.1 | General Characteristics of Mood Disorders

Mood disorders involve disabling disturbances in emotion, from the sadness of depression to the elation and irritability of mania. Mood disorders are often associated with other psychological

Depression: Signs and Symptoms

Depression was illustrated by the case of Billy. **Depression** is an emotional state marked by great sadness and feelings of worthlessness and guilt. Additional symptoms may include withdrawal from others and loss of interest and pleasure in usual activities, including a loss of sexual desire. Sleep and appetite may be

Washington DC/SUPERSTOCK

Self-portrait by Paul Gauguin. He is but one of the many artists and writers who apparently suffered from a mood disorder. Self Portrait in Caricature by Paul Gauguin/National Gallery of Art.

Archive/Photo Researchers, Inc.

Mood disorders are common among artists and writers. Van Gogh, Tchaikovsky (shown here), and Whitman were all affected.

affected in either direction: some people with depression sleep more than usual, others less. Similarly, appetite may increase or decrease, possibly leading to weight gain or weight loss. Most of us experience occasional sadness, although perhaps not to a degree or with a frequency that warrants the diagnosis of depression.

Paying attention is exhausting for depressed people. They cannot take in what they read and what other people say to them. Conversation is also a chore; depressed individuals may speak slowly, after long pauses, using few words and a low, monotonous voice. Many prefer to sit alone and remain silent. Others are agitated and cannot sit still. They pace, wring their hands, continually sigh and moan, or complain. When depressed individuals are confronted with a problem, no ideas for its solution occur to them. Every moment has a great heaviness, and their heads fill and reverberate with self-recriminations. Depressed people may neglect personal hygiene and appearance and make numerous complaints of somatic symptoms with no apparent physical basis. Utterly dejected and completely without hope and initiative, they may be apprehensive, anxious, and despondent much of the time.

The symptoms and signs of depression vary somewhat across the lifespan. Depression in children often results in somatic complaints, such as headaches or stomachaches. In older adults, depression is often characterized by distractibility and complaints of memory loss. Symptoms of depression exhibit some cross-cultural variation, probably resulting from differences in cultural standards of acceptable behaviour. For example, depression is substantially less prevalent in China than in North America, due in part to cultural mores that make it less appropriate for Chinese people to display emotional symptoms (Parker, Gladstone, & Chee, 2001). Although it is commonly believed that people from non-Western cultures emphasize somatic symptoms of depression, while people from Western cultures emphasize emotional symptoms, studies by Montreal researcher Lawrence Kirmayer suggest that people from various cultures, including Canadians, tend to emphasize somatic symptoms rather than the emotional symptoms, especially when being evaluated in a medical setting (see Kirmayer, 2001). Overall, only 15% of depressed primary care patients in Canada are what Kirmayer refers to as **psychologizers** (people who emphasize the psychological aspects of depression).

Fortunately, most depression, although recurrent, tends to dissipate with time. But an average untreated episode may stretch for months or longer. In cases where depression becomes chronic, the person does not completely "snap back" to an earlier level of functioning between bouts.

Mania: Signs and Symptoms

Mania is an emotional state or mood of intense but unfounded elation accompanied by irritability, hyperactivity, talkativeness, flight of ideas, distractibility, and impractical, grandiose plans. Some people who experience episodic periods of depression may at times suddenly become manic. Although there are clinical reports of individuals who experience mania but not depression, this condition is quite rare.

Mania at the Post Office: A Case Excerpt

MR. W., a 32-year-old postal worker, had been married for eight years. In retrospect, there appeared to be no warning of what was to happen. One morning, Mr. W. told his wife that he was bursting with energy and ideas, that his job as a mail carrier was unfulfilling, and that he was just wasting his talent. That night he slept little, spending most of the time at a desk, writing furiously. The next morning, he left for work at the usual time but returned home at 11:00 a.m., his car filled to overflowing with aquariums and other equipment for tropical fish. He had quit his job, then withdrawn all the money from the family's savings account and spent it on tropical fish equipment. Mr. W. reported that the previous night he had worked out a way to modify existing equipment so that fish "won't die anymore. We'll be millionaires." After unloading the paraphernalia, Mr. W. set off to canvass the neighbourhood for possible buyers, going door-to-door and talking to anyone who would listen.

The following bit of conversation from the period after Mr. W. entered treatment indicates his incorrigible optimism and provocativeness:

Therapist. Well, you seem pretty happy today.

Client. Happy! Happy! You certainly are a master of understatement, you rogue! *[Shouting, literally jumping out of his seat.]* Why I'm ecstatic. I'm leaving for the West Coast today, on my daughter's bicycle. Only 3,100 miles. That's nothing, you know. I could probably walk, but I want to get there by next week. And along the way I plan to contact a lot of people about investing in my fish equipment. I'll get to know more people that way—you know, Doc, "know" in the biblical sense *[leering at the therapist seductively.]* Oh, God, how good it feels. It's almost like a nonstop orgasm.

The person in the throes of a manic episode, which may last from several days to several months, is readily recognized by his or her loud and incessant stream of remarks, sometimes full of puns, jokes, rhyming, and interjections about objects and happenings that have attracted the speaker's attention. This speech is difficult to interrupt and reveals the manic person's flight of ideas. Although small bits of talk are coherent, the individual shifts rapidly from topic to topic. The need for activity may cause him or her to be annoyingly sociable and intrusive, constantly and sometimes purposelessly busy, and, unfortunately, oblivious to the obvious pitfalls of his or her endeavours. Any attempt to curb this momentum can bring quick anger and even rage. Mania usually comes on suddenly over a period of a day or two. The following description of a case of mania is from our files. The irritability that is often part of this state was not evident in this person.

Formal Diagnostic Listings of Mood Disorders

Two major mood disorders are listed in *DSM-5:* major depressive disorder, referred to earlier as unipolar depression, and bipolar disorder. As mentioned in Chapter 3, other depressive disorders added to the *DSM-5* include disruptive mood dysregulation disorder and premenstrual dysphoric disorder. Here will we focus on major depressive disorder and bipolar disorder. The dropping of the bereavement exclusion in depression was also discussed in Chapter 3. Another change in *DSM-5* is that the manual now has separate chapters for depressive disorders and bipolar and related disorders. It is mentioned specifically in the *DSM-5* that the chapter on bipolar and related disorders is located between the chapter on schizophrenia spectrum disorders and the depressive disorders chapter to connote the bipolar disorder's "place as a bridge between the two diagnostic classes in terms of symptomatology, family history, and genetics" (APA, 2013, p. 123).

Diagnosis of Depression   The formal *DSM-5* diagnosis of a **major depressive disorder (MDD)** requires the presence of five of the following symptoms for at least two weeks. Either depressed mood or loss of interest and pleasure must be one of the five symptoms:

- sad, depressed mood, most of the day, nearly every day
- loss of interest and pleasure in all, or almost all, activities
- difficulties in sleeping (insomnia); not falling asleep initially, not returning to sleep after awakening in the middle of the night, and early morning awakenings; or, in some individuals, a desire to sleep a great deal of the time
- shift in activity level, becoming either lethargic (psychomotor retardation) or agitated. This is known as psychomotor agitation or retardation
- poor appetite and weight loss, or increased appetite and weight gain
- loss of energy, great fatigue nearly every day
- negative self-concept, self-reproach and self-blame, feelings of worthlessness, and guilt
- complaints or evidence of difficulty in concentrating, such as slowed thinking and indecisiveness
- recurrent thoughts of death or suicide

While the presence or absence of MDD still involves a categorical decision, *DSM-5* incorporates dimensional ratings of the severity, frequency, and duration of the symptoms. This information is believed to be useful for both clinical and research purposes (for a discussion, see Dhingra et al., 2011).

There is no question that these are the major symptoms of depression. What is controversial, though, is whether a person with five symptoms and a two-week duration is distinctly different from one who has only three symptoms for 10 days. In an evaluation of this issue with a sample of twins, the number of symptoms and the duration of depression were used to

Fred Lum/The Globe and Mail/The Canadian Press

Canadian singer and Juno Award winner Serena Ryder described her bouts of depression in a 2012 *Chatelaine* article. Ryder had to terminate her tour when depression was combined with panic attacks. She describes eventually hitting "rock bottom" in terms of the severity of her depression. Ryder attributes much of her depression to an identity crisis and credits her recovery to combined therapy (drug treatment and psychotherapy) as well as meeting the love of her life. She also refers to music as a form of medicine. In 2016, Ryder became a spokesperson for Bell Canada's Let's Talk campaign to end the stigma surrounding mental health.

predict the likelihood of future episodes and the probability that a co-twin would also be diagnosed as depressed. Even with fewer than five symptoms and a duration of less than two weeks, co-twins were also likely to be diagnosed with depression and were likely to have recurrences (Kendler & Gardner, 1998).

Other research suggests that depression exists on a continuum of severity (Flett, Vredenburg, & Krames, 1997). The *DSM* diagnostic criteria identify people at a relatively severe end of the continuum. Whether depression is best seen as being on a continuum or as a discrete diagnostic category is far from resolved. One study with children and adolescents concluded unequivocally that depression is continuous (Hankin, Fraley, Lakey, & Waldman, 2005), while another conducted with adults found some evidence that depression reflects a taxononic, categorical structure (Solomon, Ruscio, Seeley, & Lewinsohn, 2006).

MDD is very prevalent. Lifetime prevalence rates ranged from 5.2% to 17.1% in three large-scale American studies (Kessler et al., 1994; Kessler et al., 2005; Weissman et al., 1996). This large discrepancy possibly reflects differences between studies in diagnostic criteria used, in the amount of training of the interviewers, and in the use of interviews for collecting symptom information. The 12-month prevalence of MDD in the National Comorbidity Survey—Replication (NCS-R) study (Kessler et al., 2005) was 6.7%. In Canada, using CCHS 2012 data, the lifetime prevalence of MDD was 11.3%. In a 2008 review, Scott Patten, a preeminent Canadian epidemiologist, concluded that

as defined by *DSM-IV* criteria, the lifetime prevalence of major depression exceeds 20% and may be as high as 50%. Noting the broad spectrum of severity, he concluded that, "In community populations, fulfillment of *DSM-IV* criteria for MD is probably not an effective proxy for treatment need" (Patten, 2008, p. 411). In other words, not all of these individuals necessarily require intensive treatment! Patten et al. (2015) examined the CCHS 2012 data and found that 3.9% met criteria for MDD in the past year. Of those with past-year MDD, close to two-thirds had sought some form of treatment, and about one-third were taking antidepressant medication. Prevalence was higher in women and in younger age groups. The high prevalence of depression in the general population carries through to celebrities, some of whom have gone public with their illness, such as Canadian singers Serena Ryder (see photo) and Nelly Furtado (see photo).

MDD is about two times more common in women than in men (e.g., Kessler et al., 2005; Offord et al., 1996), a gender difference found in numerous countries and in a majority of ethnic groups (Seedat et al., 2009). Clues to the etiology of depression may come from understanding the cause and timing of this gender difference. Focus on Discovery 8.1 explores some possible reasons for this gender difference.

DSM-5 also includes a diagnostic category of **persistent depressive disorder** (combining chronic depression and the condition formerly known as dysthymia) and there is a substantial research literature on people with chronic depression. A large Australian study by Murphy and Byrne (2012) found that the lifetime prevalence of chronic depression lasting at least two years was 4.6% (about 1 in 20 people). Predictors of a chronic depressive disorder included comorbid diagnoses, a younger age of onset, and not surprisingly, a history of more frequent episodes of depression. Walker and Druss (2015) examined predictors of persistent depressive disorder using American data. They found the following predictors: being female, never married, two or more medical conditions, limits on activity, and reduced contact with family. They advocated for comprehensive approaches to treatment, which include physical health, social support, and mental health. Köhler et al. (2015) compared treatment response among in-patients with chronic depression and those with episodic depression. Although they found similar rates of symptom reduction in both groups, those with chronic depression had higher symptom rates, reduced remission rates, and a longer duration of treatment. Again, there appears to be a different level of need for this subgroup of patients. Future research is recommended to identify this particular subgroup at the outset (Gunn et al., 2013).

The World Health Organization (WHO, 2004) identified major depression as one of the leading causes of "disability-adjusted life years." MDD is currently the second-leading cause of disability worldwide and it is expected to rank first in disease burden in high-income countries by the year 2030 (see Cuijpers et al., 2008). Kessler et al. (2006) assessed the effects of mood disorders on work performance. Although MDD was associated with 27.2 lost workdays per ill worker per year, bipolar disorder was associated with 65.5 lost workdays. They attributed the difference to more severe and persistent depressive episodes in workers with bipolar disorder.

Focus on Discovery 8.1

Depression in Females vs. Males: Why is there a Gender Difference?

"She sat by the window, looking inward rather than looking out. Her thoughts were consumed with her sadness. She viewed her life as a broken one, and yet she could not place her finger on the exact moment it fell apart. 'How did I get to feel this way?' she repeatedly asked herself. By asking, she hoped to transcend her depressed state; through understanding, she hoped to repair it. Instead her questions led her deeper and deeper inside herself—further away from the path that would lead to her recovery."

—*Reported by Treynor, Gonzalez, and Nolen-Hoeksema, 2003, p. 247*

A European study confirmed that the gender difference in depression was found in all 23 countries that were assessed (Van de Velde, Bracke, & Levecque, 2010). The authors concluded that "One of the most consistent findings in the social epidemiology of mental health is the gender gap in depression" (p. 305). But why does major depression generally occur about twice as often in women as in men? Nolen-Hoeksema and Girgus (1994) traced the sex difference back to adolescence and concluded that girls are more likely than boys to have certain risk factors for depression even before adolescence, but it is only when these risk factors interact with the challenges of adolescence that the gender differences in depression emerge.

Several explanations have been offered. The one referred to above is the notion that females are more likely than males to engage in **ruminative coping**, while males are more likely to engage in distracting activities such as watching a hockey game (Nolen-Hoeksema, Larson, & Grayson, 1999). Ruminators focus their attention on their depressive symptoms (e.g., saying things to themselves such as "Why do I feel this way?"). Subsequently, Treynor et al. (2003) refined this theory by differentiating between a more adaptive form of reflective pondering vs. a maladaptive rumination component referred to as **brooding** (or moody pondering). They concluded that the relationship between gender and depression could be due to the brooding component (e.g., "What am I doing to deserve this?"). Also, an interpersonal form of rumination called co-rumination, in which friends, typically female friends, discuss and brood over each other's problems as part of their friendship, has been linked with depression in adolescent girls but, on a positive note, it also fosters stronger friendships (Starr & Davila, 2009). More recent longitudinal research shows that co-rumination predicts the developmental onset, severity, and duration of depression, even after controlling for ruminative brooding (Stone, Hankin, Gibb, & Abela, 2011).

Feminist scholar Dana Jack (1999) suggested that females are more likely than males to engage in *silencing the self*—a passive style of keeping upsets and concerns to oneself in order to maintain important relationships (akin to "suffering in silence"). A definitive longitudinal test of the hypothesis remains to be conducted. Another explanation is *objectification theory* (McKinley & Hyde, 1996), based on the premise that the tendency to be viewed as an object, scrutinized and appraised by others, including appraisals of physical appearance, has a greater negative influence on the self-esteem of girls than boys. Indeed, adolescent girls, relative to boys, have higher reported levels of objectification, shame, and depression (Grabe, Hyde, & Lindberg, 2007).

Janet Stoppard from the University of New Brunswick (2000) argues that depression must be interpreted within the broad socio-cultural context and the societal conditions that influence the everyday lives of women, including stressors more germane to women and feelings of disempowerment. A Toronto study found that 52% of women receiving in-patient treatment for depression had been sexually victimized in childhood and adulthood (Sahay, Piran, & Maddocks, 2000). Other evidence for the link between childhood sexual abuse and various forms of psychopathology, including depression, was reviewed in Chapter 4.

Another possibility advanced by Hammen (1991) is that girls and women are more likely than boys and men to take a more active role in generating stress for themselves. The link between stress generation and depression is considered in Focus on Discovery 8.2. However, in terms of general life stressors, a comprehensive study failed to find a gender difference and found that the number of stressful events predicted first onsets of depression for males and females (Slopen, Williams, Fitzmaurice, & Gilman, 2011).

Finally, what about the possible role of biological differences between women and men? Evidence in support of the theory that women's vulnerability to depression is related to their hormones, specifically estrogen and progesterone, is mixed (Nolen-Hoeksema, 2002). Nonetheless, it is probable that gender differences in depression are due to multiple, interacting factors and can best be understood from a complex biopsychosocial perspective.

Canadian singer Nelly Furtado has acknowledged dealing with depression following her rapid rise to fame.

Diagnosis of Bipolar Disorder

DSM-5 defines **bipolar I disorder** as involving episodes of mania or mixed episodes that include symptoms of both mania and depression. Most people with bipolar I disorder also experience episodes of depression.

A formal diagnosis of a manic episode requires the presence of elevated or irritable mood and abnormally and persistently increased goal-directed activity or energy plus three additional symptoms (four if the mood is irritable). The inclusion of the increased activity criterion is new to *DSM-5*. Some clinicians do not regard euphoria as a core symptom and report that irritable mood and even depressive features are more common (Goodwin & Jamison, 1990). The symptoms must be sufficiently severe to impair social and occupational functioning:

- increase in goal-directed activity
- more talkative than usual or pressure to keep talking
- flight of ideas or subjective impression that thoughts are racing
- less than the usual amount of sleep needed
- inflated self-esteem; belief that one has special talents, powers, and abilities
- distractibility; attention easily diverted
- excessive involvement in pleasurable activities that are likely to have undesirable consequences, such as reckless spending

Bipolar disorder occurs less often than MDD, with a lifetime prevalence rate for both bipolar I and II of about 4.4% of the population in the NCS-R (Kessler et al., 2005). The average age of onset is in the 20s, and it occurs equally often in men and women. Among women, episodes of depression are more common and episodes of mania less common than among men (Leibenluft, 1996). More than 50% of bipolar disorder cases experience a recurrence within 12 months (Yatham et al., 2009). The severity of the disorder is indicated by the fact that at 12 months after release from hospital, 76% of clients are rated as impaired and 52% are sufficiently symptomatic that the original diagnosis is still applicable (Keck et al., 1998). Violent behaviours (e.g., child or spousal abuse) can occur during severe manic episodes (Government of Canada, 2006). People with bipolar disorder often lose insight into their condition and this can result in treatment resistance, financial and legal difficulties, substance abuse, and marital and occupational failure (Government of Canada, 2006). Anxiety comorbidity is prevalent among bipolar individuals and has a great impact on quality of life (Kauer-Sant' Anna et al., 2007). Comorbidity with personality disorders also predicts a poor outcome (Bieling, Green, & Macqueen, 2007).

Heterogeneity within the Categories

A problem in the classification of mood disorders is their great heterogeneity; i.e., people with the same diagnosis can vary greatly from one another. Some people with bipolar disorder, for example, almost every day experience the full range of symptoms of both mania and depression, termed a *mixed episode*. Others have symptoms of only mania or only depression during a clinical episode. **Bipolar II disorder** individuals have episodes of major depression accompanied by **hypomania** (*hypo* comes from the Greek for "under"), a change in behaviour and mood that is less extreme than full-blown mania. This is the kind of bipolar disorder experienced by actress Catherine Zeta-Jones (see photo).

Some people with depression may be diagnosed as having psychotic features if they are subject to delusions and

Academy Award-winning actress Catherine Zeta-Jones publicly acknowledged having bipolar disorder Type II (i.e., with slightly milder symptoms) in 2011 after her husband, Michael Douglas, inadvertently revealed his wife's depression during an interview with Oprah Winfrey.

hallucinations. The presence of delusions appears to be a useful distinction among people with major depression (Johnson, Horvath, & Weissman, 1991); depressed people with delusions do not generally respond well to the usual drug therapies for depression, but they do respond favourably to these drugs when they are combined with the drugs commonly used to treat other psychotic disorders, such as schizophrenia. Furthermore, depression with psychotic features is more severe than depression without delusions and involves more social impairment and less time between episodes (Coryell et al., 1996).

Some people with depression may have melancholic features. The term *"melancholic"* refers to a specific pattern of depressive symptoms. People with melancholic features find no pleasure in any activity (anhedonia) and are unable to feel better even temporarily when something good happens. Their depressed mood is worse in the morning. They awaken about two hours too early, lose appetite and weight, and are either lethargic or extremely agitated.

Both manic and depressive episodes may also occur during pregnancy or within four weeks of childbirth; in this case, they are noted to have a peripartum onset, more commonly known as postpartum depression, but the term "peripartum depression" reflects the reality that about half of depressive episodes actually start in pregnancy, rather than after childbirth. Postpartum, perinatal, and prenatal depression research in Canada is summarized in Canadian Perspectives 8.1.

Canadian Perspectives 8.1

Postpartum, Perinatal, and Prenatal Depression in Canadian Women

"The notion that pregnancy is a time of uninterrupted joy, happiness, and contentment has been challenged by evidence-based research showing that, to the contrary, many women are distressed by depressive disorders in pregnancy."

—*Shaila Misri, University of British Columbia, on the burden of perinatal depression, 2007, p. 477*

Many people find it difficult to understand the phenomenon of **postpartum depression (PD)**. New mothers often complain of temporary "baby blues," but how is it possible that some mothers experience profound depression even though they may be delighted by their new arrival? Even more difficult to understand are extreme cases such as that of Suzanne Killinger-Johnson, a physician and psychotherapist who apparently suffered from PD. In 2000, tragically, she took her own life and that of her infant son at a Toronto subway station.

Extensive research on postpartum depression is being conducted by Cindy Lee Dennis at the University of Toronto and her colleagues. One study used data from the Maternity Experiences Survey of the Canada Perinatal Surveillance System. Computer-assisted telephone interviews were conducted with 6,421 women who were 5 to 14 months postpartum (Dennis, Heaman, & Vigod, 2012). Depression was deemed to be present if a woman had a score of 14 or higher on the best self-report measure in this area, the Edinburgh Postnatal Depression Scale. It was found that 12% of the participants were depressed. Unique predictors of depression included a previous history of depression, low household income, low social support during the postpartum period, stressful life events, experiencing interpersonal violence, and poor self-perceived maternal health. Also using the Edinburgh Postnatal Depression Scale, but with a cut-off of 13, place of residence in Canada was examined as a risk factor (Vigod et al., 2013). Mothers in urban settings were found to have greater levels of PD compared with those in rural, semi-rural, or semi-urban settings (Vigod et al., 2013). Efforts aimed to increase social support in urban settings may be beneficial. Further, newcomer mothers, relative to Canadian-born mothers, also tend to have an increased risk for PD and report receiving less prenatal care and social support (Stewart et al., 2008). Finally, research continues to highlight the role of exposure to violence and interpersonal trauma in PD (Dennis & Vigod, 2013).

Research is also systematically examining ways to reduce PD. One study found that telephone-based peer support decreased levels of PD (Dennis, 2003). However, a more recent randomized controlled trial (RCT) investigation by Dennis and her colleagues involving the delivery of peer support yielded very surprising results; the intervention seemed to backfire in that the mothers in the control group actually ended up having better adjustment than did the mothers who received coaching on mother–child interactions from women who had recovered from postpartum depression (Letourneau et al., 2011). Perhaps the women with postpartum depression could not help engaging in upward social comparisons with the more highly functioning women who were delivering what was supposed to be a supportive intervention; instead, they may

have been reminders to currently depressed women of a more ideal level of functioning. The researchers concluded that interventions are best delivered by trained nurses.

Given the link between stressors and PD, how a woman copes with motherhood is important. Pregnant mothers in Quebec with high levels of stress during the 1998 ice storm delivered children with lower cognitive ability when assessed at the age of two (Laplante et al., 2004). Higher prenatal stress in the mother-to-be predicted poorer cognitive ability in the "ice storm" babies—children exposed to high stress, relative to those with low stress, had IQs that were 20 points lower on average. Higher stress also predicted more behavioural problems and anxiety in children at four years of age. Further, the children of mothers with high stress had abnormalities in their fingerprint profiles, suggesting that stress affected prenatal development during the crucial 14- to 22-week segment of gestation. Follow-up studies of the children at age 5.5 years continued to identify deficits associated with maternal prenatal stress exposure; for instance, deficits in motor functioning (Cao et al., 2014), as well as lower IQs and reduced language ability (Laplante et al., 2008). Follow-up studies have continued; for example, maternal prenatal stress was found to correlate with eating attitudes and behaviours of the children at age 13 (St-Hilaire et al., 2015). Given this role of prenatal stress, it is logical to assume that depression during the pregnancy period may also have a negative impact on the child's subsequent development.

What about fathers? In a review paper on men's perinatal health, Singley and Edwards (2015) report that about 10% of new fathers experience mental health problems, but they tend not to

Funded by the Ontario government, the Best Start Resource Centre is focused on maternal, newborn, and early childhood health promotion. A public awareness campaign launched in Ontario in 2007 is aimed at bringing postpartum mood disorders out into the open and encouraging new mothers to seek help.

(continued)

seek support. These findings suggest the need for support programs (like Ontario's Best Start Resource centre; see photo) to adopt a family focus that includes fathers when seeking to help PD sufferers.

Thinking Critically

1. Is it possible to develop prevention programs in connection with prenatal classes that decrease the probability of the development of PD in mothers? What strategies would you use? Despite the best possible efforts, some women will still develop depression. Design an intervention to minimize the severity and impact of these depressions. Were fathers included?

2. Prenatal and perinatal depression are relatively common. While discontinuing antidepressants may cause relapse in about 75% of women during pregnancy, continued use may pose risks to the developing fetus (Misri, 2007; Wisner et al., 2009). However, there is a balance to be achieved: "This is the reason that pregnant women are treated with pharmacotherapy; that is, the anticipated overall benefit is greater than the risk" (Wisner et al., 2013, p.490). Given unease about the safety of antidepressant use, can you think of alternative treatment modalities for this population?

Finally, both bipolar and unipolar disorders can be subdiagnosed as seasonal if there is a regular relationship between an episode and a particular time of the year. Most research has focused on depression in the winter (i.e., winter depression or seasonal affective disorder), and the most prevalent explanation is that it is linked to a decrease in the number of daylight hours. **Seasonal affective disorder** was first described by Rosenthal et al. (1984), who noted that some people's symptoms varied in response to changes in climate and latitude in a manner that suggested that reduced exposure to sunlight was causing their depressions (see photo).

In Canada, a study of community members found that the seasonal subtype of major depression was detected in 11% of the people diagnosed with depression (Levitt, Boyle, Joffe, & Baumal, 2000). The prevalence of seasonal affective disorder was 2.9%. A study of an Inuit community in the Canadian Arctic (Haggarty et al., 2002) found that 18% of the population had either seasonal affective disorder or were subsyndromal (i.e., they had fewer symptoms that did not quite meet *DSM* criteria). The authors noted that this is the highest rate of seasonal affective disorder found thus far in research involving *DSM*-based assessments. Icelanders go without light for many months in the winter, yet as a group, they have surprisingly low levels of seasonal affective disorder. A study of

Icelanders who emigrated to the Interlake District in Manitoba found a prevalence rate of only 1.2% (Magnusson & Axelsson, 1993). The authors speculated that Icelanders might have lower rates because they have adapted genetically to reduced sunlight exposure. Reduced light does cause decreases in the activity of serotonin neurons of the hypothalamus, and these neurons regulate some behaviours, such as sleep (Schwartz et al., 1997). However, this explanation does not account for why other groups have not adapted genetically to reduced sunlight, and perhaps there are other factors at play (e.g., diet, in particular the increased fish consumption found in traditional Icelandic diets).

It has long been suspected that biological factors contribute to vulnerability to seasonal affective disorder. Helpful insights have emerged from research conducted in Montreal. This research compared brain responses to different colours of light and found that for clients with seasonal affective disorder, exposure to lights influenced responses to auditory emotional stimuli in the posterior hypothalamus. This pattern was not found among control group participants (see Vandewalle et al., 2011).

In **cyclothymic disorder**, the person has frequent periods of depressed mood and hypomania, which may be mixed with, may alternate with, or may be separated by periods of normal mood lasting as long as two months. People with cyclothymic disorder have paired sets of symptoms in their periods of depression and hypomania. During depression, they feel inadequate; during hypomania, their self-esteem is inflated. They withdraw from people, then seek them out in an uninhibited fashion. They sleep too much and then too little. When depressed they have trouble concentrating, and their verbal productivity decreases; during hypomania, their thinking becomes sharp and creative and their productivity increases. People with cyclothymia do not experience full-blown episodes of mania, hypomania, or depression. However, to be diagnosed with cyclothymia, they experience periods with hypomanic symptoms and periods with depressive symptoms at least half the time, for at least two years. Cyclothymic disorder is not very common (less than 1% lifetime prevalence; APA, 2013), and may be a precursor to other mood disorders. For example, a young adult may initially present with cyclothymia, but later on in adulthood may develop bipolar disorder.

B. Boissonnet/Getty Images, Inc.

Seasonal depression is one of the subtypes of MDD. This woman is demonstrating light therapy, an effective treatment for people whose seasonal depression occurs during the winter.

8.2 Psychological Theories of Mood Disorders

Depression has been studied from several perspectives. Here, we discuss psychoanalytic views, which emphasize the unconscious conflicts associated with grief and loss; cognitive theories, which focus on the depressed person's self-defeating thought processes; and interpersonal factors, which emphasize how depressed people interact with others. These theories, for the most part, describe different diatheses in a general diathesis–stress theory that requires stressful life events in order to trigger bouts of depression (Kendler, Karkowski, & Prescott, 1999). The theories we discuss address the question: What are the psychological characteristics of people who respond to stress with a mood disorder episode?

Psychoanalytic Theory of Depression

In his celebrated paper "Mourning and Melancholia," Freud (1917/1950) theorized that the potential for depression is created early in childhood. During the oral period, a child's needs may be insufficiently or oversufficiently gratified, causing the person to become fixated in this stage and dependent on the instinctual gratifications particular to it. With this arrest in psychosexual maturation, the person may develop a tendency to be excessively dependent on other people for the maintenance of self-esteem.

From this happenstance of childhood, how can the adult come to suffer from depression? The complex reasoning is based on an analysis of bereavement. Freud hypothesized that after the loss of a loved one, whether by death or, most commonly for a child, through separation or withdrawal of affection, the mourner first introjects, or incorporates, the lost person; he or she identifies with the lost one, perhaps in a fruitless attempt to undo the loss. Because, Freud asserted, we unconsciously harbour negative feelings toward those we love, the mourner then becomes the object of his or her own hate and anger (anger turned inward). In addition, the mourner resents being deserted and feels guilt for real or imagined sins against the lost person.

The period of introjection is followed by a period of mourning work, when the mourner recalls memories of the lost one and thereby separates himself or herself from the person who has died or disappointed him or her and loosens the bonds imposed by introjection. But the mourning work can go astray and develop into an ongoing process of self-abuse, self-blame, and depression in overly dependent individuals. These individuals do not loosen their emotional bonds with the lost person; rather, they continue to castigate themselves for the faults and shortcomings perceived in the loved one who has been introjected. The mourner's anger toward the lost one continues to be directed inward.

Some research has been generated by psychoanalytic points of view, but it has been limited and does not give strong support to the theory. However, some depressed people are high in dependency and prone to depression following a rejection (see Canadian Perspectives 8.2).

Canadian Perspectives 8.2

Research on Personality Orientations in Depression

Are specific personality factors associated with depression? Do they predict susceptibility to the onset, severity, persistence, and relapse of depression? Are they related to treatment outcome? Are higher-order personality dimensions important? Much of the research in this area has a Canadian connection.

Aaron Beck (1983), taking a cognitive perspective, proposed that depression is associated with two personality styles: **sociotropy** and **autonomy**. Sociotropic individuals are dependent on others. They are especially concerned with pleasing others, avoiding disapproval, and avoiding separation. Autonomy is an achievement-related construct that focuses on self-critical goal striving, a desire for solitude, and freedom from control. Problems inherent in the original assessment of these constructs necessitated the development of alternative measures, including a multidimensional scale developed by David Clark at the University of New Brunswick, Beck, and colleagues. Their Revised Sociotropy-Autonomy Scale (SAS-R) assesses sociotropy and two aspects of autonomy: a preference for solitude and independence (Clark, Steer, Beck, & Ross, 1995). The independence component has

adaptive correlates. Mongrain and Blackburn (2005) at York University examined the recurrence of diagnosed depression in graduate students with a history of depression and showed that autonomy predicted recurrence of depression, even after controlling for history of depression and other variables. Sociotropy and autonomy were both unique predictors of the number of previous episodes.

Sidney Blatt (1974, 1995), operating from a psychoanalytic perspective, suggested that introjective and anaclitic personality styles are associated with vulnerability to depression. The anaclitic orientation involves excessive dependency on others. The introjective orientation involves excessive levels of self-criticism. Blatt developed the Depressive Experiences Questionnaire (DEQ) to assess **dependency** and **self-criticism**. Canadian researcher David Zuroff from McGill University has collaborated with Blatt and tested his predictions (see Blatt & Zuroff, 1992). Research showed a strong association between self-criticism and depression and a weaker but still significant link between dependency and depression (e.g., Mongrain & Zuroff, 1994). The DEQ actually measures maladaptive dependency (i.e., neediness) and adaptive dependency (i.e., connectedness) (see Blatt, Zohar, Quinlan, Zuroff, & Mongrain, 1995). Mongrain and Leather (2006) confirmed that self-criticism

(continued)

and maladaptive dependency interact to predict the recurrence of depression in graduate students, so it appears that students with high levels of self-criticism and neediness are particularly at risk for the return of depression.

The concept of self-criticism is linked closely with perfectionism (Blatt, 1995), and Canadian studies have examined the link between perfectionism dimensions and depression. (For an expanded description of perfectionism dimensions, see Chapter 10.) Hewitt and Flett (1991a) found that depressed people had elevated levels of self-oriented (i.e., high personal standards) and socially prescribed (i.e., expectations imposed on the self by others) perfectionism. Perfectionism has also been linked with chronic symptoms of both unipolar and bipolar depression (Hewitt, Flett, Ediger, Norton, & Flynn, 1998).

We will now focus on several substantive research approaches. One line of investigation tests the congruency hypothesis. This hypothesis reflects the diathesis–stress approach. Extensive Canadian research highlights the role of stressful life events in depression (e.g., Enns & Cox, 2005a; Wildes, Harkness, & Simons, 2002). In terms of personality and stress, the essence of the congruency hypothesis is that if a non-depressed person with a personality style (i.e., a diathesis) that makes him or her vulnerable to depression also experiences a negative life event that is congruent with or matches their vulnerability in some way (e.g., a student who wants to be perfect but fails a test), then this person will become depressed. The congruency hypothesis highlights the distinction between interpersonal and achievement-based vulnerabilities. Thus, a person characterized by interpersonal needs that indicate sociotropy and dependency will become depressed if she or he experiences interpersonal rejection or the loss of a significant other, but a person characterized by an achievement vulnerability that indicates a need to be perfect and to work autonomously will become depressed if she or he experiences a failure at school or work. The hypothesis has received only mixed support. Some personality studies have found some evidence of congruency (e.g., Hewitt, Flett, & Ediger, 1996; Segal, Shaw, Vella, & Katz, 1992); others have found a non-specific effect (i.e., stress in general combines with personality factors to produce depression) or partial or no support (Clark & Oates, 1995; Enns & Cox, 2005b).

Another area of research explores the role of personality factors in treatment outcomes. A study led by Neil Rector at the Centre for Addiction and Mental Health in Toronto (Rector, Bagby, Segal, Joffe, & Levitt, 2000) investigated the ability of self-criticism and dependency to predict treatment response among depressed clients who received either pharmacotherapy or cognitive therapy (CT). The personality factors had little impact on the outcomes associated with pharmacotherapy, but self-criticism predicted a poor response to CT. Further, the extent to which self-critical clients became less self-critical over the course of treatment was the best predictor of response to CT. These findings suggest that whether a person will respond to certain kinds of treatment will be determined, in part, by personality vulnerabilities.

Finally, Blatt's (1995) description of self-critical perfectionism suggests that personality concepts can be grouped together, both conceptually and empirically. Using a new measure named the Self-Critical Perfectionism Scale (SCPS) that incorporates items from measures of self-criticism, autonomy, and perfectionism, Wheeler, Blankstein, Antony, McCabe, and Bieling (2011) reported that among clients with MDD and various anxiety disorders, depressed and social anxiety disorder groups reported the highest levels of self-critical perfectionism, relative to other clinical groups and a control group. Further, relative to specific component measures, the SCPS was the only significant unique positive predictor of depression symptoms, and had a strong association with comorbidity. Depressed self-critical perfectionists "strive for achievement and perfection, engage in critical self-evaluation, perceive a need to reach unrealistic goals imposed by others, are concerned about criticism, disapproval, and rejection, and have a defensive separation and preference for solitude" (p. 84). These findings suggest a need to target self-critical perfectionism in psychological interventions for depression. The SCPS is unique because it captures the shared variance among variables derived from diverse theoretical frameworks, including the psychoanalytic and cognitive paradigms.

Thinking Critically

1. What other variables, in addition to stress and social support, might interact with specific personality vulnerability factors to moderate the relationship between personality and depression?

2. Given a link between certain personality factors and depression, how would you attempt to prevent the onset of depression in vulnerable people?

Cognitive Theories of Depression

Earlier discussions of the role of cognition in anxiety (Chapter 5) and of Ellis's concept of irrational beliefs (Chapter 2 and elsewhere) indicate that cognitive processes play a decisive role in emotional behaviour. In some theories of depression, thoughts and beliefs are regarded as major factors in causing or influencing the emotional state. We now discuss two cognitive theories of depression in some detail: Beck's schema theory and the helplessness/hopelessness theory.

Beck's Theory of Depression

Aaron Beck (1967; 1987; 2008) is responsible for the most important contemporary theory that regards thought processes as causative factors in depression. His central thesis is that depressed individuals feel as they do because their thinking is biased toward negative interpretations. Figure 8.1 illustrates the interactions among the three levels of cognitive activity that Beck believes underlie depression. According to Beck, in childhood and adolescence, depressed individuals acquired a negative schema—a tendency to see the world negatively—through loss of a parent, an unrelenting succession of tragedies, the social rejection of peers (see photo), the criticisms of teachers, or the depressive attitude of a parent. All of us have schemata of many kinds; by these perceptual sets, we order our lives. The negative schemata acquired by depressed persons are activated whenever they encounter new situations that resemble in some way, perhaps only remotely, the conditions in which the schemata were

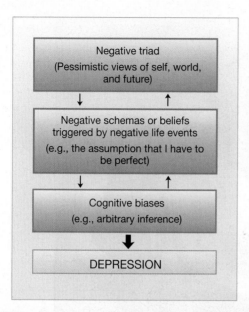

FIGURE 8.1 The interrelationships among different kinds of cognitions in Beck's theory.

learned. Moreover, the negative schemata fuel and are fuelled by certain cognitive biases that lead these people to misperceive reality. Thus, an ineptness schema can make depressed individuals expect to fail most of the time, a self-blame schema burdens them with responsibility for all misfortunes, and a negative self-evaluation schema constantly reminds them of their worthlessness.

Negative schemata, together with cognitive biases or distortions, maintain what Beck called the **negative triad**: negative views of the self, the world, and the future. The world part of Beck's depressive triad refers to the person's judgement that he or she cannot cope with the demands of the environment. Rather than having to do with a concern for global events that do not implicate the self directly (e.g., "The world has been going south since the terrorist attacks of 9/11"), it is highly personal ("I cannot possibly cope with all these demands and responsibilities").

Recall our opening description of Billy and his depression. Mobley (2008) highlighted the role of Billy's negative cognitions about his self-worth and found clear evidence of the negative triad described by Beck. According to Mobley (2008), "Billy initially had negative appraisals and irrational beliefs about (a) self and life experiences ('I do not deserve to be in college'), (b) the future ('I will not pass my classes'), and (c) the world related to my school ('There is no major for me')" (p. 93). The cognitive model posits that this negative style of looking at the world is activated after having negative life experiences.

Beck (1967, 1987) also maintains that the negative cognitions include **dysfunctional attitudes** or assumptions that bias the interpretation of events. Weissman and Beck (1978) created the Dysfunctional Attitudes Scale (DAS) to assess these attitudes. The original DAS (Form A and Form B) consisted of 40-item self-report measures. Factor analyses that were conducted originally with DAS item responses provided by university students identified two main themes: (1) dysfunctional beliefs reflecting the

need for approval (e.g., "My value as a person depends greatly on what others think of me"); and (2) dysfunctional beliefs reflecting the need for achievement and perfection (e.g., "If I don't set the highest standards for myself, I am likely to end up a second-rate person") (see Cane, Olinger, Gotlib, & Kuiper, 1986). DAS scores are higher in clients with recurrent episodes than clients who are experiencing their first episode of depression, and perfectionistic attitudes were found to best predict the number of recurrent episodes (Batmaz, Kaymak, Kocbiyik, & Turkcapar, 2015).

Here again we return briefly to the previous case of Billy. Billy's counsellor determined that there were two primary sources of his distress. First, Billy was questioning his future because he realized that he really didn't want to be a teacher after all and instead had interests in science and fantasy. It was suggested that his initial interests in being a teacher were largely a reflection of his parents' insistence that Billy demonstrate his social interest. Second, Billy had extreme dysfunctional beliefs reflecting the perfectionism theme. Mobley (2008) recounted that, "These assumptions were reflected in such statements as 'Small mistakes have amplified consequences' and 'I am what I achieve, and achievements determine worth'" (p. 89).

Given this way of viewing the world, it is apparent that Billy would be highly vulnerable following feedback and events that can be construed as mistakes or achievement failures. And, according to Beck, this will activate other negative cognitive tendencies. In Beck's (2008) words, "When the schemas are activated by an event or series of events, they skew the information processing system, which then directs attentional resources to negative stimuli and translates a specific experience into a distorted negative interpretation" (p. 970). These negatively biased cognitive schemas (cognitive vulnerability) function as efficient but maladaptive "automatic" information processors.

The following list describes some of the principal cognitive biases of depressed individuals, according to Beck:

- Arbitrary inference—a conclusion drawn in the absence of sufficient evidence or of any evidence at all. For example, a man concludes that he is worthless because it is raining the day he is hosting an outdoor party.

- Selective abstraction—a conclusion drawn on the basis of only one of many elements in a situation. A worker feels worthless when a product fails to function, even though she is only one of many people who contributed to its production.

- Overgeneralization—an overall sweeping conclusion drawn on the basis of a single, perhaps trivial, event. A student regards her poor performance in a single class on one particular day as final proof of her worthlessness and stupidity.

- Magnification and minimization—exaggerations in evaluating performance. A man, believing that he has completely ruined his car (magnification) when he notices a slight scratch on the rear fender, regards himself as good for nothing; a woman believes herself worthless (minimization) in spite of a succession of praiseworthy achievements.

In Beck's theory, our emotional reactions are a function of how we construe our world. The interpretations of depressed

Being rejected by peers may lead to the development of the negative schema that Beck's theory suggests plays a key role in depression.

individuals do not mesh well with the way most people view the world, and they become victims of their own illogical self-judgements.

A review by Rector, Segal, and Gemar (1998) noted that much of the depression research conducted in Canada has tested predictions involving Beck's schema notion. The research investigations conducted can be differentiated in terms of whether they have focused on cognitive products (i.e., the stimuli that are recalled), cognitive processes or operations involving the deployment of attention, or cognitive structures in terms of the organization of cognitive schemas. The emphasis has shifted away from initial research on cognitive products and toward cognitive processes and organization.

Initial Canadian research was dominated by investigations conducted by Nicholas Kuiper and his associates at the University of Western Ontario (e.g., MacDonald & Kuiper, 1984). They used a self-referent encoding task that involved presenting participants with positive and negative word adjectives (e.g., "smart," "stupid") and asking them to indicate whether the adjectives applied to them by stating "yes" or "no." Two key findings emerged from this research. First, depressed individuals, relative to non-depressed individuals, endorse more negative words and fewer positive words as self-descriptive. Second, they exhibit a cognitive bias: they have greater recall of adjectives with depressive content, especially if the adjectives were rated as self-descriptive. Overall, this research tests the notion that the presence or absence of depression reflects differences in the cognitive availability of negative vs. positive thoughts about the self. A British study (Dunn et al., 2009) demonstrated that the reduced positive self-judgement bias found in depressed people relates to depression-specific anhedonic (loss of pleasure) symptoms.

The next wave of research tested the possibility that the main differences of importance involved *cognitive accessibility* rather than cognitive availability per se. In other words, depressed and non-depressed people do not differ in whether their schemas involve positive or negative content; rather, they differ in cognitive processing. Depressed people pay greater attention to negative stimuli and can more readily access negative than positive information. Differences in cognitive processing are assessed via the emotional **Stroop task**. Participants are provided with a series of words in different colours and are asked to identify the colour of each word and ignore the actual word itself (i.e., if the word "sad" is presented in red ink, the correct answer is "red"). The Stroop task assesses the latency or length of time it takes to respond. Gotlib and McCann (1984) examined response patterns when students were asked to colour-name words that varied in their content: neutral, depression-oriented (e.g., "bleak"), or manic-oriented (i.e., "overly euphoric"). Non-depressed students did not differ in their response latencies across the word types, but depressed students took longer to colour-name the depression-oriented words, suggesting that these themes were more cognitively accessible for them. In subsequent research, Marlene Moretti at Simon Fraser University and her associates (Moretti et al., 1996) found that depressed individuals have reduced accessibility to positive information that is specific to themselves, not to other people.

Investigations by Scott McCabe from the University of Waterloo and his associates focused on differences in attentional processes. This experimental research has used a deployment-of-attention task to show that dysphoric and clinically depressed individuals do not seem to selectively attend to negative or positive material but that non-depressed individuals have a protective bias that involves diverting their attention away from negative stimuli and focusing instead on positive stimuli (e.g., McCabe & Tonan, 2000). In related research, people who had a history of depression but were in a neutral mood tended to divert their attention when presented with negative stimuli, once again suggesting the presence of a protective bias (McCabe, Gotlib, & Martin, 2000). However, people with a history of depression induced into a negative mood state were less able to keep themselves from noticing and paying attention to negative stimuli.

A study conducted by Dozois and Dobson (2001) is remarkable because it used multiple tasks to determine whether people with and without clinical depression differed, not only in cognitive accessibility, but also in cognitive organization. Participants completed a variety of cognitive tasks, including the self-referent encoding task, the modified Stroop task, and two tasks designed to assess cognitive structure. Four groups of participants took part: depressed, depressed and anxious, never-depressed and anxious, and non-psychiatric controls. People with anxiety disorders were included to determine whether the findings were specific to depression. Several interesting findings emerged. First, on the self-referent encoding task, depressed individuals endorsed a relatively equal number of positive and negative words as self-relevant, suggesting that the self-schema of clinically depressed people is not devoid of positive content and that there is not a lack of cognitive availability. The main group differences that emerged involved cognitive processing and cognitive organization. Dozois and Dobson (2001) summarized the cognitive structure findings by concluding that "depressed individuals have an interconnected negative self-representational system and lack a well-organized positive template of self" (p. 2), a pattern that was not evident among the anxious group and the control group. Follow-up research (Dozois, 2002) on dysphoric students found additional evidence for a deterioration of positive interconnectedness as levels of depression increased. Once again, there was evidence of greater organization of negative content among severely dysphoric students. A further follow-up study by Dozois and Dobson (2003) showed that self-schematas involving greater organization of negative content and less interconnectedness of positive content were associated with more recurrent depression.

According to Beck's expanded cognitive model (e.g., Clark & Beck, 1999; Beck, 2008), due to repeated activation, negative schemas become organized into a depressive "mode"—a network of cognitive, affective, motivational, behavioural, and physiological schemas that accounts for fully expressed depression. Negative events have an impact on the mode, making it "hypersalient," and the mode "takes control of the information processing, reflected by increased negative appraisals and rumination" (Beck, 2008, p. 972). Beck and Haigh (2014) provided an update to the generic cognitive model, which applies not just to depression but to psychological disorders in general. One important addition is the view that psychological disorders exist on the same continuum as adaptive functioning.

We must address two key issues when evaluating Beck's theory. The first is whether depressed people actually think in the negative ways enumerated by Beck. Beck initially confirmed this point in clinical observations (Beck, 1967). Further support comes from a number of sources: self-report questionnaires, laboratory studies of processes such as memory, and the Articulated Thoughts in Simulated Situations method (e.g., Segal et al., 1995). The studies outlined above confirm the presence of related differences in terms of cognitive accessibility and organization.

The second issue represents perhaps the greatest challenge for cognitive theories of depression: whether it could be that the negative beliefs of depressed people do not follow the depression, but in fact cause the depressed mood. Does depression cause negative thoughts, or do negative thoughts cause depression? The relationship in all likelihood works both ways: depression can make thinking more negative, and negative thinking can probably cause and can certainly worsen depression. Beck himself has come to this more bidirectional position.

Beck has further extended his theory by suggesting a need to focus on personality styles known as sociotropy and autonomy. The role of these factors and other personality traits is discussed in Canadian Perspectives 8.2. Despite uncertainties, Beck's theory has the advantage of being testable. It has engendered considerable research on the treatment of depression and has encouraged therapists to focus on the thinking of depressed clients in order to change their feelings. The testability is important but raises another issue: when the therapy is being tested, the therapists strictly follow protocols as they are most often recorded and treatment fidelity is assessed. These same features are not present in therapy as delivered in the community. Recent research is showing that the depression outcomes seen in a research setting may be stronger than those evidenced in a pure clinical setting (Gibbons, Stirman, DeRubeis, Newman, & Beck, 2013), an issue we revisit in Chapter 17.

Helplessness/Hopelessness Theories

In this section, we discuss the evolution of an influential cognitive theory of depression—actually, three theories: the original learned helplessness theory; its subsequent, more cognitive, attributional version; and its transformation into the learned hopelessness theory (see Figure 8.2 for a summary).

Learned helplessness The basic premise of the learned helplessness theory is that an individual's passivity and sense of being unable to act and control his or her own life is acquired through unpleasant experiences and traumas that the individual tried unsuccessfully to control. This theory began as a mediational learning theory formulated to explain the behaviour of dogs that received inescapable electric shocks. Soon after receiving the first shocks, the dogs seemed to give up and passively accept the painful stimulation. Later, when the shocks

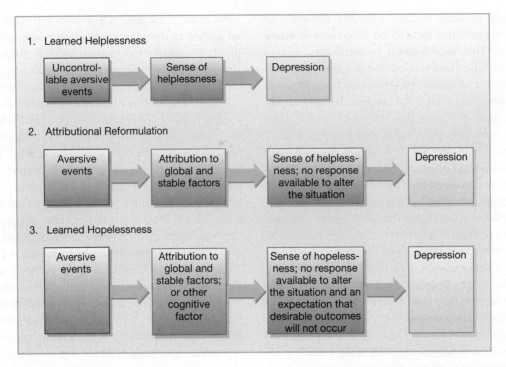

1. Learned Helplessness

Uncontrol-lable aversive events → Sense of helplessness → Depression

2. Attributional Reformulation

Aversive events → Attribution to global and stable factors → Sense of helpless-ness; no response available to alter the situation → Depression

3. Learned Hopelessness

Aversive events → Attribution to global and stable factors; or other cognitive factor → Sense of hopeless-ness; no response available to alter the situation and an expectation that desirable outcomes will not occur → Depression

FIGURE 8.2   The three helplessness theories of depression.

could be avoided, these dogs did not acquire the avoidance response as efficiently and effectively as did control animals that had not experienced the inescapable shocks. Rather, most of them lay down in a corner and whined. Seligman (1975) proposed that animals acquire a sense of helplessness when confronted with uncontrollable aversive stimulation. Later, this sense of helplessness impairs their performance in stressful situations that can be controlled. They appear to lose the ability and motivation to learn to respond in an effective way to painful stimuli.

Seligman concluded that learned helplessness in animals could provide a model for at least certain forms of human depression. Like many depressed people, the animals appeared passive in the face of stress, failing to initiate actions that might allow them to cope. They had difficulty eating or retaining what they ate, and they lost weight. Further, one of the neurotransmitter chemicals implicated in depression, norepinephrine, was depleted in Seligman's animals.

In his classic book *Helplessness,* Seligman (1975) further elaborated on the implications of helplessness for humans. He also documented cases in which profound states of helplessness actually resulted in deaths as if the person had lost the will to live.

Attribution and learned helplessness   After the original research with animals, investigators conducted similar studies with humans. By 1978, several inadequacies of the theory and unexplained aspects of depression had become apparent, and a revised learned helplessness model was proposed by Abramson, Seligman, and Teasdale (1978). Some studies with humans, for example, had indicated that helplessness inductions sometimes led to subsequent improvement of performance. Also, many

depressed people hold themselves responsible for their failures. If they see themselves as helpless, how can they blame themselves? This characteristic of feeling helpless yet blaming oneself is referred to as the **depressive paradox**.

The essence of the revised theory is the concept of **attribution**—the explanation a person has for his or her behaviour (Weiner et al., 1971). When a person has experienced failure, he or she will try to attribute the failure to some cause. Table 8.1 applies the Abramson, Seligman, and Teasdale formulation to various ways in which a university student might attribute a low score on the mathematics portion of the Graduate Record Examination (GRE). The formulation is based on answers to three questions:

1. Are the reasons for failure believed to be internal (personal) or external (environmentally caused)?

2. Is the problem believed to be stable or unstable?

3. How global or specific is the inability to succeed perceived to be?

The attributional revision of the helplessness theory postulates that the way in which a person cognitively explains failure will determine its subsequent effects:

- Global attributions ("I never do anything right") increase the generality of the effects of failure.

- Attributions to stable factors ("I never test well") make them long term.

- Attributions to internal characteristics ("I am stupid") are more likely to diminish self-esteem, particularly if the personal fault is also global and persistent.

TABLE 8.1	Attributional Schema of Depression: Why I Failed My GRE Math Exam			
	Internal (Personal)		**External (Environmental)**	
Degree	**Stable**	**Unstable**	**Stable**	**Unstable**
Global	I am stupid.	I am exhausted.	These tests are all unfair.	It's an unlucky day, Friday the 13th.
Specific	I lack mathematical ability.	I am fed up with math.	The math tests are unfair.	My math test was numbered "13."

The theory suggests that people become depressed when they attribute negative life events to stable and global causes. Whether self-esteem also collapses depends on whether they blame the bad outcome on their own inadequacies. The individual prone to depression is thought to show a depressive attributional style—a tendency to attribute bad outcomes to personal, global, and stable faults of character. When people with this style (a diathesis) have unhappy, adverse experiences (stressors), they become depressed (Peterson & Seligman, 1984).

Where does the depressive attributional style come from? In Chapter 2, we noted that the failure to answer such a central question is a problem with most cognitive theories of psychopathology. In general terms, the answer is thought to lie in childhood experiences (a common theme in many psychological theories), but few data have been collected to support this view. A promising start is the finding that depressive attributional style is related to sexual abuse in childhood, parental overprotectiveness, and harsh discipline (Rose et al., 1994).

Hopelessness theory The next version of this theory (Abramson, Metalsky, & Alloy, 1989) moved even farther away from the original formulation. Some forms of depression (hopelessness depressions) are now regarded as caused by a state of hopelessness, an expectation that desirable outcomes will not occur or that undesirable ones will occur and that the person has no responses available to change this situation. (The latter part of the definition of hopelessness, of course, refers to helplessness, the central concept of earlier versions of the theory.) As in the attributional reformulation, negative life events interact with diatheses to yield a state of hopelessness. One diathesis is the attributional pattern already described—attributing negative events to stable and global factors. However, the theory now considers two other diatheses: low self-esteem and a tendency to infer that negative life events will have severe negative consequences.

Metalsky and his colleagues (1993) conducted the first test of the hopelessness theory in a prospective study that examined how students differing in attributional style responded to success vs. failure on a class test. Two new features were the direct measurement of hopelessness and one of the newly proposed diatheses, low self-esteem. As in the earlier study, attributing poor grades to global and stable factors led to more persistent depressed mood. This pattern supported the hopelessness theory, for it was found only among students whose self-esteem was low and was mediated by an increase

in feelings of hopelessness. A similar study conducted with children in the sixth and seventh grades yielded almost identical results (Robinson, Garber, & Hillsman, 1995). Lewinsohn and his colleagues (1994) also found that depressive attributional style and low self-esteem predicted the onset of depression in adolescents. Alloy and Abramson and their colleagues (Iacoviello et al., 2006) conducted a prospective study to examine the course of depression in people at high and low cognitive risk for depression. They found that those high in negative cognitive styles experienced more episodes of depression, more severe episodes, and more chronic courses.

One advantage of the hopelessness theory is that it can deal directly with the comorbidity of depression and anxiety disorders. Alloy and her colleagues (2006) proposed that an expectation of helplessness creates anxiety. When the expectation of helplessness becomes certain, a syndrome with elements of anxiety and depression emerges. Finally, if the perceived probability of the future occurrence of negative events becomes certain (a phenomenon known as **depressive predictive certainty**), hopelessness depression develops. In a review paper, Liu, Kleiman, Nestor, and Cheek (2015) highlighted the need for greater conceptual clarity between the hopelessness theory and the earlier revised learned helplessness model.

Interpersonal Theory of Depression

In this section, we discuss behavioural aspects of depression that generally involve relationships between the depressed person and others.

Depressed individuals tend to have sparse social networks and to regard them as providing little support. Reduced social support may lessen an individual's ability to handle negative life events and increase vulnerability to depression (Billings, Cronkite, & Moos, 1983). Depressed people also elicit negative reactions from others, including rejection (Coyne, 1976). For example, the roommates of depressed students rated social contacts with them as low in enjoyment and reported high levels of aggression toward them; mildly depressed students were likely to be rejected by their roommates (Joiner, Alfano, & Metalsky, 1992). Bieling and Alden (2001) discovered that one reason why depressed people may elicit negative reactions from others is that they tend to reject their partners and display relatively few positive social behaviours. This tendency was especially evident among people high in autonomy, as described by Beck. It seems that depressed individuals with an autonomous orientation are oriented toward themselves rather than toward other people. When oriented toward others, they can act in a negative, rejecting manner. Therefore it seems that there are other factors at play, not just depressed mood that is leading to interpersonal problems. A recent study of adolescents found that not all adolescents with depression were rejected by peers; only those who engaged in conversational self-focus, a tendency to redirect conversations to the self (Schwartz-Mette & Rose, 2016). Those who were depressed but did not engage in conversational self-focus were not rejected by their friends.

Given the interpersonal problems of depressed people, it is not surprising that depression and marital discord frequently co-occur and that the interactions of depressed people and their spouses involve mutual hostility (Kowalik & Gotlib, 1987). Critical comments by spouses are a significant predictor of recurrence of depression (Hooley & Teasdale, 1989). In a longitudinal study, marital adjustment and perceived criticism were assessed during the first year of marriage among 132 married couples (Peterson-Post, Rhoades, Stanley, & Markman, 2014). Lower marital adjustment and higher perceived criticism were both associated with depressive symptoms 10 years later.

Studies have also demonstrated that depressed people are low in social skills across a variety of measures: interpersonal problem-solving speech patterns (speaking very slowly, with silences and hesitations, and more negative self-disclosures), and maintenance of eye contact (e.g., Gotlib & Robinson, 1982).

Another specific idea examined by researchers is that constant reassurance seeking is a critical variable in depression (Joiner & Schmidt, 1998). In a longitudinal study, Stewart and Harkness (2015) found that excessive reassurance seeking was related to partner rejection. Perhaps as a result of being reared in a cold and rejecting environment (Carnelley, Pietromonaco, & Jaffe, 1994), depressed people seek reassurance that others truly care, but even when reassured, they are only temporarily satisfied. Their negative self-concept causes them to doubt the truth of the feedback they have received, and their constant efforts to be reassured come to irritate others. Later, they actually seek out negative feedback, which, in a sense, validates their negative self-concept. Rejection ultimately occurs because of the depressed person's inconsistent behaviour. Focus on Discovery 8.2 explores the possibility that people become depressed because they generate stress for themselves.

Focus on Discovery 8.2

Stress Generation and Depression

Constance Hammen (1991) advanced the theory that some people are more prone to depression because they take an active role in creating or generating the stress for themselves that contributes to distress and despair. This is a radical notion because it portrays people as active agents in their own stress. Implicit in this work is the notion that females are more interpersonally sensitive and may engage in more stress generation.

The concept of stress generation is highly relevant to interpersonal theories because one of the major ways to create stress is to act in a way that creates interpersonal conflict. Another avenue is to gravitate toward peers or partners who are volatile or non-supportive, perhaps even abusive. Stress generation can also result from being so high in the need for reassurance that the constant reassurance seeking alienates other people.

The measurement of stress generation involves making the distinction between *independent events* (i.e., not due to oneself) and *dependent events* (i.e., stemming from personal choices or actions dependent on the self). Dependent vs. independent events are assessed via a rigorous contextual interview of life experiences.

Thus far, strong empirical findings, often in longitudinal research, have supported the role of stress generation in depression among adolescents and adults. It has been suggested that stress generation accounts for the gender differences in depression that emerge during adolescence. Shih, Eberhart, Hammen, and Brennan (2006) found that interpersonal episodic stress that was self-generated predicts depression in girls; for boys, chronic stress in general contributed to depression. Another longitudinal investigation confirmed that stress generation predicted depression in

adolescent girls but not in boys (Rudolph et al., 2009). In addition, generation of stress among already depressed girls predicted subsequent bouts of depression.

Stress generation may interact with other vulnerability factors. Research by Harkness and associates at Queen's University found evidence that higher rates of interpersonal stress generation predicted depression in a sample of adolescent girls with a history of childhood maltreatment (Harkness, Lumley, & Truss, 2008). This effect was not found among the subset of girls without a history of maltreatment. These data underscore the need to examine stress generation within the context of other individual difference factors associated with vulnerability to depression.

Harkness and colleagues (Harkness, Bagby, et al., 2015) have also investigated the role of genetic factors (e.g., serotonin transporter gene polymorphisms) and childhood maltreatment on stress generation. They found an interaction between history of maltreatment (maternal emotional maltreatment or sexual maltreatment) and genetic factors (specifically having the risk s-allele), leading to higher rates of dependent life events. These same factors were not predictive of independent life events. Further, these same genetic factors interacted with childhood maltreatment in predicting symptoms of depression (Harkness, Strauss et al., 2015).

Finally, longitudinal research led by Amanda Uliaszek from the University of Toronto has examined whether stress generation simply keeps stress going (i.e., stress continuation) or creates new stress (i.e., stress causation). This work, conducted in collaboration with Susan Mineka and Constance Hammen and others, found substantial evidence in favour of stress causation but also found that stress generation among adolescents is implicated in anxiety as well as in depression (Uliaszek et al., 2012).

Do any interpersonal characteristics of depressed people precede the onset of depression, suggesting a causal relationship? Some research using the high-risk method suggests the answer is yes. For example, low social competence predicted the onset of depression among children (Cole, Martin, Powers, & Truglio, 1990) and poor interpersonal problem-solving skills predicted increases in depression among adolescents (Davila et al., 1995). Thus, social skills deficits may be a cause and consequence of depression. Interpersonal behaviour clearly plays a major role in depression.

Psychological Theories of Bipolar Disorder

While bipolar disorder has been relatively neglected by psychological theorists and researchers, there is now an increasing focus on psychological aspects of bipolar disorder. As with major depression, life stress seems important in precipitating episodes (e.g., Malkoff-Schwartz et al., 1998).

Cognitive factors may also play a role. Scott et al. (2000) showed that people with bipolar depression have elevated levels of the dysfunctional attitudes described by Beck, as well as problems in autobiographical memory and the ability to generate solutions in a problem-solving task. The manic phase of the disorder is seen as a defence against a debilitating psychological state. The specific negative state that is being avoided varies from theory to theory; however, many theorists have concluded that the manic state serves a protective function. Clinical experience with people with manic episodes and studies of their personalities when they are in remission indicate that they appear relatively well-adjusted between episodes. But if mania is a defence, it must be a defence against something, suggesting that the apparently good adjustment between manic episodes may not be an accurate reflection of their true state. Individuals who experience mania, even when between episodes, have very low self-esteem (Lyon, Startup, & Bentall, 1999).

One promising theory is the behavioural activation system dysregulation theory (Alloy & Abramson, 2010). This model is based on findings such as the association that mania has with excessive goal striving and greater cognitive reactivity to success experiences (Johnson, 2005). The essence of this model is that at the root of mania and bipolar disorder is a hyperresponsiveness to reward cues that can be traced back to high behavioural activation system (BAS) activation (Alloy & Abramson, 2010). The BAS is a reward-sensitive system postulated by Gray (1990, 1991) that mediates goal-directed behaviour (Gray & McNaughton, 2000). The BAS is believed to react to rewards or the cessation of punishments by activating emotions such as hope or happiness that encourage approach behaviours (Gray, 1991; Gray, 1990). Mania may reflect extremely high levels of BAS. Research suggests that high BAS sensitivity follows the differential exposure hypothesis, which is the notion that high BAS individuals seek out rewarding stimuli more often in order to experience stronger affect (Gable, Reis, & Elliot, 2000).

8.3 Biological Theories of Mood Disorders

Since biological processes are known to have considerable effects on moods, it is not surprising that investigators have sought biological causes for depression and mania. Furthermore, disturbed biological processes must be part of the causal chain if a predisposition for a mood disorder can be genetically transmitted, and evidence that a predisposition for a mood disorder is heritable would provide some support for the view that the disorder has a biological basis. In the treatment of mood disorders, the effectiveness of drug therapies that increase the levels of certain neurotransmitters suggests that biological factors are important. In this century, there have been tremendous advances by researchers in behaviour genetics and cognitive neuroscience, in part, due to technological changes, such as functional neuroimaging, that have facilitated breakthroughs in our understanding of relations among biological, cognitive, and experiential factors in the development of depression. We will look at some of the research in the areas of genetics, neurochemistry, and the neuroendocrine system. There is also a growing literature on structural abnormalities of the brains of people with mood disorders. These abnormalities are similar to those found in schizophrenia (see Chapter 11). As noted by Beck (2008), new research has provided "a preliminary basis for formulating the neurobiological correlates of such psychological constructs as cognitive vulnerability, cognitive reactivity, and cognitive biases" (p. 972). The genetic and neurobiological discoveries also suggest some probable causal pathways to depression.

Genetic Vulnerability

Research on genetic factors in bipolar disorder and MDD has used twin, family, and adoption methods. Bipolar disorder is one of the most heritable of disorders. Overall, the concordance rate for bipolar disorder is as high as 85% (McGuffin et al., 2003). That is, genes account for possibly 85% of the variance in whether a person becomes manic. These data plus the results of adoption studies (e.g., Wender et al., 1986) support the notion that bipolar disorder has a strong heritable component. However, genetic factors do not determine when manic symptoms will occur. The risk for mania is apparently also related to a higher risk for depression (McGuffin et al., 2003). The information available on MDD indicates that genetic factors, although influential, are not as decisive as they are in bipolar disorder, with heritability estimates approximating 35% (Sullivan, Neale, & Kendler, 2000). Furthermore, relatives of MDD probands are at somewhat increased risk for MDD; however, this risk is less than the risk among relatives of bipolar probands (Andreasen et al., 1987).

Linkage analysis, which focuses on identifying the chromosomes involved, has also been applied to mood disorders. In a widely reported study of the Old Order Amish, Egeland and her colleagues (1987) found evidence favouring the hypothesis that bipolar disorder results from a dominant gene on the 11th chromosome. However, attempts to replicate the Egeland study as well as other apparently successful linkage studies have had mixed success (e.g., Smyth et al., 1996). Research on linkage has broadened to focus on other genes on other chromosomes. Muller et al. (2006) from the University of Toronto reported that within bipolar disorder, variation in the brain-derived neurotrophic factor (BDNF) gene appears to predict risk for developing rapid cycling. However, subsequent research, across various ethnicities, has been inconsistent regarding the relationship between BDNF and bipolar disorder (Wang, Li, Gao, & Fang, 2014). Genome-wide association studies are aimed at identifying the specific genes involved; however, for depression, these studies have generally not yielded significant findings (i.e., there has been little success in identifying specific genes; Ripke et al., 2013).

Some people seem to be genetically predisposed to the onset of MDD when confronted with a series of adverse life events. The pioneering work by Caspi et al. (2003) suggested that people who possess one or two copies of the short variant of the 5-HTTLPR (serotonin transporter) gene, which is involved in modulating serotonin levels, experienced higher levels of depression and suicidality following a recent stressful event (a gene–environment interaction). Wilhelm et al. (2006) also reported that the serotonin transporter gene-linked promoter region (5-HTTLPR) is a significant predictor of first major depression onset following multiple adverse events. These findings were initially supported by other studies, but more recently there have been conflicting results (Smoller, 2016). Kaufman et al. (2006) reported that in abused children, depression severity was predicted in part by an interaction of the 5-HTTPLR (short allele) with the brain-derived neurotrophic factor (*Val/Met*) genotype, especially in children receiving low social support (a gene–gene interaction).

Many studies that have investigated gene–environment interactions in the etiology of MDD have focused on a single candidate gene; however, many genes are known to be involved in the development of MDD, making it polygenic (Smoller, 2016). As such, Mullins and colleagues (2016) examined the gene–environment interaction for MDD, specifically looking at polygenic risk interacting with stressful life events or childhood trauma. The polygenic risk score did not interact with stressful life events, but did interact with a history of childhood trauma. Surprisingly the interaction was opposite to what was expected: lower polygenic risk interacted with more severe childhood trauma in predicting MDD status. Childhood trauma is a known significant risk factor for depression and it may be more strongly related to depression among people with lower genetic risk, although this requires replication. They concluded by emphasizing the importance of examining multiple risk factors, both genetic and environmental, to understand the complex etiology of MDD, and doing so with larger samples.

Accumulating evidence also suggests that a genetic predisposition is related to biases in information processing (see Beck, 2008). For example, Hayden et al. (2008) found that non-depressed children homozygous for the 5-HTTLPR short allele demonstrated greater negative processing on a self-referential encoding task after a negative mood induction than children with other genotypes.

Neurochemistry, Neuroimaging, and Mood Disorders

Researchers have sought to understand the role played by neurotransmitters in mood disorders. The most-studied neurotransmitters have been norepinephrine, serotonin, and dopamine. The original theory posited that low levels of norepinephrine and dopamine led to depression and high levels led to mania. The serotonin theory suggests that serotonin, a neurotransmitter presumed to play a role in the regulation of norepinephrine, also produces depression and mania. However, the weight of the evidence does not completely support the notion that *levels* of neurotransmitters are critical in the mood disorders.

The actions of drugs that were used to treat depression provided the clues on which the theories are based. In the 1950s, two groups of drugs, tricyclics and monoamine oxidase inhibitors, were found effective in relieving depression. **Tricyclic drugs** (e.g., imipramine, or Tofranil) are a group of antidepressant medications so named because their molecular structure is characterized by three fused rings. They prevent some of the reuptake of norepinephrine, serotonin, and/or dopamine by the presynaptic neuron after it has fired, leaving more of the neurotransmitter in the synapse so that transmission of the next nerve impulse is made easier (see Figure 8.3). **Monoamine oxidase (MAO) inhibitors** (e.g., tranylcypromine, or Parnate) are antidepressants that keep the enzyme monoamine oxidase from deactivating neurotransmitters, thus increasing the levels of serotonin, norepinephrine, and/or dopamine in the synapse. This action produces the same facilitating effect described for tricyclics, compensating for the abnormally low levels of these neurotransmitters in depressed people. These drug actions suggest that depression and mania are related to serotonin, norepinephrine, and dopamine. Newer antidepressant drugs, called **selective serotonin reuptake inhibitors (SSRIs)** (e.g., fluoxetine, or Prozac), act more selectively than older ones, specifically inhibiting the reuptake of serotonin. Because these drugs are presumed effective in treating MDD, a stronger link has been apparently shown between low levels of serotonin and depression.

It now appears that the explanation of why these drugs work is not as straightforward as it first seemed. The therapeutic effects of tricyclics and MAO inhibitors do not depend solely on an increase in levels of neurotransmitters. The earlier findings were correct—tricyclics and MAO inhibitors do indeed increase levels of norepinephrine, serotonin, and/or dopamine when they are first taken—but after several days the neurotransmitters return to their earlier levels. This information is crucial because it does not fit with data on how much time must pass before antidepressants become effective. Both

(a)

Presynaptic neuron

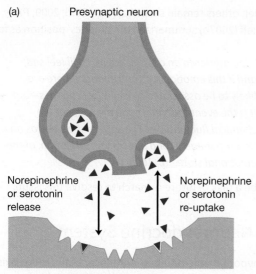

Norepinephrine or serotonin release

Norepinephrine or serotonin re-uptake

Postsynaptic neuron

(b)

Presynaptic neuron

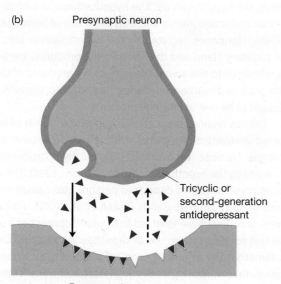

Tricyclic or second-generation antidepressant

Postsynaptic neuron

FIGURE 8.3 (a) When a neuron releases norepinephrine or serotonin from its endings, a pump-like reuptake mechanism immediately begins to recapture some of the neurotransmitter molecules before they are received by the postsynaptic (receptor) neuron. (b) Tricyclic drugs block this reuptake process, enabling more norepinephrine or serotonin to reach, and thus fire, the post-synaptic (receptor) neuron. Serotonin reuptake inhibitors act more selectively on serotonin. Adapted from Snyder (1996, p. 106).

tricyclics and MAO inhibitors take from 7 to 14 days to relieve depression, but by that time, the neurotransmitter level has already returned to its previous state.

Another approach to further evaluate the theories involved measuring metabolites of these neurotransmitters, the by-products of the breakdown of serotonin, norepinephrine, and/or dopamine found in urine, blood serum, and the cerebrospinal fluid. The problem with such measurements is that they are not direct reflections of levels of neurotransmitters in the brain; metabolites measured in this way could reflect neurotransmitters anywhere in the body. Indeed, the

majority of neurons that use serotonin are found in the intestines and norepinephrine is also an important neurotransmitter in the peripheral nervous system. Further, despite the fact that some people showed the expected levels of neurotransmitters in connection with their depression or mania, the expected high or low metabolites were not found consistently. Thus, many people with depression or mania did not have disturbances in absolute levels of neurotransmitters (e.g., Placidi et al., 2001).

It would seem, then, that a simple change in the level of norepinephrine or serotonin or dopamine is not a sufficient explanation for why people become depressed and/or manic. What is the impact of these findings? Researchers then focused on the postsynaptic effects of antidepressants and developed theories of depression that implicate postsynaptic mechanisms. One line of research examined whether antidepressants alter the chemical messengers that a postsynaptic receptor sends into the postsynaptic neuron (Duman, Heninger, & Nestler, 1997). If receptors are overly sensitive they should respond to very small amounts of a neurotransmitter in the synaptic cleft. Researchers have focused primarily on dopamine and serotonin in this line of research. For example, drugs that increase dopamine levels have triggered manic behaviour in people with bipolar disorder, suggesting the possibility that dopamine receptors are overly sensitive (Anand et al., 2000).

Delgado et al. (1990) used a special diet to reduce the level of serotonin in depressed people in remission by lowering the level of its precursor, tryptophan. They found that 67% of clients experienced a return of their symptoms. A gradual remission followed when clients resumed their normal diet. Another study used this same tryptophan-depletion strategy in normal participants who had either a positive or a negative family history of depression. Again, as predicted by the low-serotonin theory, those with a positive family history experienced an increase in depressed mood (Benkelfat et al., 1994). Beck (2008) reviewed several studies that he interpreted as showing linkages between cognitive vulnerability and genetic vulnerability expressed as a hyperreactive serotonergic system (a neurochemical vulnerability).

Fakhoury (2015) recently summarized the research on the role of neurotransmitters in depressive disorders: "the mechanisms underlying their mode of action are still not very well characterized" (p. 174).

Both structural and functional activation brain-imaging studies have been conducted in research on mood disorders in an attempt to determine how depression relates to brain activity (see Davidson et al., 2002; Wise et al., 2014 for reviews). The amygdala, hippocampus, prefrontal cortex, and the anterior cingulate are the main brain structures implicated in MDD and bipolar disorder. For example, many findings have tied amygdala hyperactivity to depression. This hyperactivity in short 5-HTTLPR variant carriers is related to increased sensitivity to negative stimuli (see Munafò, Brown, & Hariri, 2008). Further, Siegle et al. (2007) reported that almost all depressed people have reduced prefrontal function. Beck (2008) suggests that a hyperactive amygdala in combination with hypoactive prefrontal regions is related to diminished cognitive appraisal and depression and represents a neurophysiological correlate of cognitive bias.

Ravindran and Kennedy (2007a) summarized several major neuroimaging studies and among the conclusions were that structural imaging studies show that recurrent depression and long-duration untreated depression are related to decreased hippocampal volume and neurocognitive impairment. However, quantitative meta-analyses of imaging studies in depression have found considerable heterogeneity in the results of resting studies and serotonin reuptake inhibitor antidepressant treatment (e.g., Fitzgerald et al., 2006). Margaret McKinnon and her colleagues at McMaster University (2009) conducted a meta-analysis of 32 MRI studies of hippocampal volume in people with MDD. It was concluded that hippocampal volume reductions occur among people whose duration of MDD was longer than two years or who had multiple episodes, suggesting that the reductions occur *after* onset of MDD.

In a major breakthrough study, Jeffrey Meyer and colleagues (2006) from the Centre for Addiction and Mental Health attempted to determine whether MAO-A levels in the brain are elevated during untreated depression. Monoamine oxidase A (MAO-A) is an enzyme that metabolizes monoamines such as serotonin, norepinephrine, and dopamine. The study compared healthy and depressed people with MDD who had been medication-free for at least five months. MAO-A was elevated by almost 35% throughout the brain during major depression. Meyer et al. (2006) concluded that "elevated MAO-A density is the primary monoamine-lowering process during major depression" (p. 1209). Follow-up research in Toronto established that elevated MAO-A density is found in postpartum mothers during the period that is typically associated with the postpartum blues (Sacher et al., 2010). Further, Meyer's team has confirmed the elevated MAO-A density in a sample of 15 women with postpartum depression who were compared with 21 control participants (Sacher et al., 2011).

Results also vary for neuroimaging studies for bipolar disorder. "Neurobiological mechanisms of bipolar disorder (BD) are still unclear and subject to debate" (Houenou, Perlini, & Brambilla, 2015, p. 117). Houenou and colleagues (2015) outline several reasons for the inconsistent findings across studies: (1) small sample sizes, leading to difficulties replicating results; (2) different equipment (e.g., MRI scanners) used across studies; and (3) different patient characteristics (e.g., ages of onset, suicide attempt status). They suggest using large samples and focusing on specific characteristics of bipolar disorder, rather than the whole disorder. For example, a neuroimaging study could focus on emotional reactivity, which is a core feature of bipolar disorder but is also present in other disorders (e.g., borderline personality disorder). Emotional reactivity could be assessed dimensionally (i.e., on a scale, rather than as an "all-or-none" diagnosis) and a possible correlation with a neuroimaging variable would be examined.

Should we assume that any biochemical, structural, or functional irregularities associated with depression mean that they play a causal role? Many experts believe that they do;

however, others remain skeptical (e.g., Gold, 2009; Paris, 2009). Moncrieff (2007b) summarized the skeptics' position as follows:

"If I experience an adverse event, I will feel sad, and if this emotion is strong enough, there are likely to be associated biochemical changes—but it is the event that has made me sad, not the chemical fluctuations. They are best viewed as an accompaniment, or a biological correlation, of the emotional state." (p. 100)

It will be a task of future research to resolve this issue.

The Neuroendocrine System

The hypothalamic-pituitary-adrenocortical (HPA) axis may also play a role in depression (see Figure 9.6 in Chapter 9). The limbic area of the brain is closely linked to emotion and also affects the hypothalamus. The hypothalamus in turn controls various endocrine glands and thus the levels of hormones they secrete. Hormones secreted by the hypothalamus also affect the pituitary gland and the hormones it produces. Because of its relevance to the so-called vegetative symptoms of depression, such as disturbances in appetite and sleep, the HPA axis is thought to be overactive in depression.

Various findings support this proposition. Levels of cortisol (an adrenocortical hormone) are high in depressed people, perhaps because of oversecretion of thyrotropin-releasing hormone by the hypothalamus (Garbutt et al., 1994). The excess secretion of cortisol in depressed persons also causes enlargement of their adrenal glands (Rubin et al., 1995). These high levels of cortisol have even led to the development of a biological test for depression: the dexamethasone suppression test. Dexamethasone suppresses cortisol secretion, but when given dexamethasone during an overnight test, some depressed people, especially those with delusional depression, do not experience cortisol suppression (Nelson & Davis, 1997). It is believed that the failure of dexamethasone to suppress cortisol reflects overactivity in the HPA axis of clients. The failure to show suppression ceases when the depressive episode ends, suggesting such failure is a non-specific response to stress.

Gotlib and his colleagues (2008) reported that carriers of the short 5-HTTLPR show elevated cortisol response, cognitive biases, and amygdala activation during a mood repair procedure. These and other converging findings led Beck (2008) to suggest the following pathway to depression: stress leads to distorted appraisal leads to engagement of the HPA axis leads to cortisol leads to depressive symptoms.

Finally, a review of research on the neuropsychology of depression led the authors to conclude that there is solid evidence implicating both the right and left hemispheres in the experience of depression (Shenal, Harrison, & Demaree, 2003). However, the depression itself may vary. Right hemisphere dysfunction involves symptoms of indifference or flat affect, while left hemisphere dysfunction involves more overt symptoms of agitation and sadness.

TABLE 8.2	**Summary of Main Biological Hypotheses About Major Depression and Bipolar Disorder**
Major depression	Genetic diathesis, low serotonin or serotonin-receptor dysfunction, high levels of cortisol.
Bipolar disorder	Genetic diathesis, low serotonin or low norepinephrine in depressed phase, high norepinephrine in manic phase.

All these data lend some support to theories that mood disorders have biological causes. (See Table 8.2 for a summary of major biological positions.) Does this mean that psychological theories are irrelevant or useless? Not in the least. To assert that behavioural disorders have a basis in biological processes is to state the obvious. No psychogenic theorist would deny that behaviour is mediated by some bodily changes. The biological and psychological theories may well be describing the same phenomena, but in different terms (such as learned helplessness vs. low serotonin). They should be thought of as complementary, not incompatible.

Deconstructing Depression?

Beck (2008) interpreted research comparing components of the cognitive model of depression with neurophysiological studies and proposed that it is possible to present a "pragmatic formulation of the interaction of the two levels" (p. 974). A summary of his "deconstructing" of the phenomenon of depression is presented in Figure 8.4. He proposed a hypothetical pathway that begins with a genetic vulnerability (probably the 5-HTTLPR polymorphism), which leads to excessive amygdala reactivity. Heightened limbic reactivity to stressful events causes deployment of increased attentional resources to these emotional events, which is manifested in negative attentional bias and recall (cognitive reactivity). Selective focus on the "negative" results in cognitive distortions (e.g., overgeneralization) and formation of dysfunctional attitudes (e.g., "I must be perfect"). Frequent occurrences of negative interpretations shape the content of schemas (e.g., worthless). At the same time, the negative interpretations affect the HPA axis and set in motion a cycle involving the overreactive serotonergic system, which leads to depression.

Beck (2008) notes that his formulation is tentative and subject to further research. There are methodological pitfalls in analyses of gene–environment analyses, including the 5-HTTLPR gene, and some aspects of his cognitive theory are speculative.

Further, the model's biological component undoubtedly involves complex circuits in multiple brain regions (see Mayberg, 2006). A series of multiple wave prospective studies starting in early childhood will be necessary to address various problems and questions and investigate the causal sequence.

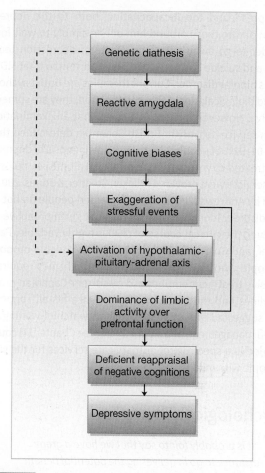

FIGURE 8.4 A developmental model of depression based on anomalous genes* Beck, A. T. (2008). The evolution of the cognitive model of depression and its neurobiological correlates. *American Journal of Psychiatry, 165*, 969–977. Reproduced with permission from The American Journal of Psychiatry. (Copyright 2008) American Psychiatric Association.

*Multiple interactions are not shown. Genetic pathways leading to reduced prefrontal activity have not been determined as yet. Increased limbic activity overrides prefrontal control.

8.4 Therapies for Mood Disorders

"The burden (of depression) persists because individuals do not seek treatment for their depression when they relapse and effective proactive treatment is not always provided when they do seek it."

—Gavin Andrews, 2008, p. 420

Most episodes of depression lift after a few months, although the time may seem immeasurably longer to the depressed individual and to those close to him or her. That most depressions are self-limiting is fortunate. However, depression is too widespread and too incapacitating, both to the depressed person and to those around him or her, simply to wait for the disorder to go away untreated. Bouts of depression tend to recur, and suicide is a risk. Thus, it is important to treat MDD, as well as bipolar disorder. Current therapies are both psychological and biological; singly or in combination, they are somewhat effective. However, it should be noted that an examination of health service delivery in British Columbia determined that in 2000–01, 92% of people who received a diagnosis of depression were treated by a primary care physician alone; i.e., no psychiatric services were provided (Bilsker, Goldner, & Jones, 2007). As noted by Andrews (2008), many depressed people do not have their disorder identified and are thus not given proactive care. However, the clinical course of MDD is highly variable. Patten, Bilsker, and Goldner (2008) argued that a sizeable proportion of people who meet criteria for MDD might not require the intensive treatment emphasized by current Canadian practice guidelines and they eschewed "a one-size-fits-all" approach. They suggested that strategies such as watchful waiting, self-guided management, and stepped care (see Chapter 17) could be included in a spectrum of primary care services for the subset of people with mild MDD.

Psychological Therapies

"It is probably fair to say that we have a great distance to go in delivering the potential benefit that psychosocial treatment could provide to people with depression in Canada."

—Elliot M. Goldner of Simon Fraser University in a 2008 guest editorial in the Canadian Journal of Psychiatry, p. 410

Psychodynamic Therapies Because depression is considered to be derived from a repressed sense of loss and from anger unconsciously turned inward, psychoanalytic treatment tries to help the client achieve insight into the repressed conflict and often encourages outward release of the hostility directed inward. The aim is to uncover latent motivations for the client's depression. People may, for example, blame themselves for a lack of parental affection but repress this belief because of the pain it causes. The therapist must first guide clients to confront the fact that they feel this way and then help them realize that any guilt is unfounded. The recovery of memories of stressful childhood circumstances should also bring relief.

Research on the effectiveness of dynamic psychotherapy in alleviating depression is sparse (e.g., Craighead, Evans, & Robins, 1992) and characterized by mixed results, in part owing to the high degree of variability among approaches that come under the rubric of psychodynamic or psychoanalytic psychotherapy. A report from the American Psychiatric Association (1993) concluded that there are no controlled data attesting to the efficacy of long-term psychodynamic psychotherapy or psychoanalysis in treating depression. Although

a more contemporary meta-analytic review (Leichsenring, 2001) concluded that short-term psychodynamic treatment and cognitive-behavioural therapy (CBT) are equally effective in alleviating depression, it was acknowledged that this conclusion must remain tentative because of the relatively small number of studies conducted. A more recent "mega-analysis" based on three randomized clinical trials (de Maat et al., 2008) concluded that a short psychodynamic supportive psychotherapy was as effective as antidepressants for people with mild to moderate MDD. Combined therapy was superior to pharmacotherapy alone.

Findings from a well-known large-scale study (Elkin et al., 1989) suggest that a form of psychodynamic therapy that concentrates on present-day interactions between the depressed person and the social environment—Klerman and Weissman's interpersonal therapy (IPT) (Klerman et al., 1984)—is effective for alleviating unipolar depression, as well as for maintaining treatment gains (Frank et al., 1990). The core of the therapy is to help depressed people examine the ways in which their current interpersonal behaviour might interfere with obtaining pleasure from relationships. For example, the clients might be taught how to improve communication with others to meet their own needs better and to have more satisfying social interactions and support. This psychodynamic therapy is not as much intrapsychic as it is interpersonal. It emphasizes better understanding of the interpersonal problems assumed to give rise to depression and aims at improving relationships with others. As such, the focus is on better communication, reality testing, developing effective social skills, and meeting present social-role requirements. Actual techniques include discussion of interpersonal problems, exploration of and encouragement to express negative feelings, improvement of both verbal and non-verbal communications, problem-solving, and suggesting new and more satisfying modes of behaviour. The focus is on the client's current life, not on an exploration of past, often-repressed causes of present-day problems. A meta-analysis of 38 studies involving IPT found that IPT is effective but overall, it was not superior to other treatments. IPT was more effective than control conditions, and IPT added significantly to pharmacotherapy, but pharmacotherapy was more effective overall (Cuijpers et al., 2011). However, IPT was the better predictor of protecting people who had recovered from their depressions from relapse. Overall, Cuijpers et al. (2011) concluded that "IPT deserves its place in treatment guidelines as one of the most empirically validated treatments for depression" (p. 581).

Cognitive and Behavioural Therapies In keeping with their contention that depression is caused by errors in thinking, Beck and his associates devised a cognitive therapy (CT) aimed at altering maladaptive thought patterns. The therapist works collaboratively with depressed persons to change their opinions of events and of the self. When a client expresses worthlessness because "Nothing goes right; everything I try to do ends in a disaster," the therapist works with the client to identify examples contrary to this overgeneralization. The therapist also encourages clients to monitor private monologues and to identify all patterns of thought that contribute to depression. The therapist then helps clients to think through negative prevailing beliefs to understand how these beliefs prevent them from making more realistic (more positive) assumptions.

Although developed independently of Ellis's rational-emotive method, Beck's analyses are similar to it in some ways. For example, Beck suggests that depressed people are likely to consider themselves totally inept and incompetent if they make a mistake (see Brown & Beck, 2002). This schema can be considered an extension of one of Ellis's irrational beliefs (i.e., the individual must be competent in all things in order to be worthwhile).

Beck also includes behavioural components in his treatment. When clients are severely depressed, he encourages them to do things, such as get out of bed in the morning or go for a walk. He gives his clients activity assignments to provide them with successful experiences and allow them to think well of themselves. But the overall emphasis is on cognitive restructuring, on persuading the person to think differently. If a change in behaviour will help achieve that goal, fine. However, behavioural change by itself is not expected to alleviate depression.

Over the past several decades, considerable research has been conducted on Beck's therapy, beginning with a widely cited study by Rush et al. (1977), which indicated that CT was more successful than tricyclic imipramine (Tofranil) in alleviating unipolar depression. The unusually low improvement rate found for the drug in this clinical trial suggests that these clients might have been poorly suited for pharmacotherapy and that this was therefore not a fair comparison. Nonetheless, subsequent research confirmed that Beck's therapy has a prophylactic effect in preventing subsequent bouts of depression (Hollon, DeRubeis, & Seligman, 1992). Other research (Parrish et al., 2009) using a daily diary designed to evaluate depressed people's changes on daily stress-related variables during CT confirmed that CT has its intended effects: after six sessions, clients reported a reduction in daily sad affect, daily negative thoughts, and sad affect reactivity to daily stressors, as well as an increase in daily positive affect.

A meta-analysis by Hamilton and Dobson (2002), while confirming the efficacy of CT, identified several factors that contribute to less favourable outcomes. CT is less effective when used to treat people with high levels of dysfunctional attitudes and high pre-treatment severity scores on measures of depression; it is also less effective for those with more chronic forms of depression, an increased number of previous episodes, and earlier onsets. Further, Fournier et al. (2008) determined that a comorbid personality disorder predicts a poor response to 16 weeks of CT (44%), relative to an antidepressant (paroxetine) group (66%), in people diagnosed with moderate to severe depression; however, sustained response rates over a 12-month follow-up were virtually identical in the prior CT and a continuation medication group (38%). People withdrawn from medication showed a very low sustained response rate (6%).

In another RCT, Bagby et al. (2008) established that depressed clients with higher scores on neuroticism were more responsive to pharmacotherapy, perhaps because pharmacotherapy "may

directly target neural systems involved in dysregulated emotions, circumventing the cognitive requirements for response to CBT" (Bagby et al., 2008, p. 367). The authors suggested that these individuals might benefit from treatment sequencing: initial treatment with pharmacotherapy followed by CBT when they are better able to use CBT strategies.

Bell and D'Zurilla (2009) conducted a meta-analysis of problem-solving therapy for depression, a CBT intervention that focuses on training in adaptive problem-solving attitudes and skills (see D'Zurilla & Nezu, 2010). Problem-solving therapy was deemed as effective as other psychosocial interventions and pharmacotherapy and significantly more effective than support/attention control groups and no treatment.

When treatments are compared and yield similar effects, people start to question whether there is anything unique in any form of psychotherapy. A multiple treatments meta-analysis found support for the specificity of CBT for depression, with the specificity increasing as the number of CBT sessions increased (Honyashiki et al., 2014). Also, better outcomes tend to be obtained at sites with more experienced therapists (Strunk, Brotman, DeRubeis, & Hollon, 2010). There is also a meta-analysis supporting the use of CBT for children with depression (Arnberg & Öst, 2014).

Other research shows that CBT for depression is becoming less effective over time. Rather than seeing improvements in the efficacy of CBT as treatment techniques are being refined, the effect sizes are actually falling as time goes on (Johnsen & Friborg, 2015). The decreasing trend was found for self-report, clinician ratings, and rates of remission.

Mindfulness-Based Cognitive Therapy

A treatment known as mindfulness-based cognitive therapy (MBCT) has been developed specifically to prevent relapse among people who have been depressed. MBCT is an extension of Kabat-Zinn's stress-reduction program that teaches people how to combat stress through mindfulness meditation. In contrast, the MBCT approach developed by Zindel Segal from Toronto (see photo), John Teasdale from England, and Mark Williams from Wales combines mindfulness meditation designed to increase awareness of changes in the body and the mind with cognitive intervention techniques (see Segal, Williams, & Teasdale, 2012). The key component is developing metacognitive awareness (i.e., the ability to step back from one's thoughts and feelings, and see them as just thoughts and feeling). Extensive research indicates that MBCT is effective. Rates of relapse are substantially reduced (cut in half) among clients who have had at least three previous episodes of depression (Teasdale et al., 2000), and reduced relapse following either MBCT or CT is associated with increases in metacognitive awareness (Teasdale et al., 2002).

Although originally developed as a treatment for people who are currently well, but formerly depressed, MBCT has been evaluated by more recent research regarding its use for people with current symptoms of depression, as well as other forms of psychopathology. MBCT appears to be successful in reducing current symptoms in people suffering from chronic-recurrent depression with a history of suicidal ideation (Barnhofer et al., 2009). A meta-analysis established that MBCT is effective in the treatment of both anxiety and depression (Hofmann, Sawyer, Witt, & Oh, 2010). This analysis of 39 studies found that MBCT has a moderate level of effectiveness but treatment improvements are indeed retained over time. Finally, a recent review highlighted the continued success seen across many samples, but there is one noteworthy limitation: comparisons with credible control conditions are limited (MacKenzie & Kocovski, 2016).

Why does MBCT work? We already touched on increases in metacognitive awareness as one possible mechanism of action (Teasdale et al., 2000). Another study found that CBT and MBCT seemed to yield improvements by reducing the cognitive tendency to engage in rumination (Manicavasagar, Perich, & Parker, 2012). Other potentially helpful aspects of training include exposure to negative moods and arousal states, relaxation, and acceptance of unwanted experiences. Williams, Teasdale, Segal, and Soulsby (2000) also showed that MBCT reduces the overgenerality of autobiographical memory effect. When asked to recall specific past events in their lives, depressed people, relative to non-depressed people, tend to provide broad, categorical memories lacking in specificity (e.g., "My father was cruel") rather than specific, detailed events. The **overgenerality effect** is believed to reflect the negative schema described by Beck. Depressed people who receive MBCT show reduced overgenerality; they have learned new encoding and retrieval skills that involve processing their past and current experiences in non-judgemental ways.

There are other approaches to the prevention of relapse, most notably preventive cognitive therapy, which is delivered to clients after a successful response to CT. Bockting and colleagues (2015) completed a 10-year follow-up study of a randomized controlled trial in which participants had received treatment as usual or preventive cognitive therapy in addition to treatment as usual. Similar to the results we reviewed on MBCT, the number of previous episodes of depression played a role. Preventive cognitive therapy helped those who had

Zindel Segal is the director of training in the new Graduate Department in Psychological Clinical Science at the University of Toronto Scarborough. He is one of the developers of Mindfulness-Based Cognitive Therapy.

experienced more than three previous episodes stay well longer. They suggested that booster sessions may be helpful.

The primary goal of MBCT, as originally developed, is to prevent depressive relapse among people with a history of depression. But what about preventive interventions focused on reducing the likelihood of experiencing depression among people in general? Their use is illustrated in Student Perspectives 8.1, which examines the prevalence of depression in university and college students and what we know thus far about whether depression in students can be prevented.

Psychological Treatment of Bipolar Disorder

Psychological therapies also show promise in dealing with many of the interpersonal, cognitive, and emotional problems of clients with bipolar disorder. If a client in a manic phase commits an indiscretion such as having an extramarital affair or spending everything in the family bank account, stress is likely to be higher as a result, and stress can trigger a subsequent mood swing. A cognitive-behavioural intervention targeted at the thoughts and interpersonal behaviours that go awry during wide mood swings appears to be effective (Basco & Rush, 1996).

One problem in getting bipolar clients to take their medication regularly is that they often lack insight into the self-destructive nature of their behaviour. A small but significant number of empirical studies show that careful education about bipolar disorder and its treatment can improve adherence to medication, which is helpful in reducing the mood swings of this disorder, thereby bringing more stability into the client's life (e.g., Craighead et al., 1998). Obviously, an effective drug is beneficial only to the extent that it is taken as prescribed. It is also important to recognize that, in addition to improving adherence to a drug regimen, education about the illness is likely to increase social support from family and friends (Craighead et al., 1998).

People with bipolar disorder relapse more quickly if they return from hospital to family settings characterized by high levels of hostility and overinvolvement (called "expressed emotion") than if they return to a less-charged emotional climate in the home (Miklowitz et al., 1996). Research indicates the effectiveness of educating the family about the disorder, the desirability of working to reduce stress at home, and the need to continue medication to help maintain improvements of the discharged bipolar client (Glick et al., 1991).

There is currently considerable controversy about the usefulness of psychotherapy for severe and recurrent bipolar disorders. Scott et al. (2006) conducted the largest multicentre pragmatic RCT of psychological therapy for bipolar disorder. They compared the effectiveness of "treatment as usual" with an additional 22 sessions of CT. It was concluded that CT was effective only for a minority of clients with fewer than 12 previous episodes. However, in an invited commentary, Dominic Lam (2006) was critical of the study design, which made interpretation of the results difficult, and contrasted the study with four other major pragmatic RCTs of structured psychological interventions (including two on which he was senior author) that reported beneficial results.

Student Perspectives 8.1

Prevalence and Prevention of Depressive Disorders in University and College Students

It seems that being a university student, in and of itself, affords little protection against experiencing depression. Indeed, over 20 years ago, Vredenburg, Flett, and Krames (1993) outlined several factors that could result in pushing vulnerable students into a bout of depression and most of these factors still apply today. Key issues that face most students include the sense of uncertainty in personal identity associated with their developmental stage, the tendency for many university students to live away from home (often for the first time), and the extensive evaluations and personal feedback that students receive about their capabilities along with social comparison pressures.

As was the case with anxiety disorders, the prevalence of depression among students is quite elevated. The large and nationally representative epidemiological study in the United States conducted by Blanco et al. (2008) that was introduced in Chapter 5 found that in terms of the prevalence of depression, there was a 12-month prevalence rate of almost 12% in college students aged 19 to 25. Another large investigation by Eisenberg and colleagues found that 13.8% of undergraduates had some type of depression compared with 11.3% of graduate students (Eisenberg, Gollust, Golberstein, & Hefner, 2007). A European study of university women that included diagnostic interviews found that the three most common disorders were nicotine dependence, depression, and generalized anxiety disorder (Vasquez, Torres, Otero, & Diaz, 2011). The current one-year prevalence of depression among the European female students was 9.0% and the lifetime prevalence was 15.1%.

A systematic review of existing studies by Ibraham, Kelly, Adams, and Glazebrook (2013) reported a whopping mean prevalence of 30.6%, but this included studies where the focus was on self-reported depressive symptoms that exceeded a threshold rather than on diagnosed depression. Still, as argued by Vredenburg et al. (1993), symptoms of depression can be very troubling for anyone, including students.

The prevalence of clinical depression and depressive symptoms suggests a need for preventive efforts. A meta-analysis of interventions devised for children and adolescents found that such programs resulted in small but significant improvements. Programs were most effective when delivered by trained professionals and when they included a specific focus on reducing negative cognitions and increasing problem-solving training (Stice et al., 2009).

As for at-risk university students, Martin Seligman and colleagues found that students in an eight-week workshop, vs. those in a control group, had significantly fewer depressive and anxious symptoms but the two groups did not differ in terms of the number of depression or anxiety episodes at the six-month follow-up (Seligman, Schulman, & Tryon, 2007). Supplementary analyses linked improvements with the development of an optimistic explanatory style. However, few students used the web-based materials that were developed to supplement the specific components of the intervention (i.e., CBT techniques, interpersonal skill training, and stress management).

A more recent RCT by Vasquez et al. (2012) found that both CBT and relaxation training were useful. This research focused on depression in students in general. Another alternative is a targeted approach. That is, certain factors that put students at risk can become a key focus for prevention. This type of preventive intervention was done for students who had problematic levels of perfectionistic thoughts as measured by the Perfectionism Cognitions Inventory (PCI; Flett, Hewitt, Blankstein, & Gray, 1998). Research conducted in Ontario by Arpin-Cribbie and colleagues pre-selected students based on high PCI scores. They demonstrated the benefits of an online intervention that combined CBT with stress management and that addressed specific issues associated with dysfunctional perfectionism (Arpin-Cribbie et al., 2008; Arpin-Cribbie, Irvine, & Ritvo, 2012). CBT reduced levels of depression and anxiety, and reductions in perfectionistic thoughts were linked with reductions in depression and anxiety. Still, some students may have been at risk following the preventive intervention because the intervention tended to reduce perfectionism to a more moderate level but it did not eliminate this type of perfectionism thinking.

Overall, it seems that cognitive, behavioural, and mindfulness interventions can be helpful to reduce stress in university students, but the availability of these programs could be improved (Regehr, Glancy, & Pitts, 2013). Regehr and colleagues (2013) note that male students are underrepresented; they suggest developing programs that would be more appealing to male students.

Thinking Critically

1. Do you think there is something inherent in the stress of being a student that causes depression, or do you think the roots of becoming depressed are well-established prior to university?

2. Do you believe that universities can design programs to reduce levels of depression among their students? Should universities invest resources in alleviating distress or do you feel that they should concentrate resources on enhancing the quality of education that their students receive?

Lam outlined the common features in psychological treatments for relapse prevention in bipolar disorder, including the following:

- psychoeducation
- promotion of medication adherence
- promotion of regular daily routines and sleep
- monitoring of mood

- detection of early warnings and relapse prevention strategies
- general coping strategies and problem-solving techniques

Lam (2006) concluded on the weight of evidence that structured psychological interventions are beneficial in relapse prevention. However, the evidence continues to be mixed. Beynon and her colleagues (2008) conducted a review and meta-analysis of psychosocial interventions and concluded that CBT, group psychoeducation, and possibly family therapy may be beneficial as adjuncts to pharmacological maintenance treatment for the prevention of relapse in bipolar disorder. On the contrary, a more recent systematic review on psychosocial interventions for bipolar disorder concluded that only psychoeducation is useful, and only under certain specific conditions (Miziou et al., 2015). Approximately one-third of clients with bipolar disorder seek psychotherapy, and they score higher on illness severity than those who do not seek psychotherapy (Sylvia et al., 2015).

Biological Therapies

"The quest for the magic bullet for depression may be a wild goose chase."

—Moncrieff, 2007a, p. 97

"Although we agree that there is no magic bullet to cure depression, antidepressants play a significant role in its treatment, and to suggest they have no effect is tantamount to throwing the baby out with the bathwater."

—Ravindran and Kennedy, 2007b, p. 102

There are a variety of biological therapies for depression and mania. The two most common are electroconvulsive shock and various drugs.

Electroconvulsive Therapy   Perhaps the most dramatic, and controversial, treatment for severe depression is **electroconvulsive therapy (ECT)**. ECT was introduced in the early twentieth century by two Italian physicians, Cerletti and Bini. More rudimentary treatment methods were used historically prior to the advent of ECT; for instance, in the sixteenth century, electric catfish were used to induce shock in people in an attempt to expel devils (see Endler & Persad, 1988).

Previously, Cerletti was interested in epilepsy and sought a means to induce seizures. The solution became apparent to him during a visit to a slaughterhouse, where he saw seizures induced in animals by electric shocks administered to the head. Shortly thereafter, he found that by applying electric shocks to the sides of the human head, he could produce full epileptic seizures. Then, in Rome in 1938, he used the technique on a person with schizophrenia. In the decades that followed, ECT was administered to people with both schizophrenia and severe depression, usually in hospital settings. Its use is restricted today to profoundly depressed individuals.

ECT is being used with increased frequency in Canada and elsewhere. Why? One reason is that when it works, it is faster than antidepressants and psychotherapy. The increased use of ECT was brought to the attention of the public thanks to an independent review conducted in British Columbia. A psychiatrist had expressed concern that the use of ECT had increased dramatically at the Riverview Hospital in Coquitlam, B.C. Indeed, it was determined that ECT use had more than doubled between 1996 and 1999 as a way of treating depression in people aged 65

or older. The review panel concluded that the use of ECT at the hospital was appropriate.

ECT entails the deliberate induction of a seizure and momentary unconsciousness by passing a current between 70 and 130 volts through the client's brain (see photo). Electrodes were formerly placed on each side of the forehead, allowing the current to pass through both hemispheres, a method known as **bilateral ECT**. Today, **unilateral ECT**, in which the current passes through the non-dominant (right) cerebral hemisphere only (e.g., Abrams, Swartz, & Vedak, 1991), is used. In the past, the person was usually awake when the current triggered the seizure and the electric shock often created frightening contortions of the body, sometimes even causing bone fractures. Now the client is given a short-acting anaesthetic, then an injection of a strong muscle relaxant, before the current is applied. The convulsive spasms of the body muscles are barely perceptible to onlookers, and the client awakens a few minutes later remembering nothing about the treatment. The mechanism through which ECT works is unknown. It reduces metabolic activity and blood circulation to the brain and may thus inhibit aberrant brain activity. A recent study found that ECT led to improvements in problem solving, compared with a control group, and these improvements were related to changes in spontaneous brain activity (Du et al., 2016).

Inducing a seizure is still a drastic procedure. Why should anyone agree to undergo such radical therapy? How could a parent or a spouse consent to such treatment for a person judged legally incapable of giving consent? The answer is simple. Although we don't know why, ECT may be the optimal treatment for extremely severe depression. Most professionals acknowledge the risks involved: confusion and memory loss that can be prolonged. However, unilateral ECT to the non-dominant hemisphere erases fewer memories than does bilateral ECT, and no detectable changes in brain structure result (Devanand et al., 1994). Clinicians typically resort to ECT only when the depression is unremitting and after less-drastic treatments have been tried and found wanting. In considering any treatment that has negative side effects, the person making the decision must be aware of the consequences of not providing any treatment at all. Given that suicide is a real possibility, the use of ECT, at least after other treatments have failed, is regarded by many as defensible and responsible.

Recent research has focused on comparing right unilateral brief and ultrabrief pulse ECT. The rationale for investigating the ultrabrief protocol was that it may be associated with fewer cognitive deficits (e.g., memory loss). The jury is still out, as evidenced by a recent exchange in the *Journal of Clinical Psychiatry*. Some research has suggested that the standard brief protocol is more effective, with no differences in cognitive side effects (Spaans et al., 2013). However, in a letter to the editor, Kellner and colleagues (2014) state that "given the study limitations, we suggest that it is premature to conclude that right unilateral (RUL) ultrabrief pulse ECT confers inferior efficacy and no cognitive advantage"(p. 777). Although there are differences of opinion, both groups advocate for more research on the optimal procedures for ECT.

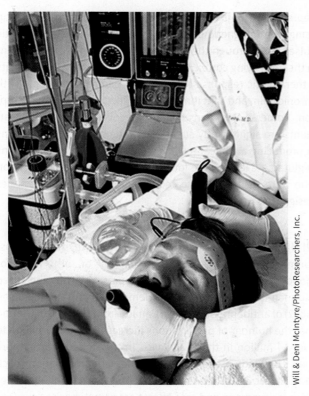

ECT was first used on a person with schizophrenia in 1938.

Will & Deni McIntyre/PhotoResearchers, Inc.

One issue that has emerged is the high relapse rate of people treated with ECT. A meta-analysis of six studies concluded that ECT was quite effective, and equally so for both unipolar and bipolar depression, but the overall remission rate was 51.5% (Dierckx, Heijnen, van den Broek, & Birkenhager, 2012). Jelovac, Kolshus, and McLoughlin (2013) completed a more extensive meta-analysis of 32 studies and found similar results. Those treated with continuation pharmacotherapy following successful ECT had a relapse rate of 51.1% by 12 months. Overall, it is discouraging that about half of those successfully treated with ECT will relapse within a year.

Many activist groups have expressed concerns about the use of ECT, and these protests continue. The groups maintain that the procedure is inhumane, involves considerable risk, and is not effective. In addition, there are published accounts by former clients who believe that ECT led to permanent damage. Wendy Funk of Cranbook, B.C., for example, wrote a book detailing her negative experiences and claimed that ECT wiped out her lifetime of memories (see Funk, 1998). Clearly, as with most treatments, there is variability in the outcomes experienced, for other people feel that ECT saved their lives. Several public inquiries conducted throughout Canada led to conclusions that support the use of ECT (Endler & Persad, 1988). An Ontario report (Clark, 1985) concluded that ECT is effective but that safeguards must remain in place to protect the well-being of clients, including the right to informed consent. Full, informed consent is crucial, given that some people have indeed had negative experiences with ECT. Parenthetically, a series of articles in the *Toronto Star* in December 2012 brought public attention to this issue when it was noted that Ontario

Popperfoto/Getty Images

Ernest Hemingway, author and former reporter for the *Toronto Daily Star*, shot himself in 1961. He attributed the fatal step he would take, in part, to receiving more than 20 sessions of ECT. He questioned: "What is the sense of ruining my head and erasing my memory, which is my capital, and putting me out of business? It was a brilliant cure, but we lost the patient." See Meyers, 1999.

leads Canada in the use of ECT (see photo). Particular note was made of an "incomprehensible" increase such that "in the year 2010–2011, the most recent year for which statistics are available, 16,259 ECT treatments were administered throughout Ontario, an increase of more than 350 per cent in seven years" (Wells & Zlomislic, 2012). Concerns were also raised about certain people receiving a large number of treatments. It was also noted that the 1985 call that was issued for guidelines and standards as a result of a government inquiry has not resulted in such standards despite this extreme increase in the number of treatments.

Norman Endler (see Canadian Contributions 9.2 in Chapter 9) was one of Canada's leading proponents of ECT. Why? Because Endler was twice treated successfully with ECT when he suffered from bipolar depression. He chronicled his experiences in his memoir *Holiday of Darkness* (Endler, 1982). Endler

Courtesy of Glenn Lowson

One Ontario resident, Annette VanEs (shown here), reported undergoing 40 electroshock treatments in a series by the *Toronto Star* on the increased use of ECT in Ontario.

also examined ECT from a scientific perspective in a book entitled *Electroconvulsive Therapy: The Myths and the Realities* (see Endler & Persad, 1988). ECT is not successful for everyone, however. For example, ECT had tragic consequences for famous author Ernest Hemingway (see photo).

Deep Brain Stimulation and Repetitive Transcranial Magnetic Stimulation

We will now consider two newer forms of biological treatment, starting with **deep brain stimulation**. Helen Mayberg and colleagues (2005) from the Rotman Research Institute in Toronto reported on preliminary success in a small number of people with a deep brain electrical stimulation procedure for treatment-resistant depression, a severely disabling disorder with no treatment options once ECT, medication, and psychotherapy have failed. The experimental treatment is based on the observation that the subgenual cingulate region (Brodmann area 25) is metabolically overactive in treatment-resistant depression. Mayberg et al. (2005) concluded that "disrupting focal pathological activity in limbic-cortical circuits using electrical stimulation of the subgenual cingulate white matter can effectively reverse symptoms in otherwise treatment-resistant depression" (p. 651). Follow-up research on the efficacy of deep brain stimulation was similarly successful (Lozano et al., 2008) and it has been shown to be equally safe and effective in treating unipolar and bipolar depression (Holtzheimer et al., 2012). Moreover, it has been tested and shown to also be effective for treating various conditions, including obsessive-compulsive disorder, substance abuse, traumatic brain injury, and Alzheimer's type dementia (Sankar, Tierney, & Hamani, 2012). In fact, a pilot study done in Toronto suggests that it also is effective in treating anorexia nervosa (Lipsman et al., 2013).

One issue with deep brain stimulation is that the cost of device implantation can run as high as $250,000 per person (Cusin & Dougherty, 2012). This includes the cost of a multidisciplinary team of neurosurgeons, psychiatrists, neuropsychologists, and support staff.

Repetitive transcranial magnetic stimulation (rTMS) is a second new development in the biological treatment of depression. This is a non-invasive method of brain stimulation using brief magnetic pulses to stimulate the brain. Magnetic pulses pass through the skull and produce an electric current in the underlying cortex. Initial studies suggest that rTMS elicits a therapeutic response in depressed people and people with chronic pain, and that it may be as effective as ECT (see Sampson, Rome, & Rummans, 2006). Moreover, active rTMS treatments are significantly superior to "sham" control conditions in producing a clinical response (Lam et al., 2008). Elevations in glutamate levels were found in adolescents with depression who were successfully treated with rTMS, using a case series design (Yang et al., 2014).

Drug Therapy For Depression

Drugs are the most commonly used treatments—biological or otherwise—for mood disorders. The use of antidepressants has increased exponentially. An analysis by Hemels, Koren, and Einarson (2002) of antidepressant use in Canada from 1981 to 2000 found that the number of prescriptions increased from 3.2 million to over 14 million in those 20 years. In the United States, more than $10 billion is spent on antidepressant prescriptions each year (Potter, 2009). However, antidepressants definitely do not work for everyone and side effects are sometimes serious (see Table 8.3). Moreover, it is difficult to identify personal characteristics that might predict treatment response. Response to drug treatment is not reliably predicted by age, sex, age at onset, symptom duration, or number of reoccurrences of the disorder.

In our earlier discussion of biological research on depression, we mentioned three major categories of antidepressant drugs:

1. monoamine oxidase (MAO) inhibitors, such as tranylcypromine (Parnate)

2. tricyclics, such as imipramine (Tofranil) and amitriptyline (Elavil)

3. selective serotonin reuptake inhibitors (SSRIs), such as fluoxetine (Prozac, which was successful in treating author Robert Munsch; see photo) and sertraline (Zoloft)

TABLE 8.3	**Drugs for Treating Mood Disorders**		
Category	**Generic Name**	**Trade Name**	**Side Effects**
Tricyclic antidepressants	imipramine, amitriptyline	Tofranil, Elavil	Heart attack, stroke, hypotension, blurred vision, anxiety, tiredness, dry mouth, constipation, gastric disorders, erectile failure, weight gain
MAO inhibitors	tranylcypromine	Parnate	Possibly fatal hypertension, dry mouth, dizziness, nausea, headaches
Selective serotonin reuptake inhibitors	fluoxetine	Prozac	Nervousness, fatigue, gastrointestinal complaints, dizziness, headaches, insomnia
Lithium	lithium	None	Tremors, gastric distress, lack of coordination, dizziness, cardiac arrhythmia, blurred vision, fatigue, death

The CCHS 1.2 offered the first opportunity to characterize Canadian psychotropic medication use on a national level within the assessed diagnostic groups. Beck et al. (2005) reported that SSRIs were the most commonly used antidepressants for those who had a major depressive episode in the past year (17.8%). Among people 15 to 19 years old with past-year depression, antidepressant use (primarily SSRIs) was 11.7%. Unfortunately, a detailed assessment of treatment quality was not possible. The researchers predicted that antidepressant use among younger participants will decline in future in view of the lack of evidence for antidepressant efficacy.

Antidepressant medication often is used in combination with some kind of psychotherapy. If, for example, a person's depression is (partly) caused by a lack of personal satisfaction because of social skills problems, it is probably essential for the drug treatment to be supplemented by attention to those behavioural deficits. A review by Segal, Vincent, and Levitt (2002) led to the conclusion that combination therapy involving medication and CT works better than either in isolation, but this conclusion is qualified by the relatively small number of participants in existing studies. Thus, a conclusive answer is not available.

The STAR*D project is a clear example of the flexible, individual-focused approach. STAR*D stands for Sequence Treatment Alternatives to Relieve Depression. It focuses on a modifiable treatment process for major depressive disorder in adults in outpatient settings. The main premise in a sense is "whatever works." Clients first receive medication (citalopram, an SSRI medication), but if symptoms remain after 8 to 12 weeks of treatment, other types of treatment are used, including other medications but also CBT. Often, clients experience two or more types of treatment in order to derive maximum benefit. Up to 30 clinic visits may be required and there is a one-year follow-up. In general, data are accumulating in support of a sequenced approach for people who initially receive medication. Meta-analytic results confirm that following medication with psychotherapy is quite effective in reducing relapse rates among individuals with a history of depression (Guidi, Fava, Fava, & Papakostas, 2010).

According to Rush (2011), STAR*D is now concluded and has resulted in over 100 published journal articles. It yielded some important findings and these are summarized below. But what is the overall picture? Rush (2011) concluded that "the results of STAR*D were both encouraging and a bit disappointing. The response and remission rates were neither terrific nor terrible" (p. 523). However, it is possible to be much more negative about the results, and indeed, some authors have been more critical in their overall assessment. As summarized by Rush (2011), some of the main findings that emerged were:

1. The cumulative remission rate after four treatment steps was under 70%, meaning that there is still a large proportion of depressed people who did not significantly improve.

2. No helpful pre-treatment factors (e.g., having anxious symptoms, insomnia, atypical melancholia) provided helpful clues about which specific medication is best for a particular client.

3. One-third of those people receiving medication who had remitted depression by 12 weeks had not shown improvement by 6 weeks. This suggests that decisions made to stop or change a medication for the initial non-responders may be premature decisions; that is, some people just need a longer treatment course.

4. Depressed clients with signs of anxiety had poorer response and remission rates to various antidepressants. This is in keeping with comorbidity being associated with reduced treatment effectiveness in general.

5. Minority participants, especially Black participants, had more comorbidity, poorer quality of life, and greater attrition. Rush (2011) suggested that minority participants may not seek treatment until a more severe psychological state has been reached and that earlier intervention for these people is clearly preferable.

Collectively, these findings confirm a general trend from years of research: that is, combined treatments offer relief for many but not all depressed people and there are still many treatment-resistant people who will be in need.

At present, there is growing controversy over the efficacy of antidepressants. In a feature called "In Debate" in the *Canadian Journal of Psychiatry,* Moncrieff (2007a, b) argued that not only are antidepressants not as effective as claimed, they are not effective at all! She claimed that the effects seen in randomized controlled trials can be accounted for by "nonspecific pharmacologic and psychological actions" (Moncrieff, 2007a, p. 96). In rebuttal, Ravindran and Kennedy (2007a) argued that "antidepressant medications are the most available first-line treatments for moderate-to-severe major depressive episodes" (p. 98).

Will future research lead to definitive conclusions and consensus among stakeholders about the efficacy and/or effectiveness and safety of antidepressants? Probably not, especially since pharmaceutical companies will continue to introduce and market new-generation antidepressants.

Drug Therapy for Bipolar Disorder

People with the mood swings of bipolar disorder are often helped by carefully monitored dosages of the element lithium, taken in a salt form, **lithium carbonate** (the first "mood stabilizer"). Up to 80% of individuals with bipolar disorder experience at least some benefit from taking this drug (Prien & Potter, 1993). Lithium is effective for clients with bipolar disorder when they are depressed as well as when they are manic, and it is much more effective for bipolar clients than for unipolar clients—another bit of evidence that these two mood disorders are different from each other. Because the effects of lithium occur gradually, therapy typically begins with both lithium and an antipsychotic, such as Haldol, which has an immediate calming effect.

Interestingly, according to Shorter (2009), lithium was never approved for use in the United States by the Food and Drug Administration (FDA) because of varying opinions about its usefulness, despite strong appeals made back in the early 1970s by Gerald Klerman, who was the chair of psychiatry at

Harvard University. Also, according to Shorter (2009), the frequency of use of lithium is threatened by the growth in popularity of "mood stabilizers."

Because of possibly serious, even fatal, side effects, lithium has to be prescribed and used very carefully. Although it has great value in the elimination of a manic episode and forestalling future episodes if it is taken regularly, discontinuation of lithium actually increases the risk of recurrence (Suppes et al., 1991). Thus, it is recommended that lithium be used continuously. Unfortunately, many clients discontinue treatment after release from the hospital (Maj et al., 1998).

Rates of use of lithium have decreased in recent years due to concerns about lasting side effects. An analysis of 385 studies was conducted by researchers at the University of Oxford (see McKnight et al., 2012). This study reaffirmed the continuing use of lithium as the treatment of choice. It found little evidence of one side effect (i.e., renal failure) but did find that about 1 in 4 clients taking lithium experience abnormalities in the thyroid and parathyroid glands. This possible side effect points to the need for calcium levels to be monitored in people taking lithium.

Although lithium is the treatment of choice for bipolar disorder (see Yatham et al., 2013 for the revised Canadian guidelines), the psychological aspects of the disorder must be considered, if only to encourage the person to continue taking the medication (Goodwin & Jamison, 1990). A friend of one of the authors put it this way (paraphrased): "Lithium cuts out the highs as well as the lows. I don't miss the lows, but I have to admit that there were some aspects of the highs that I do miss. It took me a while to accept that I had to give up those highs. Wanting to keep my job and my marriage helped!" A drug alone does not address this kind of concern.

Robert Munsch, well-known author of children's books, experienced depression for many years and attributes his recovery to taking Prozac.

Treatment for Seasonal Affective Disorder

Therapy for winter depressions typically involves exposing clients to bright, white light. According to the Canadian Consensus Guidelines, exposure to bright, white light (known as **phototherapy**) is a highly effective treatment for seasonal affective disorder (Lam & Levitt, 1999). Lam and his co-workers at the University of British Columbia have shown that phototherapy does indeed alleviate seasonal affective disorder and the associated symptoms of depression, including suicidal tendencies (see Lam et al., 2000; Levitt, Lam, & Levitan, 2002). More recent research conducted in the United States by Kelly Rohan and colleagues shows that phototherapy is more effective if combined with CBT, and long-term follow-ups confirmed the effectiveness of this combination. However, in terms of clinician ratings of the severity of depression, CBT may be somewhat more effective than phototherapy (Rohan et al., 2007; Rohan, Roecklein, Lacy, & Vacek, 2009). So, how is CBT tailored and modified as an intervention for seasonal affective disorder? Thinking focuses on how to identify the specific negative thoughts experienced during seasonal affective disorder and aggressively counteracting these thoughts, while the behavioural component involves encouraging people to engage every day in pleasurable activity during the winter months (Rohan, 2008). This emphasis on engaging in pleasurable activities is directly derived from earlier work by Lewinsohn on the protective role of frequent pleasant events in buffering depressive symptoms (see Lewinsohn & Graf, 1973). This classic view of depression regards it primarily as a lack of positive reinforcement that is made worse by having poor social skills or perceiving a deficit in social skills.

Preventing the Onset of Depressive Disorders

Is prevention of new cases of depressive disorders possible? This issue was discussed briefly in our earlier analysis of depression in students. Relatively few studies have focused on this possibility. Most prevention studies measured change in protective factors, including social, cognitive, or problem-solving skills, or outcomes such as severity of symptoms. However, in recent years researchers have examined whether prevention-focused programs can actually reduce the incidence of cases of depression as defined by diagnostic criteria. Cuijpers et al. (2008) identified 19 RCTs in which the incidence of depressive disorders in an experimental group could be compared with that of a control group. Their analyses revealed an average reduction of 22 percentage points in the incidence of depressive disorders. The findings further suggested that prevention based on IPT might be more effective than prevention based on CBT. A more recent review of 156 trials concluded that efforts aimed at prevention are worthwhile, as most lead to small or medium effect sizes (Bellón et al., 2015).

Collins and Dozois (2008) adopted a different approach. They examined empirically supported prevention programs in an effort to identify "active" components that facilitate stronger outcomes. They concluded that targeted, multi-component pro-grams with at-risk children (see Chapter 15) yielded promising results; however, which elements have the greatest impact was unclear. Nonetheless, important mechanisms of change pos-sibly included cognitive skills, interpersonal approaches, and inclusion of parent treatment components. Clearly, additional outcome and dismantling studies are needed.

8.5 Suicide

"'I just looked out over the water and it was beautiful. I felt that this was the right time and place to kill myself. The last thing I saw leave the bridge was my hands. It was at that time that I realized what a stupid thing I was doing. And there was nothing I could do but fall. The next thing I knew I was in the water hoping that someone would save me, saying, "Please God save me, somebody save me." It was incredible how quickly I had decided that I wanted to live once I realized everything that I was going to lose, my wife, my daughter, the rest of my family.'

He is currently in his thirtieth year of marriage. He is a high school teacher and part-time coach. His daughter is an elementary school teacher."

—From Blaustein and Fleming, Suicide from the Golden Gate Bridge, 2009, pp. 1115–1116

The man in this case was one survivor. Tragically, many die. Sui-cide was the ninth leading cause of death in Canada in 2012, when there were 3,926 suicides (10.4 per 100,000 population), and the second leading cause of death (after accidents) in both males and females aged 15 to 24 years (Statistics Canada). Sui-cides were the seventh leading cause of death among males; there were 2,972 suicides of males in Canada in 2012, with only about 1 out of 4 suicides being committed by females. A recent report in the United States found suicide rates are increasing and are at the highest levels in 30 years. There were 10.5 sui-cides per 100,000 population in 1999 compared with 13.0 in 2014, an increase of 24% (Curtin, Warner, & Hedegaard, 2016).

Typically, females have lower rates of suicide mortality than males but higher rates of suicidal attempts, a phenomenon called the gender paradox of suicidal behaviour. It is pro-nounced in industrialized, English-speaking countries such as Canada (see Canetto, 2008 for review). However, it is not a universal pattern, suggesting the importance of cultural perspectives. For example, in some societies (e.g., China and India) suicide is considered to be an act of the powerless and is most common in young women (Canetto, 2008). Men are also more likely to commit suicide by violent means than women (see photo).

Suicide is discussed in this chapter because many depressed persons and persons with bipolar disorder have suicidal thoughts and sometimes make attempts to take their own lives. A significant number of people who are not depressed, however, also make suicidal attempts, some with success (see the section on Suicide and Psychological Disorders).

Before proceeding, it is important to distinguish among sui-cide ideation, suicide attempts, suicide gestures, and suicide.

- Suicidal ideation refers to thoughts and intentions of killing oneself. It is often associated with a sense of hopelessness, helplessness, and despair. Many people may have such thoughts and not report them or they may be unwilling to disclose them.

- Suicide attempts involve self-injury behaviours intended to cause death but that do not lead to death. Some attempts may not be reported because they do not result in hospi-talization or medical attention. Suicide attempters may not appear in suicide attempt data even when they result in medical attention because the attempters are identified by the medical problem only (e.g., lacerations).

- Suicide gestures involve self-injury in which there is no intent to die. Rather, there is an intent to give the appearance of an attempt in order to communicate with others.

- Suicide involves behaviours intended to cause death and death actually occurs.

What are some of the factors that help distinguish when think-ing about suicide leads to an actual attempt? And what dif-ferentiates attempts that do or do not result in death? Borges et al. (2006) determined that ideators with a plan are more likely to make an attempt (31.9%) than those without a plan (9.6%); however, 43% of attempts were unplanned. A history of prior attempts is the strongest correlate of 12-month attempts. In analyses of National Comorbidity Survey data, Nock and Kess-ler (2006) differentiated suicide attempters from suicide gestur-ers. Suicide attempters had the following characteristics: male gender; fewer years of education; psychiatric diagnoses, includ-ing depressive, impulsive, and aggressive symptoms; comor-bidity; and a history of multiple physical and sexual assaults. A team of Canadian researchers also investigated this issue. Cox, Enns, and Clara (2004) found that after controlling for socio-demographic and psychiatric variables, indices of hopelessness and self-criticism were robust predictors of suicide attempts.

What factors predict actual deaths due to suicide? An impressive 20-year prospective study by Brown, Beck, Steer, and Grisham (2000) followed almost 7,000 psychiatric outpa-tients. Long-term predictors of completed suicides included severity of suicide ideation, hopelessness, depression, a diag-nosis of bipolar depression, and being unemployed. The role of hopelessness will be discussed in more detail below.

Suicide is tragic not only because a person dies unnec-essarily, but also because no other kind of death leaves loved ones, friends, and relatives with such enduring negative feel-ings that can include distress and emotional pain, shock and disbelief, guilt, shame, anger, puzzlement, and abandonment (Government of Canada, 2006). These survivors are themselves victims, having an especially high mortality rate in the year

Jitalia17/Vetta/Getty Images

Suicide involving violent death, such as jumping off a building, is more common among men than among women.

after the loved one's suicide. If the person who committed suicide also had a psychiatric disorder, then those left behind have to cope with the double stigma of suicide and mental illness (Government of Canada, 2006). Even more, the family of writer Sylvia Plath (see photo) have had many interpretations made about her life based on her writing, mental illness, and suicide. Myths about suicide abound (see Focus on Discovery 8.3).

Suicide and Psychological Disorders

It is believed that more than half of those who try to kill themselves are depressed and despondent at the time of the act (Henriksson et al., 1993), and it is estimated that 15% of people who have been diagnosed with MDD ultimately commit suicide (Maris et al., 1992). Alexander McGirr and colleagues (2007) from the McGill Group for Suicide Studies used a psychological autopsy method to examine depressive symptoms among suicides who died in the context of a major depressive episode and major depressive controls. Depressive symptoms of suicide relative to those of non-suicide included weight or appetite loss, insomnia, feelings of worthlessness or inappropriate guilt, as well as recurrent thoughts of death or suicidal ideation. Insomnia was an immediate indicator of suicide risk. Claassen et al. (2007) examined clinical differences among people with MDD with and without a history of suicide attempts. More than 16% of participants reported prior suicide attempts, and they had more current general medical conditions, more current alcohol or substance abuse, and onset of MDD occurred about nine years earlier in life. They also reported more current suicidal ideation. Comorbid anxiety disorders (especially panic disorder, generalized anxiety disorder, and anxiety disorder not otherwise specified) also increase risk of suicide death among depressed individuals (Pfeiffer et al., 2009). Valtonen et al. (2007) assessed people diagnosed with bipolar disorder and determined that hopelessness predicted suicidal behaviour during depressive phases, whereas a subjective rating of severity of depression and younger age predicted suicide attempts during mixed phases. A study of depressed people who had been referred to a mood disorders clinic (Ehnvall, Parker, Hadzi-Pavlovic, & Malhi, 2008) reported that females (but not males)

Photo courtesy of Paul Links

Paul Links was the first holder of the only endowed research chair in suicide studies in North America. He held the Arthur Sommer Rotenberg Chair in Suicide Studies at St. Michael's Hospital in Toronto, before moving to St. Joseph's Health Care in London, Ontario. The chair is named after Dr. Arthur Sommer Rotenberg, a family physician from Toronto who committed suicide.

who perceived themselves as rejected or neglected by either parent in childhood were more likely to make a lifetime suicide attempt. There are numerous other sex differences in predictors of suicidal acts (see Oquendo et al., 2008, for review).

A significant number of people who are not depressed, however, make suicidal attempts, and some succeed—most notably people diagnosed with borderline personality disorder (Links, Gould, & Ratnayake, 2003). Paul Links (see photo) and his colleagues (Links, Eynan, Heisel, & Nisenbaum, 2008) determined that the presence of negative mood intensity and mood variability (affective instability) appears to define a subgroup of borderline individuals at elevated risk for suicidal behaviour.

The suicide rate for male alcoholics is greater than that for the general population of men, and it becomes extremely high in alcoholic men who are also depressed (Linehan, 1997). Disinhibition during intoxication might render people less able to resist their thoughts of suicide. In a psychological autopsy study of completed suicides, Schneider et al. (2006) found that alcohol-related disorders, major depression, and co-occurrence of personality disorders of more than one cluster were independent predictors for suicide in males and females. Further, co-occurrence of personality disorders of more than one cluster contributed to risk of completed suicide after controlling for Axis I disorders.

A Canadian study of completed suicides found that the number of completed suicides among people with schizophrenia was comparable with the number of completed suicides among people with depression (see Martin, 2000). McGirr et al. (2006) reported that psychotic people at risk for suicide can be identified by depressive disorders, moderate to severe psychotic symptoms, a family history of suicidal behaviour, few negative symptoms, and comorbid diagnoses.

Focus on Discovery 8.3

Some Myths about Suicide

There are many prevalent misconceptions about suicide (e.g., Fremouw, de Perczel, & Ellis, 1990; Shneidman, 1987), some of which are included below. It is as important to be familiar with the myths as it is to know the facts.

1. *People who discuss suicide will not commit the act.*

   At least three-quarters of those who take their own lives have communicated their intention beforehand, perhaps as a cry for help.

2. *Suicide is committed without warning.*

   The person usually gives many warnings, such as saying that the world would be better off without him or her or making unexpected and inexplicable gifts to others.

3. *Suicidal people clearly want to die.*

   Most people who contemplate suicide appear to be ambivalent about their own deaths. For many people, the suicidal crisis passes, and they are grateful for having been prevented from self-destruction.

4. *The motives for suicide are easily established.*

   The truth is that we do not fully understand why people commit suicide. For example, that a severe reverse in finances precedes a suicide does not mean that it adequately explains the suicide.

5. *All who commit suicide are depressed.*

   This fallacy may account for the fact that signs of impending suicide are often overlooked. Many people who take their lives are not depressed; some even appear calm and at peace with themselves.

6. *Improvement in emotional state means lessened risk of suicide.*

   Those who commit suicide, especially those who are depressed, often do so after their spirits and energy begin to rise.

A Finnish study (Sourander et al., 2009) is informative because it is the only prospective, population-based study in existence that examined predictive associations between early child psychopathology and later completed suicides. Of males who completed suicide and/or made suicide attempts that prompted hospital admission in adolescence or early adulthood, 78% screened positive on parent or teacher scales of psychopathology at the age of 8 years. Self-reports of depression did not predict suicide outcome. Outcome was predicted most strongly by comorbid conduct and internalizing problems (primarily anxiety). Female severe suicidality was not predicted by any of the variables measured at age 8.

Given that people with various diagnoses commit suicide, our focus here is on issues and factors in suicide that transcend specific diagnoses, despite our inclusion of this section on suicide in a chapter on depression. Oquendo et al. (2008) noted that suicidality in high-risk groups often goes unidentified by assessing clinicians, and even when it is identified, "the patient receives a diagnosis that does not highlight suicide risk as a focus of concern" (p. 1383). They recommended that possible suicidal behaviour be included as a separate diagnosis on a sixth axis in *DSM-5,* but, of course, the axis system itself was removed in *DSM-5.*

Perspectives on Suicide

> *"...while the act of suicide itself is a relatively clear-cut observable behaviour, it is based on a multiplex of interacting, mediating, moderating, independent, overlapping, and proxy risk factors from biopsychosocial perspectives."*
>
> —Sakinofsky, 2007b, p. 8S

Self-intentioned death is a complex, multi-faceted act and no single model can hope to explain it. We turn now to several different perspectives on suicide, each of which attempts to shed light on this disturbing aspect of humankind. Large-scale longitudinal studies are needed to validate different theories of suicidality.

Durkheim's Sociological Theory

Emile Durkheim (e.g., 1951), a renowned sociologist, analyzed the records of suicide for various countries and during different historical periods and concluded that self-annihilation could be understood in sociological terms. He distinguished three different kinds of suicide:

- **Egoistic suicide** is committed by people who have few ties to family, society, or community. These people feel alienated from others and cut off from the social supports that are important to keep them functioning adaptively as social beings.

- **Altruistic suicide** is viewed as a response to societal demands. Some people who commit suicide feel very much a part of a group and sacrifice themselves for what they take to be the good of society. The self-immolations of Buddhist monks and nuns to protest the fighting during the Vietnam War fits into this category. Some altruistic suicides, such as the hara-kiri of the Japanese, are required as the only honourable recourse in certain circumstances.

- **Anomic suicide** may be triggered by a sudden change in a person's relationship to society. A successful executive who suffers severe financial reverses may experience anomie, a sense of disorientation, because what he or she believed to be a normal way of living is no longer possible. Anomie can pervade a society, such as the Guarani Indians of Brazil, in disequilibrium, making suicide more likely (see photo).

As with all sociological theorizing, Durkheim's hypotheses have difficulty accounting for the differences among individuals

Writers who killed themselves, such as Sylvia Plath, have provided insights into the causes of suicide.

The suicide of Nirvana's lead singer, Kurt Cobain, triggered an increase in suicide among teenagers. The note believed to be written by Cobain emphasized his sense that he would become a burden to his young daughter.

in a given society in their reactions to the same demands and conditions. Not all those who unexpectedly lose their money commit suicide, for example. It appears that Durkheim was aware of this problem, for he suggested that individual temperament would interact with any of the social pressures that he found causative.

Psychological Theories

Many motives for suicide have been suggested: Freud's aggression turned inward; retaliation by inducing guilt in others; efforts to force love from others; efforts to make amends for perceived past wrongs; the desire to rejoin a dead loved one; and the desire or need to escape from stress, deformity, pain, or emotional vacuum.

Still—and this is of central importance in prevention—most people who contemplate or actually commit suicide are ambivalent. "The prototypical suicidal state is one in which an individual cuts his or her throat, cries for help at the same time, and is genuine in both of these acts. . . . Individuals would be happy not to do it, if they didn't have to" (Shneidman, 1987, p. 170). There is a narrowing of the perceived range of options. When not in a highly perturbed suicidal state, the person is capable of seeing more choices for dealing with stress. People planning suicide usually communicate their intention, sometimes as a cry for help, sometimes as a withdrawal from others. Typical behaviours include giving away treasured possessions and putting financial affairs in order.

Suicide is so complex that numerous psychological variables undoubtedly play a role; however, researchers have developed models that attempt to identify the variables and the moderators and mediators that will help determine who is at highest risk. The critical factors and mechanisms of action are not all well understood.

A risk factor model

A general model of the causes of suicidal behaviour is summarized in the 2006 Government of Canada report on mental health and mental illness in Canada. In this model, recommended as a guide for suicide prevention programs, there are four categories of relevant factors:

- Predisposing factors are enduring factors that make a person vulnerable to suicidal behaviour (e.g., psychological disorder, abuse, early loss).
- Precipitating factors are acute factors that create a crisis (e.g., end of a relationship, job loss, loss of stature, rejection, pressure to succeed).
- Contributing factors increase exposure to predisposing or precipitating factors (e.g., physical illness, sexual identity issues, isolation).
- Protective factors decrease the risk of suicidal behaviour (e.g., personal resilience, adaptive coping skills, positive future expectations, and perceived social support).

Childhood sexual abuse is one potent predisposing risk factor. Bebbington and colleagues (2009) reported findings from the British National Survey of Psychiatric Morbidity, which indicated that a history of childhood sexual abuse is strongly associated with suicide intent and attempts, especially among women. The risk factor model provides a broad framework for our discussion of more specific psychological models that focus on psychological diatheses.

Baumeister's escape theory

A theory about suicide based on work in social and personality psychology holds that some suicides arise from a strong desire to escape from aversive self-awareness; that is, from the painful awareness of shortcomings and failures that the person attributes to himself or herself (Baumeister, 1990). This awareness is assumed to produce severe emotional suffering, perhaps depression.

The high suicide rate of the Guarani Indians of Brazil, who were forced onto crowded reserves, illustrates Durkheim's concept of anomic suicide. Maurice da Silva Goncalves is one of the local Guarani leaders who accused Norwegian millionaire Erling Lorentzen of stealing their land.

Unrealistically high expectations—and therefore the probability of failing to meet these expectations (cf. Beck and Ellis)—play a central role in this perspective. Of particular importance is a discrepancy between high expectations for intimacy and a reality that falls short, such as when someone's expectations for intimacy are dashed because a loved one cannot possibly deliver what the person needs. Because perfectionists have impossibly high standards, they are more likely to experience such discrepancies. A model that incorporates multi-dimensional perfectionism is outlined below.

The perfectionism social disconnection model

Elevated levels of trait perfectionism and self-criticism have been implicated in suicidal acts, especially among people who are quite talented. In his classic paper titled *The Destructiveness of Perfectionism,* Blatt (1995) described three highly talented yet self-critical perfectionists who took their own lives. One of these individuals was Vince Foster, the attorney who was a friend of Bill and Hillary Clinton.

At present, perfectionism is clearly regarded as a risk factor for suicide, with one analysis leading to the conclusion that there is "strong evidence in favor of perfectionism as an amplifier of risk" (Johnson et al., 2011, p. 572). O'Connor (2007) conducted a systematic review and concluded that there is a link between perfectionism and suicidality but he also noted that there is an urgent need for longitudinal research testing the predictive utility of perfectionism vs. other predictors. Most research has supported the role of socially prescribed perfectionism (see Hewitt, Flett, Sherry, & Caelian, 2006). For example, Blankstein, Lumley, and Crawford (2007) found that socially prescribed perfectionism in University of Toronto students was a significant predictor of current suicide ideation, interpersonal hopelessness, and achievement hopelessness.

Hewitt et al. (2006) have advanced the Perfectionism Social Disconnection Model (PSDM). The essence of this model is that interpersonal perfectionism creates a sense of alienation and isolation that amplifies the hopelessness and self-loathing that sometimes accompanies extreme forms of perfectionism. Interpersonal perfectionism also comes in the form of perfectionistic self-presentation (i.e., needing to seem perfect in public). This need would be clearly violated when a potentially suicidal perfectionist actually undergoes or perceives that he or she has experienced a public humiliation. Roxborough et al. (2012) tested the PSDM in a sample of adolescent psychiatric outpatients and found that both trait socially prescribed perfectionism and perfectionistic self-presentation were associated with a measure of suicide potential. Also, the association between suicide potential and the need to avoid seeming imperfect was mediated by a history of being bullied and elevated interpersonal hopelessness. These data suggest that when it is the case that being bullied has played a role in an attempted or completed suicide, the traumatic experience of being bullied is felt most acutely by interpersonally sensitive perfectionists who would prefer to maintain an image of being flawless and totally in control at all times.

Joiner's interpersonal theory of suicide   Thomas Joiner (see photo) is arguably the leading psychologist studying suicide and he is currently the editor of one of the most influential journals on the topic, *Suicide and Life-Threatening Behavior.* Part of his interest and influential work is personal given that Joiner's father committed suicide.

According to Joiner's model, the proclivity to commit suicide is a product of two interpersonal constructs: a thwarted

According to Joiner's interpersonal theory of suicide, people are at risk for suicide when they feel alone and feel like a burden on those around them.

need to belong and perceived burdensomeness (see Van Orden et al., 2010). Thus, people are at risk when they feel excluded and alienated (i.e., "I am alone") and they also feel at risk when they regard themselves as burdens (i.e., "I am a burden") and that other people would be better off without them. This general notion of being a burden was a core theme in the suicide note attributed to Kurt Cobain of the group Nirvana (see photo).

Extensive research has established a link between perceived burdensomeness and various indices of suicidality. One study highlighted a possible way to combine explanatory models by showing that perceived burdensomeness mediated the link between maladaptive perfectionism and suicide (Rasmussen et al., 2012). However, a study of suicide notes found that the thwarted need to belong was represented in about 30% of the notes, while feeling like a burden was present in less than 5% of instances (Gunn, Lester, Haines, & Williams, 2012).

This model also holds that the desire to commit suicide is separate and distinguishable from the capability to commit suicide. That is, suicide occurs when the person has both the will and ways to commit suicide. The capability to commit suicide helps account for differences between those who are thinking about it vs. those who are actually going to do it. One factor linked with greater capability is a heightened ability to tolerate physical pain, and this tolerance can be built up by having a history of nonsuicidal self-injury (Joiner, Ribeiro, & Silva, 2012). Research is now focusing on factors that predict the acquired capacity to actually commit suicide. Data from university students indicates that greater capacity is found among those students who are high in sensation seeking and who have a higher level of distress tolerance (Bender et al., 2012). Distress tolerance involves a tendency to not be overwhelmed and not find it too problematic to experience negative affect.

An intriguing aspect of the interpersonal model is that it has clear implications for prevention. Joiner (2009) outlined various ways in which the need to belong can be a focus of prevention efforts in schools.

Shneidman's approach

Edwin Shneidman (1987, 1993), a pioneer in the study of suicide and its prevention, reminded us that the overwhelming majority of people with psychiatric disorders do not commit suicide. He suggested that the perturbation of mind that he posits as a key feature in a person who commits suicide is not a mental illness. Shneidman regarded suicide as a conscious effort to seek a solution to a problem that is causing intense and intolerable psychological suffering and pain, or what he referred to as **psychache**. To the sufferer, this solution ends consciousness and unendurable pain—what Melville in Moby Dick termed an "insufferable anguish." Hope and a sense of constructive action are gone. Shneidman's concept of psychological pain was referred to in the journal of Richard Edmunds, who killed himself by hanging in Calgary at age 27. Edmunds wrote, "I was born and bred to be frustrated. I cannot stand the pain any longer. I negate the past, and I have negated all of the future" (Edmunds, 1998, p. 371). This excerpt is from a moving account of the impact of a family member's suicide on survivors, as related by Anne Edmunds, Richard's mother.

Thus, in Shneidman's view, other psychological factors, such as depression, are relevant only insofar as they are related to psychache. According to this view, psychache is a more proximal predictor of suicide and one that mediates more distal risk factors.

Important empirical work on psychache is being conducted by Ron Holden and his colleagues at Queen's University. They developed the Psychache Scale. It has items that reflect profound psychological pain; the items are almost upsetting to read even when not answering them. Representative items that are clearly high in face validity include "My soul aches," "My pain makes my life seem dark," and "My psychological pain affects everything I do."

An extensive program of research on psychache by Holden and his colleagues has yielded several noteworthy findings. For instance, Flamenbaum and Holden (2007) found that psychache fully mediated the relation between socially prescribed perfectionism and suicidality. Patterson and Holden (2012) found among homeless men that psychache was more of a predictor of suicide ideation than was depression, hopelessness, or life meaning. Other longitudinal research has confirmed in high-risk students that psychache predicts susceptibility to suicide ideation and it is more predictive than measures such as hopelessness (see Troister & Holden, 2012).

Additional psychological factors

Research on personality and cognition has identified many other factors implicated in the development and course of suicidal behaviour (e.g., Brezo, Paris, & Turecki, 2006), including problem-solving deficits, hopelessness, negative cognitive styles, neuroticism, and impulsivity. For example, many contemporary mental health professionals regard suicide in general as an individual's attempt at problem-solving, conducted under considerable stress and marked by consideration of a very narrow range of alternatives, of which self-annihilation appears the most viable (Linehan & Shearin, 1988). Problem-solving deficits predict suicide attempts in prospective studies (Diesrud et al., 2003). It has also been suggested that suicidal individuals are more rigid in their approach to problems and less flexible in their thinking. Constricted thinking could account for the apparent inability to seek solutions to life's problems other than that offered by taking one's own life (Linehan et al., 1987). Research confirms the hypothesis that people who attempt suicide are more rigid than others, lending support to the clinical observations of Shneidman and others that people who attempt suicide seem incapable of thinking of alternative solutions to problems.

Especially noteworthy are the findings described earlier that hopelessness is a strong predictor of suicide (Brown et al., 2000). The expectation that at some point in the future things will be no better than they are right now seems to be more instrumental than depression per se in propelling a person to take his or her life. Smith, Alloy, and Abramson (2006) found that hopelessness partially mediated the rumination-suicide ideation link. The cognitive distortions described as part of Beck's model earlier were also found to be related to suicidality (Jager-Hyman et al., 2014). A group of participants who attempted suicide within the past month scored higher on measures of cognitive distortions than a group of psychiatric controls. In particular, the patients who had attempted suicide were more likely to engage in fortune telling, a cognitive distortion that involves making negative predictions on what is going to happen in the future. However, fortune telling was no longer a significant predictor once hopelessness was taken into account. The authors still highlighted the importance of challenging cognitive distortions when working with suicidal clients. Hopelessness is a predominant theme in Canadian Perspectives 8.3, which addresses the exceptionally high levels of suicide among certain Aboriginal groups.

Knowing what there is in a person's life that prevents him or her from committing suicide has both assessment and intervention value. Rather than focusing only on negativism and pessimism, Marsha Linehan's Reasons for Living (RFL) Inventory (Linehan, 1985) taps six themes of importance to the individual: (1) survival and coping beliefs, (2) responsibility to family, (3) concerns about children, (4) fear of social disapproval, (5) fear of suicide, and (6) moral objections (i.e., a belief that suicide is morally wrong). This approach can help the clinician with intervention by identifying the reasons the person has for not wanting to die. The RFL was associated negatively with suicide ideation when the scale was adapted for use with French Canadian populations (see Labelle, Lachance, & Morval, 1996). People with reasons to live are less suicidal than people who report few reasons to live (Ivanoff et al., 1994).

Physical Factors in Suicide

The role of physical factors in vulnerability to suicide and the capacity to commit suicide has been a public topic that is now receiving much attention as a result of the growing number of athletes with a history of head injuries who have taken their own lives or died under unclear circumstances. In Canada, attention has been focused on "enforcer" hockey players who died too young, possibly as a result of suicide in some instances and the brain trauma due to head injuries incurred while fighting in hockey. But the definitive evidence has come from post-mortem studies

ZUMA Press Inc/Alamy Stock Photo

Bennet Omalu discovered chronic traumatic encephalopathy (CTE). The Bennet Omalu Foundation funds research, care, and awareness related to CTE. Their cause was the subject of the 2015 movie *Concussion* in which actor Will Smith played the role of Bennet Omalu.

of former NFL football players who took their own lives (e.g., Dave Duerson, Junior Seau). These players were found to have a condition known as **chronic traumatic encephalopathy (CTE)**, which is a progressive degenerative neurological disease involving atrophy of key areas of the brain. This can include the amygdala in advanced cases. Symptoms include cognitive confusion, decision-making problems, irritability, and impulsivity.

CTE was discovered in 2002 by Dr. Bennet Omalu (see photo). Because CTE can only be deemed to be present via autopsies, at least at the moment, most published studies have been in the form of case studies led by Omalu. Omalu and his colleagues have published case accounts implicating CTE in the suicide of an NFL player (Omalu et al., 2010) as well as the suicide of a former U.S. Marine who was an Iraqi War veteran with post-traumatic stress disorder who committed suicide eight months after receiving an honourable discharge (Omalu et al., 2011).

More general work in this area has examined the possible role of genetic factors. Monozygotic twins have a much higher

Canadian Perspectives 8.3

Suicide among Canadian Aboriginal People

"Innu youth talk openly about their pain and sense of hopelessness. They acknowledge that they drink, take drugs and sniff gasoline to forget the boredom, the beatings, the abuse . . . The prospect of a future without change is too much for some to bear."

"The Tragedy of Andrew Rich," by John DeMont, Maclean's, November 22, 1999

"This is a wounded community. A nightmare place where no one seems to have any hope."

—*Lynne Gregory, addictions counsellor in Sheshatshiu (DeMont. 1999)*

World attention focused on Canada because of the alarming situation that emerged in Davis Inlet and Sheshatshiu, Newfoundland and Labrador, where excessively high rates of suicide and dysfunctional behaviours, such as solvent abuse, sexual abuse, and domestic violence were documented.

One tragic story among many is that of Andrew Rich, the son of Jean-Pierre Ashini. Andrew went with his father to the airport in Goose Bay to see him off to London, England. Ashini was going to address a news conference about the "suicide epidemic" among Canada's Innu people.

"But he worried about his son, a shy 15-year-old who went by the nickname of 'Mr. T.' Andrew spoke little English and had always seemed most comfortable

(continued)

camping and hunting in Nitassinan, the Innu wilderness homeland. But in Sheshatshiu, 32 km north of Goose Bay, he had, like so many Innu youths, fallen into despair. He drank, did drugs, and inhaled gasoline fumes when nothing else was available to dull the pain of his life. Sometimes, he talked about suicide. Preparing to board the plane, Ashini, a tee-totalling fisherman, urged his son to stay clean and behave himself while he was away. Once on the plane, he recalls, 'I mouthed the words "don't drink" through the glass of the window. I saw him nod yes, and I felt good when I left.'

But minutes after arriving in London, Ashini received news that shattered his world. Sometime in the early morning of Nov. 6, Andrew had swallowed a vial of pills. He then walked into his bedroom and shot himself in the head while his 13-year-old girlfriend sat a few rooms away—the third youth in the past year to commit suicide in the community of 1,500."

(DeMont, 1999)

According to a report released in 2000 by the human rights group Survival for Tribal People, the Innu people of Labrador and Quebec are 13 times more likely to kill themselves than other people in Canada, and the Innu formerly of Davis Inlet, 200 km north to end of Sheshatshiu, have the highest suicide rate in the world (178 per 100,000 people). Moreover, the suicide rate among children and adolescents is extremely high, with estimates ranging from three to seven times the national average for children.

What factors contribute to such astronomically high suicide rates? The organization's report points to a multitude of factors, including loss of cultural identity, industrial development and depletion of natural resources on Innu land, and even physical and sexual abuse experienced when the Innu visited Roman Catholic missionaries at trading posts (see Samson, Wilson, & Mazower, 1999).

Although the Innu situation has garnered much public attention, other native groups also experience high suicide levels. British sociologist Colin Samson, co-author of the Innu study, reported that the Ojibwa reserve in Pikangijum (300 km northeast of Winnipeg) had an even higher suicide rate of 213 per 100,000 people between 1992 and 2000; these data included the suicides of eight females (including five 13-year-olds) who killed themselves in 2000 (Canadian Press, 2000). Some Aboriginal communities have experienced "cluster suicide"—multiple suicides by groups of individuals in the same community. Ward and Fox (1977) reported "a true suicide epidemic" among a rural community of just 37 families on a reserve on Manitoulin Island, Ontario. A 17-year-old boy, upset by the expected separation of his parents, drank a large volume of alcohol and shot himself. In less than a year, eight other youths were dead, an astronomical suicide rate of 267 per 100,000. Wilkie, Macdonald, and Hildahl (1998) described a small First Nations community in Manitoba of fewer than 1,500 people that had six suicides and many more attempted suicides in a three-month span in 1995. Alcohol and previous sexual assault were factors in four suicides. Wilkie et al. also noted that those who had attempted suicide reported that they had experienced dreams of beckoning in which voices urged them to kill themselves. A new report suggests that from 2004 to 2008, children and adolescents in Inuit Nunangat (the Inuit regions of northern Canada), relative to children from the rest of Canada, were 30 times as likely to die from suicide (Oliver, Peters, & Kohen, 2012).

These alarming situations led researchers to focus attention on this issue. A study of Inuit between the ages of 14 and 25 found that 34% had attempted suicide and 20% had made two or more attempts (Kirmayer, Malus, & Boothroyd, 1996). Risk factors associated with attempts included being male, having a friend who had attempted or committed suicide, a history of physical abuse, solvent abuse, and having a parent with an alcohol or drug problem. Two protective factors were degree of church attendance and doing well at school. A follow-up (Kirmayer, Boothroyd, & Hodgins, 1998) found the best predictors of attempted suicide among females were presence of a psychiatric problem, recent alcohol abuse, and cocaine or crack use. The best predictors among males were solvent use and the number of recent traumatic life events.

There are substantial differences in suicide rates among the various indigenous and First Nations groups, with some communities having rates that are 800 times the national average (Chandler & Lalonde, 1998). A key contributing factor is the degree to which cultural identity is maintained and preserved over time. Analysis of 196 bands in B.C. showed that a key factor that mitigates against suicide is the extent to which the community makes a collective effort to maintain and strengthen its own cultural continuity. Cooper, Corrado, Karlberg, and Adams (1992) also reported risk factors among bands in B.C. with high suicide rates, including overcrowding, numerous low-income and single-parent families, households with numerous children, and few elders in the community. The rates of suicide for Aboriginals who lived outside of the reserves were comparable with suicide rates for the general population.

The problem of suicide among Aboriginal people resulted in the formation of the Suicide Prevention Advisory Group (SPAG) in 2001. The SPAG was appointed jointly by then national chief Matthew Coon Come of the Assembly of First Nations and then federal minister of health Allan Rock. The initial report, entitled *Acting on What We Know: Preventing Youth Suicide in First Nations,* was published in January 2003 (Advisory Group on Suicide Prevention, 2003). The recommendations addressed four primary themes: (1) increasing knowledge about what works in suicide prevention; (2) developing more effective and integrated health care services; (3) supporting community-driven approaches; and (4) creating strategies for building youth identity, resilience, and culture. The SPAG acknowledged that no single approach will be effective by itself and that multi-level changes to family and community systems are needed. Unfortunately, there are no well-controlled treatment studies of suicidality among Aboriginals in Canada (see Sakinofsky, 2007b). Walls, Hautala, and Hurley (2014) reported on focus groups on youth suicide with adult First Nations community members. The discussions were not aimed at individual psychopathology leading to suicide, but were complex, involving many interrelated factors including stress, trauma, social problems, and the historical context.

The crisis continues. On one evening in April 2016, 11 people attempted to end their lives in Attawapiskat, Ontario, a remote First Nations community of about 2,000 people on James Bay, leading to the declaration of a state of emergency. They ranged in age from 11 to 71 years.

Thinking Critically

1. A new town was built in Labrador by the federal government for the Innu of Davis Inlet and they moved in February 2002. At a cost of more than $150 million, Natuashish was intended to provide a bright new future for the children and adults removed from the squalor of Davis Inlet. According to Toughill (2003), the move did not end the tragedies of the Innu—the problems were

simply exported to the new town! Would you have predicted this outcome? Why?

2. Do you think that young Innu like Andrew Rich feel pressure to belong to traditional Innu culture and at the same time pressure to achieve in mainstream Canadian culture? Is it possible that they perceive a lack of support in both directions?

3. Solutions to the problem of suicide among our Aboriginal peoples will require psychological, societal, and economic interventions. Does the fact that the suicide rate is relatively low in some Aboriginal communities suggest to you that community-based solutions are, in fact, possible?

concordance for suicidality than dizygotic twins (Baldessarini & Hennen, 2004), suggesting that the risk is partially inherited. McGirr et al. (2009) from the McGill Group for Suicide Studies examined familial transmission of suicide, controlling for depression, and concluded that Cluster B personality traits and impulsive-aggressive behaviour represent intermediate phenotypes of suicide that partially mediate the relation between familial predisposition and suicide attempts among relatives.

Other research has established a connection among serotonin, suicide, and impulsivity. Low levels of serotonin's major metabolite, 5-HIAA, have been found in people in several diagnostic categories—depression, schizophrenia, and various personality disorders—who committed suicide (e.g., van Praag, Plutchik, & Apter, 1990). Post-mortem studies of the brains of people who committed suicide have revealed increased binding by serotonin receptors (presumably a response to a decreased level of serotonin itself) (Turecki et al., 1999). The link between 5-HIAA levels and suicide is especially compelling in the case of violent and impulsive suicide (e.g., Roy, 1994). In a more recent SPECT study, Ryding et al. (2006) found no significant differences between suicide attempters and control subjects with respect to regional levels of serotonin reuptake (5HTT) and dopamine reuptake binding potential; however, in suicide attempters but not controls they found significant regional correlations between levels of measures of impulsiveness/initiative and mental energy and SPECT results. The latter were interpreted as "due to a disability of the suicide attempters to regulate their serotonin and dopamine levels, e.g., in response to external stress" (Ryding et al., 2006, p. 195).

Preventing Suicide

"Population-based and high-risk approaches must go forward synergistically, and each is integral to the hope of reducing suicide rates."

—Sakinofsky, 2007b, p. 17S

The need to prevent suicide is garnering increased attention, not only in Canada, but around the world. In 1999, the World Health Organization began a worldwide initiative—known as SUPRE-MISS—to prevent suicidal behaviours (World Health Organization, 2000). "SUPRE" refers to suicide prevention, and "MISS" refers to the multi-site intervention study on suicidal behaviours. The study focuses on the evaluation of treatment strategies for people attempting suicide, as well as on community surveys of suicidal thoughts and behaviours.

An important step forward that will hopefully soon be emulated by Canada is the 2012 U.S. National Strategy for Suicide Prevention (U.S. Department of Health and Human Services (HHS) Office of the Surgeon General and National Action Alliance for Suicide Prevention, 2012). A basic premise outlined in the national strategy document is that everyone has a role to play in suicide prevention. The strategy is based on four strategic and thematic directions with associated actions and several goals and objectives within each strategic direction. The four themes are: (1) health and empowered individuals, families, and schools; (2) clinical and community preventive services; (3) treatment and support services; and (4) surveillance, research, and evaluation. As an example of a specific goal, the strategy includes the promotion of responsible media reporting of suicide and countering the misperception that some people have that suicides cannot be prevented. Unfortunately, Canada remains one of the few developed countries without a national strategy for suicide prevention. In response to the slow pace of government in addressing this important issue, the Canadian Association for Suicide Prevention (CASP), a non-profit organization, developed a suicide prevention blueprint in 2004 (revised in 2009) to serve as a starting point for public debate and input. The Mental Health Commission of Canada (MHCC), established in 2007, released a document in 2012 entitled, "Changing Directions, Changing Lives: The Mental Health Strategy for Canada" (2012). The report cites the work of the CASP in addressing suicide, but a national strategy focused on suicide prevention remains to be crafted. Fortunately, the CASP and the MHCC are working together, along with other relevant organizations, to co-lead a National Collaborative on Suicide Prevention.

Treating the Underlying Mental Disorder

One way to look at the prevention of suicide is to bear in mind that most people who attempt to kill themselves are suffering from a treatable mental disorder. A Canadian study of young men who committed suicide showed that almost everyone who had been examined had a diagnosable Axis I disorder such as depression and 57.3% had a diagnosable personality disorder (Lesage et al., 1994). Thus, when following Beck's cognitive approach successfully lessens a client's depression, that client's suicidal risk is reduced. The same is true for the dialectical behaviour therapy of Marsha Linehan (1993b), whose therapy for individuals with borderline personality disorder is described in Chapter 13. Many experts hold the view that efforts to prevent suicide should focus on the underlying psychological disorder.

Treating Suicidality Directly   Another tradition in suicide prevention downplays mental disorder and concentrates instead on the particular characteristics of suicidal people that transcend mental disorders. One of the best-known approaches of this nature is that of Edwin Shneidman. We have already reviewed some of his thinking on suicide. His general strategy of suicide prevention (1987) was threefold:

1. Reduce the intense psychological pain and suffering.

2. Lift the blinders; that is, expand the constricted view by helping the individual see options other than the extremes of continued suffering or nothingness.

3. Encourage the person to pull back even a little from the self-destructive act.

Shneidman cited the example of a college student who was single, pregnant, and suicidal and had a clearly formed plan. The only solution she could think of besides suicide was never to have become pregnant, even to be virginal again.

> *"I took out a sheet of paper and began to widen her blinders. I said something like, 'Now, let's see: You could have an abortion here locally.' She responded, 'I couldn't do that.' I continued, 'You could go away and have an abortion.' 'I couldn't do that.' 'You could bring the baby to term and keep the baby.' 'I couldn't do that.' 'You could have the baby and adopt it out.' Further options were similarly dismissed. When I said, 'You can always commit suicide, but there is obviously no need to do that today,' there was no response. 'Now,' I said, 'let's look at this list and rank them in order of your preference, keeping in mind that none of them is optimal.'"*

> —Shneidman, 1987, p. 171

Shneidman reported that just drawing up the list had a calming effect. The student's lethality—her drive to kill herself very soon—receded, and she was able to rank the list even though she found something wrong with each item. But an important goal had been achieved; she had been pulled back from the brink and was in a frame of mind to consider courses of action other than dying or being a virgin again. "We were then simply 'haggling' about life, a perfectly viable solution" (Shneidman, 1987, p. 171).

Suicide Prevention Centres   Many **suicide prevention centres** are modelled after the Los Angeles Suicide Prevention Center, founded in 1958 by Farberow and Shneidman.

Staffed largely by non-professionals under the supervision of psychologists or psychiatrists, these centres attempt to

Photo courtesy of Hayley Flett

The Golden Gate Bridge in San Francisco was rated the number-one suicide site in the world (Blaustein & Fleming, 2009). In 2012, there were 33 confirmed suicides and there were 37 in 2011. A call box and this accompanying sign were put on the bridge in the hope that this would prevent some suicides, and there are plans for a stainless steel net to be manufactured and installed on both sides. The suicide deterrent net construction project is estimated to cost about $76 million, with construction bids received in the summer of 2016. It was expected to take an estimated four years to implement the net. A barrier was erected at the Bloor Viaduct in Toronto (once rated as the number-two suicide site) and it has stopped suicides from taking place there.

provide 24-hour consultation to people in suicidal crises (see photo). Usually the initial contact is made by telephone, and the centre's phone number is well publicized in the community. Workers rely heavily on demographic factors to assess risk. They have before them a checklist to guide their questioning of each caller. For example, a caller would be regarded as a lethal risk if he were male, middle-aged, divorced, and living alone, and had a history of previous suicide attempts. Usually the more detailed and concrete the suicide plan, the higher the risk. The worker tries to assess the likelihood that the caller will make a serious suicide attempt and, most important, tries to establish personal contact and dissuade the caller from suicide. Staffers are taught to adopt a phenomenological stance, to view the suicidal person's situation as he or she sees it and not to convey in any way that the client is a fool or is crazy to have settled on suicide as a solution to his or her woes. This empathy for suicidal people is sometimes referred to as "tuning in."

Many students who take abnormal psychology are eager to "make a difference" in the lives of others, and one common route to achieving this goal is to volunteer as a member of a suicide or crisis telephone line. Indeed, according to Leenaars (2000), throughout the world, suicide prevention depends on volunteerism. The telephone service is available in many locations throughout Canada and is becoming increasingly available in more remote regions. Levy and Fletcher (1998) described the origins and development of the first crisis line in the North,

Kamatsiaqtut, the Baffin Crisis Line, "a community response to the cries of hopelessness and helplessness that have been vibrating through the North" (p. 355). The first two phone lines were established in 1990, after start-up funds were provided by CBC employees who put together a curl-a-thon. The crisis line received more than 400 calls the first year, a large number considering that these lines served only the 3,700 people in Iqaluit. Callers report a number of problems, but the most common centre on losses involving relationships, family members, and friends. Levy and Fletcher (1998) noted that the decision to provide a crisis line in the North is inconsistent with Inuit cultural beliefs because the crisis line focuses on the individual, while Inuit society emphasizes community. Still, the crisis line is made available by the volunteer efforts of the community, and Levy and Fletcher (1998) concluded that it plays a vital role in providing distressed individuals with a chance to express their concerns and not simply keep things to themselves.

The first telephone centre in Canada was started in Sudbury, Ontario, in 1965; however, the real push in Canada came from the Suicide Prevention and Distress Centre in Toronto (Leenaars, 2000). The 48 trained volunteers started answering the telephones on November 1, 1967, and the first three calls came from people contemplating suicide. It is estimated that the centres in the Greater Toronto Area now receive approximately 800,000 calls each year. Suicide Action in Montreal is the largest French-language telephone crisis service in Canada. Such community facilities are potentially valuable because people who attempt suicide give warnings—cries for help—before taking their lives. Ambivalence about living or dying is the hallmark of the suicidal state (Shneidman, 1987). Usually, pleas are directed first to relatives and friends, but many people contemplating suicide are isolated from these sources of emotional support. A hotline service may save the lives of such individuals. The Canadian Distress Line Network is working on a number of initiatives, including the creation of a single national phone number and online presence.

Victims of suicide include survivors, especially those among the unfortunate who were speaking to or in the presence of the person when the act was committed, which occurs in an estimated 25% of suicides (Andress & Corey, 1978). Sometimes these survivors are therapists or hospital emergency room personnel. All are subject to strong feelings of guilt and self-recrimination, second-guessing what they might have done to prevent the suicide. Even dispassionate analysis does not invariably allay the guilt and anger. Grieving after a suicide death tends to last much longer than a death that is not self-inflicted. For these many reasons, peer support groups exist to help survivors cope with the aftermath of a suicide. They provide social support, opportunities to vent feelings, constructive information, and referrals to professionals if that seems advisable (Fremouw et al., 1990). McDaid et al. (2008) reviewed controlled studies of interventions for people bereaved through suicide and concluded that there is evidence of some benefit (e.g., a psychologist-led 10-week group intervention for children) but the effects were not robust.

Clinical and Ethical Issues in Dealing with Suicide

"I want to ask you gentlemen, if I cannot give consent to my own death, then whose body is this? Who owns my life?"

—*Sue Rodriguez, victim of ALS (amyotrophic lateral sclerosis, or Lou Gehrig's disease, a terminal illness), appearing in a videotaped presentation to a House of Commons committee in November 1992, in which she urged amendments to the section of the Criminal Code that makes it a crime for any person to assist another's suicide*

Therapists' Responsibilities

Professional organizations charge their members to protect people from harming themselves even if doing so requires breaking the confidentiality of the therapist–client relationship. The suicide of a therapist's client is frequently grounds for a malpractice lawsuit, and therapists tend to lose such suits if it can be proved that they failed to make adequate assessments and to take reasonable precautions according to generally accepted standards of care for suicide prevention (see Ingram & Roy, 1995).

It is not easy to agree about what constitutes reasonable care, particularly when the client is not hospitalized and therefore not under surveillance and potential restraint. Clinicians must work out their own ethic regarding a person's right to end his or her life. What steps is the professional willing to take to prevent a suicide? Confinement in a hospital? Or, as is more common today, sedation administered against the person's wishes and strong enough that the person is virtually incapable of taking any action at all? And for how long should extraordinary measures be taken? Clinicians realize that most suicidal crises pass; the suicidal person is likely to be grateful afterward for having been prevented from committing suicide.

Physician-Assisted Suicide

Physician-assisted suicide is a highly charged issue. It came to the fore in the early 1990s when a Michigan physician, Jack Kevorkian, helped a 54-year-old Oregon woman in the early stages of Alzheimer's disease, a degenerative and fatal brain disease, to commit suicide. Not yet seriously disabled, she was helped by Kevorkian to press a button on a machine designed to inject a drug that induced unconsciousness and a lethal dose of potassium chloride that stopped her heart (Egan, 1990). Death was painless. For almost 10 years, Kevorkian (see photo) played an active role in assisting upwards of 100 terminally ill people take their lives.

One such person was Austin Bastable from Windsor, Ontario. Bastable suffered from multiple sclerosis and went public with his desire to die. He lobbied the Canadian government to legalize assisted suicide. His story drew nationwide attention when it was broadcast on CBC's *Man Alive* on February 8, 1996. Right-to-life advocates attempted to intervene by pleading with Bastable, via a "Save Austin Bastable" website, not to commit suicide. On May 6 that year, Bastable travelled with his wife across the border to Detroit. He died later that same night in the presence of four physicians, including Kevorkian, who was standing trial at that time for the death of two people. Kevorkian was acquitted in 1996. He was brought to trial several times but was not convicted of murder or professional misconduct until the spring of 1999, when he was found guilty of murder and sentenced to 10 to 25 years in prison. He was released on parole in 2007 and died in 2011. Assisted suicides have continued to make news in Canada. In a 2006 case, a 60-year-old mother from Quebec was found guilty and given three years' probation for assisting the suicide of her son in 2004. He suffered from the early stages of multiple sclerosis. In another high-profile case, on December 12, 2008, a Quebec jury acquitted Stephan Dufour of an assisted suicide charge. He had helped his ill uncle to commit suicide. In 2013, the Province of Quebec announced it had found a way around federal provisions and would legalize assisted suicides.

This is a topic of great current interest in Canada due to the publicity garnered by the 2012 case of Gloria Taylor, a woman from British Columbia who petitioned for assisted suicide to alleviate her suffering from Lou Gehrig's disease (see photo). In her own words: "What I fear is a death that negates, as opposed to concludes, my life. I do not want to die slowly, piece by piece. I do not want to waste away unconscious in a hospital bed. I do not want to die wracked with pain" (taken from Carter v. Canada (Attorney General), 2015 SCC 5). The Supreme Court of British Columbia ruled in Taylor's favour after hearing from expert witnesses for several months. It was deemed that to deny her request would violate the rights of the physically disabled granted under Canada's Charter of Rights and Freedoms. However, Taylor died of an infection months later.

Taylor's case, in combination with several other parties, was then before the Supreme Court of Canada. On February 6, 2015, the Supreme Court of Canada decided that the laws against assisted suicide were unconstitutional. A year was given to create new laws, followed by a four-month extension, resulting in a revised deadline of June 6, 2016. Bill C-14 was passed by the House of Commons and Senate in mid-June 2016. There were concerns that the bill was too restrictive, granting medically assisted suicide only to mentally competent adults with an advanced state of a serious illness in which death is foreseeable. Others felt it was not restrictive enough.

Jack Kevorkian provoked a searching and emotional discussion about the conditions under which a physician may take the life of a dying person. Passionate arguments pro and con continue. Interestingly, a 1999 study sought to determine physicians' attitudes toward assisted suicide (Heath et al., 1999). Anonymous questionnaires were sent to almost 3,000 family physicians in Canada. It was found that 60% of physicians

Jack Kevorkian, a Michigan physician, assisted many people in taking their own lives. The controversy stimulated by his actions focused attention on the moral issues surrounding suicide. In 2010, HBO produced a biopic about the controversial doctor called *You Don't Know Jack*. Kevorkian was played in the movie by actor Al Pacino. Pacino indicated during a 2013 appearance at Massey Hall in Toronto that he regards Kevorkian as a great humanitarian.

THE CANADIAN PRESS/Darryl Dyck

Brian Zak/Sipa Press/Newscom

Assisted suicide crusader Gloria Taylor, shown here, sparked a national debate about assisted suicide but died suddenly due to a severe infection in October 2012. The court case continued after Taylor's death, with Taylor's daughter successfully continuing the fight against the federal government on behalf of her deceased mother.

with an opinion on this issue were in favour of the legalization of assisted suicide. One factor that predicted a more positive view was whether the physician provided care to HIV patients. Another factor was the physician's location, with more favourable attitudes coming from physicians practising in British Columbia, Ontario, and Quebec.

Caring for the Suicidal Client

The clinician treating a suicidal person must be prepared to devote more energy and time than usual. The therapist should realize that he or she is likely to become a singularly important figure in the suicidal person's life and should be prepared both for the extreme dependency of the client and for the hostility and resentment that sometimes greet efforts to help.

The *Canadian Journal of Psychiatry* (see Sakinofsky, 2007a) published a special supplement of 10 papers on caring for the suicidal person from a uniquely Canadian perspective. It was restricted to suicidal individuals who seek out or are brought into contact with mental health services and focused on topics where the findings of evidence-based investigations are available (Sakinofsky, 2007a). It was concluded that psychological treatments, particularly CBT and IPT, possibly combined with antidepressants, have demonstrated efficacy in the treatment of suicidal ideation in depression and non-fatal suicidality in borderline personality disorders. Although controversial, there is evidence that the new antidepressants possibly play a role in falling suicide rates. Further, lithium plays a positive role in reducing suicidality in bipolar disorder and possibly unipolar depression, and clozapine clearly plays a role in reducing suicidality in schizophrenia and schizoaffective psychosis. However, Sakinofsky noted that, "By default, we must sometimes use interventions where validity has not been proven" (2007b, p. 18S). The supplement is an excellent educational resource.

A recent review of help-seeking behaviour among people with current suicide ideation, plans, and/or attempts found that the rate was 29.5%, meaning that most suicidal people are not seeking mental health services (Hom, Stanley, & Joiner, 2015). These authors concluded that more research is necessary to understand how to increase help-seeking behaviour among this population.

Summary

8.1 *DSM-5* lists two principal kinds of mood disorders. In major depression, a person experiences profound sadness, as well as related problems such as sleep and appetite disturbances and loss of energy and self-esteem. In bipolar I disorder, a person has episodes of mania alone, distinct episodes of mania and depression, or mixed episodes, in which both manic and depressive symptoms occur together. With mania, mood is elevated or irritable, and the person becomes extremely talkative and distractible. *DSM-5* also lists various other mood disorders, including two chronic mood disorders, cyclothymic disorder and persistent depressive disorder. In cyclothymic disorder, the person has frequent periods of depressed mood and hypomania; in persistent depressive disorder, the person is chronically depressed.

8.2 Psychological theories of depression have been couched in psychoanalytic, cognitive, and interpersonal terms. Beck's cognitive theory ascribes causal significance to negative schematas and cognitive biases and distortions. According to the helplessness/hopelessness theories, early experiences in inescapable, hurtful situations instill a sense of hopelessness that can evolve into depression. Individuals are likely to attribute failures to their own general and persistent inadequacies and faults. Interpersonal theory focuses on the problems depressed people have in relating to others and on the negative responses they elicit from others. These same theories are applied to the depressive phase of bipolar disorder. The manic phase is considered a defence against a debilitating psychological state, such as low self-esteem.

8.3 There may be an inherited predisposition for mood disorders, particularly for bipolar disorder. Early neurochemical theories related depression to low levels of serotonin and bipolar disorder to norepinephrine (high in mania and low in depression). Overactivity of the HPA axis is also found among depressive people, indicating that the endocrine system may influence mood disorders.

8.4 Several psychological and somatic therapies are effective for mood disorders, especially for depression. Psychoanalytic treatment tries to give the client insight into childhood loss and inadequacy and later self-blame. The aim of Beck's cognitive therapy is to uncover negative and illogical patterns of thinking and to teach more realistic ways of viewing events, the self, and adversity. Interpersonal therapy, which focuses on the depressed person's social interactions, also is an effective therapy. Biological treatments are often used in conjunction with psychological treatment. ECT and several antidepressant drugs have possibly proved their worth in lifting depression, with the caveat that ECT clients relapse at high rates if they do not receive follow-up antidepressant treatment. New techniques such as deep brain stimulation, while expensive, seem to offer great promise. Other findings indicate that clients may avoid the excesses of manic and depressive periods through careful administration of lithium carbonate.

8.5 Our exploration of suicide reveals that self-annihilatory tendencies are not restricted to those who are depressed. Many methods can be applied to help prevent suicide, although no single theory is likely to account for the wide variety of motives and situations behind it. Most perspectives on suicide regard it as usually an act of desperation to end an existence that the person feels is unendurable. Physician-assisted suicide is controversial. Legislatures and the courts are wrestling with the issue of the proper role of doctors in releasing terminally ill patients from the extreme pain and disability that can accompany the last months or days of life. In Canada, the stage is set for physician-assisted suicides. Most communities have suicide prevention centres, and most therapists at one time or another deal with people in suicidal crisis. Suicidal people need to have their fears and concerns understood but not judged; clinicians must gradually and patiently point out to them that there are alternatives to self-destruction to be explored.

Key Terms

altruistic suicide
anomic suicide
attribution
autonomy
bilateral ECT
bipolar I disorder
bipolar II disorder
brooding
chronic traumatic encephalopathy (CTE)
congruency hypothesis
cyclothymic disorder
deep brain stimulation
dependency
depression
depressive paradox

depressive predictive certainty
dysfunctional attitudes
egoistic suicide
electroconvulsive therapy (ECT)
hypomania
learned helplessness theory
lithium carbonate
major depressive disorder (MDD)
mania
monoamine oxidase (MAO) inhibitors
mood disorders
negative schema
negative triad
overgenerality effect
persistent depressive disorder

phototherapy
postpartum depression (PD)
psychache
psychologizer
repetitive transcranial magnetic
   stimulation
ruminative coping
seasonal affective disorder
selective serotonin reuptake inhibitors (SSRIs)
self-criticism
sociotropy
Stroop task
suicide prevention centres
tricyclic drugs
unilateral ECT

Reflections: Past, Present, and Future

1. Most of the abnormalities in neurotransmitters that have been identified in people with the various mood disorders are "state dependent," meaning that the differences are evident when the mood disorder occurs but tend to dissipate when mood changes. What are the implications of this fact for our understanding of the mood disorders?

2. There is now extensive research on depression in children despite many authors in the 1970s and 1980s questioning whether depression exists in children. Do you think depression can occur in very young children or does it develop only during adolescence? Does depression in young people differ from depression in adults? Is it possible to find a way to prevent first depressions in vulnerable children?

3. In Chapter 4, we discussed the issue of sexual abuse among Canada's Aboriginal peoples. In this chapter, we discussed the extremely high rates of suicide among Aboriginals. In Chapter 12, you will learn that Aboriginal people have a very high rate of substance abuse. Based on your understanding of the history of the treatment of Aboriginal peoples, their current life circumstances, the identified risk factors for different psychological disorders, and factors related to suicide and substance abuse, design a comprehensive, diathesis–stress model to explain the psychological problems seen in Aboriginal people, especially children.

4. If you had the power and resources to try to change the destiny of Innu children, what would you do? Outline a comprehensive, multi-faceted intervention plan. What role would the Innu themselves play in the design and implementation of the plan?

CHAPTER 9

Stress-Related Disorders and Health Psychology

LEARNING OBJECTIVES

1. Describe various ways of assessing stress and identify ways that it can affect health.

2. Contrast biological and psychological theories of the stress–illness link.

3. Describe how stress contributes to cardiovascular disorders from a physical and a psychological perspective and the factors implicated in coronary heart disease, and discuss how therapies for psychophysiological disorders reflect the link between the mind and the body.

4. List the types of symptoms and events involved in post-traumatic stress disorder (PTSD) and summarize classic biological and psychological views of the etiology of PTSD.

Brief Case Example

Coping with Irritable Bowel Syndrome and Depression: A Case Excerpt

MS. A, a 46-year-old married lawyer, was referred for psychiatric evaluation by her gastroenterologist, who follows her for long-standing irritable bowel syndrome. She has had irritable bowel syndrome since the age of 20, with complaints of intermittent constipation, diarrhea, crampy abdominal pain, and bloating. She feels that these symptoms have gradually worsened, particularly in the last month. She describes a highly pressured job and a stressful marriage. She has specifically noted a precipitous increase in intestinal symptoms immediately after arguments with her husband and when facing deadlines at work. Three months ago, she developed depressed mood, early morning awakening, anorexia, fatigue, crying spells, impaired concentration, irritability, and preoccupation

with thoughts of ill health. Her family physician diagnosed major depression and prescribed amitriptyline, which was discontinued after it worsened her constipation. Her psychiatrist then tried fluoxetine (discontinued because of diarrhea) and trazodone (too sedating). She then responded well to nortriptyline, with disappearance of the symptoms of depression and improvement in her irritable bowel syndrome. However, several irritable bowel syndrome symptoms continued to follow the frequent marital arguments. The psychiatrist asked the patient to invite her husband to join one of their sessions so that marital issues could be explored further. He did so, resulting in the discovery that her husband was himself significantly depressed. He was referred to another psychiatrist for treatment, the marital discord abated, and her irritable bowel syndrome symptoms returned to a manageable level. (Levenson, 2003, p. 1651)

The account of Ms. A illustrates several important themes that are addressed in this chapter. First, stress can come in various forms and it will take a significant toll on the health and well-being of the individual person. There are different levels of stress; we will consider milder forms of stress and how people react to it. But we will also consider extreme stressors that often can result in post-traumatic stress disorders.

Second, the vignette describing Ms. A accords with increasing evidence of a strong association between physical health

problems and deficits in emotional well-being. People with medical illnesses have an increased risk of disorders such as depression and anxiety, and their situation is worsened when they have sleep difficulties. We will discuss the increasingly evident link between the mind and body in several sections of this chapter.

Third, significant life stressors play an important role in exacerbating health problems and contributing to psychological distress. This chapter will explore the role of stress in general but also consider it within the context of the experience and nature of post-traumatic stress disorders.

Finally, ill people suffering from distress must be viewed within their social context in ways that fit well with the biopsychosocial model. In the case of Ms. A, disputes with her husband exacerbated her symptoms, but her husband also experienced profound distress.

The importance of the social context is reflected in the very insightful tips that former Saskatchewan Premier Roy Romanow outlined in an important 2003 speech on the future of health care in Canada. These tips are summarized in the 2004 report *Improving the Health of Canadians* (Canadian Population Health Initiative, 2004). Here are eight important things to keep in mind. Some can be addressed, some you have probably already addressed, and some cannot be addressed. Some points seem obvious, others less so:

1. Don't be poor: rich people tend to live longer on average and are healthier at every life stage. Socio-economic status relates to physiological health (e.g., Chen, 2007; Chen & Miller, 2013; Marin, Chen, & Miller, 2008). Poverty also limits access to health services (Raphael, 2009). New data also suggest that the protective factors vary and are different for people of different levels of socio-economic status (see Chen & Miller, 2013). The link between low socio-economic status and poorer health is clearly evident in Canada, where it has been referred to by Kosteniuk and Dickinson (2003) as the **social gradient of health** (i.e., inequalities in socio-economic status reflect inequalities in health status). These researchers analyzed data from the 1994–95 Canadian National Population Health Survey and found that lower stressor levels were associated with higher household income, being retired, and growing older. Lower stressor levels were also linked with greater levels of control, self-esteem, and social support. How much impact does poverty have? A Canadian Medical Association (CMA) report based on a series of town hall meetings across Canada led the CMA to conclude that poverty is the number-one predictor of long-term health status and the top recommendation was that the federal and provincial priority should be developing an action plan to eliminate poverty in Canada (CMA, 2013).

2. Get a good start in life: prenatal and early childhood experiences have a profound effect on many outcomes, including long-term health status.

3. Graduate from high school (and preferably from college or university): as education level increases, so does health status.

4. Get a job: unemployment is linked with lower levels of functional health and increased levels of stress.

5. Choose your community: data on healthy vs. unhealthy communities illustrate that where you live matters as does the community's values and your sense of belonging and mattering in the community, and these can have a substantial impact on your health and well-being (e.g., Chen, Chim, Strunk, & Miller, 2007).

6. Live in quality housing: exposure to environmental risks often translates into subsequent health problems.

7. Look after yourself: much is to be gained by eating well, exercising, and not abusing alcohol or drugs. Self-care and knowing when to advocate for yourself are essential to your well-being.

8. Men and women are different: men do not live as long as women, on average, though women report poorer health status.

As indicated, Chapter 9 focuses on stress-related disorders and health. The version of Chapter 9 in this new edition has been modified significantly to reflect a key change introduced in the *DSM-5* (American Psychiatric Association, 2013). Historically, post-traumatic stress disorder (PTSD) in the *DSM* had been included among the anxiety disorders that are listed in Chapter 5 of this edition due to the anxiety inherent in PTSD. However, the *DSM-5* created a new chapter titled "Trauma- and Stressor-Related Disorders" to reflect the unique elements of stress-related disorders.

Other disorders included in this new segment of the *DSM-5* include reactive attachment disorder, disinhibited social engagement disorder, acute stress disorder, and adjustment disorders. This chapter concludes with a detailed description and analysis of PTSD. PTSD and the other disorders it is listed with all involve prolonged maladaptive reactions to stress. Reactive attachment disorder is characterized by emotionally withdrawn behaviour toward adult caregivers following neglect or other forms of deprivation. In contrast, in disinhibited social engagement disorder, the child is overly willing to interact with unfamiliar adults due to a history of neglect, deprivation, or a chaotic upbringing involving multiple caregivers. Acute stress disorder is diagnosed when trauma symptoms last between three days up to one month following a traumatic event that was experienced directly or witnessed or happened to a family member. It can also be a result of repeated exposure to traumatic events such as would be the case with first responder personnel (e.g., paramedics, police, firefighters). Adjustment disorders involve the development of emotional or behavioural symptoms following the occurrence of a major life stressor (e.g., the death of a loved one) but the symptoms do not fit the description of other disorders. For instance, a person can have an adjustment disorder with a depressed or anxious mood but not enough symptoms to warrant an anxiety or depression diagnosis.

Much is currently known about the nature of stress and its effects, but much remains to be learned. Stress is often implicated in the development of psychophysiological disorders. **Psychophysiological disorders**, such as asthma, hypertension, headache, and gastritis, are characterized by genuine physical symptoms that are caused by or can be worsened by emotional factors. The term *psychophysiological disorders* is preferred today to a term that was formerly used and is perhaps better known, **psychosomatic disorders**. Nevertheless, the term *psychosomatic* connotes quite well the principal feature of these disorders: that the psyche, or mind, is having an untoward effect on the soma, or body.

Psychophysiological disorders are real diseases involving damage to the body. That such disorders are viewed as being related to emotional factors does not make the afflictions imaginary. People can just as readily die from psychologically produced high blood pressure or asthma as from similar diseases produced by infection or physical injury.

The many demonstrations of the pervasive role of psychological factors in health form the basis for the fields of **behavioural medicine** and **health psychology**. Since the 1970s, these fields have dealt with the role of psychological factors in all facets of health and illness. Beyond examining the etiological role that stress can play in illness, researchers in these fields study psychological treatments (e.g., biofeedback for headache) and the health care system itself (e.g., how better to deliver services to underserved populations) (Appel et al., 1997; Stone, 1982).

Prevention is also a major focus of health psychology. As the twentieth century progressed and infectious diseases were brought under better control, people were dying more often from such illnesses as cardiovascular disease (CVD). It is estimated that 45% of all causes of death are cardiovascular in nature (Linden & Moseley, 2003) and CVD remains the leading cause of death in Canada (Manuel et al., 2003). The causes of CVD involve behaviour—people's lifestyles—such as smoking, eating too much, and excessive alcohol use. Thus, it is believed that many CVD cases can be prevented by changing unhealthy lifestyles. Health psychologists are at the forefront of prevention efforts that address CVD and other illnesses.

9.1 The Nature and Experience of Stress

We begin by reviewing general findings on the relationship between stress and health, as well as theories about how stress can produce illness.

Defining the Concept of Stress

In earlier chapters, the term "stress" was used to refer to some environmental condition that triggers psychopathology. We also examined the concept of self-generated stress. Here we shall examine the term more closely and consider the difficulties in its definition.

Hans Selye created the term **stress**. Selye was a world-renowned researcher who eventually became a Canadian citizen and conducted much of his research in Montreal. Selye is also known for identifying the **general adaptation syndrome (GAS)**, which is described more fully in Canadian Contributions 9.1.

Selye's concept of stress eventually found its way into the psychological literature, but with substantial changes in its definition. Some researchers followed Selye's lead and considered stress a response to environmental conditions, defined on the basis of such diverse criteria as emotional

Canadian Contributions 9.1

Hans Selye: The Father of Stress

Dr. Hans Selye is regarded as the father of the stress concept and the inventor of the common term "stress." Selye was born in Europe but immigrated to the United States when he was awarded a Rockefeller fellowship. In 1932, he immigrated to Canada when he was hired as an associate professor of histology at McGill University in Montreal. Selye was to remain in Canada the rest of his life. He became a Canadian citizen, was recognized as a Companion of the Order of Canada in 1968 for his pioneering research on the nature of stress, and was even featured on a postage stamp (see illustration). He authored 30 books and hundreds of research articles on the nature of stress in animals and people.

Most doctors focus on precise illnesses caused by specific factors, but Selye was an endocrinologist who was interested in the "general syndrome of being sick." He noticed early in his career that organisms exposed to a diverse array of stimuli (e.g., trauma, cold, heat, nervous irritation) often exhibit a similar, non-specific response. Accordingly, he viewed stress as a non-specific response of the body to any demand for change.

In 1936 Selye introduced the general adaptation syndrome (GAS), a description of the biological response to sustained and unrelenting physical stress (i.e., a biological stress syndrome). There are three phases of the syndrome, as shown in Figure 9.1.

1. During the first phase, the alarm reaction, the autonomic nervous system is activated by the stress. If the stress is too

powerful, gastrointestinal ulcers form, the adrenal glands become enlarged, and the thymus undergoes atrophy (wasting away).

2. During the second phase, resistance, the organism adapts to the stress through available coping mechanisms. The length of resistance depends on the body's innate adaptability and the intensity of the stressor (Selye, 1974).

3. If the stressor persists or the organism is unable to respond effectively, the third phase, a stage of exhaustion, follows, and the organism dies or suffers irreversible damage (Selye, 1950).

Selye is especially well-known for promoting the view that stress plays a role, for better or worse, in all diseases (see Selye, 1974). The role of stress in various illnesses is discussed in subsequent sections of this chapter.

Selye made an important distinction between negative and positive forms of stress, and this was reflected in his use of the terms **distress** and **eustress**. Distress is damaging or unpleasant stress. Eustress is positive, pleasant stress. He believed that pleasant and unpleasant emotional arousal result in increased levels of physiological stress, but only negative emotional arousal results in distress.

In time, Selye came to believe that the term "stress" was misleading and that he should have used the term "strain" instead, since "stress" has other meanings in the field of physics. But, according to Rosch (1998), Selye is regarded as the creator of the

(continued)

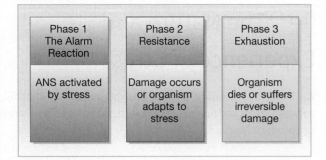

Phase 1 The Alarm Reaction	Phase 2 Resistance	Phase 3 Exhaustion
ANS activated by stress	Damage occurs or organism adapts to stress	Organism dies or suffers irreversible damage

FIGURE 9.1 Selye's general adaptation syndrome.

word as it is used commonly because many other languages lack a suitable word or phrase that can convey what is meant by the word "stress."

Interestingly, it appears that Selye's own medical history served as an illustration of the role that psychological factors play in stress and illness. According to Rosch, at one point, Selye "developed a rare and usually fatal malignancy, and attributed his rather remarkable recovery to his strong desire to continue his research. He was convinced that stress could cause cancer, and that a strong

faith could reverse this" (Rosch, 1998, p. 5). Indeed, the role of psychological factors in cancer is detailed in a subsequent section of this chapter.

© Canada Post Corporation. 1999. Reproduced with permission.

Canada Post stamp commemorating the important contributions to our understanding of stress that were initiated by Hans Selye.

upset, deterioration of performance, or physiological changes such as increased skin conductance or increases in the levels of certain hormones. The problem with these response-based definitions of stress is that the criteria are not clear-cut. Physiological changes in the body can occur in response to a number of stimuli that we would not consider stressful (e.g., anticipating a pleasurable event).

Stress affects the nervous system. The autonomic nervous system and its responsiveness to stress are described in Focus on Discovery 9.1.

Many researchers have focused on stress as a stimulus, often referred to as a **stressor**, and identified it with a long list of environmental conditions: electric shock, boredom, uncontrollable stimuli, catastrophic life events, daily hassles, and sleep deprivation. Stimuli that are considered stressors can be major (the death of a loved one), minor (being stuck in traffic), acute (failing an exam), or chronic (a persistently unpleasant work environment). According to one Canadian researcher, chronic stress can take many forms, including persistent threats, demands, and conflicts, as well as a sense of being

under-rewarded and being deprived of essential resources, as might be the case with individuals from disadvantaged groups (see Wheaton, 1997).

Stressors can also be distinguished in terms of whether they are psychogenic or neurogenic (see Anisman & Merali, 1999). Psychogenic stressors stem from psychological factors (e.g., anticipation of an adverse event), while neurogenic stressors stem from a physical stimulus (e.g., bodily injury or recovery from surgery). Anisman and Merali (1999) noted that various stressors can differ in a number of ways, including whether they are controllable (i.e., stress can be lessened or eliminated by engaging in a certain response) or uncontrollable, predictable or unpredictable, short in duration or chronic, and intermittent or recurring. Anisman and Merali (1999) also described how different stressors have different physiological implications; for example, chronic, intermittent, and unpredictable stressors are less likely to result in neurochemical adaptation, while intense and prolonged demands on neurochemical systems may create a condition known as **allostatic load**, which can lead to a variety of pathological outcomes.

Focus on Discovery 9.1

The Autonomic Nervous System and Stress

The **autonomic nervous system (ANS)** is involved when we react involuntarily or automatically to stimuli. Our nervous systems have two separate parts: the ANS and the **somatic nervous system**, which is the voluntary nervous system. The voluntary nervous system is involved when we consciously express movements. However, much of our behaviour reflects a nervous system that tends

to operate outside of our awareness and has been viewed traditionally as beyond voluntary control, hence the term "autonomic." However, research on biofeedback has shown that the ANS is under greater voluntary control than previously believed.

The ANS stimulates the endocrine glands, the heart, and the smooth muscles found in the walls of the blood vessels, stomach, intestines, kidneys, and other organs. The ANS is divided into two parts, the **sympathetic nervous system** and the **parasympathetic**

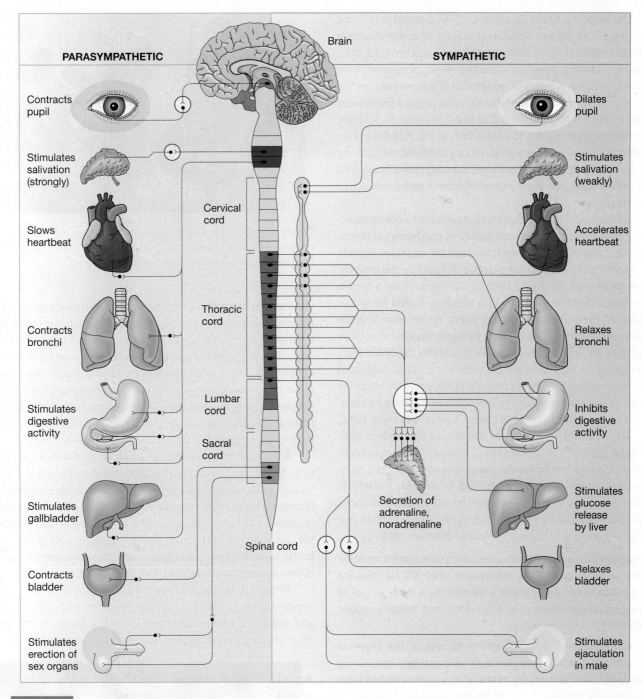

PARASYMPATHETIC

Contracts pupil

Stimulates salivation (strongly)

Slows heartbeat

Contracts bronchi

Stimulates digestive activity

Stimulates gallbladder

Contracts bladder

Stimulates erection of sex organs

Brain

Cervical cord

Thoracic cord

Lumbar cord

Sacral cord

Spinal cord

SYMPATHETIC

Dilates pupil

Stimulates salivation (weakly)

Accelerates heartbeat

Relaxes bronchi

Inhibits digestive activity

Secretion of adrenaline, noradrenaline

Stimulates glucose release by liver

Relaxes bladder

Stimulates ejaculation in male

FIGURE 9.2   The autonomic nervous system.

nervous system (Figure 9.2), which may work in tandem or in opposition to each other. The sympathetic nervous system, when energized, accelerates the heartbeat, dilates the pupils, inhibits intestinal activity, increases electrodermal activity, and initiates other smooth-muscle and glandular responses. The experience of stress or the anticipation of stress activates the sympathetic nervous system. The parasympathetic nervous system is involved in deactivation and restoring the organism to a lower state of activation.

If a person is chronically stressed, this means that the sympathetic nervous system is also chronically activated. Eventually,

significant health problems may result from this activation and prolonged exposure to stress hormones, which is described subsequently in this chapter. These health problems may reflect having a diminished immune system, given that the nervous system sends signals that influence the immune system (Segerstrom & Miller, 2004).

There is growing evidence that chronic activation of the sympathetic nervous system is implicated directly in health problems. For instance, Guyenet (2006) reviewed the growing empirical work linking activation of the sympathetic nervous system and hypertension.

Like response-based definitions, stimulus-based definitions also present problems. Stipulating exactly what constitutes a stressor is difficult. More than negativity is clearly involved; marriage, for instance, generally a positive event, is regarded as a stressor because it requires adaptation. Furthermore, people vary widely in how they respond to life's challenges. A given event does not elicit the same amount of stress in everyone. A family that has lost its home due to events such as the 2016 fire in Fort McMurray, Alberta, but has enough money to rebuild and a strong network of friends will experience less hardship than a family that has neither adequate money to rebuild nor a social network to provide support.

Some people believe that it is not possible to define objectively what events or situations qualify as psychological stressors (e.g., Lazarus, 1966). They emphasize the cognitive aspects of stress; that is, the way we perceive or appraise the environment determines whether a stressor is present. When a person determines that the demands of a situation exceed his or her resources, the person experiences stress. A final exam may be merely challenging to one student, yet highly stressful to another who does not feel equipped to take it (whether his or her fears are realistic or not). Similarly, as shown in a study conducted with women from the Ottawa area, the stress experienced during breast cancer screening is closely tied to how the stressful situation is perceived and appraised (Sweet, Savoie, & Lemyre, 1999).

Also relevant to individual differences in responding to stressful situations is the concept of **coping**, how people try to deal with a problem or handle the emotions it produces. Even among those who appraise a situation as stressful, the effects of the stress may vary depending on how the individual copes with the event. Lazarus and his colleagues have identified two broad dimensions of coping (Lazarus & Folkman, 1984):

- *Problem-focused coping* involves taking direct action to solve the problem or seeking information that will be relevant to the solution. An example is developing a study schedule to pace assignments over a semester and thereby reduce end-of-semester pressure.

- *Emotion-focused coping* is efforts to reduce the negative emotional reactions to stress; for example, by distracting oneself from the problem, relaxing, or seeking comfort from others (see photo).

Lazarus (1966) developed a transactional model of stress based on the premise that stress is not solely due to the situation or to an individual's cognitive appraisals and coping responses; rather, stress results from a transaction or interaction between situational factors and factors inside the person (see photo). A model of stress and coping developed by Neufeld (1999) at the University of Western Ontario also acknowledges the dynamic and ongoing interplay of these factors. A key element of this model is the recognition that stressors and related situations change over time.

The effectiveness of attempts to cope varies with the situation. Various investigators (e.g., Endler, Speer, Johnson, & Flett, 2000; Felton & Revenson, 1984; Forsythe & Compas, 1987) have tested a **goodness of fit hypothesis** that suggests that

Coping can focus on solving the problem itself or on regulating the negative emotions it has created. Seeking comfort or social support from others is an example of emotion-focused coping.

whether a particular coping response is adaptive depends on the match between the coping response and what is called for ideally by the problem situation. Distraction may be an effective way of dealing with the emotional upset produced by impending surgery, but it would be a poor way to handle the upset produced by the discovery of a lump on the breast (Lazarus & Folkman, 1984). Similarly, continuing efforts to seek a solution to an unsolvable problem lead to increases in frustration rather than to any psychological benefit (Terry & Hynes, 1998).

A key factor is whether a problem or situation is controllable or uncontrollable. Problem-focused coping is most adaptive when there is something that an individual can do to improve the situation; emotion-focused coping is less adaptive in these situations. However, when a situation is uncontrollable, problem-focused coping is not adaptive; here it may be better to vent and express one's emotions to release tension (Stanton, Kirk, Cameron, & Danoff-Burg, 2000).

Finally, it should be noted that, in terms of cognitive appraisals and strategies, people often respond with denial and avoidance when confronted with stressors of varying levels of severity, including shocking events. In general, however,

According to Richard Lazarus, the way a life event is appraised is an important determinant of whether it causes stress. An exam, for example, may be viewed as a challenge or as an extremely stressful event.

the evidence indicates that escape/avoidance coping (such as wishing that the situation would go away or be over with) is the least effective method of coping with many life problems (Suls & Fletcher, 1985), especially over the long term.

Types of Stress and How It is Measured

Given the difficulty of defining stress with precision, it is not surprising that measuring stress is difficult, as well. Research on the effects of stress on human health has sought to measure the amount of life stress a person has experienced and then to correlate this measurement with illness. Various scales have been developed to measure life stress. Here we examine two: the Social Readjustment Rating Scale and the Assessment of Daily Experience.

The Social Readjustment Rating Scale   In the 1960s, two researchers, Holmes and Rahe (1967), gave a list of life events to a large group of people and asked them to rate each item according to its intensity and the amount of time they thought they would need to adjust to it. Marriage was arbitrarily assigned a stress value of 500; all other items were then evaluated using this reference point (see photo). For example, an event twice as stressful as marriage would be assigned a value of 1,000, and an event one-fifth as stressful as marriage would be assigned a value of 100. The average ratings assigned to the 12 most stressful events by the respondents in Holmes and Rahe's study are shown in Table 9.1.

The Social Readjustment Rating Scale emerged from this study. A respondent checks off the life events experienced during the time period in question. Ratings are then totalled for all the events actually experienced to produce a Life Change Unit (LCU) score, a weighted sum of events.

iStock.com/jessicaphoto

Experiencing major life events such as marriage statistically increases risk of illness. Research on the effect of these major stressors assesses them with the Social Readjustment Rating Scale.

Rank	Life Event	Mean Value
1	Death of spouse	100
2	Divorce	73
3	Marital separation	65
4	Jail term	63
5	Death of close family member	63
6	Personal injury or illness	53
7	Marriage	50[a]
8	Fired from work	47
9	Marital reconciliation	45
10	Retirement	45
11	Change in health of family member	44
12	Pregnancy	40

TABLE 9.1   Social Readjustment Rating Scale

[a]Marriage was arbitrarily assigned a stress value of 500; no event was found to be any more than twice as stressful. Here the values are reduced proportionally and range up to 100.

Source: Holmes, T. H., & Rahe, R. H. (1967). The social readjustment rating scale. *Journal of Psychosomatic Research, 11(2),* 213–218. Reprinted with permission of Elsevier.

Miller and Rahe (1997) rescaled the events on the SRSS and added some events in recognition of the possibility that the impact of life changes in the 1990s might be different from the impact experienced in the 1960s and 1970s. Once again, the event of marriage was used as the reference point and was assigned a score of 50. The top five LCU ratings were given to death of a child (123), death of a spouse (119), death of a brother or sister (102), death of a parent (100), and divorce (96). Overall, Miller and Rahe (1997) found that the life-change intensity scores rose 45%. Changing to a different line of work, for example, went from an LCU of 36 to an LCU of 51.

The original LCU score has been related to several different illnesses, including heart attacks (Rahe & Lind, 1971), onset of leukemia (Wold, 1968), and colds and fevers (Holmes & Holmes, 1970). The results demonstrated a correlation between psychological stress and physical illness, but they do not necessarily mean that stress causes or contributes to illness. We know from work by Rahe and Ransom (1968) that the experience of illness itself can cause a high life-change score, as when chronic absenteeism caused by the illness brings dismissal from a job. This reality underscores the fact that psychological factors may contribute to illness onset but are also involved in how an ill person responds and reacts to the illness. We will examine this issue in more detail in further discussions of how chronically ill people can differ and be quite heterogeneous in how they cope with their illnesses.

Given the fact that it often takes many years for stress to contribute to illness, research on stress and health should, ideally, be longitudinal and involve multiple assessment phases. Longitudinal research offers several advantages; for instance, the biases of retrospective self-reports are minimized and changes in stress can be shown to precede changes in health.

Assessment of Daily Experience

Consideration of problems with the Social Readjustment Rating Scale led Stone and Neale (1982) to develop a new assessment instrument, the Assessment of Daily Experience (ADE). Rather than relying on retrospective reports, the ADE allows individuals to record and rate their daily experiences in prospective or longitudinal investigations. A day was used as the unit of analysis because a thorough characterization of this period should be possible without major retrospective-recall bias. Although the events reported on a day will generally be less severe than those reported over a longer time period, there is now direct evidence that these minor events are related to illness (Jandorf, Deblinger, Neale, & Stone, 1986). Part of the ADE is shown in Figure 9.3.

WORK-RELATED ACTIVITIES

Concerning Boss, Supervisor, Upper Management, etc.

► Praised for a job well done ☐ ○ ○ △ 01
► Criticism for job performance, lateness, etc. ☐ ○ ○ △ 02

Concerning Co-workers, Employees, Supervisees, and/or Clients

► Positive emotional interactions and/or happenings with co-workers, employees, supervisees, and/or clients (work-related events which were fulfilling, etc.) ☐ ○ ○ △ 03

► Negative emotional interactions and/or happenings with co-workers, employees, supervisees, and/or clients (work-related events which were frustrating, irritating, etc.) ☐ ○ ○ △ 04

► Firing or disciplining (by Target) ☐ ○ ○ △ 05

► Socializing with staff, co-workers, employees, supervisees, and/or clients ☐ ○ ○ △ 06

General Happenings Concerning Target at Work

► Promotion, raise ☐ ○ ○ △ 07

► Fired, quit, resigned ☐ ○ ○ △ 08

► Some change in job (different from the above, i.e., new assignment, new boss, etc.) ☐ ○ ○ △ 09

► Under a lot of pressure at work (impending deadlines, heavy workload, etc.) ☐ ○ ○ △ 10

FIGURE 9.3 Sample page from Assessment of Daily Experience Scale. Respondents indicate whether an event occurred by circling the arrows to the left of the list of events. If an event has occurred, the respondents then rate it on the dimensions of desirability, change, meaningfulness, and control, using the enclosed spaces to the right.

Reproduced with permission of Taylor & Francis Group LLC, from ENVIRONMENT AND HEALTH by Stone, A. A., & Neale, J. M. pp. 49–83. p. 70; conveyed through Copyright Clearance Centre, Inc.

With an assessment of daily experiences in hand, Stone, Reed, and Neale (1987) examined the relationship between undesirable and desirable events and the onset of episodes of respiratory illness. Respiratory illness was selected as the criterion variable because it occurs with sufficient frequency to allow it to be analyzed as a distinct outcome.

After reviewing the participants' data, the researchers identified 30 individuals who had experienced episodes of infectious illness during the assessment period. Next, they examined the daily frequency of undesirable and desirable events that occurred from 1 to 10 days before the start of an episode. For each person, a set of control days, without an episode, was also selected. The results showed that, for desirable events, there were significant decreases three and four days before the onset of respiratory infection; for undesirable events, there were significant increases at four and five days before the onset of the illness.

These results, which have been replicated (Evans & Edgerton, 1990), were the first to show a relationship between life events and health, with both variables measured in a daily, prospective design. Most sources of confounding in prior life-events studies were avoided in this study, and we can now come much closer to asserting that life events play a causal role in increasing vulnerability to episodes of infectious illness.

Other research has studied daily events by having people complete self-report measures of their **daily hassles**. These studies often show that not only does a link exist between self-reported daily hassles (see photo) and poor psychological

Daily hassles such as being stuck in traffic can be emotionally upsetting and also increase risk of illness.

iStock.com/Stouffer

and physical adjustment, but measures of daily hassles are often better than measures of major life events at predicting adjustment problems (DeLongis, Coyne, Dakof, Folkman, & Lazarus, 1982; Kanner, Coyne, Schaefer, & Lazarus, 1981).

Researchers have responded to two problems that plagued earlier research on daily hassles. First, the original Hassles Scale (Kanner et al., 1981) has been described as "contaminated" because it included items that could be construed as a symptom of distress (e.g., feeling tired) rather than a hassle per se. These symptoms were removed in a subsequent version of the Hassles Scale created by Anita DeLongis, who conducts research at the University of British Columbia (see DeLongis, Folkman, & Lazarus, 1988).

Second, the original Hassles Scale was developed for use with a middle-aged community sample, and as such, it contained daily hassles that may not be relevant to other populations. Researchers have addressed this problem by developing daily hassles tailored to the experiences of specific groups of people. Canadian researchers have developed hassles measures for university and college students (Kohn, Lafreniere, & Gurevich, 1990) and for adolescents (Kohn & Milrose, 1993). The Brief College Hassles Scale (BCHS; Blankstein, Flett, and Koledin, 1991) is shown in Figure 9.4. It taps three main themes: (1) academic hassles (e.g., academic bureaucracy, academic deadlines); (2) interpersonal hassles (e.g., contact with boyfriend/girlfriend, relationship with mother and/or father); and (3) financial hassles

---

Hassles are irritants that can range from minor annoyances to fairly major pressures, problems, or difficulties. They can occur few or many times. Each item listed below concerns a specific hassle. Please rate the persistence of the hassles shown below, over the past month including today. Persistence is defined as the combination of the frequency and duration of a hassle. Some hassles may occur very frequently and last for a long time whereas others may occur rarely and not be very enduring. Various other combinations are possible.

Please indicate the persistence of each hassle over the past month by checking a number between "1" and "7", according to the rating scale shown below:

1	2	3	4	5	6	7
No hassle; **Not at all persistent**						**Extremely persistent;** **High frequency**

	1	2	3	4	5	6	7
Academic deadlines							
Contact with girlfriend/boyfriend							
Future job prospects							
Relationship with people at work							
Money for necessary expenses							
Noise							
Organization of time							
Weight							
Household chores							
Family expectations							
Relationship with mother and/or father							
Academic bureaucracy							
Preparing meals							
Exercise							
Owing money							
Job satisfaction							
Financial security							
Relationship with girlfriend/boyfriend							
Relationship with brother/sister							
College program requirements							

Note: The typical mean score for students is approximately 75 with a standard deviation of 17. Scores are the sum of all 20 items. Scores that are considerably higher than the typical mean (e.g., 100 or greater) suggest that stress counselling could be helpful.

FIGURE 9.4   The Brief College Hassles Scale.

(e.g., owing money). It also assesses common general hassles such as organization of time, noise, future job prospects, and household chores. These hassles were identified via extensive interviews and feedback from students gathered over a three-year period.

Higher scores on the BCHS have been linked with greater psychological distress (Blankstein et al., 1991) and frequency of headaches (Bottos & Dewey, 2004). Other research at St. Mary's University with the BCHS showed that elevated hassles occurred among students with lower levels of emotional intelligence and stress management. Hassles were also associated with psychological and physical symptoms (Day, Therrien, & Carroll, 2005).

Illness-specific hassles can also be assessed. Fillion, Kohn, and their associates developed a hassles measure to assess the stressors faced by cancer patients, including stressors involving future concerns (e.g., thinking about how family members will manage if the patient dies), functional disability (e.g., difficulty walking and moving about), and body-image concerns (Fillion et al., 2001). Research with cancer patients from Quebec and Ontario indicates that this new measure is associated with higher levels of anger, fatigue, and depression. These population-specific measures are more precise and offer more meaningful ways of assessing hassles for respondents. It is important to remember, however, that the findings from this research apply to the specific group being studied and should not be overgeneralized to other groups.

We have already noted that two measures of daily hassles have been created to assess the specific daily stressors experienced by college and university students. Student Perspectives 9.1 continues our emphasis on the specific health issues facing college and university students. Although it is generally the case that health matters become more important as we get older, a considerable proportion of students are confronted with significant health concerns.

Stress in Specific Contexts   In addition to examining the hassles associated with specific illnesses, it is possible and meaningful to examine stress in specific life contexts. We have already seen that students list stress as the top factor that undermines their academic performance. We will further illustrate this issue with a brief discussion of a particular form of stress: **job stress**. People may experience high levels of job stress either because of their own unique personal characteristics or because they have a high-stress occupation (e.g., doctors, nurses, accountants at tax filing time). Job stress is linked consistently with depression (Tennant, 2001) and other negative outcomes. Consider, for instance, the results of the

---

Student Perspectives 9.1

The Health Status of Students

Contrary to expectations, there is little evidence that college and university students enjoy comparatively good health relative to other segments of the population. Students do not rate their health more positively than do older adults (Svenson & Campbell, 1992; Vingilis, Wade, & Adlaf, 1998). What factors predict less positive ratings of health status? Vingilis et al. (1998) found that more negative assessments by students from Canada were associated with poorer child–parent relationships, lower interest and achievement in school, lower self-esteem, smoking, and being female. The more negative assessments of female students were replicated in a study conducted with students from Germany, Bulgaria, and Poland (Mikolajcdyk et al., 2008). The best predictor of negative self-ratings in this European study was the presence of psychosomatic symptoms.

How would you rate your health if asked whether it is excellent, very good, good, fair, or poor? Did you assess your health as relatively good? We will now report some results from the 2008 National College Health Assessment conducted by the American College Health Association (ACHA, 2009a). This study was conducted with responses from over 80,000 students. Overall, 66% of students listed their general health as excellent or very good, and another 27% listed their health as good. Only 7% listed their health as fair or poor; hopefully, there is something that these students can do about it. The same survey was taken at six Ontario university campuses by almost 6,000 students. In Ontario, 10.8% students rated their health as fair or poor (ACHA, 2009b). More revealing is that 21.2% (over 1 in 5) of the students in Ontario reported a personal health problem in the past 12 months that was traumatic or very difficult to handle. What was especially alarming was reported

stress levels: 43.2% indicated more than average stress over the past 12 months and another 11.4% indicated "tremendous stress." Chronic exposure to this level of stress is bound to contribute eventually to a higher preponderance of health problems.

Of course, health problems have potentially life-threatening consequences. A meta-analysis of 163 studies with students found that those who rated their health as poor, relative to those who rated their health as excellent, had a twofold higher mortality risk (DeSalvo et al., 2005).

The top health problems experienced by students in the National College Health Assessment in the past year were: (1) allergy (47.9%), (2) back pain (46.1%), (3) sinus infection (30.7%), (4) depression (17.0%), and (5) strep throat (13.8%). About 1 in 10 students experienced asthma. The top health problems were comparable for men and women.

When asked to indicate factors that undermined their academic performance, students identified several things that seem intuitive (see ACHA, 2009b). The top five factors were stress (33.9%), cold/flu/sore throat (28.8%), sleep difficulties (25.6%), concern for troubled friend or family member (18.8%), and Internet use/computer games (16.9%). Other specific sources of stress mentioned were relationship difficulties and death of a family member or friend.

Given these health problems and levels of stress, it is never too soon to start engaging in positive health behaviours (e.g., exercising, regular checkups). Hopefully, good health habits will carry over throughout one's life and serve a protective role. Here again, however, the 2009 survey established that about 1 in 4 Ontario students reported that they failed to engage in even moderate exercise activity even once a week, and this inactivity can amplify the stress experienced by these students.

first-ever nationally representative survey of work and health of nurses in Canada (see Shields & Wilkins, 2005). This study involved interviews with 18,676 nurses across Canada, with participation from 4 out of 5 nurses contacted. Overall, approximately one-third of nurses were deemed to have high-job stress and strain, and this job strain predicted poorer physical and mental health (e.g., depression), as well as lengthier and more frequent absences from work. Job stress can also have an impact on family life, according to the concept of **job spillover**. This is the notion that stressed workers bring their work stress home with them and it causes family stress.

One of the potential by-products of extreme job stress is that a person may experience **job burnout**. The concept of burnout has been assessed most extensively by Christina Maslach and her colleagues (Maslach & Jackson, 1981). Burnout involves three components: (1) a sense of emotional exhaustion; (2) depersonalization (i.e., a tendency to be insensitive and not respect the needs of other people); and (3) a sense of lack of personal accomplishment. Job burnout has been linked with a vast array of physical problems including cardiovascular disease (Melamed et al., 2006) and psychological difficulties such as depression (see Maslach, Schaufeli, & Leiter, 2001). In some people, job burnout appears to be a reflection of having developed a work addiction and suffering from workaholism (for a review, see Burke, 2006). An extreme form of burnout is a condition known as **vital exhaustion**, a physical depletion that is also linked to cardiovascular disease (Melamed et al., 2006).

Assessing Coping

We have already mentioned the importance of coping. Coping is most often measured by questionnaires that list a series of coping strategies and ask respondents to indicate to what extent they used each strategy to handle a recent stressor. An example of one such measure, the COPE, is presented in Table 9.2.

As with the effects of stressors, the best way to examine coping is to use a battery of measures and to conduct a longitudinal study; this approach would demonstrate that particular ways of coping with stress precede the outcomes in which the researcher is interested. Breast cancer has been investigated in this way. The diagnosis of breast cancer, which strikes about 1 woman in 9, is a major stressor on many levels. It is a life-threatening illness; surgical interventions are often disfiguring and thus have serious implications for psychological well-being, and both radiation therapy and chemotherapy have very unpleasant side effects.

Carver et al. (1993) selected women who had just been diagnosed with breast cancer and assessed how they were coping at several times during the following year. Women who accepted their diagnosis and retained a sense of humour had lower levels of distress. Carver et al. also found that avoidant coping methods, such as denial and behavioural disengagement (see Table 9.2), were related to higher levels of distress. This negative effect of denial on adjustment to breast cancer has been replicated (Heim, Valach, & Schaffner, 1997). Another longitudinal study of several types of cancer found that avoidant coping ("I

TABLE 9.2	Scales and Sample Items from the COPE

Active Coping
I've been concentrating my efforts on doing something about the situation I'm in.

Suppression of Competing Activities
I've been putting aside other activities in order to concentrate on this.

Planning
I've been trying to come up with a strategy about what to do.

Restraint
I've been making sure not to make matters worse by acting too soon.

Use of Social Support
I've been getting sympathy and understanding from someone.

Positive Reframing
I've been looking for something good in what is happening.

Religion
I've been putting my trust in God.

Acceptance
I've been accepting the reality of the fact that it happened.

Denial
I've been refusing to believe that it has happened.

Behavioural Disengagement
I've been giving up the attempt to cope.

Use of Humour
I've been making jokes about it.

Self-Distraction
I've been going to movies, watching TV, or reading, to think about it less.

Source: Copyright © 1993 by the American Psychological Association. Reproduced with permission. Carver, C. S., et al. (1993). How coping mediates the effect of optimism on distress: A study of women with early stage breast cancer. *Journal of Personality and Social Psychology, 65(2)*, pp. 375–390. The use of APA information does not imply endorsement by APA.

try not to think about it") predicted greater progression of the disease at a one-year follow-up (Epping-Jordan, Compas, & Howell, 1994). These data show that it is not merely the presence of stress that produces physical and emotional effects: how the person reacts to the stressor is crucial as well. In the case of cancer, reducing stress by ignoring the problem is not a good idea.

Canadian psychologist Norman Endler made important contributions to the research literature on coping, stress, and anxiety (see Canadian Contributions 9.2). Endler teamed in the latter segment of his career with James Parker from Trent University (see photo) and they worked closely together to develop measures of trait coping and coping with health and illness problems. Parker holds a Canada Research Chair in emotion and health and he continues to examine predictors of stress-related, emotion, and health outcomes such as emotional intelligence and alexithymia.

Work by Endler, Parker, and their associates highlights the role of emotional preoccupation as a maladaptive coping response to illness. Emotional preoccupation is quite similar to the ruminative response style described in Chapter 8 as a way of prolonging depression. Intriguing research is beginning to illuminate the role of rumination in stress and illness. Collectively, a series of laboratory studies indicate that prolonged rumination

Canadian Contributions 9.2

Norman Endler and the Interaction Model of Anxiety, Stress, and Coping

Dr. Norman Endler from York University was one of Canada's most influential psychologists (see photo). In 1997, the Canadian Psychological Association gave him the Donald O. Hebb Award for Distinguished Contributions to Psychology as a Science, and the Royal Society of Canada gave him the Innis-Gerin medal "for distinguished and sustained contributions to the social sciences." Endler died in 2003.

What contributions did he make? Endler was known initially for his interaction model of anxiety and his work on **interactionism** with David Magnusson (see Endler & Magnusson, 1976; Endler, 1983). The essence of this model is that personality traits interact dynamically with situational factors to produce behaviours. The model's initial focus was on how different facets of trait anxiety (i.e., the person's usual level of anxiety) combine with congruent situational factors to produce immediate levels of state anxiety. Endler hypothesized that people will experience state anxiety when they experience a situation that matches the aspect of trait anxiety that is central to their personal identity; that is, people high in physical danger anxiety, say, will be anxious in dangerous situations, while people concerned about social evaluation will be anxious in situations involving the possibility of public failures.

This work is mentioned here because Endler (2002) later added stress and coping components to the interaction model based on his work with James Parker at Trent University, as was noted above. This revised model is similar in some key respects to models described earlier (see Lazarus, 1966), but it emphasizes coping as an aspect of personality. When people deal with situational

Courtesy of Norman Endler/York University.

Dr. Norman S. Endler was a distinguished research professor from York University in Toronto. He was an international expert on anxiety, stress, and coping.

stressors, a key determinant of their emotional response is their typical coping style. The Coping Inventory for Stressful Situations (CISS; Endler & Parker, 1990, 1994, 1999) measures three stable, dispositional aspects of coping: (1) emotion-oriented coping; (2) task-oriented coping; and (3) avoidance-oriented coping. These stable coping styles interact with situational stressors and cognitive appraisals of these stressful situations to determine the nature (positive or negative) and intensity of the emotional response.

This model has clear implications for health outcomes, so Endler and Parker created a new coping measure to assess how people respond to specific health problems (see Endler, Parker, & Summerfeldt, 1993). Their scale is called Coping with Health Injuries and Problems (CHIP; Endler & Parker, 2000). It has four scales that assess emotional preoccupation, distraction, instrumental coping (i.e., task-oriented strategies), and **palliative coping** (i.e., attempts to feel better via self-soothing and self-help by doing things such as staying in bed or resting when tired). The CHIP has been used to assess the ability to cope with specific health problems such as cancer (Endler, Courbasson, & Fillion, 1998; Jadoulle et al., 2006), Type II diabetes (Macrodimitris & Endler, 2001), and chronic pain (Hadjistavropoulos, Asmundson, & Norton, 1999), as well as to compare individuals with acute vs. chronic illness (Endler, Kocovski, & Macrodimitris, 2001). More recently, as part of a study of people with Crohn's disease and colitis, links were established between emotional preoccupation and greater sickness impact and dysfunctional perfectionism (Flett, Baricza, Gupta, Hewitt, & Endler, 2011). This finding accords with the results of an earlier study in which Endler et al. (2001) predicted and confirmed that chronic illnesses tend to be associated primarily with the CHIP measure of emotional preoccupation. Data from cancer patients suggest that CHIP factor scores are relatively stable during acute phases (i.e., waiting for diagnostic results) and chronic phases (Jadoulle et al., 2006). However, instrumental coping is lower in the chronic phase, presumably when seeking information is less essential. Correlational results indicated that palliative coping predicted emotional distress during the chronic phase.

Other studies with the CHIP yield interesting and meaningful results. Women in Montreal with fibromyalgia who were not adhering to their prescribed drug treatment regimen were shown to have reduced instrumental coping (Sewitch et al., 2004). Other research revealed that well-being was higher among patients with HIV and AIDS if they had elevated levels of instrumental coping (Farber et al., 2003). Finally, mindfulness training results in higher scores on palliative coping (Dobkin, 2008).

Beyond Endler's important scientific contributions, his own personal story documented in his autobiographical book *Holiday of Darkness* has proved uplifting to other people who have struggled with emotional distress (see Endler, 1982). In this book, Endler chronicled his bout of bipolar depression. Endler's experiences with depression were discussed in more detail in Chapter 8.

contributes to a heightened stress response, and, presumably, chronic rumination should translate into a chronic stress reaction that can take a long-term toll on the body. The tendency to ruminate has been referred to as **perseverative cognition** and the **perseverative cognition hypothesis** is the notion that rumination prolongs the stress response and thus contrib-

utes to health problems (see Brosschot, Gerin, & Thayer, 2006). Evidence suggests that chronic rumination can exacerbate the distress of people already attempting to cope with a chronic illness (Soo, Burney, & Basten, 2009). Related work has linked obsessive forms of ruminative thinking with blood pressure issues (Johnson, Key, Routledge, Gerin, & Campbell, 2014) and

Photo courtesy of James Parker

James Parker, who holds a Canada Research Chair at Trent University, teamed with Norman Endler to develop new measures of trait coping and coping with health, injuries, and illness. Parker has explored a wide range of topics, including the role of emotional intelligence in life outcomes and the assessment of alexithymia via the Toronto Alexithymia Scale and the newly developed Toronto Structured Interview for Alexithymia. Alexithymia is an individual difference factor involving difficulties in identifying and describing emotions. It is implicated substantially in health problems.

researchers are now beginning to explore how other vulnerability factors such as perfectionism combine with a tendency to ruminate to produce not only mental health problems but also physical health problems (see Flett, Hewitt, & Nepon, 2016).

Recall that public speaking is exceptionally stressful for many people. One laboratory investigation showed that relative to being in a non-stressful situation, being exposed to a stressful evaluation condition (i.e., having to make a speech) elicited greater rumination and those who ruminated the most had the most prolonged stress responses (Zoccola, Dickerson, & Zaldivar, 2008). Stress was measured in this study in terms of elevated cortisol. Another study conducted in Calgary examined stress responses in undergraduate women. This study by Key, Campbell, Bacon, and Gerin (2008) yielded evidence suggesting that rumination contributes to stress and hypertension by prolonging cardiovascular activation following a stressful experience. In this instance, the stressful situation was recalling a recent stressful negative life event that the participant found difficult to stop thinking about. Measures of state rumination and trait rumination (i.e., a dispositional tendency to ruminate) showed that state rumination was especially likely to contribute to prolonged physiological activation in young women who typically do not ruminate (i.e., low trait rumination). Important follow-up research also conducted at the University of Calgary has shown that repeated exposure to taxing mental stressors is particularly problematic for high trait ruminators; quite simply, ruminators show less adaptation and prolonged physiological responses to stress (Johnson, Lavoie, Bacon, Carlson, & Campbell, 2012).

People are particularly likely to ruminate about the distress that arises from negative interpersonal interactions. A 14-day study of daily experiences found that undergraduate students who ruminated extensively about an interpersonal transgression also had elevated levels of salivary cortisol (McCullough, Orsulak, Brandon, & Akers, 2007). A subsequent study confirmed the stress-producing effects of rumination in the laboratory but then continued to assess the 60 students in this experiment during the 24 hours after the experiment as they went about their role of being a university student. Ottaviani, Shapiro, and Fitzgerald (2011) confirmed that what happens in the laboratory does not stay in the laboratory; that is, ruminators continued to ruminate over the subsequent 24 hours and this tendency to ruminate was linked with higher blood pressure and heart-rate activation.

Given the stress inherent in negative social interactions, people with a personality characterized by high hostility should be particularly at risk. Indeed, a related study showed that when asked to ruminate about a time they were very angry, the tendency to experience autonomic dysregulation occurred among participants who have personalities characterized by hostility, self-directed anger (see the subsection titled Psychoanalytic Theories), depression, and anxiety (Ottaviani et al., 2009). Individuals with these features should be most prone to health problems as a result of brooding about negative social interactions.

What can be done to limit the negative effects of rumination on one's body? Initially, there are benefits associated with cognitively distracting one's attention away in order to limit the repetitive cycle of unwanted negative thoughts. Ultimately, however, ruminators must learn to gain cognitive control over the thought cycle and engage in a cognitive process of thought stopping when the ruminative cycle and the distress it generates is getting out of control.

Other Moderators of Stress

Although we can demonstrate that life events are related to the onset of illness, important questions remain. We have already noted that the same life experience apparently can have different effects on different people. This situation raises the possibility that other variables moderate or change the general stress–illness relationship. We have described one significant moderator—coping—and we have seen that the use of avoidant coping increases the likelihood of both emotional and physical effects of stress. Social support is another important factor that can lessen the effects of stress.

There are various types and conceptualizations of social support. **Structural social support** is a person's basic network of social relationships (e.g., marital status and number of friends). **Functional social support** is concerned more with the quality of a person's relationships (e.g., whether the person believes he or she has friends to call on in a time of need) (Cohen & Wills, 1985).

Social support can also be discussed in terms of the kinds of assistance provided. **Emotional support** provides the recipient with a sense of being cared for by warm and sensitive others, while **instrumental support** provides the recipient with more tangible forms of assistance (e.g., someone helps by making dinner or paying the bills). A study by Muller, Goh, Lemieux, and Fish (2000) serves as a reminder that different kinds of support vary in their relevance as a function of the stressful situation being experienced. This Canadian study found that adult survivors of abuse were more likely to receive emotional support than instrumental support and that friends were most likely to provide this emotional support.

Structural support is a well-established predictor of mortality. People with few friends or relatives tend to have a higher mortality rate than those with a higher level of structural support (Kaplan et al., 1994). Higher levels of functional support have been found to be related to lower rates of atherosclerosis (clogging of the arteries) (Seeman & Syme, 1989) and to the ability of women to adjust to chronic rheumatoid arthritis (Goodenow, Reisine, & Grady, 1990). Consistent with this theme, there is now well-designed longitudinal research leading to the conclusion that the feeling of loneliness is a risk factor for higher morbidity and mortality (Cacioppo, Cacioppo, Capitanio, & Cole, 2015).

How does social support exert its beneficial effects? One possibility is that people who have higher levels of social support perform positive health behaviours more frequently: eating a healthy diet, not smoking, and moderating alcohol intake. This possibility is consistent with the results of a University of Alberta study that found that adults who reported higher levels of social support also indicated a greater intention to exercise (Courneya, Plotnikoff, Hotz, & Birkett, 2000). Alternatively, social support (or lack thereof) could have a direct effect on biological processes. Low levels of social support, for example, are related to an increase in negative emotions, which may affect some hormone levels and the immune system (Kiecolt-Glaser, McGuire, Robles, & Glaser, 2002).

In recent years, social support has been studied in the laboratory, where cause and effect can be more readily established than in the naturalistic studies already described. In one such study, university-aged women were assigned to high- or low-stress conditions, which they experienced alone or with a close friend. In one part of the study, stress was created by having the experimenter behave coldly and impersonally, telling participants to improve their performance as they worked on a challenging task. In each case where the woman had the social support of a close friend, the friend "silently cheered her on" and sat close to her, placing a hand on her wrist. The dependent variable was blood pressure, measured while participants performed the task. As expected, high stress led to higher blood-pressure levels. But, as Figure 9.5 shows, the high-stress condition produced its effects on blood pressure primarily in those women who experienced the stress alone (Kamarck, Annunziato, & Amateau, 1995). Social support was thus shown to have a causal effect on a physiological process. Further laboratory research has shown that such results are produced only when the support comes from a friend and not when it comes from a stranger (Christenfeld et al., 1997). Perhaps only a friend can lead someone to appraise a stressful situation as less threatening.

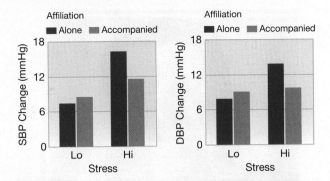

FIGURE 9.5 Results of a laboratory study of the effects of social support on blood pressure (both systolic [SBP] and diastolic [DBP] blood pressure, which are described later in this chapter). Stress led to increased blood pressure, but the increase was less pronounced among people who experienced the stressor with a friend. From Kamarck et al., 1995.

A possible biological mechanism for the stress-reducing effects of social support is suggested by some research with animals. A hormone called oxytocin may be released during social interaction. Oxytocin decreases activity of the sympathetic nervous system and may thereby lessen the physiological effects of a stressor (Uvnas-Moberg, 1997).

Not all research has found that social support has positive effects. With very severe stressors, some people may be so overwhelmed that support does no good. However, other people in the same situation may derive great benefit from the support of others.

9.2 Theories of the Stress–Illness Link

In considering the etiology of psychophysiological disorders, we are confronted with three questions:

1. Why does stress produce illness in only some people who are exposed to it?
2. Why does stress sometimes cause an illness and not a psychological disorder?
3. When stress produces a psychophysiological disorder, what determines which one of the many disorders will be produced?

Although answers to these questions have been sought by biologically and psychologically oriented researchers, theories in this domain are invariably diathesis–stress in nature. They differ primarily in whether the diathesis is described in psychological or biological terms.

Before we review some theories that describe how stress causes or exacerbates physical illness, it is important to note that much of the research in the field has attempted to link stress to self-reports of illness. The problem with this approach is that self-reports may not be an accurate reflection of physical illness, as we have already noted. Watson and Pennebaker (1989) concluded that an apparent association between negative emotional states and health was actually only a relationship between negative emotions and illness reporting. Similarly, Stone and Costa (1990) noted that neuroticism predicted reports of higher numbers of somatic complaints of all kinds (recall our discussion of hypochondriasis and somatization disorder) but did not predict "hard endpoints," such as death or verified coronary artery disease. Because of such problems, our discussion focuses mainly on research that goes beyond illness self-reports.

Biological Theories

Biological approaches attribute particular psychophysiological disorders to specific organ weaknesses, to overactivity of particular organ systems in responding to stress, to the effects of exposure to stress hormones, or to changes in the immune system that are caused by stress.

Somatic-Weakness Theory
Genetic factors, prior illnesses, diet, and the like may disrupt a particular organ system, which may then become weak and vulnerable to stress. According to the **somatic-weakness theory**, the connection between stress and a particular psychophysiological disorder is a weakness in a specific body organ. For instance, a congenitally weak respiratory system might predispose the individual to asthma.

Specific-Reaction Theory
People have been found to have their own individual patterns of autonomic response to stress. The heart rate of one individual may increase, whereas another person may react with an increased respiration rate but no change in heart rate (Lacey, 1967). According to the **specific-reaction theory**, individuals respond to stress in their own idiosyncratic ways, and the body system that is the most responsive becomes a likely candidate for the locus of a subsequent psychophysiological disorder. For example, someone reacting to stress with elevated blood pressure may be more susceptible to essential hypertension. Later in this chapter, when we consider specific psychophysiological disorders, evidence in support of both the somatic-weakness theory and the specific-reaction theory will be presented.

Prolonged Exposure to Stress Hormones
Another theory attempts to deal with the finding described earlier that the biological changes that stress produces are adaptive in the short run; for example, the mobilization of energy resources in preparation for physical activity (McEwen, 1998). The major biological responses to stress involve activation of the sympathetic nervous system and the hypothalamic-pituitary-adrenal axis (HPA). Under conditions of stress, catecholamines such as epinephrine are released from nerves and from the adrenal medulla and lead to secretion of corticotropin from the pituitary. Corticotropin then leads to the release of cortisol from the cortex of the adrenal gland (see Figure 9.6).

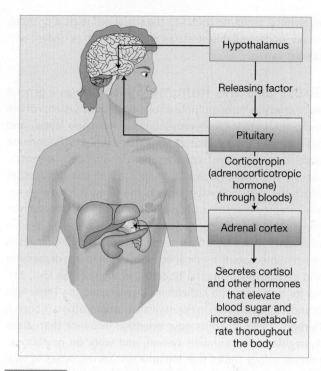

FIGURE 9.6 The HPA axis.

The key to McEwen's theory is that the body pays a price if it must constantly adapt to stress. Through exposure to high levels of stress hormones, it may become susceptible to disease because of altered immune system functioning. Furthermore, high levels of cortisol can have direct effects on the brain; for example, high levels can kill cells in the hippocampus, which itself regulates the secretion of cortisol. Over time, the person may become even more susceptible to the effects of stress.

Some people may have consistently high levels of stress hormones because they experience frequent stress. Other people may have less difficulty in adapting to repeated exposure to stressful situations. Most people react to the stress of public speaking, for example, with an increase in cortisol secretion; but after repeated exposure, most adapt and the amount of cortisol secreted declines. However, about 10% of people show no adaptation and even increase their secretion of cortisol (Kirschbaum et al., 1995). According to McEwen's theory, these are the individuals at risk for disease.

Actual research on stress and the HPA axis activation suggests that the link is exceedingly complex. A review by Gregory Miller from the University of British Columbia and his associates involved a meta-analysis of existing studies involving the HPA axis (see Miller, Chen, & Zhou, 2007). The authors concluded that several factors must be taken into account to explain why data across studies suggest that stress has been associated with both increased and reduced HPA axis activity. One key factor is the timing of the assessment. Time elapsed following the stress was associated negatively with HPA activity; as the months go by, cortisol secretion eventually goes back to normal. The nature of the stressor is also important; as might be expected, prolonged high activation resulted from more traumatic stressors, stressors that threaten survival, and stressors involving a profound threat to the social self (e.g., a divorce). Finally, uncontrollable stressors are linked with persistent HPA axis activation.

Stress and the Immune System

On a general level, stressors have multiple effects on various systems of the body: the autonomic nervous system, hormone levels, and brain activity. One major area of current interest is the immune system, an important consideration in infectious diseases, cancer, and allergies, as well as in autoimmune diseases, in which the immune system attacks the body. It is now generally accepted that stress triggers autoimmune diseases such as rheumatoid arthritis (see Stojanovich & Marisavljevich, 2008). A wide range of stressors have been found to produce changes in the immune system: medical-school examinations, depression and bereavement, marital discord and divorce, job loss, caring for a relative with Alzheimer's disease, and the Three Mile Island nuclear disaster in Pennsylvania, among others (Cohen & Herbert, 1996). There is now extensive evidence that stress dysregulates the immune system, and work on psychoneuroimmunology shows that immune system responses to viral and bacterial vaccines can be delayed, weakened, and shorter in duration for stressed or distressed people (Kiecolt-Glaser, 2009). The role of stress in disease progression is indicated by data linking stress and distress with cytokine secretion by tumour cells (Antoni, 2006). So it appears that for certain individuals, stress can kill. However, there is one clear caveat here. According to Sizemore (2012), short-term stress may actually be beneficial in activating the immune system; it is the long-term stress that tends to undermine and weaken the immune system.

The area of research that comes closest to documenting a role for stress and immune system changes in actual illness is the study of infectious diseases. To illustrate, we will discuss one aspect of the immune system—secretory immunity—in some detail.

The secretory component of the immune system exists in the tears, saliva, and gastrointestinal, vaginal, nasal, and bronchial secretions that bathe the mucosal surfaces of the body. A substance found in these secretions, called secretory immunoglobulin A, or sIgA, contains antibodies that serve as the body's first line of defence against invading viruses and bacteria. They prevent the virus or bacterium from binding to mucosal tissues.

A study by Stone and his colleagues (Stone, Cox, et al., 1987) showed that changes in the number of sIgA antibodies were linked to changes in mood. Throughout an eight-week

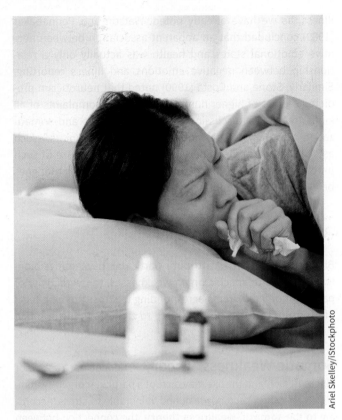

Ariel Skelley/iStockphoto

Stone and his colleagues have found that changes in the frequency of daily life events precede the onset of episodes of respiratory infection. The mechanism may be a stress-induced lowering of sIgA.

study period, a group of dental students came to the laboratory three times a week to have their saliva collected and a brief psychological assessment conducted. On days when the students experienced relatively high levels of negative mood, fewer antibodies were present than on days when the students had low levels of negative mood. Similarly, antibody level was higher on days with higher levels of positive mood.

Prior research (e.g., Stone & Neale, 1984) had shown that daily events affect mood. It is therefore quite possible that daily events affect fluctuations in mood, which in turn affect the synthesis of the secretory sIgA antibodies. The process could operate as follows: an increase in undesirable life events coupled with a decrease in desirable life events produces increased negative mood, which in turn depresses antibody levels in secretory sIgA. If during this period a person is exposed to a virus, he or she will be at increased risk for infection (see Figure 9.7 and the photo).

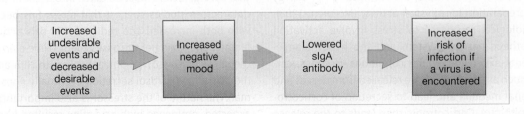

FIGURE 9.7 Mechanism through which stress could increase risk for viral infection.

Several other studies have confirmed the relationship between stress and respiratory infection. In each of them, volunteers took nasal drops containing a mild cold virus and completed a battery of questionnaires concerning recent stress. The advantage of this method was that exposure to the virus was an experimental variable under the investigators' control. Researchers found that stress was clearly linked to developing a cold (Cohen, Tyrell, & Smith, 1991; Stone et al., 1992). The stressors most often implicated were interpersonal problems and work difficulties (Cohen et al., 1998). In a similar study, social support was found to moderate the relationship between viral exposure and colds (Cohen et al., 1997). People with more diverse social networks were less likely to develop a cold following exposure to a virus. More recent work shows that a positive emotional style (i.e., being happy, calm, and full of vigour) protects people from illness after being exposed to a virus, and the presence of this positive emotional style is more predictive than the presence or absence of a negative emotional style (i.e., depressed, anxious, and hostile) (see Cohen et al., 2006). These findings illustrate the complex interplay between psychological and biological variables in the etiology of psychophysiological disorders.

The investigations described above represent only a small proportion of the research conducted in this area. A seminal meta-analysis by Suzanne Segerstrom from the University of Kentucky and Gregory Miller from the University of British Columbia of more than 300 studies has provided a wealth of useful information (see Segerstrom & Miller, 2004). They concluded that stress can be adaptive in the short term when it results in upgrades to the body's natural immunity and when it acts as a catalyst for engaging in adaptive flight-or-fight responses to challenging situations. However, even short-term stressors such as taking an exam can result in suppressed cellular immunity, and chronic stress can suppress cellular immunity and humoral immunity. Important individual differences can also come into play. Research by Bandura and his associates has expanded investigation of Bandura's concept of **self-efficacy** (i.e., a personal sense of perceived capability). Bandura's research team has shown that deficits in self-efficacy are linked to diminished immune system functioning.

Psychological Theories

Psychological theories try to account for the development of various disorders by considering such factors as unconscious emotional states, personality traits, cognitive appraisals, and specific styles of coping with stress.

Cognitive and Behavioural Factors

Physical threats obviously create stress, but humans perceive more than merely physical threats. We experience regrets about the past and worries about the future. All these perceptions can stimulate sympathetic-system activity and the secretion of stress hormones. But negative emotions, such as resentment, regret, and worry, cannot be fought or escaped as readily as can external threats, nor do they easily pass. They may keep the body's biological systems aroused and the body in a continual state of emergency, sometimes for far longer than it can bear, as suggested by McEwen's theory. In addition, the high level of cognition made possible in humans through evolution creates the potential for distressed thoughts, which can bring about bodily changes that persist longer than they were meant to. Our higher mental capacities, it is theorized, subject our bodies to physical storms that they were not built to withstand.

We saw in our general discussion of stress that the appraisal of a potential stressor is central to how it affects the person. People who continually appraise life experiences as exceeding their resources may be chronically stressed and at risk for the development of a psychophysiological disorder. How people cope with stress may also be relevant. We will shortly describe some findings that show that hypertension is related to how people cope with anger. Personality traits are implicated in several disorders, most notably CVD. People who chronically experience high levels of negative emotions, for example, are at high risk for the development of heart problems.

Psychoanalytic Theories

Psychoanalytic theories propose that specific conflicts and their associated negative emotional states give rise to psychophysiological disorders. Franz Alexander is the psychoanalytic theorist who has the greatest impact in accounting for psychophysiological disorders, relative to other psychoanalytic theorists. He maintained that each of the various psychophysiological disorders is the product of unconscious emotional states specific to that disorder. For example, undischarged hostile impulses are believed to create the chronic emotional state responsible for essential hypertension.

> *"The damming up of hostile impulses will continue and will consequently increase in intensity. This will induce the development of stronger defensive measures in order to keep pent-up aggressions in check. Because of the marked degree of their inhibitions, these patients are less effective in their occupational activities and for that reason tend to fail in competition with others ... [E]nvy is stimulated and hostile feelings toward more successful, less inhibited competitors are further intensified."*
>
> *(Alexander, 1950, p. 150)*

Alexander formulated this theory of unexpressed anger, or **anger-in theory**, on the basis of his observations of clients undergoing psychoanalysis. His hypothesis continues to be pursued in present-day studies of the psychological factors in essential hypertension, as discussed shortly.

We turn now to a detailed review of disorders that have attracted much attention from researchers: cardiovascular disorders.

9.3 | Cardiovascular Disorders

Cardiovascular disorders (CVDs) are diseases involving the heart and blood-circulation system. In this section, we focus on two forms of CVD that appear to be adversely affected by stress: hypertension and coronary heart disease. Of the cardiovascular diseases, coronary heart disease causes the greatest number of deaths. It is generally agreed that many of the deaths resulting from cardiovascular diseases could be prevented by dealing with one or more of the known risk factors.

In 1997, it was estimated that the average annual cost of CVD to the Canadian medical system was $17 billion (Statistics Canada, 1997). This estimate rose to $22.2 billion in 2000, with $7.6 billion in direct health care costs and $14.6 billion in indirect costs due to lost economic productivity (Public Health Agency of Canada, 2009). Cardiac-related illnesses continue to be the leading reason for hospitalization in Canada (Public Health Agency of Canada, 2009). Diseases of the heart represent the second-leading cause of death in Canada and account for about 1 in 5 deaths (Statistics Canada, 2012). It is a leading cause of morbidity and mortality in Canada (for a discussion, see Grace, Bennett, Ardern, & Clark, 2014). Levels of risk vary according to location, with rates higher in Eastern Canada, and by ethnic background, with South Asian Canadians particularly at risk (see Grace et al., 2014).

Some alarming results emerged between 1986 and 1992 from analyses of the Canadian Heart Health Survey. Langille et al. (1999) described the findings from probability samples of more than 5,000 women and men between the ages of 55 and 74 drawn from all 10 provinces. Participants were visited by a trained nurse who collected demographic and lifestyle data, including an assessment of each participant's knowledge of cardiovascular disease risk factors. Blood pressure was measured at a clinic within two weeks of the initial visit. Blood samples were also provided. The results showed that 52% of the participants were hypertensive, 26% suffered from isolated systolic hypertension, and 30% had levels of blood cholesterol requiring intervention. The presence of hypertension was untreated in 52% of the afflicted. Langille et al. (1999) found that almost 50% of the participants had three or more major risk factors, and they found this situation particularly troubling because risk factors tend to act synergistically rather than in an additive fashion, resulting in a substantial magnification of risk.

A related study by Kirkland et al. (1999) used data from the same sample but focused on the participants' knowledge and awareness of risk factors for cardiovascular disease. Participants were asked, "Can you tell me what are the major causes of heart disease or heart problems?" (Kirkland et al., 1999, p. S10). The most frequently mentioned causes were stress (44%), worry (44%), and smoking (41%). High blood cholesterol was mentioned by only 23% of the respondents, and hypertension was mentioned by only 16%. The authors concluded that Canadians have very low awareness of the major causes of cardiovascular disease. They also noted that of those people in the

Dr. Norm Campbell from the University of Calgary is a leading researcher, and the Canadian Institutes of Health Research Canada Chair in Hypertension Prevention and Control. He also developed and helped lead the Canadian Hypertension Education Program. He suggests that it is more than a coincidence that after the program's first 10 years, there are fewer deaths due to strokes and heart failure or heart attacks.

study identified as having a risk factor, approximately two-thirds of the women and the men involved were unaware of their high cholesterol status, while 33% of the women and 43% of the men were unaware of their hypertensive status.

These alarming findings likely helped Canadian efforts to proactively address risk. A key part of the Canadian initiative is the Canadian Hypertension Education Program, which is led by Norm Campbell (see photo). This unique initiative is designed to improve awareness, treatment, and control of hypertension by educating health care professionals (Feldman, Campbell, & Wyard, 2008). It is regarded as an international model for knowledge translation (i.e., imparting information that can be put into practice) and promoting collaboration among health care professionals. Progress is being made. Deaths due to cardiovascular disease have declined over time in Canada and the United States (Lee et al., 2009). Mortality rates and rates of hospitalization declined 30% between 1994 and 2004 (Tu, Nardi, & Fang, 2009). Reductions in major risk factors accounted for most of this change. According to Capewell and O'Flaherty (2009), over 80% of premature cardiovascular disease is avoidable.

Essential Hypertension

Why is it important to be aware of hypertension? Hypertension, commonly called high blood pressure, disposes people to atherosclerosis (clogging of the arteries), heart attacks, and strokes; it can also cause death through kidney failure. Yet no more than 10% of all cases of hypertension in the United States

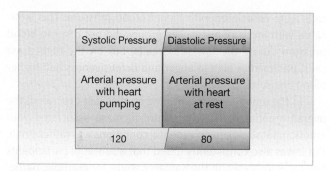

FIGURE 9.8 Normal young-adult blood pressure.

are attributable to an identifiable physical cause. Hypertension without an evident biological cause is called **essential** (or sometimes **primary**) **hypertension**. Unless people have their blood pressure checked, they may go for years without knowing that they are hypertensive. Thus, this disease is known as the silent killer.

Blood pressure is measured by two numbers: one represents systolic pressure, and the other represents diastolic pressure. The systolic measure, the upper number, is the amount of arterial pressure when the ventricles contract and the heart is pumping; the diastolic measure, the lower number, is the degree of arterial pressure when the ventricles relax and the heart is resting. Pressure is measured in mmHg (millimetres of mercury). A normal blood pressure in a young adult is 120 mmHg (systolic) over 80 mmHg (diastolic) (Figure 9.8). The guidelines for determining high blood pressure were extended and revised by the American Medical Association (AMA) in an attempt to heighten public awareness and detection of problems by physicians (see Chobanian et al., 2003). The AMA concluded that among people 50 years of age or older, systolic blood pressure (BP) of more than 140 mmHg is a much more important CVD risk factor than diastolic BP. In addition, the risk of cardiovascular disease has now been pegged at beginning at 115/75 mmHg, and it doubles with each increment of 20/10 mmHg.

A study by Wolf-Maier et al. (2003), using a BP of 140 over 90 as indicative of hypertension, found that 28% of Canadian and American adults had hypertension, while an astronomical 44% of Europeans had the condition. Currently, it is estimated that more than one billion people worldwide have hypertension (Chobanian et al., 2003). Hypertension is regarded as the leading risk factor for death in the world, causing about 7.5 million deaths per year, or 13% of all deaths (World Health Organization, 2009). While great strides in hypertension control have been made in Canada, the prevalence of hypertension remains unacceptably high. A national survey conducted between 2007 and 2009 found hypertension in 19% of adults, similar to rates in 1992, and another 20% had blood pressure in the pre-hypertension range (Wilkins et al., 2010). Sex differences do not tend to exist, except among older adults, where levels of hypertension are demonstrably higher among women (Wilkins, Gee, & Campbell, 2012).

While the overall situation has improved considerably, it is still the case that about 1 in 5 Canadians has hypertension (McAlister et al., 2011). However, according to McAlister et al.

(2011), huge gains have occurred in Canada between 1992 and 2009. There have been increases among Canadian adults with hypertension in awareness that they have hypertension (56.9% in 1992 vs. 82.5% in 2009), in how many achieve hypertension control (only 13.2% in 1992 vs. 64.6% in 2009), and in how many are receiving treatment (34.6% in 1992 vs. 79.0% in 2009). Thus, we can estimate that only about 1 in 5 Canadians with hypertension are not receiving some form of treatment.

Essential hypertension is viewed as a heterogeneous condition brought on by many possible disturbances in the various systems of the body that are responsible for regulating blood pressure. Genes play a substantial role in controlling blood pressure; other risk factors for hypertension include obesity, excessive intake of alcohol, and salt consumption. Blood pressure may be elevated by increased cardiac output (the amount of blood leaving the left ventricle of the heart), by increased resistance to the passage of blood through the arteries (vaso-constriction), or by both. The physiological mechanisms that regulate blood pressure interact in an extremely complex manner. Activation of the sympathetic nervous system is a key factor, but hormones, salt metabolism, and central nervous system mechanisms are all involved. How important is salt intake? A study of the Inuit in Northern Quebec found that levels of hypertension have doubled in recent years as a function of moving away from a salt-reduced diet consisting mostly of fish products and moving toward a more traditional salt-laden Western diet (Picard, 2009).

Table 9.3 lists the 10 major risk factors for high blood pressure, as identified by the Canadian Expert Working Group on high blood pressure prevention and control. You can see in Table 9.3 that the risk factors are varied and include physical factors (e.g., excess weight) and the importance of exercise, but they also include lifestyle factors (e.g., degree of heavy alcohol use), socio-economic status, and psychological factors involving stress and coping.

TABLE 9.3	**Risk Factors for High Blood Pressure**
Excess weight (body mass index greater than 25)	
Central obesity (i.e., waist to hip ratio greater than 1)	
Lack of regular physical activity	
Heavy alcohol use (per week, 14 or more drinks for men, 9 or more drinks for women)	
Lack of diet with high fibre, fruit, vegetables, and low saturated fat	
Inadequate dietary intake of calcium and potassium	
Excessive salt intake	
Poor coping response to stress; chronic stress	
Low socio-economic status (reflecting its association with other risk factors and daily living challenges)	
Low birth weight	

Psychological Stress and Blood-Pressure Elevation

Various stressful conditions have been examined to determine their role in the etiology of essential hypertension. Stressful interviews, natural disasters such as earthquakes, and job stress have all been found to produce short-term elevations in blood pressure (e.g., Niedhammer et al., 1998).

It is also relatively easy to produce increased blood pressure in the laboratory. The induction of various emotional states, such as anger, fear, and sadness, all increase blood pressure (Cacioppo et al., 1993). Similarly, challenging tasks, such as mental arithmetic, mirror drawing, putting a hand in ice water (the cold pressor test), and giving a speech in front of an audience all lead to increased blood pressure (e.g., Manuck, Kaplan, & Clarkson, 1983; Tuomisto, 1997). A classic series of studies by Obrist and his colleagues (e.g., 1978) used a reaction-time task in which participants were told they would receive an electric shock if they did not respond quickly enough. Good performance led to a monetary bonus. The reaction-time task yielded significant increases in both heart rate and systolic blood pressure.

Ultimately we must understand why blood pressure increases in people's natural environments. Therefore, researchers have also undertaken studies of ambulatory blood pressure, wherein participants wear a blood-pressure cuff that takes readings as they go about their daily lives. Many of these studies have asked participants about their emotional state at the time a blood-pressure reading is taken. The general finding has been that both positive and negative emotional states are associated with higher blood pressure (e.g., Jacob et al., 1999; Kamarck et al., 1998).

Other ambulatory monitoring studies have examined environmental conditions associated with blood pressure. A series of studies examined the effects of stress on blood pressure among paramedics (Shapiro, Jamner, & Goldstein, 1993; see photo). In one of these analyses, ambulance calls were divided into high- and low-stress types. As expected, the high-stress calls were associated with higher blood pressure. This interacted with levels of anger. The groups did not differ in blood pressure during the low-stress calls, but on the high-stress calls, paramedics high in anger and defensiveness had higher blood pressure.

In the ambulatory monitoring studies just described, the overall amount of blood-pressure increase associated with emotional states or environmental conditions was rather small. But it was also consistently found that a subset of participants had large increases. In the Kamarck study, for example, participants in the top 10% of the magnitude of association between negative mood and blood pressure showed a 20-point increase in systolic blood pressure. These data suggest that only people who have some predisposition, or diathesis, will experience large blood-pressure increases that over time may lead to sustained hypertension. We turn next to these possible diatheses.

Predisposing Factors

It is generally accepted that blood pressure and hypertension are highly heritable but there has been very little success thus far in identifying the genes involved. Papers published in the journal *Nature Genetics* represent important breakthroughs. These papers describe the results of meta-analyses conducted collaboratively by two huge research consortiums. Collectively, data on over 159,000 people resulted in the identification of 13 gene regions not associated previously with blood pressure (Levy et al., 2009; Newton-Cheh et al., 2009). The investigators concluded that each region may have only a small effect but there are now many specific regions to explore in subsequent research.

In the past 15 years, there has been a great deal of interest in cardiovascular reactivity as a biological predisposition to hypertension (and coronary heart disease, as well). Cardiovascular reactivity is the extent to which blood pressure and heart rate increase in response to stress. The general research strategy is to assess cardiovascular reactivity to a laboratory stressor (or, even better, a battery of stressors) among people who are not currently hypertensive and then to follow up with the participants some years later to determine whether the reactivity measure (usually the amount of change from a baseline condition after exposure to the stressor) predicts blood pressure.

What are the results of the studies that have tried to predict blood pressure from reactivity? A longitudinal study of almost 3,000 men and women between the ages of 20 and 35 found that blood pressure changes during a video game predicted coronary calcification of the arteries 13 years later (Matthews, Zhu, Tucker, & Whooley, 2006). The reaction to the video game represents a general tendency to be physiologically reactive to stress and challenge. Subsequent research sought to identify the neural systems mediating blood pressure reactivity. It was found that individuals with greater stress-evoked changes in mean arterial pressure had greater amygdala activation, lower amygdala grey matter volume, and stronger connectivity between the amygdala and both the perigenual anterior cingulate cortex and the brainstem pons (Gianaros et al., 2008). A follow-up study found that there is a neurobiological correlate (i.e., heightened resting corticolimbic activity) of high blood

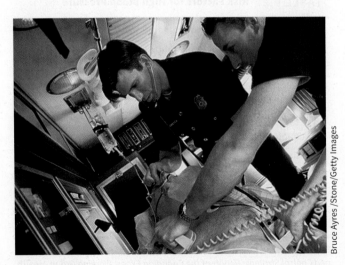

High-stress ambulance calls, such as those requiring the revival of the victim, led to greater blood-pressure increases in paramedics than low-stress calls in the Shapiro, Jamner, and Goldstein study (1993).

Bruce Ayres /Stone/Getty Images

pressure reactivity (Gianaros et al., 2009). These data are promising in pointing to neurobiological factors and associated neural circuits that may predispose certain people to greater blood pressure reactivity and cardiovascular risk.

Coronary Heart Disease

Coronary heart disease (CHD) takes two principal forms: angina pectoris and myocardial infarction, or heart attack.

Characteristics of the Disease

The symptoms of angina pectoris are periodic chest pains, usually located behind the sternum and frequently radiating into the back and sometimes the left shoulder and arm. The major cause of these severe attacks of pain is an insufficient supply of oxygen to the heart (called ischemia), which in turn is due to coronary atherosclerosis, a narrowing or plugging of the coronary arteries by deposits of cholesterol, a fatty material, or constriction of the blood vessels. In many patients with coronary heart disease, episodes of ischemia do not result in the report of pain. These are called episodes of silent ischemia. Both angina and episodes of silent ischemia are precipitated by physical or emotional exertion and are commonly relieved by rest or medication. Serious physical damage to heart muscle rarely results from an angina or ischemia attack, for blood flow is reduced but not cut off. If, however, the narrowing of one or more coronary arteries progresses to the point of producing a total blockage, a myocardial infarction, or heart attack, is likely to occur.

Myocardial infarction is a much more serious disorder. Like angina pectoris, it is caused by an insufficient supply of oxygen to the heart. But unlike angina, a heart attack usually results in permanent damage to the heart.

Several factors increase risk for CHD and the risk generally increases with the number and severity of these factors:

- age
- sex (males are at greater risk)
- cigarette smoking
- elevated blood pressure
- elevated serum cholesterol
- an increase in the size of the left ventricle of the heart
- obesity
- long-standing pattern of physical inactivity
- excessive use of alcohol
- diabetes

Stress and Myocardial Infarction

In the short term, physical exertion can trigger a myocardial infarction, as can episodes of anger (Mittleman et al., 1997). Acute stress is another factor; the frequency of myocardial infarction, for example, increased among residents of Tel Aviv on the day of an Iraqi missile attack (NHLBI, 1998). More chronic stressors, such as marital conflict and financial worries, are also relevant. One current theory is that chronic stress activates the immune system and contributes to inflammation, which, in turn, produces CHD (Miller & Blackwell, 2006).

Consistent with our earlier observations about the destructive effects of job stress, many studies have found that a high level of job strain is associated with increased risk for myocardial infarction (Schnall, Landsbergis, & Baker, 1994). In one of the most well-known investigations, more than 10,000 British civil servants were assessed for the degree of control they could exercise on their jobs. They were then followed for about five years to determine the incidence of CHD. Replicating earlier studies, more CHD was found at follow-up among workers in lower-status jobs (e.g., clerical work). This result, in turn, was related to these workers' reports of having little control on the job (Marmot et al., 1997). In a large-scale study being conducted in Finland, highly demanding jobs have also been related to the progression of atherosclerosis (Lynch et al., 1997a) and to CVD mortality and morbidity (Lynch et al., 1997b).

Diatheses for Coronary Heart Disease

The traditional risk factors still left at least half the instances of coronary heart disease unexplained as recently as the 1970s (see Jenkins, 1976). Indeed, people used to pay less attention to contributing causes, such as obesity, poor exercise habits, consumption of fatty foods, and smoking, than they do now, yet in earlier decades the incidence of CHD and related CVDs was much lower. Furthermore, in the midwestern United States, where people's diets are highest in saturated fats and smoking rates are especially high, the incidence of coronary heart disease is low compared with that in more industrialized parts of the United States. Anyone who has visited Paris is aware of the heavy smoking and the fat-rich diets of the French population, yet CHD is relatively low there. Why?

Psychological diatheses The search for predispositions for coronary heart disease has focused on psychological factors. Initial evidence linking CHD to psychological variables stems from investigations pioneered by two cardiologists: Meyer Friedman and Ray Rosenman (Friedman, 1969; Rosenman et al., 1975). In 1958, they identified a coronary-prone behaviour pattern called Type A behaviour pattern. As assessed by a structured interview, the Type A individual has an intense and competitive drive for achievement and advancement, an exaggerated sense of the urgency of passing time and of the need to hurry, and considerable aggressiveness and hostility toward others (see photo).

Initial evidence supporting the idea that the Type A pattern predicts coronary heart disease came from the classic Western Collaborative Group Study (Rosenman et al., 1975). In this double-blind, prospective investigation, 3,154 men aged 39 to 59 were followed over a period of eight and a half years. Individuals who had been identified as Type A by interview were more than twice as likely to develop CHD as were Type B men, characterized by a less driven and less hostile way of life. Traditional risk factors, such as high levels of cholesterol, were also found to be related to CHD, but even when these factors were controlled for, Type A individuals were still twice as likely to develop CHD.

One characteristic of the Type A personality is feeling under time pressure and consequently trying to do several things at once.

Subsequent research did not support the predictive utility of Type A behaviour. Instead, researchers focused on the role of one element of Type A behaviour: hostility. This focus on hostility is well-founded. A meta-analysis of 25 studies found that anger and hostility are associated with coronary heart disease outcomes in initially healthy populations and coronary heart disease populations (Chida & Steptoe, 2009).

Other research has increasingly examined the relationship between other negative emotions—particularly anxiety and depression—and CHD. Anxiety has been shown to be related to CHD in humans (Kawachi et al., 1994), and animal research demonstrates that inducing anxiety in animals with atherosclerosis can precipitate a heart attack (Carpeggiani & Skinner, 1991).

With regard to depression, about 1 in 5 CHD patients meets diagnostic criteria for depression (Miller & Blackwell, 2006), and many others do not meet diagnostic criteria but have depressive symptoms that warrant intervention, and depression heightens the risk of death. Research in Quebec found that cardiac patients who also have depressive symptoms are about three times more likely than other patients without depressive symptoms to die within five years (Lésperance, Frasure-Smith, Talajic, & Bourassa, 2002). Also, elevated depression and anxiety at baseline predict subsequent major adverse cardiac events (cardiac death, myocardial infarction, cardiac arrest) in the two years after baseline assessment among patients with stable coronary artery disease (Frasure-Smith & Lésperance, 2008). Collectively, there is now ample evidence of greater mortality and morbidity among depressed cardiac patients than those who are non-depressed (Nemeroff & Goldschmidt-Clermont, 2012).

Many plausible biological mechanisms for these relationships have been proposed. Likely factors and processes include increased inflammation, increased susceptibility to blood clotting, oxidative stress, and increased activation of the HPA axis (Nemeroff & Goldschmidt-Clermont, 2012).

Tying together this interest in CHD and negative emotions—anger, anxiety, and depression—is the proposed Type D

personality, with "D" standing for distressed type (Denollet & Brutsaert, 1998). Type D is defined as high scores on negative affectivity (a tendency to experience high levels of anxiety, anger, and depression) plus social inhibition, including inhibiting the expression of these emotions. A review by Pedersen and Denollet (2003) concluded unequivocally that Type D cardiac patients are at increased risk for cardiovascular morbidity and mortality, independent of other cardiac risk factors. Type D patients also had an impaired quality of life, benefited less from treatment, and had increased psychological distress. Recent data continue to support the predictiveness of the Type D style. For instance, a longitudinal study linked Type D with lower health-related quality of life in patients with a history of heart failure. Several factors mediated this association with lower quality of life, including elevated depression and anxiety and lower levels of social support (Staniute et al., 2015).

Type D personality seems to be accompanied by a tendency to engage in fewer positive health behaviours and it is linked with negative appraisals of social support (Williams et al., 2008). A recent study with Indonesian participants confirmed the link between Type D and more negative health behaviours and fewer positive health behaviours (Ginting, van de Ven, Becker, & Naring, 2016). Type D patients tend to report poorer health status both before and after cardiac rehabilitation (Pelle et al., 2008). How prevalent is the Type D personality? It may depend on where you live. A study of healthy British and Irish adults found that 38.5% of participants had Type D personality as determined by scores on 10 or more of the distress and social inhibition Type D factors (Williams et al., 2008). The prevalence in other European countries is lower (21–33%) and Williams et al. (2008) suggested that the greater prevalence in Ireland and England may reflect reduced emotional expressiveness found among people in Ireland and England. Note that a recent survey of 100 cardiac rehabilitation patients in Toronto found that about one-third of the participants were deemed to have a Type D personality according to established scoring criteria (Shanmugasegaram et al., 2014), while a study of Lithuanian coronary artery disease patients with heart failure also found that about one-third had the Type D personality (Staniute et al., 2015).

How does Type D personality relate to coping styles? There have been few empirical attempts to examine coping and Type D personality, other than some evidence linking Type D personality with repressive coping (Denollet, 2005) and evidence from a study in Montreal by Dunkley et al. (2012) that linked Type D with avoidance coping and low levels of problem-focused coping. Another recent investigation found with a general measure of coping that Type D was again associated with avoidance coping but, somewhat surprisingly, Type D was also associated negatively with emotion-oriented coping (Williams & Wingate, 2012). To our knowledge, research has not examined possible links between Type D personality and illness-specific coping tendencies. Accordingly, the study of 100 Canadian cardiac rehabilitation patients described earlier (Shanmugasegaram et al., 2014) also explored Type D personality and scores on Endler and Parker's CHIP. This investigation established strong links between Type D and emotional preoccupation when coping with cardiac health problems. Presumably, patients with this Type D personality engage in the deleterious ruminative style that was discussed earlier.

Biological diatheses   Of course, biological vulnerabilities also play a role in susceptibility to cardiac problems. One key factor receiving extensive attention is heart rate reactivity, more commonly referred to as **cardiovascular reactivity**. This is an individual difference factor that reflects the magnitude of physiological changes from a baseline resting state in response to some form of stress or challenge. For instance, two women start running to catch a bus but perhaps only one woman has a biological propensity for her heart to go "on alert" and start pounding. Excessive changes in heart rate and the consequent alterations in the force with which blood is pumped through the arteries may injure them, increasing risk for a myocardial infarction.

Evidence has now accumulated for the role of differences in cardiovascular reactivity in the development of cardiovascular disease (Bongard, al'Absi, & Lovallo, 2012). Research is now trying to link cardiovascular reactivity with other vulnerability factors reflecting psychological influences; here it is interesting to note that new research on cardiovascular reactivity in patients with Type D personalities and a history of chronic heart failure suggests that these patients have an inadequate stress response when put into a psychosocial stress condition (i.e., having to give a public speech) (see Kupper, Denollet, Widdershoven, & Kop, 2013).

Treating Hypertension and Reducing CHD Risk

Because some antihypertensive drugs have undesirable side effects, such as drowsiness, light-headedness, and, for men, erectile difficulties, many investigations have been undertaken on nonpharmacological treatments for borderline essential hypertension. Efforts have been directed at weight reduction, restriction of salt intake, giving up cigarettes, aerobic exercise, and reduction in alcohol consumption. Losing weight, reducing salt intake, and exercising regularly can also help reduce harmful levels of cholesterol. Drugs, too, can lower cholesterol levels; for example, lovastatin (trade name Mevacor) lowers low-density lipid cholesterol (LDL, the so-called bad cholesterol) and appears to be successful in forestalling the progression of atherosclerosis. Such drugs, plus improvements in eating habits observed since the 1960s and other modifiable risk factors, are associated with decreased mortality from cardiovascular diseases (see Patel & Adams, 2008).

A study with older adults highlights the importance of losing weight and reducing salt intake. The controlled 1998 Trial of Nonpharmacologic Interventions in the Elderly (TONE) (Whelton et al., 1998) indicated for the first time that significant benefits can be achieved by obese people between the ages of 60 and 80 who are taking blood-pressure medication. Specifically, half the overweight people in the study who reduced their salt intake by 25% and lost as little as eight pounds (3.5 kg) over the course of three months were able to come off their antihypertensive medications and maintain normal blood pressure. The ability to maintain normal blood pressure was achieved by 31% of the patients who reduced their salt intake, 36% of those who lost weight, and more than half of those who reduced both their salt intake and their weight. Furthermore, these results—the dietary and weight changes, as well as the maintenance of normal blood pressure without medication—lasted for more than three years.

Regular exercise is another avenue for reducing blood pressure, one that is available to everyone at little or no cost. Research has shown that increasing exercise through so-called lifestyle activities—for example, walking up stairs rather than using an elevator or walking short distances rather than driving—yields as much benefit as a structured program of aerobic exercise (Dunn et al., 1999).

Other research indicates that people with essential hypertension, as well as those whose blood pressure is within the normal range, should adopt regular exercise habits, such as walking briskly most every day for about half an hour or engaging in other aerobic exercise that raises the heart and respiration rates (see Pescatello et al., 2004). Most people can engage in such activity without even checking with their physician if the activity is not so strenuous that it prevents them from carrying on a conversation at the same time.

Research suggests that people with high blood pressure and no other health complications should try exercise for about a year before turning to drugs to lower their blood pressure. The prescribed exercise for someone with high blood pressure is engaging in moderately intense exercise every day of the week. It should involve 30 minutes or more of continuous activity (Pescatello et al., 2004). For those already taking antihypertensive drugs, a regular and not necessarily strenuous exercise regimen can sometimes reduce or even eliminate dependence on medication. Decreases of 10 points—a significant figure—in both systolic and diastolic blood pressure can be achieved by most people after just a few weeks. Exercising regularly can also reduce mortality from cardiovascular disease (Wannamethee, Shaper, & Walker, 1998). All these beneficial results may be mediated by the favourable effects that exercise has on stress, weight, and blood cholesterol. And if the sense of well-being that accompanies regular exercise and weight loss leads to the adoption of other health-enhancing habits, such as stopping smoking and avoiding drinking to excess, the positive effects on blood pressure will be all the stronger and more enduring.

Another psychological approach has been to teach hypertensive individuals to lower sympathetic nervous system arousal, primarily via training in muscle relaxation, occasionally supplemented by biofeedback. A review of relaxation therapy did find evidence of significant but small reductions in both diastolic and systolic blood pressure (Dickinson et al., 2008). However, serious methodological problems in several studies led the authors to conclude that there is weak evidence of a causal link between relaxation therapy and lower blood pressure. Perhaps relaxation therapy is helpful for some people more than others.

Biofeedback

A visit to the commercial exhibit area of any psychological or psychiatric convention will reveal a plentiful display of complex biofeedback apparatuses, touted as an efficient, even miraculous, means of helping people control one or another bodily mental state. By using sensitive instrumentation, **biofeedback** gives a person prompt and exact information, otherwise unavailable, on muscle activity, brain waves, skin temperature, heart rate, blood pressure, and other bodily functions. It is assumed that a person can achieve greater voluntary control over these phenomena—most of which were once considered under involuntary control only—if he or she knows immediately, through an auditory or visual signal, whether a somatic activity is increasing or decreasing. Because anxiety has been viewed generally as a state involving the autonomic (involuntary) nervous system, and because psychophysiological disorders often afflict organs innervated by this system, researchers and clinicians have been intrigued by biofeedback. For a time, biofeedback was virtually synonymous with behavioural medicine.

In a series of classic studies at Harvard Medical School, Shapiro, Tursky, and Schwartz (1970; Schwartz, 1973) demonstrated that volunteers could consciously achieve significant short-term changes in blood pressure and heart rate. They found that some people could even be trained to increase their heart rate while decreasing their blood pressure. Achievement of this fine-grained control lent impetus to biofeedback work with human beings and awakened hope that certain clinical disorders might be alleviated in this new way.

Reviews of research on the use of biofeedback to treat patients with essential hypertension have yielded results questioning its usefulness. The results of more than 100 studies indicated that these interventions reduce blood pressure "to a modest degree," with multi-component, individualized treatments resulting in the greatest improvements (Linden & Moseley, 2006, p. 51). More recently, however, another extensive review indicated that biofeedback treatment is ineffective when compared with no treatment, pharmacotherapy, or placebos (Greenhalgh, Dickson, & Dundar, 2009). These authors concluded that current treatment standards would suggest using biofeedback only if it is a supplement to other treatments.

Cardiac Rehabilitation Efforts

Frasure-Smith and her colleagues at the Montreal Heart Institute Research Centre have been evaluating the results of a long-term intervention program known as the Ischemic Heart Disease Life Stress Monitoring Program (IHDLSM) (Frasure-Smith & Prince, 1989). The IHDLSM is a cardiac rehabilitation program in which participants are assigned to a control condition or a stress-monitoring condition. The stress-monitoring condition involves the receipt of psychosocial support and advice from nurses who assess the patients' stress levels each month and intervene when stress is elevated. The initial results showed that this non-specific psychosocial intervention led to significant reductions in mortality and in reoccurrences of heart

attacks (Frasure-Smith & Prince, 1989). Unfortunately, replication studies found less successful outcomes (Frasure-Smith et al., 2002). There was no treatment impact among men overall, and women in the treatment group actually had a worse prognosis. Secondary analyses showed that coping styles were important (Frasure-Smith et al., 2002). People characterized as repressors (i.e., those who have high arousal yet use defensive strategies to avoid acknowledging the arousal) had worse outcomes. Still, some findings from the IHDLSM project did show that some people can benefit from a focus on the alleviation of stress. Specifically, highly anxious men seemed to benefit from the program (Frasure-Smith et al., 2002). This finding with anxious men is more in line with the general pattern of findings across several studies.

There is now extensive evidence summarized in meta-analyses that attest to the effectiveness of comprehensive cardiac rehabilitation preventions and interventions (e.g., Sandercock, Hurtado, & Cardoso, 2013; Zwisler et al., in press). Grace et al. (2014) expressed concern that overall, it is still the case that about two-thirds of eligible people in Canada who could be benefitting from cardiac rehabilitation programs do not access these programs. Barriers to access include lack of physician referral and issues involving travel and distance. Hopefully this situation will improve now that there is a national policy position drafted by researchers that recommends that patients be referred systematically to cardiac rehabilitation programs.

We conclude this chapter by now considering the reactions and responses that people have when they have experience exceptionally intense stress that tends to traumatize people. Much of what has been learned about trauma and stress comes from research in miltary contexts.

9.4 Post-Traumatic Stress Disorder

Post-traumatic stress disorder (PTSD) entails an extreme response to a severe stressor, including increased anxiety, avoidance of stimuli associated with the trauma, and a numbing of emotional responses.

Description, Symptoms, and Prevalence

"I always wake up just before they kill me." These words were uttered by Sergeant Bob Bilodeau to describe his dreams. Bilodeau, a 26-year veteran of the Royal Canadian Mounted Police, spent three months as a United Nations police officer inside the Muslim enclave of Srebrenica in the former Yugoslavia in 1993 (see Cowan, 1999). Bilodeau acknowledged that he has low self-esteem and problems concentrating. He experiences flashbacks and has many symptoms of post-traumatic stress disorder. Bilodeau turned to alcohol as a way to cope with his anxiety symptoms. He observed, "It's called self-medication. . . . It works, but it will kill you in the end" (Cowan, 1999, p. 29).

Brief Case Example

PTSD and its Aftermath after Witnessing an Accident

The case of Nicholas John Arnold is a precedent in Canadian law because he is the first person to be awarded money ($11,000) because of the distress experienced after witnessing an event that resulted in the deaths of people he did not know. Arnold saw a horrible car accident that killed three people on the Pattulo Bridge in British Columbia in 2001. Arnold tried to help the victims but to no avail. It was an exceptionally traumatic event that resulted in panic attacks, PTSD, and bipolar depression. Arnold got blood on his arms while trying to assist the victims and he experienced the lingering smell of one of the victim's perfume on him. In total, he was off work for 2.5 years following the traumatic event. He continued to experience anxiety while driving and flashbacks in which he recalled the event. Not surprisingly, he suffered from sleep difficulties as well.

A controversial aspect of this case is that Arnold sued the estate of the driver who caused the accident, who died as a result of the incident. Do you think this is callous or does Arnold's suffering warrant compensation? If compensation is warranted in your opinion, how much would you have awarded him? (Adapted from Hall, 2008.)

Bilodeau described a flashback that he experienced in October 1999. In talking about his experiences in Yugoslavia, he said, "It used to be very dangerous out there to drive at night because of robberies and car jackings. . . . One time I was late, and as I came around a corner, there were two guys stopped in the middle of the road—I just did a U-turn and got out of there. A month ago, about dusk, I was going with my brother out to the lake lot we rent when we came across this vehicle with the doors open and two guys—my brain was just shouting 'danger, danger'" (Cowan, 1999, p. 29). Although Bilodeau has returned to the relative safety of Canada, he continues to experience nightmares involving the men on the road, but, as he reported, "I always wake up just before they kill me."

Although there had been prior awareness that the stresses of combat could produce powerful and adverse effects on soldiers, it was the aftermath of the Vietnam War that spurred the acceptance of the new diagnosis. However, as the following case excerpt demonstrates, PTSD can be experienced in non-war contexts. PTSD is often experienced by first responder emergency workers, including police officers and firefighters. As shown in the Brief Example of Nicholas John Arnold, witnessing horrific events is a general risk factor.

PTSD is defined by a cluster of symptoms. However, unlike the definitions of other psychological disorders, the definition of PTSD includes part of its presumed etiology—namely, a traumatic event or events.

The definition of PTSD was changed considerably in *DSM-5*. Most notably, in the previous version, the event was supposed to have created intense fear, horror, or helplessness. However, it is now recognized that people can be quite variable in their emotional reactions, so this specific symptom is no longer required. A significant change across various versions of the *DSM* is what type of event is considered to be a trauma-inducing event. In previous editions of the *DSM,* the traumatic event was defined as "outside the range of human experience." Thus, the traumatic event could be a life-threatening natural disaster such as Hurricane Katrina and the aftermath for those in the southeastern United States, some of whom experienced PTSD, referred to previously as "Katrina Brain." This definition of being outside the range of human experience was considered too restrictive, as it would have ruled out the diagnosis of PTSD following such events as automobile accidents or the death of a loved one, or even prolonged exposure to abuse. Some have also considered the current broadened definition too restrictive, because it focuses on the event's objective characteristics rather than on its subjective meaning (King et al., 1995).

As noted by McNally (2009) and by Rosen and Frueh (2007), there is considerable controversy and debate about the PTSD diagnosis. A major issue is that of "conceptual bracket creep" in how trauma is defined. Various forms of trauma are now recognized.

What about witnessing traumatic events experienced by others, such as the events of September 11, 2001? One of the authors of this text watched those horrific events unfold on television, saw the second plane hit the south tower, was horrified to see people leaping to their deaths to escape the flames and searing heat, cried as the towers crumbled to the ground, and understood the tragic consequences, but did not develop PTSD. Can the author's "virtual" stress possibly compare with the experiences of those who were there and affected directly? Are we all trauma survivors? McNally (2009) recommended that *DSM-5* "eliminate indirect, informational exposure as qualifying as trauma" (p. 598). Indeed, *DSM-5* now stipulates that the event that might have happened to other people must have been witnessed in person.

A person can also experience trauma if it occurred to a close family member or close friend rather than the self. However, the event only applies if it involved violence or an accident. Hoge et al. (2015) have criticized the narrow criterion here and noted that it would exclude the parent who loses a child as a result of an aggressive cancer, as well as the soldier who loses a trusted leader who was not a close friend. They also questioned the introduction of certain new symptoms and changing the descriptions of other symptoms to the point that they concluded that the revised criteria are not a step forward. Another team involved with the development of the revised criteria contends that this conclusion is overstated and the new criteria do represent a positive step forward (Friedman, Kilpatrick, Schnurr, & Weathers, 2015).

The previous PTSD diagnostic criteria included 17 symptoms, while the current criteria involve 20 symptoms across four symptom categories, and some symptoms that still remain have experienced significant wording changes in how they are described. The fourth general category that has been newly added is negative alterations in cognitions and moods associated with the traumatic event.

The other symptoms for PTSD are grouped into three major categories. The diagnosis requires that symptoms in each category last longer than one month.

1. *Intrusion symptoms associated with the traumatic event.*

These intrusions come in various forms including distressing dreams or distressing memories. The individual frequently recalls the event and experiences nightmares about it. Intense emotional upset is produced by stimuli that symbolize the event (e.g., thunder reminding a veteran of the battlefield) or on anniversaries of some specific experience. Kuch and Cox (1992) examined PTSD symptoms in a sample of 124 Holocaust survivors living in the Toronto area. This sample included subsamples of 78 concentration camp survivors and 20 tattooed concentration camp survivors. Nightmares were experienced by more than 87% of the concentration camp survivors and by 90% of the tattooed concentration camp survivors.

The importance of re-experiencing in the form of intrusions cannot be underestimated, for it is the likely source of the other categories of symptoms. Some theories of PTSD make re-experiencing the central feature by attributing the disorder to an inability to successfully integrate the traumatic event into an existing schema (the person's general beliefs about the world) (e.g., Foa, Zinbarg, & Rothbaum, 1992; Horowitz, 1986). The tendency to re-experience the traumatic memory has sparked much research on PTSD and memory.

2. *Persistent avoidance of stimuli associated with the event beginning after the event has occurred.*

The person tries to avoid thinking about the trauma or encountering stimuli that will bring it to mind. Hoge et al. (2015) have expressed their concern with the emphasis on avoidance because it is emerging as a key factor when there are discordant diagnoses and it does not allow for the fact that certain military personnel can have PTSD symptoms warranting a diagnosis but have learned through their training to not be avoidant.

3. *Marked alterations in arousal and reactivity associated with the traumatic event.*

These symptoms include irritable behaviour, reckless or self-destructive behaviour, difficulties falling or staying asleep, difficulty concentrating, hypervigilance, and an exaggerated startle response. Laboratory studies have confirmed these clinical symptoms by documenting the heightened physiological reactivity of PTSD participants to combat imagery (e.g., Orr et al., 1995) and their high-magnitude startle responses (Morgan et al., 1997).

Not surprisingly, more extreme trauma tends to have more impact in terms of the number of disorders and associated levels of dysfunction. This was shown clearly in follow-up research on the effects of the terrorist attacks in the United States on September 11, 2001 (see photo). A dose-response relationship has been found: those with direct exposure to 9/11 vs. not being exposed showed a sixfold higher incidence of PTSD (Henriksen, Bolton, & Sareen, 2010). Exposure was associated with a higher likelihood of other disorders as well, including

The Canadian Press/Paul Chiasson

Unlike most other diagnoses, PTSD includes a traumatic event as part of its cause in its definition. On September 11, 2001, terrorists hijacked two passenger jets and deliberately crashed them into the twin towers of the World Trade Center in New York City. Thousands of people perished in the explosions and collapse of the 110-storey buildings. Firefighters, police officers, and other rescue workers, such as these men at "ground zero," could be vulnerable to PTSD.

depression. It can be reasonably assumed that more extreme exposure played a role in a recent finding about the chronicity of PTSD in Vietnam veterans; this long-term longitudinal study found that 40 years later, over 1 in 4 veterans alive today still meet full or partial criteria for PTSD, with more than twice as many deteriorating in their symptoms over time rather than improving (Marmar et al., 2015). It is estimated that 271,000 Vietnam War veterans still have full or partial PTSD.

There is a difference between PTSD and acute stress disorder, which was briefly described at the beginning of this chapter. Nearly everyone who encounters a trauma experiences stress, sometimes to a considerable degree. This is normal. If the stressor causes significant impairment in social or occupational functioning that lasts for at least three days and less than one month, an acute stress disorder is diagnosed. The proportion of people who develop an acute stress disorder varies with the type of trauma they have experienced. Following rape, the figure is extremely high—over 90% (Rothbaum et al., 1992). Other severe traumas, such as exposure to a mass shooting or being in a motor vehicle accident, yield much lower figures, such as 13% for motor vehicle accident victims (Bryant & Harvey, 1998). Although some people get over an acute stress disorder, many go on to develop PTSD (Harvey & Bryant, 2002).

Estimates of the prevalence of PTSD vary substantially depending on how people are assessed. Data suggest that the lifetime prevalence of PTSD in Canada is almost 1 in 10 and the one-month prevalence is about 1 in 25 Canadians (Van Ameringen et al., 2008). Prevalence varies depending on the severity of the trauma experienced; it is about 3% among civilians who have been exposed to a physical attack, 20% among people wounded in the Vietnam War, and about 50% among rape victims and people who were POWs (prisoners of war) in either the Second World War or the Korean War (Engdahl et al., 1997; Rothbaum et al., 1992). Mitchell, Griffin, Stewart, and Loba (2004) found that 46% of community volunteers had probable PTSD after helping with the cleanup and recovery of bodies following the 1998 Swissair disaster off the coast of Nova Scotia. Overall, 69% of volunteers reported intrusive thoughts about the disaster. Factors that were deemed to increase PTSD symptoms included community silence, limited help-seeking (due to the stigma of seeking help), and insufficient proactive provision of therapeutic resources. Similar high rates of PTSD have been experienced by Canadian military personnel (see Canadian Perspectives 9.1).

On May 12, 2008, a massive earthquake devastated a vast area of China, destroying 6.5 million homes and affecting about 46 million people. Over 70,000 people perished and about 15 million were evacuated from their homes. Peng Kun and colleagues (2009) surveyed people in August 2008 in a region severely affected by the earthquake. The prevalence of PTSD was 45.5% (using structured interviews and *DSM-IV* criteria). Numerous factors were related to increased likelihood of PTSD: low household income, being from an ethnic minority, living in a shelter or temporary house, death in the family, and household damage.

Hurricane Katrina was the deadliest hurricane in the United States in over 70 years and the most expensive natural disaster in U.S. history. Kessler et al. (2008) interviewed a representative sample of residents of areas affected by Hurricane Katrina five to eight months after the hurricane and again one year later. Contrary to some past studies, where post-disaster disorders decreased with time, prevalence increased significantly for PTSD (20.9% vs. 14.9% at baseline), serious mental

Canadian Perspectives 9.1

PTSD in Canadian Veterans and Peacekeepers

Published accounts of mental disorders in Canadian soldiers can be traced back to the First World War. Farrar (1917) concluded that 10% of invalided Canadian soldiers were "nervous and mental cases" (p. 389). The majority of cases (58%) were said to suffer from "neurotic reactions," and of these, a subgroup suffered from "shell shock." The second group (14%) were said to suffer from "mental diseases and defects" (p. 389) that included cases of "dementia praecox," "primary mental defect," and "psychopathic inferiority."

Research on PTSD in Canadian military personnel has startling implications. It is estimated that over 20,000 Canadians volunteered in the United States military to assist with the Vietnam War effort. Stretch (1990, 1991) examined the impact of participating in the war on 164 Canadian veterans who had an average of 54 months of duty with 15 months in Vietnam. An alarming 65.4% reported experiencing PTSD symptoms either during or after their Vietnam experience. PTSD was associated with poorer health, nervous system problems, depression, anxiety, anger, and shame. The sense of shame was, in part, a response to the perceived reaction of Canadian society. Comparisons of PTSD sufferers and veterans without PTSD showed that PTSD sufferers reported more negative reactions from people upon their return, more negative reactions to their involvement in the war, and homecomings that were significantly worse. Relative to American veterans, Canadian veterans were particularly vulnerable to long-lasting forms of PTSD because they were more isolated and received less recognition and support for their war efforts.

Beal (1995) conducted the longest follow-up study of PTSD published thus far. The 50-year follow-up focused on 276 Canadian veterans of the Dieppe Raid, regarded as one of the bloodiest events of the Second World War, with a casualty rate of 68%. Beal (1995) found alarming levels of PTSD in both POWs and non-POWs. Overall, 43.4% of the POWs and 29.9% of the non-POWs were diagnosed with PTSD based on their 1992 self-reports. Comparisons of POWs

with and without PTSD showed that those with PTSD reported more maltreatment in the form of beatings, personal intimidation, interrogation, group death threats, solitary confinement, and witnessing acts of torture. POWs with PTSD also had higher levels of depression, anxiety, and suicidal thoughts. A key point to remember is that these extreme levels of distress persisted for 50 years. Most men reported experiencing little anxiety or depression prior to the Dieppe Raid. Beal (1995) noted further that despite the level of disability experienced by these veterans, with 37% having PTSD in 1992, relatively few qualified for government assistance, according to 1992 Canadian government criteria. Only 5.4% were receiving psychological disability pensions from the Department of Veterans Affairs.

In 2000, the Canadian government opted finally to recognize PTSD symptoms as a form of disorder that merits a psychological disability pension (Thorne, 2000). This change was a response, in part, to the growing number of public accounts of severe forms of PTSD experienced by Canadian peacekeepers. The most well-known example is retired Lt. Gen. Roméo Dallaire (see photo), who served as the United Nations commander in Rwanda in 1994, when more than 800,000 Tutsis and Hutu moderates were killed by the ruling Hutu extremists. Dallaire and his men witnessed these atrocities (including children killing other children) as well as the slaughter of 10 Belgian soldiers by a machete-wielding mob. Dallaire's compelling account of his personal struggles and the genocide he witnessed were summarized in his book (Dallaire, 2003). His personal difficulties became public when he was discovered unconscious and apparently inebriated in a park in Hull, Quebec, on June 26, 2000. He revealed his difficulties in a letter that was sent to CBC Radio and read on-air on July 3, 2000. Dallaire has acknowledged his problems with PTSD and his suicide attempts (Growe, 2000). In his letter to CBC Radio, Dallaire said:

*"The anger, the rage, the hurt and the cold loneliness
that separates you from your family, friends and society's*

(continued)

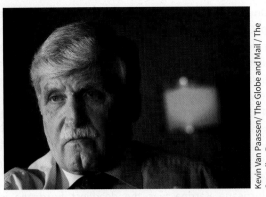

Kevin Van Paassen/The Globe and Mail / The Canadian Press

Lt. Gen. Roméo Dallaire, former commander of United Nations forces in Rwanda, who retired because of PTSD. Lt. Gen. (Retired) Dallaire is a former Senator.

normal daily routine are so powerful that the option of destroying yourself is both real and attractive. That is what happened last Monday night. . . . It appears, it grows, it invades and it overpowers you. In my current state of therapy, which continues to show very positive results, control mechanisms have not yet matured to always be on top of this battle."

A Canadian investigation of deployed peacekeepers and non-deployed military personnel confirmed that PTSD symptoms have a direct negative impact on health status. Moreover, this link was evident for both deployed peacekeepers and non-deployed personnel (Asmundson, Stein, & McCreary, 2002; also see McNally, 2005a). Thus, PTSD was associated with poor health, regardless of deployment status. PTSD was also closely linked with depression. In a study of French-Canadian male veterans seeking assessment or treatment for deployment-related PTSD, Poundja, Fikretoglu, and Brunet (2006) reported that nearly 87% of the sample reported significant current pain. The PTSD–pain relation was fully mediated by depression. Another study (Richardson et al., 2008) examined deployed Canadian Forces peacekeeping veterans and found that PTSD and depression severity predicted both mental and physical health-related quality of life.

Deniz Fikretoglu, Alain Brunet, and their colleagues (Fikretoglu, Brunet, Guay, & Pedlar, 2007) examined rates, characteristics, and predictors of mental health treatment seeking by military members with PTSD. Their sample of 549 who met the criteria for lifetime PTSD (out of 8,441 assessed) was drawn from the CCHS-Canadian Forces Supplement (CFS), the first nationally representative epidemiological survey of mental health in the Canadian military. Approximately one-third of those with PTSD never sought any form of mental health treatment. However, those with comorbid depression were 3.75 times more likely to seek treatment. Unfortunately, treatment adequacy was not assessed. There was also a greater likelihood of treatment seeking after multiple types of trauma.

A growing concern in Canada is that when treatment is sought, there are not enough treatment providers to meet our ever-increasing needs. Canada's military ombudsman, Peter Daigle, released a report in September 2012 that was accompanied by a call for more therapists. Daigle estimated that there is a need for up to 22% more staff to treat PTSD and there is a big gap between what families need and what services are available (see Brewster, 2012). Concerns about access to timely treatment remain. Dallaire went public in February 2015 and called for better support for veterans. He also alleged that the Department of Veterans Affairs was cheap. Previously, the Auditor General of Canada, Michael Ferguson, issued a scathing report about the lack of timely access for veterans to mental health services and noted specifically that 20% of those needing treatment are forced to wait up to eight months just to get approved for treatment (Auditor General of Canada, 2014).

Part of the problem is the increased demand for mental health services due to more military personnel coming forward and no longer stigmatizing themselves, but also the mental health needs for those military personnel who took part in the war in Afghanistan. According to separate reports, 54 soldiers and veterans took their own lives after returning from the war in Afghanistan (D'Alesio, 2016) and the number of PTSD diagnoses among veterans tripled between 2007 and 2015, with more than 14,000 veterans now having PTSD (CBC News, 2015). The 2013 Canadian Forces Mental Health Survey was conducted with data from all full-time regular members of the Canadian Forces. Overall, about 1 in 6 soldiers reported symptoms of depression, anxiety, PTSD, alcohol abuse, or alcohol dependence (Pearson, Zamorski, & Janz, 2014). Overall, 5.3% of respondents had PTSD over 12 months and 11.1% of respondents had a lifetime PTSD diagnosis. Rates of PTSD were about twice as high for those military personnel who had served in Afghanistan.

An earlier study of U.S. soldiers returning from combat in Afghanistan and Iraq (Pietrzak et al., 2009) suggests that interventions that bolster resilience (in this instance, increased personal control and positive acceptance of change), together with post-deployment social support, protect against the development of traumatic stress and depression.

Thinking Critically

1. Lt. Gen. Dallaire, like so many Canadian peacekeepers, had difficulty coping with the atrocities he witnessed. What steps would you take to help our peacekeepers or military on operational deployments better prepare for the psychological consequences of their missions? What preventive strategies would you recommend that the military employ during the missions? Would it be appropriate to have military psychologists available during the mission?

2. It was revealed in 2011 that a substantial number of Canadian Forces veterans with PTSD are redeployed and sent back into action after treatment for PTSD. Is this at all advisable? Do you accept the possibility that being re-exposed to this stress can actually result in improvements for those who have learned to cope with their PTSD?

3. Research on PTSD in Canadian Forces members demonstrates that there are complex relationships among PTSD, physical health, pain, and depression and their link to trauma exposure and types of traumatic events. However, these studies were correlational and preclude drawing conclusions about the direction of causation. Design a longitudinal study to replicate current findings. Also, design an intervention program to increase treatment seeking. Intervention programs should assess conditions comorbid with PTSD, particularly depression. Design a comprehensive, multi-faceted treatment program for Canadian Forces members who have experienced trauma.

illness (14.0% vs. 10.9%), suicidal ideation (6.4% vs. 2.8%), and suicide plans (2.5% vs. 1.0%). The increases were judged to be due to "unresolved hurricane-related stresses." These are residual stressors attributable to the weather (e.g., living elsewhere due to needing to relocate). When exposed to the trauma of Hurricane Katrina, women were more likely than men to develop PTSD (Galea et al., 2007). The lasting effects of traumatic stress is just one of many reasons why the Alberta government added $50 million in October 2013 for mental health treatment to help address the psychological after math of the 2012 floods in Alberta.

While most research and theory in this field focuses on PTSD in military personnel (see Canadian Perspectives 9.1), it is of course the case that the experience of a significant trauma by anyone can create PTSD. The key question when many people experience the same event at the same time is "Why do only some people develop PTSD?" This is the overarching question in research being conducted on the passengers of Air Transat Flight 236, which lost all power in August 2001. The flight originated from Toronto and was on its way to Portugal when all fuel was lost. The captain and co-pilot informed the over 300 passengers of their predicament but ultimately were able to make a successful emergency landing in the Azores after more than 30 harrowing minutes. Overall, it is believed that about one-half of the passengers developed PTSD as a result of this huge trauma. Intriguing research involving the passengers has been conducted by Margaret McKinnon and her colleagues in Hamilton, Ontario. One investigation found that all passengers showed robust autobiographic recall of event details, but PTSD sufferers recalled more nontraumatic event details for the averted disaster and other events (McKinnon et al., 2015). Other research by Palombo, McKinnon, and associates on the Air Transat passengers confirmed that amygdala activation is involved in trauma processing (see Palombo et al., 2016). This research is deeply personal for Margaret McKinnon. Why? She was one of the passengers on Flight 236!

A topic of growing interest is the fact that university and college students can also be prone to PTSD. A study conducted with 803 York University students found that an alarming 30% of them met or exceeded the recommended cut-off for significant trauma symptomatology on the Trauma Symptom Checklist-40 (Briere & Runtz, 1988) (see Muller, Thornback, & Bedi, 2012). How many students actually qualify for a diagnosis? An examination of 3,014 students at two U.S. universities found that 66% reported exposure to a significant trauma and 9% met clinical criteria for post-traumatic stress disorder. The authors concluded that a very substantial proportion of incoming university students have significant trauma exposure (Read, Ouimette, White, Colder, & Farrow, 2011). Follow-up research by Read, Bachrach, Wright, and Colder (2016) showed that when students were assessed throughout their first year of college, the majority of them resolved their PTSD symptoms, but about 1 in 5 students had severe symptoms at the start of the school year and 11% (1 in 9) still had severe symptoms at the end of the year. More severe symptoms were associated with greater trauma exposure throughout the school year and

a personality style by elevated neuroticism and lower levels of agreeableness and conscientiousness.

A study by Frazier and associates (2009) found that about 1 in 5 students experienced a traumatic event when assessed during a two-month period at university. Sexual assaults were associated with the most PTSD symptoms.

Of course, levels of PTSD are much higher in campus contexts where tragedies have actually occurred. A survey conducted four months after the 2007 Virginia Tech mass shooting found high levels of PTSD symptoms among 15% of students, with PTSD more prevalent among those who had a friend who was killed (Hughes et al., 2011). The PTSD prevalence here might have been higher but the study included only a small proportion of those with direct trauma contact.

Analyses of responses to the 2006 Dawson College shooting in Montreal (Miquelon et al., 2014; Séguin et al., 2013) focused on 948 students and staff who were assessed 18 months after the shooting. About one-third of the participants witnessed someone being wounded or killed, and half of the participants heard gunshots. Overall, 30% of participants had one or more diagnosable disorders following the shooting, which was seen as about double the prevalence of disorders in the general population. Overall, 18% developed a disorder for the first time in their lives. Here it was found that the closer the exposure to the event, the greater the risk of developing a disorder (Miquelon et al., 2014; Séguin et al., 2013). Unfortunately, the majority of people in the Dawson College study did not seek professional assistance.

Etiology of Post-Traumatic Stress Disorder

Research and theory on the causes of PTSD focus on risk factors for the disorder, as well as on psychological and biological factors.

Risk Factors
When examining risk factors, it is important to consider not only risk factors for PTSD, but also risk factors for the likelihood of being exposed to trauma. Research indicates that males, relative to females, have higher levels of trauma exposure across various event types, with the exception of child sexual abuse and sexual assaults in general, yet females have higher levels of PTSD (Breslau, 2002; Tolin & Foa, 2006).

There are several risk factors for PTSD. Given exposure to a traumatic event, predictors of PTSD, in addition to gender, include perceived threat to life, early separation from parents, family history of a disorder, previous exposure to traumas, and a pre-existing disorder (an anxiety disorder or depression) (Breslau et al., 1997, 1999; Ehlers, Malou, & Bryant, 1998; Stein, 1997). Previous exposure to trauma is regarded as one of the strongest predictors of whether the individual is exposed subsequently to trauma (Testa, VanZile-Tamsen, & Livingston, 2007). A detailed analysis of this phenomenon was conducted by Cougle, Resnick, and Kilpatrick (2009). They performed a longitudinal study with multiple phases of a nationally representative sample of women and differentiated various types of

PTSD symptoms. They found that re-experiencing PTSD symptoms predicted subsequent exposure to interpersonal violence victimization by a non-intimate perpetrator, but not subsequent exposure instigated by an intimate partner. Also, PTSD hyperarousal symptoms were uniquely predictive of other traumatic stressors. Thus, different types of PTSD symptoms played different roles in subsequent exposure to different types of events.

Longitudinal research continues to show that in addition to being exposed to less severe events, having high intelligence (an IQ of 115 or greater) seems to be a protective factor, perhaps because it is associated with having better coping skills (see Breslau, Lucia, & Alvarado, 2006).

Dissociative symptoms (including amnesia and out-of-body experiences) at the time of the trauma also increase the probability of developing PTSD, as does trying to push memories of the trauma out of one's mind (Ehlers et al., 1998). Dissociation may play a role in maintaining the disorder, as it keeps the person from confronting traumatic memories. A compelling study of dissociation assessed rape survivors within two weeks of the assault. While the women talked about either the rape or neutral topics, psychophysiological measures and self-reports of stress were taken. The women were divided into two groups based on their scores on a measure of dissociation during the rape (e.g., "Did you have moments of losing track of what was going on?"). Women with high dissociation scores were much more likely to have PTSD symptoms than were low scorers. High scorers also had a dissociation between their subjective stress ratings and their physiological responses. Although they reported high levels of stress when they were talking about being raped, they showed less physiological arousal than did the women with low dissociation scores.

Another risk factor was discovered in a study of Israeli veterans of the 1982 war with Lebanon. Development of PTSD was associated with a tendency to take personal responsibility for failures and to cope with stress by focusing on emotions ("I wish I could change how I feel") rather than on the problems themselves (Mikulincer & Solomon, 1988).

Attachment style has been identified as a PTSD risk factor by York University researcher Robert Muller and his associates in their study of high-risk adults with a history of childhood physical or sexual abuse (see Muller, Sicoli, & Lemieux, 2000; Muller, Kraftcheck, & McLewin, 2004). Attachment styles (e.g., how an infant reacts when left alone with a stranger when the mother leaves) are discussed in more detail in Chapter 15. Muller et al. (2000) reported that 76% of the participants endorsed an insecure attachment style. They found that PTSD is likely among people with an insecure attachment style that involves a negative view of the self; a negative view of others was not linked with PTSD symptoms. A treatment study by Muller and Rosenkrantz (2009) found that reductions in PTSD symptoms were accompanied by increases in secure attachment and these increases were maintained six months after treatment.

Psychological Theories Learning theorists assume that PTSD arises from a classical conditioning of fear (e.g., Fairbank & Brown, 1987). A woman who has been raped, for example, may come to fear walking in a certain neighbourhood (the CS) because of having been assaulted there (the UCS). Based on this classically conditioned fear, avoidances are built up, and they are negatively reinforced by the reduction of fear that comes from not being in the presence of the CS. In a sense, PTSD is an example of the two-factor theory of avoidance learning proposed years ago by Mowrer (1947). There is a developing body of evidence in support of this view (Foy et al., 1990) and of related theories that emphasize the loss of control and predictability felt by people with PTSD (Chemtob et al., 1988).

Cognitive theorists characterize PTSD as a disorder of memory with the hallmark feature being the constant involuntary recollection of the traumatic event (McNally, 2006). Contemporary research suggests that there are many cognitive tendencies that are problematic for those with PTSD. For instance, it has been shown across several studies that PTSD is associated with impaired memory of emotionally neutral stimuli. Specifically, there is a robust association between PTSD and memory impairment, and this tendency is stronger for verbal memory than visual memory (Brewin, Kleiner, Vasterling, & Field, 2007). Other research links PTSD with insufficient working memory systems (Shaw et al., 2009). Researchers are now attempting to show a connection with distinct memory patterns and cognitive deficits with brain regions and brain functions. For instance, an fMRI study conducted in Montreal shows that memory performance is linked with ventral medial prefrontal cortex activity (Dickie, Brunet, Akerib, & Armony, 2008). McNally (2006) summarized extant work on the cognitive features of PTSD by suggesting that PTSD involves a hyporesponsive prefrontal cortical region or hyporesponsive amygdala region. Moreover, having above-average cognitive ability protects people from experiencing PTSD, but reduced hippocampal volume escalates the risk of PTSD (e.g., Bremner, 2006).

A psychodynamic theory proposed by Horowitz (1990) posits that memories of the traumatic event occur constantly in the person's mind and are so painful that they are either consciously suppressed (by distraction, for example) or repressed. People are believed to engage in a kind of internal struggle to make some sense of a trauma by integrating it into their existing beliefs about themselves and the world.

Biological Theories We touched on biological factors as part of our discussion of memory and cognition in PTSD. Additional research on twins shows a possible diathesis for PTSD (True et al., 1993). A study conducted with twin pairs from the Vancouver area demonstrated that exposure to certain kinds of trauma (e.g., violent crimes) was influenced by genetic and environmental factors, but only environmental factors contributed to other types of trauma (e.g., natural disasters); in addition, PTSD symptoms following exposure to non-combat trauma were moderately heritable (Stein, Jang, Taylor, Vernon, & Livesley, 2002). This study is unique in two ways: it is one of the few genetic studies conducted on a non-military, community sample, and it is the first study of its kind to include women. Stein et al. (2002) concluded that a personality characterized by trait neuroticism might be the genetic vulnerability factor that serves as a diathesis for PTSD.

Gilbertson et al. (2006) evaluated neurocognitive functioning in monozygotic twin pairs who were discordant for combat exposure. They grouped pairs according to whether the brother exposed to combat developed PTSD. The combat-unexposed twins of combat veterans with PTSD displayed similar neuropsychological performance as their brothers, which was significantly poorer than that of non-PTSD combat veterans and their brothers. The researchers concluded, "The results support the notion that specific domains of cognitive function may serve as premorbid risk or protective factors in PTSD" (p. 484).

Trauma may activate the noradrenergic system, raising levels of norepinephrine and thereby making the person startle and express emotion more readily than is normal (Krystal et al., 1989). Consistent with this view is the finding that norepinephrine was higher in PTSD clients than in those diagnosed as having schizophrenia or mood disorders (Kosten et al., 1987). In addition, stimulating the noradrenergic system induced a panic attack in 70% and flashbacks in 40% of PTSD clients; none of the control participants had such experiences (Southwick et al., 1993). Also, there is extensive evidence for increased sensitivity of noradrenergic receptors in people with PTSD and this sensitivity has been linked with specific PTSD symptom clusters (O'Donnell, Hegadoren, & Coupland, 2004).

Because of the unique features of PTSD, emerging treatments for PTSD are being designed to address the specific themes that are relevant for PTSD sufferers. Some of these newer developments are outlined below.

Tailoring Treatment for Post-Traumatic Stress Disorder

Many experts on trauma agree that it is best to intervene in some fashion as soon as possible after a traumatic event, well before PTSD has a chance to develop. The need to intervene as soon as possible has resulted in the novel suggestion that training and expertise needs to come in the form of "psychological first aid." *The Psychological First Aid Field Operations Guide* was developed to provide guidance to frontline practitioners who must respond immediately to mental health needs following a disaster or terrorist event (see Vernberg et al., 2008).

Intervening when people are in the acute phase of a post-trauma period and are at risk of developing acute stress disorder is referred to as *crisis intervention*. As reviewed by Foa and Meadows (1997), intervention includes such procedures as recreating the event by having participants discuss with each other as many details as they can remember, encouraging them to describe their thoughts at the time of the event, and normalizing their anxiety reactions by reminding them that they have just been through an event that causes extreme distress for most people (Mitchell & Bray, 1990). A promising approach for people who have been sexually assaulted is a cognitive-behavioural therapy (CBT) strategy that involves, in combination, exposing clients to trauma-related cues in imagination, teaching them relaxation, and helping them think differently about what happened (e.g., to not blame themselves) (Foa et al., 1995).

Edna Foa and her colleagues have developed the PTSD treatment intervention that is seen as most effective and this has been confirmed by extensive empirical research and an associated meta-analysis (Powers et al., 2010). **Prolonged exposure therapy** was developed specifically to treat PTSD. According to Foa and McLean (2016), this therapy is derived from Foa's emotion processing theory, which sees PTSD as a failure to process trauma memories due to avoidance of trauma-related thoughts and situations. Thus, the treatment goal is to promote emotional processing and overcome avoidance by confronting the traumatic stimuli. This therapy is a combined CBT approach that involves a step-by-step process of being exposed to imagery reflecting traumatic memories as well as actual life situations reflecting trauma. It typically involves between 8 to 15 sessions of 90 minutes each (Foa & McLean, 2016). Exposure is accompanied by changing thoughts and cognitive appraisals as well as being taught specific skills such as regulating and controlling breathing (see Foa, Hembree, & Rothbaum, 2007). Research indicates that prolonged exposure therapy is effective; this conclusion was supported by a comprehensive meta-analysis (see Powers et al., 2010). Moreover, the evidence indicates that structured exposure to trauma-related events, sometimes in imagination, contributes something beyond the benefits of medication, social support, or a safe therapeutic environment (e.g., Foa & Meadows, 1997). However, it is important to recognize that exposure does not work for everyone. A recent review of psychotherapy for people with military-related PTSD noted that between one-third to one-half of people with PTSD did not experience clinically meaningfully significant symptom change and some studies show that up to two-thirds of current or former military personnel with a diagnosis still warrant the diagnosis after treatment. Also, as many as one-fourth of the people in treatment drop out of treatment (see Steenkamp, Litz, Hoge, & Marmar, 2015). So, conclusions about the effectiveness of exposure therapy for PTSD need to be qualified.

How does exposure work? We have already discussed the possibility that it leads to the extinction of the fear response. But it may also change the meaning that stimuli have for people. This cognitive view has been elaborated by Foa and her colleagues. They emphasize the corrective aspects of exposure to what is feared:

> "Exposure promotes symptom reduction by allowing patients to realize that, contrary to their mistaken ideas: (a) being in objectively safe situations that remind one of the trauma is not dangerous; (b) remembering the trauma is not equivalent to experiencing it again; (c) anxiety does not remain indefinitely in the presence of feared situations or memories, but rather it decreases even without avoidance or escape; and (d) experiencing anxiety/PTSD symptoms does not lead to loss of control."

(Foa & Meadows, 1997, p. 462)

Skip Rizzo is a creator of the "Virtual Iraq" simulation program used to promote resilience in military personnel exposed to trauma. This kind of exposure has been shown to be quite effective in initial empirical research.

Virtual reality exposure treatment has taken some great leaps forward when it comes to the treatment of PTSD. Particularly impressive is the work of Albert "Skip" Rizzo and his colleagues. Rizzo has developed a VR program known as "Virtual Iraq." Virtual Iraq is a three-dimensional program that allows the therapist to gradually introduce a variety of sensations including audio cues, visual cues, vibrations, and even smells (see photo). It comes in two scenarios: (1) the participant is in a Humvee that is part of a line of vehicles that comes under attack in the desert; or (2) the participant is in a middle Eastern town and must travel several blocks in streets and lanes with attack possible at any point. Rizzo indicated in a 2008 radio interview that VR is a treatment modality that is typically introduced in the fourth session after a therapeutic bond has been established. He also noted during this interview that using Virtual Iraq is much less stigmatizing for military personnel than "going to see the shrink" (National Public Radio, 2008, May 27). Initial outcome studies have attested to the effectiveness of Virtual Iraq in currently enlisted soldiers with PTSD (McLay et al., 2012; Rizzo et al., 2010) and it is now being used as a type of PTSD prevention in resilience training in the pre-deployment phase for those who will eventually see service (Rizzo et al., 2013).

Insights into the specific details at a case level were provided in a case reported by Gerardi, Rothbaum, Ressler, Heekin, and Rizzo (2008). A 29-year-old man who had served for a year in Iraq sought treatment six months after returning to the United States. This college-educated man had intrusive memories of military-related trauma that had limited his ability to drive and his ability to interact with other people. He had poor concentration, mood irritability, angry outbursts, sleep disorder with cold sweats, a high startle response, and hypervigilance. It was decided that the Humvee scenario would be best and he experienced four 90-minute individual sessions. Initially, the first sensations in the Humvee setting triggered his trauma and associated symptoms. However, as a result of increasing exposure and the gradual introduction of sights and sounds (explosions, gunfire, helicopter flyovers), the levels of PTSD symptoms decreased. Gerardi et al. (2008) noted that a key change in emotions occurred, with the man's initial feelings

of horror, guilt, and grief giving way to feelings of pride as he recognized the bravery needed to serve in Iraq. He developed a general acceptance of what had happened.

As is the case with CBT treatments, when treatments are effective, researchers still must try to identify the specific factors and processes that account for effectiveness. In the case of the soldier treated in the Humvee scenario, we noted that there was a change in emotions. In addition, another key factor was outcome expectancy. The initial beliefs were quite optimistic; when asked to complete the Expectancy of Therapeutic Outcome Scale (Foa, Rothbaum, Riggs, & Murdoch, 1991), the soldier with PTSD described by Gerardi et al. (2008) expressed his belief that treatment was logical and would be effective in reducing trauma-related stress and related personal problems.

Important new research insights about effective CBT components have come from a multi-stage treatment study by Kleim et al. (2013). This study established that CBT seems to be effective to the extent that it results in changes in dysfunctional appraisals of trauma and the presumed after-effects of trauma. This study helped clarify that changes in trauma appraisal occur before improvements in symptoms rather than after.

In 1989, Shapiro (1989) began to promulgate an approach to treating trauma called Eye Movement Desensitization and Reprocessing (EMDR). This method is purported to be extremely rapid—often requiring only one or two sessions—and more effective than the standard exposure procedures just reviewed. In this procedure, the client imagines a situation related to his

Twenty-six miners lost their lives in an explosion at the Westray Mine in Stellarton, Nova Scotia, in May 1992. The disaster triggered acute stress and PTSD disorders in many of the people who worked or who were otherwise associated with those who died. Westray provides a good example of the importance of a proactive community response to disasters and the importance of social support in reducing the risk of developing PTSD.

or her problem, such as the sight of a horrible automobile accident. Keeping the image in mind, the client follows with his or her eyes the therapist's fingers as the therapist moves them back and forth about a foot in front of the client. This process continues for a minute or so or until the client reports that the horror of the image has been reduced. Then the therapist has the client verbalize whatever negative thoughts are going through his or her mind, again while following the moving target with his or her eyes. Finally, the therapist encourages the client to think a more positive thought, such as "I can deal with this," and this thought, too, is held in mind as the client follows the therapist's moving fingers.

A great deal of controversy surrounds this technique (and related techniques), and opinions are polarized in ways not often found in science. On the one hand are EMDR proponents who argue that combining eye movements with thoughts about the feared event promotes rapid deconditioning or reprocessing of the aversive stimulus (e.g., Shapiro, 1999). On the other hand are numerous studies that show that eye movements do not add anything to what may be happening as a result of exposure itself (e.g., Cahill, Carrigan, & Frueh, 1999), as well as a study showing that exposure therapy appears to be more effective than EMDR (Taylor et al., 2003). Moreover, earlier claims of EMDR's effectiveness rest on experiments that have major methodological shortcomings (cf. Rosen, 1999). However, a Canadian study found that alternating right-left stimulation as part of the procedure resulted in rapid reductions in clients' subjective distress (see Servan-Schreiber et al., 2006), and a recent meta-analysis that differentiated studies that did or did not have significant flaws concluded that tests of addictive effects of EMDR in treatment studies yielded a moderate and significant effect (Lee & Cuijpers, 2013). Moreover, no one disputes the important role played by exposure to memories or images of traumatic events, and the well-established role of exposure to aversive stimuli is probably the key ingredient in whatever efficacy EMDR has.

Horowitz's (1990) psychodynamic approach has much in common with the CBT approach, for he encourages clients to discuss the trauma and otherwise expose themselves to the events that led to the PTSD. But Horowitz emphasizes the manner in which the trauma interacts with a client's pre-trauma personality, and the treatment he proposes also has much in common with other psychoanalytic approaches, including discussions of defences and analysis of transference reactions by the client. A few controlled studies lend a small degree of empirical support to its effectiveness (Foa & Meadows, 1997).

A meta-analysis conducted by Bradley et al. (2005) attests to the usefulness of psychotherapy in order to treat PTSD. This meta-analysis of 26 studies using 44 treatment conditions showed that of those who completed treatment, two-thirds no longer met diagnostic criteria for PTSD. The authors concluded that psychotherapy interventions are "highly efficacious" (Bradley et al., 2005, p. 225). However, it was still the case that the majority of clients had residual symptoms despite no longer warranting a diagnosis, and, as has been often found, treatments for combat-related trauma yielded the lowest effect

sizes. A subseqeuent meta-analysis (Benish, Imel, & Wampold, 2008) focused on the relative efficacy of *bona fide* psychotherapies using direct comparison studies only. The authors concluded that, "despite strong evidence of psychotherapy efficaciousness vis-à-vis no treatment or common factor controls, bona fide psychotherapies produce equivalent benefits for patients with PTSD" (p. 746).

Finally, various psychoactive drugs have been used with PTSD clients, including antidepressants and tranquilizers. Sometimes medication is used to deal with conditions comorbid with PTSD, such as depression; improvement in the depression can contribute to improvement in PTSD regardless of how the PTSD itself is treated (by a psychological intervention of the kinds just described, for example [Marshall et al., 1994]). Some modest successes have been reported for antidepressants, especially the serotonin reuptake inhibitors (e.g., Yehuda, Marshall, & Giller, 1998). What would you choose if you were diagnosed with PTSD: sertraline (an SSRI) or prolonged exposure?

One controversial development is the recent use of ecstasy (MDMA) in the treatment of PTSD. Mithoefer et al. (2011) conducted an RCT with 12 PTSD clients receiving ecstasy and 8 PTSD clients in the control condition receiving a placebo. Ten of the 12 clients (83%) in the treatment condition had clinically significant improvement vs. only two people in the control group. As a result of this development, two Vancouver researchers received approval at the end of 2012 to begin a clinical trial even though ecstasy has been banned for decades in Canada (see photo).

Overall, we know very little about the relative efficacy of drug and psychological interventions for chronic PTSD. Feeny et al. (2009) asked this question of female trauma victims, including women with chronic PTSD. An overwhelming majority of the women chose exposure, although those with comorbid major depression were more likely to choose sertraline than those without depression. As noted by the authors, it's important to assess clients' preferences, because they potentially affect outcome, and to rethink "one-size fits all approaches to treatment" (p. 724).

Whatever the specific mode of intervention, experts in PTSD agree that social support is critical. Sometimes finding ways to

David P. Ball for National Post

Psychiatrist Dr. Ingrid Pacey and psychologist Andrew Feldmár are leading research on MDMA-assisted therapy trials that were slated to begin with 12 trauma patients in Vancouver. Ecstasy helps people stay in the present moment and be less distressed by earlier traumas.

lend support to others can help the giver as well as the receiver (Hobfoll et al., 1991). Belonging to a religious group; having family, friends, or fellow traumatized individuals listen non-judgementally to one's fears and recollections of the trauma; and having other ways to feel that one belongs and that others wish to help ease the pain may spell the difference between post-traumatic stress and PTSD. When a disaster influences an entire community, as was the case with the Westray mining disaster in Canada, community support is vital (see photo).

In summary, our review of several therapeutic approaches to dealing with psychophysiological disorders, many of which can be subsumed under the rubric of behavioural medicine, illustrates the complex relationships between the soma and the psyche, the body and the mind. We come full circle to how we began this chapter, namely, to an appreciation of the inseparability of bodily and mental processes. Stress is a part of everyone's life. As much as it can pose problems, so, too, can it promote well-being as we learn ways to cope with or manage it.

Summary

9.1 Stress involves a sense of uncontrollability over events that impact the self. Stress can be measured in terms of uncontrollable major life events, but also daily experiences and hassles. Stress has both multiple physiological and psychological impacts and is implicated in a vast array of health conditions. The ability to predict who develops stress and copes better or worse with illness depends on individual differences in coping styles. When events are appraised as stressful, coping efforts are engaged. If coping fails to lessen the amount of stress experienced, the risk of becoming ill increases. Important issues in current work on life stress and health include looking at moderators of the relationship (e.g., social support lessens the effects of stress) and specifying the physiological mechanisms (e.g., the immune system) through which stress can exert its effects.

9.2 Psychophysiological disorders are physical diseases produced in part by psychological factors, primarily stress. Such disorders usually affect organs innervated by the autonomic nervous system, such as those of the respiratory, cardiovascular, gastrointestinal, and endocrine systems. Research has pursued a number of different paths to discover how psychological stress produces a particular psychophysiological disorder. Some researchers have looked at the specifics of the stressor or the psychological characteristics of the person, such as the links between anger/hostility and hypertension and between Type A personality and myocardial infarction. Others have emphasized that psychophysiological disorders occur only when stress interacts with a biological diathesis. Cardiovascular disorders occur in individuals who have a tendency to respond to stress with increases in blood pressure or heart rate. Although we have spoken of psychological stress affecting the body, it must be remembered that the mind and the body are best viewed as two different approaches to the same organism.

9.3 Cardiovascular disease is highly prevalent in Canada and is a reflection of hypertension arising from several factors, including diet, stress, and exercise. The tendency for hypertension to contribute to coronary heart disease is a reflection of a host of factors, including psychological diatheses or vulnerabilities that can include personality factors and biological diatheses or vulnerability factors. Psychophysiological disorders represent true physical dysfunctions. As a result, treatment usually includes medication. The general aim of psychotherapies for these disorders is to reduce anxiety or anger and there is growing evidence of the destructive impact of anger and hostility on health functioning. Researchers in the field of behavioural medicine try to find psychological interventions that can improve the client's physiological state by changing unhealthy behaviours and reducing stress. They have developed ways of helping people relax, smoke less, eat fewer fatty foods, and engage in behaviours that can prevent or alleviate illnesses, such as breast self-examination and adhering to medical treatment recommendations.

9.4 Post-traumatic stress disorder is diagnosed in some people who have experienced a traumatic event that would evoke extreme distress in most individuals. It is marked by symptoms such as re-experiencing the trauma, increased arousal, and avoidance of stimuli associated with the trauma. PTSD is highly prevalent, especially among people who encounter traumatic situations, such as military personnel and first responders. PTSD can result from directly experiencing trauma, witnessing trauma, or learning of the trauma experienced by a close friend or relative. Accounts of the etiology of PTSD must consider risk factors such as degree of exposure to trauma and demographic factors such as sex, with males more likely to be exposed to trauma. Psychological theories range from PTSD being a learned response to it being a reflection of cognitive processes implicated in memory and appraisals of life situations and circumstances. A biopsychosocial account would accord with biological theories and models that attempt to account for heightened susceptibility to experience traumatic symptoms as a function of genetic risk factors and physiological sensitivities.

Key Terms

allostatic load
anger-in theory
angina pectoris
autonomic nervous system (ANS)
behavioural medicine
biofeedback
cardiovascular disorders (CVDs)

cardiovascular reactivity
coping
coronary heart disease (CHD)
daily hassles
distress
emotional support
essential (or primary) hypertension

eustress
functional social support
general adaptation syndrome (GAS)
goodness of fit hypothesis
health psychology
instrumental support
interactionism

Reflections: Past, Present, and Future

1. Jemmott and Magliore (1988) demonstrated that among college students who were experiencing the stress of final examinations, those students with more social support had superior immune function, as assessed by secretory immunoglobulin A. What are the implications of their finding? If you were working as a student mentor in a university academic skills centre, what advice would you give your charges?

2. Research has shown that many people who develop psychological disorders also have various physical illnesses. Does this correlation allow us to conclude that mental disorders contribute to the development of physical illnesses? Design a study that would allow you to conclude that there is a causal effect of psychological disorders on physical illness.

3. Diathesis–stress, biopsychosocial, and cognitive-behavioural paradigms all emphasize that psychological and social factors play a vital role in influencing people's health. Does this mean that people are responsible for their own health? How might these perspectives affect public health policy in Canada?

4. Research (e.g., Maccoby & Altman, 1988; Schooler, Flora, & Farquhar, 1993) has demonstrated that community-based programs have the potential to reduce significantly the incidence and seriousness of many medical illnesses beyond what is achievable by strictly medical practices. It is increasingly accepted that people's physical health is often very much in their own hands and that changing lifestyle practices is sometimes the best means of reducing the risk of illness (Bandura, 1986). How could you use the mass media to reduce cardiovascular disease? What would you inform people they could do to reduce their risk of premature disease? Can people learn how to reduce their overall risk for cardiovascular and other diseases from properly designed and delivered mass media and other large-scale educational programs?

CHAPTER 10

Eating Disorders

LEARNING OBJECTIVES

1. Describe the various types of eating disorders.

2. Explain the etiology of eating disorders from a biopsychosocial perspective, including the role of the family.

3. Describe the treatment of eating disorders, including the role of cognitive-behavioural therapy.

4. Discuss the need to prevent eating disorders.

Brief Case Example

Recovering from Anorexia Nervosa

WHEN MS. A was first evaluated for admission to an inpatient eating disorders program, she had been restricting her food in take for approximately 5 years and had been amenorrheic for 4 years. At the time of her admission, this 24-year-old, single, white woman weighed 71 lb at a height of 5 feet 1.5 inches. In 12th grade, Ms. A menstruated for the first time and also developed "very large" breasts. She had a difficult first year at college, where she gained to her maximum weight of 120 lb. The following year, Ms. A transferred to a smaller college, became a vegetarian for "ethical reasons," and began to significantly restrict her food intake. She limited herself to a total of 700 to 800 calories per day, with a maximum of 200 calories per meal, and gradually lost weight in the next 5 years. Ms. A did not binge, vomit, abuse laxatives, or engage in excessive exercise. She considered herself to be "obsessed with calories" and observed a variety of rituals regarding food and food preparation (e.g., obsessively weighing her food) . . .

During her first five-month hospitalization, Ms. A was treated with a multimodal program (behavioural weight gain protocol, individual and family therapy, fluoxetine at 60–80 mg for obsessive-compulsive traits and depressive symptoms) and gained to a weight of 98 lb. At discharge, she was maintaining her weight on food but remained concerned about her weight and was particularly frightened of reaching "the triple digits" (i.e., 100 lb). After leaving the hospital, Ms. A continued with outpatient psychotherapy and fluoxetine for several months . . .

About 3.5 years after discharge, at age 27 years, Ms. A again sought inpatient treatment. At admission, she weighed 83 lb but still felt "fat." During hospitalization, she steadily gained weight and was prescribed sertraline at 100 mg/day for feelings of low self-esteem, anxiety, and obsessional thinking. When she was discharged five months later, at a weight of 108 lb, she noted menstrual bleeding for the first time in more than 7 years. After leaving the hospital, Ms. A continued taking medication and began outpatient cognitive-behavioral psychotherapy. For the next year, she continued to struggle with eating and weight issues but managed to maintain her weight and successfully expand other aspects of her life by independently supporting herself with a full-time job, making new friends, and becoming involved in her first romantic relationship. (Walsh, 2003, pp. 1516–1517)

Many cultures are preoccupied with eating. In North America today, gourmet restaurants abound and numerous magazines and television shows are devoted to food preparation. At the same time, many people are overweight. Dieting to lose weight is common, and the desire of many people, especially women, to be slimmer has created a multi-billion-dollar-a-year business. Given this intense interest in food and eating, it is not surprising that this aspect of human behaviour is subject to disorder. The case of Ms. A in the brief case example illustrates several relevant themes, including how eating disorder symptoms

often reflect transitions involving physiological processes (e.g., puberty) and life transitions (e.g., going to university).

Although clinical descriptions of eating disorders can be traced back many years, these disorders appeared in the *DSM* for the first time only in 1980, as one subcategory of disorders beginning in childhood or adolescence. With the publication of *DSM-IV*, the eating disorders anorexia nervosa and bulimia nervosa formed a distinct category, reflecting the increased attention they have received from clinicians and researchers over the past three decades. As will be discussed, binge eating disorder is another distinct diagnostic category that is now officially included in *DSM-5*. Improved criteria for anorexia nervosa and bulimia nervosa have also been introduced.

Just how common are eating disorders? The prevalence and correlates of eating disorders were assessed in a nationally representative household survey conducted in the United States between 2001 and 2003 (see Hudson, Hiripi, Pope, & Kessler, 2007). The lifetime prevalence estimates of anorexia nervosa were 0.9% for women and 0.3% for men. The lifetime prevalence estimates of bulimia nervosa were 1.5% for women and 0.5% for men. Finally, the lifetime prevalence estimates of binge eating disorder were 3.5% for women and 2.0% for men. While there is a clear sex difference, it is still the case overall that 1 in 3 or 1 in 4 cases involve boys or young men. A follow-up study of the prevalence of binge eating disorder around the world conducted by Kessler et al. (2013) used World Health Organization data gathered on over 24,000 participants from 14 countries. They found that the lifetime prevalence of binge eating disorder was higher than the rate for bulimia nervosa (1.4% vs. 0.8%). The disorders were similar in terms of age of onset (late teen years to early 20s) but it was slightly earlier for those with bulimia nervosa. Bulimia was also distinguished by having a longer persistence (6.5 years vs. 4.3 years). An extended analysis later showed that the two disorders had comparable levels of role impairment associated with them (Kessler et al., 2014).

According to Statistics Canada's 2002 Mental Health and Well-being Survey (CCHS, 1.2; see Government of Canada, 2006), 0.5% of Canadians 15 years of age or older reported an eating disorder diagnosis in the preceding 12 months. Women were once again more likely than men to report an eating disorder: 0.8% vs. 0.2%, respectively. Among young women aged 15 to 24, 1.5% reported that they had an eating disorder. Analyses of the CCHS data also determined that 1.7% of Canadians met 12-month criteria for an eating attitude problem.

Particularly alarming is the growing tendency for children between the ages of 5 and 9 years old to be admitted to a hospital for an eating disorder. This was noted in a 2012 British survey, which found that 197 children in the past three years had received treatment. Leora Pinhas confirmed that this is also taking place in Canada (see Chung, 2012). According to Pinhas, the eating disorders program at Sick Kids Hospital provided treatment to 166 children (aged 5 to 12 years old) in the same three-year period.

Eating disorders can cause long-term psychological, social, and health problems. Hospitalization is sometimes necessary. Hospitalization rates are highest among young women in the 15 to 19 age range (Government of Canada, 2006; see Figure 10.1). However, rates are also high among those aged 10 to 14 and 20 to 24.

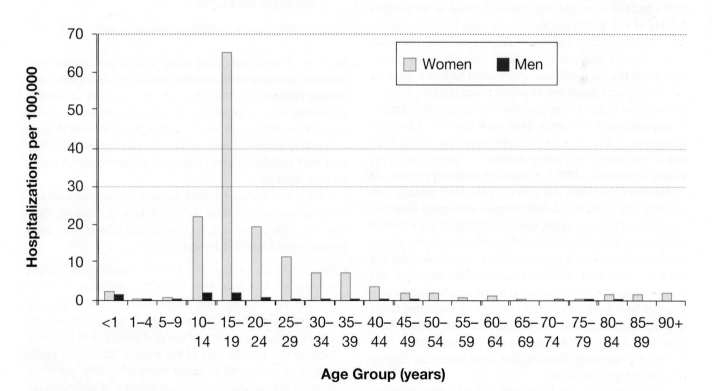

FIGURE 10.1   Hospitalizations for eating disorders* in general hospitals per 100,000 by age group, Canada, 1999–2000.

*Using responsible diagnosis only established by professionals.

10.1 Clinical Description of Eating Disorders

We begin by describing anorexia nervosa and bulimia nervosa. First, however, some key points related to diagnosing and classifying eating disorders should be noted. Do you think anorexia nervosa or bulimia nervosa is the most common type of eating disorder? The correct answer is that neither is. There is greater heterogeneity in eating disorder symptom expression; thus, the most common diagnosis (occurring in between 40 to 70% of clients) is a category called **eating disorder not otherwise specified (EDNOS)** (see Thomas, Vartanian, & Brownell, 2009). This general diagnostic category has been seen as a residual "catch-all" category that underscores problems inherent in the current diagnostic system. However, one caveat needs to be stated. EDNOS is called a "clinical condition" rather than a category *per se* because more evidence is needed to elevate it to a diagnostic category. The extensive use of the EDNOS category reflects the great heterogeneity among individuals all deemed to have an eating disorder of some sort, but it also suggests that the categories themselves need refinement. Thomas et al. (2009) reviewed research on people with EDNOS and concluded that it is an eating disorder at least comparable in severity and degree of dysfunction to anorexia nervosa and bulimia nervosa.

DSM-5 dropped the EDNOS description in favour of new *DSM-5* designations. One designation is called an unspecified feeding or eating disorder that can be used for any condition that causes clinically significant distress or impairment but does not meet diagnostic thresholds. This diagnosis can be used when there is insufficient information such as in hospital emergency room situations. The other broad category is "other specified feeding or eating disorder." This designation applies to atypical, mixed, or subthreshold conditions and it includes a variety of conditions, including subthreshold bulimia nervosa and subthreshold binge eating disorder. It also includes **night eating syndrome**, which is a repetitive tendency to wake up and eat during the night and then get quite upset about it. This category also includes a variation known as **purging disorder**. As described by Keel, Haedt, and Edler (2005), this is a form of bulimia that involves self-induced vomiting or laxative use at least once a week for a minimum of six months. Subsequent work (e.g., Keel et al., 2007) has supported the validity of this disorder. Fink et al. (2009) concluded that people with purging disorder have levels of disturbed eating and associated forms of psychopathology that are comparable with patients with other eating disorders, but people with purging disorder have certain distinguishing features. One clear feature of purging disorder is high impulsivity.

As we will see below in the revised *DSM-5* descriptions of anorexia nervosa and bulimia nervosa, the criteria now come with fewer restrictions that preclude making a diagnosis, so there should be a much lower proportion of EDNOS/other specified diagnoses than in the past. Fairburn and Cooper (2011)

applied the new *DSM-5* criteria to their cases and predicted that the changes will be only partly successful; EDNOS cases dropped from 52.7% to 25.1%, so with the new diagnostic criteria, 1 in 4 people receiving a diagnosis would still have the other specified feeding or eating disorder diagnosis, suggesting that additional scrutiny and further revisions beyond *DSM-5* are needed. However, a new analysis showed that whereas 55 women met lifetime criteria for anorexia nervosa according to previous criteria, an additional 37 cases were found using the new criteria; this amounts to about a 60% increase (see Mustelin et al., 2016).

With the diagnostic complexities in mind, we turn to a discussion of anorexia nervosa and bulimia nervosa. The diagnoses of anorexia nervosa and bulimia nervosa share several clinical features, the most important being the intense fear of being overweight, as already mentioned. There are some indications that these may not be distinct diagnoses but may be two variants of a single disorder. Co-twins of people diagnosed with anorexia nervosa, for example, are themselves more likely than average to have bulimia nervosa (Walters & Kendler, 1994).

Anorexia Nervosa

> "Between the ages of 14 and 18, I struggled with anorexia and bulimia . . . The pressure was hard-core. For four to six months at a time, I would barely eat so I was constantly dizzy. I lived on Melba toast, carrots and black coffee."
>
> —singer Alanis Morissette (from Heller, 2005, p. A4)

Ms. A, the woman described at the start of this chapter, had **anorexia nervosa (AN)**. *Anorexia* means loss of appetite, and *nervosa* indicates that this is for emotional reasons. The term is something of a misnomer because most people with anorexia nervosa actually do not lose their appetite or interest in food; in fact, they are often preoccupied with food. For instance, they may read cookbooks constantly and prepare gourmet meals for their families.

Ms. A met all four features required in previous *DSM* versions for anorexia nervosa diagnostic criteria. Here we illustrate the criteria and indicate how certain criteria have been revised in the *DSM-5* description.

- The person must refuse to maintain a normal body weight and weighs less than 85% of what is considered normal for that person's age and height. Weight loss is typically achieved through dieting, although purging (self-induced vomiting, heavy use of laxatives or diuretics) and excessive exercise can also be part of the picture. *DSM-5* has modified this criterion and no longer refers to the 85% guideline. Instead, the revised criterion is restriction of energy intake resulting in significantly low body weight within the context of a person's age, sex, and physical health status.

- The person has an intense fear of gaining weight, and the fear is not reduced by weight loss. They can never be thin enough.

AP Photo/Eugenio Savio

Anorexia nervosa can be a life-threatening condition. It is especially prevalent among young women who are under intense pressure to keep their weight low. Brazilian model Ana Carolina Reston died in November 2006 of complications from anorexia, one of several deaths of high-profile people due to eating disorders in Brazil. It has been suggested that there is currently an epidemic of eating disorders in Brazil.

TABLE 10.1	Subscales and Illustrative Items from the Eating Disorders Inventory
Drive for thinness	I think about dieting.
	I am preoccupied with the desire to be thinner.
Bulimia	I have thought of trying to vomit in order to lose weight.
	I have gone on eating binges where I have felt that I could not stop.
Body dissatisfaction	I think that my thighs are too large.
	I think that my buttocks are too large.
	I feel inadequate.
Ineffectiveness	I feel empty inside (emotionally).
Perfectionism	Only outstanding performance is good enough in my family.
	I hate being less than best at things.
Interpersonal distrust	I have trouble expressing my emotions to others.
	I need to keep people at a certain distance.
Interoceptive awareness	I get confused about what emotion I am feeling.
	I don't know what's going on inside me.
Maturity fears	I wish that I could return to the security of childhood.
	The demands of adulthood are too great.

Note: Respondents use a six-point scale ranging from "always" to "never."

Source: From Garner, Olmsted, and Polivy, 1983. Reprinted with permission from John Wiley & Sons, Inc.

- People with AN have a distorted sense of their body shape. They maintain that even when emaciated, they are overweight or that certain parts of their bodies, particularly the abdomen, buttocks, and thighs, are too fat. To check on their body size, they typically weigh themselves frequently, measure the size of different parts of the body, and gaze critically at their reflections in mirrors (see photo).

- In females, the extreme emaciation causes **amenorrhea**, the loss of the menstrual period. This criterion has been eliminated from *DSM-5* for several reasons. Many adolescents and young women clearly have anorexia nervosa but not this particular symptom and comparisons conducted in Canada show few differences between women who meet all four criteria and women who meet the other three but not amenorrhea. Moreover, amenorrhea occurs in a significant minority of women before any significant weight loss and the symptom can persist after weight gain (Garfinkel, 2002). In addition, by definition, boys and men with anorexia cannot meet the criterion.

The self-esteem of people with anorexia nervosa is closely linked to maintaining thinness. The tendency to link self-esteem and self-evaluation with thinness is known as **overevaluation of appearance**. A new investigation found for the first time that among people with acute anorexia nervosa, lower body weight was actually associated with increased self-esteem! This same association was not found among control participants or people who had recovered from anorexia (see Brockmeyer et al., 2013. This tendency for weight loss to be associated with better self-esteem is in keeping with clinical observations that young people with anorexia strive for bodily perfection through starvation due to a misguided sense that attaining the goal of being ultra-thin will make them feel better about themselves and their lives.

The distorted body image that accompanies anorexia nervosa has been assessed in several ways, most frequently by questionnaires such as the Eating Disorders Inventory (EDI; Garner, Olmsted, & Polivy, 1983). The EDI was developed in Canada and is one of the most widely used measures to assess self-reported aspects of eating disorders. The subscales and items on this questionnaire are presented in Table 10.1.

In another type of assessment, people are shown line drawings of women with varying body weights and asked to choose the one closest to their own and the one that represents their ideal shape (see Figure 10.2). Clients with AN overestimate their own body size and choose a thin figure as their ideal.

Anorexia nervosa typically begins in the early to middle teenage years, often after an episode of dieting and exposure to life stress. Halmi (2009) surveyed data from five continents and concluded that rates among younger people are definitely on the rise; moreover, the presence of anxiety disorder is a significant risk factor among younger people.

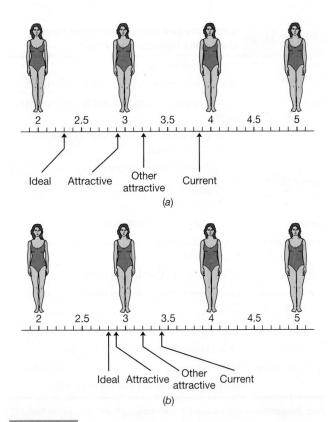

Ideal   Attractive   Other attractive   Current

(a)

Ideal   Attractive   Other attractive   Current

(b)

FIGURE 10.2 In this assessment of body image, respondents indicate their current shape, their ideal shape, and the shape they think is most attractive to the opposite sex. The figure actually rated as most attractive by members of the opposite sex is shown in both panels. Ratings of women who scored high on a measure of distorted attitudes toward eating are shown in (*a*); ratings of women who scored low are shown in (*b*). The high scorers overestimated their current size and chose a thin form as their ideal.

Source: From Zellner, Harner, and Adler (1989).

Comorbidity is high. Analyses of data from the Canadian Community Health Survey found that both men and women at risk for eating disorders were also prone to depression, panic disorder, and social phobia (Gadalla, 2008). However, some gender differences did emerge. Women were at substantially greater risk for mania, agoraphobia, and substance dependence.

A growing concern is the high rate of co-occurring eating disorders and substance use disorders, as documented in Canadian studies (see Courbasson, Smith, & Cleland, 2005; Piran & Gadalla, 2006). Also, a meta-analysis conducted in Spain found that there was no link between anorexia nervosa and illicit drug use, but there was a clear link evident between bulimia nervosa and drug use (Calero-Elvira et al., 2009). Canadian investigators have specifically tied drug use to the bingeing and dieting cycle (see Gadalla & Piran, 2007). As a result, the Centre for Addiction and Mental Health in Toronto has created a separate Eating Disorder and Addiction Clinic, directed by Christine Courbasson. Courbasson and Schelkanova (2008) have outlined the various ways that eating and appearance-related concerns become significant barriers to recovery among women with extreme forms of addiction. Given growing evidence of the link between eating

disorders and substance abuse, Harrop and Marlatt (2010) have noted the need for a sophisticated treatment approach for individuals with these comorbid conditions.

Physical Changes in Anorexia Nervosa   Self-starvation and use of laxatives produce numerous undesirable biological consequences in people with anorexia nervosa. Blood pressure often falls, heart rate slows, kidney and gastrointestinal problems develop, bone mass declines, the skin dries out, nails become brittle, hormone levels change, and mild anemia may occur. Some people lose hair from the scalp, and they may develop laguna, a fine, soft hair, on their bodies. Levels of electrolytes, such as potassium and sodium, are altered. These ionized salts, present in various bodily fluids, are essential for the process of neural transmission, and lowered levels can lead to tiredness, weakness, cardiac arrhythmias, and even sudden death. Brain size declines in people with anorexia, and EEG abnormalities and neurological impairments are frequent (Garner, 1997; Lambe et al., 1997). Research in Canada by Lambe and associates has established that deficits in white-matter volumes in the brain are restored upon recovery from anorexia nervosa, but deficits in grey-matter volumes appear irreversible, at least in the short term.

Prognosis   About 70% of clients with AN eventually recover. However, recovery often takes six or seven years, and relapses are common before a stable pattern of eating and maintenance of weight is achieved (Strober, Freeman, & Morrel, 1997). As we discuss later, for people with AN, changing their

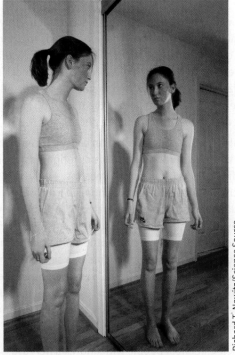

Richard T. Nowitz/Science Source

Despite being thin, women with anorexia believe that parts of their bodies are too fat, and they spend a lot of time critically examining themselves in front of mirrors.

distorted views of themselves is very difficult, particularly in cultures that value thinness.

AN is a life-threatening illness (see photo); death rates are about 10 times higher among clients with the disorder than among the general population and twice as high as among clients with other psychological disorders. There is no other disorder that matches the mortality risk inherent in anorexia nervosa (Attia, 2010). A meta-analysis of 36 studies found that there were 5.1 deaths per 1,000 person years for anorexia, vs. 3.0 deaths per 1,000 person years for eating disorders not otherwise specified and 1.7 deaths per 1,000 person years

for bulimia nervosa. A new unique longitudinal investigation found 5.35 deaths per 1,000 person years for anorexia nervosa—a mortality rate five times higher than the rate for the general population (Fichter & Quadflieg, 2016). A shorter time to death was associated with chronicity, later age of onset, and not living in a relationship. Suicidality was not linked with shorter time to death among people with anorexia nervosa but it was a factor among participants with bulimia nervosa.

One growing concern is the link between eating disorders and intentional acts of self-injury. Acts of intentional self-harm (e.g., cutting) are discussed in Focus on Discovery 10.1.

Focus on Discovery 10.1

Eating Disorders and Intentional Self-Harm

"Natalie, a 19-year-old woman in her sophomore year of college, was referred for a mandatory psychological evaluation by the resident advisor of her college dormitory after Natalie's roommate walked in one afternoon to find her crying and cutting at her wrists with a pocket knife. Natalie told her resident advisor 'It's really not a big deal at all . . . I don't want to kill myself and I know what I am doing so you don't need to worry about me.' Nevertheless, she was referred for an evaluation by a psychologist. Natalie reluctantly went to a local outpatient clinic and upon first meeting the psychologist informed her: 'Look, I have been to like a dozen shrinks already so save whatever it is you have to say. Cutting works better than any psychologist I have seen so I know you can't help me. I am only coming here because my school is making me. So what do I have to do to get out of here?.'"

(Nock, Teper, & Hollander, 2007, p. 1081)

The tendency to engage in intentional forms of self-injury and self-harm is becoming all too common and engaging in this behaviour is a risk factor for subsequent suicide attempts. Our discussion of this topic is in this chapter because intentional self-injury is associated with the experience of eating disorders and vulnerability to eating disorders (Paul et al., 2002), and as shown in one Canadian study, this is particularly likely among those with high levels of impulsivity (Ross, Heath, & Toste, 2009).

Patterns of intentional self-harm have been documented among well-known people such as Diana, Princess of Wales (see photo), and the singer Amy Winehouse (see photo). Diana revealed her self-harm behaviours in 1995 during a BBC1 interview with journalist Martin Bashir. Diana stated the following to explain why she engaged in self-harm behaviour (i.e., cutting, scratching of her arms and legs):

"When no one listens to you, or you feel no one's listening to you, all sorts of things start to happen. For instance you have so much pain inside yourself that you try and hurt yourself on the outside because you want help, but it's the wrong help you're asking for. People see it as crying wolf or attention-seeking, and they think because you're in the media all the time you've got enough attention. But I was

AP Photo/Kirsty Wigglesworth

Georges De Keerle/Getty Images

Singer Amy Winehouse had acknowledged bouts of substance abuse, depression, and eating disorder along with her extensive history of self-harm. Winehouse died in July 2011 in what the coroner ruled was a "death by misadventure." Winehouse died due to acute alcohol poisoning after drinking excessively following a period of abstinence. Diana, Princess of Wales, was characterized jointly by bulimia and an impulsive tendency toward self-harm.

actually crying out because I wanted to get better in order to go forward and continue my duty and my role as wife, mother, Princess of Wales. So yes, I did inflict upon myself. I didn't like myself, I was ashamed because I couldn't cope with the pressures."

(Bashir, 1995)

So, how common is intentional self-injury? Results from the Victoria Health Survey, a longitudinal study of Canadian youth between the ages of 14 and 21, found that 96 of 568 participants (16.9%) indicated engaging in non-suicidal self-harm. The mean age of onset was 15 years old. The most common forms of self-harm were cutting, scratching, and self-hitting (Nixon, Cloutier, & Jansson, 2008). A greater frequency of self-harm was linked with depression and difficulties regulating attention and impulsivity. The Collegiate Health Study at York University found that almost 3 in 10 first-year students admitted to engaging in at least one act of intentional self-harm (Goldstein, Flett, Wekerle, & Wall, 2009). Cutting was the most common form for young women, while young

(continued)

men acknowledged intentionally engaging in behaviours that they knew were risky, such as driving in a reckless manner. Significant correlates of intentional self-harm in these first-year university students included a history of emotional abuse, illicit drug use, depression, and various personality factors (e.g., sensation seeking and openness to experience). Follow-up analyses established that self-harm among young women was related to bodily shame and a reported history of parental criticism (Flett, Goldstein, Hewitt, & Wekerle, 2012).

Why do people engage in self-harm? Nock and Prinstein (2004) have advanced a four-factor model that focuses primarily on self-harm as reflecting various types of reinforcement. Self-injury occurs (1) for interpersonal reasons; (2) to suppress an unwanted social stimulus (i.e., social negative reinforcement); (3) to suppress negative emotion (i.e., automatic negative reinforcement); and (4) to generate feelings (i.e., automatic positive reinforcement) among those who need to feel emotion. Consistent with the emphasis on interpersonal reasons, a recent daily interaction study conducted at Simon Fraser University showed that thoughts of intentional self-harm and actual acts of intentional self-harm were preceded by the experience of interpersonal conflicts (Turner, Cobb, Gratz, & Chapman, 2016).

A separate model developed by Santa-Mina et al. (2006) assesses five factors associated with self-injury. The first factor is self-injury for reasons of regulating or controlling negative emotional feelings. Other factors include self-injury for coping, protection, stimulation, and dissociation (i.e., detachment).

Multiple factors must be taken into account when determining the etiology of self-injury. For instance, one contemporary factor is the role of Internet self-injury message boards. One study identified more than 400 of these message boards (Whitlock, Powers, & Eckenrode, 2006). This study referred to the Internet as "the virtual cutting edge." The study concluded that online social interaction provided much-needed support to those with a history of intentional self-harm, but that these boards also normalize and encourage further acts of self-injury.

Clearly, more work is needed to identify risk factors. A new meta-analysis by Fox et al. (2015) found that the strongest predictors were prior history of intentional self-injury, higher hopelessness, and personality disorder involving dramatic and erratic symptoms. However, Fox et al. (2015) concluded that other variables need to be considered because relatively few strong risk factors have been identified.

Bulimia Nervosa

"I know that so many women are slowly killing themselves and mutilating their bodies. I am not going to sit there and do nothing. I am going to use what I know about it and work with a team of experts to make a difference."

—Sophie Grégoire, television journalist and wife of Prime Minister Justin Trudeau, who acknowledged in Chatelaine *magazine her struggles with bulimia and her role as spokesperson for the Montreal-based BACA Eating Disorders Clinic (see photo)*

Ms. B's behaviour in the brief case example below illustrates the features of bulimia nervosa (BN). *Bulimia* is from a Greek word meaning "ox hunger." This disorder involves episodes of rapid consumption of a large amount of food, followed by compensatory behaviours, such as vomiting, fasting, or excessive exercise, to prevent weight gain. The *DSM-5* defines a binge as eating an excessive amount of food within a defined period (e.g., two hours). The episode of binge eating must also include a sense of lack of control over the behaviour. *DSM-5* now stipulates that the binge eating and compensatory behaviour must continue at least once a week for three months.

Bulimia nervosa is not diagnosed if the bingeing and purging occur only in the context of anorexia nervosa and its extreme weight loss; the diagnosis in such a case is anorexia nervosa, binge eating-purging type. Like AN, BN represents a discrete category that has been shown to differ qualitatively from normality (see Keel et al., 2012).

Binges typically occur in secret, may be triggered by stress and the negative emotions it arouses, and continue until the person is uncomfortably full (Grilo, Shiffman, & Carter-Campbell,

1994). Stressors that involve negative social interactions may be particularly potent elicitors of binges. Steiger et al. (1999) found in a study of daily experiences that bulimics have high levels of interpersonal sensitivity, as reflected in large increases in self-criticism following negative social interactions. Further, binge episodes tend to be preceded by poorer than average

The Canadian Press/Ryan Remiorz

Sophie Grégoire, who is married to Prime Minister Justin Trudeau, acknowledged in 2006 that she had bulimia that began when she was 17 years old. She has served as a spokesperson for BACA, a Montreal-based eating disorders clinic. Grégoire has attributed her eating disorder to an excessive need to please others, peer pressure, and socio-cultural pressures from the media to attain a prescribed physical appearance.

Brief Case Example

A Student Struggles with Bulimia Nervosa

When Ms. B, a 20-year-old white college student, was first evaluated for treatment at an outpatient eating disorders program, she had been binge-eating and purging for approximately 5 years. Each evening, she consumed large quantities of food, vomited three or four times, and took two to six laxatives. She also occasionally used herbal diuretics but had never abused diet pills or prescription diuretics. Ms. B's weight was well within the normal range (106 lb at a height of 5 feet 2 inches). She was extremely concerned about her shape and weight, was afraid of becoming fat, and wanted to weigh no more than 100 lb ("the double digits are nice too . . . may be 90 lb, but I don't think I could run at that weight").

Ms. B always binged alone in her dormitory room while watching television and flipping through magazines. A typical binge might consist of two packages of cookies, a half-gallon of ice cream, one box of cereal, one can of spaghetti, one bag of pretzels, one can of soup, one package of fishsticks, one bag of candy, and six bagels with butter, eaten during a three- to four-hour period. She would vomit every hour or so, each time making room for more food. Throughout the day, she would severely restrict her food intake, usually eating nothing but fruit, salad, oatmeal, diet hot chocolate, coffee, and chewing gum. She was an avid cross-country runner, totalling about 50 miles per week, but denied running to compensate for her eating binges. (Walsh, 2003, p. 1517)

---

social experiences, self-concepts, and moods. Indeed, another required *DSM-5* symptom is that self-evaluation is influenced unduly by body shape or body weight. Steiger et al. (1999) also reported that the binge episodes are followed by deterioration in self-concept, mood state, and social perception.

The person who is engaged in a binge often feels a loss of control over the amount of food being consumed. Foods that can be rapidly consumed, especially sweets such as ice cream or cake, are usually part of a binge. Although research suggests that people with bulimia nervosa sometimes ingest an enormous quantity of food during a binge—often more than what a normal person eats in an entire day, as was the case with Ms. B—binges are not always as large as the *DSM* implies, and there may be wide variation in the caloric content consumed by individuals with bulimia nervosa during binges. They are usually ashamed of their binges and try to conceal them. They report that they lose control during a binge, even to the point of experiencing something akin to a dissociative state, perhaps losing awareness of what they are doing or feeling that it is not really they who are bingeing.

After the binge is over, disgust, feelings of discomfort, and fear of weight gain lead to the second step of bulimia nervosa—purging to undo the caloric effects of the binge. As seen with Ms. B, purging can involve induced vomiting and excessive exercise. The use of laxatives and diuretics is common, even though this does not actually result in weight loss.

Although many people binge occasionally and some people also experiment with purging, the *DSM-IV* diagnosis of bulimia nervosa required that the episodes of bingeing and purging occur at least twice a week for three months. But the twice-a-week criterion was not a well-established cut-off point. Epidemiological research conducted in Canada found few differences between people who binge twice a week and those who do so less frequently, suggesting that there is a continuum of severity rather than a sharp distinction (Garfinkel, Kennedy, & Kaplan,1995; Garfinkel, 2002). Accordingly, in *DSM-5,* there is a lower frequency threshold as noted above, with once a week for binging now sufficient to meet the criterion.

People with bulimia nervosa are also afraid of gaining weight, and their self-esteem depends heavily on maintaining normal weight. Garfinkel (2002) observed that "a morbid fear of fat" is an essential diagnostic criterion for bulimia nervosa because it (1) covers what clinicians and researchers view as the "core psychopathology" of bulimia nervosa; (2) makes the diagnosis more restrictive; and (3) makes the syndrome more closely resemble the related disorder of anorexia nervosa.

This focus on fear of becoming fat and negative appraisals of the self for being fat are involved in a relatively new line of research on a phenomenon known as **fat talk**. Fat talk is the tendency for friends, particularly female friends, to take turns disparaging their bodies to each other. New research on "fat talk" among women in university is the topic of Student Perspectives 10.1.

Bulimia nervosa typically begins in late adolescence or early adulthood. A recent longitudinal study of bulimic symptom onset in young girls found that there are different developmental trajectories for binge eating behaviour, with one group having high steady symptoms and another having increasing behaviours. Analyses of characteristics measured when girls were in Grade 5 found that those who eventually engaged in binge eating behaviour and purging had personalities characterized by negative affect and negative urgency (i.e., the tendency to act impulsively and rashly when distressed). Purging was also predicted by expecting reinforcement from thinness (see Pearson & Smith, 2015).

Many females may not meet existing diagnostic criteria for eating disorders but show signs of vulnerability to subsequent problems, thus suggesting an important role for timely prevention effort. One study of more than 1,800 12- to 18-year-old adolescent females in Ontario found that 27% had disordered-eating attitudes and behaviours, and approximately 1 in 7 participants engaged in binge eating with associated loss of control (Jones et al., 2001). More recently, extreme body dissatisfaction was found among 7–8% of both girls and boys in Nova Scotia, and these children were only in Grade 5; these data suggest that children particularly at risk can be identified at a fairly young

Student Perspectives 10.1

Fat Talk and Why "Chewing the Fat" is a Risk

Here we focus on fat talk among students and their friends, but this is by no means limited to students. In fact, perhaps one way of internalizing extreme appearance standards is for young girls to overhear fat talk conversations that their mothers have had with friends about feeling or being overweight. However, much of the existing research focuses on university students because fat talk is a very salient construct among students and because students are easily available for research purposes.

The introduction of the term "fat talk" is attributed to Nichter (2000), an anthropologist who suggested that "fat talk" reflects a conversational norm in that it is somewhat expected that people will express negative opinions about their bodies as a way of fitting in. This view is supported by experimental research showing that university women perceive that it is less surprising for a portrayed target person to engage in negative fat talk instead of positive body talk. Both average weight and overweight target people were seen as more likeable if they were depicted engaging in fat talk (Barwick et al., 2012).

Unfortunately, these positive evaluations do not seem to be shared by the people who actually engage in fat talk. Fat talk seems to reflect a highly defensive and negative sense of self. One study with college women found that the tendency to engage in fat talk was associated with a host of negative indicators, including body shame, greater body self-consciousness, a lower sense of empowerment, and maladaptive eating attitudes (MacDonald Clarke, Murnen, & Smolak, 2010). One naturalistic study using ecological momentary assessment confirmed that naturally occurring fat talk among university women is linked with increases over time in body dissatisfaction and negative affect (Jones, Crowther, & Ciesla, 2014). It was also linked with more disordered eating and more frequent checking of one's body.

Interestingly, according to Engeln-Maddox, Salk, & Miller, 2012), fat talk is not associated with BMI (body mass index), meaning that fat talk is not necessarily more common among people who weigh more. **Body mass index** is a statistic calculated by taking the individual's body mass in kilograms and dividing by the square of their height in metres. BMI scores are often used as a covariate by researchers who wish to control for individual differences in actual body weight.

University student participants were instrumental in research conducted to create and develop various new measures to assess the frequency of fat talk. One of the original measures created by Clarke et al. (2010) involved imagining an interaction between a young woman named Naomi and her friends, who were all of normal height and weight. Several scenarios are presented. In one scenario, Naomi gets up from the lunch table to get dessert and says "I am now officially a huge fatty" (see MacDonald Clarke et al., 2010, p. 2). Participants must indicate the extent to which they would make similar statements if in this situation.

Another new measure was developed at Ryerson University in Toronto by Royal, MacDonald, and Dionne (2013). The Fat Talk Questionnaire (FTQ) is a 14-item scale that asks participants to indicate the frequency with which they audibly express to friends a series of complaints about themselves. Representative items include "When I am with one or several close female friends, I complain that my stomach is fat," and "When I am with one or several close female friends, I complain that I hate my whole body." Royal et al. (2013) found that higher FTQ scores were correlated strongly with negative appraisals of body shape, body consciousness, and social physique anxiety. Psychometric analyses indicated that the FTQ had a very high level of test–retest reliability, suggesting that it reflects enduring and reliably measured individual differences.

What are some of the factors that account for why people engage in negative body talk? A recent review confirmed that fat talk is prevalent among those people seeking anxiety reduction and greater social cohesion (Shannon & Mills, 2015). Clearly, the tendency to be overly concerned with social comparisons is also a related factor. People high in **social comparison orientation** have a style that involves judging themselves in relation to others. Corning and Gondoli (2012) confirmed that a dispositional tendency to be high in social comparison orientation is associated with the frequency of fat talk. Social comparison is so central here that when another fat talk measure known as the Negative Body Talk Scale was developed, Engeln-Maddox, Salk, and Miller (2012) included both a general negative body talk subscale and a separate body talk social comparison subscale with items such as "She has a perfect body," and "Why can't my body look like hers?" Both factors were associated with body dissatisfaction, abnormal eating attitudes, and a tendency to internalize thinness ideals.

Research and theory on fat talk is still in its early stages. One issue of obvious importance for further inquiry is to assess the developmental factors contributing to stable individual differences in fat talk. Also urgently needed is research on fat talk in females with clinical forms of eating disorder. Finally, a critical evaluation is needed of the fat talk concept and how it is measured. One potential source of bias is that because "fat talk" is focused on interactions among friends, it may not capture the appearance concerns of people who have become socially isolated.

---

age (Austin, Haines, & Veugelers, 2009). It was found among only girls that as their body mass index increased, their body satisfaction decreased.

Temporal studies of the course of the disorder indicate that many people with BN are somewhat overweight before the onset of the disorder and that the binge eating often starts during a dieting episode. Long-term follow-ups of BN clients reveal that about 70% recover, although about 10% remain fully symptomatic (Keel et al., 1999). Temporal studies also identify

diagnostic crossover. That is, more than 18% with AN eventually develop BN, while approximately 7% of those with BN eventually develop AN (see Keel et al., 2012).

Like anorexia, bulimia is associated with several physical side effects. Frequent purging can cause potassium depletion. Heavy use of laxatives induces diarrhea, which can also lead to changes in electrolytes and cause irregularities in the heartbeat. Recurrent vomiting may lead to tearing of tissue in the stomach and throat and to loss of dental enamel as stomach acids eat away at the teeth, making them ragged. The salivary glands may become swollen. However, mortality appears to be much less common in BN than in AN (Keel & Mitchell, 1997).

Binge Eating Disorder

DSM-IV-TR introduced **binge eating disorder (BED)** as a diagnosis in need of further study, and BED is now officially included in *DSM-5*. This disorder includes recurrent binges (at least once per week for at least three months), lack of control during the bingeing episode, and distress about bingeing, as well as other characteristics. For instance, binge eating episodes must involve at least three of the following: (1) eating more rapidly than normal; (2) eating until feeling uncomfortably full; (3) eating alone due to feelings of embarrassment; (4) eating large amounts of food when not feeling hungry; and (5) feeling disgusted with oneself or depressed or very guilty. It is distinguished from AN by the absence of weight loss and from BN by the absence of compensatory behaviours (purging, fasting, or excessive exercise). Support for BED as a diagnostic category was provided by Tanofsky-Kraff et al. (2013), who focused on the clinical utility of BED and how it is distinguished from EDNOS. Fairburn and Cooper (2011) also endorsed recognizing BED in *DSM-5*. They stated that this decision "seems reasonable given that we now know that binge eating disorder has a distinctive presentation, distribution, and course. It also seems more treatment responsive than anorexia nervosa or bulimia nervosa" (p. 9).

As indicated above, BED has several features that support its validity as a disorder in *DSM-5*. It is linked with impaired work and social functioning, depression, low self-esteem, substance abuse, and dissatisfaction with body shape (Spitzer et al., 1993; Striegel-Moore et al., 1998). Risk factors for developing BED include childhood obesity, critical comments regarding being overweight, low self-concept, depression, and childhood physical or sexual abuse (Fairburn et al., 1998). Also, the average life-term duration of BED (14.4 years) may be greater than the duration of AN (5.9 years) or BN (5.8 years) (see Pope et al., 2006).

10.2 Etiology of Eating Disorders

As with other psychopathologies, a single factor is unlikely to cause an eating disorder. The biopsychosocial model is clearly relevant when seeking to understand the origins and various clinical expressions of eating disorders. Several areas of current research—including genetics, the role of the brain, socio-cultural pressures to be thin, the role of the family, and the role of environmental stress—suggest that eating disorders result when several influences converge in a person's life. The Government of Canada (2006) recognizes numerous eating-specific and generalized factors from a complex biopsychosocial perspective. These direct and indirect risk factors are outlined in Table 10.2.

Biological Factors

Genetics   In a 2009 review paper, de Krom et al. (2009) observed that the role of genetic factors in eating disorders has been largely ignored, relative to other types of disorders, because of a prevailing emphasis on socio-cultural factors; it is only within the last decade that systematic research on genetic factors has started to take place. However, this field is now progressing at an exponential rate. A role for genetics is suggested by the fact that both anorexia nervosa and bulimia nervosa run in families. First-degree relatives of young women with anorexia nervosa are about four times more likely than average to have the disorder themselves (Strober et al., 1990). Twin studies of eating disorders also suggest a genetic influence. Most studies of both anorexia and bulimia report higher identical than fraternal concordance rates. One study included more than 30,000 participants from Sweden (see Bulik et al., 2006). A strong genetic component was found with a heritability estimate of 56% (relative to the 5% and 38% estimates of variance attributable to the shared environment and unique environment, respectively). Research has also shown that key features and correlates of eating disorders appear to be heritable to some degree.

The current state of knowledge was summarized accurately in a recent review paper on the genetics of anorexia nervosa (see Brandys et al., 2015). That is, there is strong evidence of a role for genetics but "the underlying genetic mechanisms remain poorly understood" (p. 814). Rapid advances should occur as researchers begin to co-operate with each other in large consortiums and researchers are able to gather genome-wide genotype data. Such a collaboration was conducted recently with data from cases and controls from 14 countries; however, while a few key genetic variants were identified, they did not achieve what is known as "genome-wide significance" (see Boraska et al., 2014). Brandys et al. (2015) noted that this effort was limited by the sample size (under 5,000 participants) and they concluded that at least 25,000 participants with anorexia nervosa will be needed.

Research is also beginning to more fully examine the interplay of genetic and psychological factors. For instance, a study showed a genetic basis to the internalization of the thin ideal with an additive genetic effect found along with a role for nonshared environmental factors (Suisman et al., 2012). Thus, there was greater concordance for monozygotic twins. There may therefore be a genetic basis that helps partly explain why some people are more susceptible than others to body image pressures.

Eating Disorders and the Brain   The hypothalamus is a key brain centre in regulating hunger and eating (see de Krom et al., 2009). Research on animals with lesions to the

TABLE 10.2   **Summary of Possible Risk Factors for the Development of Eating Disorders**

	Eating-Specific Factors (Direct Risk Factors)	Generalized Factors (Indirect Risk Factors)
Biological Factors	Eating disorder-specific genetic risk	Genetic risk for associated disturbance
	Physiognomy and body weight	Temperament
	Appetite regulation	Impulsivity
	Energy metabolism	Neurobiology (e.g., 5-HT mechanisms)
	Sex	Sex
Psychological Factors	Poor body image	Poor self-image
	Maladaptive eating attitudes	Inadequate coping mechanisms
	Maladaptive beliefs about shape and weight	Self-regulation problems
	Specific values or meanings assigned to food, body	Unresolved conflicts, deficits, post-traumatic reactions
	Overvaluation of appearance	Identity problems
		Autonomy problems
		Overprotection
		Neglect
Developmental Factors	Identifications with body-concerned relatives or peers	Felt rejection, criticism
	Aversive mealtime experiences	Traumata (physical, emotional, and sexual abuse)
	Trauma affecting bodily experience	Object relationships (interpersonal experience)
Social Factors	Maladaptive family attitudes to eating and weight	Family dysfunction
		Aversive peer experiences
	Peer-group weight concerns	Social values detrimental to stable, positive self-image
	Pressures to be thin	
	Body-related teasing	Destabilizing social change
	Specific pressures to control weight (e.g., through ballet, athletic pursuits)	Values assigned to gender
		Social isolation
		Lack of social support
	Maladaptive cultural values assigned to body	Impediments to means of self-definition
		Gender
	Gender	Media imagery concerning girls and women
		Pressures for thinness among girls
		Increasing population and availability of cosmetic surgery and body improvements
		Cultural differences and sex difference affecting ideal weight images and calculations

lateral hypothalamus (see Chapter 2) indicates that they lose weight and have no appetite (Hoebel & Teitelbaum, 1966); thus, it is not surprising that the hypothalamus has been proposed to play a role in anorexia. The paraventricular nucleus has also been implicated (Connan & Stanley, 2003). The levels of some hormones regulated by the hypothalamus, such as cortisol, are indeed abnormal in people with anorexia; rather than causing the disorder, however, these hormonal abnormalities occur as a result of self-starvation, and levels return to normal following weight gain (Doerr et al., 1980). Furthermore, the weight loss of animals with hypothalamic lesions does not parallel what we know about anorexia; these animals appear to have no hunger and become indifferent to food, whereas clients with anorexia

continue to starve themselves despite being hungry and having an interest in food. Nor does the hypothalamic model account for body-image disturbance or fear of becoming fat. A dysfunctional hypothalamus thus does not seem a highly likely factor in anorexia nervosa.

Endogenous opioids are substances produced by the body that reduce pain sensations, enhance mood, and suppress appetite, at least among those with low body weight. Opioids are released during starvation and have been viewed as playing a role in both anorexia and bulimia. Starvation among people with anorexia may increase the levels of endogenous opioids, resulting in a positively reinforcing euphoric state (Marazzi & Luby, 1986) that has been characterized as "powerfully reinforcing" (Luby & Koval,

Cultural standards regarding the ideal feminine shape have changed over time. Even in the 1950s and 1960s, the feminine ideal was considerably heavier than what it has been since then.

2009, p. 407). Furthermore, the excessive exercise seen among some people with eating disorders would increase opioids and thus be reinforcing (Davis, 1996; Epling & Pierce, 1992). Hardy and Waller (1988) hypothesized that bulimia is mediated by low levels of endogenous opioids, which are thought to promote craving; a euphoric state is then produced by the ingestion of food, thus reinforcing bingeing.

Some data support the theory that endogenous opioids do play a role in eating disorders, at least in bulimia (see Connan & Stanley, 2003). Waller et al. (1986) found low levels of the endogenous opioid beta-endorphin in people with bulimia; the more severe cases of bulimia had the lowest levels of beta-endorphin. Bencherif et al. (2005) used brain MRI techniques to establish that clients with bulimia have decreased regional mu-opioid receptor binding in the insular cortex and this is inversely correlated with fasting behaviour. Perhaps low levels of endogenous opioids can help account, at least partly, for the intentional acts of self-harm expressed by those with eating disorders. Bresin and Gordon (2013) reviewed evidence linking non-suicidal self-injury with the release of opioids as well as evidence linking this release of opioids with regulation of negative affect.

Finally, some research has focused on several neurotransmitters related to eating and satiety (feeling full). Several studies have identified low levels of serotonin metabolites in people with bulimia (e.g., Steiger et al., 2003), and serotonin metabolites have been linked with the negative mood and self-concept changes that precipitate binge episodes (Steiger et al., 2005). Evidence has now accumulated and continues to support the role of a serotonin deficit in bulimia nervosa (see Hildebrandt, Alfano, Tricamo, & Pfaff, 2010). In fact, Hildebrandt et al. (2010) have advanced a development model that links serotonin and estrogen in bulimia nervosa. Key premises of this model are that genetic polymorphisms at birth limit the serotonergic system, and associated genes may be further limited by exposure to harsh environments in the form of maladaptive parenting styles. Subsequent environmental estrogens predispose female adolescents to weight gain, thus increasing the perceived need to engage in dieting that may become excessive.

This model's initial emphasis on genetic polymorphisms is in keeping with recent attempts by researchers to link the neurotransmitters implicated in eating disorders with genetic differences. Indeed, one meta-analysis of eight studies focusing on serotonin found strong evidence of a role in anorexia nervosa for genetic variance in the serotonin transporter gene promoter (Lee & Lin, 2010). However, there was no apparent link between genetic variance in the serotonin transporter for bulimia nervosa.

Though we can expect further significant advances in biochemical research in the future, keep in mind that this work focuses principally on brain mechanisms relevant to hunger, eating, and satiety and a key question is whether attempts are made to account for other key features of both disorders, particularly the intense fear of becoming fat. Clearly, the social and cultural environments appear to play a role in the faulty perceptions and eating habits of those with eating disorders, and it is to these influences we now turn.

Socio-Cultural Variables

Throughout history, the standards societies have set for the ideal body—especially the ideal female body—have varied greatly. Think of the famous nudes painted by Rubens in the seventeenth century; according to modern standards, these women are chubby (see images). In recent times in our culture, there has been a steady progression toward increasing thinness as the ideal. *Playboy* magazine centrefolds became thinner between 1959 and 1978 (Garner, Garfinkel, Schwartz, & Thompson, 1980). A follow-up investigation of *Playboy* centrefolds found the trend toward portrayals of increasing thinness has levelled off and may even be reversing somewhat (Sypeck et al., 2006). However, while the images have suggested increasing heaviness, the normative weight displayed is still considerably lower than is healthy.

When it comes to the promotion of unrealistic images, females consistently feel more pressure than males. Even toys reflect the unrealistic pressures on females; to achieve the same figure as another ideal, the Barbie doll, the average American woman would have to increase her bust by 12 inches, reduce her waist by 10, and grow to over seven feet in height (Moser, 1989)! (See photo.) The insidious effects of exposing young girls to Barbie dolls with unrealistic body images was shown in an experiment (see Dittmar, Halliwell, & Ive, 2006). Five- and six-year-old girls exposed to Barbie images suffered lower body esteem and greater desire to achieve the thin ideal. The manufacturer of the Barbie doll responded to public pressue by introducing several new versions of Barbie in 2016 in an effort to not only increase sales, but to also be more realistic and inclusive and decrease the body image pressures on girls. And now a contemporary analysis of the top 150 video games has confirmed this tendency to portray female body types as being too thin, especially in games geared toward children, as opposed to games for adults (Martins, Williams, Harrison, & Ratan, 2009). This same research team has established that males portrayed in video games are systematically large on every body dimension measured vs. the actual norms for males (Martins, Williams, Ratan, & Harrison, 2011). There is an increasing focus in the research literature on how many of the same issues that have been focused on among females also tend to apply to males as well. There is growing evidence of the role of body dissatisfaction and how the idealization of a hyper-mesomorphic lean and muscular body ideal for males is providing the kind of pressure and dissatisfaction that underscores problems in body image, eating behaviours, and associated problems in health and well-being (see McFarland & Petrie, 2012). As a result, a measure of male body dissatisfaction has been created recently (McFarland & Petrie, 2012).

The dangers inherent in trying to live up to the unrealistic Barbie image were illustrated in a unique case study reported by Simeunovic Ostojic and Hansen (2013). They provided an account of a 28-year-old Dutch woman with a 10-year history of bulimia nervosa who was exceptionally sensitive to sociocultural pressures to be thin despite being congenitally blind.

While she could not visually perceive unrealistic body images, appearance pressures were conveyed in other ways. How does Barbie come into this situation? This young woman with bulimia nervosa said that she first became aware of unrealistic beauty standards when she first played with her Barbie doll when she was 13 years old. She noted Barbie's "amazingly long legs, small waist, and small face" and that "she became incredibly angry with her Barbie doll because she did not look like her" (p. 2). As she picked up on other cues via Internet searches and in conversations, this young woman indicated that "she started to feel a pressure to be thin because she learned from the media that if she wanted to be accepted and successful, she needed to be perfect" (p. 2).

Body image pressures can contribute to restrictive eating behaviours in various ways. Chaiken and Pliner (see Chaiken & Plainer, 1987; Pliner & Chaiken, 1990) advanced the theory that women respond to these socio-cultural pressures by eating lightly in an attempt to project images of femininity. Research in laboratory and naturalistic settings has confirmed that women who are portrayed as eating heavily are indeed seen as less feminine and more masculine than women who are portrayed as eating light meals. Pliner and Chaiken have coined the term the **Scarlett O'Hara effect** to refer to this phenomenon of eating lightly to project femininity. In *Gone with the Wind,* Mammy admonishes Scarlett to eat a meal prior to going to a barbecue so that she would appear dainty by eating very little.

While cultural standards and pressures to be thin were increasing, more and more people were becoming overweight. The prevalence of obesity has doubled since 1900; currently 20 to 30% of North Americans are overweight and there are continuing references to an obesity epidemic. Pinel, Assanand, and Lehman (2000) attribute the increasing prevalence of obesity to an evolutionary tendency for humans to eat to excess to store energy in their bodies for a time when food may be less plentiful. If so, this tendency to overconsume is clearly at odds with unrealistic pressures to maintain ideal body weights.

Kevin Thompson and his associates have documented differences among females and males in the extent of their

© Stephen Aviano

The photographs above demonstrate what a woman would look like if her proportions were changed to match those of a Barbie doll (bust 39", waist 18", hips 33"). Her neck and legs have also been elongated to match the doll's proportions.

TABLE 10.3	Sample Items from the Internalization Subscale of the Sociocultural Attitudes Towards Appearance Scale–3

I would like my body to look like the people who are in the movies.

I compare my body to the bodies of people who appear in magazines.

I wish I looked like the models in music videos.

I try to look like the people on TV.

I compare my appearance to the appearance of TV and movie stars.

Source: Adapted from J. K. Thompson et al. (2003), pp. 293–304. Reprinted with permission from John Wiley & Sons, Inc.

internalization and acceptance of prescribed body image standards. Sample items from their measure (the Sociocultural Attitudes Towards Appearance Scale–3) are shown in Table 10.3. Growing evidence points to internalization of these standards as a key component of risk for eating disorder and related dysfunctional behaviours (see Thompson et al., 2003; Thompson & Stice, 2001). In fact, a recent analysis of developmental trajectories of disordered eating symptoms in adolescents showed that escalating symptoms were predicted robustly by internalization of the thin ideal (Fairweather-Schmidt & Wade, 2016).

According to the World Health Organization's 2013–2014 Health Behaviour in School-Aged Children study, more than 1 in 4 Canadian girls felt they were too fat and by the time they reached the age of 15 years old, 43% indicated they were too fat (see Figure 10.3). It can be seen in Figure 10.3 that the percentage of fifteen year-old girls who felt they were too fat has increased from 2009.

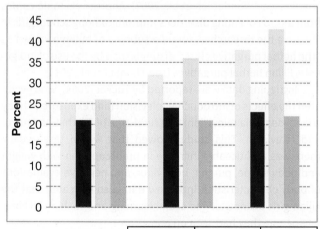

		Eleven	Thirteen	Fifteen
2009	Girls	25	32	38
	Boys	21	24	23
2014	Girls	26	36	43
	Boys	21	21	22

Age

FIGURE 10.3 Proportion of Canadian students who rated their body image as too fat, 2013/2014 vs 2008/2009.

Source: Health Policy for Children and Adolescents, No. 7. Health Behaviour in School-aged Children (HBSC) study: international report from the 2013/2014 survey.

As society has become more health and fat conscious, dieting to lose weight has become more common. The number of dieters increased from 7% of men and 14% of women in 1950 to 29% of men and 44% of women in 1999 (Serdula et al., 1999). An Ontario study found that among more than 2,000 girls aged 10 to 14, 29.3% were dieting and 1 in 10 had maladaptive eating attitudes, suggesting the presence of an eating disorder (McVey, Tweed, & Blackmore, 2004). Similarly, according to the 2002 HBSC Canadian survey, by Grades 9 and 10, more than 25% of young women were on a diet when the survey was conducted (Government of Canada, 2006). The diet industry (books, pills, videos, special foods) is valued at more than $50 billion per year. Also, liposuction (vacuuming out fat deposits just under the skin) is a very common (and sometimes risky) procedure in plastic surgery (Brownell & Rodin, 1994).

The socio-cultural ideal of thinness shared by most Western industrialized nations is a likely vehicle through which people learn to fear being or even feeling fat. Excessive body fat has negative connotations, such as being unsuccessful and having little self-control. Obese people are viewed by others as less smart and are stereotyped as being lazy. Investigations suggest this anti-fat bias is pervasive so that even the most obese people tend to endorse these views; however, the bias seems more automatic among thinner people, according to measures of implicit cognitive processing (Schwartz et al., 2006). Unfortunately, the media continue to promote these stereotypes. A content analysis of 18 prime-time television situation comedies conducted by researchers in Calgary found that females with below average weights were overrepresented in these shows; also, the heavier the female character, the more likely she was to have negative comments directed toward her (Fouts & Burggraf, 2000). Moreover, these negative comments were especially likely to be reinforced by audience laughter.

Even worse than the media's promotion of thinness is the proliferation of pro-anorexia websites. These "pro-ana" websites glorify starvation and reinforce irrational beliefs about the importance of thinness and the perceived rewards of being dangerously thin. While some people seem to turn to these websites in a desperate search for coping advice, others may simply be looking for tips and techniques to help become more anorexic (see Mulveen & Hepworth, 2006). A survey of 29 members of a French site found that they used the site to gain social support and to get specific weight loss advice. A common theme among these people is they equated thinness with happiness (Rodgers, Skowron, & Chabrol, 2012). Increasingly, organizations representing psychologists and psychiatrists are issuing calls for a ban on these pro-ana sites. Such calls are well-founded in light of evidence confirming that exposure to these sites is reliably associated with body image dissatisfaction, dieting, and negative affect; however, these pro-eating-disorder sites were not linked with bulimia (Rodgers, Lowy, Halperin, & Franko, 2016).

The double-edged nature of the Internet was illustrated further in a study conducted at the University of Waterloo on the functions of online forums for people with eating problems (Ransom, LaGuardia, Woody, & Boyd, 2010). This survey of 60 members of online forums found that they can be good or bad for one's health. Online forum members reported that, relative to their peers, they get less "offline support" from family members and friends and that online forums help them get the social support they need. At the same time, online forums encouraged adaptive and maladaptive behaviour and can actually encourage dysregulated eating behaviour because there was evidence that these forums do have an influence on their members.

Gender Influences

The primary reason for the greater prevalence of eating disorders among women than among men is that women appear to have been more heavily influenced by the cultural ideal of thinness. Women are typically valued more for their appearance, whereas men gain esteem more for their accomplishments. Women apparently are more concerned than men about being thin, are more likely to diet, and are thus more vulnerable to eating disorders. However, there is a growing belief that appearance pressures are increasing on young males as well. These increasing pressures are reflected by a heightened drive for muscularity, which can take the extreme form of muscle dysmorphia (i.e., an obsession about not being as muscular as desired).

Of course, everyone who diets will not develop an eating disorder. Other factors are described in subsequent sections.

Cross-Cultural Studies

Eating disorders are far more common in industrialized societies, such as the United States, Canada, Australia, and Europe, than in non-industrialized nations, and it is also accepted that eating disorders are more evident in Western cultures (Keel & Klump, 2003). However, it is also generally concluded that the gap is closing, with rising levels of eating disorders in non-Western cultures as well as rising levels of research interest, as reflected by an increasing number of publications (see Soh & Walter, 2013). To illustrate, while cases of eating disorder in Japan were once relatively rare, a review of research on eating disorders in Japan by Chisuwa and O'Dea (2010) found a prevalence between 0.025% to 0.2% for AN and 1.9% to 2.9% for BN. The researchers concluded that there are clear indications that the prevalence of eating disorders has increased substantially but is still low relative to the prevalence in Western countries. Moreover, according to a review conducted by University of Windsor researchers (Geller & Thomas, 1999), young women who emigrate to industrialized Western cultures may be especially prone to developing eating disorders owing to the experience of rapid cultural changes and pressures.

The wide variation in the prevalence of eating disorders across cultures suggests the importance of culture in establishing realistic vs. potentially disordered views of one's body (see painting). As yet, however, there have been no cross-cultural epidemiological studies employing similar assessments and

Standards of beauty vary cross-culturally as shown by Gauguin's painting of Tahitian women, Femmes de Tahiti (Sur la Plage).

Femmes de Tahiti (Sur la Plage) by Paul Gauguin/Musee d'Orsay/Lauris-Giraudon. Paris/SUPERSTOCK

diagnostic criteria, so it is difficult to compare prevalence rates across cultures accurately or make definitive statements about cultural differences in symptom expression.

A review concluded that at present, it is unclear whether the presentation of eating disorder symptoms varies across cultures (Soh, Touyz, & Surgenor, 2006). However, allowances must still be made for possible cultural differences in the expression of symptoms. In China, for instance, there have been suggestions that the "fear of fat" criterion seen for many years as an indication of anorexia nervosa may not apply to anorexic females (see Wonderlich et al., 2007). Another example comes from a study of eating disorder symptoms among school girls in Fiji; here the researchers found a subtype of bulimia known as "the herbal purgative class," distinguished by the use of indigenous Fijian herbal purgatives (see Thomas et al., 2011).

Intriguing data were reported by Tucker (2004), who evaluated the effects of introducing television (and exposure to body shape ideals via television) to a rural area of Fiji that had never had television. This study showed that within three years, there was a noticeable increase in preoccupation with weight and body shape, purging behaviour, and negative evaluations of body characteristics. Interview data also indicated that the Fijian girls acknowledged social learning and wishing to emulate people they had seen on television.

Cognitive-Behavioural Views

Cognitive-behavioural theories of anorexia nervosa emphasize fear of fatness and body-image disturbance as the motivating factors that make self-starvation and weight loss powerful reinforcers. Behaviours that achieve or maintain thinness are negatively reinforced by the reduction of anxiety about becoming fat. Furthermore, dieting and weight loss may be positively reinforced by the sense of mastery or self-control they create (Fairburn, Shafran, & Cooper, 1999; Garner, Vitousek, & Pike, 1997). Some theories also include personality and socio-cultural variables to explain how fear of fatness and body-image disturbances develop. For example, perfectionism and a sense of personal inadequacy may lead a person to become especially concerned with his or her appearance, making dieting a potent reinforcer.

Similarly, the media's portrayal of thinness as an ideal, being overweight, and a tendency to compare oneself with especially attractive others all contribute to dissatisfaction with one's body (Stormer & Thompson, 1996). As shown in one Canadian study, even brief exposure to pictures of fashion models can instill negative moods in young women, and women who are dissatisfied with their bodies seem especially vulnerable when exposed to these images (Pinhas et al., 1999).

Somewhat ironically, research by Jennifer Mills from York University and her associates showed that, initially, chronic dieters actually feel thinner after looking at idealized images of the thin body and this motivates them to diet (Mills, Polivy, Herman, & Tiggemann, 2002). This effect, labelled the **thinspiration effect**, can begin a process of dieting that can ultimately lead to distress among dieters unable to attain unrealistic body-image standards.

Another important factor in producing a strong drive for thinness and disturbed body image is criticism from peers and parents about being overweight (Paxton et al., 1991). In one study supporting this conclusion (Paxton et al., 1991), adolescent girls aged 10 to 15 were evaluated twice, with a three-year interval between assessments. Obesity at the first assessment was related to being teased by peers and at the second assessment to dissatisfaction with their bodies. Dissatisfaction was in turn related to symptoms of eating disorder.

It is known that bingeing results frequently when diets are broken (Polivy & Herman, 1985). Thus, a lapse that occurs in the strict dieting of a person with anorexia nervosa is likely to escalate into a binge. The purging following an episode of binge eating can again be seen as motivated by the fear of weight gain that the binge elicited. Clients with anorexia who do not have episodes of bingeing and purging may have a more intense preoccupation with and fear of weight gain (Schlundt & Johnson, 1990) or may be more able to exercise self-control.

Psychodynamic Views

There are many psychodynamic theories of eating disorders. Most propose that the core cause lies in disturbed parent–child relationships and agree that certain core personality traits, such as low self-esteem and perfectionism, are found among individuals with eating disorders. Psychodynamic theories also propose that the symptoms of an eating disorder fulfill some need, such as the need to increase one's sense of personal effectiveness (the person succeeds in maintaining a strict diet) or to avoid growing up sexually (by being very thin, the person does not achieve the usual female shape) (Goodsitt, 1997). According to Canadian researchers Howard Steiger and Mimi Israel

(1999), early psychodynamic models interpreted symptoms of anorexia from a conflict perspective (i.e., a defence against conflict drives, often of a sexual nature), while contemporary psychodynamic models interpret symptoms of anorexia from a deficit perspective, with a particular emphasis on anorexia as a way to compensate for defects in the self.

Several psychodynamic theories focus on family relationships. One view, proposed by influential theorist Hilde Bruch (1980), is that anorexia nervosa is an attempt by children who have been raised to feel ineffectual to gain competence and respect and to ward off feelings of helplessness, ineffectiveness, and powerlessness. This sense of ineffectiveness is created by a parenting style in which the parents' wishes are imposed on the child without considering the child's needs or wishes. Children reared in this way do not learn to identify their own internal states and do not become self-reliant. When faced with the demands of adolescence, the child seizes on the societal emphasis on thinness and turns dieting into a means of acquiring control and identity.

Steiger and Israel (1999) have a similar view of the origins of anorexia, and they maintain that "obstinate, avoidant, or controlling reactions on the part of these clients often constitute adaptations, justified by past experiences of parental overcontrol" (p. 745).

Consider the case of Susie, a 23-year-old woman who experienced anorexia following the death of her father from cancer. Below is an excerpt written by Susie's therapist to her as part of her fourth treatment session:

"You have an eating disorder that started at the unexpected death of your father two years ago. Your eating disorder has helped you to feel in control and your life has been both physically and emotionally affected by this eating disorder. It is making you feel depressed and ashamed...

You described to me a pleasant childhood, and also that you were told that you were a very demanding baby who your mother found difficult to cope with. When you started school you felt all of your demanding behaviour stopped and you needed to control yourself, but often felt bad...

As an adolescent you felt you couldn't rebel as you caused your father particular distress because you were so bad at maths. He used to tutor you and shout at you because you were so bad at it. You again tried to control yourself emotionally and learn to do maths. But perhaps you were unable to express your fear, anger and shame at his treatment and your inability to be good at maths. When your father died, perhaps such distressing emotions as fear, loss, anger and grief made you feel ashamed again, as they did not seem able to be expressed by your family. So again you went out of control, this time using control of your eating and body as a way of managing your distress."

(Tanner & Connan, 2003, p. 286)

Family Systems Theory

Salvador Minuchin and his colleagues proposed another influential position, known as the family systems theory, a theory relevant to both anorexia and bulimia. This position holds that the symptoms of an eating disorder are best understood by considering both the afflicted person and how the symptoms are embedded in a dysfunctional family structure. In this view, the child is seen as physiologically vulnerable (although the precise nature of this vulnerability is unspecified), and the child's family has several characteristics that promote the development of an eating disorder. Also, the child's eating disorder plays an important role in helping the family avoid other conflicts. Thus, the child's symptoms are a substitute for other conflicts within the family.

According to Minuchin et al. (1975), the families of children with eating disorders exhibit the following characteristics:

- **Enmeshment.** Families have an extreme form of over involvement and intimacy in which parents may speak for their children because they believe they know exactly how they feel.
- **Overprotectiveness.** Family members have an extreme level of concern for one another's welfare.
- **Rigidity.** Families have a tendency to try to maintain the status quo and avoid dealing effectively with events that require change (e.g., the demand that adolescence creates for increased autonomy).
- **Lack of conflict resolution.** Families either avoid conflict or are in a state of chronic conflict (see photo).

Characteristics of Families

Studies of the characteristics of families of people with eating disorders are relevant to both the family systems theory and the psychodynamic theory. Results have been variable. Some of the variation stems, in part, from the different methods used to collect the data and from the sources of the information. For example, self-reports consistently reveal high levels of conflict in the family among people with eating disorders (e.g., Hodges, Cochrane, & Brewerton, 1998). However, reports of parents do not necessarily indicate high levels of family problems. In one study in which the reports of parents of clients with eating disorders differed from those of parents in the control group, parents of clients reported high levels of isolation and lower levels of mutual involvement and support (Humphrey, 1986). Disturbed family relationships do seem to characterize some families; however, the characteristics that have been observed, such as low levels of support, only loosely fit the family systems theory. And again, these family characteristics could be a result of the eating disorder and not a cause of it.

A study more directly linked to Minuchin's family systems theory assessed both eating disorder clients and their parents on tests designed to measure rigidity, closeness, emotional overinvolvement, critical comments, and hostility (Dare et al., 1994). Contrary to Minuchin's theory, the families showed considerable variation in enmeshment and were quite low in conflict (low levels of criticism and hostility). Though this latter finding could reflect the conflict-avoiding pattern Minuchin has described, the parents' lack of overinvolvement is clearly inconsistent with his clinical descriptions. Also inconsistent with Minuchin's theory is a family study conducted in Toronto in which assessments were conducted before and after treatment of the client (Woodside et al., 1995). Ratings of family functioning improved after treatment, contradicting the idea that improvement in the client should bring other family conflicts to light and supporting the idea that eating disorders may cause family problems rather than the other way around.

To better understand the role of family functioning, we must begin to study these families directly, by observational measures, rather than by reports alone. Although a child's *perception* of his or her family's characteristics is important, we also need to know how much of reported family disturbance is perceived and how much is real.

Child Abuse and Eating Disorders

Some studies have indicated that self-reports of childhood sexual abuse are higher than normal among people with eating disorders. A study conducted in Toronto found that 25% of women with eating disorders reported the experience of previous sexual abuse; it also correlated a history of sexual abuse with greater psychological disturbance (DeGroot, Kennedy, Rodin, & McVey, 1992). Similarly, research conducted in Verdun, Quebec, confirmed that bulimic women, relative to normal eaters, had higher levels of childhood abuse and that the presence and the severity of abuse predicted more extreme psychopathology (Leonard, Steiger, & Kao, 2003). The most comprehensive recent study examined nationally representative data from the 2012 Canadian Community Health Survey (Afifi et al., 2014). Both physical abuse and sexual abuse were predictors of having an eating disorder and having at least three types of abuse, relative to one or two types, amplified the risk of having an eating disorder.

Personality and Eating Disorders

Researchers study personality factors in the hope of identifying vulnerability factors that may be involved in the etiology of eating disorders. Enough evidence for the role of personality factors has now accumulated to support the conclusion by Culbert, Racine, and Klump (2015) that factors such as trait negative emotionality and perfectionism have achieved "risk status" along with other factors such as socio-cultural pressures for thinness and thin-ideal internalization. Another recent meta-analysis conducted by Canadian researchers implicated six personality factors as linked consistently with eating disorders: avoidance motivation, lower extroversion and self-directedness, neuroticism, perfectionism, and sensitivity to social rewards (Farstad, McGeown, & von Ransom, 2016).

In assessing the role of personality, it is important to keep in mind that the eating disorder itself can affect personality. A study of semi-starvation in male conscientious objectors (who volunteered for the study instead of serving in the Second World War) conducted in the mid-1940s supports the idea that the personality of people with eating disorders, particularly those with anorexia, is affected by their weight loss (Keys et al., 1950). For a period of six weeks, the men were given two meals a day, totalling 1,500 calories, to simulate the meals in a concentration camp. On average, they lost 25% of their body weight. All the men soon became preoccupied with food. They also reported increased fatigue, poor concentration, lack of sexual interest, irritability, moodiness, and insomnia. Four became depressed, and one developed bipolar disorder. This research shows vividly how severe restriction of food intake can have powerful effects on personality and behaviour. We need to consider these effects when evaluating the personality of people with anorexia and bulimia.

Of course, it is very unlikely that such a study involving starvation would be permitted today. Still, people in Canada today can be alarmed and outraged by research practices in the past. This was the case in 2013 following the publication of a report written by Ian Mosby from the University of Guelph. Hunger and malnutrition experiments had been conducted in Aboriginal communities in the 1940s and 1950s by leading nutritional experts employed by the Government of Canada. According to Mosby (2013), unethical, controlled experiments involving lack of informed consent were conducted in various regions, including research on the Northern Cree people in Northern Manitoba. It is alleged that researchers identified people, both young and old, who were starving and denied some of them

food and nutrients so they could study them. Up to 1,000 children were kept malnourished and sometimes starved because it suited research purposes.

In part as a response to the earlier findings about how starvation can influence people, some researchers have collected retrospective reports of personality before the onset of an eating disorder. This research described clients with anorexia as having been perfectionistic, shy, and compliant before the onset of the disorder. It described people with bulimia as having the additional characteristics of histrionic features, affective instability, and an outgoing social disposition (Vitousek & Manke, 1994). It is important to remember, however, that retrospective reports that involve recalling what the person was like before diagnosis can be inaccurate and biased by awareness of the person's current problem.

Numerous studies have also measured the current personality of people with eating disorders, relying on results from established personality questionnaires such as the MMPI. Both people with anorexia and people with bulimia are high in neuroticism and anxiety and low in self-esteem (Bulik et al., 2000). The role of neuroticism as a long-term predictor of anorexia was also confirmed in a twin study (Bulik et al., 2006). Those people with AN or BN also score high on a measure of traditionalism, indicating strong endorsement of family and social standards (Bulik et al., 2000).

Researchers have also examined the personality trait of narcissism in clients with eating disorders. Narcissists are characterized by an excessive focus on the self and a heightened sense of self-importance and grandiosity. These individuals are believed to be overcompensating for a fragile sense of

People with eating disorders consistently report that their family life was high in conflict.

self-esteem, however, and they are highly sensitive and reactive to criticism. Pathological narcissism at extreme levels can take the form of a narcissistic personality disorder (see Chapter 13). Steiger and his associates have shown that AN and BN clients are characterized by high levels of narcissism that persist even when the eating disorder is in remission (Lehoux, Steiger, & Jabalpurlawa, 2000; Steiger et al., 1997). Narcissism is not always elevated among people with eating disorders (see Waller et al., 2007), but the use of a narcissistic defensive "poor me" style has treatment implications because it predicts greater treatment dropout (Campbell, Waller, & Pistrang, 2009).

As suggested earlier, perfectionism is believed to be highly relevant to an understanding of eating disorders. The initial research in this area was conducted with the perfectionism subscale of the Eating Disorders Inventory (EDI; see Table 10.1), and it confirmed that perfectionism is elevated in individuals with eating disorders (Garner et al., 1983). The EDI perfectionism subscale provides a single, global measure of perfectionism. Subsequent researchers, however, have found that the perfectionism construct is multi-dimensional, and this was even demonstrated by a reanalysis of the EDI items that showed the perfectionism subscale actually consisted of two factors reflecting self-standards and external pressures imposed on the self (Sherry et al., 2005).

Hewitt and Flett (1991b) created a multi-dimensional perfectionism scale that assesses self-oriented perfectionism (setting high standards for oneself), other-oriented perfectionism (setting high standards for others), and socially prescribed perfectionism (the perception that high standards are imposed on the self by others). One possible manifestation of socially prescribed perfectionism of relevance here is a sense that there is social pressure to attain unrealistic standards of physical perfection.

Eating disorder research with the Hewitt and Flett (1991b) Multidimensional Perfectionism Scale suggests that self-oriented and socially prescribed perfectionism are both elevated in eating disorders. Bastiani et al. (1995) reported that weight-restored and underweight anorexics had elevated scores on self-oriented perfectionism. In addition, the underweight anorexics had higher scores on socially prescribed perfectionism, relative to the control group.

Other research conducted in Toronto found that self-oriented and socially prescribed perfectionism were elevated once again in people with eating disorders, and that anorexic individuals who engage in excessive exercise are distinguished by remarkably high levels of self-oriented perfectionism (Davis, Kaptein, Kaplan, Olmsted, & Woodside, 1998). Perfectionism is relevant to both anorexia and bulimia.

One line of investigation has provided support for a three-factor interactive model of perfectionism and bulimic symptom development (for a review, see Bardone-Cone et al., 2007). According to this interactive model, bulimic symptoms are elevated among females who are characterized not only by perfectionism, but also by body dissatisfaction and low self-esteem. Thus, they have exceptionally high standards yet recognize a sense of self-dissatisfaction for not attaining these impossible standards.

Follow-up research has linked eating disorders with the tendency for some individuals to respond to social pressures to be perfect by engaging in a form of behaviour known as perfectionistic self-presentation; that is, these individuals try to create an image of perfection and are highly focused on minimizing the mistakes they make in front of other people (see Hewitt, Flett, & Ediger, 1995; Hewitt et al., 2003). Perfectionistic self-presentation seems dominated by a focus on self-image goals (Nepon, Flett, & Hewitt, in press), and, as such, it is not surprising that evidence indicates that it is elevated among eating disorder clients (see Cockell et al., 2002; Geller, Cockell, Hewitt, Goldner, & Flett, 2000).

A focus on perfectionistic self-presentation is in keeping with indications that women with eating disorders are high in public self-consciousness and overly concerned with how they are viewed by others, in part because they often feel like imposters and frauds who have not been detected yet by other people and are mistakenly seen by them as competent (Striegel-Moore, Silberstein, & Rodin, 1993). People who feel like imposters and fear detection of their self-perceived inadequacies can respond defensively by trying to create an impression of being perfect; this strategy can include attempts to portray their physical appearance in the best possible way. This need to seem perfect can go to very extreme lengths, especially among university and college students. Research is now exploring the need for some people to seem "effortlessly perfect" (see Flett et al., 2016; Travers et al., 2015). This tendency is believed to underscore such phenomena as "the Stanford Duck Syndrome." This syndrome refers to the tendency for students at Stanford University to respond to strong social pressures and expectations by trying to seem very calm and collected on the surface when in public, while hiding their anxieties, fears, and tendencies to work especially hard.

Overall, the studies outlined above suggest that diverse perfectionism dimensions are indeed elevated in the various eating disorders. However, one significant limitation of this work is that the causal role of these dimensions of perfectionism has yet to be firmly established by longitudinal, prospective research on the role of these dimensions in the onset of eating disorders. Such designs are critical to determine whether perfectionism is a true risk factor for eating disorders (see Bardone-Cone et al., 2007).

10.3 Treatment of Eating Disorders

It is often difficult to get a person with an eating disorder into treatment because the person typically denies that he or she has a problem. For this reason, the majority of people with eating disorders—up to 90% of them—are not in treatment (Fairburn, C. et al., 1996) and those who are in treatment are often resentful. Some people with bulimia only wind up in treatment because their dentist has spotted one key indicator—the erosion of teeth enamel as a result of the stomach acid coming into contact with the teeth during vomiting.

Hospitalization is required frequently to treat people with anorexia so that their ingestion of food can be gradually increased and carefully monitored. Weight loss can be so severe that intravenous feeding is necessary to save the person's life. Clearly, weight restoration is the immediate primary goal in the treatment of anorexia (for a discussion, see Attia, 2010). The medical complications of anorexia, such as electrolyte imbalances, also require treatment. For anorexia and bulimia, both biological and psychological interventions have been employed.

In the sections below we provide an overview of available treatments and their effectiveness. One vexing problem is a high rate of relapse. For instance, a recent study of 100 anorexia nervosa clients in Toronto who were treated successfully found that 41% of them relapsed during the one-year follow-up period (Carter et al., 2012). Given this problem, the search is on for predictors of relapse and ways to mitigate it. Carter et al. (2012) found in their study that relapse was more likely for those clients who had the binge-purge anorexia subtype and who had more obsessive-compulsive disorder-like checking behaviours. Most notably, and perhaps not too surprisingly, lower motivation to recover predicted subsequent relapse.

Biological Treatments

Because bulimia nervosa is often comorbid with depression, it has been treated with various antidepressants in research conducted over the past 20 years. Interest has focused on fluoxetine (Prozac) (e.g., Fluoxetine Bulimia Nervosa Collaborative Study Group, 1992). In one multi-centre study, 387 women with bulimia were treated as outpatients for eight weeks. Fluoxetine was shown to be superior to a placebo in reducing binge eating and vomiting; it also decreased depression and lessened distorted attitudes toward food and eating. Unfortunately, however, optimism about the use of fluoxetine in treatment was reduced substantially by a well-designed study conducted jointly in Toronto and New York City; this investigation of patients with anorexia found no benefits following weight restoration (Walsh et al., 2006). Thus, fluoxetine is not consistently effective. However, as noted by McElroy, Guerdjikova, Mori, and Keck (2015), fluoxetine is the only medication approved for the treatment of an eating disorder.

Drugs have also been used in attempts to treat anorexia nervosa and binge eating disorder, but there is only preliminary evidence. McElroy et al. (2015) expressed their concern about the relative paucity of pharmacotherapy research given the magnitude of eating disorders as a public health problem.

Psychological Treatment of Anorexia Nervosa

There is limited controlled research on psychological interventions for anorexia nervosa, but we will present what appear to be the most promising approaches to this life-threatening disorder.

Therapy for anorexia is generally believed to be a two-tiered process. The immediate goal is to help each person gain weight in order to avoid medical complications and the possibility of death. The client is often so weak and his or her physiological functioning so disturbed that hospital treatment is medically imperative (in addition to being needed to ensure that the patient ingests some food). The second goal of treatment is long-term maintenance of weight gain.

Fairburn, Shafran, and Cooper (1999) proposed a cognitive-behavioural theory of the maintenance of anorexia nervosa. They argued that the central feature of the disorder is an extreme need to control eating. A tendency to judge self-worth in terms of shape and weight is assumed to be superimposed on the need for self-control. According to Fairburn et al. (1999), the theory has two major treatment implications:

- The issue of self-control should be the principal focus of treatment, including "the use of eating, shape, and weight as indices of self-control, and self-worth, the disturbed eating itself and the associated extreme weight behaviour, the body checking and, of course, the low body weight" (Fairburn et al., 1999, p. 10). They suggest that other targets for change in traditional cognitive-behavioural approaches (e.g., Garner, Vitousek, & Pike, 1997), such as low self-esteem, difficulty recognizing and expressing emotions, and interpersonal and family difficulties, do not need to be addressed unless they interfere with treatment progress.

- Treatment should also focus on the person's need for self-control in general. Thus, the "focus of control can be gradually shifted away from eating by helping clients derive satisfaction and a sense of achievement from other activities, and by demonstrating that control over eating does not provide what they are seeking" (Fairburn et al., 1999, p. 10).

A non-randomized clinical trial conducted at Toronto General Hospital found that relative to a no-treatment control group, cognitive-behavioural maintenance therapy for people with anorexia nervosa resulted in significant improvements and it was significantly better at preventing relapse (see Carter et al., 2009). Thus, cognitive-behavioural therapy (CBT) has promise as a means of treating anorexia, and this was supported in more recent research comparing CBT with interpersonal therapy using a randomized control trial (RCT) design; in this investigation, both kinds of treatment were quite effective (see Carter et al., 2011). According to Wilson, Grilo, and Vitousek (2007), CBT is regarded as the treatment of choice for bulimia nervosa and binge eating disorder, while a specific version of family therapy is most favoured for treating anorexia nervosa.

Let us take a closer look at the well-known family therapy of Salvador Minuchin and his colleagues, which is based on the family systems theory described earlier. In Minuchin's view, the family member with an eating disorder deflects attention away from underlying conflicts in family relationships. To treat the disorder, Minuchin attempts to redefine it as interpersonal rather than individual and to bring the family conflict to the fore. In this way, he theorizes, the symptomatic family member is freed from having to maintain his or her problem, for it no longer deflects attention from the dysfunctional family.

Although Minuchin provided the theoretical impetus for focusing on the family, his views have been rejected in recent years. Why? Minuchin placed too much emphasis on a specific family type and this does not allow for the great heterogeneity among families that we discussed earlier. Also, it has been seen as an approach that places blame on the family.

Current efforts focus on an intervention known as the Maudsley Approach (see Lock, Le Grange, Agras, & Dare, 2001). The Maudsley Approach is a labour-intensive method that recruits parents and requires them to find creative ways to feed their children and restore them to a healthy weight. Parents are taught that they are not to blame, but at the same time, they are key "agents of change" who are taught new ways to be supportive and not critical.

More recent results continue to support the effectiveness of family therapy (see photo). A meta-analysis of 12 RCTs involving adolescents with either anorexia or bulimia and their families found that family-based therapy and individual-focused therapy were equally effective at the end of treatment; however, family-based treatment yielded superior outcomes assessed six to 12 months post-treatment (Couturier, Kimber, & Szatmari, 2013).

While CBT studies have had the greatest impact and the relevance of CBT is described in more detail below, a growing number of investigations have explored the effectiveness of psychodynamic treatments for eating disorders. A survey covering the years 1980 to 2015 identified 47 studies. These studies, by and large, had significant methodological flaws and RCTs are clearly needed. However, it was concluded that psychodynamic interventions yielded promising results both post-intervention and at follow-up (Abbate-Daga, Marzola, Amianto, & Fassino, in press). This is fitting given that it is Hilde Bruch's pioneering work from a psychodynamic perspective that launched much of this field.

Finally, Lock and Couturier (2007) noted that there have been no longitudinal studies showing that family dysfunction precedes anorexia; perhaps having a child develop anorexia causes family dysfunction.

Psychological Treatment of Bulimia Nervosa

People with bulimia nervosa, according to cognitive-behavioural accounts (see Fairburn, 1997), are usually overconcerned with weight gain and body appearance; indeed, they judge their self-worth mainly by their weight and shape. They also have low self-esteem, and because weight and shape are somewhat more controllable than other features of the self, they tend to focus on weight and shape, hoping their efforts will make them feel better. They adhere to a rigid pattern of eating that has strict rules regarding how much to eat, what kinds of food to eat, and when to eat. These rules are inevitably broken, and the lapse escalates into a binge. After the binge, feelings of disgust, shame, and fear of becoming fat build up, leading to compensatory actions such as purging via vomiting. Although purging temporarily reduces the anxiety from having eaten too much, this cycle lowers the person's self-esteem, which triggers still more bingeing and purging, a vicious circle that maintains desired body weight but has serious medical consequences. (See Figure 10.4 for a summary of this theory.)

The cognitive-behavioural therapy approach of Fairburn (1985; Fairburn, Marcus, & Wilson, 1993) is the best-validated and current standard for the treatment of bulimia. In Fairburn's therapy, which reflects his theoretical views, the client is encouraged to question society's standards for physical attractiveness. They must also uncover and then change beliefs that encourage them to starve themselves to avoid becoming overweight. They must be helped to see that normal body weight can be maintained without severe dieting and that unrealistic restriction of food intake can often trigger a binge. They are taught that all is not lost with just one bite of high-calorie food and that snacking need not trigger a binge that would be followed by induced vomiting or taking laxatives. Altering this all-or-nothing thinking can help clients begin to eat more moderately. They are also taught assertion skills to help them cope with unreasonable demands placed on them by others, and they learn more satisfying ways of relating to people, as well.

The overall goal of treatment of bulimia nervosa is to develop normal eating patterns. People with BN need to learn to eat three meals a day and even to eat some snacks between meals without sliding back into bingeing and purging. Regular meals control hunger and thereby, it is hoped, control the urge to eat enormous amounts of food, the effect of which—being overweight—is counteracted by purging. To help clients develop less extreme beliefs about themselves, the CBT therapist gently but firmly challenges such irrational beliefs as "No one will love or respect me if I am a few pounds heavier than I am now." A generalized assumption underlying such cognitions for female clients might be that a woman has value to a man only if she is a few pounds underweight—a belief that is put forth in the media and advertisements.

Family therapy is the main treatment for anorexia nervosa.

Bruce Ayres/Getty Images

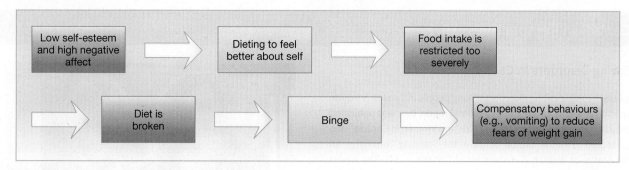

FIGURE 10.4 Schematic of the cognitive-behavioural theory of bulimia nervosa.

This CBT approach has the client bring small amounts of forbidden food to eat in the session. Relaxation is employed to control the urge to induce vomiting. Unrealistic demands and other cognitive distortions—such as the belief that eating a small amount of high-calorie food means that the person is an utter failure and doomed never to improve—are continually challenged. The therapist and client work together to determine the events, thoughts, and feelings that trigger an urge to binge and then to learn more adaptive ways to cope with these situations. For example, if the therapist and the client, usually a young woman, discover that bingeing often takes place after the client has been criticized by her boyfriend, therapy could entail any or all of the following:

- encouraging the client to assert herself if the criticism is unwarranted;
- teaching her, à la Albert Ellis, that it is not a catastrophe to make a mistake and it is not necessary to be perfect, even if the boyfriend's criticism is valid; and
- desensitizing her to social evaluation and encouraging her to question society's standards for ideal weight and the pressures on women to be thin—not an easy task by any means.

A 2006 review concluded that CBT is the most commonly used and empirically supported treatment for body image disturbance in the normal population (Farrell, Shafran, & Lee, 2006). These data and other recent developments have led some authors to conclude that no other treatment has greater efficacy than CBT (see Mitchell, Agras, & Wonderlich, 2007). However, if we focus on the clients themselves rather than on numbers of binges and purges across clients, almost half relapse after four months (Halmi et al., 2002). Predictors of relapse include less initial motivation for change and higher initial levels of food and eating preoccupation (Halmi et al., 2002).

Waller and associates have argued that if CBT is extended and takes the form of a schema-focused cognitive behaviour therapy (SFCBT), it will prove to be more effective in treating bulimia (see Waller & Kennerley, 2003). The goal of this approach is to identify and modify deeply ingrained and painful core belief systems that reflect the individual's cognitive schemas (i.e., mental filters). Waller argues that a negative core belief system involving negative aspects of the self (e.g., "I am unlovable") must be replaced by positive core beliefs in order for improvements to occur. Research on SFCBT is still in its early stages.

Recall that CBT is regarded as the psychological treatment of choice for bulimia nervosa. In several other studies, Weissman and Klerman's Interpersonal Therapy (IPT) fared well in comparisons with CBT (see Carter et al., 2011; Wilfley, Stein, & Welch, 2003). A contemporary comparison conducted by Fairburn et al. (2015) of people with various disorders including bulimia nervosa found that about two-thirds of the participants who were treated with CBT achieved remission versus about one-third who received IPT. Also, CBT appeared to work quicker than IPT. It is noteworthy that IPT is effective at all, considering that it does not focus, as CBT does, on maladaptive eating patterns, but focuses instead on improving interpersonal functioning. Such success suggests that, at least for some people, disordered-eating patterns might be caused by poor interpersonal relationships and associated negative feelings about the self and the world.

Although the outcomes from these two leading psychological treatments, especially the cognitive-behavioural one, appear to be superior to those from other modes of intervention, including drugs, a good deal more remains to be learned about how best to treat bulimia nervosa. Part of the reason at least half of the clients in some controlled studies do not recover may be that significant numbers of the clients in these studies have psychological disorders in addition to eating disorders, such as borderline personality disorder, depression, anxiety, and marital distress (Wilson, 1995). Another possibility is suggested by data indicating that those people who begin with negative self-efficacy judgements about their ability to recover actually tend to be the ones who are more treatment resistant and do indeed take longer to recover (Pinto et al., 2008). This finding underscores the role of cognitive appraisal in terms of beliefs about the expected benefits of treatment.

10.4 Prevention of Eating Disorders

Given the possible difficulties associated with the treatment of individuals with eating disorders, serious consideration has to be given to prevention of the disorders before onset. Efforts to prevent eating disorders in Canada and elsewhere are summarized in Canadian Perspectives 10.1.

Canadian Perspectives 10.1

Eating Disorders in Canada

Issues involving eating disorders among people in Canada are quite salient right now as a result of a federal report that was published in 2014. "Eating Disorders Among Girls and Women in Canada" was presented to Parliament on behalf of the Standing Committee on the Status of Women (Government of Canada, 2014). The report was based on presentations and testimony from various stakeholders, Canadian citizens, and experts.

Overall, the report paints a bleak picture of the prevalence of eating disorders and challenges in accessing effective treatment. The report calls on the federal government to respond to 25 recommendations. Key recommendations include more research on the impact of media messaging and marketing that supports the thin ideal and "a narrow definition of beauty." The report also called for broad public education programs as well as programs designed to boost the knowledge of eating disorders among general medical practitioners. The report also recommends extending the scope and quality of care, including the formation of multidisciplinary care teams (combining psychiatrists, psychologists, other necessary therapists, and dieticians), and having the various levels of government work together. Finally, the recommendations call for increased funding for research and research training so that we have more researchers in Canada focused on eating disorder issues. Most notably, several recommendations address the need to develop and implement a preventive approach.

Why was such an emphasis placed on prevention? One reason is the results of a survey conducted with family doctors and psychologists in Ontario that indicated low perceptions of competence and frustration with several barriers to practice, including lack of knowledge and lack of resources (Lafrance Robinson, Boachie, & Lafrance, 2013). The reality is that the demand will always outpace available services in Canada and elsewhere. There is now extensive research on the prevention of eating disorders and the results are encouraging for only certain programs. Stice and Shaw (2004) conducted a meta-analysis of 23 prevention studies and confirmed that the intervention effects have varied widely and have ranged from no effect to significant effects. The overall effect of prevention was deemed to range from small to medium in magnitude. Tests of mediator effects showed that larger effects occurred when the prevention was aimed at high-risk participants vs. all participants. Stronger effects were also associated with an interactive program that was more engaging than a didactic, lecture-style program. Multiple sessions also increased the effect, as did the use of well-validated measures.

A more recent open access review of the prevention and treatment of eating disorders in young people (see Bailey and associates, 2014) summarized 197 empirical trials and 22 systematic reviews. They noted that prevention research is dominated by psychoeducation efforts and the evidence base is still not well-established. A recent comprehensive review by Pennessi and Wade (2016) concluded that "there still remains a pressing need to develop more effective interventions" (p. 175). A significant problem noted by these investigators was the lack of a close link in the eating disorder field between theoretical orientations and the interventions that are developed.

Gail McVey is a leader in Canada when it comes to active attempts to prevent eating disorders (see photo). McVey is

Nicole Lee

Gail McVey, shown with one of her mentors, Harvey Skinner, the founding Dean of York University's Faculty of Health, is one of Canada's leading experts on the prevention of eating disorders.

employed by the Hospital for Sick Children; she is also the Director of the Ontario Community Outreach Program for Eating Disorders. She has also created a national prevention strategy group that is a research, practice, and policy group with members from across Canada. The group's goal is to prevent eating disorders and obesity and advance awareness of public health issues. McVey et al. (2010) showed the effectiveness of an intervention for university women. Components of the intervention included media literacy training, self-esteem enhancement strategies, stress management skills, and instruction on how to recognize healthy vs. unhealthy relationships.

McVey and Davis (2002) created a program designed to reduce the impact of media portrayals of unrealistic body images and to promote a non-dieting approach to eating and exercise. This multifaceted program also includes a focus on stress-management skills and social problem-solving strategies, along with strategies to promote a positive self-image. An additional aspect is parent education on the nature and prevention of eating problems. Initial results have found no specific effects of the program because both the prevention and control groups in this study showed increases in body-image satisfaction and decreases in eating problems over time (McVey & Davis, 2002).

One prevention approach involves forming school-based peer support groups (McVey, Lieberman, Voorberg, Wardrope, & Blackmore, 2003). Thus far, McVey and colleagues have found mixed evidence for the impact of peer support groups, with one study leading to improvements in Grade 7 and 8 girls and another study finding no improvement. Regardless, this multi-faceted approach to prevention recognizes that a multitude of factors can contribute to the development of eating disorders and that a complex prevention program is required to combat this problem.

More recent efforts focus on enlisting teachers in preventive efforts. Initial results from a web-based training program for teachers suggests that the program is effective in improving teachers' knowledge and empowering them to monitor and address any weight-related biases that creep into teaching practices (McVey, Gusella, Tweed, & Ferrari, 2009).

Information on eating disorders can be obtained from the National Eating Disorder Information Centre (www.nedic.ca) in Toronto.

Thinking Critically

1. Prevention efforts often take place under the auspices of school boards. Do you think that all school boards should be required to include a focus on the prevention of disorders such as eating disorders and depressive disorders? If you were to set up such a program for eating disorders, what would you emphasize?

2. Governments have taken steps to make sure that there are warning labels on products such as cigarettes because they can be harmful to your health. Do you think there is merit in including warnings about television shows that promote unhealthy body images and/or restricting ads that promote unhealthy body images? Or would this simply draw even more attention to these body images?

Summary

10.1 The two main eating disorders in terms of awareness among researchers and the general public are anorexia nervosa and bulimia nervosa. The symptoms of anorexia nervosa include refusal to maintain normal body weight, an intense fear of being fat, and a distorted sense of body shape. Amenorrhea in females is no longer a required symptom in the *DSM-5*. Anorexia typically begins in the mid-teens, is 10 times more frequent in women than in men, and is comorbid with several other disorders, notably depression. Its course is not favourable, and it can be life-threatening. The symptoms of bulimia nervosa include episodes of binge eating followed by purging, fear of being fat, and a distorted body image. Like anorexia, bulimia begins in adolescence, is much more frequent in women than in men, and is comorbid with other diagnoses, such as depression. Prognosis is somewhat more favourable than for anorexia. Some people with an eating disorder have a clinical condition designated as EDNOS (i.e., eating disorder not otherwise specified). This applies to people with less severe and overt symptoms or ones who do not meet the rigid criteria for anorexia or bulimia. The other main eating disorder is binge eating disorder, which applies to people who have at least one binge episode every week for at least three months. The characteristics of a binge episode include eating more rapidly, eating past the point of being comfortably full, eating alone out of shame and embarrassment, and feeling disgusted or depressed due to the amount eaten.

10.2 Biological research in the eating disorders has examined both genetics and brain mechanisms. There is strong evidence of a role for genetics but the specific genetic factors remain to be identified. Endogenous opioids and serotonin, both of which play a role in mediating hunger and satiety, have been examined in eating disorders. Low levels of both these brain chemicals have been found (see Steiger et al., 2001). Psychological and social factors are also extensively considered. On a psychological level, several factors play important roles. As cultural standards changed to favour a thinner shape as the ideal for women, the frequency of eating disorders increased. The prevalence of eating disorders is higher in industrialized countries, where the cultural pressure to be thin is strongest. The prevalence of eating disorders is very high among people who are especially concerned with their weight, such as models, dancers, and athletes. Initial psychodynamic theories of eating disorders emphasize parent–child relationships and personality characteristics. Bruch's theory, for example, proposes that the parents of children who later develop eating disorders impose their wishes on their children without considering the children's needs. The family systems approach embeds dysfunction in the family dynamic. But research on the role of family factors is not consistent in terms of pointing to the role of family characteristics. Contemporary intervention approaches enlist the parents as key agents of positive change and support.

10.3 Cognitive-behavioural theories of eating disorders propose that fear of being fat and body-image distortion make weight loss a powerful reinforcer. Among people with bulimia nervosa, negative mood and stress precipitate binges that create anxiety, which is then relieved by purging. Cognitive-behavioural treatment for bulimia focuses on questioning society's standards for physical attractiveness, challenging beliefs that encourage severe food restriction, and developing normal eating patterns. Outcomes are promising. The main biological treatment of eating disorders is the use of antidepressants. There are not extensive data indicating that drugs are effective.

10.4 The need for services to treat people with eating disorders far outweighs the available services in Canada, according to a recent federal report. The level of demand points to the clear need for prevention, which has some evidence of limited success but more extensive research is required.

Key Terms

amenorrhea
anorexia nervosa (AN)
binge eating disorder (BED)
body mass index
bulimia nervosa (BN)
diagnostic crossover

eating disorder not otherwise specified (EDNOS)
fat talk
lateral hypothalamus
night eating syndrome
over evaluation of appearance

purging disorder
Scarlett O'Hara effect
social comparison orientation
thinspiration effect

Reflections: Past, Present, and Future

1. Bulimia nervosa and depression are often associated with each other. Do you think that bulimia nervosa plays a causal role in the development of depression, or that depression contributes to the development of bulimia, or is each of the disorders caused by common third variables? What biological, personality, family, or socio-cultural factors might lead to the development of both bulimia nervosa and depression?

2. If you had a friend, loved one, or significant other with an eating disorder, how would you want that person to be treated? Assume that members of the individual's family would be included in the treatment program. Would you recommend cognitive or cognitive-behavioural therapy, behaviour therapy (no cognitive elements), interpersonal therapy, family therapy, or antidepressant medication such as Prozac? Defend the reasons for your choice.

3. Assume that you were able to design and implement the "perfect" multi-faceted intervention program for a specific eating disorder. What would it look like? What elements would you include? Would the program differ from one person to another even though they might receive the same *DSM-5* diagnosis? (Review our discussions about assessment strategies in Chapter 3.) How would you deal with comorbid conditions or associated problems, including mood disorders (see Chapter 8), anxiety disorders (Chapter 5), substance-related disorders (Chapter 12), personality disorders (Chapter 13), and even sexual problems (Chapter 14)?

CHAPTER 11

Schizophrenia

LEARNING OBJECTIVES

1. Describe the various clinical symptoms of schizophrenia, including the different subtypes of schizophrenia.

2. List the key developments in the history of schizophrenia.

3. Identify the genetic and environmental factors that are believed to contribute to the complex development of schizophrenia.

4. Discuss the therapies used to treat schizophrenia and the relative effectiveness of these therapeutic interventions.

5. Identify contemporary efforts in Canada designed to reduce the likelihood and degree of life impairment associated with schizophrenia.

Case Study 11.1

Case Excerpt: A Ticket Agent Copes with Psychosis

AS AN AIR CANADA ticket agent in Calgary during the early 1980s, Michele Misurelli was convinced that Communist agents were plotting against her. "I believed that some of the people I worked with were Communist spies who travelled from airport to airport trying to blow things up," recalls Misurelli, 31, whose own illness has now been largely controlled by antipsychotic drugs. She adds, "You take in information from all five senses properly but you interpret it wrong. If someone followed me down a hallway, I thought they were going to kill me." Overwhelmed by paranoia, Misurelli finally resigned from Air Canada in June 1988 to evade the colleagues she believed were trying to kill her. "I thought," she says, "that I was thinking normally."

The turning point came two months later. "I thought Communists sprayed gas under my apartment door at night and performed brain surgery on me while I was sleeping," says Misurelli, who at the time was obsessed with politics and wanted to run for public office. "I thought they stuck a pick in my ear and pulled my brain out bit by bit. I woke up screaming in my apartment. I phoned my mother and told her that the Communists were going to kill me." Misurelli finally agreed to go to the local hospital, where doctors diagnosed her as schizophrenic and put her on antipsychotic drugs.

Over the next year, as she struggled with schizophrenia, Misurelli tried several times to hold a job. She lasted only a couple of days as a receptionist in Calgary because she repeatedly disconnected callers. "Again, I thought the phones were bugged," she remembers. "I became paranoid and had another confrontation." Several months later, Misurelli landed a ticket agent's job with American Airlines and was sent to Montreal for on-the-job training. But the stress triggered a new bout of psychotic paranoia. "I was afraid in my hotel room," she says. "I thought the walls were closing in on me. I needed to be surrounded by friends and family, so I said that I had the flu and went back to Calgary. My boss fired me for leaving the training."

Although stress can still cause her to experience hallucinations, Misurelli works as a volunteer for the Schizophrenia Society of Alberta, visiting schools and talking to senior students about her illness. In 1993, Misurelli, who is unmarried, gave birth to a daughter, Jennifer, after a brief relationship, and she now lives in Calgary with her parents. "With schizophrenia," says Misurelli, "everything was taken away from me. All my hopes and opportunities were gone. Now, my job is to look after my daughter. I have a purpose." (Nichols, 1995, January 30)

Case Study 11.1 illustrates the profound symptoms that confront people who develop schizophrenia. Although the diagnosis of schizophrenia has existed for over a century and spawned more research than any other psychological problem, we are far from understanding this serious mental disorder.

Schizophrenia is a psychotic disorder characterized by major disturbances in thought, emotion, and behaviour: disordered thinking in which ideas are not logically related, faulty perception and attention, flat or inappropriate affect, and bizarre disturbances in motor activity. People with schizophrenia withdraw from other people and reality, often into a fantasy life of delusions and hallucinations.

The term schizophrenia (meaning "split mind") was introduced by Bleuler (1911). But Keshavan, Tandon, and Nasrallah (2013), the editors of the journal *Schizophrenia Research*, have concluded that the term urgently needs to be updated and replaced for at least two key reasons. First, they argue that the reference should be to "schizophrenias" to reflect the various types of schizophrenia. Second, the name does not reflect perhaps the most salient symptom—aberrant perception—and the current name promotes stereotypes of people with schizophrenia. They predict that over time, the diagnostic term "schizophrenia" will be replaced by suggested alternatives such as "integration disorder," "psychosis susceptibility syndrome," or "dopamine dysregulation disorder." However, while logical, this is unlikely, given the longstanding use of the term "schizophrenia."

Schizophrenia is one of the most severe psychopathologies we will describe. Its severity is reflected by mortality rates. People with schizophrenia have earlier mortality at all age levels and it is estimated that people with schizophrenia have a life expectancy that is 20 years shorter than people from the general population. Moreover, recent data suggest that this "mortality gap" may be on the increase (see Laursen, Nordentoft, & Mortensen, 2014). Factors that seem to predict this risk of earlier death include illicit drug use, lower family involvement, and longer time to the initial remission of symptoms (Reininghaus et al., 2015).

How prevalent is schizophrenia? A recent review of 65 studies conducted between 1990 and 2013 indicated that the median 12-month prevalence was 0.33% and the median lifetime prevalence was estimated at 0.48% (Simeone et al., 2015). As indicated earlier, these values are considerably lower than the estimates found in research conducted before 1990.

Are the diagnostic criteria applicable across cultures? Does the expression of symptoms of schizophrenia vary across cultures? A meta-analysis of prevalence and incidence rates conducted by Canadian researchers (see Goldner, Hsu, Waraich, & Somers, 2002) concluded that there may be real variation in schizophrenia across geographical regions around the world, with Asian populations having the lowest prevalence rates. The incidence is significantly higher in males than in females (male:female ratio = 1.4) (McGrath, 2006). Myers (2011) summarized existing data on this topic by stating, "Provocative new research continues to indicate that the incidence of schizophrenia, as well as the symptoms, course, and outcomes for individuals so diagnosed seems to vary across cultural contexts" (p. 305).

Analyses continue to find cultural differences, and this extends to refugees and immigrants in Canada, who are more or less susceptible to schizophrenia depending on their country of origin, as shown by a recent analysis of first-generation immigrants and refugees in Ontario (see Anderson et al., 2015). Higher rates of psychotic disorders were detected among immigrants from the Caribbean and Bermuda. Typically, prevalence rates of symptoms such as auditory and visual hallucinations are comparatively higher among people from African nations (Bauer et al., 2011) while other countries such as India are known for having substantially better recovery rates, especially among people in southern India. While a plethora of factors likely contribute, key factors that may vary across cultures include the likelihood of experiencing adverse life events, degree of social disadvantage, and family differences across cultures in terms of reactions to and interpretations of symptoms of schizophrenia (see Myers, 2011). Myers (2012) has incorporated these factors into a proposed applied neuroanthropological model of psychosis that is very much in keeping with the biopsychosocial model because it incorporates the interplay of "culture, brains, and experience" (p. 113). She highlighted the need for "culturally grounded" studies that take life experiences into account when studying the brain and the experience of psychotic episodes.

Although schizophrenia sometimes begins in childhood, it usually appears in late adolescence or early adulthood, somewhat earlier for men than for women. People with schizophrenia typically have a number of acute episodes of their symptoms. Between episodes, they often have less severe but still very debilitating symptoms. Most people with schizophrenia are treated in the community; however, hospitalization is sometimes necessary. Whitehorn, Richard, and Kopala (2004) examined newly diagnosed cases in Nova Scotia and concluded that almost one half (46%) do not require inpatient services. However, people who were first diagnosed while inpatients and those residing in rural areas were more likely to require additional inpatient services in the first year of treatment.

In Canada, hospitalization rates are typically much higher among young men than young women (see Figure 11.1). Schizophrenia accounts for 19.9% of hospitalizations in general hospitals and 30.9% of hospitalizations in psychiatric hospitals. About 10% of people with schizophrenia commit suicide (Government of Canada, 2006). Despite recent advances in treatment, many people with schizophrenia remain chronically disabled. The disability can be attributed to symptoms inherent to schizophrenia, as well as the comorbid disorders from which approximately 50% of those with schizophrenia suffer (e.g., Rosen et al., 2006).

Rates of symptom remission were more variable prior to 2005 until standard remission criteria were agreed upon by the Remission in Schizophrenia Working Group. According to a review published in the *Harvard Review of Psychiatry*, rates vary widely across studies. However, it was concluded that slightly more than 1 in 3 have symptom remission (i.e., 35.6% in first-episode schizophrenia and 37.0% in multiple-episode schizophrenia) (see AlAqeel & Margolese, 2012). Remission was most frequently associated with milder initial symptoms, better premorbid functioning, earlier treatment response, and a shorter duration of untreated psychosis.

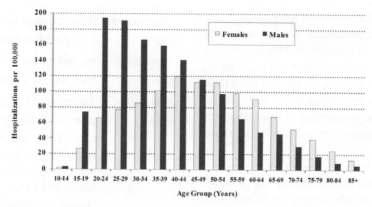

* Using most responsible diagnosis only

FIGURE 11.1 Hospitalizations for schizophrenia* in general hospitals per 100,000, by age group, Canada, 2002–03.

In 2004, there were an estimated 234,305 people in Canada with schizophrenia. Overall, 374 deaths that year in Canada were attributed to schizophrenia. The disorder's total estimated costs, including health care and lost productivity due to early morbidity and mortality, were nearly $6.9 billion, 70% of which was the cost of lost productivity (Goeree et al., 2005).

Comorbid conditions appear to play a role in the development, severity, and course of schizophrenia. Canadian researchers (McMillan, Enns, Cox, & Sareen, 2009) examined the comorbidity of Axis I and II disorders within a community-based sample of adults with schizophrenia (the U.S. National Epidemiologic Survey of Alcohol and Related Conditions). They reported that (1) comorbid personality disorders (e.g., avoidant, paranoid, dependent, and anti-social) are common and have implications for the course and clinical management of schizophrenia; (2) treatment should include evaluation of co-occurring substance use disorders (especially alcohol and cannabis abuse or dependence); and (3) attention to associated mood (especially major depressive disorder) and anxiety syndromes (particularly social phobia) may be important for optimal outcomes.

Comorbid substance abuse is a major problem for people with schizophrenia. Swartz et al. (2006) reported that 37% of a sample of people with schizophrenia showed current evidence of substance use disorders, that the relationship was especially common among men, and that childhood conduct disorder problems are potent risk factors for substance use disorders in schizophrenia.

Conley and colleagues (2007) prospectively measured the link between depressive symptoms and functional outcomes in long-term treatment of people with schizophrenia. About 40% of the participants were depressed at the outset. Over the next three years, those diagnosed with schizophrenia who were also depressed, relative to a non-depressed group, were more likely to use relapse-related mental health services; to be a safety concern (violent, arrested, victimized, suicidal); to have substance-related problems; and to report poorer life satisfaction, quality of life, mental functioning, family relationships, and medication adherence.

Comorbid anxiety disorders can impose an additional burden on people with schizophrenia and result in further decline in their perceived quality of life (e.g., Braga, Mendlowicz, Marrocos, & Figueira, 2005). A team of Canadian researchers conducted a meta-analysis that showed that there is a high prevalence of comorbid anxiety disorder for every anxiety disorder when examining schizophrenia and associated spectrum disorders. The most prevalent comorbid condition was social anxiety disorder, which was estimated as being found in 14.9% of people with schizophrenia (see Achim et al., 2011).

In this chapter, we describe the clinical features of schizophrenia, consider the history of the concept and how it has changed over the years, and examine research on the etiology of schizophrenia and therapies for the disorder.

11.1 Clinical Symptoms of Schizophrenia

"When I'm psychotic I feel like I'm a disembodied soul. I'm in contact with fairy kings, delusionary people. Sometimes I'm not even aware there are normal people around me, I'm so caught up in the fantasy. Sometimes I've thought I was Peter Rabbit and I would only eat rabbit food. Sometimes, like when I thought I was Brother Michael, Michael the Archangel, I thought I had the power to heal people. One time I felt like I had electricity flowing through my body and that it was controlling me and if I didn't keep control of it that it would kill people. It's very frightening. It's not imaginary. It's real at the time."

—Sandy, a 37-year-old woman with schizophrenia. From the National Film Board of Canada film Full of Sound and Fury

The symptoms of people with schizophrenia involve disturbances in several major areas: thought, perception, and attention; motor behaviour; affect or emotion; and life functioning. The range of problems of people diagnosed as schizophrenic is extensive, although only some of these problems may be present at any given time. The *DSM* determines for the diagnostician how many problems must be present and in what degree to justify the diagnosis. The duration of the disorder is also important in diagnosis.

No essential symptom must be present for a diagnosis of schizophrenia. Thus, people with schizophrenia can differ from each other more than do people with other disorders. Walter Heinrichs (1993, 2001) of York University suggested that the key to understanding schizophrenia is to recognize its heterogeneity at the empirical and conceptual levels. He noted that:

> "... the presentation, course, and outcome of schizophrenia are variable and diverse. Some clients develop delusions but no hallucinations. Others become isolated socially and show 'positive' psychotic symptoms only later. Some clients have histories of poor social and academic adjustment that predate their illness. Other clients seem to have thrived until stricken with their first psychotic episode. Current evidence indicates that it is hard to find specific traits or characteristics that are shared by all persons with a diagnosis of schizophrenia."
>
> (Heinrichs, 1993, p. 222)

This heterogeneity suggests that it may be appropriate to subdivide people with schizophrenia into types that manifest particular constellations of problems. We will examine several recognized types later in this chapter, but here we present the main symptoms of schizophrenia in two categories, positive and negative, and also describe some symptoms that do not fit neatly into these two categories.

Positive Symptoms

Positive symptoms comprise excesses or distortions, such as disorganized speech, hallucinations, and delusions. They are what define, for the most part, an acute episode of schizophrenia. Positive symptoms are the presence of too much of a behaviour that is not apparent in most people, while the negative symptoms (described later) are the absence of a behaviour that should be evident in most people. We will now discuss positive symptoms involving excesses.

Disorganized Speech   Also known as **formal thought disorder**, **disorganized speech** is a disorder in which the client has problems in organizing ideas and in speaking so that a listener can understand.

"*Interviewer*: Have you been nervous or tense lately?

Client: No, I got a head of lettuce.

Interviewer: You got a head of lettuce? I don't understand.

Client: Well, it's just a head of lettuce.

Interviewer: Tell me about lettuce. What do you mean?

Client: Well, . . . lettuce is a transformation of a dead cougar that suffered a relapse on the lion's toe. And he swallowed the lion and something happened. The . . . see, the . . . Gloria and Tommy, they're two heads and they're not whales. But they escaped with herds of vomit, and things like that.

Interviewer: Who are Tommy and Gloria?

Client: Uh, . . . there's Joe DiMaggio, Tommy Henrich, Bill Dickey, Phil Rizzuto, John Esclavera, Del Crandell, Ted Williams, Mickey Mantle, Roy Mantle, Ray Mantle, Bob Chance . . .

Interviewer: Who are they? Who are those people?

Client: Dead people . . . they want to be fucked . . . by this outlaw.

Interviewer: What does all that mean?

Client: Well, you see, I have to leave the hospital. I'm supposed to have an operation on my legs, you know. And it comes to be pretty sickly that I don't want to keep my legs. That's why I wish I could have an operation.

Interviewer: You want to have your legs taken off?

Client: It's possible, you know.

Interviewer: Why would you want to do that?

Client: I didn't have any legs to begin with. So I would imagine that if I was a fast runner, I'd be scared to be a wife, because I had a splinter inside of my head of lettuce."

(Neale & Oltmanns, 1980, pp. 103–104)

This excerpt illustrates the **incoherence** sometimes found in the conversation of individuals with schizophrenia. Although the person may make repeated references to central ideas or a theme, the images and fragments of thought are not connected; it is difficult to understand exactly what the person is trying to tell the interviewer.

Speech may also be disordered by what are called **loose associations**, or **derailment**. In these cases, the person may be more successful in communicating with a listener but has difficulty sticking to one topic. He or she seems to drift off on a train of associations evoked by an idea from the past. Clients have themselves provided descriptions of this state.

Disturbances in speech were at one time regarded as the principal clinical symptom of schizophrenia, and they remain one of the criteria for the diagnosis. But evidence indicates that the speech of many people with schizophrenia is not disorganized and that the presence of disorganized speech does not discriminate well between schizophrenia and other psychoses, such as some mood disorders (Andreasen, 1979). For example, people in a manic episode exhibit loose associations as much as do people with schizophrenia.

Delusions

Consider the anguish you would feel if you were firmly convinced that many people did not like you—indeed, that they disliked you so much that they were plotting against you. Imagine that your persecutors have sophisticated listening devices that allow them to tune in on your most private conversations and gather evidence in a plot to discredit you. Those around you, including your loved ones, are unable to reassure you that these people are not spying on you. Even your closest friends are gradually joining your tormentors and becoming members of the persecuting community. You are naturally quite anxious or angry about your situation, and you begin your own counteractions against the imagined persecutors. You carefully check any new room you enter for listening devices. When you meet people for the first time, you question them at great length to determine whether they are part of the plot against you.

Such **delusions**, beliefs held contrary to reality, are common positive symptoms of schizophrenia. Persecutory delusions like these were found in 65% of a large, cross-national sample of people with schizophrenia (Sartorius, Shapiro, & Jablonsky, 1974). Delusions may take several other forms, as well. German psychiatrist Kurt Schneider (1959; see photo) introduced some of the most important delusions. The following descriptions of these delusions are drawn from Mellor (1970):

- The person may be the unwilling recipient of bodily sensations or thoughts imposed by an external agency.

  One man described "X-rays entering the back of my neck, where the skin tingles and feels warm, they pass down the back in a hot tingling strip about six inches wide to the waist. There they disappear into the pelvis which feels numb and cold and solid like a block of ice. They stop me from getting an erection." (p. 16)

- People may believe that their thoughts are broadcast or transmitted, so that others know what they are thinking.

  "As I think, my thoughts leave my head on a type of mental ticker-tape. Everyone around has only to pass the tape through their mind and they know my thoughts." (p. 17)

- People may think their thoughts are being stolen from them, suddenly and unexpectedly, by an external force.

  "I am thinking about my mother, and suddenly my thoughts are sucked out of my mind by a phrenological vacuum extractor, and there is nothing in my mind, it is empty." (pp. 16–17)

- Some people believe that their feelings are controlled by an external force.

  "I cry, tears roll down my cheeks and I look unhappy, but inside I have a cold anger because they are using me in this way, and it is not me who is unhappy, but they are projecting unhappiness onto my brain. They project upon me

laughter, for no reason, and you have no idea how terrible it is to laugh and look happy and know it is not you, but their emotions." (p. 17)

- Some people believe that their behaviour is controlled by an external force.

  "When I reach my hand for the comb it is my hand and arm which move, and my fingers pick up the pen, but I don't control them. . . . I sit there watching them move, and they are quite independent, what they do is nothing to do with me. . . . I am just a puppet who is manipulated by cosmic strings. When the strings are pulled my body moves and I cannot prevent it." (p. 17)

- Some people believe that impulses to behave in certain ways are imposed on them by some external force.

  [A patient who emptied the contents of a urine bottle over the ward dinner trolley tried to explain the incident.] "The sudden impulse came over me that I must do it. It was not my feeling, it came into me from the X-ray department, that was why I was sent there for implants yesterday. It was nothing to do with me, they wanted it done. So I picked up the bottle and poured it in. It seemed all I could do." (p. 18)

Although delusions are found among more than half of people with schizophrenia, as with speech disorganization, they are also found among people with other diagnoses—notably, mania and delusional depression. The delusions of people with schizophrenia, however, are often more bizarre. They are highly implausible (Junginger, Barker, & Coe, 1992).

Hallucinations and Other Disorders of Perception

People with schizophrenia often report that the world seems somehow different or even unreal to them. A person may mention changes in how his or her body feels, or the person's body may become so depersonalized that it

Tita Binz. Courtesy Heidelberg University.

Kurt Schneider, a German psychiatrist, proposed that particular forms of hallucinations and delusions, which he calls first-rank symptoms, are central to defining schizophrenia.

feels like a machine. As described in the case beginning this chapter, some people report having difficulty in attending to what is happening around them.

The most dramatic distortions of perception are **hallucinations**, sensory experiences in the absence of any stimulation from the environment. They are more often auditory than visual; 74% of one sample reported having auditory hallucinations (Sartorius et al., 1974). Like delusions, hallucinations can be very frightening experiences.

Some hallucinations are thought to be particularly important diagnostically because they occur more often in people with schizophrenia than in other psychotic people. They include the following (taken from Mellor, 1970, pp. 15–23):

- Some people with schizophrenia report hearing their own thoughts spoken by another voice.

  One woman complained of a man's voice speaking in an intense whisper from a point about two feet above her head. The voice would repeat almost all the patient's goal-directed thinking—even the most banal thoughts. The patient would think, "I must put the kettle on," and after a pause of not more than one second the voice would say, "I must put the kettle on." It would often say the opposite, "Don't put the kettle on." (p. 16)

- Some people claim that they hear voices arguing.

  One man reported hearing voices coming from the nurse's office. One voice, deep in pitch and roughly spoken, repeatedly said, "G. T. is a bloody paradox," and another higher in pitch said, "He is that, he should be locked up." A female voice occasionally interrupted, saying, "He is not, he is a lovely man." (p. 16)

- Some people hear voices commenting on their behaviour.

  One woman heard a voice coming from a house across the road. The voice went on incessantly in a flat monotone describing everything she was doing with an admixture of critical comments. "She is peeling potatoes, got hold of the peeler, she does not want that potato, she is putting it back, because she thinks it has a knobble like a penis, she has a dirty mind, she is peeling potatoes, now she is washing them." (p. 16)

Negative Symptoms

The **negative symptoms** of schizophrenia consist of behavioural deficits, such as avolition, alogia, anhedonia, flat affect, and asociality, all of which are described below. Attentional deficits contribute to clear reductions and impairments in working memory. These symptoms tend to endure beyond an acute episode and have profound effects on people's lives. The presence of many negative symptoms is a strong predictor of a poor quality of life (e.g., occupational impairment, few friends) two years following hospitalization (CME Institute, 2007). There is also some evidence that negative symptoms are associated with earlier onset brain damage (e.g., enlarged ventricles) and progressive loss of cognitive skills (e.g., IQ decline) (see Rummel, Kissling, & Leucht, 2005).

It is important to distinguish among negative symptoms that are truly symptoms of schizophrenia and those that are due to some other factor (Carpenter, Heinrichs, & Wagman, 1988). For example, flat affect (a lack of emotional expressiveness) can be a side effect of antipsychotic medication. Observing clients over extended periods is probably the only way to address this issue. Also, as Heinrichs (1993) has noted, negative symptoms (e.g., flat affect) are difficult to distinguish from aspects of depression, so specificity is an issue.

Avolition Apathy or **avolition** is a lack of energy and a seeming absence of interest in or an inability to persist in what are usually routine activities. Clients may become inattentive to grooming and personal hygiene, with uncombed hair, dirty nails, and dishevelled clothes. They have difficulty persisting at work, school, or household chores and may spend much of their time sitting around doing nothing.

Revealing new research being conducted primarily in Canada suggests that some negative symptoms are particularly deleterious and the motivational deficits associated with avolition or apathy appear to be especially problematic. Collectively, these studies indicate that a deficit in motivation is perhaps the key determinant of life functioning among people with schizophrenia (see Foussias, Mann, Zakzanis, van Reekum, Agid, & Remington, 2011; Foussias et al., 2009). These findings are in keeping with the results of a 10-year longitudinal study showing that apathy was a unique predictor of poorer life functioning and negative ratings of quality of life (see Evensen et al., 2012).

Alogia A negative thought disorder, **alogia** can take several forms. In poverty of speech, the sheer amount of speech is greatly reduced. In poverty of content of speech, illustrated in the following excerpt, the amount of discourse is adequate, but it conveys little information and tends to be vague and repetitive.

"*Interviewer*:	O.K. Why is it, do you think, that people believe in God?
Patient:	Well, first of all because, He is the person that is their personal savior. He walks with me and talks with me. And uh, the understanding that I have, a lot of peoples, they don't really know their personal self. Because they ain't, they all, just don't know their personal self. They don't know that He uh, seems to like me, a lot of them don't understand that He walks and talks with them. And uh, show 'em their way to go. I understand also that, every man and every lady, is not just pointed in the same direction. Some are pointed different. They go in their different ways. The way that Jesus Christ wanted 'em to go. Myself, I am pointed in the ways of uh, knowing right from wrong, and doing it, I can't do any more, or not less than that."

(American Psychiatric Association, 1987, pp. 403–404)

Anhedonia   An inability to experience pleasure is called anhedonia. It is manifested as a lack of interest in recreational activities, failure to develop close relationships with other people, and lack of interest in sex. Clients are aware of this symptom and report that normally pleasurable activities are not enjoyable for them.

Flat Affect   In people with flat affect, virtually no stimulus can elicit an emotional response. The client may stare vacantly, the muscles of the face flaccid, the eyes lifeless. When spoken to, the client answers in a flat and toneless voice. Flat affect is found in a majority of people with schizophrenia. The concept refers only to the outward expression of emotion and not to the person's inner experience, which may not be impoverished at all. In a study by Kring and Neale (1996), people with schizophrenia and normal participants watched excerpts from films while their facial reactions and skin conductance were recorded. After each film clip, participants self-reported on the moods the films had elicited. While the clients were much less facially expressive than were the non-clients, they reported about the same amount of emotion and were even more physiologically aroused.

Asociality   Some people with schizophrenia have severely impaired social relationships, a characteristic referred to as asociality. They have few friends, poor social skills, and little interest in being with other people. A study of clients from the Hamilton (Ontario) Program for Schizophrenia showed that people diagnosed with schizophrenia have lower sociability and greater shyness (Goldberg & Schmidt, 2001). People with schizophrenia also reported more childhood "social troubles." These manifestations of schizophrenia are often the first to appear, beginning in childhood before the onset of more psychotic symptoms. Some of these interpersonal deficits could reflect related deficits in the ability to recognize emotional cues displayed by others (Addington & Addington, 1998).

Other Symptoms

Some authors (e.g., Heinrichs, 1993, 2001) have taken issue with the usefulness of the positive vs. negative symptom distinction. One problem is that positive and negative symptoms do not necessarily reflect exclusive subtypes because they are dimensions that often coexist within the same person. Moreover, several other symptoms of schizophrenia do not fit neatly into the positive-negative scheme. Two important symptoms in this category are catatonia and inappropriate affect. Many people also exhibit various forms of bizarre behaviour. They may talk to themselves in public, hoard food, or collect garbage.

Catatonia   Catatonia is defined by several motor abnormalities. Some clients gesture repeatedly, using peculiar and sometimes complex sequences of finger, hand, and arm

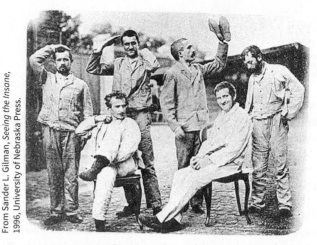

From Sander L. Gilman, *Seeing the Insane*, 1996, University of Nebraska Press.

An 1896 photo showing a group of people with catatonic immobility. These men held these unusual positions for long periods of time.

movements that often seem to be purposeful, odd as they may be. Others manifest an unusual increase in their overall level of activity, which might include much excitement, wild flailing of the limbs, and great expenditure of energy similar to that seen in mania. At the other end of the spectrum is catatonic immobility: clients adopt unusual postures and maintain them for very long periods of time (see photo). A person may stand on one leg, with the other tucked up toward the buttocks, and remain in this position virtually all day. Catatonic people may also have waxy flexibility, whereby another person can move the persons' limbs into strange positions that they maintain for extended periods.

Inappropriate Affect   Some people with schizophrenia have inappropriate affect. The emotional responses of these individuals are out of context; for example, the client may laugh on hearing that his or her mother just died or become enraged when asked a simple question about how a new garment fits. These clients are likely to shift rapidly from one emotional state to another for no discernible reason. This symptom is quite rare, but its appearance is of considerable diagnostic importance because it is relatively specific to schizophrenia.

The symptoms of schizophrenia have a profound effect on people's lives, as well as the lives of their families and friends. Delusions and hallucinations may cause considerable distress, compounded by the fact that hopes and dreams have been shattered. Cognitive impairments and avolition make stable employment difficult, with impoverishment and often homelessness the result. Strange behaviour and social-skills deficits lead to loss of friends and a solitary existence. The strongest predictor of this social disability is chronic cognitive impairment (Liddle, 2000). High substance abuse rates perhaps reflect an attempt to achieve relief from negative emotions (Blanchard et al., 1999). Little wonder, then, that the suicide rate among people with schizophrenia is high.

11.2   History of the Concept of Schizophrenia

We turn now to a review of the history of the concept of schizophrenia and how ideas about this disorder have changed over time.

Early Descriptions

The concept of schizophrenia was formulated by two European psychiatrists, Emil Kraepelin and Eugen Bleuler. Kraepelin(see photo) first presented his notion of **dementia praecox**, the early term for schizophrenia, in 1898. He differentiated two major groups of endogenous, or internally caused, psychoses: manic-depressive illness and dementia praecox. Dementia praecox included several diagnostic concepts—dementia paranoides, catatonia, and hebephrenia—that had been regarded as distinct entities by clinicians in previous decades. Kraepelin believed that they shared a common core: an early onset (praecox) and a deteriorating course marked by a progressive intellectual deterioration (dementia). The "dementia" in dementia praecox is not the same as the dementias we discuss in the chapter on aging (Chapter 16), defined principally by severe memory impairments. Kraepelin's term refers to a general "mental enfeeblement."

The formulation of the next major figure, Eugen Bleuler (see photo), represented both a specific attempt to define the core of the disorder and a move away from Kraepelin's emphasis on age of onset and course. Bleuler broke with Kraepelin on two major points: he believed that the disorder did not necessarily have an early onset, and he believed that it did not inevitably progress toward dementia. Thus, the label *dementia praecox* was no longer appropriate, and in 1908 Bleuler first proposed the term "schizophrenia," from the Greek words *schizein*, meaning "to split," and *phren*, meaning "mind," to capture what he viewed as the essential nature of the condition.

With age of onset and deteriorating course no longer considered defining features of the disorder, Bleuler faced a conceptual problem. Since the symptoms of schizophrenia could vary widely among clients, he needed some justification for putting them into a single diagnostic category. Bleuler therefore tried to specify a common denominator, or essential property, that would link the various disturbances. The metaphorical concept that he adopted for this purpose was the "breaking of associative threads." For Bleuler, associative threads joined not only words but thoughts. Thus, goal-directed, efficient thinking and communication were possible only when these hypothetical structures were intact. The notion that associative threads were disrupted in people with schizophrenia could then account for other problems. Bleuler viewed attentional difficulties—for example, as might result from a loss of purposeful direction in thought—as the cause of passive responses to objects and people in the immediate surroundings. Also, he viewed

blocking—an apparently total loss of a train of thought—as a complete disruption of the person's associative threads.

Although Kraepelin recognized that a small percentage of clients who originally manifested symptoms of dementia praecox did not deteriorate, he preferred to limit this diagnostic category to clients who had a poor prognosis. Bleuler's work, in contrast, led to a broader concept of schizophrenia. He diagnosed clients with a good prognosis as schizophrenic, and he also included in his concept of schizophrenia many clients who would have received different diagnoses from other clinicians.

The Historical Prevalence of Schizophrenia

Data from several countries throughout the world suggest that rates of schizophrenia have fallen sharply since the 1960s.

Over the years, the number of people diagnosed with schizophrenia has varied considerably depending on how schizophrenia has been conceptualized and defined, and this has hampered attempts to determine accurately the extent of changes in prevalence over time. Bleuler had a great influence on the concept of schizophrenia as it developed in the United States. Over the first part of the twentieth century, the breadth of the diagnosis was extended considerably. At the New York State Psychiatric Institute, for example, about 20% of the clients were diagnosed with schizophrenia in the 1930s. The numbers increased through the 1940s and in 1952 peaked at a remarkable 80%. In contrast, the concept of schizophrenia prevalent in Europe remained narrower. The percentage of clients diagnosed with schizophrenia at the Maudsley Hospital in London, for example, stayed relatively constant, at 20%, for a 40-year period (Kuriansky, Deming, & Gurland, 1974).

The reasons for the increase in the frequency of diagnoses of schizophrenia in the United States are easily discerned. Several prominent figures in U.S. psychiatry expanded Bleuler's already broad concept of schizophrenia even more. In 1933, for example, Kasanin described nine patients who had been diagnosed with dementia praecox. For all of them, the onset of the disorder had been sudden and recovery relatively rapid. Noting that theirs could be said to be a combination of both schizophrenic and affective symptoms, Kasanin suggested the term "schizoaffective psychosis" to describe the disturbances of these clients. This diagnosis subsequently became part of the U.S. concept of schizophrenia and was listed in *DSM-I* (1952) and *DSM-II* (1968).

The concept of schizophrenia was further broadened by three additional diagnostic practices:

1. U.S. clinicians tended to diagnose schizophrenia whenever delusions or hallucinations were present. Because these symptoms, particularly delusions, occur also in mood disorders, many people with a *DSM-II* diagnosis of schizophrenia may actually have had a mood disorder (Cooper et al., 1972).

2. People whom we would now diagnose as having a personality disorder (notably schizotypal, schizoid, borderline, and

Radio Times/Hulton Picture Library.

Emil Kraepelin (1856–1926), a German psychiatrist, articulated descriptions of dementia praecox that have proved remarkably durable in light of contemporary research.

Public Domain

Eugen Bleuler (1857–1939), a Swiss psychiatrist, contributed to our conceptions of schizophrenia and coined the term.

paranoid personality disorders, discussed in Chapter 13) were diagnosed as having schizophrenia according to *DSM-II* criteria.

3. People with an acute onset of schizophrenic symptoms and a rapid recovery were diagnosed as having schizophrenia.

The *DSM-IV-TR* Diagnosis

Beginning in *DSM-III* and continuing in *DSM-IV-TR*, the U.S. concept of schizophrenia shifted considerably from the broad definition to a new definition that narrowed the range of people diagnosed as schizophrenic in five ways:

1. The diagnostic criteria were presented in explicit and considerable detail.

2. People with symptoms of a mood disorder were specifically excluded. Schizophrenia—schizoaffective type was listed as schizoaffective disorder in a separate section as one of the psychotic disorders, but this was dropped from *DSM-5*. It comprised a mixture of symptoms of schizophrenia and mood disorders.

3. *DSM-IV-TR* required at least six months of disturbance for the diagnosis. The six-month period stipulated at least one month of the active phase, which is defined by the presence of at least two of the following: delusions, hallucinations, disorganized speech, grossly disorganized or catatonic behaviour, and negative symptoms. (Only one of these symptoms is required if the delusions are bizarre or if the hallucinations consist of voices commenting or arguing.)

4. Some of what *DSM-II* regarded as mild forms of schizophrenia instead became diagnosed as personality disorders (e.g., schizotypal personality disorder).

5. *DSM-IV-TR* differentiated between paranoid schizophrenia, to be discussed shortly, and delusional disorder. A person with **delusional disorder** is troubled by persistent persecutory delusions or by delusional jealousy, which is the unfounded conviction that a spouse or lover is unfaithful. There are also delusions of being followed, somatic delusions (believing that some internal organ is malfunctioning), and delusions of erotomania (believing that one is loved by some other person, usually a complete stranger with a higher social status). A highly publicized case of apparent erotomania occurred when Tricia Miller, a 31-year-old factory worker, was arrested in July 1995 at the SkyDome Hotel in Toronto. Miller was obsessed with Roberto Alomar, who was then a star of the Toronto Blue Jays and is now a member of the Baseball Hall of Fame. Miller was frustrated that she was unable to reach him despite her persistent attempts. Miller had a loaded gun. She had planned to kill Alomar and then commit suicide, despite having no prior relationship or face-to-face contact with the athlete. Unlike the person with paranoid schizophrenia, the person with delusional disorder does not have disorganized speech or hallucinations, and his or her delusions are less bizarre. Delusional disorder is quite rare and typically begins later in life than schizophrenia. In most family studies, it appears to be related to schizophrenia, perhaps genetically (Kendler & Diehl, 1993).

Categories of Schizophrenia in *DSM-IV-TR* and Their Elimination in *DSM-5*

"Elizabeth II is named as the monarch of record in Canada, but she's not the true king. I am the true king. She is simply a puppet of Satan, kept as a figurehead to fool the people. To try the king of Canada is high treason."

— Stanley Almeida, who suffers from paranoid schizophrenia, lashing out at a judge whom he accused of engaging in a "conspiracy of evil" aimed at crucifying "the king" (Boyle, 1998, February 10, E1)

Earlier, we mentioned that the heterogeneity of schizophrenic symptoms suggested the presence of subtypes of the disorder. Three types of schizophrenic disorders included in *DSM-IV-TR*—disorganized (hebephrenic), catatonic, and paranoid—were proposed initially by Kraepelin many years ago. The descriptions of Kraepelin's original types demonstrate the great diversity of behaviour that relates to the diagnosis of schizophrenia. Below, we will describe these subtypes for historical purposes and to further illustrate the heterogeneity theme. It is very important to note though that the *DSM-5* work group successfully proposed discontinuing all of the "classic" subtypes of schizophrenia and rejected alternatives to take their place. One major argument for discontinuing the subtypes was that they are rarely used diagnostically, with the exception of paranoid schizophrenia. It is stated in the *DSM-5* (APA, 2013) that the subtypes had "limited diagnostic stability, low reliability, and poor validity" (p. 810). Instead, *DSM-5* includes a dimensional rating of symptoms that enables clinicians to consider the heterogeneity in symptom expression.

The validity question was the subject of a systematic review conducted by Linscott, Allardyce, and van Os (2009), who focused on subtypes within schizophrenia and within psychotic disorders as a whole. It was concluded that the findings do not point to a single system of subtyping. Similarly, as noted earlier in this book, it was decided to not formally include another variation, psychosis risk syndrome, for various reasons.

Disorganized Schizophrenia

Kraepelin's hebephrenic form of schizophrenia was called **disorganized schizophrenia** in *DSM-IV-TR*. Speech is disorganized and difficult for a listener to follow. Clients may speak incoherently, stringing together similar-sounding words and even inventing new words, often accompanied by silliness or laughter. They may have flat affect or experience constant shifts of emotion, breaking into inexplicable fits of laughter and crying. Their behaviour is generally disorganized and not goal directed; for example, a client may tie a ribbon around a big toe or move incessantly, pointing at objects for no apparent reason. Clients sometimes deteriorate to the point of incontinence, voiding anywhere and at any time, and completely neglect their appearance, never bathing or combing hair.

Catatonic Schizophrenia

The most obvious symptoms of **catatonic schizophrenia** are the catatonic symptoms described earlier. Clients typically alternate between catatonic immobility and wild excitement, but one of these symptoms may predominate. These clients resist instructions and suggestions and often echo (repeat back) the speech of others. The onset of catatonic reactions may be more sudden than the onset of other forms of schizophrenia, although the person is likely to have previously shown some apathy and withdrawal from reality.

Catatonic schizophrenia is seldom seen today, perhaps because drug therapy works effectively on these bizarre motor processes. A cohort study stretching over 40 years found that even when catatonic schizophrenia was more common, it accounted for only about 7% of the cases of people with schizophrenia (Kleinhaus et al., 2012). Boyle (1991) maintained that the apparent high prevalence of catatonia during the early part of the 20th century reflected misdiagnosis and that apparent catatonic schizophrenia was actually lethargica (sleeping sickness). Lethargica was portrayed in the film *Awakenings*, which was based on the writings of neurologist Oliver Sacks.

Paranoid Schizophrenia

The diagnosis **paranoid schizophrenia** is assigned to a substantial number of recently admitted clients to psychiatric hospitals. The key to this diagnosis is the presence of prominent delusions. Delusions of persecution are most common, but clients may experience **grandiose delusions**, in which they have an exaggerated sense of their own importance, power, knowledge, or identity. Some clients are plagued by **delusional jealousy**, the unsubstantiated belief that their partner is unfaithful. The other delusions described earlier, such as the sense of being persecuted or spied on, may also be evident. Vivid auditory hallucinations may accompany the delusions. Clients with paranoid schizophrenia often develop **ideas of reference**; they incorporate unimportant events within a delusional framework and read personal significance into the trivial activities of others. For instance, they think that overheard segments of conversations are about them, that the frequent appearance of a person on a street where they customarily walk means that they are being watched, and that what they see on television or read in magazines somehow refers to them. Individuals with paranoid schizophrenia are agitated, argumentative, angry, and sometimes violent. They remain emotionally responsive, although they may be somewhat stilted, formal, and intense with others. They are also more alert and verbal than are people with other types of schizophrenia. Their language, although filled with references to delusions, is not disorganized.

Additional Ways of Conceptualizing Heterogeneity

While perhaps useful from an heuristic perspective, Kraepelin's system of subtyping has not proved to be a useful way of dealing with the variability in schizophrenic behaviour. The *DSM-IV-TR* included other flawed subtypes in addition to the ones outlined above. The diagnosis of **undifferentiated schizophrenia** applies to people who meet the diagnostic criteria for schizophrenia but not the criteria for any of the three subtypes. The diagnosis of **residual schizophrenia** is used when the client no longer meets the full criteria for schizophrenia but still shows some signs of the disorder.

Despite the problems with subtyping systems, there is continuing interest in differentiating the forms of schizophrenia. A radically different and promising approach focuses on schizophrenia subtypes that differ qualitatively in terms of neurocognitive features that involve brain abnormalities. Regarding the heterogeneity issue, Heinrichs and Awad (1993) conducted a cluster analysis that identified subtypes of schizophrenia based on performances on a battery of neuropsychological tests that

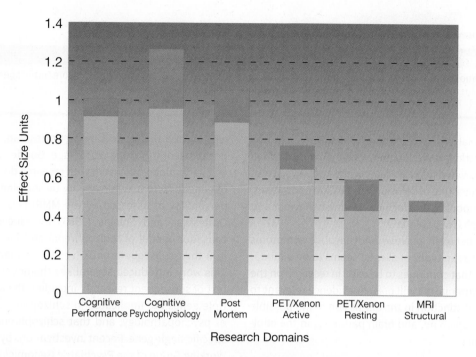

FIGURE 11.2 Meta-analytic findings of impairment in different domains of schizophrenia research.

Source: Copyright © 2005 by the American Psychological Association. Reproduced with permission. Heinrichs, R. W. (2005). The primacy of cognition in schizophrenia. *American Psychologist, 60* (3), pp. 229–242. The use of APA information does not imply endorsement by the APA.

Note: This summary includes grand mean effect sizes and their 95% confidence intervals derived from clinical and experimental tests of cognitive performance (Heinrichs, 2001; Heinrichs & Zakzanis, 1998); smooth pursuit eye tracking and evoked potential measures of cognitive psychophysiology (Heinrichs, 2001); post-mortem neuroanatomical and neurotransmitter receptor binding studies (Heinrichs, 2001); positron emission tomography (PET) and xenon inhalation studies of regional metabolism and blood flow conducted with participants engaged in cognitive activation tasks (Davidson & Heinrichs, 2003); PET studies of regional metabolism, blood flow, and receptor binding and xenon blood flow studies with participants in a resting state (Davidson & Heinrichs, 2003; Heinrichs, 2001); and regional volumetric measurements of the frontal and temporal lobes based on structural magnetic resonance imaging (MRI) (Davidson & Heinrichs, 2003).

included the Wisconsin Card Sorting Test (a test of executive functioning), the Wechsler Adult Intelligence Scale (WAIS), and measures of motor function and verbal memory. The cluster analysis identified five subtypes, including one group with normative, intact cognition. The other four groups included an "executive subtype," which was distinguished by impairment on the Wisconsin Card Sorting Test; an "executive-motor subtype," which had deficits in card sorting and motor functioning; a "motor subtype," which had deficits only in motor functioning; and a "dementia subtype," which had pervasive and generalized cognitive impairment. These subtypes differed on other variables, such as duration of symptoms and extent of hospitalization. A subsequent study of a subset of the clients showed that most of the neurocognitive and functional differences persisted over time, even though there were no apparent symptom differences among the subtypes (Heinrichs, Ruttan, Zakzanis, & Case, 1997). A continuing focus on neuropsychological differences may provide important insights into the heterogeneity of schizophrenia.

Heinrichs (2005) compared average effect sizes across various ways of assessing cognition vs. physiological functioning and structures in schizophrenia. He concluded that there is a "primacy of cognition" (p. 229) in schizophrenia,

with average effect sizes from studies of memory, attention, language, and reasoning being at least twice as large as those obtained in studies that examine schizophrenia with structural brain MRI and PET scans. The results are shown in Figure 11.2. Heinrichs (2005) then went on to identify several explanations for why the link between schizophrenia and cognition is much stronger. One factor he suggested is that there is disorder-related brain disturbance that could have a pervasive influence on brain systems that are active in information processing. Another possible factor is that cognitive deficits reflect genetically determined constraints. A third factor is the possible influence of chronic stress and distress on cognition in people prone to schizophrenia.

The system that distinguishes between positive and negative symptoms, described earlier, has received much attention. Initially, Andreasen and Olsen (1982) evaluated 52 people with schizophrenia and found that 16 could be regarded as having predominantly negative symptoms, 18 predominantly positive symptoms, and 18 mixed symptoms. Although these data suggest that it is possible to talk about types of schizophrenia, subsequent research found that most people with schizophrenia show mixed symptoms (e.g., Andreasen et al., 1990) and that very few clients fit into the pure positive or pure negative types.

TABLE 11.1 Summary of the Major Symptom Dimensions in Schizophrenia

Positive Symptoms	Negative Symptoms	Disorganization
Delusions, hallucinations	Avolition (apathy), alogia (poverty of speech and poverty of content of speech), anhedonia, flat affect, asociality	Bizarre behaviour, disorganized speech

Subsequent analyses revealed three dimensions, not two (Lenzenweger, Dworkin, & Wethington, 1991). That is, positive symptoms can be divided into two categories: a positive symptom component consisting of delusions and hallucinations and a disorganized component that includes bizarre behaviour and disorganized speech (see Table 11.1).

A distinction between positive and negative symptoms (as opposed to between types of clients) seems to be a fundamental distinction that continues to be used in research on the etiology of schizophrenia. We will present evidence relevant to the validity of this distinction in the discussion of the possible roles of genetics, dopamine, and brain pathology in the etiology of schizophrenia.

11.3 Etiology of Schizophrenia

"The search to uncover the genetic and molecular secrets of the brain has not solved the riddle of psychosis, nor has it eradicated its disabling symptoms. . . . Perhaps the time has come for the field of psychiatry to reassess the role of social factors in the etiology of psychosis."

—G. Eric Jarvis, from a 2007 guest editorial in the
Canadian Journal of Psychiatry, p. 275

We have described how people with schizophrenia differ from normal people in thought, speech, perception, and imagination. What can explain the disconnection of their thoughts, their inappropriate emotions or lack of emotion, and their misguided delusions and bewildering hallucinations? We look here at the major areas of etiological research.

The Genetic Data

What would you do if you wanted to find an individual who had a very good chance of being diagnosed one day with schizophrenia and you could not consider any behaviour patterns or other symptoms? Indeed, imagine that you could not even meet the person. This problem, suggested by Paul Meehl (1962), has a solution that offers you a close-to-even chance of choosing a person who is potentially schizophrenic: find an individual who has an identical twin with schizophrenia.

Today, the role of genetic factors in various forms of psychopathology is widely acknowledged and a large proportion of research finding is detected to the study of genetic factors. This was not the case back in the 1960s. The recognized pioneer

who started this work is Irving Gottesman, who passed away unexpectedly in June 2016 (see Goode, 2016). Gottesman began his pioneering work with research documenting the role of genetic factors in personality by showing the heritability of personality as assessed by the MMPI (see Gottesman, 1963). Gottesman and Shields (1966) introduced their polygenic causation model of schizophrenia and further elaborated on it in their subsequent book (see Gottesman & Shields, 1972). This work introduced several key themes that have stood the test of subsequent research, including the assertion that multiple genes are implicated in schizophrenia and other forms of psychopathology, and that schizophrenia is not due to a specific single gene. Recent investigations by the Schizophrenia Working Group of the Psychiatric Genomics Consortium (2014) resulted in the identification of 108 schizophrenia-associated genetic loci, and a recent development by this same group is strong evidence for the role of the complement component 4 (C4) genes (see Sekar et al., 2016).

Although he is identified as synonymous with the role of genetic factors, Gottesman also consistently emphasized the role of environmental factors, thus setting the stage for biologically based diathesis–stress models.

A convincing body of literature indicates that a predisposition to schizophrenia is transmitted genetically. The family, twin, and adoption methods employed in this research have led researchers to conclude that a predisposition to schizophrenia is inherited by the majority of people who experience schizophrenia (e.g., Kendler & Gruenberg, 1984). Still, it is important to put this statement in context; as noted in one review (see Svrakic et al., 2013), while genetic factors play a clear role, schizophrenia, of course, is not limited to twins. When the family is viewed from a broader perspective, 90% of people who develop schizophrenia have parents who do not have schizophrenia, and between 60 and 80% do not have a sibling with schizophrenia.

Family Studies Table 11.2 presents a summary of the risk for schizophrenia in various relatives of index cases with schizophrenia. Quite clearly, relatives of people with schizophrenia are at increased risk, and the risk increases as the genetic relationship between proband and relative becomes closer.

More recent data continue to confirm what is shown in Table 11.2 (see L. Rodriguez-Murillo, Gogos, & Karayiorgou, 2012). Further, the negative symptoms of schizophrenia appear to have a stronger genetic component (Malaspina et al., 2000). The relatives of people with schizophrenia are also at increased risk for other disorders (e.g., schizotypal personality disorder) that are thought to be less severe forms of schizophrenia (Kendler, Neale, & Walsh, 1995). The data gathered by the family method thus support the notion that a predisposition to schizophrenia can be transmitted genetically. Of course, relatives of a schizophrenic index case may share not only genes but also common experiences and shared distinguishing characteristics such as atypical eye tracking (see photo). The behaviour of a parent with schizophrenia, for example, could be very disturbing to a developing child. Therefore, the influence of the environment cannot be discounted as a rival explanation for the higher morbidity risks.

Twin Studies

Concordance rates for MZ and DZ twins are also given in Table 11.2. Concordance for identical twins (44.30%), although greater than that for fraternal twins (12.08%), is less than 100%.

Cardno and Gottesman (2000) reviewed the results since 1995 from European and Japanese studies and reported concordance rates for MZ twins of 41 to 65%, and for DZ twins of 0 to 28%. The less than 100% concordance in MZ twins is important: if genetic transmission alone accounted for schizophrenia and one twin had schizophrenia, then the other twin would also have schizophrenia because MZ twins are genetically identical. Consistent with a genetic interpretation of these data, concordance among MZ twins does increase when the proband is more severely ill (Gottesman & Shields, 1972).

There is a critical problem in interpreting the results of twin studies. A common "deviant" environment rather than common genetic factors could account for the concordance rates. By common environment we mean not only similar child-rearing practices, but also a more similar intrauterine environment, for MZ twins are more likely than DZ twins to share a single blood supply.

A clever analysis supporting a genetic interpretation of the high concordance rates found for identical twins was performed by Fischer (1971). She reasoned that if these rates indeed reflected a genetic effect, the children of even the discordant, or non-schizophrenic, identical co-twins of people with schizophrenia should be at high risk for the disorder. These non-schizophrenic twins would presumably have the genotype for schizophrenia, even though it was not expressed behaviourally, and thus might pass

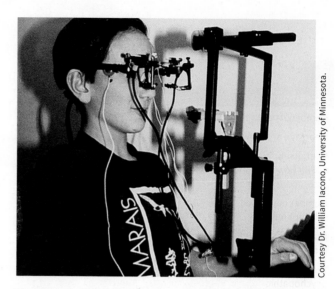

This apparatus is used to assess a person's ability to track a moving target. This ability is impaired in both people with schizophrenia and their relatives, suggesting that eye tracking is a genetic marker for the disorder.

Courtesy Dr. William Iacono, University of Minnesota.

along an increased risk for the disorder to their children. In agreement with this line of reasoning, the rate of schizophrenia and schizophrenic-like psychoses in the children of non-schizophrenic co-twins of people with schizophrenia was 9.4%. The rate among the children of the people with schizophrenia themselves was only slightly, and not significantly, higher at 12.3%. Both rates are substantially higher than the less than 1% prevalence found in an unselected population.

Dworkin and his colleagues re-evaluated the major twin studies according to the positive–negative symptom distinction (e.g., Dworkin, Lenzenweger, & Moldin, 1987; Dworkin et al., 1988). The analyses suggested that negative symptoms have a stronger genetic component than do positive ones.

Adoption Studies

The study of children whose mothers had schizophrenia but who were reared from early infancy by non-schizophrenic adoptive parents has provided more-conclusive information on the role of genes in schizophrenia by eliminating the possible effects of a deviant environment. Heston (1966) was able to follow up on 47 people born between 1915 and 1945 to women with schizophrenia in a state mental hospital. The infants were separated from their mothers at birth and raised by foster or adoptive parents. Fifty control participants were selected from the same foundling homes that had placed the children of the women with schizophrenia.

The follow-up assessment, conducted in 1964, included an interview, the MMPI, an IQ test, and social class ratings. A dossier on each participant was rated independently by two psychiatrists, and a third evaluation was made by Heston. Clinical ratings were made on a 0–100 scale of overall disability. Overall, the control participants were rated as less disabled than the children of mothers with schizophrenia. Thirty-one of the 47 children of mothers with schizophrenia

TABLE 11.2	Summary of Major European Family and Twin Studies of the Genetics of Schizophrenia
Relation to Proband	**Percentage with Schizophrenia**
Spouse	1.00
Grandchildren	2.84
Nieces/nephews	2.65
Children	9.35
Siblings	7.30
DZ twins	12.08
MZ twins	44.30

Source: From Gottesman, McGuffin, & Farmer (1987).

TABLE 11.3	Characteristics of Participants Separated from Their Mothers in Early Infancy	
Assessment	Offspring of Schizophrenic Mothers	Control Offspring
Number of participants	47	50
Mean age at follow-up	35.8	36.3
Overall ratings of disability (low score indicates more pathology)	65.2	80.1
Number diagnosed schizophrenic	5	0
Number diagnosed mentally defective	4	0
Number diagnosed psychopathic	9	2
Number diagnosed neurotic	13	7

Source: From Heston (1966).

(66%) but only nine of the 50 controls (18%) were given a *DSM* diagnosis. None of the controls was diagnosed as schizophrenic, but 16.6% of the offspring of women with schizophrenia were so diagnosed. Children of women with schizophrenia were also more likely to be diagnosed as mentally defective, psychopathic, and neurotic (Table 11.3). They had been involved more frequently in criminal activity, had spent more time in penal institutions, and had more often been discharged from the armed services for psychiatric reasons. Heston's study provides strong support for the importance of genetic factors in the development of schizophrenia. Children reared without contact with their so-called pathogenic mothers were still more likely to become schizophrenic than were the control participants. A similar study was conducted in Denmark (Kety et al., 1975, 1994) and it produced similar results.

Molecular Genetics

It does not appear that the genetic predisposition to schizophrenia is transmitted by a single gene; several multi- or polygenic models remain viable.

Thaker (2007) noted that the hunt for schizophrenia-related genes turned out to be more difficult than expected for several reasons, including:

1. Lack of preciseness in defining the boundaries of the clinical phenotype
2. Absence of biological tests that confirm diagnostic categorization
3. Clinical heterogeneity and the complex nature of schizophrenia

One of the most remarkable emerging findings from genome-wide analyses is that five major psychiatric disorders including schizophrenia may all stem from several specific genetic variations that apply to all five disorders (Cross-Disorder Group of the Psychiatric Genomics Consortium, 2013). This work builds on earlier work suggesting an overlap in genetic susceptibility across traditional classification categories, including schizophrenia and bipolar disorder (Craddock, O'Donovan, & Owen, 2006). The Cross-Disorder Group is a large international team led by Jordan Smoller. They have focused on five disorders that appear to share a common genetic vulnerability: schizophrenia, major depressive disorder, bipolar disorder, autism spectrum disorder, and attention-deficit/hyperactivity disorder. Initial work indicates that these disorders involve single-nucleotide polymorphisms in regions on chromosomes 3p21 and 10q24, and in two calcium subunits: CACNA1C and CANB2. Several implications follow from these findings. For instance, the role of common genetic factors could help explain certain factors that are not specific to schizophrenia and also apply to disorders such as depression. In addition, the obvious question becomes, "Why does one person with a similar genetic vulnerability develop schizophrenia while another person develops depression?" We must wait for this answer because this research is still in its very early stages.

Other recent developments illustrate just how complex the situation is in terms of different etiological routes to schizophrenia. Intriguing new results have emerged from research on people without a family history of schizophrenia who nevertheless developed schizophrenia (who are referred to as "sporadic cases") and these studies have illustrated the neural complexity involved in schizophrenia. It has been found in these investigations that schizophrenia seems to reflect relatively rare protein-altering gene mutations that have implicated up to 40 genes, including a disruption in DCGR2 (Xu et al., 2011, 2012). This is a gene found in the 22q11.2 microdeletion region known for vulnerability to schizophrenia (see Rodriguez-Murillo et al., 2012). Many of these gene mutations may have taken place in early development. According to Rodriguez-Murillo et al. (2012), these new advances are a result of being able to use more powerful technologies and being able to study genome-wide panels of genetic markers with larger samples of participants than were typically available in past research. Another important development identified by researchers from the Salk Institute in California is that the cells of people with schizophrenia had fewer synapses; that is, their neurons make fewer connections than do healthy nerve cells (Brennand et al., 2011). The practical implication of this work is that it points to the usefulness of antipsychotic drugs that can help nerve function return to normal levels.

Despite these new advances, we cannot conclude that schizophrenia is a disorder completely determined by genetic transmission and by biological factors, for we must keep in mind the distinction between phenotype and genotype and Gottesman's early emphasis on environmental factors. Like other mental disorders, schizophrenia is defined by behaviour; it is a phenotype and thus reflects the influence of both genes and environment. The role of both factors is suggested by outcomes experienced by the Genain quadruplets (see Focus on Discovery 11.1). The diathesis–stress

Focus on Discovery 11.1

The Genain Quadruplets—Heredity or Environment in Schizophrenia?

The schizophrenia manifested by the Genain quadruplets represents a fascinating illustration of the mutual influence played by genetic factors and life experiences. All of the Genain sisters had developed schizophrenia by the time they reached the age of 24. Genain is a pseudonym used to protect the identity of the four sisters who live in a U.S. midwestern state (see Rosenthal, 1963). The story of Hester, Nora, Iris, and Myra is fascinating for many reasons. First, it was estimated in 1963 that the odds of identical quadruplets (see photo) all developing schizophrenia were 1 in 1.5 billion births! Second, the Genain sisters have been studied throughout much of their life, initially by David Rosenthal and his associates at the U.S. National Institute of Mental Health (NIMH), and more recently by Allan Mirsky and his co-investigators. The latter published a 39-year follow-up investigation of the sisters (see Mirsky et al., 2000). The sisters experienced very different life outcomes even though they share the same genetic background. Hester experienced severe impairment, never completed high school, and was incapable of independent functioning. Iris and Nora showed better functioning but never had substantial careers and never got married. In contrast, Myra was able to work, marry, and raise a family despite developing schizophrenia.

The differences among the sisters demonstrate that the course of the disorder can be variable and, clearly, that all people diagnosed with schizophrenia are not alike. The sisters' different outcomes illustrate the need to consider genetic factors and environmental factors jointly. Scholars such as Mirsky point to the differential treatment of the girls by their father, who was especially cruel to Hester and

Nancy R. Cohen/Getty Images

Identical quadruplets share identical genetics. Studies of the identical Genain quadruplets (not pictured) who all developed schizophrenia later in life illustrated the need to consider both genetic and environmental factors.

Iris and kinder to Myra and Nora. The girls' father was described by Rosenthal (1974) as paranoid, and this may have contributed to his variability in his behaviours. Of course, it is impossible to pinpoint exactly the factors that contributed to the outcomes experienced by the Genain quadruplets. Still, the lives of the four sisters were quite different despite their common history of schizophrenia.

and biopsychosocial models seem appropriate for guiding theory about and research into the etiology of schizophrenia. Genetic factors can only predispose individuals to schizophrenia. Some kind of stress is required to render this predisposition an observable pathology. The importance of considering the gene by environment interaction was reiterated in a conclusion reached by Svrakic et al. (2013); that is, environmental factors that tend to produce small effects can have very large effects when combined with genetic vulnerability.

Biochemical Factors

The demonstrated role of genetic factors in schizophrenia suggests that biochemicals should be investigated, for it is through body chemistry and biological processes that heredity may have an effect. Research is examining different neurotransmitters, including norepinephrine and serotonin. No biochemical theory has unequivocal support. We shall review one of the best-researched factors: dopamine.

Dopamine Activity   According to Howes, McCutcheon, Owen, and Murray (in press), the dopamine hypothesis is

the longest standing biologically based theory of schizophrenia and it has predominated for over four decades. Initially, the hypothesis that schizophrenia is related to excess activity of dopamine is based principally on the knowledge that drugs effective in treating schizophrenia reduce dopamine activity. Antipsychotic drugs, in addition to being useful in treating some symptoms of schizophrenia, produce side effects resembling the symptoms of Parkinson's disease. Parkinsonism is known to be caused in part by low levels of dopamine in a particular nerve tract of the brain. It has been confirmed that because of their structural similarities to the dopamine molecule (Figure 11.3), molecules of antipsychotic drugs fit into and thereby block postsynaptic dopamine receptors. The dopamine receptors that are blocked by first-generation or conventional antipsychotics are called D2 receptors. Like other neurotransmitters, there are several subclasses of dopamine receptors that differ in the specifics of how they signal the postsynaptic neuron. Some of the second-generation or atypical antipsychotics (see the section called "Second-generation (atypical) antipsychotics" later in this chapter) have effects on additional kinds of dopamine receptor sites (D3, D4) and on some types of serotonin receptor sites (S2, S3), as reviewed by Lehmann and Ban (1997). From this knowledge about the action of the drugs that help people with schizophrenia, it is but a short inductive

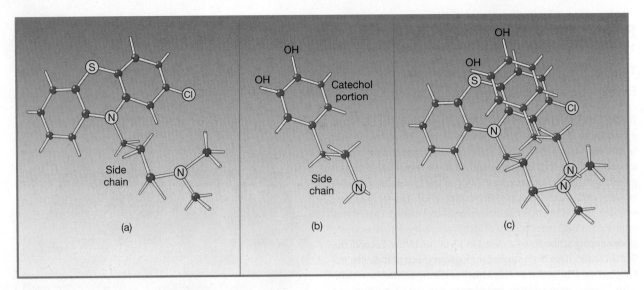

FIGURE 11.3 Conformation of (a) chlorpromazine, an antipsychotic, and (b) dopamine, and (c) their superimposition, determined by X-ray crystallographic analysis. Chlorpromazine blocks impulse transmission by dopamine by fitting into its receptor sites. Adapted from Horn and Snyder (1971).

leap to view schizophrenia as resulting from excess activity in dopamine nerve tracts.

Further indirect support for the **dopamine theory** came from the literature on amphetamine psychosis. Amphetamines can produce a state that closely resembles paranoid schizophrenia, and they can exacerbate the symptoms of schizophrenia (Angrist, Lee, & Gershon, 1974). Amphetamines cause the release of catecholamines, including norepinephrine and dopamine, into the synaptic cleft and prevent their inactivation. Additional evidence for the dopamine hypothesis came from post-mortem studies of people with schizophrenia. More recently, a key piece of evidence is the link between more potent antipsychotic drugs and dopamine D2 receptors (see Howes et al., in press). Relevant findings are discussed in more detail below.

Based on the data just reviewed, researchers at first assumed that schizophrenia was caused by a dopamine excess. But as other studies progressed, this assumption did not gain support. For example, the major metabolite of dopamine, homovanillic acid (HVA), was not found in greater amounts in people with schizophrenia (Bowers, 1974). Such data, plus improved technologies for studying neurochemical variables in humans, have led researchers to propose excess or oversensitive dopamine receptors, rather than a high level of dopamine, as factors in schizophrenia. Research on the antipsychotics' mode of action suggests that the dopamine receptors are a more likely locus of disorder than the level of dopamine itself. Some post-mortem studies of brains of schizophrenic people, as well as PET scans of schizophrenic people, have revealed that dopamine receptors are greater in number or are hyper-sensitive in some people with schizophrenia (e.g., Goldsmith, Shapiro, & Joyce, 1997). Having too many dopamine receptors would be functionally akin to having too much dopamine. The reason is that when dopamine (or any neurotransmitter) is released into the synapse, only some of it actually interacts with postsynaptic receptors. Having more receptors gives a greater opportunity for the dopamine that is released to stimulate a receptor.

Subsequent developments in the dopamine theory (e.g., Davis et al., 1991) expanded its scope. The key change involved the recognition of differences among the neural pathways that use dopamine as a transmitter. The excess dopamine activity that is thought to be most relevant to schizophrenia is localized in the mesolimbic pathway (see Figure 11.4), and the therapeutic effects of antipsychotics on positive symptoms occur by blocking dopamine receptors there, thereby lowering activity in this neural system.

The mesocortical dopamine pathway begins in the same brain region as the mesolimbic, but it projects to the prefrontal cortex. The prefrontal cortex also projects to limbic areas that are innervated by dopamine. These dopamine neurons in the prefrontal cortex may be underactive and thus fail to exert inhibitory control over the dopamine neurons in the limbic area, with the result that there is overactivity in the mesolimbic dopamine system. Because the prefrontal cortex is thought to be especially relevant to the negative symptoms of schizophrenia, the underactivity of the dopamine neurons in this part of the brain may also be the cause of the negative symptoms of schizophrenia (see Figure 11.5). This proposal has the advantage of allowing the simultaneous presence of positive and negative symptoms in the same person with schizophrenia. Furthermore, because antipsychotics do not have major effects on the dopamine neurons in the prefrontal cortex, we would expect them to be relatively ineffective as treatments for negative symptoms, and they are. When we examine research on structural abnormalities in the brains of people with schizophrenia, we will see some close connections between these two domains.

Although dopamine remains the most actively researched biochemical factor in schizophrenia, it is not

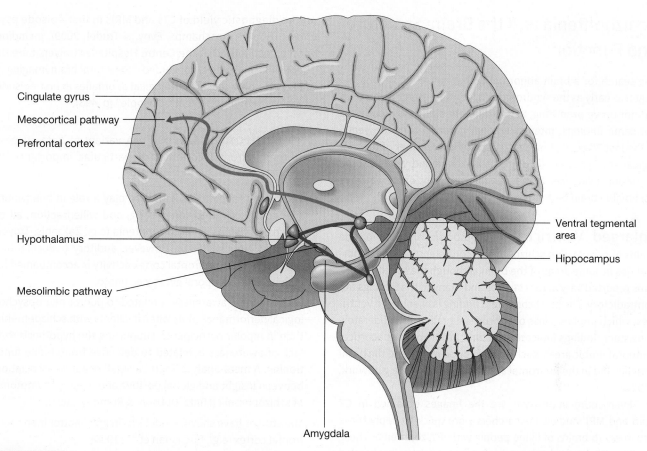

Cingulate gyrus

Mesocortical pathway

Prefrontal cortex

Hypothalamus

Mesolimbic pathway

Ventral tegmental area

Hippocampus

Amygdala

FIGURE 11.4 The brain and schizophrenia. The mesocortical pathway begins in the ventral tegmental area and projects to the prefrontal cortex. The mesolimbic pathway also begins in the ventral tegmental area, but projects to the hypothalamus, amygdala, hippocampus, and nucleus accumbens.

Source: Weinberger, Berman, & Illowsky, 1988.

likely to provide a complete explanation of the biochemistry of the disorder. Schizophrenia has widespread symptoms covering perception, cognition, motor activity, and social behaviour. It is unlikely that a single neurotransmitter could account for all of them. Researchers are casting a broader biochemical net, moving away from an emphasis on dopamine.

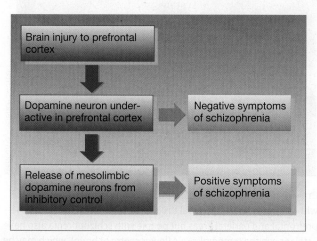

Brain injury to prefrontal cortex

Dopamine neuron under-active in prefrontal cortex

Negative symptoms of schizophrenia

Release of mesolimbic dopamine neurons from inhibitory control

Positive symptoms of schizophrenia

FIGURE 11.5 Dopamine theory of schizophrenia.

Other Neurotransmitters

Newer drugs used in treating schizophrenia implicate neurotransmitters such as serotonin in the disorder. Dopamine neurons generally modulate the activity of other neural systems; for example, in the prefrontal cortex, they regulate GABA neurons. Similarly, serotonin neurons regulate dopamine neurons in the mesolimbic pathway. Thus, dopamine may be only one piece in a much more complicated puzzle. Glutamate, a transmitter that is widespread in the human brain, may also play a role (Carlsson et al., 1999). Low levels of glutamate have been found in cerebrospinal fluid of people with schizophrenia (Faustman et al., 1999), and post-mortem studies have revealed low levels of the enzyme needed to produce glutamate (Tsai et al., 1995). The street drug PCP can induce a psychotic state, including both positive and negative symptoms, in normal people. It produces this effect by interfering with one of glutamate's receptors (O'Donnell & Grace, 1998). Furthermore, a decrease in glutamate inputs from either the prefrontal cortex or the hippocampus (brain areas implicated in schizophrenia) to the corpus striatum (a temporal-lobe structure) can result in increased dopamine activity (O'Donnell & Grace, 1998). Glutamate and serotonin may well be at the forefront of these inquiries, perhaps in conjunction with dopamine activity.

Schizophrenia and the Brain: Structure and Function

The search for a brain abnormality that causes schizophrenia began as early as the syndrome was identified, but the research did not prove promising, as the different studies did not yield the same findings. Interest gradually waned over the years. In the last 25 years, however, spurred by a number of technological advances, the field has reawakened and yielded some promising evidence. Some people with schizophrenia have observable brain pathology.

Enlarged Ventricles

Post-mortem analyses of the brains of people with schizophrenia consistently reveal abnormalities in some areas of the brain, although the specific problems reported vary across studies and many of the findings are contradictory. The most consistent finding is of enlarged ventricles, which implies a loss of subcortical brain cells. Moderately consistent findings indicate structural problems in subcortical temporal-limbic areas, such as the hippocampus and the basal ganglia, and in the prefrontal and temporal cortex (e.g., Dwork, 1997).

Even more impressive are the images obtained in CT scan and MRI studies. Researchers were quick to apply these new tools to brains of living people with schizophrenia. These images of living brain tissue have most consistently revealed that some people, especially males (Nopoulos, Flaum, & Andreasen, 1997), have enlarged ventricles. Research also shows a reduction in cortical grey matter in both the temporal and frontal regions (Goldstein et al., 1999) and reduced volume in basal ganglia (e.g., the caudate nucleus) and limbic structures (e.g., Velakoulis et al., 1999), suggesting deterioration or atrophy of brain tissue. Further evidence concerning large ventricles comes from an MRI study of 15 pairs of MZ twins who were discordant for schizophrenia (Suddath et al., 1990). For 12 of the 15 pairs, the twin with schizophrenia could be identified by simple visual inspection of the scan. Because the twins were genetically identical, these data suggest that the origin of these brain abnormalities may not be genetic.

Large ventricles in people with schizophrenia are correlated with impaired performance on neuropsychological tests, poor adjustment prior to the onset of the disorder, and poor response to drug treatment (e.g., Andreasen et al., 1982). A Canadian study found that large ventricles can be detected both in people with a first episode of schizophrenia and in people with chronic schizophrenia. It is likely that the large ventricles have a neurodevelopmental origin and are not progressive. Thus, enlarged ventricles do not simply reflect chronic, untreated schizophrenia (see Malla, Mittal, et al., 2002). The extent to which the ventricles are enlarged, however, is modest, and many clients do not differ from normal people in this respect. Furthermore, enlarged ventricles are not specific to schizophrenia, as they are also evident in the CT scans of people with other psychoses, such as bipolar disorder (e.g., Zipursky et al., 1997). Finally, a review of evidence

on the diagnostic yield of CTs and MRIs in first-episode psychosis (Goulet, Deschamps, Evoy, & Trudel, 2009), including people hospitalized at the Centre Hospitalier Universitaire de Sherbrooke in Quebec, concluded, "Structural brain imaging is unlikely to show causal neurological anomalies in first-episode psychosis in otherwise healthy people" (p. 493).

The Prefrontal Cortex

A variety of data suggest that the prefrontal cortex is of particular importance in schizophrenia.

- The prefrontal cortex is known to play a role in behaviours such as speech, decision-making, and willed action, all of which are disrupted in schizophrenia (e.g., Zakzanis, Troyer, Rich, & Heinrichs, 2000). However, auditory hallucinations result when this prefrontal cortex activity is accompanied by activity in the temporal gyrus (see photo).

- Lack of illness awareness is related to poorer neuropsychological performance more often in clients with schizophrenia than in bipolar participants, supporting the hypothesis that lack of awareness is related to defective frontal-lobe functioning. A meta-analysis found a small negative association between insight and global positive and negative symptoms of schizophrenia (Mintz, Dobson, & Romney, 2003).

- MRI studies have shown reductions in grey matter in the prefrontal cortex (e.g., Buchanan et al., 1998).

- In a type of functional imaging in which glucose metabolism is studied in various brain regions while clients perform psychological tests, clients with schizophrenia have shown low metabolic rates in the prefrontal cortex (Buchsbaum et al., 1984). Glucose metabolism in the prefrontal cortex has also been studied while clients are performing neuropsychological tests of prefrontal function. Because the tests place demands on the prefrontal cortex, glucose metabolism

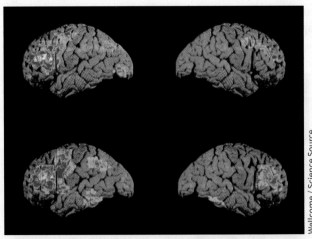

Wellcome / Science Source

Brain scans comparing people with schizophrenia (bottom) or without (top) show that verbal tasks elicit common activation in the prefrontal and parietal areas but people with schizophrenia also have activation in the temporal gyrus (lower centre of brain), which may be contributing to auditory hallucinations (see Palaniyappan et al., 2012).

normally goes up as energy is used. People with schizophrenia do poorly on the tests and also fail to show activation in the prefrontal region (e.g., Fletcher et al., 1998).

- Failure to show frontal activation has also been detected by the fMRI (e.g., MacDonald & Carter, 2003). Ragland et al. (2009) conducted a meta-analysis of functional imaging studies that contrasted people with schizophrenia and "healthy" volunteers during episodic encoding and retrieval. Clients with schizophrenia showed less prefrontal activation (prominent dysfunction) in specific areas relative to comparison participants, suggesting that "cognitive control deficits strongly contribute to episodic memory impairment in schizophrenia" (Ragland et al., 2009, p. 863).

- The frontal hypoactivation is less pronounced in the non-schizophrenic twin of discordant MZ pairs, again suggesting that this brain dysfunction may not have a genetic origin (Torrey et al., 1994). Failure to show frontal activation is related to the severity of negative symptoms (O'Donnell & Grace, 1998) and thus parallels the work on dopamine underactivity in the frontal cortex already discussed.

- In an interesting new direction, Joyal et al. (2007) used fMRI to test the hypothesis that violent people with schizophrenia and comorbid anti-social personality and substance use disorders show a different pattern of prefrontal functioning than seriously violent people with schizophrenia only. The results suggested that violent people with schizophrenia and a history of anti-social and/or substance use manifest neural dysfunction affecting basal or orbital parts of the prefrontal cortex.

Congenital and Developmental Considerations

A possible interpretation of these brain abnormalities is that they are the consequence of damage during gestation or birth. Waddington and colleagues (2008) used the Congenital Anomalies data set in the Prenatal Determinants of Schizophrenia study to conduct a systematic, prospective examination of the relation between congenital anomalies, early associated functional impairments, and risk of schizophrenia in adulthood. It was reported that the presence at birth or in infancy of "craniofacial/midline anomalies and/or early functional impairments that commonly occur as a symptom of CNS [central nervous system] anomaly" were associated with a doubling of the risk for schizophrenia spectrum disorder (a group or array of disorders related to and including schizophrenia) (Waddington et al., 2008, p. 266). These anomalies involve areas that share the embryological origins of the CNS, especially frontal cortical regions.

Many studies have shown high rates of delivery complications when babies were born to women with schizophrenia; such complications could have led to a reduced supply of oxygen to the brain, resulting in damage (e.g., Verdoux et al., 1997). These obstetrical complications do not raise the risk of schizophrenia in everyone who experiences them; rather, the risk is increased in those who experience complications and have a genetic predisposition (Cannon & Mednick, 1993).

Although the data are not entirely consistent, another possibility is that a virus invades the brain and damages it during fetal development (e.g., Mednick, Huttonen, & Machon, 1994). In 1957, Helsinki, Finland, experienced an epidemic of influenza. Researchers examined rates of schizophrenia among adults who had likely been exposed during their mothers' pregnancies. People who had been exposed to the virus during the second trimester of pregnancy had much higher rates than those who had been exposed in either of the other trimesters or among non-exposed control adults. Subsequently, Brown et al. (2004) reported that serologically documented influenza exposure during early to mid-gestation was associated with a threefold increase of schizophrenia, and that first trimester exposure conferred a sevenfold increased risk. These findings are intriguing. Cortical development is in a critical stage of growth during the second trimester—neurons are being produced in the rudimentary brain called the neural tube. These neurons then have to move to their appropriate location, passing through layers of cells as they do so. Perhaps this process of cell migration is disrupted in people who later develop schizophrenia.

Consistent with this speculation, post-mortem analyses of neurons in the brains of individuals with schizophrenia have shown reduced numbers of cells in the outer layers of the cortex in both the prefrontal and the temporal areas (Akbarian et al., 1995). Similarly, a widespread thinning of the cortex of people with schizophrenia has been reported, apparently resulting from loss of dendrites and axons (Selemon, Rajkowska, & Goldman-Rakic, 1995), and neurons in the frontal cortex have been shown to be smaller than normal in people with schizophrenia (Rajkowska, Selemon, & Goldman-Rakic, 1998).

Brown and Derkits (2010) reviewed the accumulating evidence that suggests that prenatal exposure to infections, including influenza, rubella, and toxoplasmosis (an intracellular parasite), and maternal cytokines (known to mediate the host response to infection), are associated with increased risk of schizophrenia. Brown and Derkits (2010) noted that it is important to identify pathogenic mechanisms and to investigate interactions between infection and susceptibility genes. The relevance of prenatal exposure was shown by new data qualifying past links between low birth weight and the subsequent development of schizophrenia by showing that low birth weight is a risk factor only when it is combined with prenatal exposure to influenza or hypoxia (Fineberg et al., 2013).

Brown and Patterson (2011) highlighted the practical implications of these findings by arguing that the three leading ways of becoming at risk (i.e., maternal influenza, toxoplasmosis, and genital/reproductive infections among mothers) can and should be the target of preventive interventions that should lower the number of cases of schizophrenia. For instance, greater awareness of the role of sexually transmitted infections and the possible role of influenza can both be addressed with basic methods such as aggressive treatment with antibiotics along with a general role of practical, inexpensive public health campaigns.

While there is a clear role for prenatal exposure, a comprehensive meta-analysis also points to a role for infections in early childhood that involve the central nervous system. This research established that childhood infection doubles the risk of adult schizophrenia (Khandaker et al., 2012).

If, as the findings suggest, the brains of people with schizophrenia are damaged early in development, why does the disorder begin many years later, in adolescence or early adulthood? Weinberger (1987) proposed that the brain injury interacts with normal brain development and that the prefrontal cortex is a brain structure that matures late, typically in adolescence. Thus, an injury to this area may remain silent until the period of development when the prefrontal cortex begins to play a larger role in behaviour. Notably, dopamine activity also peaks in adolescence, which may further set the stage for the onset of symptoms.

Related Research　Work on the relationship of the brain and schizophrenia is proceeding rapidly. Recognizing that the symptoms implicate many areas of the brain, research has moved away from trying to find some highly specific "lesion" and is examining neural systems and the way different areas of the brain interact with one another. This work calls attention to the possible role of a wider range of brain structures (e.g., the thalamus, cerebellum) in schizophrenia (e.g., Levitt et al., 1999). Indeed, quantitative and conceptual reviews such as those conducted in Canada by Zakzanis and Heinrichs and their associates (e.g., Zakzanis, Poulin, Hansen, & Jolic, 2000) led to the conclusion that the specific role of deficits in the temporal lobes has been overstated and that more diffuse dysfunction exists. Moreover, the extent of a more broad-based cognitive impairment needs to be examined with respect to the heterogeneity of schizophrenia. It may be the case that specific deficits exist in only a subset of those afflicted with schizophrenia.

Nonetheless, a meta-analysis of quantitative, non-invasive MRI studies reported a subtle (4%) but significant bilateral hippocampal volume reduction in people with schizophrenia (Nelson et al., 1998). A subsequent meta-analysis (Wright et al., 2000) concluded that regional volume reductions are especially marked in bilateral medial temporal lobe regions (i.e., amygdala, hippocampus, and parahippocampal areas). Related to this, van Erp et al. (2004) reported finding reduced hippocampus volume among twins with schizophrenia relative to twins without schizophrenia. Sim et al. (2006) followed up on the frequent finding of smaller medial temporal lobe volume by investigating the relative contributions of the hippocampus and three surrounding cortical regions (entorhinal cortex, perirhinal cortex, and parahippocampal cortex). They reported that clients had smaller overall medial temporal lobe volumes relative to controls, but that the volume difference was not specific for either region or hemisphere and concluded that the findings "have important implications for studying the functional role of the hippocampus and surrounding cortical regions in schizophrenia" (Sim et al., 2006, p. 332). Brambilla and colleagues (Brambilla et al., 2007) used an MRI procedure and determined that reduced cerebral blood volume accompanies brain size decrement in schizophrenia and proposed that chronic cerebral blood volume eventually results in neuronal loss and cognitive impairments.

A special theme issue of *Schizophrenia Bulletin* (see Potkin & Ford, 2009) presented a series of related articles that described fMRI data that were collected as part of a multi-site brain imaging consortium (the Functional Imaging Biomedical Information Research Network or FIBIRN) on the same participant population. A unique feature is that the publications indicate the power of multi-site neuroimaging since the consortium allowed a larger sample (125 clients and 125 controls) from a broader range of clients than could have been possible from a single site. The studies demonstrated widespread cortical dysfunction in schizophrenia. In their summary of several of the studies, Potkin and Ford (2009) suggested that "abnormal circuitry characterizes schizophrenic performance in both auditory target detection and memory retrieval, and that clients who hallucinate have reduced left auditory cortical activation on both tasks" (p. 15). Anatomical differences between clients and controls were reported, as was the identification of six genes that have functions related to forebrain development and stress responses in schizophrenia.

A growing body of work suggests that schizophrenia is related to dysfunction of functionally and anatomically connected networks of brain regions (see Tregellas, 2009 for a summary). For example, Wexler et al. (2009) reported smaller white matter volumes in neuropsychologically impaired participants with schizophrenia relative to a group of schizophrenics with near-normal cognition and healthy subjects. White matter forms the physical connections of the functional networks. The authors concluded that white matter pathology plays a critical role in the cognitive impairments seen in schizophrenia. In the future we can expect to learn more about other important developments in our understanding of brain structure and function in people with schizophrenia.

Psychological Stress and Schizophrenia

We have discussed several possible neurobiological diatheses for schizophrenia, but more than biology is responsible. Psychological stress plays a key role by interacting with a biological vulnerability (genetic or neurobiological) to produce schizophrenia in keeping with the biopsychosocial model. Data show that, as with other disorders, increases in life stress increase the likelihood of a relapse (e.g., Hirsch et al., 1996). Moreover, clients who take part in a stress-management program are less likely to be readmitted to the hospital in the year following treatment, especially if they had attended treatment sessions regularly (Norman et al., 2002). More recent data indicate that biological vulnerabilities involving the dopamine system are vulnerable to acute stress in ways that fit well with the biopsychosocial model (see Howes et al., in press).

Phillips et al. (2007) reviewed the available research and concluded that there is only limited evidence that stressful experiences precipitate a psychotic episode due to serious methodological limitations, including retrospective designs, inadequate control groups, overreliance on the life events approach to assessing stress, and, especially, failure to consider a person's appraisal of the meaning and potential impact of events or personal characteristics that might mediate any relations. Further, it was concluded that the physiological mechanisms that underlie a stress-psychosis onset relation have not been determined. With these limitations in mind, we turn now to the role of life stress in the actual development of schizophrenia. Two stressors that have played an important part in schizophrenia research are social class and the family.

Social Class and Schizophrenia

We know that the highest rates of schizophrenia are found typically in central city areas inhabited by people in the lowest socio-economic class (e.g., Harvey et al., 1996; Hollingshead & Redlich, 1958; see photo) and that the higher rates of schizophrenia among people with lower social class is regarded as an established fact in the schizophrenia field (see Tandon, Keshavan, & Nasrallah, 2008). The relation between social class and schizophrenia does not show a continuous progression of higher rates of schizophrenia as the social class becomes lower. Rather, there is a decidedly sharp difference between the number of people with schizophrenia in the lowest social class and the number in other social classes. In the classic 10-year Hollingshead and Redlich (1958) study in New Haven, Connecticut, the rate of schizophrenia was found to be twice as high in the lowest social class as in the second-lowest class. This finding was confirmed cross-culturally by similar community studies carried out in countries such as Denmark, Norway, and the United Kingdom (Kohn, 1968).

The correlations between social class and schizophrenia are consistent, but they are difficult to interpret in causal terms. Some people believe that stressors associated with being in a low social class may cause or contribute to the development of schizophrenia—the **sociogenic hypothesis**. The degrading treatment a person receives from others, the low level of education, and the lack of rewards and opportunity taken together may make membership in the lowest social class such a stressful experience that an individual—at least

one who is predisposed—develops schizophrenia. Alternatively, the stressors encountered by those in the lowest social class could be biological; for example, we know that children of mothers whose nutrition during pregnancy was poor are at increased risk for schizophrenia (Susser et al., 1996).

Another explanation of the correlation between schizophrenia and low social class is the **social-selection theory**, which reverses the direction of causality between social class and schizophrenia. During the course of their developing psychosis, people with schizophrenia may drift into the poverty-ridden areas of the city. The growing cognitive and motivational problems besetting these individuals may so impair their earning capabilities that they cannot afford to live elsewhere. Or, they may choose to move to areas where little social pressure will be brought to bear on them and they can escape intense social relationships.

One way of resolving the conflict between these opposing theories is to study the social mobility of people with schizophrenia. Consistent with the social-selection theory, some studies (e.g., Turner & Wagonfeld, 1967) found that people with schizophrenia are downwardly mobile in occupational status. But an equal number of studies have shown that people with schizophrenia are not downwardly mobile (e.g., Dunham, 1965). Clearly, this approach has not resolved the issue. Kohn (1968) suggested another way of examining this question: Are the fathers of people with schizophrenia also from the lowest social class? If they are, this could be considered evidence in favour of the sociogenic hypothesis that lower-class status is conducive to schizophrenia, for class would be shown to precede schizophrenia. If the fathers are from a higher social class, the social-selection hypothesis would be the better explanation. Turner and Wagonfeld (1967) found evidence for the social-selection hypothesis: of 26 clients in the lowest social class, only four had fathers in the lowest class.

A subsequent study in Israel employed a new methodology, simultaneously investigating both social class and ethnic background (Dohrenwend et al., 1992). The rates of schizophrenia were examined in Israeli Jews of European ethnic background and in more recent immigrants to Israel from North Africa and the Middle East. Those in the latter group experience considerable racial prejudice and discrimination. The sociogenic hypothesis would predict that because all social classes of this disadvantaged ethnic group experience high levels of stress, all should have consistently higher than normal rates of schizophrenia. However, this pattern did not emerge, supporting the social-selection theory.

In sum, the data are more supportive of the social-selection theory than of the sociogenic hypothesis. But we should not conclude that the social environment plays no role in schizophrenia. For example, the prevalence of schizophrenia among Africans from the Caribbean who remain in their native country is much lower than among those who have emigrated to London (Bhugra et al., 1996)—perhaps caused by the stress associated with trying to assimilate into a new culture. Cantor-Graae (2007) has reviewed evidence since 1996 and argues that research on migrants to western Europe supports the hypothesis that social

Courtesy of Seaton House.

The prevalence of schizophrenia is highest among people in the lowest socio-economic class. Seaton House in Toronto provides a safe place for those who are homeless and suffering from severe mental illness, including schizophrenia.

factors do contribute to the development of schizophrenia. For example, the extremely high risk for schizophrenia in second-generation immigrants is difficult to explain solely on the basis of biological and genetic factors. Studies also implicate childhood exposure to social adversity, and neighbourhood and urban effects as risk factors. She proposed a mechanism by which social factors could generate psychotic symptoms: social defeat or social exclusion might lead to alterations in CNS dopamine sensitivity and the regulation of dopaminergic systems.

The Family and Schizophrenia

Etiology and the role of the family   Early theorists regarded family relationships, especially those between a mother and her son, as crucial in the development of schizophrenia. At one time, the view was so prevalent that the term **schizophrenogenic mother** was coined to describe the supposedly cold and dominant, conflict-inducing parent who was said to produce schizophrenia in her offspring (Fromm-Reichmann, 1948). These mothers were characterized as rejecting, overprotective, self-sacrificing, impervious to the feelings of others, rigid and moralistic about sex, and fearful of intimacy—a very destructive view since it basically blamed the mother (or other family members) for a severe psychiatric disorder in a child. Controlled studies evaluating the theory have not yielded supporting data.

Some findings do suggest that the faulty communications of parents play a role in the etiology of schizophrenia. For example, in a longitudinal study of adolescents with behaviour problems, a family communication pattern characterized by hostility and poor communication predicted the later onset of schizophrenia or schizophrenia-related disorders (Norton, 1982). However, it does not appear that communication deviance is a specific etiological factor for schizophrenia, since parents of manic clients are equally high on this variable (Miklowitz, 1985).

Further evidence favouring some role for the family comes from an adoption study by Tienari and his colleagues (1994) in Finland. A large sample of adopted offspring of mothers with schizophrenia was studied along with a control group of adopted children. Data were collected on various aspects of family life in the adoptive families, and these family data were related to the adjustment of the children. The families were categorized into levels of maladjustment. Long-term follow-up confirmed that more serious psychopathology was evident among the adoptees if they were reared in a disturbed family environment; children having a biological parent with schizophrenia showed a greater increase in psychopathology than did the control participants who were reared in a disturbed family environment. A problem in interpretation remains. The disturbed family environment could be a response to a disturbed child. Thus, we cannot conclude that an etiological role for the family has been established.

Relapse and the role of the family   A series of studies initiated in London, England, indicate that the family can have an important impact on the adjustment of people with schizophrenia after they leave the hospital. Brown et al. (1966) conducted a nine-month follow-up study of a sample of clients with schizophrenia who returned to live with their families after discharge. Interviews were conducted with parents or spouses before discharge and rated for the number of critical comments made about the client and for expressions of hostility toward or emotional overinvolvement with him or her. The following statement is an example of a critical comment made by a father about his daughter's behaviour. The father claims that his daughter is deliberately symptomatic to avoid housework: "My view is that Maria acts this way so my wife doesn't give her any responsibilities around the house" (Weisman et al., 1998).

On the basis of this variable, referred to as **expressed emotion (EE)** by Brown and colleagues, families were divided into two groups: those revealing a great deal of expressed emotion, called high-EE families, and those revealing little, called low-EE families. At the end of the follow-up period, 10% of the clients returning to low-EE homes had relapsed. In marked contrast, 58% of the clients returning to high-EE homes had gone back to the hospital!

EE, as it is currently conceptualized, has several elements including criticism, emotional overinvolvement, hostility, and low warmth, but the main focus has been on the amount of perceived criticism in a person's closest, most meaningful relationship (see Masland & Hooley, 2015). This emphasis on perceived criticism is largely due to its clinical utility in terms of predicting relapse.

What else is known about perceived criticism? First, it is transdiagnostic in that it is linked with several clinical conditions, including depression, and it is not limited to schizophrenia (see Masland & Hooley, 2015). Second, the negative symptoms of schizophrenia are the ones most likely to elicit critical comments (King, 2000) and relatives who make the most critical comments tend to view the clients as being able to control their symptoms (e.g., Provencher & Fincham, 2000).

What is not yet clear is exactly how to interpret the effects of EE. Is EE causal, or do these critical comments reflect a reaction to the clients' behaviour? For example, if the condition of a person with schizophrenia begins to deteriorate, does family concern and involvement increase? Indeed, bizarre or dangerous behaviour by the client might seem to warrant the setting of limits and other familial efforts that could increase the level of expressed emotion.

Research indicates that both interpretations of the operation of EE—the causal and the reactive—may be correct (Rosenfarb et al., 1994). Discharged schizophrenia clients and their high- or low-EE families were observed as they engaged in a discussion of a family problem. Two key findings emerged:

1. The expression of unusual thoughts by the clients ("If that kid bites you, you'll get rabies") elicited higher levels of critical comments by family members who had previously been characterized as high in EE.

2. In high-EE families, critical comments by family members led to increased expression of unusual thoughts.

Thus, this study found a bidirectional relationship: critical comments by members of high-EE families elicited the increased expression of unusual thoughts by clients, and unusual thoughts expressed by clients led to increased critical comments in high-EE families. Another study conducted in Montreal is more consistent with the position that critical comments and emotional overinvolvement may be responses to schizophrenia (i.e., effects) rather than causes (see King, 2000). It is important not to minimize the major effects that a disturbed family member can have on other members of the family and on the overall functioning of the family. Further, we need to consider a "third variable" issue, namely, that relapse on the part of the person with schizophrenia and disturbed communication in the family could both be caused by genetic factors associated with the transmission of an increased risk for schizophrenia. Thus, other family members could appear "strange" because they have some, but not all, of the gene code for full-blown schizophrenia.

How could stress, such as a high level of EE, increase the symptoms of schizophrenia and precipitate relapses? Attempts to understand the factors and processes that may be involved have resulted in investigations seeking to establish links between expressed emotion and biological factors and processes. Support for a possible gene by environment interaction came from a study of expressed emotion in which schizophrenic clients interacted with family members in either a neutral condition or in a family conflict situation (see Keri, Kiss, Seres, & Kelemen, 2009). Researchers focused their attention on a polymorphism of the neuregulin 1 gene because this gene is implicated in risk for psychosis and it also influences prefrontal cortical activation. They found that schizophrenic clients with the genetic polymorphism displayed more unusual thoughts in the conflict situation and not the control condition. Thus, being in an unsupportive environment may interact with a genetic diathesis.

Another study sought to link exposure to expressed emotions with brain activation. Rylands et al. (2011) used an fMRI paradigm to study brain responses of 11 people with schizophrenia. They found evidence for a neural network that may mediate reactions to high expressed emotion. The processing of harsh social feedback was associated with activation in such areas as the rostral anterior cingulate, the middle superior frontal gyrus, and the left temporal pole. Perhaps some vulnerable people who have high interpersonal sensitivities have a hypersensitivity and chronic activation in these areas of the brain.

Developmental/High-Risk Studies of Schizophrenia

What are people who develop schizophrenia like before their symptoms begin? An early method of answering this question was to construct developmental histories by examining the childhood records of those who had later become schizophrenic. Individuals who became schizophrenic were different from their contemporaries even before any serious problems were noted in their behaviour. In the 1960s, Albee and Lane and their colleagues repeatedly found that children who later developed schizophrenia had lower IQs than did members of various control groups (e.g., Lane & Albee, 1965). Investigations of the social behaviour of preschizophrenic people yielded some interesting findings, as well. For example, teachers described preschizophrenic boys as disagreeable in childhood and preschizophrenic girls as passive (e.g., Watt, 1974). Both men and women were described as delinquent and withdrawn in childhood (Berry, 1967). Researchers have also examined home movies of family life taken before the onset of a child's schizophrenia (e.g., Walker, Davis, & Savoie, 1994). Compared with their siblings who did not later become schizophrenic, preschizophrenic children showed poorer motor skills and more expressions of negative affect.

As intriguing as these findings are, the major limitation of such developmental research is that the data were not originally collected with the intention of describing preschizophrenic people or of predicting the development of schizophrenia from childhood behaviour. More specific information is required if developmental histories are to provide clear evidence regarding etiology. The high-risk method can yield this information. The first such study of schizophrenia was begun in the 1960s by Sarnoff Mednick (see photo) and Fini Schulsinger (1968). They chose Denmark because the Danish registries of all people make it possible to keep track of them for long periods of time. Mednick and Schulsinger selected as their high-risk subjects 207 young people whose mothers had chronic schizophrenia. The researchers decided that the mother should be the parent with the disorder because paternity is not always easy to determine. Then, 104 low-risk subjects, individuals whose mothers did not have schizophrenia, were matched to the high-risk subjects on variables such as sex, age, father's occupation, rural or urban residence, years of education, and institutional upbringing vs. rearing by the family. In 1972, the now-grown men and women were the subject of follow-up for a number of measures, including a diagnostic battery. Fifteen of the high-risk subjects were diagnosed with schizophrenia; none of the control men and women was so diagnosed. Looking back to the information collected on the subjects when they were children, the investigators found that several circumstances predicted the later onset of schizophrenia.

These data suggest that the etiology of schizophrenia may differ for positive- and negative-symptom clients. In subsequent analyses, the clients with schizophrenia were divided into two groups: those with predominantly positive and those with predominantly negative symptoms (Cannon, Mednick, & Parnas, 1990). Variables predicting schizophrenia were different for the two groups. Negative-symptom schizophrenia was preceded by a history of pregnancy and birth complications and by a failure to show electrodermal responses to simple stimuli. Positive-symptom schizophrenia was preceded by a history of family instability, such as

Sarnoff Mednick, a psychologist at the University of Southern California, pioneered the use of the high-risk method for studying schizophrenia. He has also contributed to the hypothesis that a maternal viral infection is implicated in this disorder.

separation from parents and placement in foster homes or institutions.

In the wake of this pioneering study, several other high-risk investigations were undertaken, some of which have also yielded information concerning the possible causes of adult psychopathology. The New York High-Risk Study found that a composite measure of attentional dysfunction predicted behavioural disturbance at follow-up (Cornblatt & Erlenmeyer-Kimling, 1985). Furthermore, low IQ was a characteristic of the first high-risk children to be hospitalized (Erlenmeyer-Kimling & Cornblatt, 1987). In an Israeli study, poor neurobehavioural functioning (poor concentration, poor verbal ability, lack of motor control and coordination) predicted schizophrenia-like outcomes, as did earlier interpersonal problems (Marcus et al., 1987).

An Australian high-risk study was initiated by Yung and colleagues (see Yung, Phillips, Hok, & McGorry, 2004). The research group followed people between the ages of 14 and 30 who were referred to a special clinic in the early 1990s and identified as at "ultra" high risk (UHR) of developing a psychotic disorder. Since the study began, 41 of the 104 participants developed psychotic disorders, including schizophrenia (Yung et al., 2004). A cross-sectional and longitudinal MRI comparison determined that participants who developed a psychotic disorder, relative to those who did not, had reduced grey matter volumes, suggesting that lower grey matter volume predates the onset of psychotic disorders, including schizophrenia (also see Lui et al., 2009). Another study of these people (Mason et al., 2004) found that responses to a measure of the experience of life events did not predict the onset of psychosis in the UHR group. Unfortunately, measurement was limited to the quantitative assessment of life events (see Phillips et al., 2007). Phillips et al. (2007) concluded that "Longitudinal studies with high-risk cohorts might provide clearer information about the process underlying the onset of psychosis and could influence the development of preventive interventions" (p. 314).

11.4 Therapies for Schizophrenia

The puzzling, often frightening array of symptoms displayed by people with schizophrenia makes treatment difficult. The history of psychopathology is in many respects a history of humankind's efforts, often brutal and unenlightened, to deal with schizophrenia. Although some of the profoundly disturbed people confined centuries ago in foul asylums may have suffered from problems as prosaic as syphilis, there seems little doubt that many, if examined now, would carry a diagnosis of schizophrenia. Today we know a good deal about the nature and etiology of schizophrenia, but although we can treat its symptoms somewhat effectively, a cure remains elusive.

With the notable exception of an intensive behaviour-therapy project based on social learning principles implemented by Paul and Lentz (1977), research indicates, for the most part, that traditional hospital care does little to effect meaningful, enduring changes in the majority of mentally disordered people (see the descriptions of mental hospitals in Chapter 1). Studies designed specifically to follow clients with schizophrenia after discharge from a hospital show generally poor outcomes (Robinson et al., 1999).

A major problem with any kind of treatment for schizophrenia is that many clients lack insight into their impaired condition and refuse any treatment (Amador et al., 1994). As they don't believe they have a disorder, they don't see the need for professional intervention, particularly when it includes hospitalization or drugs. This is especially true of those with paranoid schizophrenia, who may regard any therapy as a threatening intrusion by hostile outside forces. Family members face a major challenge in getting their relatives into treatment, which is one reason they sometimes turn to involuntary hospitalization via civil commitment as a last resort or lobby for community treatment orders. Clinicians who treat schizophrenia also face numerous challenges, including risks of client suicide and the possibility of violent behaviour, nonadherence to the preferred treatment regimen, relapse of symptoms, and deterioration of functioning over time (CME Institute, 2007). The ultimate goal of treatment is to help the individual to remain in or re-enter and function in the community.

The American Psychiatric Association (2004) treatment guidelines for schizophrenia recommend a multi-point treatment course that consists of several strategies known to improve functional outcome:

1. Selection and application of antipsychotic medication to control acute psychotic symptoms, including strategies for maintaining adherence.

2. Identification and treatment of comorbid disorders, including substance use and depressive disorders.

3. Use of psychosocial treatment approaches with demonstrated effectiveness in improving symptoms and ability to function socially and vocationally.

Psychosocial treatment strategies supported by the American Psychiatric Association include family interventions and psycho-education, social skills training, cognitive-behavioural therapy, assertive community treatment, and supported employment. Unfortunately, few of the psychosocial treatments are used frequently in the practice setting despite research demonstrations of beneficial outcomes (CME Institute, 2007).

Biological Treatments

Shock and Psychosurgery

The general warehousing of people in mental hospitals earlier in the twentieth century, coupled with the shortage of professional staff, created a climate that allowed, perhaps even subtly encouraged, experimentation with radical biological interventions. In the early 1930s, the practice of inducing a coma with large dosages of insulin was introduced by Sakel (1938), who claimed that up to three-quarters of the schizophrenics he treated showed significant improvement. Later findings were less encouraging, and insulin-coma therapy—which presented serious risks to health, including irreversible coma and death—was gradually abandoned. As discussed in Chapter 8, ECT was also used after its development in 1938 by Cerletti and Bini; it, too, proved to be only minimally effective.

In 1935, Egas Moñiz, a Portuguese psychiatrist, introduced the **prefrontal lobotomy**, a surgical procedure that destroys the tracts connecting the frontal lobes to lower centres of the brain (see photo). His initial reports claimed high rates of success (Moñiz, 1936), and for 20 years thereafter, thousands of people—not only those diagnosed with schizophrenia—underwent variations of psychosurgery. A related procedure known as a leucotomy is a more circumscribed and specific procedure than a lobotomy. The lobotomy procedure was used especially for those whose behaviour was violent. Many clients did indeed quiet down after undergoing a lobotomy and could even be discharged from hospitals. During the 1950s, however, this intervention fell into disrepute. After surgery,

Scene from *One Flew Over the Cuckoo's* Nest. The character on whose shoulders Jack Nicholson is sitting was lobotomized in the film.

many clients became dull and listless and suffered serious losses in their cognitive capacities (e.g., becoming unable to carry on a coherent conversation with another person). This is not surprising given the destruction of parts of their brains believed responsible for thought. Overall, the principal reason for the abandonment of lobotomies was the introduction of drugs that seemed to reduce the behavioural and emotional excesses of many clients. Today, a more modern and non-invasive approach is repetitive transcranial magnetic stimulation; initial evidence suggests that this stimulation is effective in relieving the symptoms of schizophrenia, especially auditory hallucinations (Cole et al., 2015).

Drug Therapies

Without question, the most important development in the treatment of schizophrenia was the advent in the 1950s of several medications collectively referred to as **antipsychotic drugs**. These drugs are also called "neuroleptics" because they produce side effects similar to the symptoms of a neurological disease.

First-generation (conventional) antipsychotic drugs One of the more frequently prescribed antipsychotic drugs in the past 50 years, phenothiazine, was first produced by a German chemist in the late nineteenth century. Not until the discovery in the 1940s of the antihistamines, which have a phenothiazine nucleus, did phenothiazines receive much attention. Reaching beyond their use to treat the common cold and asthma, the French surgeon Laborit pioneered the use of antihistamines to reduce surgical shock. He noticed that they made his patients somewhat sleepy and less fearful about the impending operation. Laborit's work encouraged pharmaceutical companies to re-examine antihistamines in light of their tranquilizing effects. Shortly thereafter, a French chemist, Charpentier, prepared a new phenothiazine derivative, which he called chlorpromazine. This drug proved very effective in calming people with schizophrenia. As already mentioned, phenothiazines derive their therapeutic properties from their ability to block dopamine receptors in the brain, thus reducing the influence of dopamine on thought, emotion, and behaviour.

Chlorpromazine (trade name Thorazine) was first used therapeutically in the United States in 1954 and rapidly became the preferred treatment for schizophrenia. Thorazine was actually introduced to North America by Canadian psychiatrist Heinz Lehmann (Lehmann & Hanrahan, 1954), as described in Canadian Contributions 11.1. By 1970, more than 85% of all clients in state and provincial mental hospitals in the United States and Canada were receiving chlorpromazine or another phenothiazine. Other antipsychotics that were used for years in the treatment of schizophrenia include the butyrophenones (e.g., haloperidol, Haldol) and the thioxanthenes (e.g., thiothixene, Navane). Both types seem generally as effective as the phenothiazines and work in similar ways. These classes of drugs reduce the positive symptoms of schizophrenia but have much less effect on the negative symptoms.

Canadian Contributions 11.1

Heinz E. Lehmann and the "Discovery" of Neuroleptics in North America

"Look, you can't imagine. You know we saw the unthinkable—hallucinations and delusions eliminated by a pill! I suppose if people had been told well they'll die 2 years later they'd still have said it's worth it. It was so unthinkable and so new and so wonderful."

—*Heinz Lehmann, 1996*

Recall for a moment the contributions of Philippe Pinel (described in Chapter 1), who in 1793 removed the chains of mentally ill people at La Bicêtre asylum in Paris and ushered in many humanitarian reforms. Pinel lived on the asylum grounds and took his meals with the patients in order to be available to them and to practise his compassionate treatment of them throughout the day. Perhaps his intent was to serve as an appropriate role model for his charges. Can you imagine the director of a mental hospital living on the institution's grounds in the modern era? One such person was Heinz Lehmann (see photo). Lehmann, who passed away in 1999, must be considered one of the most important historical and contemporary figures in Canadian psychiatry.

In 1937, a young physician escaped from the Nazis in Germany and made his way to Canada, where he obtained a position at the Verdun Protestant Hospital in Montreal, a psychiatric hospital now known as the Douglas Hospital. According to Dongier (1999), Lehmann was initially placed in charge of about 750 clients, who accounted for almost half the beds at the hospital during that era. By 1947, he was clinical director. Subsequently, he became the director of research and education (1962), a full professor at McGill University (1965), and chair of the Department of Psychiatry (1971–74). For 60 years, Lehmann remained on staff at the Douglas, where

Photo ca. 1960s by Pichette Studio (LaSalle, QC). Courtesy of the Archives of the Centre for Addiction and Mental Health (CAMH), Toronto.

Heinz E. Lehmann (1911–1999), Clinical Director of Douglas Hospital (formerly Verdun Protestant Hospital) in Montreal, published the first North American paper on the treatment of schizophrenia using chlorpromazine. Following his success at the hospital, the use of neuroleptics spread to the rest of the continent.

he lived with his family in a small house on the hospital grounds. He kept a personal tradition of meeting and shaking hands with all of his clients on Christmas Day.

In the early years, Lehmann was unable to purchase phenobarbital, the main sedative used at the time, in capsule form. The resourceful physician overcame the obstacle: "At night, once my visits to patients were over, I was busy making capsules using bottles of powder. Incidentally, this started the rumour that I was an addict because nobody in his right mind would work in the pharmacy at 2 am" (Dongier, 1999, p. 362). In the 1950s, Lehmann and some of his clients were featured in a series of short films produced by the National Film Board (NFB) of Canada. He interviewed clients and summarized the symptoms of the disorders that led to commitment to a mental hospital during the era when available drugs and psychosocial interventions were not especially effective. The disorders included the schizophrenias, manic depression, depression, and organic psychoses. These films are informative and educational even today, especially because the clients demonstrated some of the more florid symptoms of psychotic disorders that are now frequently controlled by modern neuroleptic drugs. Today it would be considered unethical to deprive people suffering from schizophrenia and other serious mental disorders of an intervention that could reduce their suffering.

Of this NFB series, the favourite film of one of the authors, *Folie à Deux* (literally, madness shared by two), illustrates a disorder referred to in the *DSM-IV-TR* as shared psychotic disorder—the development of a delusional system within a close relationship with a delusional person. (However, shared psychotic disorder was eliminated as a separate psychotic disorder in *DSM-5*.) In the film, a client, Zena, developed delusions that she was being persecuted by doctors, the police, lawyers, and judges following what she perceived to be unsuccessful cosmetic surgery on her nose. Her mother subsequently developed the same delusions. Zena attributed her problems to a conspiracy on the part of the entire criminal justice system, whereas her mother, who was less sophisticated medically and psychologically, blamed "witches" hidden among the clients and staff. You might ask that if Zena's mother's delusions are caused by her close association with Zena's delusions, why not separate the two of them? Presumably, when no longer influenced by her daughter, the mother would give up her own delusions. This would seem to be a logical strategy. In fact, Dr. Lehmann did exactly this, and as predicted, the mother's delusions disappeared. Unfortunately, she became so clinically depressed and suicidal that, for humane reasons, Lehmann decided to put mother and daughter back together on the same ward. Parenthetically, the case of Zena and her mother illustrates an important difference between the treatment of the mentally ill during that era and the treatment today. Despite ongoing concerns about current practices, it is very improbable that today's doctors would lock Zena and her mother away for much of the remainder of their lives, as often occurred back in the 1950s. We will discuss current mental health laws in Canada, especially as they relate to civil commitment, in Chapter 18.

In 1953, Lehmann noticed in a French journal an article about the effects of chlorpromazine as a tranquilizer and antipsychotic medication and decided that it would be worth trying the new drug with his own clients. He obtained a supply from the manufacturer's representative and administered it with considerable success to more than 200 people who had a diagnosis of schizophrenia. He published his findings in the scientific journal *Archives of Neurology and Psychiatry*. This journal article was the very first paper published in North America on the use of a neuroleptic to control symptoms of psychosis. Just as Philippe Pinel unchained the chained in the asylums of Paris, Heinz Lehmann attempted to liberate his clients with schizophrenia from the torments of their delusional thoughts. The use of chlorpromazine soon spread throughout North America. Subsequently, Lehmann read in a Swiss journal the first published paper on the use of the tricyclic antidepressant imipramine for the treatment of major depression. According to Dongier (1999), Lehmann deserves the credit for introducing these treatment advances to North America.

Although Lehmann received numerous international honours for his clinical psychopharmacology research, it should be noted that his research and clinical interests were not wedded to biological interventions. Some of his more than 300 publications

in journals and books focused on psychotherapy, psychosocial approaches to treatment of the mentally ill, aftercare services in the community, community psychiatry, and assessment tools to measure the severity of psychiatric disorders (Dongier, 1999). In fact, Lehmann was opposed to the reductionist trends in biological psychology. He also resisted the process of psychiatric hospital deinstitutionalization when it was not accompanied by appropriate supports in the community.

In the concluding section of his eulogy to Lehmann in the Canadian Medical Association's *Journal of Psychiatry and Neuroscience*, Dongier (1999) stated, "Without any doubt, no contemporary Canadian psychiatrist had the international prestige or commanded such high unanimous respect as Heinz Lehmann" (p. 362). His body rested at Douglas Hall, in the heart of the hospital to which he had devoted his life.

Source: Adapted from Dongier (1999).

Although the antipsychotics reduce some of the positive symptoms of schizophrenia, they are not a cure. Furthermore, about 30 to 50% of people with schizophrenia do not respond favourably to conventional antipsychotics, although some of these clients may respond to some of the newer antipsychotic drugs (e.g., clozapine). Where do things stand at present? Carpenter and Davis (2012) concluded that more than 60 years after the introduction of chlorpromazine, the "advances in pharmacotherapy of schizophrenia have been modest" (p. 1168). In particular, they noted that while there has been success in treating psychosis, effective treatments for cognitive aspects and negative symptoms are "unmet therapeutic challenges" (p. 1168). However, they did hold out some hope that developments from neuroscience research will yield key insights that will translate into more effective treatments. A more recent review concluded that clozapine is the only medication for treatment-resistant schizophrenia that has proven to be effective. Moreover, the great heterogeneity in how afflicted people respond to drugs in general and specific drugs in particular result in a trial-and-error treatment choice strategy for each individual (see Lally & MacCabe, 2015). These same authors concluded, "It remains the case that there has been no fundamental innovation in psychopharmacology for schizophrenia since the discovery of clozapine in the late 1950s. This is further exacerbated by the recent retreat of the pharmaceutical industry away from research and development in psychiatric disorders" (pp. 176–177).

Another concern about antipsychotics is possible side effects. Some advances have been made in controlling side effects of second-generation antipsychotics, but now there are emerging concerns of side effects that enhance the risk of cardiometabolic dysfunction (Lally & MacCabe, 2015). Historically, commonly reported side effects of antipsychotics include dizziness, blurred vision, restlessness, and sexual dysfunction. In addition, a group of particularly disturbing side effects, *extrapyramidal side effects*, stem from dysfunctions of the nerve tracts that descend from the brain to spinal motor neurons. Extrapyramidal

side effects resemble the symptoms of Parkinson's disease. People taking antipsychotics may develop tremors of the fingers, a shuffling gait, and drooling. Other side effects include dystonia, a state of muscular rigidity, and dyskinesia, an abnormal motion of voluntary and involuntary muscles, producing chewing movements, as well as other movements of the lips, fingers, and legs. Together, these side effects cause arching of the back and a twisted posture of the neck and body. Akathisia is an inability to remain still; people pace constantly and fidget. These perturbing symptoms can be treated by drugs used by people who have Parkinson's disease.

In a muscular disturbance of clients with schizophrenia, called tardive dyskinesia, the mouth muscles involuntarily make sucking, lip-smacking, and chin-wagging motions. In more severe cases, the whole body can be subject to involuntary motor movements. This syndrome affects about 10 to 20% of clients treated with antipsychotics for a long period of time and it is not responsive to any known treatment (Sweet et al., 1995). Finally, a side effect called *neuroleptic malignant syndrome* occurs in about 1% of cases. In this condition, which can sometimes be fatal, severe muscular rigidity develops, accompanied by fever. The heart races, blood pressure increases, and the client may lapse into a coma.

Because of the side effects of the whole range of antipsychotic drugs, studies have found that about half the people who take them quit after one year and up to three-quarters quit after two years (e.g., Lieberman et al., 2005). A Canadian survey of people taking antipsychotics found that 56% reported that, without seeking their doctor's approval, they had stopped taking their medication; the most common reason given for non-compliance was drug side effects (Schizophrenia Society of Canada, 2002). Because of these high non-compliance rates, clients are frequently treated with long-lasting antipsychotics (e.g., fluphenazinedecanoate, Prolixin), which are injected every two to six weeks.

Clients who respond positively to antipsychotics are kept on so-called *maintenance* doses of the drug, just enough to continue the therapeutic effect. They take their medication and return to the hospital or clinic on occasion for adjustment of the dose level. Clients who are maintained on medication may make only marginal adjustment to the community, however. For example, they may be unable to live unsupervised or to hold down the kind of job for which they would otherwise be qualified. Their social relationships are likely to be sparse. And again, although conventional antipsychotics keep positive symptoms from returning, they have little effect on negative symptoms such as flat affect. Antipsychotics have significantly reduced long-term institutionalization, but they have also initiated the revolving-door pattern of admission, discharge, and readmission seen in some clients.

Second-generation (atypical) antipsychotics

". . .we have new evidence from larger pragmatic studies that the second-generation antipsychotics have, quite literally, been oversold. . ."

—Jan Scott (2008, p. 401) on the failures to replicate the initial impressive benefits of second-generation antipsychotics in subsequent effectiveness trials

In the decades following the introduction of antipsychotic drugs, there was little apparent interest in developing new drugs to treat schizophrenia. This situation changed markedly following the introduction of clozapine (Clozaril), which appeared to produce therapeutic gains in people with schizophrenia who do not respond well to traditional antipsychotics (e.g., Buchanan et al., 1998) and appeared to produce greater therapeutic gains than traditional antipsychotics (e.g., Rosenheck et al., 1999). A survey of clients' attitudes conducted at Hamilton (Ontario) Psychiatric Hospital concluded that most had a favourable view of clozapine, reporting improvements in levels of satisfaction, quality of life, thinking, mood, and alertness (Waserman & Criollo, 2000).

According to Meltzer (2013), the key distinguishing feature of **atypical antipsychotics**, relative to antipsychotics in general, is that at effective dose levels, the atypical antipsychotics are less likely to cause side effects. Because side effects such as tardive dyskinesia can prove fatal for some people, Meltzer (2013) strongly favours atypical antipsychotics and their reduced likelihood of morbidity and mortality. At the same time, Meltzer (2013) noted that there is one camp of scholars that has concluded that with the exception of the creation of clozapine, which is discussed in more detail below, there have been no meaningful advances since the original discovery of chlorpromazine.

An international study that included data obtained in Montreal found that clozapine, relative to olanzapine (another atypical medication), resulted in fewer suicide attempts among clients with schizophrenia (Meltzer et al., 2003). Furthermore, maintaining discharged clients on clozapine appeared to reduce relapse rates (Conley et al., 1999). Although the precise biochemical mechanism of the therapeutic effects of clozapine is not fully known, we do know that it has a major impact on serotonergic neurotransmitters and 5HT receptors (see Meltzer, 2013).

The apparent success of clozapine stimulated drug companies to search for other drugs that might be more effective than traditional antipsychotics. Two results are olanzapine (Zyprexa) and risperidone (Risperdal). Both produce fewer motor side effects than traditional antipsychotics, and they appear to be as effective as traditional antipsychotics in reducing symptoms (e.g., Wirshing et al., 1999), perhaps even better (Sanger et al., 1999). The Canadian Risperidone Study compared the effects of risperidone and haloperidol in an eight-week, double-blind, randomized study (Chouinard et al., 1993). This study found that 6 mg of risperidone was the most effective dosage level and that risperidone was significantly more effective than haloperidol at reducing negative and positive symptoms. Another study conducted in Canada showed that risperidone may lead to reduced use of health services because it was associated with a lower length of first hospitalization and less use of inpatient beds (Malla et al., 2001). Another randomized controlled trial (RCT) study (van Nimwegen et al., 2008) reported that both olanzapine and risperidone are associated with improvement in subjective well-being in adolescents with first psychosis. More recently, Addington, Labelle, Kulkarni, and colleagues (2009) compared the efficacy, tolerability, and safety of risperidone and a newer antipsychotic, ziprasidone, in a multi-centre RCT. Both drugs were effective as continuation and maintenance treatments in people recovering from an acute exacerbation of schizophrenia. However, ziprasidone was associated with fewer adverse effects (e.g., extrapyramidal symptoms) and greater improvement in depressive symptoms. See Table 11.4 for examples of major drugs used in treating schizophrenia.

Antipsychotic drugs are an indispensable part of treatment for schizophrenia and will undoubtedly continue to be an important component. They are surely preferable to the straitjackets formerly used to restrain clients. Nonetheless, some people with schizophrenia do not respond favourably to any of the current medications. However, the apparent success of clozapine, olanzapine, risperidone, and other atypical antipsychotics in treating some people has stimulated a continued effort to find new and more effective drug therapies for schizophrenia.

TABLE 11.4 Examples of Major Drugs Used in Treating Schizophrenia

Drug Category	Generic Name	Trade Name
phenothiazine	Chlorpromazine	Thorazine
	Fluphenazine	Prolixin
	Decanoate	
butyrophenone	Haloperidol	Haldol
thioxanthene	Thiothixene	Navane
tricyclic	Clozapine	Clozaril
dibenzodiazepine		
thienobenzodiazepine	Olanzapine	Zyprexa
benzisoxazole	Risperidone	Risperdal
dibenzothiazepine	Quetiapine	Seroquel

Our growing knowledge of biological diatheses for schizophrenia should not lead to a neglect of psychosocial factors in both the causes of and the efforts to control schizophrenia. Indeed, in his review of dopamine dysregulation and related biological factors, Kapur (2003) concluded eloquently that "[d]opamine dysregulation may provide the driving force, but the subject's cognitive, psychodynamic, and cultural context gives form to the experience. Psychosis is seen as a dynamic interaction between a bottom-up neurochemical drive and a top-down psychological process, not an inescapably determined outcome of a biology" (p. 17). This view is very much in keeping with the tenets of the biopsychosocial model.

Psychological Treatments

Psychological treatments for schizophrenia typically come in two forms: psychosocial treatments and cognitive behavioural interventions. Clearly, neglect of the psychological and social aspect of schizophrenia would compromise efforts to deal with people and their families who are struggling with that disorder. Moreover, evidence indicates that psychosocial strategies can play an important role in increasing the effectiveness of medication treatment and decreasing the relapse rate (CME Institute, 2007). Freud believed that people with schizophrenia were incapable of establishing the close interpersonal relationship essential for analysis. Although Harry Stack Sullivan and Frieda Fromm-Reichman subsequently developed similar ego-analytic approaches for schizophrenia that led to great claims of success, results from a long-term follow-up confirmed a lack of success (Stone, 1986). However, more recent psychosocial interventions hold considerable promise for success. We turn now to a consideration of various psychological treatments, beginning with elements of psychosocial interventions.

Social Skills Training   Social skills training is designed to teach people with schizophrenia behaviours that can help them succeed in a wide variety of interpersonal situations— discussing their medications with their psychiatrist, ordering meals in a restaurant, filling out job applications, saying no to offers to buy drugs on the street—all things that most of us take for granted and give little thought to in our daily lives. For people with schizophrenia, these life skills are not to be taken for granted; such individuals need to work hard to acquire or reacquire them.

The theoretical basis of this work was provided by Robert Liberman and his associates (see Liberman, DeRisi, & Mueser, 1989; Liberman et al., 1987). This model and therapeutic approach focuses on three key elements: receiving skills (i.e., social cognition), processing skills, and behavioural responses in social interaction. The techniques used in general for social skills training are utilized (e.g., modelling, role playing, and training in goal setting).

Studies conducted with groups of people with schizophrenia (e.g., Liberman et al., 1998) indicate that severely disturbed clients can be taught new social behaviour and independent living skills that may help them function better in their communities. A large and growing body of research supports the effectiveness of social skills training for people with schizophrenia, and a meta-analysis of RCT investigations concluded that this approach yields significant improvements across a variety of indicators, including skill acquisition, social interaction, and appropriate personal assertiveness in social situations (Kurtz & Mueser, 2008).

Kopelowicz, Liberman, and Zarate (2006) outlined many features of social skills training tailored to meet the needs of people with schizophrenia, including special adaptations and applications for improved generalization into the community, supported employment, and training to overcome cognitive deficits and negative symptoms. Social skills training nowadays is usually a component of treatments for schizophrenia that go beyond the use of medications alone, including family therapies for lowering expressed emotion. We turn to that work now.

Family Therapy and Reducing Expressed Emotion   Many people with schizophrenia who are discharged from psychiatric hospitals go home to their families. Earlier we discussed research showing that high levels of expressed emotion (including being hostile, hypercritical, and overprotective within the family) have been linked to relapse and re-hospitalization. Accordingly, family interventions have been developed. While they differ in length, setting, and specific techniques, these therapies have several features in common beyond the overall purpose of calming things down for the client by calming things down for the family:

- They educate clients and families about the biological vulnerability that predisposes people to schizophrenia, cognitive problems inherent to schizophrenia, the symptoms of the disorder, and signs of impending relapse.
- They provide information about and advice on monitoring the effects of antipsychotic medication.
- They encourage family members to blame neither themselves nor the client for the disorder and for the difficulties all are having in coping with it.
- They help improve communication and problem-solving skills within the family.
- They encourage clients and their families to expand their social contacts, especially their support networks.
- They instill a degree of hope that things can improve, including the hope that the client may not have to return to the hospital.

Programs employ various techniques to implement these strategies. Examples include identifying stressors that could cause relapse, providing training in communication and problem solving, and having high-EE (expressed emotion) family members watch videotapes of interactions of low-EE families (e.g., Penn & Mueser, 1996). Compared with medication only, family therapy plus medication typically lowers relapse over periods of one to two years, a finding particularly evident in studies in which the treatment lasted for at least nine months (e.g., Kopelowicz & Liberman, 1998).

The role of families is clearly illustrated in the early interventions that have been developed. These interventions are described later in this chapter in Canadian Perspectives 11.1. One of the leading proponents of this approach is Jean Addington (see photo), who teamed with Donald Addington to establish a clinic in Calgary. She then did the same in Toronto before returning to Calgary. This approach incorporates and involves family members right from the start (Addington, Collins, McCleery, & Addington, 2005) and longitudinal research indicates that one clear benefit is a lasting reduction in family distress and dysfunction (see Addington, McCleery, & Addington, 2005).

The central role of the family was illustrated in an intriguing case study of an adolescent boy named Peter that was described by Addington, Collins, McCleery, and Baker (2009). This case illustrates how symptoms are expressed in first-episode psychosis. The family was a focus in the decision to seek treatment, the actual expression of symptoms, and the intervention:

> "Alex and Marina reported that they had noticed a change in Peter's behaviour approximately 18 months ago. At that time, Peter, a relatively mild-mannered adolescent, became increasingly irritable with his parents and his grades started dropping at school. He stopped going out socially and spent hours in his room, alone on the computer, playing Dungeons and Dragons. He appeared concerned about the safety of his family. As a result he started sleeping with a baseball bat in this room to fend off potential attackers.

Courtesy Jean Addington

Jean Addington is Professor of Psychiatry at the University of Calgary and holds the inaugural Alberta Centennial Mental Health Research Chair. Her research is focused on determining means to identify young people in the earliest stages of psychosis and developing effective early treatments.

> During the interview with the psychiatrist, Peter was vague about when his difficulties started but went on to describe an elaborate belief system that involved a conspiracy against him and his parents. He endorsed hearing voices that were calling him names and threatening to kill him. When questioned, Peter said that he would take his life and the lives of his parents if he were unable to stop the perpetrator of these threats. Of particular concern was that Peter could not be dissuaded from his ideas. He grew increasingly agitated and lost in his thoughts as the interview went on. Given the severity of his symptoms, the psychiatrist was unable to obtain a comprehensive history. The collateral information at the first assessment interview is always important, but in this situation, it became a crucial part of the assessment process."

(Addington, Collins, McCleery, & Baker, 2009, p. 52)

Peter's parents received parenting skills training to help them cope with this challenging situation, but the family became a much bigger focus when Marina, Peter's mother, arrived at the clinic in tears one day because there had been marital conflict involving much screaming and shouting and Peter had been drawn into it. According to Addington, Collins, McCleery, and Baker (2009), it is likely the family conflict and Peter's return to school that contributed to Peter making the decision to stop his medication. What happened next? Addington et al. (2009) reported that over the next two months, Peter "began to decompensate and became increasingly isolated, irritable, and suspicious. His behaviour grew increasingly bizarre and Peter refused to meet with his psychiatrist and case manager. The outpatient team decided to enlist the help of the first-episode mobile team . . ." (p. 60).

Peter's story illustrates the role of psychosocial factors in relapse vs. recovery and it is very much in keeping with reviews that emphasize the importance of the social context and how social experience relates directly to illness experience (see Kidd, 2013). According to Kidd (2013), psychological factors that must be considered include social cognition and social processing difficulties, communication, emotion, and the self-concept. These psychological factors are experienced in a social context. At some point, the client returns to his or her daily life and the life context can be protective and supportive or maladaptive and undermining. In the case of Peter, he eventually became suicidal and the team worked with Peter and his parents for over two and a half years so that he achieved good remission from psychotic symptoms and he was no longer at high risk for suicide, but he was still socially isolated and displayed negative symptoms. Part of his recovery is that Peter resumed taking his medications. Addington, Collins, McCleery, and Baker (2009) noted that Peter passed his high school equivalency test and his parents "were devastated that he would not become an engineer or a doctor as they had hoped. However, as they noticed their son's steady gains, they became relieved that he was alive and could formulate new goals for himself" (p. 62).

We now turn to the very hot topic of cognitive-behavioural therapy as a way of treating schizophrenia. Beck's increasing focus on the role of cognitive factors in schizophrenia seems to have been the catalyst for extensive new work.

Cognitive-Behavioural Therapy Whereas it used to be assumed that it was futile to try to alter the cognitive distortions, including delusions, of people with schizophrenia, an emerging clinical and experimental literature has demonstrated that the maladaptive beliefs of some clients can be changed with interventions. In fact, Beck and Rector (2005) concluded that people with schizophrenia can benefit from cognitive techniques designed to address their delusions and hallucinations. Furthermore, in their conceptual model of cognition and schizophrenia, they suggested that cognitive-behavioural therapy (CBT) can facilitate motivation and engagement in social and vocational activities. This is in keeping with observations that people who have been psychotic for some time incorporate their psychotic beliefs into their broader cognitive schemas (see Kapur, 2003). In their theoretical analysis, Beck and Rector (2005) integrated the complex interaction of predisposing neurobiological, environmental, cognitive, and behavioural factors with the diverse symptomatology of schizophrenia. For example, the impaired integrative functions of the brain, in conjunction with domain-specific cognitive deficits, increases vulnerability to negative life events (e.g., job loss), leading to dysfunctional beliefs and behaviours.

Support for a cognitive approach was provided by Kieron O'Connor (2009) from the Université de Montreal, who reviewed cognitive accounts of psychosis, including claims that it is "cognitive and meta-cognitive appraisals (attributions and beliefs) about the significance of the symptoms that cause distress and dysfunction" (p. 152). He concluded that hallucinations and delusions possibly result not from perceptual distortion but from cognitive styles (e.g., inferential confusion, cognitive slippage, and fantasy proneness) that encourage the psychotic person "to live in fictional narratives as if they were real" (p. 152). A more recent meta-analysis found that CBT for psychosis yields small but significant benefits beyond the effects of medication for those people with medication-resistant psychosis (Burns, Erickson, & Brenner, 2014).

Empirical support for the cognitive model has come from a variety of sources, including a line of investigation focusing on dysfunctional attitudes in schizophrenia that is clearly derived from early work by Weissman and Beck on dysfunctional attitudes in depression. Dysfunctional attitudes predict reduced life functioning in people with schizophrenia (Horan et al., 2010) and they have even been linked with the internalization of stigma (Park, Bennett, Couture, & Blanchard, 2013). Work by Grant and Beck and colleagues has focused on a cluster of dysfunctional attitudes in a factor described as "defeatist beliefs." An example of a defeatist belief is "If you cannot do

something well, there is little point in doing it at all." Defeatist beliefs distinguish a group of people with schizophrenia with a particularly troubling form of negative symptoms called "the deficit syndrome" (see Beck et al., 2013). The presence of defeatist beliefs is associated with greater neurocognitive impairment and the defeatist beliefs also seem to mediate the links that cognitive impairment has with negative symptoms and with poor vocational functioning (Grant & Beck, 2009). A recent meta-analysis of past research confirmed the presence of a small but positive link between defeatist attitudes and negative symptoms of schizophrenia (Campellone, Sanchez, & Kring, 2016). What researchers in the schizophrenia field have failed to emphasize so far in this research on defeatist beliefs is that the measure of defeatist beliefs is composed primarily, indeed almost entirely, of the perfectionistic dysfunctional attitudes that Blatt and associates have seen as playing a key role in treatment-resistant forms of depression (for a review, see Blatt & Zuroff, 2002). Overall, it is plausible that some of the motivational deficits and apathy that plague certain people with schizophrenia can be traced back to a sense of feeling defeated stemming from rigid, absolute assumptions and a perceived inability to live up to perfectionistic standards and unrealistic expectations.

Figure 11.6 illustrates how cognitive beliefs and cognitive schemas can become intertwined with key symptoms of schizophrenia. According to Birchwood and Meaden (2013), a hallucination in which the person believes that they are being commanded to do something (i.e., command hallucinations) is the symptom that is the most distressing, high-risk, and treatment resistant of all symptoms of schizophrenia. Figure 11.6 is part of a case formulation described by Birchwood and Meaden (2013) for a client named Brian. It can be seen that the voices that Brian reported experiencing are quite severe in a way that would only exacerbate the symptoms (e.g., "Cut your wrists" and "Don't take your medication"). The cognitive elements are represented by "power beliefs" related to the voices themselves (i.e., they are omniscient and know all about my past, they are controlling me and keeping me awake at night). The numbers reflected in Figure 11.6 reflect the acknowledged strength or power of the belief; 100% would reflect an exceptionally strong belief that is dominating cognition. Also playing a role is a "dominant-subordinate overarching schema" that reflects the theme that "Others are stronger" and a sense of personal weakness due to the belief that "I am a bad person." The ability to address and remove these beliefs may limit the command hallucinations from occurring; even if the hallucinations continue to occur, limiting these maladaptive beliefs could still be beneficial by reducing Brian's subjective levels of distress.

How has CBT fared as a way of treating schizophrenia? Initial comparative research indicated that CBT plus enriched treatment as usual is as effective as treatment as usual alone, and that CBT seems to be particularly effective at reducing negative symptoms of schizophrenia (Rector, Seeman, & Segal, 2003).

Meta-analytic reviews (e.g., Zimmerman et al., 2005) support the efficacy of individualized CBT for people with persistent

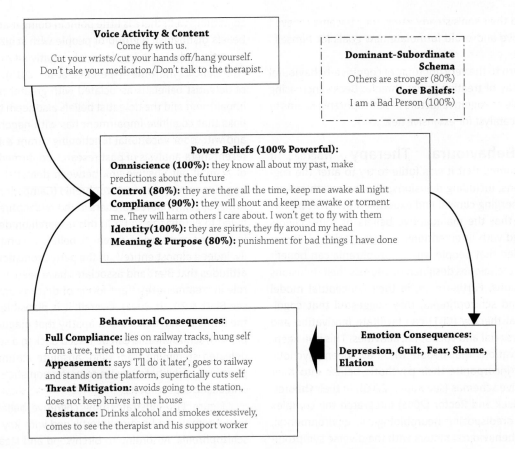

Voice Activity & Content
Come fly with us.
Cut your wrists/cut your hands off/hang yourself.
Don't take your medication/Don't talk to the therapist.

Dominant-Subordinate Schema
Others are stronger (80%)
Core Beliefs:
I am a Bad Person (100%)

Power Beliefs (100% Powerful):
Omniscience (100%): they know all about my past, make predictions about the future
Control (80%): they are there all the time, keep me awake all night
Compliance (90%): they will shout and keep me awake or torment me. They will harm others I care about. I won't get to fly with them
Identity(100%): they are spirits, they fly around my head
Meaning & Purpose (80%): punishment for bad things I have done

Behavioural Consequences:
Full Compliance: lies on railway tracks, hung self from a tree, tried to amputate hands
Appeasement: says 'I'll do it later', goes to railway and stands on the platform, superficially cuts self
Threat Mitigation: avoids going to the station, does not keep knives in the house
Resistance: Drinks alcohol and smokes excessively, comes to see the therapist and his support worker

Emotion Consequences:
Depression, Guilt, Fear, Shame, Elation

FIGURE 11.6   The Cognitive Therapy and Command Hallucinations (CTCH) template summarizing the extent to which voice hallucinations are experienced as strong and powerful by Brian. The greater the perceived power and omnipotence of the voice, the more likely a client such as Brian is to follow it and act upon it. In Brian's case, the omniscience rating suggests that the voices know all about him and what he has been up to in the past. Identity reflects the sense of who is providing the voice, and meaning and purpose reflects attempts to cognitively appraise and understand why it is happening.

Source: Birchwood, M., & Meaden, A., 2013. Cognitive therapy for reducing distress and harmful compliance with command hallucinations. In C. Steel (Ed.), *CBT for schizophrenia: Evidence-based interventions and future directions* (pp. 13–34). Chichester, West Sussex: Wiley-Blackwell.

positive psychotic symptoms. Several qualifications of this finding are needed. First, the efficacy of a group format is less clear-cut. Barrowclough et al. (2006) concluded that group CBT is probably not the optimum treatment for reducing hallucinations and delusions, though it possibly has important benefits, including feeling less negative about oneself and less hopeless for the future.

Second, a comprehensive meta-analysis of approximately 30 RCT efficacy trials (Wykes, Steel, Everitt, &Tarrier, 2008) concluded that CBT plus usual treatment, relative to usual treatment alone, demonstrates significant effects on depression, anxiety, symptoms (both positive and negative), and social functioning but not relapse rates. Further, those who benefited the most from CBT for psychosis had medication-refractory positive symptoms. The authors noted that effect sizes decreased as sample sizes and methodological rigour increased.

Third, a recent meta-analytic comparison confirmed once again that CBT was effective. However, supportive therapies

were also effective and there was no significant difference between CBT and supportive therapy (Newton-Howes & Wood, 2013).

Fourth, most of the CBT studies have been conducted in the United Kingdom and official organizations there have given stronger endorsements of CBT than has the American Psychiatric Association. A comparison of clinicians in the United Kingdom and the United States found no differences in awareness; however, the UK clinicians were more likely to actually practise CBT for schizophrenia. Moreover, they rated CBT as more effective and were more positive about possible recovery for clients treated with CBT (see Kuller et al., 2010).

Finally, what about the generalizability of CBT to the "real world?" Is it just as effective? As noted by Jan Scott (2008) in an editorial in the *British Journal of Psychiatry*, generalizability may be a problem; Scott pointed to a study that found limited effectiveness. Indeed, the authors of this study concluded that it may be best to reserve generic CBT for psychosis for clients with medication-unresponsive positive symptoms (see Garety et al., 2008). Are these results a major setback for CBT research? Probably not, but as Scott (2008) observed:

> "...it introduces some healthy realism about the limits for the role of adjunctive therapy in severe mental disorders. It is also a timely reminder that, away from the 'therapy for all' media hysteria, the world of routine psychiatric practice brings us into contact with some clients who do not want or do not respond optimally to antipsychotic medication, but who also do not always want or benefit from psychological therapies either."

(p. 402)

Treatment Focus on Basic Cognitive Functions

It is well established that people diagnosed with schizophrenia, as a group, have deficits in virtually all facets of cognitive functioning and show performance deficits on a range of simple and complex tasks (see CME Institute, 2007; Heinrichs, 2005; Walker, Kestler, Bollini, & Hochman, 2004). Moreover, these deficits are apparent in first-episode, non-medicated clients, so deficits are not a by-product of receiving treatment. Consequently, researchers have been attending to fundamental aspects of cognition that are disordered in schizophrenia in an attempt to improve these functions and thereby produce a favourable effect on behaviour. This more molecular approach concentrates on trying to normalize such fundamental cognitive functions as attention and memory, which are known to be deficient in many people with schizophrenia and are associated with poor social adaptation and other deficits in functional ability (see CME Institute, 2007).

One approach called **cognitive enhancement therapy (CET)**, developed by Hogarty and his colleagues (Hogarty et al., 2004), was evaluated in a two-year RCT of clients who were also taking medication. The approach was compared with an enriched supportive therapy that included educational and supportive aspects of personal therapy. The CET-specific focus is on computer-based training in attention, memory, and problem solving, as well as social-cognitive skills (such as initiating conversations). CET proved successful in improving cognition and processing speed and there was evidence to suggest that it also had a positive effect on functional outcomes. A subsequent two-year RCT investigation provided further evidence of the effectiveness of CET, including evidence that it protected against grey matter loss in the brain. Structural MRIs indicated that CET preserved grey matter in areas such as the left hippocampus and actually resulted in grey matter increases in the left amygdala (Eack et al., 2010).

Other studies have shown that a schizophrenia client's ability to recognize facial affect in others, working memory, and attention can all be improved through cognitive training (CME Institute, 2007). Canadian research conducted by Young and Zakzanis and their colleagues (2002) demonstrated the *utility of scaffolding* in the remediation of cognitive deficits. Scaffolded instruction is a concept derived from a proposal

that everyone has a zone of current development and that the complexity of tasks must be tailored to account for individuals' current skill level and level of potential development. The scaffolding model requires instructors to select tasks that reflect the clients' current capabilities so that eventually they are able to solve problems for themselves. The ultimate goal is to develop general problem-solving skills and processes that clients can generalize to new situations. Young et al. (2002) found that the delivery of scaffolded instruction to participants with schizophrenia, relative to direct instruction, significantly increased the number of categories created during the Wisconsin Card Sorting Test and that cognitive improvements were still evident one month later. The scaffolded group also had relatively higher levels of positive affect and self-esteem. Thus, scaffolding may lead to improvements in self-regulation and self-conceptualization.

A meta-analysis of 26 RCTs (McGurk et al., 2007) concluded that cognitive remediation in schizophrenia produces moderate improvements in cognitive performance. Further, when combined with psychiatric rehabilitation, it also improves psychosocial functioning. On a negative note, a more comprehensive meta-analysis of 53 longitudinal studies (Szoke et al., 2008) concluded that while people with schizophrenia showed improvement on most cognitive tasks, "practice was more likely than cognitive remediation to account for most of the improvements observed" (p. 248).

Research on psychosocial approaches to improving cognition in people with schizophrenia is vitally important because the innovative approaches offer an alternative to medications for improving functional outcomes.

Case Management/Assertive Community Treatment

After deinstitutionalization began in the 1960s, many people with schizophrenia no longer resided in mental hospitals and often had to fend for themselves in securing needed services. Without a centralized hospital as the site where most services were delivered, the mental health system became more complex. In 1977, fearing that many clients were not accessing services in the United States, the National Institute of Mental Health established a program that gave grants to states to help clients cope with the mental health system. Out of this program, a new mental health specialty, the case manager, was created. Canada adopted the strategy (Health Canada, 1991), but the practice varies widely across provinces and territories and in different places in the same province or territory.

Initially, case managers were basically brokers of services. Being familiar with the system, they were able to get clients into contact with providers of whatever services the clients required. As the years passed, different models of case management developed. The major innovation was the recognition that case managers often needed to provide direct clinical services and that these services might best be delivered by a team.

The Assertive Community Treatment model (ACT; Stein & Test, 1980; Stein & Santos, 1998) and the Intensive Case Management model (ICM; Surles, Blanch, Shern, & Donahue, 1992) both entail a multidisciplinary team that provides community services ranging from medication, treatment for substance abuse, help in dealing with the kind of stressors clients face regularly (such as managing money), psychotherapy, vocational training, and assistance in obtaining housing and employment. ACT has the overarching goal of helping individuals to become integrated into their community (see Trawver, 2010). It is assertive in the sense of being proactive rather than waiting, and team members are mobile and deliver up to 80% of the services in the community (Trawver, 2010). Overall, as summarized by Mueser, Deavers, Penn, and Cassisi (2013), ACT effectively provides stable housing, reductions in homelessness and hospitalizations, and a moderate reduction in mental health problems.

Table 11.5 summarizes the key elements of ACT. A clear theme shown here that merits repeating is that this is an integrated team approach.

Although a short-lived hospital-based program not unlike ACT was developed at the Montreal General Hospital, according to Latimer (2005) it wasn't until the 1990s that intensive case management programs and programs more or less similar to the current ACT model (e.g., Stein & Santos, 1998) began appearing in psychiatric and general hospitals in Canada. The Greater Vancouver Mental Health Service (which is now incorporated into the Vancouver Coastal Health Authority) was considered one of the best of its kind in North America (Nichols, 1995, January 30). The agency in the 1990's served about 5,000 people with serious mental disorders each year, many of them suffering from schizophrenia. It provided housing, special programs for older clients, and community response teams that can act very quickly in crisis situations involving their clients. The latter approach proved effective in Ontario. Community-based teams of doctors, nurses, and social workers called PACT (Program for Assertive Community Treatment) have been set up to ease the pressure caused by the closing of provincial psychiatric hospitals and to reduce the number of people with schizophrenia and other serious psychiatric disorders who end up in hospital emergency wards (Latimer, 2005).

TABLE 11.5	Key Assertive Community Treatment (ACT) Features
Multidisciplinary team staffing	
Services delivered by a shared team approach	
Assertive outreach	
Community-delivered services	
Integrated, comprehensive, and individualized service delivery	
Low staff-to-consumer ratios	
Prompt access and 24/7 crisis response	
Long-term, time-unlimited services	

Adapted from K. Trawver (2010), p. 190. Reprinted with permission from John Wiley & Sons, Inc.

The mental health teams are available 24 hours a day and even make "house calls" to mentally ill people in their homes and workplaces.

A related and recent initiative established in parts of Toronto is the Mobile Crisis Intervention Team (MCIT), a partnership between six local hospitals and Toronto police that responds to 911 calls with a psychiatric or crisis component. There are currently five MCITs in Toronto. They respond to situations in 12 of 17 policing divisions (see Rush, 2012, September 26). The MCIT program is based on a similar model developed by police in Memphis, Tennessee, in 1988. Each team is composed of a mental health nurse (who wears a bulletproof vest) and a specially trained police officer who ensures the safety of the nurse and can make apprehensions and arrests if necessary, including if it's the only way to get a psychiatric client into the mental health care system. The majority of the calls the teams respond to involve people with chronic schizophrenia who are off their medication and people who are suicidal. The mobile teams work out of unmarked police cars and currently can respond to only a fraction of psychologically disturbed individuals, but they are making an impact. In 2005 the Toronto teams responded to 4.3% of total 911 calls; however, in 2008 they responded to 10.6% of calls. It is the job of the MCIT team to assess situations, try to divert the people in crisis from harm, and arrange for appropriate treatment. The teams are able to divert many people from hospital emergency rooms and, because the necessary assessment has already been initiated, reduce wait times and ensure that clients who need hospital care receive attention more quickly. Other provinces also have some similar programs. For example, Latimer (2005) noted that there are a number of programs in Quebec patterned after the ACT model.

Indications are that more intensive treatment is more effective than less intensive methods in reducing time spent in the hospital, improving housing stability, and ameliorating symptoms (Tibbo et al., 2001). However, more intensive case management has not shown positive effects on other domains, such as time spent in jail or social functioning. The actual procedures that come under the rubric of case management vary a great deal from study to study. The services provided by a case management team will have positive effects only to the extent that those services are appropriate and effective. Indeed, Kidd et al. (2011) demonstrated that promoting recovery-oriented values within the context of recovery-oriented service provision is a key factor that helps account for the positive impact of ACT.

A meta-analysis of 10 studies of the effectiveness of ACT for homeless populations with severe mental illness (Coldwell & Bender, 2007) concluded that ACT offers significant advantages over standard case management. It is not clear how to adapt the ACT model to remote and rural areas in Canada. However, Gold et al. (2006) reported success with the design and implementation of a program that blended ACT with a supported employment program in a rural South Carolina county. Vocational and mental health services were tightly integrated within each self-contained team. Programs such as this could possibly adapt well to the Canadian situation.

11.5 | Contemporary Trends and Issues

While initial attempts to account for schizophrenia focused on the family, the contemporary view is that biological factors predispose a person to develop schizophrenia and that stressors, principally of a psychological nature, trigger the disorder in a predisposed individual and interfere with that person's adaptation to community living. We turn now to current trends in the treatment and care of people with schizophrenia.

General Trends in Treatment

The most promising contemporary approaches to treatment emphasize the importance of both pharmacological and psychosocial interventions. Indeed, this conclusion was supported by a systematic review of empirically supported first-episode psychosis services by Donald Addington and associates. Addington, McKenzie, Norman, Wang, and Bond (2013) evaluated 280 articles and provided a list of essential services that are evidence-based to a team of international experts. These experts were then given the task of rating the various components and they arrived at a list of 32 essential components across six categories. The highest level of supportive evidence was found for pharmacological components followed closely by key psychosocial components such as group family psychoeducation.

This joint emphasis on pharmacological and psychosocial interventions is reflected currently in a variety of ways:

- Families and clients are given realistic and scientifically sound information about schizophrenia. They learn that it is a disability that can be controlled but is probably lifelong, and that, as with many other chronic disabilities, medication is necessary to help maintain control and allow clients to perform daily activities. What is not necessary, and is counterproductive, is the guilt of family members, especially parents, who may have been led to believe that something in the client's upbringing initiated the problem. Considerable effort is devoted in many treatment programs to dispelling this sense of culpability while encouraging a focus on the biological diathesis and the associated need for medication.

- Medication is only part of the whole treatment picture. Family-oriented treatment aims to lessen the stress experienced by the client after discharge from the hospital by reducing hostility, overinvolvement, intrusiveness, and criticality in the family (EE). Topics include the importance of CBT interventions that teach clients how to notice and control their own stress reactions before they snowball and lead to emotional dysregulation and disruptive behaviours.

- It is increasingly recognized that early intervention is important in influencing the course of schizophrenia over time; losing no time getting clients onto the right medications and providing support and information to the family

and appropriate psychotherapy to the client can reduce the severity of relapses in the future (Drury et al., 1996). Ongoing research in Canada and elsewhere on a variable identified as duration of untreated psychosis (DUP), typically operationalized as the period between the onset of the first psychotic symptom and the beginning of antipsychotic treatment, has found that DUP predicts remission and positive symptom outcome after one year of treatment (see Malla, Norman, et al., 2002), and poorer functional and symptomatic outcome four years later (Clark et al., 2006). It is now firmly established that a longer DUP predicts the number of positive symptoms as well as a higher relapse rate and a longer time to remission. A review of 28 studies found that DUP also predicts negative symptoms, with fewer symptoms associated with a DUP of less than nine months. This review also found that the mean DUP was 61.4 weeks (see Boonstra et al., 2012). As a result of these and similar findings, interventions have been implemented in the hope of shortening the DUP. Unfortunately, it seems that generally education programs are not very effective and it is instead suggested that intensive, multi-faceted campaigns aimed at the general public and key professionals are needed (see Lloyd-Evans et al., 2011).

- It is also important to teach clients social skills and more reality-based thinking so that they can control their emotions and function more normally outside the hospital and probably reduce the EE encountered both inside and outside the home. Families affected by schizophrenia are encouraged to join support groups and formal organizations, such as the Alliance for the Mentally Ill or the Schizophrenia Society of Canada or its provincial or local counterparts, to combat and reduce the isolation and stigma associated with having a family member who has schizophrenia (Health Canada, 1991).

Canadian early intervention programs for schizophrenia that were alluded to earlier are summarized in Canadian Perspectives 11.1. These programs illustrate the benefits of active preventive efforts.

Further Issues in the Care of People with Schizophrenia

As people with schizophrenia grow older, they are less likely to be living with their families. The transition to living arrangements outside the parents' home is fraught with risk. Aftercare is one of society's thorniest social problems. To what extent do people with schizophrenia end up on the streets by falling through cracks in the mental health system?

The Homeless Mentally Ill   A relatively small proportion of homeless people in the United States are mentally ill, though many people with schizophrenia are without residences. In Canada, the situation is much different—the mentally ill make up a large proportion of the homeless. For

Canadian Perspectives 11.1

Early Detection and Prevention of Schizophrenia in Canada

> "It's quite horrendous. First of all, you've got somebody that you love, a child that you've raised. And then suddenly, the child becomes a crazy person."
>
> —June Beeby, former executive director of the Ontario Friends of Schizophrenics (now the Schizophrenia Society of Ontario) speaking about her 19-year-old son, Mathew, whose schizophrenia drove him to commit suicide
>
> (Nichols, 1995, January 30)

Early psychosis intervention projects have been developed in major centres across Canada for almost two decades. The focus here is on bouts of first-episode psychosis as illustrated in the earlier description of Peter and his symptoms. Early interventions are becoming increasingly popular because evidence suggests that without them, among those people showing early signs of high-risk symptoms, about one-third will not develop more full-blown psychosis with diagnosable schizophrenia, another one-third will go on to have psychotic illness, and the remaining one-third will exhibit symptoms of psychopathology and significant psychosocial impairment (see Fusar-Poli et al., 2012; Simon et al., 2013). A longitudinal study of 9- to 11-year-olds in England suggests that indicators of risk include impairments in general intelligence and specific cognitive functions, abnormalities in brain structure and function, and heightened responsivity to stressors (Laurens & Cullen, 2016).

According to a recent overview paper, Canada is considered among those countries that have been at the forefront in developing early intervention programs that have proved effective. Indeed, it is only past five to 10 years that the United States has begun implementing programs such as the Navigate Program (see Mueser et al., 2015) after the National Institute of Mental Health issued a request for proposals for the Recovery After an Initial Schizophrenia Episode (RAISE) research program was developed. But all is not rosy in Canada. At present, only three provinces (British Columbia, Ontario, and Nova Scotia) have made early intervention for psychosis a priority in the provincial mental health strategy. Moreover, programs are not accessible by people in remote and rural areas and there is no national commitment to early intervention (see Iyer et al., 2015). Indeed, a survey of 52 program sites in Ontario that included 21 small area programs showed that due to limited resources, there is only limited implementation of certain components (Durbin et al., in press).

Most programs offer outpatient services for young people and most treatment is done in the participant's home. The hope is that early intervention will help people function at the highest level possible, despite their disorder. A research component is an important feature of many programs.

While only three provinces have made this a priority, clinics exist in many provinces. For instance, Malla and his associates have developed the PEPP Clinic in Montreal (PEPP stands for Prevention and Early Intervention Program for Psychosis) and have patterned it after a similar program that Malla and colleagues developed in London, Ontario (for a description see Malla et al., 2016). The program developed by Jean Addington and her associates when she was in Toronto is outlined below.

The PRIME Clinic: Prevention through Risk Identification Management and Education

The CAMH First Episode Psychosis Clinic was established in 1992 to help individuals with schizophrenia and their families deal with the complexities of managing an initial episode of schizophrenia. The PRIME Clinic was established to facilitate early identification and treatment of people aged 12 to 45 who are possibly in the earliest stages of a first episode of psychosis (prodromal phase) and are at risk of "transitioning" to the active phase. The phase preceding acute psychosis is often confusing and traumatic for people. In addition to presenting with mild pre-psychotic symptoms, people at risk may also be experiencing a decline in their usual day-to-day functioning or way of relating to others. They may also have a family history of psychotic disorders such as schizophrenia. The PRIME Clinic is fully affiliated with the Department of Psychiatry at the University of Toronto.

Ridwan Tahseen is one person who was helped by the PRIME Clinic. According to a story published in The Globe and Mail (see Pearce, 2008), when he was 20 years old, Ridwan's university grades started to drop sharply after he experienced a romantic breakup. He started cutting himself on his arm and he developed the belief when in crowds that people were staring at him and were going to hurt him. He was referred to the PRIME Clinic due to some early symptoms of schizophrenia. His story is now one of the many compelling "Stories on Recovery" on the CAMH website (see www.camh.ca/en/hospital/about_camh/newsroom/stories_of_recovery/Pages/default.aspx). The story noted that Ridwan was able to get off of academic probation and that he was feeling quite positive because he had been accomplishing his goals.

The aim of early intervention for young people who appear to need it is to intervene during the prodromal phase to prevent (1) the onset of active phase symptoms and (2) the decline in cognitive, social, and occupational functioning associated with schizophrenia. Thus, the expectation is that through careful monitoring of identified high-risk individuals, it will be possible to prevent, delay, or attenuate active phase symptoms and improve the long-term course and outcome of the disorder. Thus, treatment should begin as soon as possible to ensure the best possible chance of recovery.

Such programs typically include an educational component that is offered for hospital staff, psychiatrists, and general practitioners in order to raise awareness about schizophrenia in the medical community and in the general public. Early signs of risk can include confusion, exaggerated self-opinion, suspiciousness, altered perceptions, odd thinking and speaking processes, lack of close friends, flat emotions, and difficulty with social activities and performing functions at school or at work.

Does the research support early intervention for schizophrenia? Is it effective? Harvey, Lepage, and Malla (2007) from the Douglas Hospital and McGill University in Montreal assessed the effectiveness of 11 "enriched" interventions relative to 6 "standard care" trials for clients with recent-onset psychosis, including the Calgary Early Psychosis Program. Enriched interventions included comprehensive programs with specialized and personalized services, a higher caregiver-to-client ratio, and a rational pharmacotherapy for at least six months, and some form of relevant, well-identified psychosocial treatment (e.g., family interventions, social skills training, CBT, or supportive psychotherapy) for at least three months. Harvey et al. (2007) concluded that enriched interventions are more effective than standard care for both symptomatic and functional improvement over a one-year period. Another multi-site Canadian study by the Douglas Hospital group (Malla et al., 2007) examined one-year symptomatic outcome in people with first-episode psychosis at three different publicly funded sites. It concluded, "Similarly enriched early intervention services may produce different outcomes, even within a relatively homogeneous mental health system" (p. 563). It was suggested that "local factors" can influence outcomes.

More recently, Malla and colleagues (Menezes, Malla, Norman, et al., 2009) conducted a one-year follow-up of 200 first-episode psychosis clients following one year of treatment from programs in four university centres in Ontario (Toronto, Western, McMaster, and Ottawa). A majority (70%) were involved in school, work, and/or relationships; however, the rate of functional recovery (51%) was lower than the rate of symptom remission (74%). Residual symptoms at six months and comorbid substance abuse predicted outcome variance.

Longer duration follow-ups are necessary, especially in light of evidence from research conducted in Europe suggesting that initial improvements do not appear to be maintained at five-year follow-up (Gafoor et al., 2010). However, other research conducted in London, Ontario, by Norman et al. (2011) indicated that their program did yield improvements that were evident five years later. Research is also exploring psychosocial factors that contribute to maintaining treatment gains. Norman et al. (2012) established that higher levels of social support predicted better functional outcomes five years later.

example, a United Way of Toronto (1997) report on homelessness in Metropolitan Toronto concluded that about 86% of the homeless have experienced a mental health or addiction problem at some point in their lives. Many of these individuals have been diagnosed with schizophrenia. The Mayor's Homelessness Action Task Force (1999) concluded that between 30 and 35% of homeless people were living with mental illness. One of its 105 recommendations called for 5,000 supportive housing units for those who are currently suffering from mental disorders and addictions.

The number of homeless people in Canada is not well-known and there is a clear need for a national study. A 2007 report by the Canadian Institute for Health Information (CIHI, 2007) yielded estimates for major cities that seem quite low, in part because the researchers had to rely on existing public health reports. The estimates of numbers of homeless were as follows: Toronto (5,052 people), Calgary (3,436 people), Edmonton (2,618 people), Vancouver (2,174 people), and Montreal (1,785 people). Overall, it was suggested that at any time, there are 10,000 homeless people in Canada, but this figure is regarded by most people as a dramatic underestimate. It was concluded in a report compiled on behalf of the Mental Health Commission of Canada that there may be over 200,000 homeless people in Canada and there is an estimated annual cost to the Canadian economy of over $7 billion (see Goering et al., 2014). Indeed, a 2007 survey done in British Columbia estimated that between 8,000 to 15,000 British Columbians with severe addiction and mental health problems were living on the streets (see Krausz & Scheutz, 2011). While researchers did not include a focus on schizophrenia per se, standardized interviews with 500 homeless people from three locations in B.C. (Vancouver, Victoria, and Prince George) found that 92.8% of the homeless people surveyed met criteria for a current mental disorder and 82.6% had alcohol or drug dependence. Overall, 60% had some form of suicide ideation and over one-third had attempted suicide. Particularly noteworthy was the high levels of multiple traumas, including abuse, that participants reported experiencing earlier in life, leading the investigators to conclude that in the vast majority of cases, mental health issues preceded homelessness rather than vice versa. Unfortunately, less than one-fifth of those with mental health problems had received treatment within the previous 12 months (Krausz & Scheutz, 2011; Krausz et al., 2013).

Supplementary analyses conducted on homeless people with a form of mental illness suggest that more than half of the people assessed had a history of schizophrenia. This work was led by a researcher from Simon Fraser University named Julian Somers (see photo), who has been quite open about his personal investment in this important area of research. This Vancouver psychologist's father was an alcoholic who lived his final years in a downtown hotel. Somers revealed that his father experienced a number of setbacks on a downward trajectory "terminating in precarious housing, untreated illness and premature death" (Shell, 2009, p. 1).

Courtesy of Julian Somers.

Julian Somers from Vancouver is the lead investigator of a multiple-site investigation of homelessness and mental illness. Somers revealed that his father experienced life challenges that resulted in precarious living situations and this fuelled his interest in this important research topic.

The research team led by Somers illustrated the importance of isolating persistent homelessness, which was defined as having a lifetime duration of being homeless for three years or more. Patterson, Somers, and Moniruzzaman (2012) found that persistent homelessness was associated with male gender, a younger age when first homeless, past-month alcohol use, and daily illicit drug use. Prolonged homelessness (i.e., having at least one single time of being homeless for a year or more) was associated with current substance dependence and a tendency to have two or more mental disorders as determined by assessment interviews. More recent data from Vancouver's Downtown Eastside indicate that there have been substantial increases over the past decade in terms of the proportion of mentally ill homeless people who have migrated to Vancouver from elsewhere (52% versus 17% ten years earlier) and these people have high levels of deterioration in their health and social welfare (see Somers, Moniruzzaman, & Rezansoff, 2016).

Fortunately, Canada has a number of national initiatives underway to address homelessness in general and homelessness and mental health problems in particular. For instance, the Canadian Observatory on Homelessness and the Homeless Hub were developed by Stephen Gaetz from York University and his colleagues (www.homelesshub.ca). This brings together researchers and advocates and provides a wealth of important information to the general public. For instance, a recent initiative was their development of a definition and typology of "homelessness." The contributions of Gaetz and his colleagues were acknowledged in 2016 when he was appointed to the Order of Canada.

On the mental health front, the most significant development was the At Home/Chez Soi project that began in 2009 and was led by the Mental Health Commission of Canada and its partners. The basic premise of this project is that it is both more affordable and more humane to address the mental health problems of homeless people by providing them with long-term housing (see www.mentalhealthcommission.ca). This is a national research project that involves building houses in five cities—Moncton, Montreal, Toronto, Winnipeg, and Vancouver—and following over 2,000 participants for over two years. The 2014 National Final Report is well worth reading not only for the cogent summary of initial research findings but also for the uplifting personal accounts provided by participants (see Goering et al., 2014). The report summarizes the benefits that have accrued to those who received housing (described as the "Housing First intervention"). Key findings include:

1. Housing First can be implemented effectively in cities of varying sizes and ethnoracial compositions.

2. Housing First rapidly puts an end to homelessness.

3. Housing First makes better use of public dollars—especially for those who are high-service users—and is a sound financial investment.

4. There are many ways in which Housing First can change lives and it yields positive benefits that go well beyond the anticipated positive outcomes.

Employment and Housing

Obtaining employment poses another major challenge for people with schizophrenia, partly because of bias against those who have been in psychiatric hospitals. It is important because evidence suggests that most people with schizophrenia have a desire to work and that being employed is linked with several benefits, including fewer symptoms of mental illness, higher self-esteem, and a greater sense of purpose (see Mueser et al., 2013). Although laws in most provinces and territories prohibit employers from asking applicants if they have a history of serious mental illness, former psychiatric hospital clients still have a difficult time obtaining regular employment. Also a factor is how much leeway employers are willing to give former mental health clients whose thinking, emotions, and behaviour are usually unconventional to some degree.

There are some positive signs, however. Twenty or 30 years after first developing symptoms of schizophrenia, about half of people with schizophrenia are able to look after themselves and participate meaningfully in society at large. Some continue to take medications, but many do not and yet still function well enough to stay out of the hospital (CME Institute, 2007). Welfare, community, and other social service agencies in Canada try to provide rent subsidies or affordable housing to former mental health clients to help them live in their own apartments or group homes, where they are occasionally checked on by mental health workers. Nonetheless, there is a chronic shortage of subsidized housing for psychiatric clients in most places in Canada. Further, a study by the Centre for Equality of Rights in Accommodation (see CERA, 2009) reported that more than one-third of people in Toronto with a psychiatric disorder would face substantial discrimination when trying to rent accommodation.

The jury at the inquest into the highly publicized case of Edmond Yu (Coyle, 1999, April 17), who was diagnosed with paranoid schizophrenia and was shot to death at age 35 by a police officer while brandishing a small hammer aboard a Toronto bus, recommended provision of safe houses for psychiatric clients and more affordable housing. The jury's list of 24 recommendations also included the provision of jobs with flexible or part-time hours that would offer the dignity of work. On January 22, 2004, the Edmond Yu Safe House Project was officially launched at the Gerstein Crisis Centre in Toronto (see photos). The house was intended to provide transition for 16 people who would be able to stay for up to 18 months while working their way into permanent housing. The organizers hoped that the city and federal governments would share the $2-million start-up costs and that the Province of Ontario would provide the annual budget ($790,000). The house, known as Edmond Place, is finally a reality and consists of 29 self-contained units at 194 Dowling Avenue in Toronto. It is a transformed building where Edmond Yu used to live (see www.parc.on.ca/edmond-place/).

Destigmatization

Further progress in the destigmatization of schizophrenia must continue to occur. Recall in Chapter 1 that we described preventive efforts to reduce stigma among students in high school and that much of this focus is on stigmatization of people with schizophrenia. Why focus on schizophrenia? Stip and associates (see Stip, Caron, & Lane, 2001; Stip, Caron, & Mancini-Marie, 2006) examined perceptions of schizophrenia in Quebec. The findings were both heartening and disheartening. Of the 1,001 people interviewed, 54% indicated that people with schizophrenia should be considered violent and dangerous, and 31% felt that an employee with schizophrenia would be fired from his or her job. With respect to the issue of integration of people with schizophrenia into the community, 49% agreed with rehabilitation in the community but 40% disagreed. Overall, relative to views on bipolar disorder, schizophrenia was seen as more severe, more stigmatized, and less tolerated (Stip et al., 2006). On a positive note that bodes well for the future, the youngest respondents were more likely to agree with rehabilitation in the community (57%) than older respondents (29%). In general, higher education and younger age was associated with more acceptance and understanding. This pattern fits with an Ontario survey of over 3,000 adolescents in grades 7 to 12 that showed that the majority of young people had some knowledge of schizophrenia and low social distancing; overall, more positive attitudes were found among those with greater knowledge and among girls (Faulkner, Irving, Paglia-Boak, & Adlaf, 2010).

Stuart and Arboleda-Florez (2001) surveyed attitudes toward people with schizophrenia in Alberta. Half the respondents knew someone who had been treated for schizophrenia or another mental illness. Social distance increased with the level of intimacy required, ranging from a low of 20% who claimed that they would be unable to remain friends with someone with schizophrenia to a high of 75% who would be unwilling to marry someone with schizophrenia. Consistent with Stip et al. (2001), respondents over 60 years of age were the least knowledgeable or enlightened about schizophrenia and the ones who practised the most social distancing. Stuart and Arboleda-Florez (2001) did, however, conclude that "most respondents were relatively well informed and progressive in their reported understanding of schizophrenia" (p. 245). The majority believed that people with schizophrenia could be treated

with some success outside of a psychiatric facility, needed to take antipsychotic medications to control their symptoms, could function adequately in regular employment, and were not a public nuisance or threat to safety. The authors further concluded that it is people's knowledge of schizophrenia rather than exposure to the mentally ill that is the "central modifiable correlate of schizophrenia" (Stuart & Arboleda-Florez, 2001, p. 245).

Perceptions of schizophrenia among university and college students are the subject of Student Perspectives 11.1. Unfortunately, the presence of mistaken beliefs suggests that a significant proportion of university students may be holding on to stigmatizing beliefs.

Much of the stigma around schizophrenia has been attributed to negative media accounts of people with the disorder, and this factor was identified by De Jong and Mather (2009) as probably being the main reason for the misconceptions held by some students that were described in Student Perspectives 11.1. Because of these concerns, the CBC Televison show *Cracked*, which is a police drama focused on solving crimes about mental illness, was aimed at providing a realistic portrayal of mental illness without fostering stigma and adding to the misconceptions.

A media intervention attempt in Calgary sought to promote more positive attitudes among Calgary newspaper journalists by providing them with accurate information and liaisons to mental health experts. Unfortunately, the intervention yielded mixed findings. In general, the number of positive stories about mental illness increased following the intervention, but the number of negative stories about people with schizophrenia also increased (Stuart, 2003). Stuart suggested that local positive stories might be undermined by a phenomenon dubbed "The CNN effect"—that is, sensationalized television stories may overshadow local anti-stigma initiatives.

Finally, what about mental health professionals? Do they hold fewer stigmatizing attitudes than the general public as would be expected? A study in Switzerland (Nordt, Rossler, & Lauber, 2006) reported that psychiatrists actually have more

Project & photo by Hilditch Architect; The Canadian Press/The Toronto Star/Dick Loek.

Edmond Place (left) is an impressive source of housing that commemorates the memory of Edmond Wai-Hong Yu (right), a one-time University of Toronto medical student who deteriorated into schizophrenia and homelessness. Yu actually lived on the same site at one point.

Perceptions of Schizophrenia and the Presence of Stigma Among Students

What perceptions and beliefs do students have about schizophrenia? Unfortunately, there is some evidence suggesting that misperceptions abound in the general student population. This was perhaps best exemplified in a survey conducted at the University of Lethbridge. De Jong and Mather (2009) presented a class of about 200 introductory psychology students with 12 questions on various issues related to schizophrenia that were drawn from a fact sheet developed by the Schizophrenia Society of Alberta. The mean number of questions answered correctly was just slightly above half (6.5 out of 12). Students seemed quite knowledgeable about social issues, as reflected by such statements as "Over 25% of the people with schizophrenia are homeless." However, there was much less knowledge of demographic issues reflected by statements as "Individuals with schizophrenia experience multiple personalities," and "More men are diagnosed with schizophrenia than women." Here, 3 out of 5 students gave incorrect answers to all three questions. Most troubling was that students were also asked how certain they were and some students held strong but incorrect beliefs on items about whether people with schizophrenia also have multiple personalities and the item "all individuals with schizophrenia experience hallucinations and delusions."

Research on stigma among university students is ongoing at the University of Western Ontario as part of a research program conducted by Ross Norman and colleagues. The key outcome variable in much of this research is social distance, which evaluates how physically close or remote someone is when in the presence of someone with a disorder such as schizophrenia. Social distance among students is influenced by the perceived norms for how people tend to react and respond to other people with schizophrenia (see Norman, Sorrentino, Windell, & Manchada, 2008). Another investigation involved 103 students reading a vignette about a young woman named Lisa who was suffering from schizophrenia. They were then presented with an opportunity to meet Lisa, and the key dependent measure of social distance was how close participants sat to Lisa. Overall, 9 participants sat right beside her, 47 sat 2 chairs away, 27 sat 3 chairs away, and 12 sat 4 chairs away. Women sat significantly closer, suggesting more favourable beliefs, but perhaps this simply reflected having the same biological sex as Lisa. Interestingly, the researchers also found that those with more reported "self-transcendent values" and who should be able to "put themselves in someone else's shoes" reported more positive attitudes toward Lisa than those with less self-transcendent values, but these values did not predict actual seating distance behaviour (see Norman et al., 2010). These data underscore the need to assess level of stigma in terms of not only attitudes and awareness, but also in terms of actual behaviours. Because this study did not include a comparison condition, we cannot be certain that the results are specific to students's reactions to people with schizophrenia versus other forms of mental illness, but the findings are still quite provocative.

Thinking Critically

1. Do you think that mistaken beliefs and perceptions of schizophrenia among students reflect a lack of awareness, a lack of contact with people with schizophrenia, or a general prejudiced view?

2. Do you believe that the media is responsible for the stigma that exists? What role do you think family beliefs play in fostering stigma?

3. In the social distance research, do you think the distance in terms of how many chairs away someone sits is a valid indicator of social distance and associated attitudes? What other measures would you use, if any?

negative stereotypes than the general population. Fortunately, a more recent study in Australia found that mental health professionals endorsed less stigmatizing attitudes than people from the general public, but general practitioners showed indications of endorsing stigma involving beliefs about the perceived dangerousness of people with schizophrenia and the personal weakness of people with a diagnosis (Reavley, Mackinnon, Morgan, & Jorm, 2014). Clearly, there is a need for more work on the anti-stigma front.

Summary

11.1 The symptoms of schizophrenia are typically divided into positive and negative types. Positive symptoms are behavioural excesses, such as delusions, hallucinations, and disorganized speech. Negative symptoms are behavioural deficits, such as flat affect, avolition, alogia, and anhedonia. Individuals with schizophrenia also show deterioration in functioning in occupational and social roles. Schizophrenia has historically been divided into subtypes, such as paranoid, catatonic, and disorganized. These subtypes are based on the prominence of particular symptoms (e.g., delusions in the paranoid subtype) and reflect the considerable variations in behaviour found among people diagnosed with schizophrenia. These distinctions were dropped in *DSM-5*, though dimensional symptom ratings have been added to capture the heterogeneity of symptom expression.

11.2 The concept of schizophrenia arose from the pioneering efforts of Kraepelin and Bleuler. Kraepelin's work fostered a descriptive approach and a narrow definition, whereas Bleuler's theoretical emphasis led to a broad diagnostic category. Bleuler introduced the term "schizophrenia" and had a great influence on the American concept of schizophrenia, making it extremely broad. By the middle of the twentieth century, the differences between the diagnosis of schizophrenia in the United States and the diagnosis of schizophrenia in Europe were vast.

11.3 Research has tried to determine the etiological role of specific biological variables, such as genetic and biochemical factors and brain pathology, as well as of stressors, such as low social class and family conflict. Much of the research fits with a biopsychosocial model. The data on genetic transmission are impressive and new research increasingly highlights the complex array of genetic factors and processes that may be involved. It appears that an increased sensitivity of dopamine receptors in the limbic area of the brain is related to the positive symptoms of schizophrenia. The negative symptoms may be due to dopamine underactivity in the prefrontal cortex. Research into biochemical factors in schizophrenia is beginning to examine the possible role played by other neurotransmitters, such as serotonin. Environmental factors are also implicated. Vague communications and conflicts are evident in the family life of people with schizophrenia and probably contribute to their disorder. A high level of expressed emotion (EE)—criticism, hostility, and emotional overinvolvement—in families has been shown to be an important determinant of relapse. Increases in general life stress have also been shown to be important precipitants of relapse. These stressors may increase cortisol levels, which, in turn, stimulate dopamine activity.

11.4 There are both biological and psychological therapies for schizophrenia. Insulin and electroconvulsive treatments and even surgery were in vogue in the early twentieth century, but they are no longer much used, primarily because of the availability of antipsychotic drugs, in particular, the phenothiazines. In numerous studies, these medications have been found to have a major beneficial impact on the disordered lives of people with schizophrenia. Newer medications such as clozapine and risperidone are at least as effective as the phenothiazines and produce fewer motor side effects but the variability of individual responses suggests the need for a trial-and-error process when it comes to the treatment of an individual person. Drugs have also been a factor in the deinstitutionalization of hospital clients.

Drugs alone are not a completely effective treatment, as clients with schizophrenia need to be taught or retaught ways of dealing with the challenges of everyday life. Family therapy, aimed at reducing high levels of expressed emotion, has been shown to be valuable in preventing relapse. In general, evidence is accumulating and showing the benefits of psychosocial interventions. Efforts to change the thinking of people with schizophrenia are showing some promise and there is growing support for cognitive theories of schizophrenia and associated interventions. The most effective treatments for schizophrenia are likely to involve both biological and psychological components.

11.5 Canadian efforts are focused on the early prevention of schizophrenia based on identifying young people at risk for the development of schizophrenia. The importance of living conditions is a key consideration in terms of a community-based response. A significant proportion of people who are homeless suffer from mental illness. Canada has implemented important initiatives such as the At Home/Chez Soi Project led by the Mental Health Commission of Canada and it has proven effective in ways that go well beyond the anticipated positive outcomes.

Key Terms

alogia
anhedonia
antipsychotic drugs
asociality
atypical antipsychotics
avolition
catatonic immobility
catatonic schizophrenia
cognitive enhancement therapy (CET)
delusional disorder
delusional jealousy
delusions
dementia praecox

disorganized schizophrenia
disorganized speech (formal thought
    disorder)
dopamine theory
expressed emotion (EE)
flat affect
grandiose delusions
hallucinations
ideas of reference
inappropriate affect
incoherence
loose associations (derailment)
negative symptoms

paranoid schizophrenia
positive symptoms
prefrontal lobotomy
residual schizophrenia
schizophrenia
schizophrenogenic mother
social distance
social-selection theory
sociogenic hypothesis
undifferentiated schizophrenia
waxy flexibility

Reflections: Past, Present, and Future

1. Most people diagnosed with schizophrenia lead a tortured, tormented existence; however, even when they respond favourably to antipsychotic medication, they often experience severe side effects and stop taking their medication. Some advocates have argued that, for this reason, people with schizophrenia should have the right to choose to continue to be psychotic. Do you agree or disagree with these advocates? Under what circumstances, if any, should we be allowed to impose treatment on psychiatric clients?

2. Assume that that you are engaged to be married. Although your future partner appears to be extremely well adjusted, he or she has a fraternal twin who has been diagnosed with schizophrenia. The two of you are concerned about the genetic implications for your children. Will they be at elevated risk for schizophrenia? What other factors could put your children at risk of developing schizophrenia? What future scientific findings would help you to decide whether or not to have children?

3. Canadian authors have made a strong recommendation that genetic counselling should be made available to everyone with schizophrenia and their families (see Hodgkinson et al., 2001).

Genetic counselling is a process of communication that involves conveying information about risk to clients and their relatives to help them make decisions, deal with current issues, and anticipate other issues associated with schizophrenia. Do you agree with the recommendation?

4. Assume that you are a psychologist who has been given carte blanche to develop a comprehensive and effective psychosocial treatment for schizophrenia (to be used in conjunction with traditional medical management). What would you focus on? Assume that the very best programs include the following components: individual case managers to work as advocates to help clients obtain necessary services; social supports that can "wrap around" clients to keep them in the community (e.g., safe houses and peer support groups); individualized proactive plans to facilitate crisis avoidance and management; and specific vocational rehabilitation plans that identify needed skills for occupational goals. Design and implement your program. Be specific. Assume that the financial cost or the availability of human resources becomes a factor. Which component(s) would you delete from your program?

CHAPTER 12

Substance-Related Disorders

LEARNING OBJECTIVES

1. Identify the signs and symptoms of alcohol abuse and dependence with reference to drinking in students, and the consequences of alcohol abuse and dependence.

2. Discuss the addictiveness of nicotine and its toll on people with reference to current trends in the prevalence of smoking.

3. Describe the psychological, physical, and therapeutic effects of marijuana and how there are complex considerations to take into account when it is decided to legalize marijuana.

4. Explain how sedatives and stimulants may seem innocuous but are potentially quite dangerous and represent emerging public health issues.

5. Describe the symptoms experienced following the ingestion of LSD and the history of how it was discovered and became well-known.

6. Explain how the etiology of substance abuse and dependence is complex and likely reflects a confluence of factors.

7. Contrast traditional approaches to the treatment of problem drinking and more modern harm-reduction approaches that reflect differences in beliefs about the nature of addiction.

8. Explain how therapies for the use of illicit drugs leave room for psychological factors and psychological approaches.

9. Describe the various treatments for cigarette smoking and why a focus on relapse prevention is necessary.

10. Identify different approaches to the prevention of substance use and the evidence for the effectiveness of prevention efforts.

"The blackouts became regular. Each time I drank there would be hours, even days I could not remember. I would start to work and manage to get three pages done. Then, thinking three pages was a wonderful amount, I would go to the bookshelf where I kept my bottle of rum and have one drink, then two. . . . Yet now, when I really wanted to stop, when I prayed to be able to drink normally, I could not. Nor could I control anything I did or said once I started drinking. It was a terrible feeling, not to know what was to happen to me once I went outside. Three-day drunks became three-week drunks, and then three-month drunks."

—*Richards, 2001, pp. 115–116*

The above excerpt is from the personal account of David Adams Richards, the acclaimed author from New Brunswick. His story is but one of 10 compelling essays by Canadian authors in the book *Addicted: Notes from the Belly of the Beast* (see Crozier & Lane, 2001). Fortunately, Richards was able to

quit drinking over 20 years ago when a friend took him to an Alcoholics Anonymous meeting. His story illustrates that some people with extreme forms of addiction can overcome it.

Unfortunately, problems with addiction are widespread and can influence people of various backgrounds and levels of accomplishment. For instance, Canadian actor Cory Monteith of the TV show *Glee* received treatment in early 2013, but he died at the age of 31 that summer in Vancouver after mixing alcohol and heroin. In an interview in 2011, Monteith (see photo) revealed that he started drinking when he was 13. He first entered into rehabilitation treatment when he was 19 after a family intervention when he was caught stealing from a family member (see Chang, 2011; Malcolm, 2011). He noted back in 2011 that "I'm not Finn Hudson. I'm lucky on so many counts. I'm lucky to be alive" (see Chang, 2011). Below we will discuss in more detail the dangers of mixing substances and the celebrity deaths that have resulted from this very dangerous practice.

One of the most striking contrasts evident in society is the distinction between the costs and consequences of addiction vs. the way that usage is portrayed in advertisements. The fun,

EXimages/Alamy Stock Photo

In spite of multiple attempts to get clean, Canadian actor Cory Monteith died of a fatal combination of heroin and alcohol at the age of 31.

exciting party atmosphere depicted in beer commercials and the cool sophistication of characters promoting liquor products simply do not fit the facts about drinking. These facts were summarized in the World Health Organization (2011) report titled *The Global Status Report on Alcohol and Health*. Here are some of the facts:

- The harmful use of alcohol results in 2.5 million deaths per year.
- Worldwide, 4% of all deaths are attributable to alcohol and this is greater than the number of deaths attributable to HIV-AIDS, violence, or tuberculosis.
- Alcohol consumption is the world's third-largest risk factor for disease and disability.
- Alcohol abuse is a causal factor in 60 types of diseases and injuries and is a contributing factor in 200 others.
- Alcohol is particularly a risk for males and is implicated as the leading cause of death for males aged 15 to 59.

Recent debate has centred on whether mild or modest drinking is protective or is associated with health risks. A recent review of the well-known link between drinking and breast cancer suggested there is risk in even modest consumption. It was estimated that in 2012, 144,000 breast cancer diagnoses and 38,000 breast cancer deaths around the world were attributable to levels of alcohol consumption, and almost 1 in 5 cases in either category were women who had been light alcohol consumers (Shield, Soerjomataram, & Rehm, 2016). A systematic review and meta-analysis from Stockwell and associates (2016) at the University of Victoria led them to conclude that there is much greater risk for heavier drinkers and former heavy drinkers, and the reduced risk for light drinkers is not as great as previously concluded because earlier research did not make adjustments for methodological problems. They concluded that it is certainly not the case that low-volume alcohol consumption is better than abstaining from drinking.

North America is a drug culture in ways that go beyond the use of alcohol. North Americans use drugs to wake up (caffeine in coffee or tea), to stay alert throughout the day (nicotine in cigarettes, caffeine in soft drinks), to relax (alcohol), and to reduce pain (aspirin). The widespread availability and frequent use of various drugs sets the stage for the potential abuse of drugs, the topic of this chapter.

Historically, the pathological use of substances was represented in two diagnostic categories: substance abuse and substance dependence. **Substance dependence** was characterized by the primary symptoms of tolerance and withdrawal. **Tolerance** is indicated by either (1) larger doses of the substance being needed to produce the desired effect or (2) the effects of the drug becoming markedly less if the usual amount is taken. **Withdrawal** symptoms—negative physical and psychological effects—develop when the person stops taking the substance or reduces the amount. The person may also use the substance to relieve or avoid withdrawal symptoms.

For the less serious diagnosis of **substance abuse**, the person must experience one of the following as a result of recurrent use of the drug:

- failure to fulfill major obligations (e.g., absences from work or neglect of children)
- exposure to physical dangers (e.g., operating machinery or driving while intoxicated)
- legal problems (e.g., arrests for disorderly conduct or traffic violations)
- persistent social or interpersonal problems (e.g., arguments with a spouse)

Unfortunately, empirical testing has indicated a lack of a clear distinction in reality between substance abuse and substance dependence (see Martin, Chung, & Langenbucher, 2008). Martin et al. (2008) concluded that there is a quantitative severity distinction rather than a qualitative distinction between substance abuse and substance dependence, and so both disorders should be included on a single continuum. Indeed, in the *DSM-5*, this distinction was dropped and there is now one overarching category: **substance-related and addictive disorders**. The American Psychiatric Association suggested that dropping the substance dependence category would help to distinguish the compulsive drug acquisition behaviours of addicted people vs. "the normal responses of tolerance and withdrawal that some patients experience when using prescribed medications that affect the central nervous system" (American Psychiatric Association, February 10, 2010).

This overarching *DSM-5* category is broken down into various substance-related disorders (e.g., alcohol-related disorders, caffeine-related disorders, hallucinogen-related disorders, opioid-related disorders). The biggest change involving the addictive disorders in the *DSM-5* is that substance use disorders are now subsumed in the new overall category called "addiction and related disorders." The *DSM-5* also includes a new category called "gambling disorder" that is listed as a non–substance-related addictive disorder.

We turn now to an overview of the major substance-related disorders, focusing on problem drinking, nicotine and cigarette smoking, marijuana, sedatives and stimulants, and the hallucinogens. We will then look at etiological factors suspected in substance abuse and dependence and conclude with an examination of available therapies. Before we do so, however, note that while we will discuss various forms of addiction as separate problems, in reality, people who are addicted often combine many substances, including prescription drugs, in a way that can prove fatal. In these instances, it is as if the person has taken a lethal cocktail of drugs. Recent deaths of famous people who have died at an early age seem a little less bewildering when autopsy reports become available. Consider the cases, for instance, of Heath Ledger (see photo), Michael Jackson, Whitney Houston, Amy Winehouse, and Philip Seymour Hoffman. The New York City medical examiner ruled in 2008 that "Mr. Heath Ledger died as the result of acute intoxication by the combined effects of oxycodone, hydrocodone, diazepam, temazepam, alprazolam and doxylamine. We have concluded that the manner of death is accident, resulting from the abuse of prescription medications" (see CNN, February 6, 2008). Ledger's death coincided with the peak of his popularity due to his unforgettable performance as the Joker in the movie *The Dark Knight*. Blood tests indicated that Michael Jackson had a combination of the anaesthetic drug propofol and several other drugs, including three sedatives (i.e., lidocaine, lorazepam, midazolam, diazepam, and nordiazepam). It was concluded that Whitney Houston "possibly overdosed on a narcotic substance, prescription medications, over the counter medications and alcohol" (County of Los Angeles, 2012, p. 1). However, in contrast, in the case of singer Amy Winehouse, a second autopsy reported early in 2013 indicated that the primary cause of death was simply "acute alcohol poisoning."

Polysubstance abuse involves the use of multiple drugs. Alcohol and nicotine are a common combination, although most people who smoke and drink in social situations do not become substance abusers.

Finally, acclaimed actor Philip Seymour Hoffman died in February 2014. The New York City medical examiner ruled that Hoffman died of acute mixed drug intoxication, which included a combination of heroin, cocaine, benzodiazepines, and amphetamine. Hoffman was found on the floor of his bathroom with a syringe in his arm. The sad fates of these famous performers underscore that fame and fortune do not equate to happiness and well-adjusted behaviour.

Alcohol abuse or dependence combined with other drugs is referred to as **polydrug** (or **polysubstance**) **abuse**, which is defined simply as using or abusing more than one drug at a time (see photo). The deaths described above underscore the fact that polydrug abuse can create serious health problems because the effects of some drugs when taken together are synergistic; the effects of each combine to produce an especially strong reaction. For example, mixing alcohol and barbiturates is a common means of suicide, both intentional and accidental (Lesage et al., 1994). Alcohol is also believed to contribute to deaths from heroin, for it can reduce the amount of the narcotic needed to make a dose lethal.

In January of 2008, Heath Ledger died of an accidental overdose of a combination of prescription medications in January 2008. The actor died from the combined effects of oxycodone, hydrocodone, diazepam, temazepam, alprazolam, and doxylamine. Polydrug use can amplify the risk of death.

12.1 Alcohol Abuse and Dependence

The term "alcoholic" is familiar to most people, yet it does not have a precise meaning. To some, it implies a person slumped against a building, to others an abusive husband or co-worker, and to still others a man or woman sneaking drinks during the day. All these images are to some extent accurate, yet none provides a full or useful definition.

Alcohol dependence may include tolerance or withdrawal reactions. People who are physically dependent on alcohol generally have more severe symptoms of the disorder (Schuckit et al., 1999). Those who begin drinking early in life develop their first withdrawal symptoms in their thirties or forties. The effects of the abrupt withdrawal of alcohol in a chronic, heavy user

The Canadian Press/Jeff McIntosh

Canadian hockey player Theoren Fleury had to leave the New York Rangers of the National Hockey League in 2001 to take part in a rehabilitation program for alcohol abuse. Fleury's struggles continued. He was suspended for six months in 2003 and prohibited from playing for his new team, the Chicago Blackhawks, because of continuing addiction problems and related behavioural difficulties. In his autobiography, Fleury acknowledged that he was sexually abused by his hockey coach as a boy.

may be dramatic because the body has become accustomed to the drug. Subjectively, the person is often anxious, depressed, weak, restless, and unable to sleep. Tremors of the muscles, especially of the small musculatures of the fingers, face, eyelids, lips, and tongue, may be marked, and pulse, blood pressure, and temperature are elevated.

In relatively rare cases, a person who has been drinking heavily for a number of years may also experience **delirium tremens** (the **DTs**, which involve alcohol withdrawal delirium) when the level of alcohol in the blood drops suddenly. The person becomes delirious as well as tremulous and has hallucinations that are primarily visual, but may be tactile as well. Unpleasant and very active creatures—snakes, cockroaches, spiders, and the like—may appear to be crawling up the wall or over the person's body, or they may fill the room. Feverish, disoriented, and terrified, the person may claw frantically at his or her skin to get rid of the vermin or may cower in the corner to escape an advancing army of fantastic animals. The delirium and physiological paroxysms caused by withdrawal of alcohol indicate that the drug is addictive.

Increased tolerance is evident following heavy, prolonged drinking. Some alcohol abusers can drink a litre of bourbon a day without showing signs of drunkenness (Mello & Mendelson, 1970). Moreover, levels of alcohol in the blood of such people are unexpectedly low after what is usually viewed as excessive drinking, suggesting that the body adapts to the drug and becomes able to process it more efficiently.

Although changes in the liver enzymes that metabolize alcohol can account to a small extent for tolerance, most researchers now believe that the central nervous system is implicated. Some research suggests that tolerance results from changes in the number or sensitivity of GABA or glutamate receptors (Tsai, Gastfriend, & Coyle, 1995). Withdrawal may be the result of increased activation in some neural pathways to compensate for alcohol's inhibitory effects in the brain. When drinking stops, the inhibitory effects of alcohol are lost, resulting in a state of overexcitation.

Although tolerance is mostly due to physiological factors, research by Vogel-Sprott and associates at the University of Waterloo highlighted the role of psychological factors. Response expectations and the consequences of behaviour can have a direct influence on tolerance and the effects of alcohol (see Vogel-Sprott, Kartechner, & McConnell, 1989; Zinatelli & Vogel-Sprott, 1993). Similarly, the development of addictions often reflects the interplay of biological and psychological factors.

The drinking pattern of people who are alcohol dependent indicates that their drinking is out of control. They need to drink daily and are unable to stop or cut down despite repeated efforts to abstain completely or to restrict drinking to certain periods of the day. They may go on occasional binges, remaining intoxicated for two, three, or more days. Sometimes they consume a litre of alcohol at a time. They may suffer blackouts and have no memory of events that took place during a bout of intoxication; their craving may be so overpowering that they are forced to ingest alcohol in a non-beverage form, such as hair tonic. Such drinking, of course, causes social and occupational difficulties, quarrels with family or friends, violent behaviour, frequent absences from work, loss of job, and arrests for intoxication or traffic accidents.

The person who abuses alcohol, in contrast to the person who is physically dependent on it, experiences negative social and occupational effects from the drug but does not show tolerance, withdrawal, or the compulsive drinking patterns seen in the person who is alcohol dependent.

Prevalence of Alcohol Abuse and Comorbidity with Other Disorders

Prevalence rates for alcohol dependence in the United States defined by *DSM-IV* criteria were estimated in 2007 as follows: the prevalence of lifetime and 12-month alcohol abuse was 17.8% and 4.7%, respectively, and the prevalence of lifetime and 12-month alcohol dependence was 12.5% and 3.8%, respectively (Hasin, Stinson, Ogburn, & Grant, 2007). That is, lifetime prevalence of alcohol misuse was more than 3 in 10 Americans. This study also found that about 3 in 4 with alcohol dependence had never received treatment. Prevalence rates were higher in men, younger cohorts, and whites. The course was often chronic, with an average of four years for alcohol dependence (Hasin et al., 2007).

A U.S. survey of over 10,000 adolescents between the ages of 13 to 18 found that 15% of the adolescents (about 1 in 7) met criteria for lifetime substance abuse. Additional analyses indicated that the median age of onset for drug or alcohol abuse with dependence was about 14 years old (Swendsen et al., 2012).

TABLE 12.1   **Rates of Hazardous Drinking in Canada**

Substance and Measure	CCHS 1.2 2002[a] Interview	CAS 2004[b] Telephone
Alcohol	**Survey Adults 15+**	**Survey Adults 15+**
Regular heavy drinking (5+ drinks on one occasion at least once a week) in the past 12 months among heavy drinkers	18.6% • 23.0% of men; 10.3% of women	
Exceeded low-risk drinking guidelines (men: 14 drinks or less per week, and women: 9 drinks or less per week)		22.6% of current alcohol drinkers • 30.2% of men; 15.1% of women who had drank in the past year
Reported symptoms meeting criteria for being dependent on alcohol or illicit drugs	3.1% • 2.6% (641,000) dependence on alcohol • 0.8% (194,000) dependence on illicit drugs • 4.5% of men; 1.7% of women	
Drinking hazardously indicating harmful use or possible dependence on alcohol[c]		17.0% of current alcohol drinkers • 25.1% of men; 8.9% of women who had drank in the past year
Cannabis		
Past-3-month cannabis users reporting problems[d]		• 42.9% reported failure to control their use at some point in their life • 40.4% reported a strong desire to use cannabis (during previous 3 months)

[a]Statistics Canada, 2002 Mental Health and Well-being Survey (Canadian Community Health Survey, Cycle 1.2)
[b]Canadian Centre on Substance Abuse, 2004 Canadian Addiction Survey (CAS)
[c]According to the World Health Organization's Alcohol Use Disorders Identification Test (AUDIT)
[d]According to the World Health Organization's Alcohol, Smoking and Substance Involvement Screening Tool (ASSIST)

Table 12.1 summarizes epidemiological data obtained in Canada. Based on the 2004 Canadian Addiction Survey, 22.6% of current alcohol drinkers exceeded low-risk drinking guidelines, which stipulate no more than two drinks per day, and 17.0% of current alcohol drinkers engaged in hazardous drinking. Strong gender differences exist, with hazardous drinking among current drinkers being evident among 25.1% of men and 8.9% of women.

Indeed, the prototypical heavy drinker in Canada is a young adult male who is not married and who is relatively well off financially (Single et al., 1995). Problem drinking is comorbid with several personality disorders; in fact, Canadian researchers have sought to identify genetic factors that are common to personality disorders and alcohol misuse (Jang, Vernon, & Livesley, 2000). Problem drinking is also comorbid with mood and anxiety disorders, as shown in a study of six countries, including Canada (Merikangas et al., 1998), and with other drug use and schizophrenia. Comorbidity is important to assess because comorbid psychiatric disorders predict higher relapse rates and less initial treatment improvement among dually diagnosed individuals with substance abuse (for a review, see Aase, Jason, & Robinson, 2008).

Drinking is on the rise in Canada and binge drinking among students remains a big problem (see Student Perspectives 12.1). With the turn of the century, there was a 9% increase in Canada overall in alcohol consumption, but the increase was almost twice as high (16%) in British Columbia (Thomas, Stockwell, & Reist, 2009). Unfortunately, alcohol-related deaths increased to a similar degree, underscoring the dangers of excessive drinking. Other analyses by this research team of the 2004 Canadian Addiction Survey results found that the heaviest-drinking 10% of respondents accounted for 50% of overall consumption (Stockwell, Zhao, & Thomas, 2009).

A new report titled Alcohol Consumption in Canada released by Canada's Chief Public Health Officer provides a concise overview of key themes and issues involving drinking in Canada (see Taylor, 2016). Some of the key findings and conclusions are as follows:

1. It is estimated that in 2013, about 22 million Canadians drank alcohol.

2. Levels of consumption suggest that 3.1 million Canadians drank enough to be at immediate risk of injury and harm.

3. About 4.4 million Canadians drank enough to have risk for chronic health effects such as liver cirrhosis and various forms of cancer. There is no "safe limit" of alcohol consumption when it comes to cancer risk.

4. Drinking patterns matter: how much and how often drinking occurs contributes to risk.

Student Perspectives 12.1

Binge Drinking and Its Consequences Among Students

Alcohol abuse is frequent among university and college students. A 1993 U.S. survey revealed that 50% of men and 40% of women engaged in the previous month in binge drinking, defined as having five drinks in a row for men and four for women (Wechsler et al., 1994). The 1993 survey was repeated in 1997 and 1999, and similar findings emerged. The 1999 survey evaluated more than 14,000 students from 119 sites and found that 44% had engaged in binge drinking within the previous month, a rate similar to those obtained in previous surveys (Wechsler, Lee, Kuo, & Lee, 2000). About 1 in 4 students were frequent binge drinkers who usually binged at least once a week. The survey results have received a great deal of attention and not just because of the alarming levels of binge drinking. Other findings point to the harmful consequences of excessive drinking on campuses. Students who binge drink are substantially more likely to damage property, get into legal trouble, miss classes, and experience injuries (Wechsler et al., 1994). One update found that in a two-year period, more than half a million U.S. students were unintentionally injured as a result of drinking (Hingson, Heeren, Winter, & Wechsler, 2005). Binge drinkers are more willing to engage in unsafe sexual practices, and nondrinking students in close proximity to binge drinkers are more likely to be the target of unwanted sexual advances and physical assaults.

What about binge drinking on Canadian campuses? The results of the first comprehensive survey of Canadian campuses were reported by Gliksman, Demers, Adlaf, Newton-Taylor, and Schmidt (2000). This study, conducted initially in 1998, used representative sampling techniques to survey 7,800 undergraduate students at 16 universities across Canada. The 2004 Canadian Campus Survey (Adlaf, Demers, & Gliksman, 2005) confirmed that binge drinking is a very significant problem on Canadian campuses. Overall, about 1 out of 6 Canadian students met criteria for "heavy frequent drinking," which is defined as the usual consumption of five or more drinks on a daily basis (Adlaf et al., 2005).

Evidence continues to indicate that binge drinking and its consequences represent a big problem on Canadian campuses. The latest survey of students from 41 Canadian campuses by the American College Health Association (2016) found that 32.0% of students had not had anything to drink within the past 30 days, but those who did often went too far. Overall, 34.5% of students reported at least one binge drinking episode (consuming five or more drinks) during the previous two weeks. The average number of drinks consumed during the last time that they partied or socialized and had something to drink was 5.96 drinks for men and 4.67 drinks for women. Again, there were many consequences. The most common consequences during the past 12 months were that they did something they regretted doing (38.0%), forgot where they were or what they did (29.1%), had unprotected sex (24.1%), and got physically injured (18.4%).

Typically, extensive sex differences are not found. The 2007 report by ESPAD (Andersson, Hibell, Beck, et al., 2007) of student drinking in 35 European countries found comparable levels of binge drinking among females and males, with females actually having higher levels of binge drinking in 9 of the 35 countries, including the United Kingdom, Ireland, and Spain.

Of course, as is the case with anyone, binge drinking can have substantial consequences for students. New research at McMaster University indicates that binge-drinking students with elevated stress and depression had clear deficits on high interference memory tasks and that students with an early history of binge drinking had poorer performance on a range of memory tasks. These researchers wanted to study whether these deficits could be reversed by stopping and no longer engaging in binge drinking, but they reported that they could not test this due to an inability to locate enough students who had stopped their tendency to binge drink (see Goldstein et al., in press).

What can be done about the binge-drinking problem? A survey of U.S. college administrators indicated that many preventive steps have been taken (Wechsler et al., 2000). Prevention efforts include providing general education about the effects of alcohol, use of policy controls to limit access to alcohol (including "dry" residences and "dry" campuses), and restrictions on media advertising involving alcohol. High-profile cases of sexual assaults committed by students under the influence of alcohol and other drugs have resulted in decisions such as the alcohol ban at undergraduate parties announced by Stanford University in California in August 2016.

More intensive alcohol interventions are feedback-based interventions that are devised for students who have been mandated to receive treatment due to an alcohol-related problem. Students in these interventions receive feedback about their drinking along with instruction in harm reduction techniques. One investigation found that a group-delivered intervention was not effective and a computer-delivered intervention was only somewhat effective, but a face-to-face intervention delivered to individuals resulted in significant reductions in alcohol use and alcohol-related harms (Alfonso, Hall, & Dunn, 2013). In general, face-to-face interventions have proven far superior to computer-delivered interventions for college drinkers (see Carey et al., 2012).

The late Alan Marlatt conducted extensive research on high-risk college drinkers with his harm reduction perspective (see Canadian Contributions 12.1). He and his associates have tested the usefulness of brief interventions that focus on controlling and reducing the drinking behaviour of high-risk students rather than on striving for complete abstinence. They have shown that even brief interventions can reduce the harmful consequences of heavy drinking and that these improvements persist over a two-year period (see Marlatt, Baer, & Larimer, 1995; Marlatt et al., 1998). However, despite these improvements, the high-risk group still experiences more alcohol-related problems than the low-risk participants.

Thinking Critically

1. Is binge drinking a problem on your university or college campus? How would you rank it relative to other possible concerns (such as vandalism, safety, and sexual assaults)? Are you in favour of cancelling homecoming events that have often been linked with excessive drinking?

2. If binge drinking is a problem, what can be done about it? Who should be responsible for doing something about it? Should it be the administration, faculty, the students themselves, or a coordinated effort on the part of all stakeholders?

3. Do you think that interventions that focus on moderating the drinking behaviour of high-risk students would work on your campus? If yes, how would you set up a program?

5. Exposure to alcohol through family and friends as well as through entertainment and advertising can strongly influence people's motives for drinking alcohol and their drinking patterns.

6. Family, friends, and all Canadians who care for or work with youth can play a positive role if they recognize their influence on youth's drinking patterns and support their healthy physical, mental, and emotional development.

7. Approaches such as a regulated alcohol industry, policies on prices and taxation, controls on sales and availability, and minimum age laws help reduce the impact on Canadians, especially youth.

This report is available online for anyone to read and it is recommended that all Canadians consider doing so.

Nature of the Disorder

An important issue to discuss from the outset is how addictive disorders such as alcohol abuse are considered and conceptualized according to different models. The **disease model** is the view that problems such as excessive drinking are due to vulnerabilities that reside within a person (e.g., a genetic predisposition, brain chemistry). It is a reflection of a medical model and the announcement in 1954 by the American Medical Association that alcoholism is a disease. In contrast, the **moral model** is the view that excessive drinking reflects personal failings and personal choices of the afflicted individual. These models have clear implications for a host of other issues: recovery, the perceived likelihood of relapse, and the role of personal responsibility and self-directed change. If a disease model is endorsed, then it follows that no cure is possible and abstinence is indicated. This also promotes the research for brain mechanisms implicated in addiction (for a discussion, see Blume, Rudisill, Hendricks, & Sanatoya, 2013).

It is worth noting that a survey of 215 university and college educators found that the prevailing view of addiction does not reflect either the disease model or the medical model. Rather, they preferred to view addiction as a maladaptive coping mechanism or coping response, while rejecting the moral view and showing ambivalence toward the disease model (see Broadus et al., 2010).

We will see below that initial beliefs about the nature and course of alcoholism were strongly influenced by the views and work of E. Morton Jellinek. According to Blume et al. (2013), Jellinek's emphasis on the stages of alcoholism that emerge over time is largely responsible for promoting the disease model.

Course of the Disorder

At one time, the life histories of alcohol abusers were thought to have a common, downhill progression. On the basis of an extensive survey of 2,000 members of Alcoholics Anonymous,

Jellinek (1952) described the male alcohol abuser as passing through four stages, beginning with social drinking and progressing to a stage at which he lives only to drink.

The available evidence does not always corroborate this stage model. The histories of alcohol-dependent people do indeed show a progression from alcohol abuse to alcohol dependence (Langenbucher & Chung, 1995); however, data reveal considerable fluctuations in drinking patterns, from heavy drinking for some periods of time to abstinence or lighter drinking at others (Vaillant, 1996). Furthermore, patterns of maladaptive use of alcohol are more variable than Jellinek implied. Heavy use of alcohol may be restricted to weekends, or long periods of abstinence may be interspersed with binges of continual drinking for several weeks (Robins et al., 1988). There is no single pattern of alcohol abuse.

Evidence also indicates that Jellinek's account does not apply to women. Difficulties with alcohol usually begin at a later age in women than in men and often after an inordinately stressful experience, such as a serious family crisis. For women, the time interval between the onset of heavy drinking and alcohol abuse is briefer than it is for men (Mezzich et al., 1994). Women with drinking problems tend to be steady drinkers who drink alone and are less likely than men to binge.

Costs of Alcohol Abuse and Dependence

The beginning of this chapter outlined some of the costs of alcohol abuse. There are some clear regional differences. Rates of hazardous alcohol drinking are exceptionally high in Russia and here it has been established indirectly that the relatively low life expectancy of Russian men is attributable to hazardous alcohol drinking. Leon et al. (2007) found that almost half of all deaths of working-aged men in a typical Russian city can be attributed to hazardous drinking.

Public awareness of the dangers of drinking and driving may have peaked when Diana, Princess of Wales, was killed and it was found that her driver was intoxicated (see photo). Although public awareness campaigns continue, significant levels of driving while impaired are still found in Canada and around the world.

Although most people who have a drinking problem do not seek professional help, people who abuse alcohol constitute a large proportion of new admissions to mental and general hospitals. Problem drinkers use health services four times more often than do non-abusers, and their medical expenses are twice as high as those of non-drinkers (Harvard Mental Health Letter, 1996). The suicide rate for alcohol abusers is much higher than that for the general population.

Although alcohol-related traffic fatalities have declined substantially in Canada, analyses of national data between 2000 and 2010 showed that 56.7% of fatally injured drivers tested positive for alcohol, drugs, or both (Beirness, Beasley, & Boase, 2013). According to statistics from the Traffic

Jerome Delay/AP Images

Diana, Princess of Wales, was killed in an automobile accident in Paris. Her driver was intoxicated.

Injury Research Foundation in Ottawa, as summarized by the Canadian division of Mothers Against Drunk Driving (MADD, 2007), drunk drivers kill an average of about 3 to 4 people per day and injure 187 people in Canada every day. Alcohol increases both the likelihood and severity of traffic accidents. Unfortunately, high-profile cases of driving under the influence (see photo) illustrate that this behaviour can be quite pervasive.

The prototypical drinking driver in Canada is a male between the ages of 25 and 34 who drinks large amounts of alcohol on a regular basis or is a social drinker who occasionally drinks heavily (MADD, 2007). Despite this profile, the social significance of drunk driving among teenagers should not be discounted. According to Chamberlain and Solomon (2008), 16- to 19-year-olds made up 5.4% of the Canadian population in 2003, yet they accounted for 23% of pedestrian fatalities where the driver had been drinking alcohol. The authors called for a nationwide requirement of zero blood alcohol for drivers aged 21 and younger, as well as greater police powers and more rigorous enforcement of existing legislation. Indeed, reviewers have concluded that enacting and enforcing more extreme legislative measures are highly effective in reducing drunk driving (Anderson, Chisholm, & Fuhr, 2009).

It seems that a substantial proportion of impaired drivers have a general tendency to engage in anti-social acts. Stewart, Boase, and Lamble (2000) examined a random sample of 100 Canadian drivers with alcohol-related driving offences and found that 45% had a history of charges or convictions for such things as robbery, assault, and narcotic offences.

Alcohol may contribute to other injuries, as well. Rape, assault, and family violence are alcohol-related crimes, as is homicide; it is believed that over half of all murders are committed under the influence of alcohol (Murdoch, Pihl, & Ross, 1990). A comprehensive review concluded that alcohol is the drug with the most evidence of there being a direct link between intoxication and violence (Hoaken & Stewart, 2003). Indeed, a telephone survey of more than 1,000 Canadian adults

Paul Fenton/ZUMA KPA/Alamy Stock Photo

Kiefer Sutherland, Canadian actor and star of *24* and *Designated Survivor*, pleaded no contest to a misdemeanour charge for driving under the influence in 2007. Sutherland was sentenced to 48 days in jail because he violated his probation for a 2004 arrest for drunk driving.

found that either the perpetrator or victim was drinking in over two-thirds of reported cases of physical aggression (Wells, Graham, & West, 2000).

These data illustrate the pervasive negative impact that excessive drinking can have on drinkers and the people around them. The human costs, in terms of broken lives, are incalculable.

Short-Term Effects of Alcohol

How does alcohol produce its short-term effects? Alcohol is metabolized by enzymes after being swallowed and reaching the stomach. Most of it goes into the small intestines where it is absorbed into the blood. It is then broken down, mostly in the liver, which can metabolize about 30 millilitres of 100-proof (50% alcohol) whisky per hour. Quantities in excess of this amount stay in the bloodstream. Absorption of alcohol can be rapid, but removal is always slow. The effects of alcohol vary with the level of concentration of the drug in the bloodstream, which in turn depends on the amount ingested in a particular period of time, the presence or absence of food in the stomach to retain the alcohol and reduce its absorption rate, the size of a person's body, and the efficiency of the liver. The effects of 60 millilitres of alcohol would vary greatly for a 180-pound (80-kilogram) man who has just eaten and a 110-pound (50-kilogram) woman with an empty stomach.

Because drinking alcoholic beverages is accepted in most societies, alcohol is rarely regarded as a drug. But it is indeed a drug, and it has a biphasic effect. This means that the initial effect of alcohol is stimulating—the drinker experiences an expansive feeling of sociability and well-being as the blood-alcohol level rises—but after the blood-alcohol level peaks and begins to decline, alcohol acts as a depressant that may lead to negative emotions. Large amounts of alcohol interfere with complex thought processes. Motor coordination, balance, speech, and vision are also impaired. At this stage of intoxication, some people become depressed and withdrawn.

Alcohol produces its effects through its interactions with several neural systems in the brain. It stimulates GABA receptors, which may be responsible for reducing tension. (GABA is a major inhibitory neurotransmitter; the benzodiazepines, such as Valium, have an effect on the GABA receptor similar to that of alcohol.) Alcohol also increases levels of serotonin and dopamine, and this may be the source of its ability to produce pleasurable effects. Finally, alcohol inhibits glutamate receptors, which may cause the cognitive effects of alcohol intoxication, such as slurred speech and memory loss (U.S. Department of Health and Human Services, 1994).

Long-Term Effects of Prolonged Alcohol Abuse

Chronic drinking creates severe biological damage in addition to psychological deterioration. Almost every tissue and organ of the body is affected adversely by prolonged consumption of alcohol. Malnutrition may be severe. Because alcohol provides calories—a pint of 80-proof spirits supplies about half a day's caloric requirements—heavy drinkers often reduce their intake of food. But the calories provided by alcohol are empty; they do not supply the nutrients essential for health. Alcohol also contributes directly to malnutrition by impairing the digestion of food and absorption of vitamins. In older chronic alcohol abusers, a deficiency of B-complex vitamins can cause amnestic syndrome, a severe loss of memory for both recent and long-past events. Memory gaps are often filled in with reports of imaginary, improbable events.

Prolonged alcohol use with reduction in the intake of proteins contributes to the development of cirrhosis of the liver, a potentially fatal disease in which some liver cells become engorged with fat and protein, impeding their function; some cells die, triggering an inflammatory process. When scar tissue develops, blood flow is obstructed.

Other common physiological changes include damage to the endocrine glands and pancreas, heart failure, hypertension, stroke, and capillary hemorrhages, which are responsible for the swelling and redness in the face, especially the nose, of chronic alcohol abusers. Prolonged use of alcohol appears to destroy brain cells; a five-year longitudinal study found

significant loss of grey matter from the temporal lobes (Pfefferman et al., 1998). Even shorter-term abuse may produce some cognitive impairment; alcohol-abusing college students show impairment on neuropsychological tests (Sher et al., 1997). Alcohol also reduces the effectiveness of the immune system and increases susceptibility to infection and cancer. For example, women's risk of breast cancer increases steadily with the amount they drink; there is a linear-dose response such that risk increases by 7% per drink; thus five drinks per day on average would increase risk by 35% (see Aronson, 2003). Even moderate drinking is linked with risk of breast cancer and some evidence suggests that alcohol can act as a breast carcinogen and a tumour promoter (see Brooks & Zakhari, 2013).

Heavy alcohol consumption during pregnancy is the leading cause of mental retardation. The growth of the fetus is slowed, and cranial, facial, and limb anomalies are produced, a condition known as **fetal alcohol syndrome (FAS)** (see photo). Other syndromes included among fetal alcohol spectrum disorders are partial fetal alcohol syndrome and alcohol-related neurodevelopmental disorder (ARND) (see Loock et al., 2005). Even moderate drinking by mothers-to-be can produce less severe but undesirable effects on the fetus, so total abstention is recommended. Research now clearly indicates that there are risks associated with sustained drinking in any of the three pregnancy trimesters (Gupta, Gupta, & Shirasaka, 2016).

FAS disorders are highly comorbid with other problems and conditions. A recent review and meta-analysis conducted by a team of Canadian investigators found a total of 428 comorbid conditions associated with FAS. The most common comorbid conditions involved problems with the peripheral nervous system, conduct disorder, receptive language disorder, and expressive language disorder (see Popova et al., 2016).

Early detection of fetal alcohol spectrum disorders is associated with better long-term outcomes (Loock et al., 2005). Early diagnosis and treatment can reduce later mental health problems, subsequent levels of inappropriate sexual behaviour, and later involvement with the law (Matlow, 2011). Early

Andy Levin/Science Source

Heavy drinking during pregnancy causes fetal alcohol syndrome. Children with this syndrome have facial abnormalities, as well as mental retardation.

universal screening is indicated and protocols exist for doing this in the most cost-effective manner (Matlow, 2011).

Initial accounts of the consequences of FAS focused on the impact on behaviours. However, in light of new findings, a growing number of researchers are arguing from a neuropsychological perspective that FAS is a disorder of brain structures and processes rather than behaviours *per se*. Riley, Infante, and Warren (2011) outlined the various pathways in which prenatal alcohol exposure influences brain development.

The human costs and economic costs of the syndrome are enormous. In terms of the economic costs, FAS disorders occur in about 1 out of every 100 live births in Canada. An estimate of direct and indirect costs in Canada for 2013 is $1.8 billion, though this could be underestimated (see Popova, Lange, Burd, & Rehm, 2015). FAS is the leading cause of developmental and cognitive disabilities in children in Canada (Stade et al., 2009).

The prevalence of FAS disorders is not simply due to a lack of awareness; it was estimated over a decade ago that 90% of Canadian women realize that drinking alcohol is not good for the unborn baby (Koren, Nulman, Chudley, & Loock, 2003). One problem realized over a decade ago is that at least half of Canadian and American women drink socially and half of all pregnancies are unplanned, so each year about 100,000 Canadian infants are exposed to some alcohol during gestation (Koren et al., 2003). About one-quarter of pregnant women in Canada drink alcohol prior to realizing that they have conceived (Koren et al., 2003). In recent years, Canada has assumed a leadership role in terms of the prevention of FAS disorders and has begun to implement a pan-Canadian prevention strategy (see Poole, Schmidt, Green, & Hemsing, 2016). The recent survey of gaps and barriers conducted by Poole and associates (2016) identified other concerns, such as maternal fears that seeking treatment for addiction will result in the infant being taken away by authorities. One very significant barrier that was identified is lack of access to suitable treatment programs in Canada for addicted pregnant women.

The psychological, biological, and social consequences of prolonged consumption of alcohol are extremely serious. Because the alcohol abuser's own functioning is so severely disrupted, the people with whom he or she interacts are also deeply affected and hurt.

Inhalant Use Disorders

We will mention briefly another class of disorders that may be a stepping stone for developing other disorders involving alcohol and drug abuse: inhalant use disorders. According to the *DSM-5*, inhalant use disorder is diagnosed when the person displays a problematic pattern of use of a hydrocarbon-based inhalant substance as indicated by two or more symptoms that occur over a 12-month period and are associated with clinically significant impairment or distress. Key symptoms include recurrent use and constant craving of inhalants.

Young people from Davis Inlet, Sheshatshiu, and Pikangikum have engaged in inhalant abuse. Unfortunately, the $150-million move from Davis Inlet, Labrador, to the new town of Natuashish in 2002 did not solve the problems of the Mushuau Innu from Davis Inlet (Toughill, 2003). The children are still sniffing gasoline.

Although inhalant use is not confined to children and adolescents, an alarming number of young people begin their substance abuse by inhaling such substances as glue, correction fluid, spray paint, cosmetics, gasoline, household aerosol sprays, and the nitrous oxide found in spray cans of whipped cream. The Director of the U.S. National Institute on Drug Abuse, Nora Volkow, has expressed concerns about increases in inhalant abuse among young people, despite evidence that inhalant use has decreased substantially since its peak in the mid-1990s (see Volkow, 2012). The greatest use in the U.S. is among 12- to 17-year-olds with it tending to peak among 14-year-olds.

This estimate fits with the findings from the Canadian Paediatric Society (1998), who concluded that the peak age of inhalant use is 14 to 15 years, with initial onsets in children as young as 6. Inhalants are inexpensive and readily available. Inhalant use disorders can involve behaviours such as sniffing (nasal inhalation of a substance), huffing (breathing fumes from a small rag stuffed in the mouth), and bagging (breathing fumes from a plastic bag held up to the mouth).

Gasoline sniffing is a widespread problem among certain groups in northern Canada and is especially prevalent among Aboriginal children and adolescents (Barnes, 1989; see photo). For instance, a study conducted with Aboriginal and rural high school students in Quebec found that solvent use was considerably higher among Aboriginal students. This finding reflected a general tendency for the Aboriginal students to make greater use of illicit drugs, while the francophone students consumed more alcoholic beverages (Lalinec-Michaud, Subak, Ghadirian, & Kovess, 1991). Harries (2001) asked children in Pikangikum, in northern Ontario, what the gas does for them.

> "'It makes you dizzy, it makes you high,'" Sylvester says. 'You get hungry.'

Is there anything else they could be doing?

'No,'Erroll says. 'It's boring,' Sylvester says.

What would make a difference?

'We wanted a community centre so we could go there, play pool,' Erroll says.

'We could paint,' Sylvester suggests.

'We want some . . .' Erroll's voice trails away. He brings the bag up to his face.

'Chips and pop,' Sylvester is sniffing from a bag too.

Erroll finds his voice. 'We want clothing, we want food, I wish that people had—I don't know.' His hands are shaking and he sniffs again to compose himself.

'To play games at the school—soccer, hockey, baseball . . . (p. A16)

Most inhalants act as depressants and, as such, can be seen as similar to alcohol and sedatives. The inhaled substance can result in feelings of euphoria and psychic numbing, but inhalants can cause damage to the central nervous system. Nausea and subsequent headaches are experienced eventually in almost all cases.

Inhalant use is linked with other adjustment problems. Howard and Jenson (1999) compared delinquents who did or did not use inhalants and found that those with inhalant use had higher levels of suicide, criminal behaviour, and family problems.

12.2 Nicotine and Cigarette Smoking

The history of tobacco smoking bears much similarity to that of other addictive drugs (Brecher, 1972). It was not long after Columbus's first commerce with Native North Americans that sailors and merchants began to imitate the Natives' habit of smoking rolled leaves of tobacco and to experience, as the Natives did, the increasing craving for it. When not smoked, tobacco was—and is—chewed or ground into small pieces and inhaled as snuff.

Nicotine is the addicting agent of tobacco. It stimulates receptors, called nicotinic receptors, in the brain. Molecular biology studies suggest that the main receptor mediating nicotine dependence is the nicotinic acetylcholine receptor subtype. Exposure to nicotine influences brain nicotinic cholinergic receptors to facilitate neurotransmitter release (e.g., dopamine), thus producing stimulation, pleasure, and mood modulation (see Benowitz, 2008).

Some idea of the addictive qualities of tobacco can be appreciated by considering how much people have sacrificed to maintain their supplies. In sixteenth-century England, for example, tobacco was exchanged for silver, ounce for ounce. Poor people squandered their meagre resources for their several daily pipefuls. Even the public tortures and executions engineered as punishment by Sultan Murad IV of Turkey during the seventeenth century could not dissuade those of his subjects who were addicted to the weed.

Growing evidence indicates that nicotine may be much more addictive than previously indicated. A study by researchers from Toronto evaluated nicotine self-administration in squirrel monkeys (Le Foll, Wertheim, & Goldberg, 2007). This study showed that nicotine had "high reinforcing efficacy," with monkeys willing to perform up to 600 lever presses in order to self-administer nicotine! The authors concluded that regardless of other factors, nicotine is a robust and highly effective reinforcer of drug-taking behaviour.

Another investigation of adolescents from Quebec found that the addictive effects of nicotine start very shortly after one's first puff. In addition, indications of mental addiction can be found well before actual physical addiction takes place (see Gervais et al., 2006). Thus, even just one puff or one cigarette can be enough for some people to begin their addiction to nicotine.

Other data suggest that nicotine may operate differently on the brains of males vs. females. Fallon et al. (2005) measured brain activity via PET scans in male and female smokers and non-smokers while they performed two tasks. The researchers identified what they described as a fundamental biological difference between women and men. That is, without nicotine involved, there were great gender differences in metabolic activity, with females having much greater brain activity, especially in the cortical and subcortical prefrontal systems (which are linked with attention and memory). However, these differences virtually disappeared when nicotine was administered to men and women. These data qualify sex differences in smoking behaviour by suggesting that they may have both biological and cultural-social origins. Female smokers have substantially greater changes in cognitive activity after nicotine exposure.

Health Consequences of Smoking

The threat to health posed by smoking has been documented convincingly since the early 1960s. In 1964, the U.S. Surgeon General's Report was issued with the dire warning that smoking causes lung cancer. Many textbooks state that this was the first major public warning about the dangers of smoking. These books are incorrect. Judy LaMarsh provided the first major public health warning in North America on June 17, 1963. LaMarsh was Canada's Minister of Health and Welfare. She declared in the House of Commons that, "There is scientific evidence that cigarette smoking is a contributory cause of lung cancer and that it may also be associated with chronic bronchitis and coronary heart disease." This was sad foreshadowing for LaMarsh, a smoker, who died of cancer in 1980. LaMarsh was given the Order of Canada. Today, the LaMarsh Centre for Child and

Youth Research at York University in Toronto is named in her honour.

It is estimated that smoking causes about 17% of deaths annually (20% in men, 12% in women) and about 100 Canadians die each day of a smoking-related illness (Rehm, Baliunas, Brochu, et al., 2006). Overall, more than 480,000 American tobacco users die prematurely each year (U.S. Department of Health and Human Services, 2014). Cigarette smoking is responsible in some way for 1 of every 5 deaths in the United States, killing about 1,200 people each day. It is the single most preventable cause of premature death. The health risks of smoking are significantly less for cigar and pipe smokers because they seldom inhale the smoke into their lungs, but cancers of the mouth are increased.

As with alcohol, the socio-economic cost of smoking is staggering. American surveys indicated that smokers compile more than 80 million lost days of work and 145 million days of disability each year, considerably more than do their non-smoking peers. This loss of productivity coupled with the health care costs associated with smoking runs to more than $65 billion annually in the United States. The costs may be disproportionate according to socio-economic status (SES). Increasing education, occupational status, and SES tend to be linked negatively with current smoking (Corsi et al., 2013). Strong concerns have been expressed that the socio-economic disparities in levels of smoking in Canada have persisted despite improvements in terms of overall smoking reductions (Reid, Hammond, & Driezen, 2010).

Emerging data that cigarette smoking contributes to erectile problems in men—not surprising, given that nicotine constricts blood vessels—resulted in 1998 in several televised public service announcements aimed at creating some second thoughts about how sexy smoking is. One ad shows a well-dressed young man looking with interest at an attractive woman at a fancy cocktail party. He lights up a cigarette, and when she looks over in his direction, the cigarette goes limp. She shakes her head and walks away (Morain, 1998). A similar theme was portrayed in public service ads in California (see photo).

Prevalence of Smoking

Recent data attest to the significant reductions in smoking in Canada in recent years:

- Approximately 17% of Canadians were smokers in 2011 according to the results of the Canadian Tobacco Use Monitoring Survey (see Health Canada, 2011). The prevalence of smoking has steadily decreased for many years. In 2014, it was estimated that 14.6% of Canadians (about 4.2 million people) were smokers, according to the *Tobacco Use in Canada: Patterns and Trends* report (see Reid, Hammond, Rynard, & Burkhalter, 2015). This report also notes that the prevalence of smoking is highest among 25- to 34-year-olds,

WARNING: SMOKING CAUSES IMPOTENCE

California's Tobacco Education Media Campaign parodies tobacco ads to illustrate potential health effects of smoking and to attack pro-tobacco influences.

followed by 20- to 24-year-olds, and that there is a sex difference, with 16% of males and 13% of females being smokers. The current estimate of 1 in 7 Canadians being a smoker compares with the estimate that 1 in 2 Canadians being a smoker in 1965 (see Reid, Hammond, Rynard, & Burkhalter, 2015).

- Daily smokers in Canada smoked an average of 13.9 cigarettes per day. Typically, males smoke three more cigarettes than do females per day (Reid et al., 2015).

- The lowest percentage of smokers by province is 11% in British Columbia. The highest percentage of smokers by province is about 20%, in New Brunswick, Newfoundland and Labrador, and Nova Scotia (Reid et al., 2015).

The good news of the reduced smoking in Canada is overshadowed by the fact that there is a global epidemic of tobacco use, and according to Wipfli and Samet (2016), this probably represents one of the first examples of the globalization of a noninfectious cause of disease. They noted that some high-income countries still have high levels of use and there are high and increasing levels of use in several low-income and middle-income countries (e.g., Bangladesh, China, India, Indonesia, and Russia). It is estimated that the global disease burden is six million deaths every year. What makes this situation even more remarkable is the willingness of the tobacco industry over four decades to deny the health risks of smoking and suppress their evidence of the health risks (for a discussion, see Wipfli & Samet, 2016). Also, as indicated by the Russell Crowe movie *The Insider*, certain factions of the tobacco industry not only denied the health risk, they also developed and implemented the use of chemicals in cigarettes designed to increase how addicted people would become. This movie documents the whistleblowing efforts of Jeffrey Wigand, a former industry executive and scientist who worked for the tobacco company Brown & Williamson. He revealed publicly what was going on (most notably during a 1996 appearance on the television show *60 Minutes*). Wigand later worked for the Canadian government in its prevention program designed to limit smoking among young people. He also provided expert testimony in 2012 in the landmark class action suit in Quebec that involved plaintiffs suing three tobacco companies. It was ruled in 2015 that the companies had to pay $15 billion in damages to more than one million smokers in Quebec.

Culver

Early recreational use of hashish occurred in a fashionable apartment in New York City. An 1876 issue of the *Illustrated Police News* carried this picture with the title "Secret Dissipation of New York Belles: Interior of a Hasheesh Hell on Fifth Avenue."

Consequences of Second-Hand Smoke

As we have known for many years, the health hazards of smoking are not restricted to those who smoke. The smoke coming from the burning end of a cigarette, so-called **second-hand smoke**, or environmental tobacco smoke (ETS), contains higher concentrations of ammonia, carbon monoxide, nicotine, and tar than does the smoke actually inhaled by the smoker. Environmental tobacco smoke is blamed for more than 50,000 deaths a year in the United States. About 6 in 10 Canadians report being exposed to second-hand smoke (Reid et al., 2015). Collectively, a massive amount of evidence now attests to the widespread negative effects of exposure to second-hand smoke. The effects can be found both in terms of health outcomes and behavioural tendencies. For instance, recent data on children in Montreal link exposure with higher self-reported aggression and teacher-rated anti-social behaviour (Pagani & Fitzpatrick, 2013).

12.3 Marijuana

Marijuana consists of the dried and crushed leaves and flowering tops of the hemp plant, *Cannabis sativa*. It is most often smoked, but it may be chewed, prepared as a tea, or eaten in baked goods. **Hashish**, much stronger than marijuana, is produced by removing and drying the resin exudate of the tops of high-quality cannabis plants (see illustration).

Marijuana use is illegal in most countries, including Canada, as many of them were bound by a United Nations treaty prohibiting its sale (Goodwin & Guze, 1984). However, in 2003, the Canadian government moved toward decriminalizing simple possession of small amounts (up to 15 grams) of marijuana (Lawton, 2003). This movement was terminated

when Stephen Harper became prime minister in 2006. However, the new government under Prime Minister Justin Trudeau has started the process of legalizing marijuana and is expected to move forward in 2017. The government has been considering a variety of issues, including public health concerns, and has held lengthy consultations with the Canadian Psychological Association on issues related to addiction and the likely impact of the change in legislation on young people. A key consideration is the age at which marijuana use should be legal given that adolescents, relative to adults, are more sensitive to the negative effects of regular marijuana use, and surveys of Canadian adolescents indicate that they lack basic knowledge and hold several misguided views of the impact and effects of cannabis (Kalant, 2015). Meanwhile, in the United States, the decision in 2012 to legalize marijuana use in the U.S. states of Washington and Colorado has resulted in corporations becoming involved in growing marijuana. Several other states (e.g., Alaska, Oregon, and the District of Columbia) have now legalized marijuana for both recreational use and medicinal use.

Effects of Marijuana

Like most other drugs, marijuana has its risks. Generally, the more we learn about a drug, the less benign it turns out to be, and marijuana is no exception (see Focus on Discovery 12.1).

Psychological Effects   The intoxicating effects of marijuana, like most drugs, depend in part on its potency and size of dose. Smokers of marijuana find it makes them feel relaxed and sociable. Large doses have been reported to bring rapid shifts in emotion, to dull attention, to fragment thoughts, and to impair memory. Time seems to move more slowly. Extremely heavy doses sometimes induce hallucinations and

Focus on Discovery 12.1

The Stepping-Stone Theory: From Marijuana to Hard Drugs

A concern prevalent for some time is expressed in the so-called *stepping-stone theory* of marijuana use, which led subsequently to the *gateway theory*. This is the premise that marijuana is dangerous not only in itself, but also because it is a first step or gateway that can lead young people to become addicted to other, more harmful drugs, such as heroin. Strong evidence for the gateway theory came from a unique study of 21- to 30-year-olds from Oslo (Bretteville-Jensen, Melberg, & Jones, 2008). A sophisticated multivariate analysis found temporal evidence of soft drugs leading to harder drugs; specifically, alcohol was a gateway drug for cannabis, which, in turn, was a gateway drug for amphetamine, which then served as a gateway drug for cocaine.

But is marijuana a stepping stone to more serious substance abuse? The question is not difficult to answer. About 40% of regular marijuana users do not go on to use such drugs as heroin and cocaine (Stephens, Roffman, & Simpson, 1993). So if by stepping stone we mean that there is an inevitability of escalating to a more serious drug, then marijuana is not a stepping stone. Still, we do know that many, but far from all, who use heroin and cocaine began their drug experimentation with marijuana. Moreover, users of marijuana are more likely than non-users to experiment later with heroin and cocaine (Miller & Volk, 1996), and the single best predictor of cocaine use in adulthood is heavy use of marijuana during adolescence (Kozel & Adams, 1986). These data are in accordance with the results of a survey conducted in Montreal of participants at "raves," gigantic parties attended by young people in warehouse-like settings (Gross, Barrett, Shestowsky, & Pihl, 2002). This study found a linear trend of experimentation with substances; that is, rave participants reported a history of using first alcohol, then cannabis, LSD, psilocybin, amphetamines, cocaine, and ecstasy. A follow-up study found that 4 out of 5 participants engaged in polysubstance use at their most recently attended rave, and the average was 2.5 psychoactive substances (excluding tobacco) per person (Barrett, Gross, Garand, & Pihl, 2005). Those who had a more extensive history of attending raves had a substantially greater degree of polydrug use.

Still, it is the case that the stepping-stone theory is fraught with problems. First, it is of limited value in terms of its main emphasis on the sequence of developing addiction problems instead of focusing on etiology from a broad perspective. Second, researchers testing the stepping-stone theory or the gateway theory continue to conclude that it has limited support. Instead, these researchers recommend focusing on factors such as life experiences (Tarter et al., 2012) or whether a young person is gainfully employed (Van Gundy & Rebellon, 2010). Thus, marijuana is part of the picture, but is only one of many factors contributing to involvement in harmful substance use.

---

other effects similar to those of LSD, including extreme panic, and there is growing evidence that cannabis use increases the likelihood of psychotic disorders in some young people, presumably due to the interactions that relate to levels of dopamine (see Kuepper et al., 2010). Dosage can be difficult to regulate because it may take up to half an hour after smoking marijuana for its effects to appear; many users thus get much higher than intended. People with psychological problems are generally believed to be at highest risk for negative reactions to marijuana or any psychoactive drug, perhaps because lack of control frightens them.

The major active chemical in marijuana is delta-9-tetrahydrocannabinol (THC). The amount of THC in marijuana is variable, but in general marijuana is much more potent now than it was two decades ago, with some estimates indicating that the THC content is two or three times higher (Zimmer & Morgan, 1995). In the late 1980s, cannabis receptors were discovered in the brain; shortly thereafter, it was found that the body produces its own cannabis-like substance, anandamide, named for the Sanskrit word for bliss (Sussman et al., 1996).

Growing evidence attests to the cognitive problems associated with marijuana use. A longitudinal study conducted by researchers at Carleton University in Ottawa found that current marijuana use resulted in an average decrease of 4.1 IQ points, but only among heavy users who smoked at least five joints per week (Fried, Watkinson, James, & Gray, 2002). Lighter use did not result in diminished IQ scores. Studies of working memory and verbal episodic memory indicate impairments in encoding, storage, manipulation, and retrieval mechanisms in long-term or heavy cannabis use (Solowij & Battisti, 2008). Neurocognitive deficits are greater among adults who began cannabis use in early adolescence and adolescents seem much more susceptible than adults to neurocognitive deficits (Schweinsburg, Brown, & Tapert, 2008). In a review for the Canadian Centre on Substance Abuse, Porath-Waller (2009) concluded that chronic cannabis use contributes to mild impairments rather than severe impairments; impairment would not be evident on simple, everyday tasks but would be apparent on complex tasks that rely on a memory component or strategic planning. More recent data point to impairment. One longitudinal study found that marijuana use was associated with IQ scores that were 5 to 6 points lower (Meier et al., 2012). Controversy arose when a Norwegian researcher used a simulated study to suggest that this conclusion was flawed because the original researchers failed to control for the strong link that poverty has with both marijuana use and lower IQ (Rogeberg, 2013). However, the original researchers subsequently clarified that their finding held after controlling for SES.

Unfortunately, problems associated with heavy marijuana use are not confined to cognitive difficulties. An Ontario study comparing daily marijuana users with non-daily users confirmed that more of the daily users reported cannabis-related cognitive problems (60% vs. 42%), but they were also more likely to report psychological problems, health problems, financial problems, and vocational problems (Strike, Urbanoski, & Rush, 2003). Daily users were found to be more likely to use multiple substances and suffer from an anxiety disorder.

Several studies have found that being high on marijuana impairs the complex psychomotor skills necessary for driving. Highway fatality and driver-arrest figures indicate that marijuana plays a role in a significant proportion of accidents and arrests (Brookoff, Cook, Williams, & Mann, 1994). Marijuana has similarly been found to impair manipulation of flight simulators. Some performance decrements measurable after smoking one or two marijuana cigarettes containing 2% THC can persist for eight hours after a person believes he or she is no longer high, creating the very real danger that people will attempt to drive or fly when they are not functioning adequately.

Somatic Effects

In recent years, physiological research has identified specific cannabinoid receptors in the brain (CB) that recognize and are activated by cannabinoids (Iversen, 2003). The CB receptors in the brain are located in various regions, and it is believed that receptors in the hippocampus account for the short-term memory loss that sometimes follows smoking marijuana. Iversen (2003) observed that the discovery of these receptors has revitalized cannabis research and resulted in much interest.

The short-term side effects of marijuana include blood-shot and itchy eyes, dry mouth and throat, increased appetite, reduced pressure within the eye, and somewhat raised blood pressure. There is no evidence that smoking marijuana has untoward effects on a normal heart.

There is growing evidence that marijuana smoking is associated with a host of respiratory disorders and related ailments, and it seriously impairs lung functioning. Symptoms include coughing, wheezing, bronchitis, injury to airway tissue, and impaired functioning of immune system components (Moore et al., 2005; Tashkin, 2005). A Vancouver study found that concurrent smoking of marijuana and regular tobacco is associated with substantially increased risk for respiratory symptoms and chronic obstructive pulmonary disease (COPD) among those people who have smoked at least 50 marijuana joints in their lifetime (Tan et al., 2009). Even though marijuana users smoke far fewer cigarettes than do tobacco smokers, most inhale marijuana smoke more deeply and retain it in their lungs for much longer periods of time. Since marijuana has some of the same carcinogens found in tobacco cigarettes, its harmful effects are much greater than would be expected were only the absolute number of cigarettes or pipefuls considered. For example, one marijuana cigarette is the equivalent of four tobacco cigarettes in tar intake, five in carbon monoxide intake, and 10 in terms of damage to cells lining the airways (Sussman et al., 1996).

Is marijuana addictive? Contrary to widespread earlier belief, it may be. The development of tolerance began to be suspected when American service personnel returned from Vietnam accustomed to concentrations of THC that would be toxic to domestic users. Controlled observations have confirmed that habitual use of marijuana does produce tolerance (see Compton, Dewey, & Martin, 1990). Analyses of data from more than 2,700 lifetime marijuana users in the Ontario Health Survey identified a threshold of use (100 to 199 uses of marijuana) that was associated with substantially greater risk for developing marijuana disorders (DeWit, Hance, Offord, & Ogborne, 2000). Interestingly, this threshold was lower for females, with using marijuana between 50 and 99 times being associated with the development of marijuana disorders. This study also found that the timing of marijuana use matters. Ontarians who were late starters and began using after the age of 17 were less likely to have a subsequent marijuana disorder than those who initiated use before the age of 14. Finally, new data indicate that nicotine dependence occurs quicker among people with an anxiety disorder (Kushner, Menary, Maurer, & Thuras, 2012). Work of this nature has given rise to the concept of **dependence susceptibility** and the notion that some people are much more sensitive and prone to becoming addictive than are other people.

The question of physical addiction to marijuana is complicated by reverse tolerance. Experienced smokers need only a few hits or puffs to become high from a marijuana cigarette, whereas less experienced users puff many times to reach a similar state of intoxication. Reverse tolerance is the direct opposite of the tolerance that occurs with an addicting drug, such as heroin. The substance THC, after being rapidly metabolized, is stored in the body's fatty tissue and then released very slowly, perhaps for a month, which may explain reverse tolerance for it.

Therapeutic Effects

In a seeming irony, therapeutic uses of marijuana came to light just as the negative effects of regular and heavy usage of the drug were being uncovered. In the 1970s, several double-blind studies (e.g., Salan, Zinberg, & Frei, 1975) showed that THC and related drugs can reduce the nausea and loss of appetite that accompany chemotherapy for some cancer patients. Later findings confirmed this result (Grinspoon & Bakalar, 1995). Marijuana often appears to reduce nausea when other anti-nausea agents fail. Marijuana is also a treatment for the discomfort of AIDS (Sussman et al., 1996), as well as glaucoma, epilepsy, and multiple sclerosis.

The potential benefits of smoking marijuana were also confirmed in a 1998 report to the U.S. National Institutes of Health (NIH) by a panel of experts. The panel suggested that medical researchers and clinicians should take the benefits more seriously (Ad Hoc Advisory Group of Experts National Institutes of Health, 1997).

In light of this evidence, and following a request from two men with AIDS, a process was set up in June 1999 whereby people wishing to use marijuana for medical reasons could apply to be exempt from the federal ban. Then, in April 2001, the Government of Canada announced that people with other medical conditions (e.g., arthritis) might be eligible for medical

The Canadian Press/Frank Gunn

On August 3, 2001, then-federal minister of health Alan Rock toured the plant where marijuana is being grown for medical purposes. The hydroponic lab (dubbed the Rock Garden by workers), located in an old shaft at Trout Lake Mine in Flin Flon, Manitoba, became Canada's first legal growing operation.

marijuana, with the caveat that they had to first demonstrate that other means (e.g., painkillers) did not alleviate their suffering. The issue received public attention following a plant tour by the federal Health Minister (see photo).

A court challenge in Ontario was launched to make it easier for people to qualify for medical marijuana use but the Ontario Court of Appeal upheld the original criteria, leading some people to complain that it is virtually impossible to get a medical marijuana exemption from a physician. This court challenge was instigated by Matthew Mernagh, who was charged in 2008 with illegally producing marijuana. He has been described as suffering from fibromyalgia, scoliosis, epilepsy, and depression (Makin, 2013).

The issue of medical marijuana use in Canada came back into the spotlight in November 2016 when the federal government announced restrictions on compensation to military veterans because of the degree of use and skyrocketing costs. The first case was in 2007 and in eight years, over 3,000 veterans have received compensation. The new restrictions allow for extra consideration for a veteran with "exceptional circumstances" (see Cullen & Zimonjic, 2016).

12.4   Sedatives and Stimulants

Addiction to drugs, including sedatives, was disapproved of but tolerated in the United States until 1914, when the *Harrison Narcotics Act* made the unauthorized use of various drugs illegal and those addicted to them criminals. The drugs we discuss here, some of which may be obtained legally with a prescription, can be divided into two general categories: sedatives and stimulants.

Sedatives

The major **sedatives**, often called downers, slow the activities of the body and reduce its responsiveness. This group of drugs includes the opiates—opium and its derivatives, morphine, heroin, and codeine—and the synthetic barbiturates and tranquilizers, such as secobarbital (Seconal) and diazepam (Valium).

Opiates

"The popular scare comes from the deaths . . . My personal opinion about OxyContin is that it was designed to be addictive. Thirty-five per cent of the drug is immediate release for a fast effect."

—*Dr. Peter Selby, Clinical Director of the CAMH Addictions Programs (as cited in MacCallum, 2012)*

The **opiates** are a group of addictive sedatives that relieve pain and induce sleep when taken in moderate doses. Foremost among them is **opium**, originally the principal drug of illegal international trafficking and known to the people of the Sumerian civilization as long ago as 7000 B.C. They gave the poppy that supplied this drug (see photo) its name (i.e., the plant of joy). When in a synthetic or semi-synthetic version, opiates are referred to as **opioids**.

One of the most predominant concerns at present, especially in Canada, is the number of people who became addicted to the painkiller **OxyContin**, which is an opioid with the active ingredient oxycodone that produced a swift and powerful high. OxyContin misuse represents the most rapidly growing addiction in Canada. The first part of this decade was known for widespread abuse of this painkiller, in part because pills could be crushed into a fine powder by drug abusers.

Dr. Jeremy Burgess/Science Source

An opium poppy. Opium is harvested by slitting the seed capsule, which allows the raw opium to seep out.

How big a problem did OxyContin become? This behaviour is known as prescription opioid (PO) related misuse (PORM). A review by Canadian researchers led to the conclusion that Canada is second in the world in PO misuse (Fischer & Argento, 2012). An Ontario survey conducted in 2010 and 2011 found that non-medically prescribed opioid misuse was reported by 15.5% of students and 5.9% of adults (see Fischer et al., 2013). Recent data suggest that Canada and the United States continue to lead the world in the rate of opioid use and that the rates of overdoses and deaths continue to escalate (Kirkup, 2016). Canada registered 74 overdose deaths in just one month—January 2016—and Vancouver declared a public health emergency in the spring of 2016 (Kirkup, 2016). Meanwhile, the United States continued to experience unprecedented problems, to the extent that then-President Obama asked the U.S. Congress to approve $1.1 billion for financial assistance to states in order to heighten public awareness and try to limit the spread and consequences of opioids. Opioid addiction has been described as an urgent public health problem, with consumption of opioid pain relievers increasing by over 500% during the past 15 years (see Kolodny et al., 2015).

Overdose deaths have skyrocketed at an alarming rate. One contributor is the increasing availability of the opioid painkiller fentanyl, which is often illegally manufactured, and is estimated to be 100 times more potent that other opioids. It was a fentanyl overdose that was determined to be the cause of death of singer and actor Prince in April 2016. Fentanyl is so toxic that just a few grains can be fatal. The drug naloxone is effective if administered right away to combat an overdose. Given the seriousness of the situation, naloxone has been made publicly available without a prescription in some U.S. jurisdictions (e.g., Texas). Recent reports of exponential increases in fentanyl overdoses in Western Canada and in northern U.S. states have led to a police warning in Ontario and in other provinces (see Van Praet, 2016). How bad is the fentanyl problem? Cincinnati, Ohio, reported 178 overdose cases over a six-day period in August 2016 (Van Praet, 2016). The problem has become so prevalent and the need so urgent that police in certain U.S. cities have had to assume the role of frontline medical personnel (see Woo, 2016).

A related concern is the growing epidemic in the United States of the use of **heroin**, a relatively inexpensive but potent opioid. Just how dangerous is the heroin epidemic? It is estimated by the U.S. Centers for Disease Control and Prevention that overdose deaths in the United States have almost quadrupled between 2002 and 2013, and the use has doubled over the past decade in people aged 18 to 25 years old (see Jones, Logan, Gladden, & Bohm, 2015). According to another recent account (see Ingraham, 2016), the police in Huntington, a small city in West Virginia, responded to 26 separate heroin overdose cases during a four-hour period one night in August 2016.

A particular concern in Canada is the exceptionally high rates of use in certain First Nations communities (Pressly, 2012). Claudette Chase, Medical Director for the Sioux Lookout First Nations Health Authority, was quoted as estimating that about one-third of the people in her community had an opioid addiction, with it being as high as 75% in some communities (Paperny, 2012).

Others have concluded that Canada is actually the world leader in this category and there is substantial concern due to the strong link between higher misuse and mortality (see Dhalla et al., 2012). It was once suggested that worldwide, PO misuse was third highest in terms of substance abuse burden of disease, behind drinking and smoking (Fischer & Argento, 2012).

While our main focus should be on the human costs, there are also financial concerns that cannot be ignored. A report compiled by the Canadian Institute for Health Information on behalf of *The Globe and Mail* suggested that spending on drugs to treat addiction to painkillers increased by 60% from 2011 to 2014 to reach a total of $93 million (see Howlett, 2016). This report appeared in conjunction with allegations that federal and provincial governments have failed to provide physicians with the training and guidelines needed to help curb what is seen as a tendency to overprescribe these drugs.

History   Where did it all begin? In 1806, the alkaloid **morphine**, named after Morpheus, the Greek god of dreams, was separated from raw opium. This bitter-tasting powder proved to be a powerful sedative and pain reliever. Before its addictive properties were noted, it was used in patent medicines. In the middle of the nineteenth century, when the hypodermic needle was introduced, morphine began to be injected directly into the veins to relieve pain. Many soldiers wounded in battle during the American Civil War were treated with morphine and returned home addicted to the drug.

Concerned about administering a drug that could disturb the later lives of patients, scientists began studying morphine. In 1874, they found that morphine could be converted into another powerful pain-relieving drug that was discussed earlier: heroin. Used initially as a cure for morphine addiction, heroin was substituted for morphine in cough syrups and other patent medicines (see illustration). So many maladies were treated with heroin that it came to be known as G.O.M., or "God's own medicine" (Brecher et al. 1972). However, heroin proved to be even more addictive and more potent than morphine, acting more quickly and with greater intensity. In 1909, U.S. president Theodore Roosevelt called for an international investigation of opium and the other opiates.

Dr. Jeremy Burgess/National Library of Medicine/Science Photo Library

Heroin was synthesized from opium in 1874 and was soon being added to a variety of medicines that could be purchased without prescription. This ad shows a teething remedy containing heroin. It probably worked.

Psychological and physical effects   Opium and its derivatives, morphine and heroin, produce euphoria, drowsiness, reverie, and a lack of coordination. Heroin has an additional initial effect: the rush, a feeling of warm, suffusing ecstasy immediately following an intravenous injection. The user sheds worries and fears and has great self-confidence for four to six hours, but then experiences letdown, bordering on stupor.

Opiates produce their effects by stimulating neural receptors of the body's own opioid system. Heroin, for example, is converted into morphine in the brain and then binds to opioid receptors. The body produces opioids, called endorphins and enkephalins, and opium and its derivatives fit into their receptors and stimulate them.

Opiates are clearly addicting, for users show both increased tolerance of the drugs and withdrawal symptoms when they are unable to obtain another dose. Reactions to not having a dose of heroin may begin within eight hours of the last injection, at least after high tolerance has built up. The individual typically has muscle pain, sneezes, sweats, becomes tearful, and yawns a great deal over the next few hours. The symptoms resemble those of influenza. The withdrawal symptoms become more severe within 36 hours. There may be uncontrollable muscle twitching, cramps, chills alternating with excessive flushing and sweating, and a rise in heart rate and blood pressure. The addicted person is unable to sleep, vomits, and has diarrhea. These symptoms typically persist for about 72 hours and then diminish gradually over a 5- to 10-day period.

Heroin used to be confined to poor neighbourhoods and the inner city, but in recent years, heroin has started to become the cool drug for middle- and upper-middle-class college students and young professionals, and it is beginning to vie with cocaine for popularity among these groups. The 2004 Canadian Campus Survey (Adlaf et al., 2005) found that 8.7% of university students had used such illicit drugs as heroin, cocaine, crack, LSD, and ecstasy, and this rate was fairly stable across various versions of the survey. Use of hallucinogens such as mescaline, mushrooms, and LSD has declined significantly, however.

Synthetic Sedatives   Barbiturates, another major type of sedative, were synthesized as aids for sleeping and relaxation. The first barbiturate was produced in 1903, and since then hundreds of derivatives of barbituric acid have been made. These drugs were initially considered highly desirable and were frequently prescribed. A campaign was mounted against them in the 1940s because they were discovered to be addictive, and physicians began to prescribe barbiturates less often. Today, the benzodiazepines, such as Valium, are more commonly used and abused. Methaqualone, a sedative sold under the trade names Quaalude and Sopor, is similar in effect to barbiturates and has become a popular street drug.

Sedatives relax the muscles, reduce anxiety, and in small doses produce a mildly euphoric state. Like alcohol, they are thought to produce these psychological effects by stimulating the GABA system. With excessive doses, however, speech becomes slurred and gait unsteady. Judgement, concentration, and ability to work may be severely impaired. The user loses emotional control and may become irritable and combative before falling into a deep sleep. Very large doses can be fatal because the diaphragm muscles relax to such an extent that the individual suffocates. Sedatives are frequently chosen as a means of suicide. However, many users accidentally kill themselves by drinking alcohol, which potentiates, or magnifies, the depressant effects of sedatives. The brain can become damaged and personality deteriorates with prolonged excessive use.

Increased tolerance follows prolonged use of sedatives, and the withdrawal reactions after abrupt termination are particularly severe and long-lasting and can cause sudden death. The delirium and convulsions resemble the symptoms that follow abrupt withdrawal from alcohol.

Stimulants

Stimulants, or uppers, such as cocaine, act on the brain and the sympathetic nervous system to increase alertness and motor activity. Cocaine is a natural stimulant extracted from the coca leaf. The amphetamines, such as Benzedrine, are synthetic stimulants. Focus on Discovery 12.2 discusses a more prevalent stimulant: caffeine. The risk of caffeine overconsumption is increasing as a result of the proliferation of energy drinks, which can contain as much or more caffeine as coffee.

Amphetamines
Seeking a treatment for asthma, the Chinese-American pharmacologist Chen studied ancient

Canadian boxing great George Chuvalo has dedicated his time to warning students about the dangers of using drugs such as heroin. Three of his four sons became addicted to heroin. Tragically, his sons George Lee Chuvalo and Steven Chuvalo died of heroin overdoses, and Jesse Chuvalo committed suicide by shooting himself. Chuvalo's wife, Lynn, could not cope with these losses and also committed suicide.

The Canadian Press/Tobin Grimshaw

Focus on Discovery 12.2

Our Tastiest Addiction: Caffeine and the Rise of Energy Drinks

What may be the world's most popular drug is seldom viewed as a drug at all, and yet it has strong effects, produces tolerance in people, and even subjects habitual users to withdrawal (Hughes et al., 1991). Users and non-users joke about it. We are, of course, referring to caffeine, a substance found in coffee, tea, cocoa, cola, some cold remedies, and some diet pills. Caffeine can contribute to serious problems, as reflected by the inclusion in the *DSM-5* of a separate section describing caffeine-related disorders (e.g., caffeine intoxication, caffeine withdrawal, other caffeine-induced disorders, and unspecified caffeine-related disorder).

Two cups of coffee, containing between 150 and 300 milligrams of caffeine, affect people within half an hour. Metabolism, body temperature, and blood pressure all increase; urine production goes up, as most of us will attest; there may be hand tremors; appetite can diminish; and, most familiar of all, sleepiness is warded off. Panic disorder can be exacerbated by caffeine because of the heightened arousal of the sympathetic nervous system occasioned by the drug. Extremely large doses can cause headache, diarrhea, nervousness, severe agitation, even convulsions and death. Death, however, is virtually impossible unless someone grossly overuses caffeine tablets, since the drug is excreted by the kidneys without any appreciable accumulation.

Although it has long been recognized that drinkers of very large amounts of regular coffee daily can experience withdrawal symptoms when consumption ceases, people who drink just two cups of regular coffee a day can suffer from clinically significant headaches, fatigue, and anxiety if caffeine is withdrawn from their daily diet (Silverman, Evans, Strain, & Griffiths, 1992). These symptoms, moreover, can markedly interfere with social and occupational functioning.

As is the case with other drugs, people ingest caffeine to obtain positive outcomes and avoid negative outcomes. Research by Kathryn Graham (1988) examined the reasons that Canadian undergraduates gave for heavy consumption of coffee and tea. Students reported drinking for reasons of sociability and affiliation with others, but also to obtain relief from aversive states. Of course, the need for a stimulant was also important. Analyses showed that relief and stimulation as reasons for caffeine use were the best predictors of overall consumption and caffeine dependence.

As we will see in a subsequent section, cognitive expectancies play a key role in substance use and misuse. A 37-item Caffeine Expectancy Questionnaire developed by Heinz, Kassel, and Smith (2009) taps four expectancy factors: (1) withdrawal symptoms (e.g., "I will get headaches if I don't drink regularly"); (2) positive effects (e.g., "Drinking caffeine is satisfying"); (3) acute negative effects (e.g., "Caffeine causes me to shake or be jittery"); and (4) mood effects (e.g., "Caffeine helps me relax"). High scores on items tapping factors 1, 2, and 4 (withdrawal symptoms, positive effects, and mood effects) were correlated strongly with self-reports of degree of addiction to caffeine (Heinz et al., 2009).

While the popularity of energy drinks grows, so do the concerns surrounding the safety of using these products.

A growing public health concern reflects the number of energy drinks with high levels of caffeine that are being ingested by Canadians, especially younger Canadians (see photo). A particularly dangerous practice is the mixing of alcoholic beverages with energy drinks. A recent study of over 23,000 Grade 9 to 12 students in Ontario found that 17.3% of respondents reported the use of energy drinks mixed with alcohol in the previous 12 months (Reid et al., 2015). Males were twice as likely to use energy drinks and one of the strongest predictors of use was the extent of binge drinking. Another survey of over 36,000 Canadian students in grades 7 to 12 showed that about 1 in 5 reported consuming alcohol mixed with energy drinks in the past year (Azagba, Langille, & Ashbridge, 2013). In addition to the added health risk, this study found that those who mixed alcohol and energy drinks had greater substance use, past-year heavy drinking, smoking, marijuana use, greater absence from school, and greater participation in team sports. Protective factors were greater connectedness to school and an average grade of 70% or greater. Equally troubling are data indicating that excessive adolescent caffeine consumption is linked with conduct disorder and more frequent violent behaviours among adolescents (Kristjannsson, Sigfusdottir, Frost, & James, 2013). However, because these data were from cross-sectional research, it could be the case that adolescents with these tendencies are more likely to seek out caffeine rather than caffeine creating these behavioural problems.

Given that having a school average of 70% or higher was protective in the study just described, it might be concluded that mixing alcohol and energy drinks among university students would be uncommon. This conclusion would be wrong. A survey of 465 university students from Western Canada found that 105 students (about 1 in 4) reported consuming alcohol mixed with caffeinated energy drinks within the previous month (Brache & Stockwell, 2011). Those who did it more frequently reported a substantially higher number of negative consequences, illustrating the importance of increasing awareness among students of the possible dangers involved.

Chinese descriptions of drugs. He found that a desert shrub, ma huang, was described as an effective remedy. After systematic effort, Chen isolated an alkaloid from this plant belonging to the genus *Ephedra*, and the result, ephedrine, proved highly successful in treating asthma. But relying on the shrub for the drug was not efficient, and so efforts to develop a synthetic substitute began. **Amphetamines** resulted from these efforts (Snyder, 1974).

The first amphetamine, Benzedrine, was synthesized in 1927. Almost as soon as it became commercially available in the early 1930s as an inhalant to relieve stuffy noses, the public discovered its stimulating effects. Physicians thereafter prescribed it and the other amphetamines that were soon synthesized to control mild depression and appetite. Soldiers on both sides in the Second World War were supplied with the drugs to ward off fatigue, and today amphetamines are sometimes used to treat hyperactive children.

Amphetamines, such as Benzedrine, Dexedrine, and Methedrine, produce their effects by causing the release of norepinephrine and dopamine and blocking the reuptake of these neurotransmitters. They are taken orally or intravenously and can be addictive. Wakefulness is heightened, intestinal functions are inhibited, and appetite is reduced—hence their use in dieting. The heart rate quickens, and blood vessels in the skin and mucous membranes constrict. The individual becomes alert, euphoric, and outgoing, and is possessed with seemingly boundless energy and self-confidence. Larger doses can make people nervous and confused, subjecting them to palpitations, headaches, dizziness, and sleeplessness. Sometimes heavy users become so suspicious and hostile that they can be dangerous to others. Large doses taken over time can induce a state similar to paranoid schizophrenia, including its delusions.

Tolerance to amphetamines develops rapidly, so that more and more of the drug is required to produce the stimulating effect. As tolerance increases, the user may stop taking pills and inject Methedrine, the strongest of the amphetamines, directly into the veins. The so-called speed freaks give themselves repeated injections of the drug and maintain intense and euphoric activity for a few days, without eating or sleeping (a run), after which they are exhausted and depressed and sleep, or crash, for several days. Then the cycle starts again. After several repetitions of this pattern, physical and social functioning deteriorates considerably. Behaviour is erratic and hostile, and speed freaks may become a danger to themselves and to others.

Amphetamine use in the workplace has been increasing. Under time pressure to produce—the saying of the 1990s was "do more with less"—many white-collar workers turned to speed to stay awake, be more productive, and in general feel more energized, even euphoric.

Cocaine

The natives of the Andean uplands, to which the coca shrubs are native, chew the leaves. Europeans, introduced to coca by Spanish conquistadors, chose instead to brew the leaves in beverages. The alkaloid **cocaine** was extracted from the leaves of the coca plant in the mid-1800s and has been used since then as a local anaesthetic. In 1884, while still a young neurologist, Sigmund Freud began using cocaine to combat his depression. Convinced of its wondrous effects, he prescribed it to a friend who had a painful disease. Freud published one of the first papers on the drug, "Song of Praise," which was an enthusiastic endorsement of the exhilarating effects he had experienced. Freud subsequently lost his enthusiasm for cocaine after nursing a physician friend, to whom he had recommended the drug, through a night-long psychotic state brought on by it. Perhaps the most famous fictional cocaine addict was Sherlock Holmes. A more contemporary case of cocaine use surfaced when Lady Gaga admitted her use (see photo).

Cocaine has other effects in addition to reducing pain. It acts rapidly on the brain, blocking the reuptake of dopamine in mesolimbic areas that are thought to yield pleasurable states; the result is that dopamine is left in the synapse and thereby facilitates neural transmission and resultant positive feelings. Self-reports of the pleasure induced by cocaine are strongly related to the extent that cocaine has blocked dopamine reuptake (Volkow, Wang, Fischman, & Foltin 1997). Cocaine increases sexual desire and produces feelings of self-confidence, well-being, and indefatigability. An overdose may bring on chills,

Wenn/Newscom

In the September 2010 issue of *Vanity Fair*, pop phenom Lady Gaga admitted to using cocaine. Of her drug use, she said "I do not want my fans to ever emulate that or be that way. I don't want my fans to think they have to be that way to be great. It's in the past. It was a low point, and it led to disaster."

nausea, and insomnia, as well as a paranoid breakdown and terrifying hallucinations of insects crawling beneath the skin. Chronic use often leads to changes in personality, which include heightened irritability, impaired social skills, paranoid thinking, and disturbances in eating and sleeping. Ceasing cocaine use appears to cause a severe withdrawal syndrome. Cocaine can take hold of people with as much tenacity as do the established addictive drugs. As with alcohol, developing fetuses are markedly and negatively affected in the womb by the mother's use of cocaine during pregnancy, and many babies are born addicted to the drug.

Cocaine, a vasoconstrictor, causes the blood vessels to narrow. Cocaine increases a person's risk for stroke and causes cognitive impairments, including problems with memory and attention. Because of its strong vasoconstricting properties, cocaine poses special dangers in pregnancy, because the blood supply to the fetus may be compromised.

In the mid-1980s a new form of freebase, called crack, appeared on the streets. The presence of crack brought about an increase in freebasing and in casualties. Because it was available in small, relatively inexpensive doses, younger and less-affluent buyers began to experiment with the drug and became addicted (Kozel & Adams, 1986).

Cocaine use seems to vary due to racial and ethnic differences; recent U.S. data indicate that past-year use among Black people in the U.S. was 0.8% and lifetime use was estimated at 4.6%; however, the levels of reported use were lower for Hispanic people (0.3% for 12 months, 3.7% lifetime) and for White people (0.1% for 12 months, 2.3% lifetime) (Substance Abuse and Mental Health Services Administration, 2013). Comparative analyses indicate that crack users versus powder cocaine users are much more likely to be arrested (Palamar, Davies, Ompad, Cleland, & Weitzman, 2015).

12.5 LSD and Other Hallucinogens

History

In 1943, a Swiss chemist, Albert Hofmann, described an illness he had seemingly contracted: "Last Friday . . . I had to interrupt my laboratory work . . . I was seized with a feeling of great restlessness and mild dizziness. At home, I lay down and sank into a not unpleasant delirium, which was characterized by extremely exciting fantasies. In a semiconscious state with my eyes closed . . . fantastic visions of extraordinary realness and with an intense kaleidoscopic play of colors assaulted me" (cited in Cashman, 1966, p. 31).

Earlier in the day Hofmann had manufactured a few milligrams of d-lysergic acid diethylamide, a drug that he had synthesized in 1938. Reasoning that he might have unknowingly ingested some and that this had caused his unusual

experience, he deliberately took a dose and confirmed his hypothesis.

After Hofmann's experiences with **LSD** in 1943, the drug was referred to as psychotomimetic because it was thought to produce effects similar to the symptoms of a psychosis. Then the term "psychedelic," from the Greek words for "soul" and "to make manifest," was applied to emphasize the subjectively experienced expansions of consciousness reported by users of LSD and often referred to by them as a trip. The term in current use for LSD is **hallucinogen**, which describes one of the main effects of such drugs—hallucinations.

Four other important hallucinogens are mescaline, psilocybin, and the synthetic compounds MDA and MDMA. In 1896, **mescaline**, an alkaloid and the active ingredient of peyote, was isolated from small, disc-like growths on the top of the peyote cactus. The drug has been used for centuries in the religious rites of Native peoples living in the U.S. Southwest and northern Mexico. **Psilocybin** is a crystalline powder that Hofmann isolated from the mushroom *Psilocybe mexicana* in 1958. The early Aztec and Mexican cultures called the sacred mushrooms "God's flesh," and the Natives of Mexico still use them in their worship. Each of these substances is structurally similar to several neurotransmitters, but their effects are thought to be due to the stimulation of serotonin receptors.

During the 1950s, researchers gave LSD, mescaline, and psilocybin to people in research settings so that they could study what were thought to be psychotic experiences.

In 1960, Timothy Leary (see photo) and Richard Alpert of Harvard University began an investigation of the effects of psilocybin on institutionalized prisoners. Their early results were encouraging and pointed to therapeutic benefits: released prisoners who had taken psilocybin proved less likely to be rearrested. However, the investigators started taking trips themselves and soon had gathered around them other people interested in experimenting with psychedelic drugs. Their

In the 1960s, psychologist Timothy Leary was one of the leading proponents of the use of hallucinogens to expand consciousness.

activities had attracted the attention of law-enforcement agencies by 1962. As the police investigation continued, the situation became a scandal, culminating in Leary's and Alpert's departures from Harvard. The affair gave tremendous impetus to the use of the hallucinogens, particularly since the manufacture of LSD and the extraction of mescaline and psilocybin were relatively easy and inexpensive. There is no evidence of withdrawal symptoms during abstinence, but tolerance seems to develop rapidly (McKim, 1991).

Another hallucinogen joined the ranks of illegal drugs in 1985. **Ecstasy**, which refers to two closely similar synthetic compounds, MDA (methylenedioxyamphetamine) and MDMA (methylenedioxymethamphetamine), is chemically similar to mescaline and the amphetamines and is the psychoactive agent in nutmeg. Ecstasy was introduced in Chapter 9 due to its controversial use in British Columbia as a potential treatment for post-traumatic stress disorder (PTSD). Ecstasy is a "designer drug" produced via chemical synthesis. It comes in many different sizes and shapes, depending on how it is manufactured. MDA was first synthesized in 1910, but it was not until the 1960s that its psychedelic properties came to the attention of the drug-using, consciousness-expanding generation of the times. Today it is popular on some college campuses, and the use of ecstasy is associated with raves (see Gross et al., 2002). The 2004 Canadian Addiction Survey found that 4.1% of Canadians reported using ecstasy during their lifetime and 1.1% had used it within the previous year. Ecstasy use among Ontario students in grades 7 to 13 increased steadily in the 1990s, with 4.8% of students reporting use in 1999 and 5.4% reporting use in 2015 (Boak, Hamilton, Adlaf, & Mann, 2015).

Users report that the drug enhances intimacy and insight, improves interpersonal relationships, elevates mood, and promotes aesthetic awareness. It can also cause muscle tension, rapid eye movements, increased heart rate and blood pressure, nausea, faintness, chills or sweating, and anxiety, depression, and confusion. Lasting side effects can include paranoia, confusion, and memory complaints (Hardaway et al., 2016). The U.S. Drug Enforcement Administration considers the use of ecstasy and other so-called designer drugs unsafe and a serious health threat. Several deaths have come from accidental overdoses, with hyperthermia being the leading cause of death (see Gross et al., 2002).

Effects of Hallucinogens

The *DSM-5* describes nine distinguishable hallucinogen-related disorders. The effects of hallucinogens depend on a number of psychological variables in addition to the dose itself. A person's set—that is, attitudes, expectations, and motivations with regard to taking drugs—is widely held to be an important determinant of his or her reactions to hallucinogens. The setting in which the drug is experienced is also important.

Among the most prominent dangers of taking LSD is the possibility of experiencing a bad trip. A bad trip can sometimes develop into a full-blown panic attack and is far more likely to occur if some aspect of taking the drug creates anxiety. Often the specific fear is of going crazy. These panics are usually short-lived and subside as the drug is metabolized. A minority of people, however, go into a psychotic state that can require hospitalization and extended treatment.

Flashbacks, a recurrence of psychedelic experiences after the physiological effects of the drug have worn off, also sometimes occur, most frequently in times of stress, illness, or fatigue (Kaplan & Sadock, 1991). Flashbacks are not believed to be caused by drug-produced physical changes in the nervous system, in part because only 15 to 30% of users of hallucinogenic drugs are estimated ever to have flashbacks (e.g., Stanton & Bardoni, 1972). Moreover, there is no independent evidence of measurable neurological changes in these drug users. Flashbacks seem to have a force of their own, haunting and upsetting people weeks and months after they have taken the drug.

12.6 Etiology of Substance Abuse and Dependence

In considering the causes of substance abuse and dependence disorders, we must recognize that becoming substance-dependent is generally a developmental process. The person must first have a positive attitude toward the substance, then begin to experiment with using it, then begin using it regularly, then use it heavily, and finally abuse or become physically dependent on it (see Figure 12.1). The general idea is that the person becomes ensnared by the biological processes of tolerance and withdrawal after engaging in prolonged, heavy use.

Certain findings have caused scholars to re-examine the role of withdrawal in the development of addiction. Historically, withdrawal has not been implicated as a factor in drug use and relapse. However, Baker et al. (2006) argued that there is a need for a more complex view of withdrawal. That is, the physical signs of withdrawal do not motivate substance misuse, but two elements do seem to play a role: (1) the intense negative affect caused by withdrawal; and (2) urges (i.e., conscious awareness of the desire to take a drug).

Variables that cause substance dependence appear to depend on the stage being considered. For example, developing a positive attitude toward smoking and beginning to experiment with tobacco are strongly related to the smoking of other family members (Robinson, Klesges, Zbikowski, & Glaser, 1997). In contrast, becoming a regular smoker is more strongly related to smoking by peers and being able to acquire cigarettes readily (Holowaty, Feldman, Harvey, & Shortt, 2000; Robinson et al., 1997).

Also, other external influences cannot be discounted. There are growing concerns about the impact of watching smoking in movies, after studies have concluded that exposure to movie smoking has a dose–response relationship with adolescent smoking behaviour (Charlesworth & Glantz, 2005).

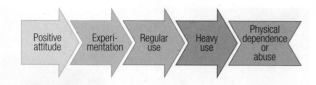

FIGURE 12.1 The process of becoming a substance abuser.

Some data suggest that compared with adolescents with low exposure, those with high exposure to smoking in movies are three times more likely to try smoking or become smokers (Heatherton & Sargent, 2009). This effect is strong enough that researchers have advocated that movies involving smoking be automatically R-rated.

This developmental model does not account for all cases of substance abuse or dependence. There are documented cases in which heavy use of tobacco or heroin did not end in addiction. Moreover, progression through the stages is not inevitable. Some people have periods of heavy use of a substance and then return to moderate use. Nevertheless, guided by this model, most research has examined variables related to initial use and its subsequent escalation. In the following sections, we discuss socio-cultural, psychological, and biological variables related to substance abuse. Note that these factors can relate to various substances differently (e.g., a genetic diathesis may contribute to alcoholism but not to hallucinogen abuse).

Social Variables

Socio-cultural variables can play a widely varying role in drug abuse. Various aspects of the social world (e.g., peers, parents, media portrayals) can affect people's interest in and access to drugs. At the broadest level, we can look at great cross-national variations in alcohol consumption. The data in Figure 12.2,

from a large-scale longitudinal study, illustrate the commonalities in the alcohol consumption of various regions. First, over the study period (1950–80), alcohol consumption rose greatly in each area studied. Second, variations in consumption across locations decreased with the passage of time, although great differences still exist. Other research has found striking cross-national differences in the prevalence of substance use despite widespread similarities in the average onset of first use (see Vega et al., 2002). For example, the highest alcohol consumption rates have typically been found in wine-drinking countries, such as France, Spain, and Italy, where drinking alcohol regularly is widely accepted (deLint, 1978). Cultural attitudes and patterns of drinking thus influence the likelihood of drinking heavily and therefore of abusing alcohol.

Family variables are important socio-cultural influences. Analyses of the National Longitudinal Survey of Children and Youth (NLSCY) data of 10- to 15-year-old Canadian youth show that a host of chronic disease behavioural risk factors (i.e., tobacco smoking, drinking alcohol) are more prevalent among those who have caregivers who smoke and peers who smoke and drink; protective factors were having high self-esteem and coming from a home with a member with post-secondary education (Alamian & Paradis, 2009). Other data from the Vancouver Family Survey indicate that heavy marijuana use among youth was predicted by the father's alcoholism, peer use of illicit drugs, and an addiction-prone personality characterized by high novelty seeking and low self-regulation (Barnes, Barnes, & Patton, 2005). A lack of emotional support from parents is also linked with increased use of cigarettes, cannabis, and alcohol (Cadoret et al., 1995a; Wills, DuHamel, & Vaccaro, 1995). Finally, a lack of parental monitoring leads to increased association with drug-abusing peers and subsequent use of drugs (Chassin, Curran, Hussong, & Colder, 1996). Meta-analytic data from 17 studies with over 35,000 participants confirmed that adolescent perceptions of greater parental monitoring are linked reliably with less marijuana use and this held across concurrent and longitudinal assessments (Lac & Crano, 2009).

Any analysis of family factors should consider the role of siblings. Data indicate that the dominant family influence in terms of behaviour was from older siblings to younger siblings, especially if the siblings are less than two years apart in age (Boyle et al., 2001). Moreover, this effect was stronger than the link between substance use in parents and their children.

The social milieu in which a person operates can also affect substance abuse. Having friends who smoke predicts smoking (Killen et al., 1997). Peer influences are also important in promoting alcohol and marijuana use (Alamian & Paradis, 2009; Kairouz & Adlaf, 2003; Stice, Barrera, & Chassin, 1998; Wills & Cleary, 1999). Although peer influence is important, those who have a high sense of self-efficacy (Bandura, 1997) are influenced less by their peers. Adolescents with this quality agree with statements like "I can imagine refusing to use tobacco with students my age and still have them like me" (Stacy et al., 1992, p. 166).

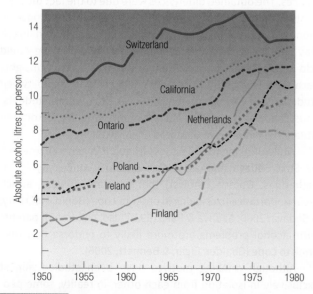

FIGURE 12.2 Annual consumption of alcoholic beverages among people aged 15 years and over from 1950 to 1980. From Mäkelä et al., 1981.

Psychological Variables

Next, we examine three classes of psychological variables. The first class essentially comprises the effects of alcohol on mood, the situations in which a tension-reducing effect occurs, and the role of cognition in this process. The second concerns beliefs about the prevalence of the drug's use and health risks associated with that drug. The third includes the personality traits that may make it more likely for some people to use drugs heavily.

Mood Alteration, Situations, and the Role of Cognition

Why do people drink?   One team of Canadian investigators proposed that it is possible to approach this issue from a cost vs. benefit perspective; for example, drinking occurs if the perceived benefits outweigh the costs (Cunningham et al., 1997). Cox and Klinger (1988) proposed another motivational model of alcohol use that suggested that motives for drinking vary along two dimensions: the valence of reinforcement (positive vs. negative) and locus (external reasons vs. internal, personal reasons); that is, people can drink to obtain pleasurable outcomes or avoid negative outcomes, and they can drink in response to external, social stimulation or in response to internal, personal cues. Four combinations involving these two dimensions are possible. Drinking for positive, internal reasons reflects drinking to enhance positive mood. Drinking for negative, internal reasons reflects drinking to reduce or avoid experiencing negative emotions. Drinking for positive, external reasons reflects drinking to obtain social rewards, and drinking for negative, external reasons involves drinking to escape punishment or to avoid being embarrassed by other people.

Cooper (1994) created a multifactorial scale to assess these four drinking motives. Positive, internal reasons are measured by the enhancement scale (e.g., drinking because it gives you a pleasant feeling). Negative, internal reasons are reflected by the coping scale (e.g., drinking because it cheers you up when you are in a bad mood). Positive, external reasons are assessed via the social scale (e.g., drinking because it makes social gatherings more fun). Finally, negative, external reasons are assessed via the conformity scale (e.g., drinking because you do not want to feel left out).

Extensive research has been conducted on these four motives. Kuntsche et al. (2005) have provided a comprehensive review of drinking motives research with young people. They concluded that young people drink primarily for social motives. They are less likely to drink for enhancement and they are even less likely to drink due to coping motives. Social motives are associated with moderate alcohol use, while enhancement motives are more likely to be associated with heavy drinking (i.e., drinking to get drunk). Coping motives predict alcohol-related problems (e.g., academic problems and legal difficulties). Researchers at Dalhousie University have developed a five-factor motive scale (Grant et al., 2007) and found that it is

The late Alberta Premier Ralph Klein and former Premier Gordon Campbell of British Columbia have both been identified as having drinking problems. Klein acknowledged his problem in December 2001 following a bizarre incident in which he stopped outside a shelter while inebriated and berated homeless people, while Campbell was arrested for drunk driving in Hawaii in January 2003.

possible and important to distinguish coping-anxiety motives and coping-depression motives within the coping motives domain (Grant, Stewart, & Mohr, 2009). This study found that coping-anxiety motives moderated the link between daily anxious mood and alcohol consumption, and as expected, coping-depression motives moderated the link between daily depressed mood and alcohol consumption.

Contemporary research conducted in Canada has provided new insights into the role of motives in drinking by using experience sampling methods to assess drinking over a 22-day period. This research showed, as expected, that high enhancement motive drinkers drink more than low enhancement drinkers when experiencing high arousal positive moods (e.g., excited, euphoric); however, the high enhancement motive drinkers do not engage in even more drinking in these circumstances. The obtained differences were due to the fact that students with low enhancement motives in high arousal positive mood situations showed substantial reductions in drinking. It was almost as if they were overstimulated and drinking would add to this sense. This longitudinal study yielded new insights because it was able to not only make comparisons between students, but to look at changes over time within students. Thus it showed the need to study temporal drinking factors and situational factors (see Gautreau et al., 2015).

While drinking to cope is less frequent in general, research by Stan Sadava and associates at Brock University in St. Catharines, Ontario, showed that problem drinkers attach great importance to drinking in order to cope (Bonin, McCreary, & Sadava, 2000; Sadava & Pak, 1993). Also, children of parents with alcohol problems are more likely to endorse that they drink to cope (Chalder, Elgar, & Bennett, 2006).

Although drinking motives have been studied almost exclusively in isolation from each other, in reality, some people will drink for multiple motives and there is surprisingly little research on these people. Goldstein and Flett (2009) focused on a group of students who drink jointly for both coping and enhancement reasons (i.e., distress relief and pleasure seeking). Empirical results showed that these students were actually quite similar to another group of students who drank primarily for coping motives. Coping-motivated drinkers and coping plus enhancement-motivated drinkers had comparable personality features (i.e., elevated neuroticism and anxiety sensitivity). It is possible that those who drink for multiple motives are at even greater risk for more serious drinking problems.

The notion of drinking in order to cope is related closely to the **self-medication theory of addiction**. That is, in the case of drinking, for instance, drinking is done with the goal of reducing an aversive state. Analyses of the data from a U.S. national survey focused on people with anxiety disorders and found that about 20% of them indicate that they drink in order to control anxiety. However, these individuals tended to drink more alcohol and longitudinally were at greater risk for developing alcohol dependence (Menary, Kushner, Maurer, & Thuras, 2011).

A recent phenomenon is the tendency for young people to drink before going out in order to then drink some more. This is known as "predrinking" or "pregaming." Its relevance to social anxiety was shown in a recent Canadian study showing that socially anxious students will engage in predrinking, but it is often done when they are alone; one unanticipated finding was that they were actually less likely to be involved in social predrinking (Keough, Battista, O'Connor, Sherry, & Stewart, 2016).

Extensive research is .now examining the role of social anxiety in the onset and persistence of drinking problems. Does social anxiety precede drinking problems or vice versa? A recent epidemiological study with a follow-up assessment at the four-year mark found that social anxiety disorder and PTSD both predicted alcohol use disorders and not vice versa (Wolitzky-Taylor et al., 2012). Other longitudinal data indicate that drinking in order to self-medicate among people suffering from anxiety is associated with greater likelihood of the development of alcohol dependence and greater persistence of the alcohol dependence (see Crum et al., 2012). Thus, anxiety seems to lead to alcohol abuse for some people. In contrast, an epidemiological study conducted in New Zealand evaluated the causal sequence involving depression and alcohol abuse and the researchers found that the evidence was more consistent with a sequence in which alcohol abuse led to subsequent depression (Fergusson, Boden, & Horwood, 2009).

Cognitive factors in drinking   There are many ways that cognitive factors may operate in drinking; for instance, by reducing tension. Findings indicate that alcohol may produce its tension-reducing effect by altering cognition and perception (Curtin, Lang, Patrick, & Strizke, 1998; Steele & Josephs, 1990). Alcohol impairs cognitive processing and narrows attention to the most immediately available cues, resulting in what Steele and Josephs (1990) term "alcohol myopia"—the intoxicated person has less cognitive capacity to distribute between

ongoing activity and worry. If a distracting activity is available, attention will be diverted to it rather than to worrisome thoughts, with a resultant decrease in anxiety.

Extensive research has been conducted on the role of positive vs. negative cognitive expectations in drinking behaviour. Positive alcohol expectations predict higher levels of consumption and alcohol-related problems, while negative expectations tend to inhibit consumption. The belief that alcohol helps one cope with stress is one of several positive beliefs. Other positive beliefs are that drinking enhances sexual pleasure and that it makes a person more friendly and assertive in social situations (see MacLatchy-Gaudet & Stewart, 2001; see photo). Negative alcohol expectations include beliefs such as that drinking contributes to physical problems (i.e., hangovers), is linked with cognitive deficits, increases negative moods, and increases one's willingness to engage in unsafe and risky behaviours.

It seems that positive expectations are stronger predictors of drinking behaviour than negative ones (Goldman, Del Boca, & Darkes, 1999). A strong self-protective bias also seems to exist. There is a discrepancy in people's beliefs about the effects of alcohol on themselves vs. others, with most people believing that alcohol has a stronger effect on other people than on themselves (see Paglia & Room, 1999).

Several factors may be involved in the development of alcohol expectations, including direct personal experiences and more indirect, vicarious influences that involve the imitation and internalization of parental beliefs and beliefs displayed in the media (see Goldman et al., 1999). For instance, having an alcoholic parent and experiencing high levels of abuse while growing up are factors that contribute to negative alcohol expectations (Wall, Wekerle, & Bissonette, 2000). Alcohol expectations are also influenced by situational factors. A Canadian study assessed the alcohol expectations of students who were surveyed either in a laboratory or in an on-campus bar (Wall, McKee, & Hinson, 2000). Students tested in the on-campus bar

CBS Photo Archive/Getty Images, Inc

Raj Koothrappali, a character in the hit TV show *The Big Bang Theory*, has coped with his social anxiety, selective mutism, and inability to converse with women by drinking alcohol in order to be engaged in a conversation.

reported higher expectations of pleasurable disinhibition and stimulation from drinking.

Contemporary work on cognitive factors has incorporated the distinction between explicit cognitions (i.e., consciously held beliefs and expectations) and implicit cognition. **Explicit cognition** reflects controlled thought processes that can be deliberated upon, while **implicit cognition** involves automatic appraisal of cues that is more uncontrolled and perhaps not subject to conscious awareness. The focus on implicit cognition reflects the reality that behaviour is often not a product of conscious cognitive reflection but is instead due to cognitions spontaneously activated during periods of temptation or periods of stress (see Stacy & Wiers, 2010). Recent data suggest that explicit cognitions are particularly salient among students who are responsive to reward cues (Keough, O'Connor, & Colder, 2016).

Wiers and Stacy (2006) have advanced a two-component, dual-process model of addictive behaviour that distinguishes between controlled, reflective behaviour and automatic impulsive processing. They summarize research indicating that as an addiction develops, the automatic processing component gains strength and fosters an impulsive orientation that is reflected in cognitive tendencies. They suggest, for instance, that as addiction develops, drug-related cues, such as the presence of a beer bottle, gain the ability to automatically capture the person's attention, even though they may not be consciously aware of their attentiveness to these cues.

While there is growing evidence of the role of implicit cognitions in addictive tendencies (Stacy & Wiers, 2010), and it is generally accepted that both implicit and explicit cognitions play a role in tandem, this area is not without its limitations. Most notably, concerns have been raised about the measures used to assess implicit cognition in terms of whether they really assess what they purport to measure (Christiansen & Field, 2013).

Much of the empirical basis of the implicit component of the dual-process model came from research using the **Drug-Stroop Task**. A Stroop task typically requires an individual to say whether a word matches a particular colour (e.g., Is the word "blue"; that is, is it written in blue letters?) and ignore the actual content of the word. The Drug-Stroop Effect is the tendency for addiction-prone people to respond slower when colour-identifying a word that reflects addiction (e.g., identifying the colour when they see the word VODKA in red letters, as opposed to a neutral word such as BASEBALL). This is known as the Stroop interference effect and is believed to stem from an attentional bias that implicitly operates. Extensive work with the Drug-Stroop Task has confirmed that people prone to addiction have an interference effect when presented with drug-related words (Cox, Fadardi, & Pothos, 2006). The Drug-Stroop Task can be used to assess vulnerability, but it can also be used to evaluate remission and treatment improvements. Indeed, one recent study of people with cocaine addiction undergoing treatment involved collecting fMRI data while participants underwent the Drug-Stroop

Task. Less responsiveness toward cocaine-related cues was associated with heightened midbrain activation, suggesting that this region is implicated in cocaine addiction (see Moeller et al., 2012).

Cognitive processes and negative affect may be linked inextricably in some drinkers. Studies of cognitive processing indicate that negative affective cues in the environment seem to activate alcohol-related concepts (e.g., target words such as "beer") in problem drinkers with high levels of psychological distress (Zack, Toneatto, & MacLeod, 1999; Zack, Poulos, Fragopoulos, & MacLeod, 2003). Thus, it seems that an orientation toward negative affect moods has cognitive implications for certain alcohol abusers.

Biological Variables

Most research on biological factors in substance abuse has addressed the possibility that there is a genetic predisposition for problem drinking. Twin studies have revealed greater concordance in identical twins than in fraternal twins for alcohol abuse (e.g., King et al., 2005), caffeine use (Kendler & Prescott, 1999), smoking (True et al., 1993), heavy use or abuse of cannabis (Kendler & Prescott, 1998), and drug abuse (Tsuang et al., 1998). More recent evidence suggests that the genetic component in drinking may be much stronger for males than females (King et al., 2005). Interesting new work on the role of genetic factors in smoking confirmed suspicions that monozygotic twins, relative to dizygotic twins, were more likely to have simultaneous smoking initiation (Pergadia et al., 2006).

According to Lerman, Schnoll, and Munafo (2007), enough evidence is accumulating to some day be able to develop genetic profiles of smokers that will guide selections of the type, dose, and duration of treatment. Moreover, in an interesting twist, evidence is accumulating in support of the position that the ability to quit smoking also has a substantial heritable component; that is, some people are genetically programmed to be able to quit smoking (see Uhl et al., 2008).

Reviews suggest that heritability estimates for alcohol dependence range between 50 to 60% (Gelernter & Kranzler, 2009). However, these authors note that environmental factors are also important; after all, if someone is never exposed to drink in their environment, they will be abstinent. Contemporary research is focusing on a polymorphism of the OPRM1 receptor gene; it has been linked with early-onset problem drinking among adolescents as well as a tendency for these adolescents to report that they drank specifically to enhance how they were feeling (Miranda et al., 2010). Finally, investigators are now suggesting that the specific genes involved in alcohol dependence are likely involved in other forms of addiction as well, such as addiction to tobacco (Li & Burmeister, 2009). However, researchers caution that many genes remain to be investigated and even those that have been identified require additional work in order to fully understand their nature and roles.

Spanagel (2009) has outlined a systems model of addictive behaviour that views molecular biology's role within a complex gene-environment model. Factors include cumulative response to alcohol exposure, genetic composition, and environmental perturbations over time. To underscore the complexity, Spanagel suggests that chronic use of alcohol interacts with brain physiology to alter gene expression and synaptic plasticity.

Although biological factors are clearly important, Siegel from McMaster University in Hamilton, Ontario, has developed a **conditioning theory of tolerance** that underscores the need to jointly consider biological processes and environmental stimuli that may be involved in the acquisition and maintenance of addictive behaviours (Siegel, 1999; Siegel et al., 2000). Siegel's initial research on the "associative basis of tolerance" was conducted with rats, but similar findings have been obtained with humans. The conditioning theory of tolerance is based on the notion that tolerance is a learned response, and the environmental cues that are present when addictive behaviours are developed can influence behaviours because these cues have come to be associated with the addictive substances via Pavlovian conditioning. For instance, if a person developed an addiction by drinking excessively in his or her recreation room at home, the room itself can become a conditioned stimulus. Drug-associated environmental cues can also elicit withdrawal symptoms.

One consistent research finding is that the presentation of environmental cues previously associated with the drug can attenuate or reduce an already established tolerance. Siegel has also postulated **feedforward mechanisms**, which are defined as anticipatory regulatory responses made in anticipation of a drug (Siegel, 1991; Siegel, Krank, & Hinson, 1987). Feedforward mechanisms reflect the fact that we learn to anticipate drug effects before they actually occur.

What are the implications of the conditioning theory of tolerance for addicted individuals? One clear implication is that factors pertaining to the environmental cues that were present when conditioning first occurred may be quite alluring and will thus have an impact when they reoccur (Siegel, 1999); that is, these environmental factors may contribute to relapses among drug addicts who have been successfully treated. Siegel's work reminds us that physiological processes must be evaluated within the context of situational factors.

Having reviewed the nature and possible causes of the several kinds of substance-related disorders, we turn now to their treatment and prevention.

12.7 | Therapy for Problem Drinking

The havoc created by problem drinking, both for the drinker and for his or her family, friends, employer, and community, makes this problem a serious public health issue. Conse-quently, a great deal of research and clinical effort has gone into the design and evaluation of treatments.

Treatment of alcohol abuse is difficult, not only because of the addictive nature of the drug, but also because of related psychological problems involving depression, anxiety, and severe disruptions in social and occupational functioning. Although some of these problems may have preceded and even contributed to the abuse of alcohol, by the time an abuser is treated, it is seldom possible to know what is cause and what is effect. But what is certain is that the person's life is usually a shambles, and any treatment that has any hope of success has to address more than merely the excessive drinking.

Interventions for problem drinking are both biological and psychological. Whatever the intervention, the first step is for the person to admit the problem and decide to do something about it.

Admitting the Problem

To admit to having a serious drinking problem may sound straightforward to someone who has never had a drinking problem or has never known someone who did. However, substance abusers of all kinds are adept at denying that they have a problem and may react angrily to any suggestion that they do. Moreover, because patterns of problem drinking are highly variable—someone physically dependent on alcohol, for example, does not always drink uncontrollably—the need for intervention is not always recognized by friends or even by health professionals.

Canadian investigations have indicated the general unwillingness of problem drinkers to seek help. Ogborne and DeWit (1999) found that, overall, only 2% of lifetime drinkers reported seeking help; this rose to 9% if the focus was restricted to those who felt that their alcohol use had resulted in some harm. Ogborne and DeWit concluded that the help-seeking rate in Canada is much lower than that among lifetime drinkers in the United States (5%). Canadians report that they would much rather receive assistance by obtaining a self-help book or getting computerized feedback than by contacting a counsellor or therapist, and this is the case even among people who have experienced drinking-related harm in at least two areas of their lives (Koski-Jannes & Cunningham, 2001).

An analysis of Canadian survey data found higher help-seeking rates, with 1 in 3 people with alcohol abuse or dependence seeking treatment (Cunningham & Breslin, 2004). Still we must ask: Why did 2 out of 3 people not seek help? One problem was reiterated in an Ontario survey: current heavy drinkers were significantly less likely than more moderate drinkers to believe that they needed treatment. There seems to also be a tendency for heavy drinkers to overestimate the extent of heavy drinking in the general population (see Cunningham, Blomqvist, & Cordingley, 2007).

Enabling the drinker to take the first step to betterment—what has been called the contemplation stage (Prochaska,

DiClimente, & Norcross, 1992)—can be achieved through questions that get at the issue somewhat indirectly.

> *Do you sometimes feel uncomfortable when alcohol is not available?*
>
> *Do you drink more heavily than usual when you are under pressure?*
>
> *Are you in more of a hurry to get to the first drink than you used to be?*
>
> *Do you sometimes feel guilty about your drinking?*
>
> *Are you annoyed when people talk about your drinking?*
>
> *When drinking socially, do you try to sneak in some extra drinks?*
>
> *Are you constantly making rules for yourself about what and when to drink?*
>
> *(Harvard Mental Health Letter, 1996, pp. 1–2)*

Once the alcohol abuser recognizes that a problem exists, many treatment approaches are available.

Traditional Hospital Treatment

Public and private hospitals worldwide have for many years provided retreats for alcohol abusers, sanctums where people can "dry out" and avail themselves of a variety of individual and group therapies. The withdrawal from alcohol, **detoxification**, can be difficult, both physically and psychologically, and usually takes about one month. Tranquilizers are sometimes given to ease the anxiety and general discomfort of withdrawal. Because many alcohol abusers misuse tranquilizers, some clinics try a gradual tapering off without tranquilizers, rather than a sudden cut-off of alcohol. This non–drug-assisted withdrawal works for most problem drinkers (Wartenberg et al., 1990). To help get through withdrawal, alcohol abusers also need carbohydrate solutions, B vitamins, and, sometimes, anticonvulsants.

When is in-patient treatment needed? One analysis indicated that an in-patient approach is probably best for people with few sources of social support who are living in environments that encourage the alcohol abuse, especially individuals with serious psychological problems in addition to their substance abuse (Finney & Moos, 1998).

Biological Treatments

Some problem drinkers who are in treatment, in-patient or out-patient, take disulfiram, or **Antabuse**, a drug that discourages drinking by causing violent vomiting if alcohol is ingested. It blocks the metabolism of alcohol so that noxious by-products are created. Adherence to an Antabuse regimen can be a

problem. The drinker must already be committed to change. If an alcohol abuser is able or willing to take the drug every morning as prescribed, the chances are good that drinking will lessen because of the negative consequences of imbibing (Sisson & Azrin, 1989). However, in a large, multi-centre study with placebo controls, Antabuse showed no specific benefit and dropout rates were as high as 80% (Fuller, 1988). Antabuse can also cause serious side effects, such as inflammation of nerve tissue (Fuller, 1988).

Biological treatments are best viewed as adjunctive; that is, they may offer some benefit when combined with a psychological intervention. Drugs such as naltrexone and naloxone are more effective than a placebo in reducing drinking and add to overall treatment effectiveness when combined with cognitive-behavioural therapy (CBT)(Volpicelli et al., 1995, 1997). Like many other drug treatments we have discussed, the benefits of naltrexone continue only for as long as the person continues to take it and long-lasting compliance with the treatment is difficult to achieve (O'Malley et al., 1996). Overall, existing evidence indicates that naltrexone is effective in the reduction of heavy drinking and craving, while another drug known as acamprosate is more effective in the maintenance of abstinence (Maisel et al., 2013).

The use of drugs to treat alcohol-abusing people carries some risk because liver function is often impaired in the people and, therefore, the metabolism of the prescribed drug in the liver can be adversely affected, leading to undesirable side effects (Klerman et al., 1994).

Alcoholics Anonymous

Alcoholics Anonymous (AA) is the largest and most widely known self-help group in the world (see photo). It was founded in 1935 in the United States by two recovered alcoholics. It currently has over 115,000 groups worldwide, and there is AA activity in more than 180 countries. Even though relatively few Canadians seek help, of those who do, the majority (60%) seek help from Canadian chapters of AA, like David

Hank Morgan/Science Source

Alcoholics Anonymous is the largest self-help group in the world. At their regular meetings, newcomers rise to announce their addiction and receive advice and support from others.

Adams Richards did (Ogborne & DeWit, 1999). An AA chapter runs regular and frequent meetings at which newcomers rise to announce that they are alcoholics, and older, sober members give testimonials, relating the stories of their problem drinking and indicating how their lives are better now. The group provides emotional support, understanding, and close counselling for the problem drinker, as well as a social life to relieve isolation. Members are urged to call on one another around the clock when they need companionship and encouragement not to relapse into drink. About 70% of Americans who have ever been treated for alcohol abuse have attended at least one AA meeting. Programs modelled after AA are available for other substance abusers; for example, Cocaine Anonymous and Marijuana Anonymous. There are even similar 12-step programs called Overeaters Anonymous and Gamblers Anonymous.

The belief is instilled in each AA member that alcohol abuse is a disease that can never be cured, so continuing vigilance is necessary to resist taking even a single drink lest uncontrollable drinking begin all over again. The basic tenet of AA was articulated vividly in the classic film *Lost Weekend*, for which Ray Milland won an Oscar for best actor. In one scene, his brother confronts him about his denial of the seriousness of his drinking problem: "Don't you ever learn that with you it's like stepping off a roof and expecting to fall just one floor?" The spiritual aspect of AA is apparent in the 12 steps of AA shown in Table 12.2, and there is evidence that belief in this philosophy is important for achieving abstinence (Gilbert, 1991).

Two related self-help groups have developed from AA. The relatives of problem drinkers meet in Al-Anon Family Groups for mutual support in dealing with their family members and in realizing that they cannot make them change their ways. Similarly, Alateen is for the children of alcohol abusers, who also require support and understanding to help them overcome the sense that they are in some way responsible for their parents' problems and responsible also for changing them. Other self-help groups do not have the spiritual overtones of AA, relying instead on social support, reassurance, encouragement, and suggestions for leading a life without alcohol. People often see mental health professionals while attending self-help meetings.

The claims made by AA about the effectiveness of its treatment have been empirically tested. Although AA does seem to confer significant benefits (Ouimette, Finney, & Moos, 1997), it has high dropout rates, and the dropouts are not always factored into the results. In addition, there is only limited long-term follow-up of AA clients. Results from one investigation showed that the degree of AA attendance was related to abstinence over time (McCrady, Epstein, & Kahler, 2004). Clearly, the needs of many people seem to be met by the fellowship, support, and religious overtones of AA. For them, it becomes a way of life; members often attend meetings regularly for many years, as often as four times a week. As with other forms of intervention, it remains to be determined for whom this particular mode is best suited.

TABLE 12.2   **Twelve Steps of Alcoholics Anonymous**

1. We admitted we were powerless over alcohol—that our lives had become unmanageable.
2. Came to believe that a power greater than ourselves could restore us to sanity.
3. Made a decision to turn our will and our lives over to the care of God as we understood Him.
4. Made a searching and fearless moral inventory of ourselves.
5. Admitted to God, to ourselves, and to another human being the exact nature of our wrongs.
6. Were entirely ready to have God remove all these defects of character.
7. Humbly asked Him to remove our shortcomings.
8. Made a list of all persons we had harmed, and became willing to make amends to them all.
9. Made direct amends to such people wherever possible, except when to do so would injure them or others.
10. Continued to take personal inventory and, when we were wrong, promptly admitted it.
11. Sought through prayer and meditation to improve our conscious contact with God as we understood Him, praying only for knowledge of His will for us and the power to carry that out.
12. Having had a spiritual awakening as the result of these steps, we tried to carry this message to alcoholics and to practice these principles in all our affairs.

Source: The Twelve Steps are reprinted with permission of Alcoholics Anonymous World Services, Inc. ("AAWS") Permission to reprint the Twelve Steps does not mean that AAWS has reviewed or approved the contents of this publication, or that AAWS necessarily agrees with the views expressed herein. A.A. is a program of recovery from alcoholism only—use of the Twelve Steps in connection with programs and activities which are patterned after A.A., but which address other problems, or in any other non-A.A. context, does not imply otherwise.

Cognitive and Behavioural Treatment

Behavioural and cognitive-behavioural researchers have been studying the treatment of alcohol abuse for many years. Indeed, one of the earliest articles on behaviour therapy concerned aversive conditioning as a treatment for alcoholism (Kantorovich, 1930). In general, cognitive and behavioural therapies represent the most effective psychological treatments for alcohol abuse (Finney & Moos, 1998).

Aversion Therapy   In aversion therapy, problem drinkers are shocked or made nauseous while looking at, reaching for, or beginning to drink alcohol. In one procedure, called **covert sensitization** (Cautela, 1966), problem drinkers are instructed to imagine being made violently and disgustingly sick by their drinking.

Despite some evidence that aversion therapy may slightly enhance the effectiveness of in-patient treatment (Smith,

Frawley, & Polissar, 1991), some well-known behaviour therapists discourage its use because it lacks empirical support and causes great discomfort (e.g., Wilson et al., 1991). Aversion therapy, if used at all, seems best implemented in the context of broad programs that attend to the client's particular life circumstances; for example, marital conflict, social fears, and other factors associated with problem drinking (Tucker, Vuchinich, & Downey, 1992).

Contingency-Management Therapy

Contingency-management therapy (a term often used interchangeably with operant conditioning) for alcohol abuse involves teaching clients and those close to them to reinforce behaviours inconsistent with drinking; for example, taking Antabuse and avoiding situations associated with past drinking. This therapy also includes teaching job-hunting and social skills, as well as assertiveness training for refusing drinks. Socially isolated individuals are encouraged and helped to establish contacts with other people who are not associated with drinking. Often referred to as the "community-reinforcement approach," contingency-management therapy has generated very promising results (Baucom et al., 1998; Sisson & Azrin, 1989).

A strategy that is sometimes termed "behavioural self-control training" (Tucker et al., 1992) builds on the work just described. This approach emphasizes patient control and includes one or more of the following:

- *stimulus control*, whereby one narrows the situations in which one allows oneself to drink (e.g., with others on a special occasion)
- *modification of the topography of drinking* (e.g., having only mixed drinks and taking small sips rather than gulps)
- *reinforcing abstinence* (e.g., allowing oneself a non-alcoholic treat if one resists the urge to drink)

An issue not formally addressed by advocates of behavioural self-control training is how to get the person to abide by restrictions and conditions that, if implemented, will reduce or eliminate drinking. In other words, the challenge with such therapies seems to be not so much discovering the means necessary to control drinking as getting the alcohol abuser to employ these tools without constant external supervision and control. There is evidence for the general effectiveness of this approach (Hester & Miller, 1989), some of it in the context of controlled-drinking programs, to which we turn now.

Moderation in Drinking

Until recently, it was generally agreed that alcohol abusers had to abstain completely if they were to be cured, for they were believed to have no control over imbibing once they had taken that first drink. Although this continues to be the belief of AA, this assumption has been called into question by research mentioned earlier indicating that drinkers' beliefs about themselves and alcohol may be as important as the physiological addiction to the drug itself. Considering the difficulty in society of avoiding alcohol altogether, it may even be preferable to teach the problem drinker to imbibe with moderation. A drinker's self-esteem will certainly benefit from being able to control a problem and from feeling in charge.

Controlled drinking in alcohol treatment was introduced by the Sobells while they were located at the Addiction Research Foundation in Toronto (see Sobell & Sobell, 1993). This approach is currently much more widely accepted in Canada and Europe than in the United States. **Controlled drinking** is a moderate pattern of alcohol consumption that avoids the extremes of total abstinence and inebriation. The results of the Sobells' initial treatment program suggested that at least some alcohol abusers can learn to control their drinking and improve other aspects of their lives, as well (Sobell & Sobell, 1976). Problem drinkers attempting to control their drinking were given shocks when they chose straight liquor rather than mixed drinks, gulped their drinks down too fast, or took large swallows rather than sips. They also received problem-solving and assertiveness training, watched videotapes of themselves inebriated, and identified the situations that precipitated their drinking so that they could settle on a less self-destructive course of action. Their improvement was greater than that of alcohol abusers who tried for total abstinence and were given shocks for any drinking at all.

People in contemporary controlled-drinking treatment programs are taught to respond adaptively to situations in which they might otherwise drink excessively. They learn various social skills to help them resist pressures to drink; they receive assertiveness, relaxation, and stress-management training, sometimes including biofeedback and meditation; and they are encouraged to exercise and maintain a healthy diet.

Clients are also taught—or more precisely, are encouraged to believe—that a lapse will not inevitably precipitate a total relapse and should be regarded as a learning experience rather than as a sign that the battle is lost, a marked contrast from the AA perspective (Marlatt & Gordon, 1985). This non-catastrophizing approach to relapse after therapy—falling off the wagon—is important because the overwhelming majority of problem drinkers who become abstinent do experience a relapse over a four-year period (Polich, Armor, & Braiker, 1980). In this therapy, alcohol abusers examine sources of stress in their work, family, and relationships so that they can become active and responsible in anticipating and resisting situations that might tempt excessive drinking (Marlatt, 1983; Sobell, Toneatto, & Sobell, 1990). The controlled-drinking approach has now been supplemented by the guided self-change approach, which was developed in Toronto. **Guided self-change**, an outpatient approach, emphasizes personal responsibility and control. The Guided Self-Change Program (GSCP; Sobell & Sobell, 2005) is an early intervention program designed for people with mild to moderate drinking problems. The goals of the program are to (1) help clients help themselves; (2) allow clients to make informed choices; (3) teach a general problem-solving approach; (4) strengthen client motivation and commitment to change; and (5) encourage self-reliance, empowerment, and personal competence.

Harm reduction therapy is another alternative to an approach that focuses on complete abstinence. The principles of harm reduction therapy are outlined in Canadian Contributions 12.1.

Canadian Contributions 12.1

G. Alan Marlatt and Harm Reduction Therapy

Courtesy of the Estate of G. Alan Marlatt

G. Alan Marlatt outlined harm reduction therapy as an alternative to treatments stemming from the medical model.

G. Alan Marlatt, a Canadian psychologist, was the director of the Addictive Behaviors Research Center at the University of Washington in Seattle (see photo). Marlatt died in 2011 after an exceptionally distinguished career. He had a substantial impact on the assessment and treatment of addictions, and his work has been widely recognized. For instance, in 1990 he was given the Jellinek Memorial Award for outstanding contributions to knowledge in the field of alcohol studies. He was also given the Senior Scientist Award from the U.S. National Institute of Alcohol Abuse and Alcoholism. In 1996, Marlatt was appointed a member of the U.S. National Advisory Council on Drug Abuse. Marlatt's research on employing brief interventions to help control and reduce binge drinking among students was discussed earlier. His harm reduction therapy (HRT) is having an increasing impact as a general approach that can be used to treat a variety of high-risk behaviours, including addictions. The basic tenets of HRT are discussed below:

- First, contrary to moral/criminal models or disease models of drug use, addiction is not a crime deserving of punishment. Rather, it is an adjustment problem that needs intervention.

- Second, HRT recognizes that abstinence is an ideal outcome, but it is not the only outcome, especially for those beginning treatment. It is quite acceptable to strive for outcomes that involve the reduction of harm rather than striving in an all-or-none fashion to eliminate harm altogether. HRT recognizes that striving for more extreme goals may be self-defeating.

- Third, HRT is a bottom-up approach that is more in line with the needs of the addict and is focused on reducing their level of suffering. It contrasts with the top-down approach favoured by those who make drug policy.

- Fourth, because HRT does not require complete abstinence, more people should be able to gain access to what Marlatt refers to as "low-threshold" services. Marlatt (1999) has suggested that the difference is reflected in the phrase "We'll meet you where you are" (p. 55), not "where you should be."

- Finally, Marlatt (1999) argues that HRT is based on the principle of "compassionate pragmatism" rather than on "moralistic idealism." Specifically, harm reduction is non-judgemental and acknowledges the realistic struggles of people as they attempt to manage their everyday affairs.

Harm reduction involves a number of goals: to stabilize the maladaptive behaviour and prevent further harm, to help the client develop an awareness of high-risk behaviours, and to give the person coping training in how to deal with high-risk situations. Another important goal is to facilitate health-promoting and risk-reducing strategies.

Marlatt's Alcohol Skills Training Program (ASTP) for students incorporates the harm reduction model. The ASTP is based on the view that drinking is normal behaviour for students and that interventions may be needed; thus, a focus on moderation rather than abstinence is more realistic. Students participate in eight sessions over several weeks. The initial sessions focus on helping students become more aware of alcohol's impact and learn practical things such as how to calculate their own blood-alcohol levels. Subsequent sessions challenge overly positive beliefs about the benefits of drinking. Students also learn specific skills and role-play so that they will know how to deal with stressful situations without turning to alcohol.

HRT can be controversial, as some of the things that are done to reduce initial harm may involve initiatives that are not accepted by everyone. These could include such things as encouraging controlled drinking or the moderate (as opposed to extensive) use of amphetamines or setting up needle-exchange programs to limit additional health risks. Marlatt acknowledged that his approach has been criticized for "enabling" drug use (see Marlatt, Blume, & Parks, 2001). Another criticism is that HRT does not have the goal of abstinence. Marlatt et al. (2001), however, stated that abstinence is a goal at the endpoint of the continuum once the addicted individual starts to improve.

According to Marlatt and Witkiewitz (2002), empirical research shows that harm reduction is at least as effective as abstinence-oriented approaches in reducing alcohol consumption and alcohol-related consequences, and new data continue to show that harm reduction is very effective (see Witkiewitz & Marlatt, 2006). Moreover, Marlatt, a firm believer in the importance of education, maintains that the basic tenets of harm reduction therapy can be taught in educational programs. High school and university students respond well to this approach. If they are heavy drinkers, for example, they can adopt the goal of drinking less and in a more responsible manner, rather than strive for absolute abstinence. According to Marlatt et al. (2001), one advantage of HRT over other treatment approaches is that it more easily forges a positive alliance between the client and therapist because the realistic goals of HRT reflect client needs.

In Canada, the harm reduction debate reached its initial peak during the 2003 mayoral election in Vancouver, when successful

(continued)

candidate Larry Campbell proposed the use of a harm reduction model as a way of combating rampant drug use in downtown Vancouver. The overall strategy, known as the Four Pillars Drug Strategy, includes the creation of supervised drug-injection sites. According to the City of Vancouver, these sites would be a "vital part of a harm reduction plan to reduce overdose and overdose deaths and the spread of HIV/AIDS and hepatitis C, and to provide access to primary health care to drug users in Vancouver." The strategy's four pillars are harm reduction, prevention, treatment, and law enforcement. This proposal resulted in the creation of Insite, North America's first safe injection site. Empirical evidence has found consistently that this innovative approach has been very successful (see Neighbors, Larimer, Lostutter, & Woods, 2006; Podymow et al., 2006; Wood, Tyndall, Montaner, & Kerr, 2006). Nevertheless, the safe injection HRT program in Vancouver has been continually at risk of extinction despite its apparent benefits (see Drucker, 2006). Supervised injection sites were not in keeping with principles endorsed by the former federal government under then-Prime Minister Stephen Harper. At that time, Insite had to seek federal approval every year. But in 2016, Insite received a four-year licence from the new Liberal government. Other communities in Canada are now considering creating safe injection sites. The leadership of the late Brooklyn McNeil and Toronto's then-Medical Officer of Health Dr. David McKeown resulted in Toronto approving three safe injection sites in 2016.

The negative attitude of the former Canadian government is in keeping with the more negative view of harm reduction that exists in areas of the United States, which can be differentiated from the more favourable views of HRT in Europe and Australia (see Neighbors et al., 2006). Drucker (2006) claimed that then-Prime Minister Harper opposed harm reduction in all forms. At the time of writing, Insite was safe. A successful 2008 constitutional challenge provided protection from the federal government. Justice Ian Pitfield of the B.C. Supreme Court ruled that closing Insite would violate Section 7 of the *Charter of Rights and Freedoms* (which governs the life, liberty, and security of the person), and he granted Insite a conditional exemption from legislation governing drug use. The federal government then appealed to the Supreme Court of Canada, but in 2011, the highest court ruled in favour of Insite on the grounds that to not keep it open would violate the *Charter of Rights and Freedoms*. Canada's Chief Justice Beverly McLachlin noted that, quite simply, Insite saves lives.

We will leave the final word on Insite to someone close to the situation, Mark Townsend, Executive Director of the Portland Hotel Society, which operates Insite. He noted the following: "There is no silver bullet to deal with the scourge of addiction. If drug enforcement really worked then we wouldn't have situations like we do in the Downtown Eastside (of Vancouver) . . . Insite is about working in the reality of the situation, and most importantly about preventing overdose deaths" (Chesser, 2009).

Clinical Considerations in Treating Alcohol Abuse

Many attempts to treat problem drinking are impeded by the therapist's often-unstated assumption that all people who drink to excess do so for the same reasons. From what we have examined thus far in this chapter, we know that this assumption is unlikely to be correct.

A comprehensive clinical assessment considers what place drinking occupies in the person's life (Tucker et al., 1992). A woman in a desperately unhappy marriage, with time on her hands now that her children are school-aged, may seek the numbing effects of alcohol to help pass the time and avoid facing life's dilemmas. Making the taste of alcohol unpleasant by pairing it with shock or a drug that induces vomiting seems neither sensible nor adequate. The therapist should concentrate on the marital and family problems and try to reduce the psychological pain that permeates the person's existence. She will also need help in tolerating the withdrawal symptoms that come with reduced consumption. Without alcohol as a reliable anaesthetic, she will need to mobilize other resources to confront her hitherto-avoided problems. Social skills training and rewarding activities outside the home may help her do so.

We have seen that problem drinking is sometimes associated with other mental disorders, in particular anxiety disorders, mood disorders, and psychopathy. Therapists of all orientations have to recognize that depression is often comorbid with alcohol abuse and that suicide is also a risk. The clinician must therefore conduct a broad-spectrum assessment of the client's problem.

Alcohol researchers recognize that different kinds of drinkers may require different treatment approaches (Mattson et al., 1994). The challenge is to determine which factors in the drinkers should be aligned with which factors in treatment. Client-treatment matching, or what the psychotherapy literature describes as "aptitude-treatment interaction," has been cited by the Institute of Medicine (1990a) as a critical issue in the development of better interventions for problem drinking. A large-scale effort to address the question was Project Match, a multi-site clinical trial designed to test the hypothesis that certain kinds of treatments are good matches for certain kinds of problem drinkers. This project is described in Focus on Discovery 12.3.

It is doubtful that a single event, even a dramatic one, can bring about the kind of profound changes necessary to wean a person from an addiction. It is more probable that successful abstinence, whether resulting from treatment or not, relies on a confluence of many life events and forces that can support the recovering alcoholic's efforts to lead a life without substance abuse. Whatever combination of factors helps problem drinkers become abstinent or controlled drinkers, a key element is social support for their efforts from family, friends, work, or self-help groups such as AA (McCrady, 1985).

Focus on Discovery 12.3

Matching Client to Treatment: Project Match

For many years, both practitioners and researchers have understood the importance of employing treatments that are suitable for particular people. This notion goes beyond the question of the general kind of therapy best suited for a particular kind of problem; rather, it involves an approach called *aptitude–treatment interaction (ATI)*, which focuses on characteristics of people with the same disorder that might make them more suitable candidates for one generally effective treatment than for another.

The question of matching the person to treatment was tested in Project Match, a large, eight-year, multi-site study on alcohol abuse (Project Match Research Group, 1997). This study has remained controversial in professional circles because it failed to find what it was looking for, namely, a way to match particular kinds of people with specific interventions.

Ten matching variables were chosen, among them severity of alcohol dependency, severity of cognitive impairment, motivation to change, severity of psychological disturbance (referred to as "psychiatric severity"), support from one's social milieu for drinking, and sociopathic tendencies, having been found in previous research to be associated with outcomes of intervention. There were three treatments:

1. The 12-step facilitation treatment (TSF) was designed to convert people to the AA view of alcoholism as an incurable but manageable disease and to encourage their involvement in AA.

2. The motivational-enhancement therapy (MET), based on William Miller's approach (see Miller & Rollnick, 2002), attempted to mobilize clients' own resources to reduce drinking. Part of this intervention involved highlighting the ways in which current maladaptive behaviour was interfering with their valued goals.

3. A cognitive-behavioural coping-skills therapy (CBT) presented to clients the idea that drinking is functionally related to problems in their lives; this treatment taught clients skills to help them cope with situations that trigger drinking or prevent relapse.

Some of the predicted interactions were that drinkers under heavy pressure to stop would do best with the 12-step facilitation therapy; those with psychological problems would do best with the cognitive therapy; and those with low motivation to change would do best with the motivational-enhancement therapy.

All treatments were carefully administered in individual sessions by trained therapists over a 12-week period. The principal dependent (outcome) measures were percentage of days abstinent and drinks per drinking day during a one-year post-treatment assessment period. Figure 12.3 portrays the main results of this study. Significant within-group improvement was observed—all treatments were very helpful on average, consistent with a subsequent study by Ouimette et al. (1997). However, interactions between treatments and matching variables (the main purpose of the study) were not found except for the interaction involving psychiatric severity. Clients in better psychological shape had more abstinent days after the 12-step facilitation program than did participants in the cognitive-behavioural therapy, although clients in worse psychological condition did not fare differently across the three treatments.

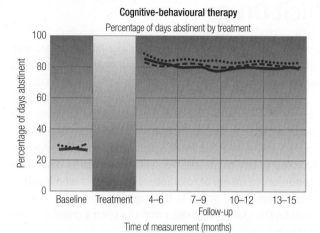

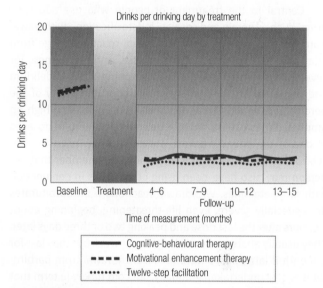

FIGURE 12.3 Monthly percentage of days abstinent and drinks per drinking day (DDD) for baseline (averaged over three months prior to treatment) and for each month of the posttreatment period (months 1–15).

According to Marlatt (1999), one shortcoming of the Project Match study as a treatment efficacy study is that it did not include a no-treatment, assessment-only control group. The extensive assessment sessions undergone by the participants may have had a positive influence on their behaviour, independent of treatment.

Another criticism of Project Match raised by Canadian researchers (Conrod, Pihl, Stewart, & Dongier, 2000) is that the therapies chosen were not precise enough and were not tailored to the specific therapy needs of the individual clients. Conrod et al. (2000) conducted their own study and showed that personality-specific motivational and coping-skills training was substantially more effective than a motivational control intervention in reducing the frequency and severity of alcohol and drug use. They concluded that matching strategies that link client personality characteristics and treatments have substantial promise.

12.8 Therapy for the Use of Illicit Drugs

Some factors involved in treatment for alcohol abuse are relevant also to treatment for addiction to illegal drugs. We focus here on issues that pertain to those who abuse illicit drugs.

People turn to drugs for many reasons, and even though, in most instances, drug use becomes controlled primarily by a physical addiction, the entire pattern of an addict's existence is bound to be affected by the drug and must therefore be addressed in any treatment. As seen in our earlier discussion of conditioning theory of tolerance, one of the chief difficulties of maintaining abstinence is the negative influence of many stimuli on the recovering addict that can elicit a craving for the substance.

Central to the treatment of people who use addicting drugs, such as heroin and cocaine, is detoxification—withdrawal from the drug itself. Heroin-withdrawal reactions range from relatively mild bouts of anxiety, nausea, and restlessness for several days to more severe and frightening bouts of delirium and panic anxiety, depending primarily on the purity of the heroin that the individual has been using. Someone high on amphetamines can be brought down by appropriate dosages of one of the phenothiazines, a class of drugs used to treat schizophrenia, although it is important to remember that the person may also have been using other drugs in conjunction with amphetamines. Withdrawal reactions from barbiturates are especially severe, even life-threatening, beginning about 24 hours after the last dose and peaking two or three days later. They usually abate by the end of the first week but may last for a month if large doses were taken. Withdrawal from barbiturates is best undertaken gradually, not cold turkey (a term that derives from the goosebumps that occur during withdrawal, making the person's skin resemble that of a plucked turkey), and should take place under close medical supervision.

Detoxification is the first way in which therapists try to help an addict or drug abuser, and it may be the easiest part of the rehabilitation process. Enabling the drug user to function without drugs after detoxification is an arduous task that promises more disappointment and sadness than success for both helper and client. A variety of approaches are available, both biological and psychological.

Biological Treatments

Two widely used drug-therapy programs for heroin addiction involve the administration of **heroin substitutes**, drugs chemically similar to heroin that can replace the body's craving for it, or **heroin antagonists**, drugs that prevent the user from experiencing the heroin high. The first category includes **methadone**, levomethadyl acetate, and buprenorphine—synthetic narcotics designed to take the place of heroin. Since these drugs are themselves addicting, successful treatment essentially converts the heroin addict into someone who is addicted to a different substance. This conversion occurs because these synthetic narcotics are **cross-dependent** with heroin; that is, by acting on the same central nervous system receptors, they become a substitute for the original dependency. Of course, methadone used as described here is legal, whereas heroin is not.

Abrupt discontinuation of methadone results in its own pattern of withdrawal reactions. Because these reactions are less severe than those of heroin, methadone can wean the addict altogether from drug dependence (Strain, Bigelow, Liebson, & Stitzer,1999).

For treatment with heroin substitutes, the addict must go to a clinic and swallow the drug in the presence of a staff member, once a day for methadone and three times a week for levomethadyl acetate and buprenorphine (see photo). Some users under treatment are able to hold jobs, commit no crimes, and refrain from using other illicit drugs (Eissenberg, Bigelow, Strain, & Walsh,1997), but many users are unable to do so. The effectiveness of methadone treatment is improved if combined with regular psychological counselling (Ball & Ross, 1991).

Pre-existing behavioural patterns and life circumstances play a role in how the individual will react to methadone treatment. Since methadone does not provide a euphoric high, many addicts will return to heroin if it becomes available to them. Many people drop out of methadone programs in part because of side effects, such as insomnia, constipation, excessive sweating, and diminished sexual functioning. Yet in this era of AIDS and the transmission of the human immunodeficiency virus through shared needles, this treatment has a big advantage because methadone can be swallowed.

In treatment with the opiate antagonists cyclazocine and naloxone, addicts are first gradually weaned from heroin. They then receive increasing dosages of one of these drugs and are thereby prevented from experiencing any high should they later take heroin. These drugs have great affinity for the receptors to which opiates usually bind; their molecules occupy the receptors without stimulating them, leaving heroin molecules with no place to go. As with methadone, however, addicts must make frequent and regular visits to a clinic, and this takes motivation and responsibility on their part.

The Waterloo Region Record-David Bebee/The Canadian Press

Methadone is a synthetic narcotic substitute. Former heroin addicts come to clinics each day and swallow their dose.

Psychological Treatments

Drug abuse is sometimes treated in the consulting rooms of psychiatrists, psychologists, and other mental health workers. Several kinds of psychotherapy are applied to drug-use disorders, as they are to other human maladjustments, often in combination with biological treatments aimed at reducing the physical dependence.

In the first direct comparison in a controlled study, the tri-cyclic antidepressant desipramine and a cognitive-behavioural treatment were found to be somewhat effective in reducing cocaine use, as well as in improving abusers' family, social, and general psychological functioning. In a 12-week study by Carroll and associates (Carroll, Rounsaville, Gordon, et al. 1994; Carroll et al., 1995), desipramine was more effective than a placebo for patients with a low degree of dependence on cocaine, whereas the cognitive treatment was better in reducing cocaine use in patients with a high degree of dependence. This finding illustrates the significance of the psychological aspects of substance abuse.

In Carroll's study, patients receiving cognitive treatment learned how to avoid high-risk situations (e.g., being around people who use cocaine), recognize the lure of the drug for them, and develop alternatives to using cocaine (e.g., recreational activities with non-users). Cocaine abusers in this study also learned strategies for coping with the craving and for resisting the tendency to regard a slip as a catastrophe ("relapse prevention training," per Marlatt & Gordon, 1985). The more depressed the patient, the more favourable the outcome from both the antidepressant drug and the cognitive therapy. Overall, the results for the psychosocial treatment were superior to those for the antidepressant drug in reducing cocaine use, and this pattern was maintained at a one-year follow-up (Carroll, Rounsaville, Nich, et al., 1994).

A more recent and more widely used approach involves the use of **motivational interviewing**. This approach combines CBT principles with the humanistic principles avowed by Carl Rogers. The central premise is that people must be motivated and ready for change in order for psychological interventions to work and motivation needs to be enhanced among ambivalent clients. Motivational interviewing (MI) is a general orientation that is broadly applicable. It is discussed in more detail as an approach to the treatment of various disorders in Chapter 17.

William R. Miller was the first clinician to systematically develop and apply motivational interviewing to problematic drinking behaviour (see Miller, 1983; Miller & Rollnick, 1991, 2002). The need for this approach is reflected in Miller and Heather's (1998) widely cited quote:

> *"Every therapist knows that motivation is a vital element of change. Nowhere is this clearer than in the treatment of addictive behaviours, which are, if one thinks about it, fundamentally motivational problems. Addictive behaviours are by definition highly motivated in that they persist against an accumulating tide of aversive consequences. When one continues to act despite great personal risk and cost, something is overriding common sense. In the context of war, we call it bravery or heroism. In the context of pleasure, we call it addiction" (p. 121).*

This approach is in the Rogerian tradition in that it involves non-judgemental empathy and the motivation to change and that the sense of responsibility must come from the client rather than the therapist or counsellor.

Three key motivational concepts identified by Rollnick and Allison (2004) that are highly related to whether someone with a drinking problem can overcome it are readiness to change, ambivalence, and resistance. Readiness to change is viewed dimensionally from a process approach and it requires the therapist to be attuned to when the client is really at a point of wanting to change. Ambivalence involves mixed feelings and a range of emotions due to wanting to change but still recognizing the perceived benefits of drinking (reflected by statements such as "I want to but. . . ."). Resistance is a clear reluctance or open opposition to making progress.

Rollnick and Allison (2004) provided the following account of resistance:

"Counsellor: I understand that you have come to see me about your drinking. Is that correct?

Client: No, it's not. I thought that what would happen here, like you go on just like my wife—drinking, drinking, drinking, as if it's all due to drinking. I tell you, if all you want to is talk about drinking, I may as well go home. It's just a waste of time . . .

Counsellor: For you, there's a much bigger picture. It's not just the alcohol that's bothering you.

Client: That's right, because time and time again I get told that my drinking is a problem, like it's the only thing that matters.

Counsellor: Other things also matter and you don't want them to be sidelined in our meeting today.

Client: No, that's exactly right. I want to talk about other things as well.

Counsellor: Tell me, taking your time, about these other things." (p. 112)

Source: Rollnick, S., & Allison, J. (2004). Motivational interviewing. In N. Heather & T. Stockwell (Eds.), *The essential handbook of treatment and prevention of alcohol problems* (pp. 105–115). Chichester, West Sussex, England: John Wiley & Sons.

The above excerpt reflects the skillful decision made by the therapist to steer away from a discussion of drinking until much later in the process after an empathic relationship has been established.

A meta-analysis of nine studies that compared brief MI with other types of interventions for excessive drinking found a moderate effect size of 0.43, leading the authors of this work to conclude that brief MI is effective (see Vasilaki, Hosier, & Cox, 2006).

12.9 Treatment of Cigarette Smoking

As we mentioned earlier, numerous laws today prohibit smoking in restaurants, trains, airplanes, public buildings, and other places. These laws are part of a social context that provides more incentive and support to stop smoking than existed in the past (see photo).

Some smokers attend smoking clinics or consult with professionals for specialized smoking-reduction programs. It is estimated that about half of those who go through smoking-cessation programs succeed in abstaining by the time the program is over; only about 20% of those who have succeeded in the short term actually remain non-smoking after a year. The greatest success overall is found among smokers who are better educated, are older, or have acute health problems (USDHHS, 1998).

Many people have turned to the use of battery-powered electronic cigarettes (e-cigarettes); they are motivated to circumvent restrictions on smoking in public and they often endorse the belief that the use of e-cigarettes will help people trying to quit smoking and is a healthier alternative. An e-cigarette consists of a vaporized liquid of varying flavours that is inhaled. A recent meta-analysis concluded that the use of e-cigarettes was not more effective than other methods of smoking cessation (Kalkhoran & Glantz, 2016).

Biological Treatments

Reducing a smoker's craving for nicotine by providing it in a different way is one biological approach to treatment. Attention to nicotine dependence is clearly important because the more cigarettes a person smokes daily, the less successful attempts to quit will be. Gum containing nicotine may help smokers endure the nicotine withdrawal that accompanies any effort to stop smoking. The nicotine in gum is absorbed much more slowly and steadily than that in tobacco. The long-term goal is for the former smoker to be able to cut back on the use of the gum as well, eventually eliminating reliance on nicotine altogether.

There is some controversy around this treatment, however, because ex-smokers can become dependent on the gum. Moreover, in doses that deliver an amount of nicotine equivalent to smoking one cigarette an hour, the gum causes cardiovascular changes (e.g., increased blood pressure) that can be dangerous to people with cardiovascular diseases. Nevertheless, some experts believe that even prolonged, continued use of the gum is healthier than obtaining nicotine by smoking, since at least the poisons in the smoke are avoided. The best results are obtained when the gum is combined with a behaviourally oriented treatment (Hughes, 1995).

Hughes (1995) pointed out that although nicotine replacement alleviates withdrawal symptoms—which justifies its use in gum and in the nicotine patches—the severity of withdrawal is related only minimally to success in stopping smoking (Hughes & Hatsukami, 1992).

In Canada, Ontario lags behind the other provinces in smoking cessation, with 20% of the population smoking and no improvements in rates since 1995 (see Selby, 2013). The STOP Study (Stop Smoking Therapy for Ontario Patients) is a massive treatment study targeting up to 50,000 smokers led by Peter Selby at CAMH. It has been ongoing since 2005 and seeks to identify novel and effective methods of combining nicotine replacement therapy with other forms of intervention, including various forms of counselling, such as counselling delivered by pharmacists throughout the province. One form of nicotine replacement therapy and pharmacist counselling has yielded an initial quit rate of 27.7% (see Costello et al., 2011). While initial results look promising in terms of quit rates, a longer follow-up period is required to fully evaluate this provincial intervention. Meanwhile, other research based at the University of Toronto has found that the CYP2A6 genotypes are associated with the slow metabolism of nicotine and that this accounts, in part, for why some people are less likely to benefit from nicotine replacement therapy (Malaiyandi et al., 2006).

Nicotine patches first became available in December 1991 with a doctor's prescription and in 1996 over the counter (see photo). A polyethylene patch taped to the arm serves as a transdermal (through the skin) nicotine delivery system that slowly and steadily releases the drug into the bloodstream and thence to the brain. An advantage of the patch over nicotine gum is that the person needs only to apply the patch each day and not remove it, making compliance easier. A program of treatment usually lasts 10 to 12 weeks, with smaller and smaller patches used as treatment progresses. A drawback is that a person who continues smoking while wearing the patch may increase the amount of nicotine in the body to dangerous levels.

Evidence suggests that the nicotine patch is superior to the use of a placebo patch in terms of abstinence, as well as subjective craving (see Hughes, 1995). However, as with nicotine gum, the patch is not a panacea. Abstinence rates are less than 40% immediately following the termination

Laws that have banned smoking in many places have probably increased the frequency of quitting.

The Canadian Press/STRCANWEST

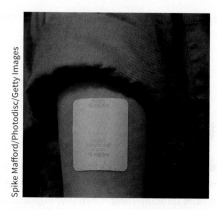

Nicotine patches are now available over the counter to help relieve withdrawal symptoms.

of treatment, and at nine-month follow-ups, differences between the drug and a placebo disappear. The manufacturers state that the patch is to be used only as part of a psychological smoking-cessation program and then for not more than three months at a time.

Varenicline is a nicotine receptor partial agonist that seems effective in reducing smoking when used over a period of three months (see Hajek et al., 2011). Varenicline not only reduces withdrawal symptoms, it tends to reduce the urges to smoke among those who have quit smoking. However, given reports linking varenicline with depression and suicidal tendencies in some people, the U.S. Food and Drug Administration insisted in 2009 that it be accompanied by a warning about these possible side effects.

Given other evidence that attempting to quit smoking can precipitate an episode of depression in someone who has previously been depressed, interest has also focused on the possible role of antidepressants in aiding smoking cessation. Evidence shows that antidepressants that have strong effects on dopamine do have some benefit, regardless of whether the person has a history of depression (Hurt, Sachs, & Glover, 1997). Clients are typically given an amount of the antidepressant that is less than would be used to treat depression. They take the drug for some period of time before trying to stop smoking and then continue taking the antidepressant for some amount of time (e.g., seven weeks) as they try to give up smoking. Hurt et al. (1997) combined brief counselling with either bupropion (an antidepressant sold under the names Wellbutrin and Zyban) or a placebo and found one-year abstinence rates of 23% in the treated group and 12% in the placebo group. Combining bupropion and nicotine patches has yielded an impressive 12-month abstinence rate of 35% (Jorenby et al., 1999).

Psychological Treatments

Although short-term results of psychological treatments are often very encouraging (some programs have reported as many as 95% of smokers abstinent by the end of treatment), longer term results are far less positive. Most smokers return to smoking within a year, especially if they tend to be heavy smokers

(DiClemente, 1993). This evidence does not belie the fact that a substantial minority of smokers can be helped; clearly, however, the task is not easy.

Many techniques have been tried. The idea behind some of them is to make smoking unpleasant, even nauseating. In the 1970s, there was considerable interest in rapid smoking treatment, in which a smoker sits in a poorly ventilated room and puffs much faster than normal, perhaps as often as every six seconds (e.g., Lando, 1977). Variations include rapid puffing (rapid smoking without inhaling), focused smoking (smoking for a long period of time but at a normal rate), and smoke holding (retaining smoke in the mouth for several minutes but without inhaling). Although such treatments reduce smoking and foster abstinence more than no-treatment control conditions, they usually do not differ from each other or from other credible interventions, showing high rates of relapse at follow-ups (Schwartz, 1987; Sobell et al., 1990).

Cognitively oriented investigators have tried to encourage more control in people who smoke with treatments that have them develop and use various coping skills, such as relaxation and positive self-talk, when confronted with tempting situations (e.g., following a good meal). One goal is to address the "internal dialogue" that smokers have and substitute positive and encouraging thoughts for negative thoughts (see cartoon). Results have yielded significant reductions in smoking cessation, but the bulk of the evidence suggests that a combined approach with counselling and pharmacotherapy is best (Raupach & Onno, 2011). But there is still the problem of relapse, which is discussed in more detail below.

Probably the most widespread intervention is advice or direction from a physician to stop smoking. Each year millions of smokers are given this counsel because of hypertension, heart disease, lung disease, diabetes, or on general grounds of preserving or improving health. Indeed, by age 65, most smokers have managed to quit (USDHHS, 1998). There is some evidence that a physician's advice can get some people to stop smoking, at least for a while, especially when the patients also chew nicotine gum (Law & Tang, 1995). But much more needs

to be learned about the nature of the advice, the manner in which it is given, its timing, and other factors that must surely play a role in determining whether an addicted individual is prepared and able to alter his or her behaviour primarily on a physician's say-so (USDHHS, 1998).

As with other addictions, psychological factors may make it difficult for smokers to quit. As these factors can vary significantly among addicts, one treatment package cannot be expected to help all smokers. People have trouble quitting for many different reasons, and diverse methods need to be developed to help them. Yet in their zeal to make an impact on the smoking problem, clinicians have until recently put smokers in standardized programs.

Relapse Prevention

Mark Twain reputedly quipped that stopping smoking was easy—he'd done it hundreds of times! Most smokers relapse within a year of stopping, regardless of the means used to stop. As might be expected, people who smoked the most—and are presumably more addicted to nicotine—relapse more often and more quickly than moderate or light smokers. It is very difficult for ex-smokers to maintain their abstinence. Data (and common sense) tell us that ex-smokers who do not live with a smoker do better at follow-up than do those who do live with a smoker (McIntyre-Kingsolver, Lichtenstein, & Mermelstein, 1986). So-called booster or maintenance sessions help, but in a very real sense they represent a continuation of treatment; when they stop, relapse is the rule (Brandon, Zelman, & Baker, 1987). However, there is considerably more social support for not smoking than there was just 20 years ago. Perhaps as time goes on, societal sanctions against smoking will help those who have succeeded in quitting remain abstinent.

One approach to the relapse problem is to focus on the cognitions of ex-smokers (Baer & Lichtenstein, 1988). Using the articulated thoughts paradigm (Davison, Robins, & Johnson, 1983), Haaga (1990) found that recent ex-smokers who tended to think of smoking without prompting relapsed more readily three months later. However, if they learned some effective ways of countering these smoking-related thoughts, such as distracting themselves with other concerns, their abstinence was better months later. Using a questionnaire measure, Haaga found that ex-smokers' self-efficacy in their most difficult challenge situation (e.g., having coffee and dessert following a pleasant dinner) was a good predictor of abstinence a year later (Haaga, 1990). These and related studies indicate that we can more reliably predict the maintenance or relapse in smoking cessation if we access the cognitions of ex-smokers. Such information may help therapists design programs that will improve a person's ability to remain a non-smoker (Compas et al., 1998).

While some gains have been realized, data continues to suggest that relapse prevention is not highly effective, both in terms of behavioural and cognitive interventions (see Hajek et al., 2009). Thus, more creative methods to prevent relapse have emerged. For instance, one recent approach that has been well-received and seems to have promise is sending people text messages designed to maintain their motivation to not start smoking again (Snuggs et al., 2012).

12.10 Prevention of Substance Abuse

From all that is known about the etiology of substance abuse, discouraging people from beginning to abuse drugs makes the most sense. It is difficult—and for many, impossible—to overcome addiction to substances that create both psychological and physical dependency. We turn our attention next to prevention efforts involving alcohol abuse, drug abuse, and smoking.

Prevention efforts typically come in one of two forms. First, there are prevention programs with multiple facets that are designed for young people. Many prevention programs are delivered through school systems (see photo), while other preventive efforts focus on the role of parents. In addition, there are specific policies and procedures enacted at the community level (e.g., warnings printed on cigarette packages) that reflect more general public health initiatives.

Many prevention efforts have been aimed at adolescents because substance abuse in adulthood often follows experimentation in the teens and earlier. Programs, usually conducted in schools, have been directed at enhancing the young adolescent's self-esteem, teaching social skills, and encouraging the young person to say no to peer pressure. Unfortunately, the results are mixed and one review concluded that while some programs yield some positive improvements, other programs have no significant impact (see Foxcroft & Tsertsvadse, 2011). For instance, a highly publicized program, Project DARE (Drug Abuse Resistance Education), which combines affective education and resistance training and is delivered by police officers in fifth- and sixth-grade classrooms, has shown disappointing results; an initial meta-analysis found that the effect size was very small (West & O'Neal, 2004).

Lifelong smoker Barbara Tarbox spoke to young people across Canada about the dangers of smoking before she died of lung cancer at age 42.

Perhaps these programs simply need to be refined and to become more extensive and more sophisticated in order to address the complex motives and the various routes to addiction for unique individuals. Because many of the riskier decisions that are made by young people often reflect identity and self-image issues, one possible alternative is to fashion school-based programs that promote a sense of resilience in conjunction with promoting a more positive self-view. Another key feature of such a program would be to provide a sense of optimism, hope, and goal-directedness, given that an optimistic future orientation is linked directly with substance use avoidance (Caravajal, Evans, Nash, & Getz, 2002).

Parent-based prevention efforts have had some success and this focus on the role of parents is in keeping with a view that is commonly shared among prevention researchers; that is, parents must be involved and engaged as agents of change. A contemporary review of the results from 13 prevention programs concluded that these programs led to desirable changes in terms of the parent–adolescent interaction (i.e., improved rule-setting, monitoring, and communication) and there is some evidence of reductions in adolescent substance use. However, the results vary depending on several factors, including the age of the adolescents, the parents included, and the intensity of the program (Kunstsche & Kunstsche, 2016). A meta-analysis suggested that the overall effectiveness is limited; parent-based prevention programs have curtailed the use of marijuana but have not prevented the use of other illicit drugs. Three studies targeting high-risk youth yielded benefits but other studies did not, leading the authors to conclude that the overall evidence is mixed (see Vermeulen-Smit, Verdurmen, & Engels, 2015).

Developing ways of discouraging young people from experimenting with tobacco has become a top priority among health researchers and politicians. Canada has an established reputation as a world leader in taking an aggressive stand against tobacco advertising, as well as in providing the public with warnings about the use of tobacco. On June 28, 2000, Canada's then-health minister, Alan Rock, announced new regulations that mandated that all cigarette packages sold in Canada carry health warnings that cover 50% of the front and back of the package. Indeed, Canada was the first country in the world to insist on these warnings.

They also seem to be effective. According to Senior (2000), research conducted by Health Canada in 1999 showed that the larger and more emotional the message on the package, the more impact it had on potential users. Another survey found that 1 in 5 adult smokers reported cutting down as a result of the graphic advertising images (Hammond et al., 2004). This conclusion was strongly supported by reviews by Fong, Hammond, and Hitchman (2009) and Hammond (2011). The World Health Organization launched a campaign to promote the World No Tobacco Day, which is held annually, and it strongly endorses the use of graphic picture warnings (see illustration). This approach accords with Hammond's (2011) conclusion that vivid, large warnings are the most effective. However, another approach is to limit the allure of positive visual cues by insisting that tobacco is sold in plain packaging. This approach was first

Each May 31, the WHO holds World No Tobacco Day, which highlights the health risks of tobacco use and advocates for effective policies for reducing tobacco consumption. The 2013 campaign focused on banning all forms of tobacco advertising, promotion, and sponsorship.

mandated in Australia in 2011 and has now been endorsed by France and Great Britain.

The most common emotional reactions to these warnings are disgust and fear, especially for more salient warnings (Hammond, 2011); those who experienced more of these negative emotions when assessed initially were more likely to have quit or reduced their smoking when assessed three months later. The use of warning labels, the decision to raise cigarette taxes to make it more difficult for young people to smoke, and preventive lectures on the topic given to Canadian schoolchildren by people such as Dr. Jeffrey Wigand, who was mentioned earlier, were all part of a multi-faceted Health Canada strategy designed at the turn of this century to decrease the number of young smokers and limit the long-term costs to the health system.

A study of more than 9,000 smokers from four countries (Canada, the United States, the United Kingdom, and Australia) found that more than three-quarters of them recognized that society does not approve of smoking and they expressed their belief that tobacco companies cannot be trusted (Hammond et al., 2005). The belief that society does not approve is called a **denormalization belief**. It was found that belief that smoking is disapproved of was associated with higher abstinence from smoking eight months later, and supplementary analyses showed that the link between warning labels and denormalization was strongest in Canada.

Advertising and media exposure also contributes to drinking. Anderson et al. (2009) conducted a review of 13 longitudinal studies with over 38,000 young participants in total. Overall, 12 of 13 studies found a significant impact of alcohol advertising and media exposure on subsequent alcohol use, including initiation of drinking, and heavier drinking among existing drinkers. Clearly, a case can be made for banning drinking ads. Reviews indicate that banning alcohol advertising is "highly cost effective" in reducing harm (see Anderson et al., 2009).

Because of evidence suggesting that potential smokers may have been misled for years by tobacco companies, most Canadian provinces have now initiated lawsuits designed to recoup some of the medical costs associated with smoking. It will be interesting to see how the courts decide.

When it comes to smoking, another approach has been to increase the cost of cigarettes through taxes. However, Canadian research indicates that pricing has a differential impact on men and women (Dedobbeleer, Béland, Contandriopoulos, & Adrian, 2004). Higher prices appear to decrease the prevalence of smoking among men but have no effect among women, who, it was suggested, tend to smoke in response to life stressors.

Summary

12.1 Alcohol use and dependence is a compulsive pattern of substance use and consequent serious psychological and physical impairments. It can involve physiological dependence, or addiction, when tolerance and withdrawal are present. Alcohol has a variety of short-term and long-term effects on human beings. Many of these effects are tragic in nature, ranging from poor judgement and motor coordination and their dire consequences for the alcohol-abusing person and society, to addiction, which makes an ordinary, productive life impossible and is extremely difficult to overcome. It is especially troubling when alcohol use results in fetal alcohol syndrome disorders. As with other addicting drugs, people come to rely on alcohol not so much because it makes them feel good as because it provides an escape from feeling bad.

12.2 Nicotine, especially when taken into the body via the inhaled smoke from a cigarette, has worked its addictive power on humankind for centuries, and despite sombrely phrased warnings from public health officials, it continues in widespread use, especially when viewed from a global perspective and when the 6 million deaths per year due to smoking are considered. Smoking by school-age youngsters and teenagers is a notable concern because nearly all adult smokers began their use in their teens. Each year, the government and private individuals spend millions of dollars to dissuade people from beginning the habit or to help those already addicted to stop smoking.

12.3 Psychological reactions to marijuana vary substantially as a function of dosage level ranging from being relaxed and sociable to possibly experiencing hallucinations, and there is growing evidence of chronic use being associated with cognitive and neurocognitive effects. Physical reactions can include susceptibility to respiratory problems and possible addiction in a subset of vulnerable users. Marijuana is used therapeutically to combat the side effects of illness and treatment of certain illnesses, and this use of medical marijuana can alleviate suffering.

12.4 Less prevalent but more notorious, perhaps because of their illegality, are the opiates, including heroin and the barbiturates, which are sedatives; and the amphetamines and cocaine, which are stimulants. All these substances are addictive, and cocaine, including crack, is especially so. Heroin has been the focus of concern in recent years because usage is up due to its relatively low cost and because stronger varieties have become available. At present, various societies are trying to deal with an epidemic of overdose deaths, most of which are seen as accidental. Barbiturates have for some time been implicated in both intentional and accidental suicides; they are particularly lethal when taken with alcohol.

12.5 People who have ingested LSD typically experience hallucinations that some people interpret and experience as an expanded state of consciousness, awareness, and wonderment. LSD was discovered by Albert Hofmann but made popular by Timothy Leary and his followers. Leary was a well-known psychologist who made important contributions to theories of interpersonal processes.

12.6 Several factors are related to the etiology of substance abuse and dependence. Family experiences, social attitudes, and culture all play a role in encouraging the abuse of drugs, alcohol, and cigarettes. Socio-cultural variables, such as attitudes toward the substance, peer pressure, and how the substance is portrayed by the media, are all related to how frequently a substance is used. Many substances are used to alter mood (e.g., to reduce tension or increase positive affect), and people with certain personality traits, such as those high in negative affect or psychopathy, are especially likely to use drugs. Cognitive variables, such as the expectation that the drug will yield positive effects, are also important. Finally, biological factors, most notably a genetic predisposition or diathesis, play a role in the use of some substances, particularly alcohol, with heritability estimates ranging from 50 to 60%.

12.7 The treatment of drinking problems is complicated by the problems people have in acknowledging their problem and being willing to seek help. The recovery process is difficult in part due to the physical difficulties experienced during detoxification and withdrawal. Classical approaches to treatment include attending Alcoholics Anonymous and engaging in various CBT strategies. An alternative that is growing in use and support is harm reduction therapy, which is based on encouraging moderation rather than abstinence. The harm reduction approach has been applied to the treatment of other addictions and has generated controversy that reflects varying opinions on the nature of addiction and whether people should be encouraged to drink or take drugs.

12.8 Therapies of all kinds have been used to help people refrain from the use of both legal (e.g., alcohol and nicotine) and illegal (e.g., heroin and cocaine) drugs. It is common for people to recover and then relapse, leading some authors to discuss chronic addiction in terms of "addiction and treatment careers." As all the drugs discussed in this chapter are addictive, biological treatments have attempted to release users from their physiological dependency. Some benefits have been observed for treatments using drugs such as methadone.

12.9 Addictions related to the use of tobacco are highly persistent and many people who attempt to quit smoking suffer a relapse. Nicotine replacement via gum or patches has met with some success in reducing cigarette smoking. None of these somatic approaches appears to lead to enduring change unless accompanied by psychological treatments with such goals as helping clients resist pressures to indulge, cope with normal life stress, control emotions without relying on chemicals, and make use of social supports such as Alcoholics Anonymous.

12.10 Health professionals recognize that substance abuse is a multi-faceted problem requiring a broad range of interventions. Because it is far easier to never begin using drugs than to stop using them, considerable effort has been expended in recent years on attempts to prevent substance abuse by implementing educational and social programs to equip young people with the skills they need to develop their lives without a reliance on drugs. Prevention programs at school and enlisting parents have met with limited success, which underscores the complex issues and multiple factors implicated in addiction.

Key Terms

amphetamines
Antabuse
barbiturates
cocaine
conditioning theory of tolerance
controlled drinking
covert sensitization
cross-dependent
delirium tremens (DTs)
denormalization belief
dependence susceptibility
detoxification
disease model
Drug-Stroop Task
ecstasy
explicit cognition
feedforward mechanisms

fetal alcohol syndrome (FAS)
flashbacks
guided self-change
hallucinogen
harm reduction therapy
hashish
heroin
heroin antagonists
heroin substitutes
implicit cognition
LSD
marijuana
mescaline
methadone
moral model
morphine
motivational interviewing

nicotine
opiates
opioids
opium
OxyContin
polydrug (polysubstance) abuse
psilocybin
second-hand smoke
sedative
self-medication theory of addiction
stimulant
substance abuse
substance dependence
substance-related and addictive
    disorders
tolerance
withdrawal

Reflections: Past, Present, and Future

1. Where do you stand on this controversial issue: Should pot be legalized in Canada? Is prohibition more harmful than marijuana itself? Or are there numerous reasons not to legalize? What is your position on the medical use of marijuana? One controversy is the age that people will have to be in order to legally use marijuana. What age do you think is appropriate?

2. Do you think the goal of substance abuse treatment should be total abstinence, or do you favour a harm reduction approach? What is your view on harm reduction efforts that involve supplying addicts with needles: Is this a wise decision? And given that only some communities will have harm reduction facilities, should the government legislate that more facilities be created from a fairness perspective?

3. Do you think that it will ever be possible to reduce the prevalence of inhalant abuse or other substance abuse by means of psychological interventions among Canada's Aboriginal peoples?

4. Do you think that if a person has a genetic predisposition to engage in alcohol abuse, it is virtually inevitable that he or she will develop a problem? If you had limited resources to allocate, would you favour treatment of existing addiction or prevention of future addictions among young people?

CHAPTER 13

Personality Disorders

LEARNING OBJECTIVES

1. List the general criteria used to determine whether someone has personality dysfunction.

2. Identify the most significant challenges that influence the assessments that are conducted when seeking to determine whether someone has a personality disorder, and explain why a categorical approach to diagnosis has been supplemented by a dimensional approach.

3. List the personality disorders grouped in the odd/eccentric cluster and describe the characteristics they have in common.

4. Compare and contrast the personality disorders in the dramatic/erratic cluster in terms of how people with these personality disorders tend to interact with other people.

5. Identify the theme of the anxious/fearful cluster and explain how avoidant personality disorder, obsessive-compulsive personality disorder, and dependent personality disorder fit this theme.

6. Explain some of the challenges facing therapists providing treatment to people with severe personality disorders and how dialectical behaviour therapy is tailored to address the vulnerabilities of people with borderline personality disorder.

Brief Case Example

A Constant Parade of Friends and Therapists

MARY WAS 26 years old at the time of her first admission to a psychiatric hospital. She had been in outpatient treatment with a psychologist for several months when her persistent thoughts of suicide and preoccupation with inflicting pain on herself (by cutting or burning) led her therapist to conclude that she could no longer be managed as an outpatient.

Mary's first experience with some form of psychological therapy occurred when she was an adolescent. Her grades declined sharply in Grade 11, and her parents suspected she was using drugs. She began to miss curfews and even failed to come home at all on a few occasions. She was frequently truant. Family therapy was undertaken, and it seemed to go well at first. Mary was enthusiastic about her therapist and asked for additional, private sessions with him.

Her parents' fears were confirmed during the family sessions, as Mary revealed an extensive history of drug use, including "everything I can get my hands on." She had been promiscuous and had prostituted herself several times to get drug money. Her relationships with her peers were changeable, to say the least. The pattern was a constant parade of new friends, at first thought to be the greatest ever but who soon disappointed Mary in some way and were cast aside, often in a very unpleasant way. Except for the one person with whom she was currently enamoured, Mary had no friends. She reported that she stayed away from others for fear that they would harm her in some way.

After several weeks of therapy, Mary's parents noticed that her relationship with the therapist had cooled appreciably. The sessions were marked by Mary's angry and abusive outbursts toward the therapist. After several more weeks had passed, Mary refused to attend any more sessions. In a subsequent conversation with the therapist, Mary's father learned that Mary had behaved seductively toward the therapist during their private sessions and that her changed attitude toward him coincided with the rejection of her advances, despite the therapist's attempt to mix firmness with warmth and empathy.

Mary managed to graduate from high school and enrolled in a local community college, but the old patterns returned. Poor grades, cutting classes, continuing drug use, and lack of interest in her studies finally led her to quit in the middle of the first semester of her second year. After leaving school, Mary held a series of clerical jobs. Most of them didn't last long, as her relationships with co-workers paralleled her relationships with her peers in high school. When Mary started a new job, she would find someone she really liked, but something would come between them and the relationship would end angrily. Mary was frequently suspicious of her co-workers and reported that she often heard them talking about her, plotting how to prevent her from getting ahead on the job. She was quick to find hidden

meanings in their behaviour; for example, she interpreted being the last person asked to sign a birthday card to mean that she was the least liked person in the office. She indicated that she "received vibrations" from others and that, even in the absence of any direct evidence, she could tell when they really didn't like her.

Mary's behaviour in Brief Case Example includes many characteristic symptoms of several personality disorders, in particular borderline personality disorder. Her frequent mood swings, with periods of depression and extreme irritability, led her to seek therapy several times. But after initial enthusiasm, her relationship with her therapist always deteriorated, resulting in premature termination of therapy. The therapist she was seeing just before her hospitalization was her sixth.

Personality disorders (PDs) are a heterogeneous group of disorders that are regarded as long-standing, pervasive, and inflexible patterns of behaviour and inner experience that deviate from the expectations of a person's culture and that impair social and occupational functioning. Some, but not all, can cause emotional distress.

As we examine the personality disorders, some may seem to fit people we know, not to mention ourselves! Although the symptoms of the personality disorders come close to describing characteristics that we all possess from time to time and in varying degrees, an actual personality disorder is defined by the extremes of several traits and by the inflexible way these traits are expressed. People with personality disorders are often rigid in their behaviour and cannot change it in response to changes in the situations they experience. This emphasis on being rigid fits with the notion that key differences between people can be conceptualized in terms of personality capabilities such as the ability to be flexible in social interactions (see Paulhus & Martin, 1987, 1988; Wallace, 1966). In contrast, people with dysfunctional personalities cannot usually adjust their thoughts, feelings, and behaviours to fit the circumstances and the people they encounter. Most of the personality field focuses on a trait perspective (i.e., what a person typically or usually does), but a capability perspective (i.e., what a person could do or has the potential to do) provides a unique view of how to conceptualize personality dysfunction.

The personality each of us develops over the years reflects a persistent means of dealing with life's challenges, a certain style of relating to other people. One person is overly dependent, another is challenging and aggressive, another is shy and avoids social contact, and still another is concerned more with appearance and bolstering his or her vulnerable ego than with relating to others. These individuals would not be diagnosed as having personality disorders unless the patterns of behaviour were long-standing, pervasive, and dysfunctional. For example, on entering a crowded room and hearing a loud burst of laughter, you might feel that you are the target of some joke and that people are talking about you. Such concerns become symptoms of paranoid personality disorder only if they occur

frequently and intensely and prevent the development of close personal relationships.

In this chapter, we look first at how we classify personality disorders and at the challenges associated with classification and assessment. Then we turn to the personality disorders themselves, the theory and research on their etiology, and therapies for dealing with them.

13.1 Classifying Personality Disorders: Clusters, Categories, and Problems

The idea that personality can be disordered goes back at least to the time of Hippocrates and his humoral theory, which we discussed in Chapter 1. Personality disorders were listed in the early *DSMs*, but the diagnoses were very unreliable. One clinician might diagnose a flamboyant client as narcissistic, whereas another might consider him or her psychopathic. As with other diagnoses, the publication of *DSM-III* began a trend toward improved reliability (Coolidge & Segal, 1998). Beginning with *DSM-III*, personality disorders were also placed on a separate axis, Axis II, to ensure that diagnosticians would pay attention to their possible presence. Axis II described many personality disorder categories that either did or did not apply to people with clinical dysfunction. The axis element was removed in *DSM-5* but it is now generally accepted that more episodic disorders may be accompanied by a long-lasting personality disorder, while for some people, the personality disorder is the main adjustment problem.

When viewed broadly, what are the indicators that a personality disorder exists? Theodore Millon, who died in 2014, made several important contributions as a prominent theorist in the personality disorders field. Millon (1986) identified three key criteria that help distinguish normal vs. disordered personality. First, disordered personality is indicated by rigid and inflexible behaviour. Thus, the afflicted person has difficulty altering his or her behaviour according to changes in the situation.

Second, the person engages in self-defeating behaviour that fosters vicious cycles. That is, behaviours and cognitions simply perpetuate and exacerbate existing conditions. Self-defeating behaviour gets us farther away from our goals rather than closer to them.

Finally, there is "structural instability." Millon used this term to refer to a fragility to the self that "cracks" under conditions of stress. This would pertain to a student who functions at a reasonably high level during the early part of a term but loses the ability to cope due to the mounting pressure of multiple deadlines.

Livesley, Schroeder, Jackson, and Jang (1994) regard personality disorder as a failure or inability to come up with adaptive solutions to life tasks. Livesley (1998) identified three types of life tasks and proposed that failure with any one task is enough to warrant a personality disorder diagnosis. The three tasks are (1) to form stable, integrated, and coherent representations of self and others; (2) to develop the capacity for intimacy and positive affiliations with other people; and (3) to function adaptively in society by engaging in prosocial and co-operative behaviours.

Below we discuss the value of a dimensional approach to personality disorders. Initially, it was believed and anticipated that the *DSM-5* personality disorders section was going to undergo a radical change by switching to dimensions rather than categories, but a decision not to do that was made very late in the process. As a result, the categorical approach still prevails in the *DSM-5*. As shown in Table 13.1, *DSM-5* contains a description of **general personality** disorder to outline when a general personality disorder exists and then assessment can establish whether someone is characterized by a particular PD. You can see in Table 13.1 that there is some overlap with the PD elements proposed by Millon and by Livesley and associates.

So what happened to the dimensional approach that was going to be used? The alternative model was also introduced in Section III of the *DSM-5* (American Psychiatric Association, 2013). This section outlines the Alternative Model for Personality

Disorders (AMPD). AMPD criterion A assesses "levels of personality functioning" according to two themes: (1) self (identity and self-direction), and (2) interpersonal (empathy and intimacy). AMPD criterion B involves rating a person across five broad trait dimensions: negative affectivity, detachment, antagonism, disinhibition, and psychoticism. Pincus, Dowgwillo, and Greenberg (2016) showed with three people suffering from moderate to severe pathological narcissism that the AMPD framework is more clinically useful than past diagnostic approaches and allows for a better representation of the differences among the three people they described. Another indication of the usefulness of the AMPD criteria is a report indicating that these traits predict unique variance in levels of psychosocial impairment among over 600 psychiatric patients after taking into consideration various other criteria including personality disorder types, other psychiatric symptoms, and other personality trait dimensions (see Simms & Calabrese, 2016).

Calls have been issued for a dimensional approach to personality disorders for more than 25 years. Why is the AMPD in the *DSM-5*? Tests of the categorical approach reflected in *DSM-5* vs. a dimensional approach provide strong support for the dimensional approach. Although Canadian researchers have provided some evidence to suggest that the psychopathy underscoring anti-social personality may represent a discrete category (Skilling, Harris, Rice, & Quinsey, 2002), one analysis indicated that even psychopathy should be considered dimensional (Edens, Marcus, Lilienfeld, & Poythress, 2006). Overall, a dimensional approach seems a better fit to existing data. Research by John Livesley from the University of British Columbia and his associates shows that when people with a personality disorder take a general personality inventory, what is revealed is a personality with a structure that is similar to that of normal people but is simply more extreme (Livesley, Jang, & Vernon, 1998). Similar research at Lakehead University revealed that dimensional differences exist when characterizing normal vs. abnormal personality: personality disorders reflect extreme and rigid response tendencies that differ in degree, not in kind, from the responses of people without disorders (O'Connor, 2002; O'Connor & Dyce, 2001). Thus, the personality disorders can be construed as the extremes of characteristics we all possess.

The personality dimensions being considered for this alternative approach have been strongly influenced by other general developments in the personality literature. Focus on Discovery 13.1 describes the popular dimensional model and alternative models. While there is a tendency to focus on multi-trait models such as those described in Focus on Discovery 13.1, there is still significant debate about which dimensions should be included whenever the shift to a dimensional approach is implemented. Perfectionism is one personality construct that clearly deserves more attention than it is receiving in terms of its role in personality dysfunction. At present, perfectionism is considered in the *DSM-5* only as one symptom of obsessive-compulsive personality disorder (OCPD), but extreme perfectionists can have a form of workaholism and relentless striving that can result in great distress for them or the people around them in ways that

---

TABLE 13.1   *DSM-5* **Criteria for General Personality Disorder**
A. An enduring pattern of inner experience and behaviour that deviates markedly from the expectations of the individual's culture. The pattern is manifest in two (or more) of the following areas:
1. Cognition (i.e., ways of perceiving and interpreting the self, other people, and events)
2. Affectivity (i.e., the range, intensity, lability, and appropriateness of emotional response)
3. Interpersonal functioning
4. Impulse control
B. The enduring pattern is inflexible and pervasive across a broad range of personal and social situations.
C. The enduring pattern leads to clinically significant distress or impairment in social, occupational, or other important areas of functioning.
D. The pattern is stable and of long duration, and its onset can be traced back at least to adolescence or early adulthood.
E. The enduring pattern is not better explained as a manifestation or consequence of another mental disorder.
F. The enduring pattern is not attributable to the physiological effects of a substance or another medical condition.

Reprinted with Permission from the *Diagnostic and Statistical Manual of Mental Disorders, Fifth Edition,* Copyright 2013. American Psychiatric Association. pp. 646–647.

Focus on Discovery 13.1

A Dimensional Approach to Personality Disorders

According to the most promising dimensional approach to personality disorders, these disorders represent extremes of personality traits found in everyone. Most contemporary research focuses on a highly influential model of personality called the five-factor model (McCrae & Costa, 1990). The five factors, or major dimensions, of personality are neuroticism, extroversion/introversion, openness to experience, agreeableness/antagonism, and conscientiousness.

How might the five-factor model apply to personality dysfunction involving psychopathy? Harpur, Hart, and Hare (1994) found that psychopaths are high in neuroticism and low in agreeableness and conscientiousness. Psychopathy is described in greater detail later in this chapter.

A meta-analysis established that each personality disorder had a meaningful combination of the five factors associated with it. Moreover, it was found that high neuroticism and low agreeableness were common to many personality disorders, and high or low extroversion was a factor that was quite useful in distinguishing among the various personality disorders (Saulsman & Page, 2004). Some personality disorders have a unique five-factor profile. For instance, according to Alden et al. (2002), avoidant personality disorder is the only personality disorder characterized by high neuroticism and introversion.

The Hopkins Epidemiology of Personality Disorder Study suggests that it has limited utility (see Nestadt et al., 2008). This study compared NEO-PI(R) responses, the five-factor measure developed by Costa and McCrae, and psychologist assessments of 742 community residents evaluated with the International Personality Disorder Examination. Only modest correspondence was found; the NEO-PI(R) dimensions explained only one-fifth to one-third of the variance in personality disorder dimensions.

Various alternatives to the five-factor model have been proposed. Table 13.2 outlines the HEXACO model developed by Canadian researchers Michael Ashton and Kibeom Lee (see Ashton, Lee, & Son, 2000; Lee & Ashton, 2004). This model has five dimensions that parallel the components of the five-factor model, but also has a key sixth dimension that reflects whether a person has a high level of honesty and humility vs. dishonesty and low humility. Representative test items are also found in Table 13.2.

Another set of dimensions is captured in Livesley and Jackson's (2002) self-report scale known as the Dimensional Assessment of Personality Pathology—Basic Questionnaire (DAPP-BQ). The DAPP-BQ has 22 scales that assess 18 personality trait dimensions (e.g., anxiousness, affective lability, callousness, insecure attachment, and narcissism) and various response styles. Statistical tests show that DAPP-BQ trait scales reflect the higher-order factors of emotional dysregulation (i.e., affective lability and impulsivity), dissocial behaviour (i.e., callousness, conduct problems, and

TABLE 13.2	Dimensions of the HEXACO Personality Inventory-Revised and Sample Items
Emotionality	I am very anxious when waiting to hear about an important decision.
Extroversion	I enjoy having lots of people around to talk with.
Openness to Experience	I think of myself as a somewhat eccentric person.
Agreeableness/Anger	I generally accept people's faults without complaining about them.
Conscientiousness	I often push myself very hard when trying to reach a goal.
Honesty-Humility	I am an ordinary person who is no better than others.

Note: The HEXACO Personality Inventory-Revised has 60-item and 100-item self-report and informant versions. HEXACO is derived as follows: H for Honesty-Humility, E for Emotionality, X for Extraversion, A for Agreeableness, C for Conscientiousness, and O for Openness.

© Kibeom Lee & Michael C. Ashton. Reprinted with permission.

narcissism), inhibitedness (i.e., avoidance of intimacy and restricted expression of emotions), and compulsivity (Livesley, Jang, & Vernon, 1998). Research linking the DAPP-BQ with variables from other personality models shows that neuroticism is linked with emotional dysregulation, dissocial behaviour is linked with high psychoticism, inhibitedness is linked with low extroversion, and compulsivity is linked with high conscientiousness (Larstone et al., 2002).

The personality dimensions proposed in the *DSM-5 AMPD* have been supported empirically; over 2,000 students provided their responses to a scale developed to parallel the changes that were initially proposed and the proposed five factors did emerge (see Wright et al., 2012). The factors are (1) negative affect (e.g., anxiousness, emotional lability); (2) detachment (e.g., withdrawal, intimacy avoidance); (3) antagonism (e.g., manipulativeness, deceitfulness); (4) disinhibition (e.g., impulsivity, irresponsibility); and (5) psychoticism (e.g., eccentricity, perceptual dysregulation). Disinhibition and psychoticism are not in the five-factor model. Perhaps the five dimensions outlined in the *DSM-5* will someday be standard criteria for how personality disorders are diagnosed. While there will be continuing controversy over which dimensions are most useful and relevant, what seems beyond debate is that the dimensional approach, relative to a categorical approach, tells us much more about someone's personality structure.

do not fit well with the description of OCPD. Ayearst, Flett, and Hewitt (2012) outlined several reasons why multi-dimensional perfectionism merits consideration, including the fact that it is a personality style that is relatively unique and it typically accounts for significant variance in personality dysfunction beyond the variance accounted for by the other personality trait dimensions that comprise the multi-trait models. Another indication

that perfectionism deserves more consideration is that treatment research suggests that perfectionism is quite persistent and ingrained and that CBT-based interventions typically lower but do not eliminate problematic perfectionism (e.g., Handley, Egan, Kane, & Rees, 2015). The need for a complex approach is reflected in an alternative interpersonal psychodynamic approach that sees perfectionism as a by-product of interpersonal experiences and unmet interpersonal needs (see Hewitt, Flett, & Mikail, 2017; Hewitt et al., 2015).

As noted earlier, Axis II and other axes are not included in the *DSM-5*, but the dimensional approach was put on hold late in the process. Instead, the various personality disorders are still listed in the disorder section, and the new "alternative model" is included in Section III of the *DSM-5* where proposals that merit further consideration are described.

Despite this setback for the proponents of the new model, a study of 337 clients who were diagnosed under the previous model and the proposed systems by clinicians familiar with them led to the conclusion that there was considerable correspondence between the two diagnostic approaches (Morey & Skodol, 2013). These top researchers focused on coming up with decision rules that would serve as diagnostic thresholds that would enable the clinician to use dimensional data to make categorical decisions. When these thresholds were established, the new diagnostic model was applied successfully to many of the specific personality disorders.

The low stability of personality disorder diagnoses is one problem that has plagued the categorical approach. Because personality disorders are presumed to be more stable over time than some episodic disorders (e.g., depression), test–retest reliability—a comparison of whether clients receive the same diagnosis when they are assessed twice with some time interval separating the two assessments—is also an important factor in their evaluation. Durbin and Klein (2006) assessed the stability of personality disorders in clients with mood disorders and found that the 10-year stability of categorical diagnoses was "relatively poor" (p. 82). Stability coefficients were greater when a dimensional view of personality disorder was used and shorter time intervals were employed. Consistent with the greater stability of anti-social disorders, cluster B disorders (see the section "Personality Disorder Clusters: Dramatic/Erratic Cluster") had the greatest stability over time.

More recently, Morey and Hopwood (2013) re-examined this issue and identified many factors that affect stability ratings, including the types of constructs being measured and the impact of how participants were sampled. They concluded that, at present, it is virtually impossible to come up with a clear, single answer to the question "How stable are personality disorders?" Still, it is believed that personality disorders are among the most enduring disorders.

Another vexing problem with personality disorders is that it is often difficult to diagnose a single, specific personality disorder because many disordered people exhibit a wide range of traits that make several diagnoses applicable (Marshall & Serin, 1997). In the Brief Case Example opening this chapter, Mary met the diagnostic criteria not only for borderline personality disorder but also for paranoid personality disorder, and she came close to meeting the criteria for schizotypal disorder, as well. One study found that 55% of patients with borderline personality disorder also met the diagnostic criteria for schizotypal personality disorder; 47%, the criteria for anti-social personality disorder; and 57%, the criteria for histrionic personality

disorder (Widiger, Frances, & Trull, 1987). These data are particularly discouraging and have implications for when we try to interpret the results of research that compares clients who have a specific personality disorder with some control group. If, for example, we find that people with borderline personality disorder differ from normal people, is what we have learned specific to borderline personality disorder or is it related to personality disorders in general?

Finally, there still seem to be problems remaining when personality disorder criteria are examined from the perspective of their clinical utility. Recent feedback from clinicians suggest that there is a need for an expanded description of at least four personality disorders: avoidant, narcissistic, obsessive-compulsive, and schizoid personality disorders (Crego, Sleep, & Widiger, 2016). This is important feedback given the goal of maximizing the clinical use of the *DSM-5*.

13.2 Assessing Personality Disorders

A significant challenge in assessing personality disorders is that many disorders are egosyntonic: the person with a personality disorder is typically unaware that a problem exists and may not be experiencing significant personal distress; that is, they lack insight into their own personality. However, the people who interact with these oblivious individuals may have a great deal of discomfort and upset. This suggests that the assessment and diagnosis of personality disorders are enhanced when the significant others in an individual's life become informants. This point was illustrated in a study of symptoms of narcissistic personality disorder. Narcissists tend to have highly inflated and grandiose self-views. Extreme narcissists are described in much greater detail later in this chapter. Informants tend to report higher symptoms than do narcissistic people and there is low or nonsignificant agreement across the nine key symptoms of narcissism (see Cooper, Balsis, & Oltmanns, 2012). Because of the lack of personal self-awareness in many cases, personality disorders typically need to be diagnosed via clinical interviews led by trained personnel.

Another significant diagnosis challenge is that a substantial proportion of clients are deemed to have a general personality disorder (referred to more generally as PD not otherwise specified, or PDNOS) and these clients do not fit clearly into existing PD diagnostic categories. Verheul and Widiger (2004) concluded that PDNOS is the third-most prevalent type of personality disorder diagnosed via structured interviews, with a prevalence ranging from 8 to 13% in clinical samples. Tyrer et al. (2007) reviewed these and other problems and concluded that "the assessment of personality disorder is currently inaccurate, largely unreliable, frequently wrong, and in need of improvement" (p. S51).

Although clinical interviews are preferable when seeking to make a diagnosis, researchers often rely on the use of self-report measures when assessing personality disorder symptoms. The MMPI-2 that was described earlier in this book also has been used for this purpose. Scoring schemes using MMPI items have been created to assess the symptoms of specific personality disorders (e.g., Morey, Waugh, & Blashfield, 1985). Harkness, McNulty, and Ben-Porath (1995) described a set of MMPI-2 scales that they developed to assess five dimensional personality constructs to reflect psychopathology. This framework, known as the PSY-5, consists of dimensions assessing negative emotionality/neuroticism, lack of positive emotionality, aggressiveness, lack of constraint, and psychoticism. The PSY-5 dimensions have been corroborated via confirmatory factor analyses (Bagby, Ryder, Ben-Dat, Bacchiochi, & Parker, 2002), and they are promising because they seem particularly relevant to certain forms of personality dysfunction. For instance, Trull et al. (1995) noted that the PSY-5 constraint scale should be robustly associated with anti-social personality disorder symptoms given that the constraint scale has items that assess lying, stealing, and getting into legal trouble. A comparative study showed that both the PSY-5 and the NEO-PI(R) were strong, significant, unique predictors of the symptoms of 10 personality disorders (Bagby, Sellbom, Costa, & Widiger, 2008). The PSY-5 was comparatively better at predicting paranoid, schizotypal, narcissistic, and anti-social personality disorder symptom counts.

Perhaps the most widely used measure of personality disorder symptoms is the Millon Clinical Multiaxial Inventory, which is now in its fourth edition (MCMI-IV; Millon, Grossman, & Millon, 2015). The MCMI-IV is a 195-item true-false inventory at a fifth-grade reading level that was revised to parallel *DSM-5*. The MCMI-IV provides subscale measures of 15 personality disorder scales that include 12 "clinical personality patterns" (schizoid, avoidant, melancholic, dependent, histrionic, turbulent, narcissistic, anti-social, sadistic, compulsive, negativistic, and masochistic) and three "severe personality pathology" scales (schizotypal, borderline, and paranoid). It also has 10 clinical syndrome scales and five validity scales, including two that detect random responses.

The updated 2009 version of the MCMI-III was modified to include "therapy-guiding facet scales" (e.g., interpersonal style, cognitive style) known as the Grossman Facet Scales that further characterize the person who answered the MCMI-III (see Millon, Davis, Millon, & Grossman, 2009). These facet scales were added to facilitate Millon and Grossman's (2007) treatment approach known as **personalized therapy**. That is, in order to be more effective and meaningful for individuals, therapies need to be modified to recognize each person's unique needs and personality styles.

Two key issues involving self-report measures of personality disorder need to be considered. First, the various self-report measures differ in their content and are not equivalent. A study done at the University of Alberta examined the prevalence of personality disorders in university students by administering three self-report personality disorder scales, including the MCMI-II, the MMPI personality disorder scale, and the Coolidge Axis Two Inventory (CATI) (Sinha & Watson, 2001). For men, narcissistic PD was the most prevalent disorder according to the MCMI-II and CATI results, but the MMPI measure indicated that paranoid PD was the most prevalent. For women, the most prevalent disorder according to MCMI-II results was avoidant PD, but it was narcissistic PD according to CATI responses and paranoid PD according to the MMPI responses.

Second, a general concern involving self-report measures, including PD measures, is that the cut-off points used with self-report responses to determine the presence of a personality disorder often overestimate the number of people who meet diagnostic criteria for particular disorders. For instance, the Sinha and Watson (2001) study found that 26.3% of women surveyed had an avoidant PD. A common pattern in comparative research is that only a proportion of those who appear to have a diagnosable disorder on the basis of the self-report measure actually are diagnosed following more detailed examination using clinical criteria.

Issues surrounding diagnoses and prevalence are discussed further in Student Perspectives 13.1, which examines clinically diagnosed personality disorders in students.

Student Perspectives 13.1

Personality Disorder Among Students

While relying on self-report measures may overestimate the prevalence of PDs, some impressive research suggests that PDs may be quite prevalent among university and college students. Various mental health problems, including personality disorder diagnoses, were evaluated in a large U.S. sample by Blanco et al. (2008). Diagnoses were based on the results of a structured clinical interview. This is in keeping with suggestions that self-reports should be supplemented by clinical interviews such as the Personality Disorder Examination (Loranger, 1988; Loranger, Oldham, Russakoff, & Susman, 1987).

Blanco et al. (2008) compared students and same-aged peers not attending college or university and estimated the 12-month

prevalence of disorders. They found that 18% of the students met criteria for a personality disorder in their lifetime vs. 22% of the non–college-attending peers. Thus, more than 1 in 6 students met criteria for one or more personality disorders.

The two most prevalent PDs among students were obsessive-compulsive PD and paranoid PD. Several PDs were significantly less common among students, relative to their peers not attending college or university, including avoidant, dependent, paranoid, schizoid, and anti-social personality disorders.

One issue that is receiving increasing attention is the notion that there is an epidemic of narcissism among younger people (narcissistic PD is described below). This conclusion stems from apparent generational increases in levels of narcissism based on student responses across cohorts to well-known measures of narcissism (see

(continued)

Twenge & Foster, 2010). Uncharitable references have been made to current students being a part of "Generation Me," focused on themselves. Narcissists have inflated self-images that are often defensive attempts to overcompensate for feelings of inadequacy, rather than feelings of self-importance. Given the findings reported by Blanco et al. (2008), could it simply be that, rather than a spate of narcissism, there is a seemingly widespread rash of general personality-related

adjustment problems among students and other younger people? Does this not suggest the need for a closer examination of contemporary life and the personal, familial, and societal factors that contribute to personality dysfunction? Unfortunately, the clinical impairment experienced by students that typically accompanies a PD may persist and result in significant impairment throughout life for many students.

13.3 Personality Disorder Clusters: Odd/Eccentric Cluster

Historically, personality disorders have been grouped into three clusters:

1. Individuals in cluster A (paranoid, schizoid, and schizotypal) seem odd or eccentric. These disorders reflect oddness and avoidance of social contact.

2. Those in cluster B (borderline, histrionic, narcissistic, and anti-social) seem dramatic, emotional, or erratic. Behaviours are extrapunitive and hostile.

3. Those in cluster C (avoidant, dependent, and obsessive-compulsive) appear fearful.

The empirical evidence on the validity of these clusters is mixed, and some evidence suggests that perhaps a fourth cluster reflecting obsession and inhibition should also be considered (see Tyrer et al., 2007). Nevertheless, despite all of the recommended changes in the assessment and diagnosis of personality disorders, the three original clusters form a very useful organizational framework for this chapter, so we will proceed on this basis, beginning with the odd/eccentric cluster.

The odd/eccentric cluster comprises three diagnoses: paranoid, schizoid, and schizotypal PDs. The symptoms of these disorders bear some similarity to the symptoms of schizophrenia, especially to the less severe symptoms of its prodromal and residual phases.

Paranoid Personality Disorder

The individual with **paranoid personality** disorder (PPD) is suspicious of others. People with this diagnosis expect to be mistreated or exploited by others and thus are secretive and always on the lookout for possible signs of trickery and abuse. Such individuals are reluctant to confide in others and tend to blame them even when they themselves are at fault. They can be extremely jealous and may unjustifiably question the fidelity of a spouse or lover.

Individuals with PPD are preoccupied with unjustified doubts about the trustworthiness or loyalty of others. They may read hidden negative or threatening messages into events

(e.g., the individual may believe that a neighbour's dog deliberately barks in the early morning to disturb him or her). This diagnosis is different from schizophrenia, paranoid type, because symptoms such as hallucinations are not present and there is less impairment in social and occupational functioning. It differs from delusional disorder because full-blown delusions are not present.

PPD occurs most frequently in men and co-occurs most frequently with schizotypal, borderline, and avoidant personality disorders (Morey, 1988). Data suggest that it is one of the more commonly diagnosed personality disorders in community samples and that paranoid personality disorder is best represented as a continuous dimension rather than a discrete category (Edens, Marcus, & Morey, 2009).

Schizoid Personality Disorder

People with **schizoid personality** disorder do not appear to desire or enjoy social relationships and usually have no close friends. They appear dull, bland, and aloof and have no warm, tender feelings for others. They rarely report strong emotions, have no interest in sex, and experience few pleasurable activities. Indifferent to praise and criticism, individuals with this disorder are loners with solitary interests. The prevalence of schizoid personality disorder is less than 1%. It is slightly less common among women than men (Weissman, 1993).

Comorbidity is highest for schizotypal, avoidant, and paranoid personality disorders, most likely because of the similar diagnostic criteria in the four categories. The diagnostic criteria for schizoid personality disorder are also similar to some of the symptoms of the prodromal and residual phases of schizophrenia.

Schizotypal Personality Disorder

The concept of the **schizotypal personality** grew out of Danish studies of the adopted children of schizophrenic parents (Kety, Rosenthal, Wender, & Schulsinger, 1968). Although some of these children developed full-blown schizophrenia as adults, an even larger number developed what seemed to be an attenuated form of schizophrenia. The diagnostic criteria for schizotypal personality disorder were devised by Spitzer, Endicott, and Gibbon (1979) to describe these individuals.

People with schizotypal personality disorder usually have the interpersonal difficulties of the schizoid personality and excessive social anxiety that does not diminish as they get to know others. Several additional, more eccentric symptoms, identical to those that define the prodromal and residual phases of schizophrenia, occur in schizotypal personality disorder.

Cognitive limitations and restrictions found in schizophrenia are also evident in schizotypal personality disorder (McClure et al., 2008). Those with schizotypal personality disorder may also have odd beliefs or magical thinking (e.g., superstitiousness, beliefs that they are clairvoyant and telepathic) and recurrent illusions (they may sense the presence of a force or a person not actually there). In their speech, they may use words in an unusual and unclear fashion; for example, "I'm not a very talkable person." Their behaviour and appearance may also be eccentric; they may talk to themselves, for example. Also common are ideas of reference (the belief that events have a particular and unusual meaning for the person), suspiciousness, and paranoid ideation. Affect appears to be constricted and flat. Widiger et al. (1987) found that paranoid ideation, ideas of reference, and illusions were the symptoms most relevant for making a diagnosis. The prevalence of this disorder is about 3%. It is slightly more frequent among men than women (Zimmerman & Coryell, 1989).

A significant problem in the diagnosis of schizotypal personality disorder is its comorbidity with other personality disorders. Morey (1988) found that 33% of people diagnosed with schizotypal personality also met the diagnostic criteria for borderline personality disorder, while 59% also met the criteria for avoidant personality disorder and for paranoid personality disorder. Epidemiological data suggest that comorbidity is higher for schizotypal personality disorder than for any other personality disorder, and the degree of comorbidity with borderline personality disorder and narcissistic personality disorder continues to be very high (Pulay et al., 2009). Clearly, these comorbidity figures are unsatisfactory if we want to consider schizotypal personality disorder a discrete diagnostic entity.

Etiology of the Odd/Eccentric Cluster

What causes the odd, sometimes paranoid thinking, bizarre behaviour, and interpersonal difficulties that appear in this cluster of personality disorders? The search for causes has been guided by the idea that these disorders are genetically linked to schizophrenia, perhaps as less severe variants of this disorder. The evidence for this idea varies depending on which of the odd/eccentric disorders is considered.

- Family studies of paranoid personality disorder for the most part find higher than average rates in the relatives of people with schizophrenia or delusional disorder (Bernstein, Useda, & Siever, 1993).

- Family studies have shown that the relatives of people with schizophrenia are at increased risk for this disorder (Nigg & Goldsmith, 1994). However, Squires-Wheeler et al. (1993) found increased rates in the first-degree relatives of people with depression, suggesting that schizotypal personality disorder is related to disorders other than schizophrenia.

Genetic factors play some role in etiology, but a study of twins in Norway found that the heritabilities of personality disorders were modest and ranged from 20 to 41%. The lowest heritability estimate was found for schizotypal personality disorder and the largest heritability estimate was found for anti-social personality disorder (Kendler et al., 2008). This study found no evidence that there were unique genetic factors distinguishing cluster A, B, and C disorders.

Overall, family studies provide at least some evidence that personality disorders of the odd/eccentric cluster are related to schizophrenia. People with schizotypal personality disorder have deficits in cognitive and neuropsychological functioning (Cadenhead, Perry, Shafer, & Braff, 1999; Chen et al., 1998) that are similar to those seen in schizophrenia. Also in keeping with schizophrenia research, schizotypal personality disorder is associated with enlarged ventricles and less temporal-lobe grey matter (Dickey et al., 1999).

Finally, given the comorbidity associated with schizotypal personality disorder, it is important to establish whether predictors are linked uniquely with the disorder. Berenbaum et al. (2008) showed that schizotypal personality disorder was linked with a history of post-traumatic stress disorder and childhood maltreatment even after controlling for the links that these factors also had with anti-social and borderline personality disorder symptoms.

13.4 Personality Disorder Clusters: Dramatic/Erratic Cluster

The diagnoses in the dramatic/erratic cluster—borderline, histrionic, narcissistic, and anti-social personality disorders—include clients with a wide variety of symptoms, ranging from variable behaviour to inflated self-esteem, exaggerated emotional displays, and anti-social behaviour.

Borderline Personality Disorder

"[She] arrived at the Institute of Living on March 9, 1961, at age 17, and quickly became the sole occupant of the seclusion room on the unit known as Thompson Two, for the most severely ill patients. The staff saw no alternative: the girl attacked herself habitually, burning her wrist with cigarettes, slashing her arms, her legs, her midsection, using any sharp object she could get her hands on.

The seclusion room, a small cell with a bed, a chair, and a tiny, barred window, had no such weapon. Yet her urge to die only deepened. So she did the only thing that made any sense to her at the time: banged her head against the wall and, later, the floor. Hard.

 'My whole experience of these episodes was that someone else was doing it; it was like "I know this is coming, I'm out of control, somebody help me; where are you God?"' she said. 'I felt totally empty, like the Tin Man; I had no way to communicate what was going on, no way to understand it.' . . .

 . . . doctors gave her a diagnosis of schizophrenia; dosed her with Thorazine, Librium, and other powerful drugs, as well as hours of Freudian analysis; and strapped her down for electroshock treatments, 14 shocks the first time through and 16 the second, according to her medical records. Nothing changed, and soon enough the patient was back in seclusion on the locked ward."

(Carey, 2011, p. A1)

The above excerpt is another illustration of someone with **borderline personality** disorder (BPD), which was adopted as an official *DSM* diagnosis in 1980. The core features of this disorder are impulsivity and instability in relationships, mood, and self-image (Blais, Hilsenroth, & Castlebury, 1997; Links, Heslegrave, & van Reekum, 1998). For example, attitudes and feelings toward other people may vary considerably and inexplicably over short periods of time. Emotions are erratic and can shift abruptly, particularly from passionate idealization to contemptuous anger. BPD sufferers are argumentative, irritable, sarcastic, quick to take offence, and very hard to live with. Longitudinal data suggest that there is also considerable instability in the personality traits of people with BPD assessed over a six-year period (Hopwood et al., 2009).

The instability in relationships is reflected in the social networks of people with BPD. A revealing glimpse of their social worlds emerged from an investigation by Lazarus and Cheavens (in press) that examined the social networks of women with BPD vs. healthy control participants. Women with BPD had significantly smaller social networks and more variability in their networks and in their close relationships. Moreover, their networks were characterized by less satisfaction and support and more conflict and criticism with their partners. Most notably, the women with BPD reported more relationships that involved a significant change or a rupture in the past month. Clearly, there was substantial evidence of greater interpersonal stress among women with BPD.

The unpredictable and impulsive behaviour of people with BPD may include gambling, spending, indiscriminate sexual activity, and eating sprees, and is thus potentially self-damaging. This impulsivity is not specific to borderline personalities; researchers in Montreal have argued that impulsivity is one trait that underscores all four disorders in the dramatic and erratic cluster (Looper & Paris, 2000).

The case excerpt is a clear illustration of what can happen because people with BPD often have not developed a clear and coherent sense of self and remain uncertain about their values, loyalties, and career choices. They cannot bear to be alone, have fears of abandonment, and demand attention. Subject to chronic feelings of depression and emptiness, they often attempt suicide and engage in various forms of self-harm and self-mutilating behaviour, as was illustrated. Self-harm was also evident in the famous case of Susanna Kaysen, who documented her experiences with borderline personality disorder in the book (and subsequent movie) *Girl, Interrupted* (see photo). Kaysen had chronic wrist banging, along with chronic feelings of depression and emptiness.

Research in Canada and elsewhere indicates that 1 in 10 people with BPD commit suicide (Paris, 2002). According to Montreal psychiatrist Joel Paris, in contrast to typical patterns, most BPD sufferers who kill themselves are female and most suicides occur after multiple attempts rather than on the first attempt. Follow-up data suggest that those who die by suicide are higher in impulsivity and violent-aggressive features linked with cluster B disorders (McGirr, Paris, Lesage, Renaud, & Turecki, 2007).

Clinicians and researchers have used the term "borderline personality" for some time but have given it many meanings. Originally, the term implied that the person was on the borderline between neurosis and schizophrenia. The *DSM* concept of borderline personality no longer has this connotation. The current conceptualization derives from two main sources. First, Gunderson, Kolb, and Austin (1981) proposed a set of specific diagnostic criteria similar to those that ultimately appeared in *DSM-III*. The second source of the diagnostic criteria was a study of the relatives of those people with schizophrenia done by Spitzer et al. (1979). As discussed earlier, some of these relatives had schizotypal personality disorder, but Spitzer and colleagues also identified another syndrome in the relatives, the characteristics of which came to identify BPD.

BPD typically begins in early adulthood. Initial estimates suggested a prevalence of 1 to 2% (Swartz et al., 1990), but a more recent assessment of almost 35,000 American adults yielded a much higher prevalence of 5.9% (Zanarini et al., 2011). BPD sufferers are more likely to be women (Swartz et al.,

Susanna Kaysen, the person portrayed by Winona Ryder in the movie *Girl, Interrupted*, was diagnosed with BPD. Her autobiography is an insightful account of what it means to have BPD and her experiences as a patient in McLean Hospital in Belmont, Massachusetts.

1990), to have a mood disorder (Zanarini et al., 1998), and to have parents who are more likely than average to have mood disorders and other forms of psychopathology (Shachnow et al., 1997; Trull, 2001). Comorbidity is found with substance abuse, post-traumatic stress disorder, eating disorders, and personality disorders from the odd/eccentric cluster (Skodol, Oldham, & Gallaher, 1999; Zanarini et al., 1998).

For many years, it has been assumed that the prognosis of BPD is not favourable, but Paris (2009) reviewed existing evidence and concluded that most clients with BPD recover over time. The results of a 27-year investigation conducted in Montreal found that gradual improvement over time occurred for most clients, such that only 7.8% met criteria for BPD 27 years later (Paris & Zweig-Frank, 2001; Zweig-Frank & Paris, 2002). Still, the mortality rate of the sample as a whole was substantially elevated, relative to Canadian norms, as many BPD patients had premature deaths. The McLean Study of Adult Development by Zanarini et al. (2005a) is a longitudinal study that also indicates a more positive long-term prognosis, with remission rates of BPD (74%) much higher than believed possible. A subsequent study examined people with BPD over 10 years and again found high rates of remission (85%) and low rates of relapse (only 12%), but severe and persistent impairments in social functioning (Gunderson, Stout, et al., 2011), a conclusion also reported by Zanarini et al. (2005b). Researchers are now shifting their focus to factors that predict who does recover vs. who does not recover. An impressive 16-year investigation found that 3 out of 5 people with BPD had at least a two-year period of recovery. Unique predictors of recovery included no prior psychiatric hospitalizations, higher IQ, a good vocational record, and a combination of personality characteristics (higher extroversion, higher agreeableness, and an absence of the anxious cluster personality disorder) (see Zanarini et al., 2014).

Even when treatment gains are realized, the overall level of functioning often remains relatively poor (see Davidson et al., 2006). Moreover, there also seems to be a lasting vulnerability to experience negative life events; a study of middle-aged people who previously had a BPD diagnosis showed that they experienced a greater frequency of negative life events, both in terms of self-reported and interviewer-assessed life events (Gleason, Powers, & Oltmanns, 2012).

Etiology of Borderline Personality Disorder

There are several views concerning the causes of BPD. Here, we discuss object-relations theory, biological research, and Linehan's diathesis–stress theory. While there are several possibilities, Paris (2009) has observed that treatment is challenging and usually not based on theory because the etiology of BPD is still largely unknown. Perhaps there are multiple routes to the experience of BPD.

Object-relations theory   Object-relations theory, an important variant of psychoanalytic theory, is concerned with the way children incorporate (or introject) the values and images of important people, such as their parents. In other words, the focus is on the manner in which children identify with people to whom they have strong emotional attachments. These introjected people (object representations) become part of the person's ego, but they can come into conflict with the wishes, goals, and ideals of the developing adult. For example, a college-age woman who has adopted her mother's notion of the "proper" role of a woman in society may find herself drawn to more modern ideals of feminism.

Object-relations theorists hypothesize that people react to their world through the perspectives of people from their past, primarily their parents or other primary caregivers. As noted, sometimes these perspectives conflict with the person's own wishes. Two leading object-relations theorists are Otto Kernberg and Heinz Kohut. (Kohut's views on narcissism will be discussed later.)

Kernberg (1985) proposed that adverse childhood experiences—for example, having parents who provide love and attention inconsistently, perhaps praising achievements but being unable to offer emotional support and warmth—cause children to develop insecure egos.

Although people with BPD have weak egos and need constant reassuring, they retain the capacity to test reality. As a result, they are in touch with reality but frequently engage in a defence mechanism called splitting: dichotomizing objects into all good or all bad and failing to integrate positive and negative aspects of another person or the self into a whole. This tendency causes extreme difficulty in regulating emotions because the person with BPD sees the world, including himself or herself, in black-and-white terms. Somehow this defence protects the client's weak ego from intolerable anxiety.

A number of studies have yielded data relevant to Kernberg's theory. As expected, people with BPD report a low level of care by their mothers (Patrick et al., 1994). They view their families as emotionally inexpressive, low in cohesion, and high in conflict. Research conducted in Toronto by Links and van Reekum (1993) indicates that people with BPD also frequently report childhood sexual and physical abuse. Also, many of those with BPD have experienced separation from parents during childhood (Paris, Zweig-Frank, & Guzder, 1994).

Biological factors   BPD runs in families, suggesting that it has a genetic component. Indeed, an analysis reported that heritability estimates range across four studies from 37% to 69%. These same researchers found in their studies that someone with a first-degree relative with BPD, vs. someone without a first-degree relative with BPD, had a three to four times greater likelihood of being diagnosed with BPD. There are also indications that genetic factors play a substantial role while environmental factors play a relatively small role (see Gunderson, Zanarini, et al., 2011).

Some data suggest poor functioning of the frontal lobes, which may play a role in impulsive behaviour. BPD clients perform poorly on neurological tests of frontal-lobe functioning and show low glucose metabolism in the frontal lobes (Goyer, Andreason, Semple, & Clayton, 1994; van Reekum et al., 1993).

More recent research has sought to illuminate the neural correlates of BPD. A meta-analysis led by Canadian researcher

Anthony Ruocco supported the conclusion that the processing of negative emotions in BPD is subserved by an abnormal reciprocal association between limbic structures implicated in the subjective feelings that people have when they experience negative emotions and the anterior brain areas involved in the regulation of emotion (Ruocco, Amirthavasagam, Choi-Kain, & McMain, 2013). This helps account for the intensive negative emotions and their persistence. That is, people with BPD have an overactivation in the insula and posterior cingulate cortex, and underactivation across a region that stretches from the amygdala to the dorsolateral prefrontal cortex. A more recent meta-analysis supported the conclusion that BPD is an emotion dysregulation disorder involving dysfunctional dorsolateral prefrontal and limbic brain regions (Schulze, Schmahl, & Niedfield, 2016).

Linehan's diathesis–stress theory

Marsha Linehan is one of the most influential theorists and therapists in the BPD field and her influence continues to grow. Her therapy is described in a later segment of this chapter and here we describe her diathesis–stress theory. What is remarkable about her contributions is that for years Marsha Linehan did not reveal her own personal story, but that changed in 2011. Incredibly, the story of the 17-year-old girl that opened this BPD segment of Chapter 13 is Linehan's own story, as recounted by Benedict Carey (2011) in an exceptional article in the *New York Times*. Linehan is now a famous theorist and therapist in the clinical world and she represents a beacon of hope for people struggling with their own profound difficulties. In her own words, she decided to participate in a published series about people coping with mental illness because "So many people have begged me to come forward, and I just thought—well, I have to do this. I owe it to them, I cannot die a coward" (Carey, 2011, p. A1).

According to this published account, Linehan was discharged in 1963 and official records indicated that she had 26 months of hospitalization and was one of the most disturbed patients in the hospital. She had a relapse and at least one suicide attempt after 1963. However, a dramatic turning point for Linehan in her recovery occurred when she was praying in a chapel, looking up at a cross, and she felt a shimmering experience that came toward her and engulfed her. This encounter was transformative and made her realize that she loved herself and it was then time to be self-accepting.

Linehan's diathesis–stress theory is described below. First, however, it is worth noting that one of the authors of this text was an element in the Marsha Linehan story in 1972 as the person who admitted Linehan as a post-doctoral student in a clinical program in behavioural therapy at Stony Brook University in New York. Admission was based on Davison's realization that Linehan was very creative with people and could challenge them without putting them down.

So what is her theory? Marsha Linehan proposes that BPD develops when people with a biological diathesis (possibly genetic) for having difficulty controlling their emotions are raised in a family environment that is invalidating. A diathesis for what Linehan calls "emotional dysregulation" can interact with experiences that invalidate the developing child, leading to the development of borderline personality.

An invalidating environment is one in which the person's wants and feelings are discounted and disrespected, and efforts to communicate one's feelings are disregarded or even punished. An extreme form of invalidation is child abuse, sexual and nonsexual: "Daddy says he loves me and yet he is hurting me and threatening even more if I tell." A recent humorous example of our own illustrates invalidation between a husband and a wife.

Wife:	Honey, could you help me with something for a minute?
Husband:	Sure, but I have to go to the bathroom first.
Wife:	No, you don't.

The two main hypothesized factors—dysregulation and invalidation—interact with each other in a dynamic fashion (see Figure 13.1). For example, the emotionally dysregulated child makes enormous demands on his or her family. The exasperated parents ignore or even punish the child's outbursts. This response can lead to the child suppressing emotions, only to have them build up to an explosion, which then gets parental attention. Parents can end up reinforcing the very behaviours they find aversive. Other patterns are possible, but they share a constant back-and-forth, a vicious circle, between the diathesis for dysregulation and the stress of invalidation.

A key piece of evidence supporting Linehan's theory concerns childhood physical and sexual abuse. As noted above, abuse is more frequent among people with BPD than among people diagnosed with most other disorders (Herman, Perry, & van der Kolk, 1989; Wagner & Linehan, 1994). One exception to this general pattern is dissociative identity disorder, which is also linked with very high rates of childhood abuse. Given the high rates of dissociative symptoms in borderline personality, the two disorders may be related and dissociation in both disorders may reflect the extreme stress of child abuse. Indeed, a study by Ross-Gower, Waller, Tyson, & Elliott (1998) found that the link between reported child sexual abuse and borderline symptoms was mediated by dissociative tendencies.

A recent case documented by Granato, Wilks, Miga, Korslund, and Linehan (2015) illustrates how the interplay of

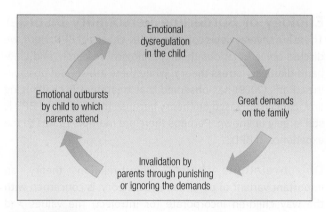

FIGURE 13.1 Linehan's diathesis–stress theory of borderline personality disorder

extreme trauma, sexual abuse, and invalidation can combine to create BPD. It is the case of Charlene, who presented with extreme BPD and post-traumatic stress disorder, as well as dissociative symptoms. The horrific circumstances she experienced were described as follows:

> *"Charlene is a 31-year-old female who was referred to the DBT clinic by her primary therapist for treatment of PTSD. Charlene reported a history of multiple traumatic events starting in childhood and a generally unsupportive and invalidating childhood environment. The index trauma targeted during the course of therapy occurred when Charlene was 12 years old. According to her recollection, a family member brought her to a party where she was drugged and subsequently gang raped. She awoke to the experience of being repeatedly raped by multiple perpetrators, beaten, and choked. She was in and out of consciousness during the assault, which lasted over 24 hours. She recalled that the assault was videotaped and believed it was for the purpose of creating child pornography and possibly to repay a family debt. After the assault, she was dumped in a remote location and left for dead.*
>
> *Charlene reported that during the event she experienced severe and intense helplessness, confusion, fear, and physical pain during and after the assault. After the assault, her family did not take her to the hospital despite multiple lacerations, contusions, and possible fractures and instead sent her away to live with another relative. She reported that no one responded to her in a comforting and supportive way. She indicated that she avoids things that remind her of the trauma, such as being out alone at night, being around crowds, and saying certain words such as 'rape.' She reported that since that time she has experienced frequent nightmares, flashbacks, and periods of memory loss. She reported that she has constantly experienced intense urges to commit suicide and self-harm."*
> (p. 806–807).

As is often the case with victims of abuse, Charlene experienced shame and guilt and she endorses the sense that somehow she was to blame for what happened. This tendency for people to blame themselves for things that they are clearly not responsible for and that are well beyond their control is due in part to our tendency to need to maintain "an illusion of control" that is fuelled by the fear inherent in realizing that some things are beyond our control. Fortunately, and somewhat remarkably, Charlene responded well to a therapeutic intervention that took place over 41 therapy sessions that combined the therapy developed by Linehan (i.e., dialectical behaviour therapy) and prolonged exposure therapy. The nature of dialectical behaviour therapy (DBT) is described later in this chapter.

As Linehan herself has cautioned, most aspects of her theory of etiology remain to be investigated. For example, self-reports of people with BPD that they suffered invalidating experiences as children are subject to the same kinds of questions as any retrospective self-report from a patient in therapy. Considering how sensitive such individuals are to invalidating experiences as adults, it is conceivable that their recollections of invalidating childhood experiences are coloured by their current psychological turmoil.

Linehan is mostly known for her treatment approach. It is described in a later segment of this chapter.

Histrionic Personality Disorder

The case of Suzanne described in Brief Case Example is an example of histrionic personality disorder (HPD). The diagnosis of **histrionic personality**, formerly called hysterical personality,

---

Brief Case Example

The Semisuicidal Sophomore

Suzanne called the university counselling centre just after midnight. She spoke softly into the answering machine and seemed to be fighting back tears. "Uh, I feel really shitty and I'm mad at everyone I know and I need to talk with someone who cares or I'm going to kill myself right now and I'm not kidding either!" Although she left her phone number at her dorm room, attempts to reach her by the on-call therapist were unsuccessful. According to her roommate, Suzanne was out "making the rounds." After a second call the next morning, she agreed to come in for evaluation.

Suzanne arrived 30 minutes late, chewing bubble gum and dressed scantily in a shocking black outfit. When her male interviewer paused immediately upon seeing her, she stated simply, "It symbolizes the way I'm feeling right now. Do you like it?" A turban covered her hair, and dark stones adorned her fingers, ears, and neck. The whole getup seemed chosen for its obvious shock value. An assessment of suicidal potential was the first objective, but Suzanne denied that she wasn't really serious. "If I was serious," she quipped dramatically, "I wouldn't be here, now would I?" "It's a good way of getting attention . . . I don't like to be ignored . . . always works on the parents. You'd be surprised what you can get if you try hard enough." At that moment, she blew a big bubble, and then suddenly sucked the air out of it, all without losing eye contact with the interviewer.

Suzanne reports problems in many areas of life. First, she is doing poorly in school and fears she may be thrown out if her grades do not improve. She is already on academic probation. When asked about her attendance, she admits that she rarely makes it to classes, because most of them are in the morning, and her social activities get started after midnight. However, "a lot of the guys in class have volunteered to take notes for me." Second, Suzanne and her roommates have had problems getting along since the beginning of the semester. They object to her "borrowing" their things, her late nights, and her frequent male visitors, who often stay overnight in various states of intoxication. Finally, her boyfriend, whom she regards as extremely and unreasonably jealous, wants to break up, objecting to her flirtatious behaviour, even though she swears she has been completely faithful to him over the month they have been together. Suzanne states that she is overwhelmed that "the closest person in the world to me would turn on me all of a sudden like that." And that, she notes, is what prompted her call to the counselling centre.

Although Suzanne speaks of her great distress and depression, her demeanour belies her words. She is animated and demonstrative, perhaps even slightly manic. She flits from topic to topic and from emotion to emotion with only minimal insight and no real transition in between. No follow-up appointment could be made, because Suzanne is "too busy." She denies continued feelings of suicidality. When asked if she wants to continue next week, she remarks teasingly "I'll get back to you," blowing another bubble and then pressing the gum under her seat on the way out (from Millon & Davis, 2000, p. 256).

is applied to people who are overly dramatic and attention-seeking. They often use features of their physical appearance, such as unusual clothes, makeup, or hair colour, to draw attention to themselves. These individuals, although displaying emotion extravagantly, are thought to be emotionally shallow. They are self-centred, overly concerned with their attractiveness, and uncomfortable when not the centre of attention. They can be inappropriately sexually provocative and seductive and are easily influenced by others. Their speech is often impressionistic and lacking in detail. For example, they may state a strong opinion yet be unable to give any supporting information.

This diagnosis has a prevalence of 2 to 3% and is more common among women than among men (Corbitt & Widiger, 1995). The prevalence of HPD is higher among separated and divorced people, and it is associated with high rates of depression and poor physical health (Nestadt et al., 1990). Comorbidity with BPD is high.

Etiology of Histrionic Personality Disorder

Unfortunately, little research has been conducted on HPD.

Psychoanalytic theory predominates and proposes that emotionality and seductiveness were encouraged by parental seductiveness, especially father to daughter. People with HPD are thought to have been raised in a family environment in which parents talked about sex as something dirty but behaved as though it was exciting and desirable. This upbringing may explain the preoccupation with sex, coupled with a fear of actually behaving sexually. The exaggerated displays of emotion on the part of histrionic persons are seen as symptoms of such underlying conflicts, and their need to be the centre of attention is seen as a defence mechanism, a way to protect themselves from their true feelings of low self-esteem (Apt & Hurlbert, 1994; Stone, 1993).

Narcissistic Personality Disorder

As discussed earlier, people with a **narcissistic personality** disorder (NPD) such as Malcolm in Brief Case Example have a grandiose view of their own uniqueness and abilities

Brief Case Example

The Long-Suffering Einstein

Malcolm stormed out of his supervisor's office, furious that he was on the edge of being terminated. He stubbornly resisted the demand that he seek counselling, asserting that the problem was the company, not him.

The immediate issue was his strained relationship with his supervisor and the subordinates in his office. Although his credentials were excellent, Malcolm had ways of inventing new procedures that impacted standard routines without much sympathy for those affected. Everyone was automatically expected to follow his whim. Sometimes his novel notions worked out, and sometimes they didn't. Regardless, the staff resented these impositions on their time and their job descriptions. When things did work out for the better, Malcolm gave only lip service to the role of his co-workers.

Worse, Malcolm never gave up any of his ideas. He was sure they were superior to the "old ways" and would work if the staff could just "get their head out their ass long enough to see the big picture and just adjust for the better." "I do not know why the magnitude of my innovations isn't obvious to everyone," he had been heard to state. When asked how he saw himself in five years,

Malcolm remarked, "I'm a firm believer in the power of positive thinking. For the most part, it's old ways that hold us down. Wherever I've gone I've found new ways, new efficiencies, some of them startling. I can only imagine that in time I will be fantastically successful. It is my destiny."

In fact, Malcolm had been pushed out at other companies for making life difficult, just as he is creating problems now. Others, he asserted loudly, "either do not recognize my ability, or else are envious when they do." The problems with the office staff he attributed to jealousy. "They want to get me fired so I don't make them all look bad. In fact, I think some of them might be deliberately sabotaging me." The same was supposedly true of his supervisor.

Malcolm also spoke about the "cretins" he was forced to work with, and how their incompetence constantly delayed him from finishing his own projects and implementing his latest ideas. Having been forced to associate with inferiors all his life, he was glad that a psychiatrist was treating him, because a medical doctor would have a better chance of understanding him and sympathizing with his plight. Asked to name people with whom he felt a bond, he mentioned Einstein and Salk, individuals who "had suffered nobly for being ahead of their time, just like me" (from Millon & Davis, 2000, p. 272).

Narcissistic personality disorder draws its name from Narcissus of Greek mythology. He fell in love with his own reflection, was consumed by his own desire, and was then transformed into a flower.

(see illustration). They are preoccupied with fantasies of great success. To say that they are self-centred is an understatement. They require almost constant attention and excessive admiration and believe that only high-status people can understand them. Their interpersonal relationships are disturbed by their lack of empathy, feelings of envy, arrogance, and their tendency to take advantage of others. Relationships are also problematic because of their feelings of entitlement—they expect others to do special, not-to-be-reciprocated favours for them. Most of these characteristics, with the exception of lack of empathy and extreme reactions to criticism, have been validated in empirical studies as aspects of NPD (Ronningstam & Gunderson, 1990). The prevalence of NPD is less than 1%. It most often co-occurs with BPD (Morey, 1988).

In recent years, much has been learned about the nature of narcissism. Aaron Pincus and his colleagues have argued that for many years the research literature has painted too rosy a view of narcissism by relying on a self-report measure that did not capture the maladjustment of extreme narcissists. Pincus et al. (2009) responded by creating the Pathological Narcissism Inventory (PNI). The PNI is a self-report scale that taps seven components of pathological narcissism. Four factors assess narcissistic grandiosity (entitlement rage, exploitativeness, grandiose fantasy, and self-entitlement) and three factors assess narcissistic vulnerability (contingent self-esteem, hiding the self, and devaluing). These factors combine into two higher order factors reflecting grandiosity and vulnerability that

are replicable and invariant across women vs. men (Wright, Lukowitsky, Pincus, & Conroy, 2010).

A less positive view of narcissism was also provided by Paulhus and Williams (2002). Their work introduced a constellation on traits known as the **dark triad**. The dark triad consists of the combination of narcissism, psychopathy, and Machiavellianism. People who are narcissistic also tend to have the other elements of the triad. The concept of psychopathy and its link with anti-social tendencies are described below. Machiavellianism is a personality style characterized by an extreme willingness to take advantage of others when the opportunity presents itself because people with this orientation essentially believe that everyone is out for himself or herself. The dark triad has recently been supplemented with the addition of the dimension of sadism and, as a result, it is now called the **dark tetrad** (see Buckels, Jones, & Paulhus, 2013). Sadism is a tendency to enjoy cruelty in everyday life. We will see in Chapter 14 that in some people it can take on extreme forms of sexual sadism.

An important point that emerges from this recent work is that when we focus on personality dimensions in research concentrated on personality variables, there is a tendency to lose sight of a person-centred approach and the fact that several correlated dimensions that reflect personality dysfunction may exist within the same person. This point was emphasized in a recent analysis of the concept of "dark perfectionism," which was inspired by those people who are not only perfectionistic, they are also narcissistic and Machiavellian (Flett, Hewitt, & Sherry, 2016).

Etiology of Narcissistic Personality Disorder

The diagnosis of NPD is rooted in modern psychoanalytic writings. Many psychoanalytically oriented clinicians have regarded it as a product of our times and our system of values. On the surface, the person with NPD has a remarkable sense of self-importance, complete self-absorption, and fantasies of limitless success, but it is theorized that these characteristics mask a very fragile self-esteem.

Constantly seeking attention and adulation, narcissistic personalities are very sensitive to criticism and deeply fearful of failure. Sometimes they seek out others whom they can idealize because they are disappointed in themselves, but others are not allowed to become genuinely close. Their relationships are few and shallow. People with NPD become angry with others and reject them when they fall short of their unrealistic expectations. Their inner lives are impoverished because, despite their self-aggrandizement, they actually think very little of themselves.

At the centre of contemporary interest in narcissism is Heinz Kohut, whose two books, *The Analysis of the Self* (1971) and *The Restoration of the Self* (1977), have established a variant of psychoanalysis known as *self-psychology*. According to Kohut, the self emerges early in life as a bipolar structure with an immature grandiosity at one pole and a dependent overidealization of other people at the other. A failure to develop healthy self-esteem occurs when parents do not respond with approval to their children's displays of competency. The child is not valued for his or her own self-worth but rather as a means to foster the parents' self-esteem.

Kohut suggests that when parents respond to a child with respect, warmth, and empathy, the child is endowed with healthy self-esteem. But when parents further their own needs rather than directly approve of their children, the result may be a narcissistic personality.

> *"A little girl comes home from school, eager to tell her mother about some great successes. But this mother, instead of listening with pride, deflects the conversation from the child to herself [and] begins to talk about her own successes which overshadow those of her little daughter."*
>
> (Kohut & Wolf, 1978, p. 418)

Children neglected in this way do not develop an internalized, healthy self-esteem and have trouble accepting their own shortcomings. They develop into narcissistic personalities, striving to bolster their sense of self through unending quests for love and approval from others.

Anti-Social Personality Disorder and Psychopathy

In current usage, the terms "anti-social personality disorder" and "psychopathy" (sometimes referred to as "sociopathy") are often used interchangeably, although there are important differences between the two. Anti-social behaviour is an important component of both terms.

Characteristics of Anti-Social Personality Disorder

The *DSM-5* concept of **anti-social personality** disorder (APD) involves two major components:

1. A conduct disorder (described in Chapter 15) is present before the age of 15. Truancy, running away from home, frequent lying, theft, arson, and deliberate destruction of property are major symptoms of conduct disorder. Upwards of 60% of children with conduct disorder later develop APD (Myers, Stewart, & Brown, 1998).

2. This pattern of anti-social behaviour continues in adulthood.

Thus, the diagnosis involves not only certain patterns of anti-social behaviour but patterns that began in childhood. Other symptoms include failure to conform to social norms, deceitfulness, impulsivity, irritability, and reckless disregard for the safety of self and others. Adults with APD show irresponsible and anti-social behaviour by working only

inconsistently, breaking laws, being irritable and physically aggressive, defaulting on debts, and being reckless. Although completely aware of lies and misdeeds, many neither show regard for truth nor experience remorse for their misdeeds.

It is estimated that between 1% and 4% of the general population have APD (Werner, Few, & Bucholz, 2015); variability in estimates reflect the methods used to determine prevalence. A community study conducted in Edmonton found that about 3% of people met *DSM* criteria for APD (Swanson, Bland, & Newman, 1994). Rates are much higher among younger than among older adults and among people of low socio-economic status. APD is comorbid with a number of other diagnoses, most notably substance abuse. Swanson et al. (1994) found that more than 90% of those with APD had at least one other lifetime psychiatric diagnosis. Men with APD tend to outnumber women at a 3:1 prevalence ratio. Women with APD are more likely to have a history of emotional neglect, sexual abuse, and victimization. Moreover, they have less violent anti-social behaviours, lower social support, and greater impairment (Alegria et al., 2013).

APD became a prominent topic in Canada as a result of the April 2013 inquest examining the death of Ashley Smith, the girl who choked herself to death in 2007 in her cell in an Ontario psychiatric prison without staff intervening. There are many troubling aspects of this case, but here, we will focus on the testimony of Dr. Olajide Adelugba. Adelugba was the clinical director at the Regional Psychiatric Centre in Saskatoon in December 2006, where the teenager was once housed. This centre is the only psychiatric facility in Canada operated by Correctional Services Canada that takes in incarcerated women. Adelugba described Ashley Smith as having a "textbook case" of APD in that she displayed every APD symptom (see Perkel, 2013). Problematic behaviours included a history of trespassing and repeated assaults—including multiple assaults of staff. But she also had severe borderline features reflecting a high need for attention and self-harm behaviours.

Characteristics of Psychopathy

Consider the following case history of a psychopath recounted by Robert Hare (1970), a University of British Columbia professor who is regarded as the world's leading expert on psychopathy:

> *"Donald S., 30 years old, has just completed a three-year prison term for fraud, bigamy, false pretenses, and escaping lawful custody. The circumstances leading up to these offenses are interesting and consistent with his past behavior. With less than a month to serve on an earlier 18-month term for fraud, he faked illness and escaped from the prison hospital. During the ten months of freedom that followed he engaged in a variety of illegal enterprises; the activity that resulted in his recapture was typical of his method of operation. By passing himself off as the 'field executive' of an*

international philanthropic foundation, he was able to enlist the aid of several religious organizations in a fund raising campaign. The campaign moved slowly at first, and in an attempt to speed things up, he arranged an interview with a local TV station. His performance during the interview was so impressive that funds started to pour in. However, unfortunately for Donald, the interview was also carried on a national news network. He was recognized and quickly arrested. During the ensuing trial it became evident that he experienced no sense of wrongdoing for his activities. He maintained, for example, that his passionate plea for funds 'primed the pump' — that is, induced people to give to other charities as well as to the one he proposed to represent. At the same time, he stated that most donations to charity are made by those who feel guilty about something and deserve to be bilked. The ability to rationalize his behavior and his lack of self-criticism were also evident in his attempts to solicit aid from the very people he misled. Perhaps it is a tribute to his persuasiveness that a number of individuals actually did come to his support. During his three-year prison term, Donald spent much time searching for legal loopholes and writing to outside authorities, including local lawyers, the Prime Minister of Canada, and a Canadian representative to the United Nations. In each case he verbally attacked them for representing the authority and the injustice responsible for his predicament. At the same time he requested them to intercede on his behalf and in the name of the justice they professed to represent.

While in prison he was used as a subject in some of the author's research. On his release he applied for admission to university and, by way of reference, told the registrar that he had been one of the author's research colleagues! Several months later the author received a letter from him requesting a letter of recommendation on behalf of Donald's application for a job."

(Hare, 1970, pp. 1–2, Psychopathy: Theory and Research *by Robert Hare, © 1970)*

The story of Donald demonstrates the true psychopath's profound tendency to lie compulsively and act without any concern or regard for social conventions or the well-being of other people. As a result, legal problems are quite common.

The concept of **psychopathy** is linked closely to the writings of Hervey Cleckley and his classic book *The Mask of Sanity* (1976). On the basis of his clinical experience, Cleckley formulated a set of criteria for recognizing the disorder. Unlike the *DSM* criteria for anti-social personality disorder, Cleckley's criteria for psychopathy refer less to anti-social

The character played by Anthony Hopkins in *The Silence of the Lambs, Hannibal,* and *Red Dragon* displayed many of the characteristics of the psychopath, especially total lack of regard for the rights of others.

behaviour per se than to the psychopathic individual's thoughts and feelings. One of the key characteristics of psychopathy is poverty of emotions, both positive and negative. Psychopathic people have no sense of shame, and even their seemingly positive feelings for others are merely an act (see photo). The psychopath is superficially charming and manipulates others for personal gain. They exploit others even if it involves the use of violence and aggression (see Porter & Woodworth, 2006). Their lack of anxiety may make it impossible for psychopaths to learn from their mistakes, and their lack of positive emotions leads them to behave irresponsibly and often cruelly toward others. Another key point in Cleckley's description is that the anti-social behaviour of the psychopath is performed impulsively, as much for thrills as for something like financial gain.

Most researchers diagnose psychopathy using a well-known checklist (the Psychopathy Checklist-Revised or PCL-R) developed by Robert Hare (1991) (see photo). An extensive description of this measure and related research is provided in Canadian Contributions 13.1.

Robert Hare is regarded as the world's leading expert on psychopathy.

Canadian Contributions 13.1

Robert Hare and the Conceptualization and Assessment of Psychopathy

Robert Hare retired recently from the University of British Columbia after conducting decades of influential research on the nature and assessment of psychopathy. Hare's work has received widespread recognition, including an award from the Canadian Psychological Association for distinguished contributions in applied psychology and citations from the director of the Federal Bureau of Investigation (FBI) for exceptional service in the public interest. Hare's most well-known measure is the Psychopathy Checklist-Revised (PCL-R; Hare, 1991). The PCL-R consists of 20 items that are rated on a three-point scale. The 20 items on the checklist assess two major clusters of psychopathic behaviours. Factor 1, referred to as emotional detachment, describes a selfish, remorseless individual with inflated self-esteem who exploits others. This factor focuses on affective and interpersonal characteristics associated with psychopathy. It assesses attributes such as egocentricity, manipulativeness, callousness, and lack of guilt. Factor 2 characterizes an unstable and anti-social lifestyle marked by impulsivity and irresponsibility. Unfortunately, the Hare checklist does not include items to assess an absence of anxiety, a key feature of psychopathy according to Cleckley (Schmitt & Newman, 1999). Note that some investigators (e.g., Patrick, Hicks, Krueger, & Lang, 2005) have split Factor 1 into an affective factor (i.e., lack of remorse) and an interpersonal factor (i.e., glibness/superficial charm), and it has been suggested that the PCL-R actually consists of three factors.

Although these two factors are highly correlated with each other and extreme psychopaths tend to receive substantially elevated scores on both, extensive research evidence indicates that the factors differ in their associations with other personality, behavioural, and demographic factors. Harpur and Hare (1994) examined whether there are age-related changes in scores on the PCL-R factors in 889 male prisoners. Factor 1 scores remained stable across the age span, but scores on Factor 2 decreased with age, suggesting that psychopaths may become less impulsive and lower in sensation-seeking with age.

Research conducted with the Hare PCL-R shows that psychopathy occurs more among men than among women (Nicholls, Ogloff, Brink, & Spidel, 2005). Overall, among prison inmates, 15.7% of men and 7.4% of women exceeded the PCL-R cut-off for psychopathy. However, in women, there is still a moderate significant association between psychopathy and aggression and violence. Canadian data based on the use of the PCL-R indicate that psychopaths, relative to non-psychopaths, commit more violent and non-violent offences, as would be expected. More troubling is evidence suggesting that psychopaths, vs. non-psychopaths, were 2.5 times more likely when incarcerated to be granted conditional release even though they were more likely to reoffend (Porter, ten Brinke, & Wilson, 2009). The researchers concluded that psychopaths are very good at conning and deceiving prison staff and parole board members.

Other research led by Stephen Porter at Dalhousie University used the PCL-R to study offenders who have committed homicides. They found that criminal homicides committed by psychopathic murderers are cold-blooded, predatory acts that are almost always premeditated and motivated by an external goal (e.g., material gain or revenge), while homicides committed by non-psychopaths are more likely to be impulsive crimes of passion (Porter & Woodworth, 2007; Woodworth & Porter, 2002). Interestingly, psychopaths downplay the instrumentality of their acts when asked to describe their behaviour, in an apparent attempt to minimize their guilt and not seem responsible (Porter & Woodworth, 2007). Other research found that psychopaths are especially likely to exhibit sadistic behaviour in their homicides (Porter et al., 2003).

The PCL-R has proven to be one of the best predictors of recidivism in global research (see Hare, Clark, Grann, & Thornton, 2000). Hemphill, Hare, and Wong (1998) concluded that psychopaths are three times more likely than non-psychopaths to recidivate in general and four times more likely to recidivate by committing acts of violence. Both factors of the PCL-R predicted violent recidivism, while only Factor 2 predicted general recidivism. Overall, the PCL-R is regarded as a key component of risk appraisal in forensic assessment. It also can predict treatment outcome. Ogloff, Wong, and Greenwood (1990) evaluated 80 male federal inmates in a therapeutic community program in British Columbia and found that the psychopaths in their sample showed less clinical improvement and had lower levels of motivation.

Controversies with Diagnoses of APD and Psychopathy The two diagnoses—APD and psychopathy—are related, but they are by no means identical. (For a detailed comparison, see Werner et al., 2015.) One study found that only about 20% of people with APD scored high on the Hare PCL-R (Rutherford, Cacciola, & Alterman, 1999). Harpur and Hare (1994) observed that almost all psychopaths are diagnosed with APD but many people diagnosed with APD do not meet the criteria for psychopathy on the PCL-R. The question of which diagnosis is preferable has raised several issues.

Hare, Hart, and Harpur (1991) criticized the *DSM* diagnosis of APD because it requires accurate reports of events from many years earlier by people who are habitual liars (recall the onset-in-childhood criterion), and many researchers believe that a *DSM* diagnostic concept should not be synonymous with criminality. Nevertheless, 75 to 80% of convicted felons meet the criteria for APD, while only 15 to 25% of convicted felons meet the criteria for psychopathy (Hart & Hare, 1989). Moreover, lack of remorse, a hallmark of psychopathy, is but one of seven criteria for the *DSM*'s anti-social personality diagnosis, and only three of these criteria need to be present to make the diagnosis. Therefore, the person diagnosed with APD by the *DSM* may not have the lack of remorse that is central to psychopathy.

Extensive research has now identified factors and processes that distinguish APD and psychopathy. For instance, clear differences have emerged in defensive reactivity (as assessed by startle blink responses) suggesting that psychopathy is distinguished by a low fear disposition (see Vaidyanathan, Hall, Patrick, & Bernat, 2011). This deficit in psychopathy is described in more detail below. Other research has found that factors believed to distinguish APD and psychopathy actually do not. For instance, Cleckley (1976) suggested that psychopaths are relatively immune to suicidal acts but there is a great deal of evidence suggesting that people with APD can be prone to suicide. However, a study of male prison inmates found that APD and features of psychopathy were both associated with a history of suicide attempts (Verona, Patrick, & Joiner, 2001). Similarly, it was believed previously that cognitive control deficits were linked with APD but psychopathic individuals had elevated cognitive control, but here again, recent data indicate that APD and psychopathy are both associated with deficits in cognitive control (Zeier, Baskin-Sommers, Racer, & Newman, 2012). Thus, some factors are common to both, but there are other factors that clearly differentiate APD and psychopathy.

Hare (1996) described the differences between APD and psychopathy in a discussion of people who kill law enforcement officers. Hare stated that a 1992 FBI report erroneously described these killers as having APD when, in fact, psychopathy was evident. Hare (1996) noted, "These killers were not simply persistently anti-social individuals who met *DSM-IV* criteria for APD; they were psychopaths—remorseless predators who use charm, intimidation, and, if necessary, impulsive and cold-blooded violence to attain their ends" (p. 39). Unfortunately, in recent years, Canada has had its share of these individuals, including infamous characters such as Clifford Olson (see photo), Paul Bernardo, and Karla Homolka, who have killed children and/or young women.

As we review the research in this area, it is important to keep in mind that it has been conducted on individuals diagnosed in different ways—some as anti-social personalities and some as psychopaths—which makes integrating these findings somewhat difficult.

Bryan Sclosser / The Canadian Press

Psychopathic serial killer Clifford Olson murdered 11 children in British Columbia. In 1982, he was sentenced to life in prison without eligibility for parole for 25 years. In 1997, he asked to have his parole eligibility reconsidered under the "faint hope" clause. The jury at his hearing rejected his application. He compared himself with the cannibalistic killer of *The Silence of the Lambs*, saying, "Hannibal Lecter is fiction—I'm real" (Worthington, 2011). Olson died of cancer in 2011. Robert Pickton, from Port Coquitlam, B.C., may have surpassed Olson's acts. He was accused of 26 counts of first-degree murder and the remains of 33 victims were found on his farm. Many of the victims were prostitutes who had disappeared from the Vancouver area. In 2007, he was convicted in six of the murders, which he appealed. The Supreme Court of Canada denied his appeal. A team of experts from British Columbia concluded in a 2012 bulletin written for the U.S. Federal Bureau of Investigation that Pickton is likely a psychopath as reflected by his emotionlessness while describing his heinous acts (see Woodworth et al., 2012).

Research and Theory on the Etiology of Anti-Social Personality Disorder and Psychopathy

We now turn to research and theory on the etiology of APD and psychopathy. We examine genetics, as well as the psychological factors that operate in the family and in emotions. A final section on response modulation and impulsivity ties together several of the individual research domains. Note again, however, that most research has been conducted on psychopathic individuals who have already been convicted as criminals. Thus, the available literature may not allow generalization to the behaviour of psychopaths who elude arrest or who do not engage in criminal activities.

Childhood roots of psychopathy   Psychopathy, like anti-social personality, is believed to have its roots in childhood and adolescence, but is less likely to be reflected by overt anti-social behaviours (see Hare & Neumann, 2009). Extensive research is now examining this possibility. This

research has been facilitated by research with the PCL-R. The PCL-R has been used successfully with adolescents. A study of juvenile psychopaths aged 14 to 18 from Quebec used the PCL-R to distinguish psychopaths and non-psychopaths and confirmed that high PCL-R scores are associated with a lack of behavioural inhibition (Roussy & Toupin, 2000). A separate version designed for youth, the Hare Psychopathy Checklist: Youth Version (PCL:YV) has been developed for 12- to 18-year-olds and for children and relies on ratings from informants to make diagnoses (see Forth, 2005; Forth, Kosson, & Hare, 2003). Lynam (1997) used it to show that psychopathic children are similar to psychopathic adults—they are impulsive and severely delinquent. Other research conducted over a six-month interval shows that levels of psychopathy have high to moderate stability, with the interpersonal and behavioural factors having the greatest stability (Lee et al., 2009). While the PCL:YV is deemed to have adequate reliability and validity, Hare and Neumann (2009) have cautioned that there are concerns about its use in the criminal justice system to the extent that it contributes to a tendency to label a child or adolescent as "a psychopath."

Evidence is accumulating on the nature of psychopathy in children and youth. Collectively, research has shown the following:

- Genetically influenced psychopathic personality in adolescents is a strong predictor of adult anti-social behaviour (Forsman et al., 2010).
- Female youth offenders, relative to males with high psychopathy, are more likely to have a history of psychiatric hospitalization if they are high in psychopathy (Cook, Barese, & Dicataldo, 2010).
- Children with psychopathic traits have abnormal prefrontal cortex responsiveness (Finger et al., 2008).
- Tests of regional grey matter volume among incarcerated male adolescents link psychopathy with decreased grey matter volumes in diffuse paralimbic brain regions, leading the researchers to conclude that psychopathy in younger people is best viewed as a neurodevelopmental disorder (Ermer et al., 2013).
- Canadian youth with pre-existing elevated levels of psychopathy are more likely to join youth gangs if they come from a neighbourhood of residential instability in terms of high neighbourhood turnover rates (Dupere et al., 2007).

The role of the family   Since much psychopathic behaviour violates social norms, many investigators have focused on the primary agent of socialization, the family, in their search for the explanation for such behaviour. McCord and McCord (1964) concluded, on the basis of a literature review, that lack of affection and severe parental rejection were the primary causes of psychopathic behaviour. Other studies have related psychopathic behaviour to parents' physical abuse, inconsistencies in disciplining their children, and failure to teach them responsibility toward others (see Johnson, Hunsley, Greenberg, & Schlinder, 1999). Furthermore, the fathers of psychopaths are likely to be anti-social in their behaviour.

Self-reported data on early rearing must be interpreted cautiously, because they were gathered by means of retrospective reports—individual recollections of past events. Information obtained in this way cannot be accepted uncritically. When people are asked to recollect early events in the life of someone now known to be psychopathic, their knowledge of the person's adult status may well affect what they remember or report about these early events. They may be more likely to recall deviant incidents and overlook more normal events. It is also risky to trust the retrospective reports of psychopaths because lying is a key feature of this disorder.

"If one wishes to choose the most likely candidate for a later diagnosis of [psychopathy] from among children appearing in a child guidance clinic, the best choice appears to be a boy referred for theft or aggression who has shown a diversity of anti-social behaviour in many episodes, at least one of which could be grounds for Juvenile Court appearance, and whose anti-social behaviour involves him with strangers and organizations as well as with teachers and parents. . . . More than half of the boys appearing at the clinic [with these characteristics were later] diagnosed socio pathic personality. Such boys had a history of truancy, theft, staying out late, and refusing to obey parents. They lied gratuitously, and showed little guilt over their behaviour. They were generally irresponsible about being where they were supposed to be or taking care of money."

(Robins, 1966, p. 157)

In addition to these characteristics, several aspects of family life were found to be consequential. Both inconsistent discipline and no discipline at all predicted psychopathic behaviour in adulthood, as did anti-social behaviour of the father.

Two important limitations to this research should be noted: (1) the harsh or inconsistent disciplinary practices of parents could be reactions to trying to raise a child who is displaying anti-social behaviour; and (2) many individuals who come from disturbed social backgrounds do not become psychopaths. This second point is important. Adults may have no problems whatsoever despite a problematic upbringing. Thus, although family experience is probably a significant factor in the development of psychopathic behaviour, it is not the sole factor. A diathesis also is required.

Genetic correlates of APD   Research suggests that both criminality and APD have heritable components. Adoption and twin studies, including those of twins reared apart, indicate that genetic factors play a significant role in the likelihood that a person will commit a criminal act (Gottesman & Goldsmith, 1994; Grove et al., 1990). For APD, twin studies show higher concordance for MZ than DZ pairs (Lyons et al., 1995). Moreover, adoption studies reveal higher than normal prevalence of anti-social behaviour in adopted children of biological parents with APD and substance abuse (Cadoret et al., 1995b; Ge et al., 1996).

More recent investigations of the role of genetic factors in APD have shown that APD and BPD have common genetic factors and that non-shared environmental factors overlap considerably in APD and BPD, especially with respect to anti-social-externalizing tendencies. However, BPD is distinguished by the role of genetic factors in affective-interpersonal tendencies (see Hunt, Bornovalova, & Patrick, 2015).

Both twin and adoption studies of APD have established that the environment plays a substantial role in APD. In the Cadoret adoption study referred to above, an adverse environment in the adoptive home (such as marital problems and substance abuse) was related to the development of anti-social personality disorder whether or not the adoptive parents had anti-social personality disorder. Furthermore, high levels of conflict and negativity and low levels of parental warmth predicted anti-social behaviour in a twin study by Reiss et al. (1995).

Adoption research has also shown that some characteristics of adoptive families that are related to anti-social behaviour in their children appear to be reactions to a "difficult" child (Ge et al., 1996); that is, the child's genetically influenced anti-social behaviour leads to environmental changes involving harsh discipline, which, in turn, exacerbate the child's anti-social tendencies.

A clear picture of the relative contribution of various factors emerged from a meta-analysis of 51 twin and adoption studies conducted by Rhee and Waldman (2002). Variance in anti-social behaviour was attributed to additive genetic influences (32%), nonadditive genetic influences (9%), nonshared environmental influences (43%), and shared environmental influences (16%). Thus, genetic and environmental factors both play strong roles.

It was noted in Chapter 2 that work by Caspi et al. (2002) illustrated how exposure to maltreatment combined with genetic vulnerability to increase the likelihood of anti-social behaviour. A recent meta-analysis confirmed that early adversity interacts with the MAOA genotype to increase the likelihood of anti-social outcomes and anti-social behaviours among males; however, there was weaker evidence of an interaction among females but maltreatment alone did contribute somewhat to anti-social tendencies (see Byrd & Manuck, 2014).

As noted earlier, Canadian researchers have been instrumental in extending research on the role of genetic factors in personality disorders such as APD (see Jang, Vernon, & Livesley, 2001; Livesley et al., 1998). They have used twin studies to show that a large genetic component accounts for much of the variability in individual differences in the personality dimension known as "dissocial behaviour" (i.e., anti-social behaviour).

Emotion and psychopathy   In defining the psychopathic syndrome, Cleckley pointed out the inability of such persons to profit from experience or even from punishment; they seem to be unable to avoid the negative consequences of social misbehaviour. Many are chronic lawbreakers despite their experiences with jail sentences. They seem immune to the anxiety or pangs of conscience that help keep most of us from breaking the law or lying to or injuring others, and they have difficulty curbing their impulses. In learning-theory terms, psychopaths have not been well socialized because they were unresponsive to punishments for their anti-social behaviour. Thus, they do not experience conditioned fear responses when they encounter situations in which the conditioned fear response should inhibit anti-social behaviour.

In a classic study based on Cleckley's clinical observations, Lykken (1957) tested the idea that psychopaths may have few inhibitions about committing anti-social acts because they experience so little anxiety. He performed several tests to determine whether psychopaths do indeed have low anxiety. One of the most important tests involved avoidance learning, which is assumed to be mediated by anxiety. Lykken studied the ability of psychopaths and control-group participants to avoid shock. He found that the psychopaths were poorer than the controls at avoiding the shocks, which supported the idea that psychopaths are low in anxiety.

Studies of the autonomic nervous system also indicate that psychopaths respond less anxiously to fear-eliciting stimuli. Psychopaths have lower than normal levels of skin conductance in resting situations, and their skin conductance is less reactive when they are confronted with intense or aversive stimuli or when they anticipate an aversive stimulus (Harpur & Hare, 1990). However, a different picture emerges when heart rate is examined. The heart rate of psychopaths is normal under resting conditions and remains normal when neutral stimuli are presented, but in situations in which they anticipate a stressful stimulus, their hearts beat faster than those of normal people anticipating stress.

These physiological reactions indicate that psychopaths cannot be regarded as simply under-aroused, since their heart rates are higher than normal in anticipation of a stressor. Basing his theorizing in part on Lacey's work (1967), Hare (1978) focused on the pattern of psychophysiological responses of psychopaths. Faster heartbeats are viewed as an indication that a person is tuning out or reducing sensory input. Thus, the increased heart rate of psychopaths who are anticipating an aversive stimulus indicates that they are tuning out the stimulus. Their skin conductance is then less reactive to an aversive stimulus because they are effective in ignoring it. Indeed, more recent experimental data have confirmed that an attentional mechanism does seem to account for the reduced fear response. That is, the apparent lack of fear reflects diminished attention to threat-relevant stimuli (Dvorak-Bertscha, Curtin, Rubinstein, & Newman, 2009).

In general, while aggression tendencies are associated positively with electrodermal reactivity, psychopaths have low electrodermal activity and reactivity. This distinction has been demonstrated in many investigations (see Lorber, 2004).

The research we have described thus far has been based on the idea that punishment does not arouse strong emotions in psychopaths and thus does not inhibit anti-social behaviour. But some researchers do not believe that punishment is the critical agent of socialization. They think that empathy—being in tune with the emotional reactions of others—is more important. For example, empathizing with the distress that callous treatment might cause in someone else could inhibit such behaviour. Some features of psychopathy may arise from a lack of empathy.

This idea has been tested by monitoring the skin conductance of psychopathic and non-psychopathic men as they viewed slides of varying content. Three types of slides were used: threatening (e.g., gun, shark), neutral (e.g., book), and distress (e.g., a crying person). No differences were found between the two groups in their responses to the first two

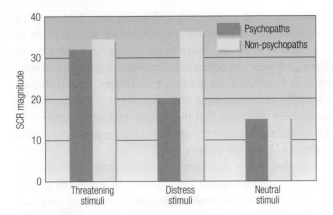

FIGURE 13.2 Skin-conductance response(SCR) of psychopathic and non-psychopathic men to three types of stimuli. The psychopathic men showed less responsiveness to the distress stimuli, indicating a deficit in empathy.

types of slides, but the psychopaths were less responsive to the distress slides (Blair, Jones, Clark, & Smith, 1997). Thus, the psychopaths indeed appeared to show less empathy for the distress of others (see Figure 13.2.).

Response modulation, impulsivity, and psychopathy
Research continues to highlight the impulsivity of psychopaths and its physiological roots. A study in British Columbia used the PCL-R to identify criminal psychopaths; subsequent functional magnetic resonance imaging tests showed that, compared with criminal non-psychopaths and control participants, criminal psychopaths had less affect-related activity in the amygdala/ hippocampal formation, suggesting that the hypoemotionality of psychopaths reflects limbic system deficiencies (Kiehl et al., 2001).

A review was conducted of 17 neuroimaging studies that focused on people with a history of engaging in impulsive violent acts (Bufkin & Luttrell, 2005). Anti-social impulsive acts are associated with decreased prefrontal activity and increased subcortical activity in the brain. A particular subcortical structure, the amygdala, is implicated in emotion regulation, and growing evidence supports the role of amygdalar dysfunction in psychopathy (Vien & Beech, 2006).

As for impulsivity, it shows up when psychopaths attempt tasks designed to test their ability to modify their responses to success or failure (Patterson & Newman, 1993). In one study, participants viewed playing cards on a computer-generated video display (Newman, Patterson, & Kosson, 1987). Psychopaths continued playing the game much longer than non-psychopaths and appeared to ignore numerous cues indicating that they were unlikely to be rewarded and should quit. The insensitivity to contextual information appears to be a general feature of psychopathy; it occurs even in situations that do not involve threat of punishment (Newman, Schmitt, & Voss, 1997). This insensitivity to context might well relate to psychopaths' insensitivity to other people.

Thus, psychopaths do not react as most of us do. In particular, they have little anxiety, so anxiety can have little deterrent effect on their anti-social behaviour. Their callous treatment of others may also be linked to their lack of empathy. Because psychopaths are deficient in using contextual information and in planning ahead, they behave impulsively. These are possible reasons for the psychopath's misconduct without regret.

13.5   Personality Disorder Clusters: Anxious/Fearful Cluster

This cluster comprises three personality disorders:

- Avoidant personality disorder applies to people who are fearful in social situations.
- Dependent personality disorder applies to those who lack self-reliance and are overly dependent on others.
- Obsessive-compulsive personality disorder applies to those who have a perfectionistic approach to life.

Avoidant Personality Disorder

The diagnosis of **avoidant personality** disorder applies to people such as Jared in Brief Case Example who are keenly

---

Brief Case Example

The Shamed Son

A first-year college student, Jared hardly associated with anyone. In the clinical interview, he seemed to want to make contact, but he frequently stuttered, causing him to retreat in embarrassment. Otherwise, he expressed almost no emotion.

His second computer programming course was the immediate problem. Though he was fluent in several computer languages, his professor wanted the students to work in groups, to collaborate in building chunks of a single large project. Jared was scared. "I try to

work on it, but I can't concentrate." His voice shrank to a whisper. "They're g..g..going to think I'm an idiot." His solution was to drop the class, though he had an A average going into this, the last assignment of the semester. In fact, his grades were exceptional overall. Nevertheless, Jared could report no friends, and confessed, "I'm lousy at meeting people. I guess I think they won't like me or something. I'm awkward. I'm a klutz. I just don't have many qualities others are interested in, I guess. But I'm great with computers." (From Millon & Davis, 2000, p. 154)

sensitive to the possibility of criticism, rejection, or disapproval and are reluctant to enter into relationships unless they are sure they will be liked. They may avoid employment that entails a lot of interpersonal contact. They are restrained in social situations owing to an extreme fear of saying something foolish or of being embarrassed by blushing or other signs of anxiety. They believe they are incompetent and inferior to others and are reluctant to take risks or try new activities.It is widely accepted that avoidant personality disorder is one of the personality disorders associated with higher levels of life impairment and it is one of the most prevalent, being diagnosed in almost 2% of the general population (Weinbrecht, Schulze, Boettcher, & Renneberg, 2016). Given that there has been less research on avoidant personality disorder than on other personality disorders (e.g., borderline) and related conditions (e.g., social anxiety disorder), Weinbrecht et al. (2016) characterized avoidant personality disorder as a neglected diagnosis in clinical research.

Many scholars emphasize that those with an avoidant personality disorder tend to avoid social situations, but this conclusion was qualified by Taylor, Laposa, and Alden (2004), who found that those with avoidant personality disorder engage in other forms of avoidance as well and that these people have a general pattern of avoidance. Regardless, avoidant personality disorder and generalized social phobia are highly comorbid, with research by Canadian investigators showing that 40% of those with avoidant personality disorder also had generalized social phobia (Cox, Pagura, Stein, & Sareen, 2009) and that avoidant personality disorder predicts greater persistence of social phobia after adjusting for socio-demographic factors (Cox et al., 2011). Perhaps this reflects the fact that those who had both disorders had demonstrably lower levels of life quality.

Avoidant personality disorder is highly comorbid with dependent personality disorder (Alden et al., 2002). Dependent personality disorder is described below. According to Alden et al. (2002), the only symptom that reliably differentiates avoidant personality disorder from dependent personality is that the avoidant person has great difficulty approaching and initiating social relationships. Avoidant personality is comorbid with depression as well as with generalized social phobia (Alpert et al., 1997). The comorbidity with generalized social phobia is likely due to the similarity between the diagnostic criteria for these disorders; avoidant personality disorder may be a more severe variant of generalized social phobia (Hofmann, Newman, Ehlerr, & Roth, 1995).

Both avoidant personality disorder and social phobia are related to a syndrome that occurs in Japan called *taijinkyoufu* (*taijin* means "interpersonal" and *kyoufu* means "fear"). Like people with avoidant personality disorder and social phobia, those with *taijinkyoufu* are overly sensitive and avoid interpersonal contact. But what they fear is somewhat different from the usual fears of those with the *DSM* diagnoses. People with *taijinkyoufu* tend to be ashamed about how they appear to others, fearing, for example, that they are ugly or have body odour (Ono et al., 1996).

Dependent Personality Disorder

The core feature of **dependent personality** disorder (DPD) is a lack of both self-confidence and a sense of autonomy. People with DPD view themselves as weak and other people as powerful. They also have an intense need to be taken care of, which makes them feel uncomfortable when alone; they may be preoccupied with fears of being left alone to take care of themselves. They subordinate their own needs to ensure that they do not break up protective relationships. When a close relationship ends, they urgently seek another relationship to replace the old one.

Existing diagnostic criteria for DPD include some features that are not well supported by the research literature. These diagnostic criteria portray people with DPD as being very passive (e.g., having difficulty initiating projects or doing things on their own, not being able to disagree with others, or allowing others to make decisions). Dependent people do whatever is necessary to maintain a close relationship. This could involve being very deferential and passive, but may also entail taking active steps to preserve a relationship (Bornstein, 1997).

An important caveat about DPD was expressed by Chen, Nettles, and Chen (2009). They suggested that DPD is perhaps the most culture-laden diagnostic category. It is rooted in the individualism of North American study. Too great a need to connect with others can constitute maladjustment in North America, but connecting with others is healthy and valued in collectivistic cultures in places such as East Asia.

Obsessive-Compulsive Personality Disorder

The **obsessive-compulsive personality** is a perfectionist, preoccupied with details, rules, schedules, and the like. These people often pay so much attention to detail that they never finish projects. They are work-oriented rather than pleasure-oriented and have inordinate difficulty making decisions (lest they err) and allocating time (lest they focus on the wrong thing). Their interpersonal relationships are often poor because they are stubborn and demand that everything be done their way. They are generally serious, rigid, formal, and inflexible, especially regarding moral issues. They are unable to discard worn-out and useless objects, even those with no sentimental value. A dysfunctional attention to work and productivity is found more often in men than in women.

Obsessive-compulsive personality disorder (OCPD) is quite different from obsessive-compulsive disorder (OCD); it does not include the obsessions and compulsions that define the latter. Although the use of the term "obsessive-compulsive" in both disorders suggests that the two disorders are related, the relationship does not appear to be very strong. Although OCPD is found more frequently among people with OCD than among those with panic disorder or depression, it is found in no more than 20% of OCD cases. OCD and OCPD are clearly distinguishable (Mancebo, Eisen, Grant, & Rasmussen, 2005).

Image Source/Getty Images

Children normally go through a phase in which separation from a parent is distressing. People with dependent personality disorder may be experiencing a similar phenomenon in their adult relationships.

Obsessive-compulsive personality disorder has a prevalence of between 1% to 2% and it often co-occurs with anorexia or depression (Fineberg et al., 2015).

Existing data provide an inconsistent view of OCPD, with low test–retest reliabilities of stability being found and almost half of the people with OCPD no longer meeting diagnostic criteria after one year. Diedrich and Voderholzer (2015) also described some evidence suggesting substantial stability and they attributed this ambiguity to the fact that some OCPD symptoms are quite stable (e.g., rigidity, perfectionism), while others are less trait-like (e.g., moral behaviours) and more prone to fluctuate across time periods.

Etiology of the Anxious/Fearful Cluster

Few data exist on the causes of the personality disorders in this cluster. Speculation about their causes has focused on parent–child relationships. It has been argued, for example, that dependent personality disorder results from an overprotective and authoritarian parenting style that prevents the development of feelings of self-efficacy (Bornstein, 1997).

Dependent personality disorder could also be a reflection of what are referred to as attachment problems (Livesley, Schroeder, & Jackson, 1990). Attachment has been studied by developmental psychologists and is regarded as important for personality development (see Chapter 15). The basic idea is that the young infant becomes attached to an adult and uses the adult as a secure base from which to explore and pursue other goals. Separation from the adult leads to anger and distress. As development proceeds, the child becomes less dependent on the attachment figure for security. The abnormal attachment behaviours seen in dependent personalities may reflect a failure in the usual developmental process arising from a disruption in the early parent–child relationship because of death, neglect, rejection, or overprotectiveness (see photo). Persons with dependent personality disorder engage in a number of tactics (originally established to maintain their relationship with their parents) to keep their relationships with other people at any cost—for example, always agreeing with them (Stone, 1993).

Much like the development of fears and phobias, avoidant personality disorder may reflect the influence of an environment in which the child is taught to fear people and situations that most of us regard as harmless. For example, the abnormal fears of one of the child's parents may be transmitted through modelling.

Freud viewed obsessive-compulsive personality traits as being due to fixation at the anal stage of psychosexual development. More contemporary psychodynamic theories emphasize a fear of loss of control that is handled by overcompensation. For example, the man who is a compulsive workaholic may fear that his life will fall apart if he relaxes and has fun.

13.6 Therapies for Personality Disorders

Over the past two decades, there have been substantial advances in research on the treatment of personality disorders. Some of these research developments are outlined below. It is important to bear in mind that a therapist working with someone with a personality disorder has many challenges to address. This person has long-standing vulnerabilities related to his or her self-concept and sense of personal identity. There are also characteristic interpersonal tendencies that likely transfer to the therapy context, along with interpersonal expectations and preconceptions. The person often has one or more additional disorders of a more episodic nature (e.g., anxiety, depression) and these disorders are often why people with PDs enter into treatment. For example, a person with anti-social personality disorder is likely to have substance abuse problems, a person with avoidant personality disorder may seek treatment for a social phobia, and a person with obsessive-compulsive personality disorder may be seen for depression. Not surprisingly, people who have a PD along with other disorders tend not to show as much improvement after various forms of psychotherapy (Crits-Christoph, 1992). The reason seems pretty clear: people with both types of diagnoses tend to be more seriously disturbed. As a result, they may require therapy that is both more intensive (because of the long-standing nature of personality disorders) and more extensive (i.e., focused on a broad range of psychological problems).

Psychodynamic therapists aim to alter the personality-disordered person's present-day views of the childhood problems assumed to underlie a personality disorder. For example, they may help an obsessive-compulsive personality to realize that the childhood quest to win the love of his or her parents by being perfect need not be carried into adulthood, that he or she need not be perfect to win the approval of others, and that it is possible to take risks and make mistakes without being abandoned.

Behavioural and cognitive therapists, in keeping with their focus on situations rather than traits, had little to say about specific treatments for the personality disorders until the publication of a seminal book edited by Beck and Freeman (1990) on the cognitive-behavioural therapy of personality disorders. Behavioural and cognitive therapists tend to analyze the individual problems that taken together reflect a personality disorder. For example, a person diagnosed as having a paranoid or an avoidant personality is extremely sensitive to criticism. This sensitivity may be treated by systematic desensitization or rational-emotive behaviour therapy (Renneberg, Goldstein, Phillips, & Chambless, 1990). The paranoid personality's argumentativeness and hostility when faced with a contrary opinion pushes others away and provokes counterattacks from them. The behavioural therapist may help the paranoid individual learn more adaptive ways of disagreeing with other people. Social skills training in a support group might be suggested to encourage avoidant personalities to be more assertive with other people. One controlled study done in Vancouver confirmed that this is a promising strategy (Alden, 1989). Such an approach, perhaps combined with rational-emotive behaviour therapy, may help these clients cope when efforts to reach out do not succeed, as is bound to happen at times (Millon, 1996).

In looking at cognitive therapy for personality disorders, Beck, Freeman, and associates (1990) applied the same kind of analysis that has been found promising in the treatment of depression. Each disorder can be analyzed in terms of logical errors and dysfunctional schemata. For example, treating obsessive-compulsive personality with cognitive therapy entails first persuading the client to accept the essence of the cognitive model: that feelings and behaviours are primarily a function of thoughts. Errors in logic are then explored, such as the person concluding that he or she cannot do anything right because of failing in one particular endeavour (an example of overgeneralization). The therapist also looks for dysfunctional assumptions or schemata that might underlie the person's thoughts and feelings; for example, the belief that it is critical for every decision to be correct. (Adherents of Ellis's methods would also take this step.) Beck's approach to personality disorders represents a combination of a variety of behavioural and cognitive-behavioural techniques, all designed to address the particular, long-standing, and pervasive difficulties that are experienced.

A related version of this approach developed primarily by Young is known as **schema therapy** for personality disorders (see Young, Klosko, & Weishaar, 2003). Young has identified a range of cognitive schemas measured by the Young Schema Questionnaire (YSQ) believed to underlie various forms of dysfunction, including personality disorder (see Young, 1994; Young & Lindemann, 2002). The YSQ taps three broad themes: (1) disconnection and rejection; (2) impaired autonomy and performance; and (3) impaired limits. Each theme is tapped by several subscale factors. For instance, the disconnection and rejection theme is assessed by abandonment/instability, mistrust/abuse, emotional deprivation, defectiveness/shame, and social isolation/alienation.

Schema therapy can be adapted to the main themes inherent in a particular personality disorder. Schema therapy for borderline personality disorder involves three phases of treatment: (1) bonding between the client and therapist and emotional regulation; (2) schema mode change; and (3) development of autonomy (see Kellogg & Young, 2006).

Schema therapy typically takes place across 50 sessions. A recent study with 323 patients with diagnosable personality disorders found that schema therapy was more effective than treatment as usual or clarification-oriented psychotherapy (Bamelis, Evers, Spinhoven, & Arntz, 2014). Evidence continues to indicate that schema therapy is effective and Wood and Johnson (in press) have suggested that schema therapy should be seen as an illustration of the power of positive psychology and the benefits of developing positive tendencies such as emotional awareness, while also benefitting from a positive alliance between the client and the therapist.

Therapy for the Borderline Personality

Few people pose a greater challenge to treatment than do those with BPD. The problems that borderline personalities have with other people are replicated in the consulting room.

With the BPD client, trust is inordinately difficult to create and sustain, thus handicapping the therapeutic relationship. The person alternately idealizes and vilifies the therapist, demanding special attention and consideration one moment—such as therapy sessions at odd hours—and refusing to keep appointments the next, imploring for understanding and support but insisting that certain topics are off-limits.

Suicide is always a serious risk, but it is often difficult for the therapist to judge whether a frantic phone call at 2 a.m. is a call for help or a manipulative gesture designed to see to what lengths the therapist will go to meet the client's needs at the moment. As happened in the case presented at the beginning of this chapter (see Brief Case Example), hospitalization is often necessary when the client's behaviour becomes unmanageable on an outpatient basis or when the threat of suicide cannot be managed without the greater supervision possible only in a psychiatric hospital.

Because seeing clients with BPD is so stressful, it is common practice for therapists to have regular consultations with another therapist, sometimes for support and advice and sometimes for professional help in dealing with their own emotions as they try to cope with the extraordinary challenges involved.

A number of drugs have been tried in the pharmacotherapy of BPD, most notably antidepressants and antipsychotic medications. There is little to recommend antidepressants, but antipsychotics show some modest effects on anxiety, suicidality, and psychotic symptoms (Bendetti et al., 1998). Because drugs are often abused and suicide is a risk, extreme caution must be used in any drug-therapy regimen, and overall, drug treatments for BPD are not very effective (see Paris, 2009).

Specific psychotherapy approaches applied to BPD are outlined below. First, however, it is important to consider the

Otto Kernberg, one of the leading object-relations theorists, has been very influential in the study of borderline personality disorder.

Courtesy Otto Kernberg

Photo by *UW Daily*, University of Washington. Courtesy Marsha M. Linehan.

Marsha Linehan created dialectical behaviour therapy, which combines cognitive-behavioural therapy with Zen and Rogerian notions of acceptance.

overall state of affairs when it comes to the treatment of BPD, as outlined in a recent editorial by Shelly McMain at the Centre for Addiction and Mental Health in Toronto. McMain (2015) observed that establishing the effectiveness of psychotherapeutic interventions was "a game changer that completely transformed our understanding of and approach to the management of BPD" (p. 741). However, it was also noted that people with BPD find it difficult to access treatment due to the limited availability of therapists trained in the treatment of BPD. Other reasons include long-standing negative beliefs about "the difficultness" of people with BPD and the fact that interventions for BPD are lengthy and resource intensive in an era of diminishing resources and a strong emphasis on reducing costs. Thus, McMain (2015) perceives major barriers to treatment access for BPD sufferers.

Object-Relations Psychotherapy

As noted earlier, object-relations theory focuses on how children identify with people to whom they have strong emotional attachments. Earlier in the chapter, we described the views of two object-relations theorists: Heinz Kohut, on narcissism, and Otto Kernberg (see photo), on the borderline personality.

As mentioned previously, Kernberg (1985) operates from the assumption that borderline personalities have weak egos and therefore have inordinate difficulty tolerating the probing that occurs in psychoanalytic treatment. Kernberg's modified analytic treatment has the overall goal of strengthening the person's weak ego so that he or she does not fall prey to splitting, or dichotomizing. Splitting is the result of an inability to form complex ideas (object representations) that do not fit a simple good–bad dichotomy. For example, the person may see the therapist as a godlike genius, only to be crushed and furious when the therapist later mentions that therapy payments are overdue; in an instant, the therapist becomes evil and incompetent. The therapist employs interpretive techniques, pointing out how emotions and behaviours are being regulated by such defences as splitting.

Kernberg's approach is more directive than that of most analysts. In addition to interpreting defensive behaviour, he gives concrete suggestions for behaving more adaptively and will hospitalize people whose behaviour becomes dangerous to themselves or others. Kernberg's opinion that such people are unsuitable for classical psychoanalysis because of their weak egos is consistent with a long-term study conducted at the world-famous analytically oriented Menninger Clinic (Stone, 1987).

Dialectical Behaviour Therapy

Linehan's personal account focused on developing a sense of personal acceptance. Thus, it is probably not surprising that Linehan (1987; see photo) introduced an approach that combines client-centred empathy and acceptance with cognitive-behavioural problem solving and social skills training. What she calls **dialectical behaviour therapy** (DBT) has three overall goals for borderline individuals—that they learn to

1. modulate and control their extreme emotionality and behaviours,
2. tolerate feeling distressed, and
3. trust their own thoughts and emotions.

Why does Linehan use the word "dialectical" in describing her therapy? The concept of dialectics comes from the German philosopher Hegel (1770–1831). For our purposes, it is enough to know that dialectics is a worldview that holds that reality is an outcome of a constant tension between opposites. Any event—called the thesis—tends to generate a force in opposition to it: its antithesis. The tension between the opposites is resolved by the creation of a new event: the synthesis. For example, John loves Mary (thesis). But he finds in her some qualities that annoy him, creating in him some doubt as to whether he truly loves her (antithesis). John then comes to realize that he can love Mary in spite of her faults, perhaps even because of them (synthesis). This synthesis can then split into another pair of dialectical opposites, with a new synthesis eventually emerging that can reconcile them into yet another synthesis. And so on and on.

Linehan uses the term "dialectic" to describe the seemingly paradoxical stance that the therapist must take with people with BPD: accepting each person as they are and yet helping them change. Linehan also uses the term to refer to the borderline person's realization that they need not split the world into black and white, but can achieve a synthesis of apparent opposites. For example, instead of a friend being either all bad (thesis) or all good (antithesis), the friend can be a person with both kinds of qualities (synthesis).

DBT centres on the therapist's full acceptance of borderline personalities with all their contradictions and acting out, empathically validating their (distorted) beliefs with a matter-of-fact attitude toward their suicidal and other dysfunctional behaviour. McMain, Korman, and Dimeff (2001) described the role of DBT in treating emotion dysregulation. They illustrated the concept of therapist acceptance by relating the case study of Jane, a BPD client with substance abuse disorder. Jane had a history of sexual abuse and experienced intense emotions of sadness, fear, and anger, along with intense self-criticism and shame. The following account stems from Jane's failure to keep self-monitoring diary cards and her emotional reactions to the treatment sessions:

> "*Client*:   Sometimes it's so upsetting. Because sometimes I could come in a good mood and then leave depressed. I end up leaving here so upset.
>
> *Therapist*:   No, I agree, that doesn't sound too comfortable.
>
> *Client*:   It's like my mother in the past, reminding me of all my faults all the time.
>
> *Therapist*:   Yeah, it's so painful to bring up this stuff. Why would anyone want that?
>
> *Client*:   Yeah, exactly!
>
> *Therapist*:   Now here's the dilemma. We could not talk about your problems, and if this would take away your pain and misery, I'd be all for it. On the other hand, if we help you figure out how to tolerate your bad feelings, then you won't have to rely on your pain medicine or resort to thinking of killing yourself when these feelings come up."
>
> (From McMain et al., 2001, pp. 192–193)

This exchange illustrates the therapist's acceptance and acknowledgement of Jane's emotional experiences. At the same time, the therapist suggests that learning to develop some emotional self-control can be substituted for the extreme emotional reactions that Jane has relied on in the past.

The cognitive-behavioural aspect of the treatment, conducted both individually and in groups, involves helping clients learn to solve problems, to acquire more effective and socially acceptable ways of handling their daily living problems, and to control their emotions. Work is also done on improving their interpersonal skills and controlling their anger and anxieties. After many months of intensive treatment, limits are set on

their behaviour, consistent with what Kernberg advocates. Basically, DBT is cognitive-behavioural therapy within the paradoxical context of validating and accepting the person for who he or she is. In Linehan's words:

> "*Stylistically, DBT blends a matter-of-fact, somewhat irreverent, and at times outrageous attitude about current and previous parasuicidal and other dysfunctional behaviours with therapist warmth [and] flexibility . . .. [A] focus . . . on active problem-solving [is] balanced by a corresponding emphasis on validating the patient's current emotional, cognitive, and behavioral responses just as they are.*"
>
> (1993b, p. 19)

Linehan and her associates published the results of the first randomized, controlled study of a psychological intervention for BPD (Linehan et al., 1991). Patients were assigned randomly either to DBT or to treatment as usual. They were assessed after one year of treatment and again six and 12 months later (Linehan, Heard, & Armstrong, 1993). The findings immediately after treatment revealed the highly significant superiority of DBT on measures of intentional self-injurious behaviour, including suicide attempts, dropping out of treatment, and in-patient hospital days. At the follow-ups, superiority was maintained; additionally, DBT patients had better work histories, reported less anger, and were judged as better adjusted overall than the comparison therapy patients. A subsequent study showed that DBT was reasonably effective in reducing drug use in BPD clients with substance dependence (Linehan et al., 1999).

As a result of Linehan's (1993a, 1993b) work, there is now widespread interest in DBT and its applicability to BPD and other disorders and adjustment problems. Some data suggest, for instance, that DBT is effective for treating suicidal college students with multiple problems, especially those who have the lower levels of functioning prior to treatment (Pistorello et al., 2012). It is not clear, however, whether DBT is the most effective form of treatment when compared with other alternatives. A Canadian study found that DBT vs. general psychiatric management were equally effective in reducing BPD symptoms, psychological distress, degree of suicidality, and health care utilization (McMain et al., 2009). This conclusion was still supported by the results of a two-year follow-up by this same team (see McMain et al., 2012), with the important caveat that even among those who maintained improvements, there were still high overall levels of functional impairment. Another longitudinal investigation by another team of investigators compared three forms of treatment across one year and confirmed that all three forms of treatment, including DBT, were somewhat effective; however, transference-focused psychotherapy, which has its roots in object-relations psychotherapy, was most effective in reducing maladjustment across six indicators, including depression and suicidality (Clarkin, Levy, Lenzenweger, & Kernberg, 2007). Transference-focused psychotherapy emphasized dominant, emotion-laden themes in individual sessions with a therapist actually trained in object-relations theory.

Therapy for Psychopathy

As for the treatment of psychopathy, there is widespread—and unfortunate—agreement among therapists of varying theoretical persuasions: psychopathy is often virtually impossible to treat (Cleckley, 1976; McCord & McCord, 1964). This negative stance has been described as "therapeutic nihilism" by Wong and Olver (2015). However, an analysis of eight treatment studies modified this conclusion somewhat by finding low to moderate treatment success (Salekin, Worley, & Grimes, 2010) and Wong and Olver (2015) concluded that more recent interventions using better research designs and more nuanced approaches offer more grounds for optimism. However, the challenges here are illustrated by research on children and adolescents who have the personality orientation believed to feed into psychopathy; that is, traits reflecting "callous unemotional" tendencies. A review of 15 treatment studies showed that children with CU (callous unemotional traits) tend to experience reductions in these traits and in their aggressive behaviour but they can also end up with higher levels of anti-social behaviour. The review found that there are many treatment difficulties at first because these children typically have very low initial levels of premorbid functioning (see Wilkinson, Waller, & Viding, 2016).

It may be that people with the classic symptoms listed by Cleckley are by their very natures mostly incapable of benefiting from any form of psychotherapy. In fact, it is unlikely that most psychopaths would even want to be in therapy. The primary reason for their unsuitability for psychotherapy is that they are unable and unmotivated to form any sort of trusting, honest relationship with a therapist. People who lie almost without knowing it, who care little for the feelings of others and understand their own even less, who appear not to realize that what they are doing is morally wrong, who lack any motivation to obey society's laws and mores, and who, living only for the present, have no concern for the future are, all in all, extremely poor candidates for therapy.

Summary

13.1 Personality disorders are defined as enduring patterns of behaviour and inner experience that disrupt social and occupational functioning. Classic theorists emphasize a lasting pattern of rigid and self-defeating behaviours that reflects insecurity and instability in the self. Personality disorders tend to be expressed in terms of dysfunctional emotional, cognitive, and interpersonal tendencies.

13.2 Personality diagnoses have become more reliable in recent years, although reliability is still a concern. Diagnoses overlap considerably and it is usual for a person to meet diagnostic criteria for more than one personality disorder. This high comorbidity, coupled with the fact that personality disorders are seen as the extremes of continuously distributed personality traits, has led to proposals to develop a dimensional rather than a categorical means of classifying these disorders. Classification schemas have retained a categorical focus while beginning to incorporate more of a dimensional focus.

13.3 Personality disorders are grouped into three clusters. Specific diagnoses in the first cluster—odd/eccentric—include paranoid, schizoid, and schizotypal. These disorders are usually considered to be less severe variants of schizophrenia, and their symptoms are similar to those of the prodromal or residual phases of schizophrenia. Behaviourgenetic research gives some support to this assumption, especially for schizotypal personality disorder.

13.4 The dramatic/erratic cluster includes borderline, histrionic, narcissistic, and anti-social personality disorders. The major symptom of borderline personality disorder is unstable, highly changeable emotions and behaviour; of histrionic personality disorder, exaggerated emotional displays; of narcissistic personality disorder, highly inflated self-esteem; and of anti-social personality disorder, seriously anti-social behaviour. Psychopathy is related to the anti-social personality disorder but it is not an official *DSM* diagnosis. More is known about anti-social personality disorder and psychopathy than about other disorders in the dramatic/erratic cluster. Though they overlap a great deal, the two diagnoses are not exactly equivalent. APD focuses on anti-social behaviour, whereas psychopathy, influenced by the writings of Cleckley, emphasizes emotional deficits, such as a lack of fear, regret, or shame. Psychopaths are thought to be unable to learn from experience, to have no sense of responsibility, to lack empathy, and to seem unable to establish genuine emotional relationships with other people.

13.5 The anxious/fearful cluster includes avoidant, dependent, and obsessive-compulsive personality disorders. The major symptom of avoidant personality disorder is fear of rejection or criticism; of dependent personality disorder, low self-confidence; and of obsessive-compulsive personality disorder, a perfectionistic, detail-oriented style. Theories of etiology focus on early experience. Avoidant personality disorder may result from the transmission of fear from parent to child via modelling. Dependent personality may be caused by disruptions of the parent–child relationship (e.g., through separation or loss) that lead to the fear of losing other relationships in adulthood. Obsessive-compulsive personality disorder may result from a fear of loss of control.

13.6 Personality disorders are difficult to treat because they typically involve long-standing self and identity issues and ingrained emotional, cognitive, and interpersonal styles that have been building up for several years. A more favourable view of outcomes is emerging from research on schema therapy that addresses core vulnerability themes, and there is promising evidence of the utility of dialectical behaviour therapy for borderline personality disorder. This approach is likely effective in addressing interpersonal needs by combining client-centred acceptance with a cognitive-behavioural focus on making specific changes in thought, emotion, and behaviour. While psychotherapy for psychopathy is rarely successful, some theorists believe that there is more reason for optimism than originally believed.

Key Terms

anti-social personality

avoidant personality

borderline personality

dark tetrad

dark triad

dependent personality

dialectical behaviour therapy

general personality disorder

histrionic personality

narcissistic personality

obsessive-compulsive personality

paranoid personality

personality disorders

personalized therapy

psychopathy

schema therapy

schizoid personality

schizotypal personality

Reflections: Past, Present, and Future

1. Assume that you are a counselling psychologist at a university counselling centre who has a female undergraduate student as a client. She has been referred to you with a diagnosis of panic disorder with agoraphobia. You already have a treatment plan in mind based on your experience in working with anxious students. However, during your assessment, you realize that the woman also meets the criteria for a dependent personality disorder. How would your case conceptualization (see Chapter 3) and intervention change as a result of this new personality disorder information?

2. Psychopaths are not highly responsive to attempts to change their anti-social behaviour through rehabilitation and treatment efforts. In fact, the clever ones probably do learn from their experiences—but only to become more successful predators and even less likely to be caught in the future. How should we then cope with them? Should Canada consider reinstating the death penalty (abolished in 1976) for serial killers and multiple murderers such as Clifford Olson and Paul Bernardo? Should such people be incarcerated for the rest of their lives as punishment for their crimes and/or because they are likely to reoffend? Or, should they be considered criminally insane and committed for treatment? We will discuss the issue of

criminal insanity, or what is now called "not criminally responsible on account of mental disorder," and the prediction of violence in Chapter 18.

3. Meta-analysis suggests that overall levels of narcissism are on the rise, especially in university student samples. What factors might be contributing to this tendency? Do you think that contemporary society plays a role in encouraging narcissism among certain well-known celebrities?

4. We have noted that Marsha Linehan, who is perhaps the most well-known contemporary theorist in the personality disorder field, has acknowledged her own previous diagnosis of borderline personality disorder. Linehan identified a religious experience as a key turning point that led to her recovery. At one point, Linehan was diagnosed with schizophrenia. Imagine you were a psychologist and were asked to reassess Linehan's behaviour and symptoms. What types of assessments would you use? And, subsequently, would you be able to keep an open mind about the religious experience that Linehan reported experiencing? Clearly, this remarkable story is useful in helping us re-examine our beliefs about people.

CHAPTER 14

Sexual Disorders and Gender Dysphoria

LEARNING OBJECTIVES

1. Describe contemporary views on gender identity disorder and how it differs from gender dysphoria.

2. Identify the various paraphilias and views of their etiology.

3. Describe the heterogeneity found among rapists and the myriad factors associated with recidivism.

4. Describe the various sexual disorders and how beliefs about their etiology reflect a complex array of factors.

Brief Case **Example**

Peeping William

WILLIAM V. is a 28-year-old computer programmer who lives alone. He grew up in a rural area within a conservative family with strong religious values. He has two younger brothers and an older sister. William began to masturbate at age 15; his first masturbatory experience took place while he watched his sister urinate in an outdoor toilet. Despite considerable feelings of guilt, he continued to masturbate two or three times a week while having voyeuristic fantasies . . .

On a summer evening at about 11:30 P.M., William was arrested for climbing a ladder and peeping into the bedroom of a suburban home. Just before this incident he had been drinking heavily at a cocktail lounge featuring a topless dancer . . . Feeling lonely and depressed [after leaving the bar], he had begun to drive slowly through a nearby suburban neighborhood, where he noticed a lighted

upstairs window. With little premeditation, he had parked his car, erected a ladder he found lying near the house, and climbed up to peep. The householders, who were alerted by the sounds, called the police, and William was arrested. Although this was his first arrest, William had committed similar acts on two previous occasions . . .

[In therapy] William described a lonely and insecure life . . . Six months before the arrest, he had been rejected in a long-term relationship . . . As an unassertive and timid individual, he had responded by withdrawing from social relationships, and increasing his use of alcohol. His voyeuristic fantasies, which were present to begin with, became progressively more urgent as William's self-esteem deteriorated. His arrest had come as a great personal shock, although he recognized that his behavior was both irrational and self-destructive. (Rosen & Rosen, 1981, pp. 452–453. Reprinted with permission of McGraw-Hill Book Company)

Sexuality is one of the most personal—and private—areas of an individual's life. Each of us is a sexual being with preferences and fantasies that may surprise or even shock us from time to time. These are part of normal sexual functioning. But when our fantasies or desires begin to affect us or others in unwanted or harmful ways, as with William's peeping in Brief Case Example, they begin to qualify as abnormal. This chapter considers the full range of human sexual thoughts, feelings, and actions that are generally regarded as abnormal and dysfunctional and are considered to be sexual disorders. Sexual disorders are listed in Table 14.1.

Our study of these disorders is divided into three major sections. First we examine theory and research in gender identity disorder, a diagnosis used previously to describe people who believe they are of the opposite sex. This controversial diagnosis was dropped in the *DSM-5*. Next we consider the paraphilias, in which people are attracted to unusual sexual activities or objects. We include a discussion of rape, which, although not a diagnostic listing, merits examination in an abnormal psychology textbook. The next major section of the chapter addresses sexual dysfunctions, which are disruptions in normal sexual functioning found in many people who are in otherwise reasonably sound psychological health.

TABLE 14.1 Paraphilic Disorders and Sexual Dysfunctions

A. Paraphilias
1. Fetishistic disorder
2. Transvestic disorder
3. Pedophilic disorder
4. Exhibitionistic disorder
5. Voyeuristic disorder
6. Frotteuristic disorder
7. Sexual masochism disorder
8. Sexual sadism disorder
9. Other specified paraphilic disorder (e.g., zoophilia, necrophilia)
10. Unspecified paraphilic disorder (i.e., not meeting full criteria for other disorders)

B. Sexual Disorders
1. Sexual Desire Disorders
   a. Male hypoactive sexual desire disorder
2. Sexual Arousal Disorders
   a. Female sexual interest/arousal disorder
   b. Erectile disorder
3. Orgasmic disorders
   a. Female orgasmic disorder (inhibited female orgasm)
   b. Male orgasmic disorder (inhibited male orgasm)
   c. Premature (early) ejaculation
   d. Delayed ejaculation
4. Genito-Pelvic Pain/Penetration Disorders
5. Substance/Medication-Induced Sexual Dysfunction

Source: Adapted from *DSM-5* (American Psychiatric Association, 2013).

Cultura RM/Alamy Stock Photo

Although dressing up is normal in childhood, most transsexuals trace their gender identity tendencies to childhood and report dressing in gender-inappropriate clothes.

14.1 Gender Identity Disorder and Gender Dysphoria

"Are you a boy or a girl?" "Are you a man or a woman?" For the vast majority of people—even those with serious mental disorders such as schizophrenia—the answer to such questions is immediate and obvious. And others would also agree unequivocally with the answer. Our sense of ourselves as male or female, our gender identity, is so deeply ingrained from earliest childhood that whatever stress is suffered at one time or another, the vast majority of people are certain beyond a doubt of their gender. In contrast, sexual identity or sexual orientation is the preference we have for the sex of a partner. For example, a man may be attracted to men—a matter of sexual orientation, without believing he is a woman—a matter of gender identity.

Characteristics of Gender Identity Disorder

A significant change in *DSM-5* is that gender identity disorder is no longer considered a disorder. How was it previously described? People with **gender identity disorder** (GID), sometimes referred to as **transsexualism,** have been described as feeling deep within themselves, usually from early childhood

(see photo), that they are of the opposite sex. They have an aversion to same-sex clothing and activities. The evidence of their anatomy—normal genitals and the usual secondary sex characteristics, such as beard growth for men and developed breasts for women—does not persuade them that they are what others see them to be. A man can look at himself in a mirror, see the body of a biological man, and yet personally experience that body as belonging to a woman. He may try to pass as a member of the opposite sex and may even want to have his body surgically altered to bring it in line with his gender identity.

Levine (2003) provided the following description of a man diagnosed with GID behaviour that bordered on a fetish and transvestite behaviour:

> "A couple married for 32 years sought help immediately after the wife unexpectedly returned home and discovered that her husband had been out in public dressed as a woman. She was certain that his public passing as a woman represented a worsening of his judgement. Thirty years before, he had revealed that he was sexually aroused by women's clothing and wanted to cross-dress for lovemaking. She adamantly refused to consider it. Since that incident, she never mentioned it again, trying to act as though she was unaware of his 'secret.' Privately, she periodically worried that he was putting on her panty hose and bra to masturbate. Their sexual frequency declined after his initial request and, over the ensuing 20 years, she slowly developed an aversion to being touched by him. Sexual behavior ceased 10 years before.

The husband, a 55-year-old masculine-appearing physical education teacher, elected to enter individual therapy where he expressed his dilemma. He wanted to spare his wife pain. She believed that his 'prurient' interest would go away if only he had more faith and prayed more, but he knew that nothing, including his fundamentalist religious patterns, diminished his periodic need to wear women's clothing. 'If I tell her about my cross-dressing, she withdraws in anger. If I do not tell her about it, her imagination about how often I am doing it runs wild and she punishes me for cross-dressing that I don't do. If I stop cross-dressing, I deprive myself of unparalleled comfort and sumptuous pleasure and the desire eventually overtakes me. I lose either way. Should I honor my wife or my own identity?' His daily rate of masturbation had not changed much. He thought he masturbated to cope with her refusal to have sexual behavior together. 'My cross-dressing has actually kept me from having affairs with other women, thankfully.'"

(From Levine, in Tasman, Kay, & Lieberman, 2003, p. 1490)

Until *DSM-5* appeared, this would have been considered a case of GID and not transvestic disorder, which is one of the paraphilias discussed later in this chapter. Although they often dress in clothing typical of the opposite sex, transvestites do not identify themselves as of the opposite sex.

Why has GID been dropped? Concerns have been expressed for many years that some people do not identify with their biological gender and they should not be stigmatized for this and assigned a diagnostic label. We are now in an era where there is much more sensitivity. But there is still a need for greater understanding, as well as more accumulated knowledge from empirical research. Accordingly, in 2014, the American Psychological Association introduced the journal *Psychology of Sexual Orientation and Gender Diversity*. It publishes articles such as a unique study of a community sample of 573 transgender women from the San Francisco area with a history of sex work (see Glynn et al., 2016). This study found that three types of gender affirmation (psychological, medical, and social) were associated with higher self-esteem and lower depression, but they were unrelated to suicide ideation. It is important to identify factors that enhance well-being due to the elevated levels of psychological distress found typically among transgender people. According to Glynn et al. (2016), factors that contribute to this distress include social oppression and greater risk of and actual exposure to violence.

There is also a greater emphasis on training and practice guidelines. In 2015, the American Psychological Association published *Guidelines for Psychological Practice with Transgender and Gender Nonconforming People* (American Psychological Association, 2015). The purpose of these guidelines is "to assist psychologists in the provision of culturally competent, developmentally appropriate, and trans-affirmative psychological practice with transgender and gender nonconforming people" (p. 832). A recent commentary article by Singh and dickey (2016) considers the significant challenges that exist, especially in terms of addressing gaps in psychological practice training, and calls for psychologists to become leaders in implementing progressive policies. They suggest that the ultimate goal is to engage in "affirmative practice" in that it is relevant and responsive to clients and takes into account how their lives and well-being reflect multiple social identities and can be impacted by multiple social inequities and systemic barriers (Singh & Dickey, 2017). The inequities that can be encountered are illustrated by the issues faced by Jenna Talackova (see photo).

Much of what we know about gender identity issues stems from work done at the Child and Adolescent Gender Identity Clinic at the Clarke Division of the Centre for Addiction and Mental Health (CAMH) in Toronto. This CAMH clinic opened in 1978, and the experts affiliated with it included Kenneth Zucker, Susan Bradley, and Ray Blanchard. Zucker chaired the *DSM-5*

Ray Tamarra/Getty Images, Inc.

Jenna Talackova is a transgendered beauty queen and model from Vancouver who successfully fought the 2012 decision to ban her from the Miss Universe competition because she was not born female. Talackova faced opposition from Donald Trump, who owned the Miss Universe pageant at the time. Her struggle to win the right to compete became the subject of a 2015 documentary film. Jenna said she felt like she was a girl from the age of four. She started hormone therapy at 14 years of age and had sex reassignment surgery in 2010.

Sexual Disorders Committee. The impact of these researchers on the field is reflected by the fact that they were part of the advising team that provided feedback on the *DSM-IV* diagnostic criteria for GID (see Bradley et al., 1991). However, controversy erupted in 2015, resulting in CAMH closing the clinic after 30 years of operation. Zucker's employment was also terminated. This controversial decision became known publicly throughout Canada and elsewhere. A CAMH official stated in a *Globe and Mail* article that the decision was made because the therapy at the clinic was "not in step with the latest thinking" (see Anderssen, 2016). This seemed to refer to complaints about the approach favoured by Zucker, which is to proceed slowly over several years if necessary and allow time for the child to accept the biological sex that he or she was born with. But there are significant differences of opinion as to what is in the best interests of the child; thus, many people in society regard this as a form of conversion therapy that clashes with the current cultural emphasis on respecting the wishes and urges of transgender people.

When gender identity issues begin in childhood, a child may express cross-gender behaviours, such as dressing in opposite-sex clothes, preferring opposite-sex playmates, and engaging in play that would usually be considered more typical of the opposite sex (e.g., a boy playing with Barbie dolls). Not surprisingly, these children have a developmental lag in achieving a sense of gender constancy or stability (i.e., acceptance that one is a boy or girl for life) (see Zucker et al., 1999). Gender identity issues in a child are usually recognized by parents when the child is between two and four years old (Green & Blanchard, 1995).

Predictably, those people with gender identity issues often arouse the disapproval of others and experience discrimination in employment when they choose to cross-dress. Cross-dressing is less of a problem for women because contemporary fashions allow women to wear clothing similar to that worn by men. People with gender identity issues often experience anxiety and depression, not surprising given their psychological predicament and the negative attitudes most people have toward them. GID in childhood is linked with separation anxiety disorder (Bradley & Zucker, 1997).

Even though GID is no longer considered a disorder, it is still worth examining the developmental factors that are involved given the distress that some people with gender identity issues may experience. Indeed, *DSM-5* has retained the category of **gender dysphoria** to account for those people suffering identity-related distress. Gender dysphoria places stronger emphasis on a sense of "gender incongruence" rather than cross-gender identification. It is now recognized that gender dysphoria can take many forms and be expressed specifically in many ways, including differences depending on the age of the person with gender dysphoria. A diagnosis is warranted only to the extent that there is clinically significant distress or impairment (see American Psychiatric Association, 2013).

The decision to retain a focus on gender dysphoria but to drop GID from the *DSM-5* is largely due to a key article by a team of Canadian scholars who provided a conceptual analysis of the existing data on GID with a view to determining whether gender

identity disorder in children should be considered a mental disorder (Bartlett, Vasey, & Bukowski, 2000). Bartlett et al. (2000) concluded that children who experience a sense of inappropriateness in the culturally prescribed gender role of their sex but who do not experience discomfort with their biological sex should not be considered to have GID. Bartlett et al. (2000) went on to suggest that GID in children should be removed from the *DSM*. Moreover, it was this team that expressed great concern that viewing GID as a mental disorder may contribute to a label that stigmatizes those children with GID who go on to express homosexuality.

Research investigations examining the etiology of gender identity issues have yielded some data indicating that these patterns can come from a physical disturbance. Specifically, evidence indicates that gender identity is influenced by hormones. A study demonstrating this point was conducted on the members of an extended family in the Dominican Republic (Imperato-McGinley, Guerrero, Gautier, & Peterson, 1974). Participants were unable to produce a hormone that shapes the penis and scrotum in males during fetal development. They were born with very small penises and scrotums that looked like labial folds. Two-thirds of them were raised as girls. However, when they reached puberty and testosterone levels increased, their sex organs changed. The penis enlarged, and the testicles descended into the scrotum. Seventeen of 18 participants then developed a male gender identity.

Other research shows that human and other primate offspring of mothers who have taken sex hormones during pregnancy frequently behave like members of the opposite sex and have anatomical abnormalities. For example, girls whose mothers took synthetic progestins, which are precursors to male sex hormones, to prevent uterine bleeding during pregnancy, were found to be tomboyish during their preschool years (Ehrhardt & Money, 1967). Young boys whose mothers ingested female hormones when pregnant were found to be less athletic as young children and to engage less in rough-and-tumble play than their male peers (Yalom, Green, & Fisk, 1973). Although such children were not necessarily abnormal in their gender identity, their mothers' ingestion of prenatal sex hormones did apparently give them higher than usual levels of cross-gender interests and behaviour.

Focus on Discovery 14.1 further examines these issues in the context of a well-known individual who experienced a tragic outcome.

Therapies for Gender Identity Issues

We turn now to the interventions available to help people with gender identity issues. These are of two main types. One attempts to alter the body to suit the person's psychology; the other attempts to alter the psychology to suit the person's body.

Body Alterations   A person who enters a program that entails alteration of the body is generally required to undergo six to 12 months of psychotherapy. The therapy typically

Focus on Discovery 14.1

Joan/John: Nature vs. Nurture in Gender Identity

In 1965, Linda Thiessen gave birth to twin boys. Seven months later, she noticed that the boys' foreskins were closing, making urination difficult. Her pediatrician recommended circumcision to correct the problem. However, because of either an equipment problem or an error by the surgeon, the penis of John, one of the twins, was destroyed. Although the Thiessens consulted with several physicians, none held out much hope of surgically reconstructing John's penis.

In December 1966, the Thiessens happened to see a television program on which John Money, a well-known sex researcher at Johns Hopkins, described the successful use of sex-change surgery for transsexuals. The Thiessens contacted Money, who proposed that turning John into Joan was the best option. The plan involved castration, construction of female genitals, and later treatment with sex hormones.

Several years later, Money shared the details of the case, describing it as a total success, consistent with his theory that gender identity is determined by the environment. Over subsequent years, he wrote several follow-ups, again claiming success. The facts reveal otherwise. Two researchers who managed to find Joan several years later conducted interviews with her and her parents and discovered a picture very different from the one Money had painted, one that suggests that there is a strong biological influence on gender identity.

Despite having been instructed to encourage feminine behaviour in Joan, her parents reported that Joan behaved in a very boyish way. At age 2, she ripped off her first dress, and during her preschool years, her play activities were clearly masculine. The same pattern continued into her elementary school years. When she reached age 11, it was time to begin her treatment with female hormones to promote the development of breasts and other feminine characteristics. Vaginal surgery was also recommended to construct a more feminine vagina. Although she reluctantly began taking estrogen, Joan steadfastly held out against the surgery.

By age 14, Joan decided to stop living as a girl. She adopted male attire, began to urinate standing up, and enrolled in a technical high school. Given Joan's refusal to have the surgery and a life filled with considerable distress, Joan's physicians finally recommended that she be told the whole story. She immediately changed her name back to John and decided to do everything possible to reverse the earlier treatments. She took male hormones, had her breasts removed, and had an artificial penis constructed. At age 21,

John had another operation to improve his artificial penis, and at age 25, he was married.

Clearly, this case demonstrates a strong biological underpinning for gender identity; despite not having a penis, being encouraged to behave in a feminine way, and developing breasts as a result of taking estrogen, John never developed a female gender identity (Colapinto, 1997).

It has since been revealed in Colapinto's (2000) book *As Nature Made Him: The Boy Who Was Raised as a Girl* that this case involved a family in Winnipeg and is actually the tragic story of Brenda/David Reimer. Reimer asked Colapinto to reveal her/his actual identity and provide more details of the case. These revelations have caused various societies to rethink their position. For instance, the American Association of Pediatrics now recommends that various factors be taken into account when deciding whether a child should be raised as male or female. Sadly, David Reimer committed suicide on May 5, 2004, at the age of 38. His suicide followed several setbacks, including a separation from his wife, and prolonged grief over the death of his twin brother Brian, who passed away unexpectedly in 2002, as a result of a toxic mix of antidepressants and alcohol. According to Colapinto (2004), the root cause of David's decision to commit suicide was brooding about his physicality, his gender identity, and his feeling of sexual inadequacy while experiencing a profound sense of social disconnection and isolation.

This ultimate outcome of the John/Joan case contrasts with a similar case in Canada reported by Bradley, Oliver, Chernick, and Zucker (1998). A two-month-old boy suffered a burn of his penile shaft during an electrocautery circumcision and eventually his penis sloughed off. The decision was made to reassign the child as a female and raise her as a girl. According to Bradley et al. (1998), long-term follow-up of this person has taken place, including an interview when she was 26 years old. In this case study, the reassigned girl continues to have a female gender identity, which Bradley et al. (1998) attributed to her being raised as a girl. However, they also noted that this young Canadian woman has a bisexual sexual identity and has had sexual experiences with both women and men. Also, she has many masculine interests and is employed in a blue-collar job that is usually dominated by men. Bradley et al. (1998) raised the possibility that this behavioural masculinity is a remnant of the masculine sexual biology and prenatal androgenization of the central nervous system. Nevertheless, the fact remains that unlike the outcome for John/Joan, this Canadian case study shows that the reassigned female gender identity is still evident, despite the presence of masculine tendencies.

---

focuses not only on the anxiety and depression that the person has likely been experiencing, but also on available options for altering his or her body. Some people may choose to have only cosmetic surgery; a male-to-female transsexual may have electrolysis to remove facial hair and surgery to reduce the size of the chin and Adam's apple. Many transsexuals also take hormones to bring their bodies physically closer to their beliefs about their gender. For example, female hormones will promote breast growth and soften the skin of male-to-female

transsexuals (Schaefer, Wheeler, & Futterweit, 1997). Many people with gender identity issues go no further than using such methods, but some take the next step of having sex-reassignment surgery.

Sex-reassignment surgery is an operation in which the existing genitalia are altered to make them more like those of the opposite sex. The first sex-reassignment operation took place in Europe in 1930, but the surgery that attracted worldwide attention was performed on an ex-soldier, Christine

After sex-reassignment surgery, author and historian James Morris (top, in a 1960 photo) became Jan Morris (bottom, in 2007). Morris was married to Elizabeth Tuckniss and they had five children together. Physicians refused to perform the surgery until Morris got a divorce, but years later after the surgery, Tuckniss and Morris were reunited legally in a civil ceremony.

(originally George) Jorgensen, in Copenhagen, Denmark, in 1952. Another well-known and more recent example is the sex reassignment of John Morris who became Jan Morris (see photo).

Sex-reassignment surgery is an option much more frequently exercised by men than by women. How beneficial is sex-reassignment surgery? There has been much controversy over this question for several decades. One of the most controversial outcome studies (Meyer & Reter, 1979) found no advantage to the individual "in terms of social rehabilitation" (p. 1015). The findings of this study led to the termination of the Johns Hopkins University School of Medicine sex-reassignment program, the largest such program at the time in the United States.

A subsequent review by Green and Fleming (1990) of reasonably controlled outcome studies published between 1979 and 1989, with at least a one-year follow-up, drew more favourable conclusions. Of 130 female-to-male surgeries, about 97% could be judged satisfactory; of 220 male-to-female surgeries, 87% were satisfactory. Preoperative factors that seemed to

predict favourable post-surgery adjustment were (1) reasonable emotional stability; (2) successful adaptation in the new role for at least one year before the surgery; (3) adequate understanding of the actual limitations and consequences of the surgery; and (4) psychotherapy in the context of an established gender identity program.

A subsequent study of 232 transsexuals who had sex-reassignment surgery (male to female) found no one acknowledging regret; any dissatisfaction was attributed primarily to dissatisfaction with subsequent physical characteristics (Lawrence, 2003). Perhaps the more relevant question is whether sex-reassignment surgery impacts psychological adjustment. A longitudinal study of sex-reassigned people conducted in Denmark found little overall change following the surgery and there were comparable results for people who were male at birth vs. female at birth; the more glaring outcome was that about 1 in 4 people overall still had significant diagnosable psychiatric morbidity (see Simonsen, Giraldi, Kristensen, & Hald, 2016).

14.2 The Paraphilias

The **paraphilias** are a group of disorders involving sexual attraction to unusual objects or sexual activities that are unusual in nature. In other words, there is a deviation (*para*) in what the person is attracted to (*philia*). The fantasies, urges, or behaviours must last at least six months and cause significant distress or impairment. A person can have the behaviours, fantasies, and urges that a person with a paraphilia has (such as exhibiting the genitals to an unsuspecting stranger or fantasizing about doing so) but not be diagnosed with a paraphilia if the fantasies or behaviours are not recurrent or if he or she is not markedly distressed by them. Indeed, surveys have shown that many people occasionally fantasize about some of the activities we will be describing. A Canadian survey found that 50% of men report voyeuristic fantasies of peeping at unsuspecting naked women (Hanson & Harris, 1997).

The *DSM* diagnostic criterion of distress or impairment has created some problems because many people with the behavioural features of a paraphilia are neither distressed nor impaired (Hudson & Ward, 1997). For example, according to the *DSM* criteria, someone who has repeatedly had sex with young children but is not distressed or impaired cannot be diagnosed as having pedophilia. Therefore, many researchers in this field hold a more behavioural definition of paraphilias and ignore the distress and disability parts of the *DSM* definition. More generally, some paraphilias may not be disorders *per se* because they are atypical but do not cause anyone apparent distress. Thus, one *DSM-5* recommendation that was ultimately endorsed and accepted was to distinguish between paraphilias and paraphilic disorders that cause some harm or distress (see www.dsm5.org). The *DSM-5* distinguishes between paraphilic behaviours (i.e., paraphilias) and paraphilic disorders. A paraphilic disorder is a "paraphilia that is currently causing distress or impairment to the individual or a paraphilia whose satisfaction has entailed personal harm, or risk of harm, to others" (American Psychiatric Association, 2013, pp. 685–686).

People often exhibit more than one paraphilia, and such patterns can be aspects of other mental disorders, such as schizophrenia, depression, or one of the personality disorders. Accurate prevalence statistics are not available for most of the paraphilias. Many people with paraphilias may choose not to reveal their deviance when responding to a community survey. Similarly, statistics on arrests are likely to be underestimated because many crimes go unreported and some paraphilias (e.g., voyeurism) involve an unsuspecting victim. The data do indicate, though, that most people with paraphilias, whatever their sexual orientation, are male; even with masochism and pedophilia, which do occur in noticeable numbers of women, men vastly outnumber women. Because some people with paraphilias seek non-consenting partners, these disorders often have legal consequences.

Russell Williams began breaking into homes to steal underwear. This behaviour escalated over time culminating in Williams murdering two women in Ontario.

Fetishism

Fetishism is the reliance on an inanimate object for sexual arousal. The person with fetishism, almost always a male, has recurrent and intense sexual urges toward non-living objects, called fetishes (e.g., women's shoes), and the presence of the fetish is strongly preferred or even necessary for sexual arousal to occur.

Feet and shoes, sheer stockings, rubber products such as raincoats, gloves, toilet articles, fur garments, and especially underpants are common sources of arousal for fetishists. Some can carry on their fetishism by themselves in secret by fondling, kissing, smelling, sucking, placing in their rectum, or merely gazing at the adored object as they masturbate. Others need their partner to don the fetish as a stimulant for intercourse. Fetishists sometimes become interested in acquiring a collection of the desired objects, and they may commit burglary week after week to add to their hoard. This pattern was clearly exemplified by the behaviour of the former colonel in the Canadian Armed Forces from Tweed, Ontario. Russell Williams (see photo) began a string of break and enter burglaries with the goal of stealing and keeping women's underwear. Williams eventually became a sexual sadist and murderer of at least two women. His case was included in an intriguing analysis that enabled a team of researchers to conclude that offenders with this type of fetish are "collectors" who are seeking to preserve a sense of control and power even though they retain evidence that is incriminating should they be detected (see Warren, Dietz, & Hazelwood, 2013).

The attraction felt by the fetishist toward the object has a compulsive quality; it is experienced as involuntary and irresistible. It is the degree of the erotic focalization—the exclusive and very special status the object occupies as a sexual stimulant—that distinguishes fetishisms from the ordinary attraction that, for example, high heels and sheer stockings

may hold for heterosexual men in Western cultures. The boot fetishist must see or touch a boot to become aroused, and when the fetish is present, the arousal is overwhelmingly strong.

The disorder usually begins by adolescence, although the fetish may have acquired special significance even earlier, during childhood. Fetishists often have other paraphilias, such as pedophilia, sadism, and masochism (Mason, 1997).

Transvestic Disorder

When a man is sexually aroused by dressing in women's clothing, although he still regards himself as a man, the term **transvestic disorder**, or transvestism, applies (see photo). The extent of transvestism varies from wearing women's underwear under conventional clothing to full cross-dressing. Some transvestites may enjoy appearing socially as women. Note that while some female impersonators become performers in nightclubs, catering to the delight that many sexually conventional people take in observing skilled cross-dressing, these impersonators are not considered transvestic unless the cross-dressing is associated with sexual arousal.

The term *autogynephilia* was coined by Ray Blanchard (1989) at the Clarke Institute in Toronto to refer to a man's tendency to become sexually aroused at the thought or image of himself as a woman. Blanchard (1992) noted that autogynephilia is typically, but not always, found in association with transvestism.

Transvestic disorder usually begins with partial cross-dressing in childhood or adolescence. Transvestites are heterosexual, always males, and by and large cross-dress episodically rather than on a regular basis. They tend to be otherwise masculine in appearance, demeanour, and sexual preference. Many are married. Cross-dressing usually takes place in private

Transvestic disorder is diagnosed when the person sexually arouses himself by dressing in opposite-sex clothing. The reference to "himself" as opposed to "himself or herself" reflects the fact that the vast majority of people with this disorder but not all people with this disorder are men.

and in secret and is known to few members of the family. This is one of the paraphilias for which the *DSM* distress and disability criteria do not seem to apply at all.

The urge to cross-dress may become more frequent over time and sometimes is accompanied by gender dysphoria—discomfort with one's anatomical sex—but not to the extent found in GID. Transvestism is comorbid with other paraphilias, notably masochism (Zucker & Blanchard, 1997).

Pedophilia and Incest

"If I can help just one person . . . then all of this will have been worth it."

—Martin Kruze on Jane Hawtin Live, February 26, 1997, concerning his revelations about being sexually abused as a child by employees at Maple Leaf Gardens in Toronto

According to the *DSM*, individuals who practise **pedophilia** (*pedos*, Greek for "child"; referred to as pedophilic disorder in *DSM-5*) are adults who derive sexual gratification through physical and often sexual contact with prepubescent children unrelated to them. *DSM-5* requires that the offender be at least 16 years old and at least five years older than the child. Research does not appear to support the *DSM*'s earlier statement that all pedophiles prefer prepubescent children; an analysis by Marshall (1997) at Queen's University revealed that some of them victimize postpubescent children who are younger than the legal age to consent to having sex with an adult.

Another qualification is that some surveys, including Internet surveys, indicate that a substantial proportion of those who identify themselves as pedophiles (more than 50% in some surveys) have no known sexual contact with children or legal history of doing so (see Seto, 2009). This calls into question the tendency to equate pedophilia with sexual contact with children and much of the research literature, which tends to focus on individuals who have come to our attention via their involvement with the legal system.

Pedophilic disorder occurs much more frequently in men than in women (Seto, 2009), though case studies of female pedophiles have been reported, including that of a young Canadian woman who had sexual relations with two four-year-old daughters of acquaintances (see Chow & Choy, 2002). Pedophilic disorder is often comorbid with mood and anxiety disorders, substance abuse, and other paraphilias (Raymond et al., 1999). The pedophile can be heterosexual or homosexual.

Public awareness of pedophilia was heightened as a result of the investigative reporting of the *Boston Globe* newspaper. The Spotlight team of investigative journalists went public in January 2002 with their investigation of priests in the Boston area, who were alleged pedophiles who sexually abused boys and girls, and the cover-up that took place. Overall, 249 priests and brothers from the Boston Archdiocese were accused publicly of sexual abuse. The Spotlight team won the Pulitzer Prize in journalism in 2003 for their work. Most noteworthy was their documentation of how the priests with a history of pedophilia were often reassigned to other churches once their transgressions became known and there was evidence with certain priests that the transgressions were still taking place. The details of their work and their findings were summarized in a follow-up book (*The Investigative Staff of the Boston Globe*, 2015). Further public awareness came in 2015 with the movie *Spotlight*, which won the Academy Award for best motion picture (see photo). The Toronto area played a role in this story, not only because it provided a filming location for the movie. The Southdown Institute, which is located north of Toronto, is well known for providing psychological treatment to members of the clergy. According to the *Boston Globe*, one of the pedophiles featured in the movie, John J. Geoghan, received treatment at the Southdown Institute in 1996. It should be noted that only a small percentage of the people receiving treatment at this facility are pedophiles. Most people at this facility are receiving treatment for adjustment issues involving anxiety, depression, or burnout.

Unfortunately, there is no shortage of cases of pedophiles in Canada who have abused children. An exceptionally long list of communities with scandals accompanies the end credits of the *Spotlight* movie. Five Canadian locations are mentioned (i.e., Antigonish in Nova Scotia, Chatham in Ontario, Igloolik in Nunavut, St. Johns in Newfoundland and Labrador, and Wilno in Ontario). It was also rumoured for many years that there was an extensive pedophile ring operating in Cornwall, Ontario. Investigation began when a 35-year old former altar

The award winning movie Spotlight depicts the investigative work of reporters at the Boston Globe. They drew attention to the widespread prevalence of the sexual abuse of children by priests with pedophilia. A January 2017 follow-up story in the Boston Globe indicated that hundreds of church sex abuse victims from around the world are still coming forward, in part, due to the awareness created by the movie and their investigative reporting.

On June 17, 2004, Michael Briere was sentenced to 25 years in prison for the brutal sexual attack and strangulation of 10-year-old Holly Jones of Toronto. Briere's "dark secret" was an overwhelming desire to have sex with a young child. His fantasy was fuelled by child pornography readily downloaded from the Internet. Canada's child pornography laws became an issue in the June 2004 federal election.

boy claimed he was abused as a youth. A lengthy public inquiry ordered by the Province of Ontario that cost an estimated $53 million failed to confirm or deny the presence of this pedophile network but it did identify 34 victims. The inquiry's commissioner, Justice G. Normand Glaude, issued a report that made over 200 recommendations and documented broad failures in the system, insensitivity to victim complaints, and a reluctance to act on the part of several groups, including the church, schools, and Children's Aid. It is now the case in Ontario that anyone who performs professional or official duties with respect to children has a duty to report any suspected abuse or neglect of children.

The Internet has played an increasing role in pedophilic disorder (Seto, 2009); pedophiles use the Internet to acquire child pornography and to contact potential victims (Durkin, 1997). Extensive international networks of Internet users of child pornography have been detected and shut down by police. One high-profile Canadian child pornography case involved Benjamin Levin, who pled guilty in 2015 in Toronto to three child pornography-related changes. Levin had once been Ontario's Deputy Minister of Education. A more extreme and troubling case involved Michael Briere (see illustration).

It is noteworthy that a Canadian study by Seto, Cantor, and Blanchard (2006) found that a child pornography offence is a stronger diagnostic indicator of pedophilia than is an actual history of sexually offending against child victims! Another follow-up study conducted in Canada found that more frequent pornography use was a strong predictor of recidivism, especially among those already deemed to be higher-risk offenders. Also, the use of pornography with more deviant content was a risk factor for offenders of various levels of risk (see Kingston et al., 2008). A more recent investi-

gation of almost 2,000 young men from Sweden found that 84 of them (4.2%) acknowledged accessing Internet child pornography (see Seto et al., 2015). These young men were distinguished by a greater likelihood of actually having sex with children and a tendency to watch extremely violent pornography. Not surprisingly, the extensive, aberrant use of the Internet has resulted in Internet sex offender treatment programs (see Middleton, 2008).

One meta-analysis found noteworthy similarities among "offline" offenders, who perpetrate their crimes in the physical world, and "online" offenders, who perpetrate their crimes electronically. For instance, both have greater levels of childhood physical and sexual abuse relative to people from the general population. However, there were also several differences. Online offenders are slightly younger and have greater victim empathy but they also have lower impression management tendencies and greater sexual deviancy. The authors concluded that the online offenders, relative to offline offenders, may have greater self-control and more barriers to acting on their more extreme deviant tendencies (see Babchishin, Hanson, & Hermann, 2011).

Convicted pedophiles who are granted parole often have their access to the Internet restricted as a condition of their release. This was the case for Robert Noyes, who was granted a full parole release in June 2003 but with restricted Internet access. Noyes, a teacher and a school principal in British

Columbia, was arrested in 1985 and charged in connection with approximately 600 separate assaults, involving at least 65 children (mostly boys) between the ages of 6 and 15. Noyes was one of the first pedophiles to be designated as a dangerous offender, so he could have been in prison for an indefinite term.

The Internet has also been used to facilitate research on pedophilia. A growing trend is to evaluate the nature and correlates of pedophilia by having pedophiles take part in studies conducted online, with their anonymity protected (see Seto, 2004, for a discussion). While responses obtained via the Internet may be subject to socially desirable responding, perhaps it also facilitates a level of candidness that is not found when face-to-face interactions are involved.

Pedophilia in Canada has received great public attention because of a number of highly publicized cases, including the Maple Leaf Gardens scandal. It was revealed in 1997 that about 90 children had been sexually abused by some Maple Leaf Gardens employees, including George Hannah, Gordon Stuckless, and John Paul Roby. The tragedy of Martin Kruze, one of the boys victimized who "blew the whistle" on a shameful event in Canadian sports history, is told by Cathy Vine and Paul Challen's (2002) moving account, *Gardens of Shame*. Kruze worked as a spokesperson for sexual abuse survivors. Sadly, he jumped off a bridge to his death at age 35 just three days after Stuckless was sentenced to two years less a day in a reformatory. Previously, we also learned of the abuse experienced by Sheldon Kennedy, a former player in the National Hockey League. In 1997, Kennedy's coach in junior hockey, Graham James, pleaded guilty to charges of sexual assault.

Another disturbing case occurred in New Brunswick at the Kingsclear Youth Training Facility near Fredericton. Karl Toft, who worked at the facility, is a convicted pedophile who was found guilty in 1992 of buggery, bestiality, and more than 30 counts of sexual assault involving children (see photo). Toft has since admitted to abusing more than 150 children over two decades. He was denied parole in August 2000. The parole board's decision at that time was based on several factors, including Toft's apparent lack of empathy for his victims, his lack of an "internal control mechanism," and his unwillingness to submit to medication as a form of treatment. Then, in August 2001, the decision was made to grant Toft parole and send him to a halfway house in Edmonton. The Edmonton Police Service issued a public warning that outlined his convictions, noted his participation in a sex offender program, and included a physical description with a photo. In response to vigorously expressed public concern, Correctional Service Canada reversed the decision and sent him to a regional psychiatric centre in Saskatoon, a secure treatment facility (Auld, 2001).

Violence is seldom a part of molestation, although it can be, as occasionally comes to people's attention through lurid media accounts. But even if most pedophiles do not physically injure their victims, some intentionally frighten the

Convicted pedophile Karl Toft. The group Mad Mothers Against Pedophiles planned rallies to protest his release.

child by, for example, killing a pet and threatening further harm if the youngster tells his or her parents. Sometimes the pedophile is content to stroke the child's hair, but he may also manipulate the child's genitalia, encourage the child to manipulate his, and, less often, attempt intromission. Molestations may be repeated for weeks, months, or years if they are not discovered by other adults or if the child does not protest.

A minority of pedophiles, who might also be classified as sexual sadists or anti-social (psychopathic) personalities, inflict serious bodily harm on the object of their passion. These individuals, whether psychopathic or not, are perhaps best viewed as child rapists and are different from pedophiles in that they wish to hurt the child physically at least as much as they wish to obtain sexual gratification (Groth, Hobson, & Guy, 1982). Indeed, research by Firestone et al. (1998, 2000) at the University of Ottawa shows that although it is often difficult to distinguish homicidal child molesters from non-homicidal child molesters, homicidal child molesters show a greater physiological response to and preference for descriptions of assaults on children. Although psychopathy is more elevated in these men than in incest offenders, rapists tend to have even higher levels of psychopathy when assessed by Hare's PCL-R (see Chapter 13) and they are more likely to endorse anti-social attitudes in general (Firestone et al., 2000; Mills, Anderson, & Kroner, 2004).

Incest is sexual relations between close relatives for whom marriage is forbidden. It is most common between brother and sister. It can involve multiple siblings as shown in the case of the Miller family from British Columbia (see photo).

The Canadian Press/Darryl Dyck

Two of the four sisters who were sexually abused by their brother, John Henry Miller, held a press conference in British Columbia in 2009. Miller committed incest between 1956 and 1974 and only stopped after being arrested for killing an RCMP officer, Constable Roger Pierlet. The sisters reported the case to the police in 2008 and Miller was sentenced to an additional five years in a halfway house in July 2009. However, he died in hospital of a stroke less than one week later.

The next most common form is between father and daughter. Although father–daughter incest is considered more pathological, data from Quebec question this conclusion because brother–sister incest was associated with just as much distress among victims as incest involving fathers or stepfathers; moreover, brother–sister incest was associated with a much higher frequency of sexual penetration (Cyr, Wright, McDuff, & Perron, 2002).

The taboo against incest seems virtually universal in human societies, a notable exception being the marriages of Egyptian pharaohs to their sisters or other females of their immediate families. In Egypt, it was believed that royal blood should not be contaminated by that of outsiders. The incest taboo makes sense according to present-day scientific knowledge. The offspring from a father–daughter or a brother–sister union have a greater probability of inheriting a pair of recessive genes, one from each parent. For the most part, recessive genes have negative biological effects, such as serious birth defects. The incest taboo, then, has adaptive evolutionary significance.

There is evidence that the structure of families in which incest occurs is unusually patriarchal and traditional, especially with respect to the subservient position of women (Alexander & Lupfer, 1987). Parents in these families also tend to neglect and remain emotionally distant from their children (Madonna, Van Scoyk, & Jones, 1991). Furthermore, it is believed that incest is more prevalent when the mother is absent or disabled (Finkelhor, 1979), because mothers usually protect their daughters from intrafamilial sexual abuse.

Incest was listed in *DSM-IV-TR* as a subtype of pedophilia but this designation was dropped from the *DSM-5*. Several major distinctions are drawn between incest and pedophilia. First, incest is by definition between members of the same family. Second, incest victims tend to be older than the victims of a pedophile's desires. It is more often the case that a father becomes interested in his daughter when she begins to mature physically, whereas the pedophile is usually interested in the youngster precisely because he or she is sexually immature.

An archival study of cases in Saskatchewan examined the nature of incest vs. extrafamilial (outside the family) forms of child sexual abuse and found that incest had an earlier onset and longer duration (Fischer & McDonald, 1998). Also, victims of incest had comparatively greater levels of physical injury and emotional distress. The impacts of experiencing sexual abuse are highlighted in Focus on Discovery 14.2 and Student Perspectives 14.1.

Focus on Discovery 14.2

Child Sexual Abuse: Effects on the Child and Modes of Intervention

A 1997 survey of police forces in six provinces found that 62% of all victims of a sexual offence were young people under the age of 18, with 30% being young children under the age of 12 (Statistics Canada, 1999). The prototypical act is a sexual offence committed against a female by someone familiar to her. Overall, fewer than 1 in 5 victims are males, but the proportion of males being victimized rises to 31% for children under the age of 12. Half of the sexual offences were committed by a friend or acquaintance, and another 28% were committed by family members.

Pedophilia and incest are forms of **child sexual abuse** (CSA) and should be distinguished from non-sexual child abuse (i.e., physical abuse, emotional abuse, neglect). In Canada, anyone aware of abuse taking place is required by law to report it to the police or child protective agencies.

Effects on the Child

The short-term effects of CSA are variable. A subset of children are seemingly resilient after disclosing severe abuse (Hébert, Parent, Daignault, & Tourigny, 2006). However, the majority are negatively affected, with problems including anxiety, depression, low self-esteem, and conduct disorder. Hébert et al. (2006) identified a group of children who mostly had severe anxiety symptoms vs. other children who had a range of symptoms. The negative impact on self-esteem can influence numerous self-esteem domains, including physical self-esteem and social self-esteem (Murthi, Servaty-Seib, & Elliott, 2006).

Several factors likely contribute to how CSA affects a child. One is the nature of the abuse itself. Consider, for example, the probable differences in consequences between a case involving the repeated rape of a 7-year-old girl by her father and that of a 12-year-old boy who has a sexual relationship with an older woman. Results from a sample of 50 girls from Quebec who experienced CSA found one year later that the duration of the abuse was linked, not surprisingly, with poor functioning (Daignault & Hébert, 2008). Poorer functioning was also found among the girls with dissociative symptoms. Protective factors were approach coping and engagement in extracurricular activities. In general, an earlier onset of the abuse also predicts more extreme levels of distress (Kaplow & Widom, 2007).

Sometimes the aftermath of CSA is post-traumatic stress disorder (PTSD). Indeed, *DSM-5* lists threatened or actual sexual violence including sexual assault as being among the stressors that can be traumatic. A team of researchers from Université Laval and Université du Québec à Montréal conducted a study in which they compared the characteristics of three groups of children between the ages of 7 to 12: a sexually abused group, a medical control group, and a community group (Tremblay, Hébert, & Piché, 2000). The authors found that the sexually abused group had higher levels of symptoms than the other two groups, in terms of both Type I and Type II symptoms. A high level of self-blame and lack of a supportivefamily environment also increase the chances that the CSA will produce negative reactions (Kuehnle, 1998).

A history of CSA is also associated reliably with sexual revictimization according to a review conducted by Catherine Classen from the University of Toronto and her colleagues (see Classen, Palesh, & Aggarwal, 2005). That is, those with a history of CSA, relative to those lacking this history, are more likely to be a victim of sexual assault in adulthood. Predictive factors include experiencing multiple traumas and childhood sexual abuse that happened more recently. Revictimization was also associated with greater distress, self-blame, and shame. Victims of CSA are also more likely to be victims of assaults in general. Researchers are seeking to explain why this revictimization occurs.

Some sexually abused children become suicidal in subsequent years. Victims of child sexual abuse, such as comedian Drew Carey (see photo) and former NHL hockey players Sheldon Kennedy and Théoren Fleury, have acknowledged that they have had suicidal tendencies. In his remarkable 2012 autobiography, Toronto Blue Jays pitcher R. A. Dickey (see photo) described being sexually abused at the age of 8 by his female babysitter, and then in a separate incident by an adolescent male (Dickey & Coffey, 2012). While Dickey's overall story is one of great resilience, he, too, experienced subsequent thoughts of suicide.

An epidemiological study found that a history of sexual abuse had a strong link with suicide attempts and suicide ideation, and the association was stronger among women (Bebbington et al., 2009). This association was mediated by negative affective states such as depression. Analyses of interpersonal functioning show that CSA is also associated with interpersonal distress such as marital distress and with problems in sexual functioning (see Rumstein-McKean & Hunsley, 2001).

Prevention

An important goal of any prevention program is to reduce the incidence, prevalence, and severity of a particular problem. For CSA, prevention efforts have focused on elementary schools. The ESPACE program is offered in schools throughout Quebec. An evaluation of this program found that the Grades 1 and 3 students who took part were better able to identify appropriate behavioural responses when presented with vignettes of situations that could involve abuse (Hébert, Lavoie, Piché, & Poitras, 2001). Parents reported that this program also had indirect, unintended effects, such as raising the level of self-confidence and assertiveness among children, even to the point that approximately 29% of the children became so assertive that they started to disobey appropriate requests from their parents!

Summaries of prevention efforts provided by Canadian researchers (Hébert et al., 2001; Wolfe, 1990) indicate that their content varies from program to program, but common elements include teaching children to recognize inappropriate adult behaviour, resist inducements, leave the situation quickly, and report the incident to an appropriate adult. Children are taught to say no in a firm, assertive way when an adult talks to or touches them in a manner that makes them feel uncomfortable. Instructors may use comic books, films, and descriptions of risky situations to teach children about the nature of sexual abuse and how they can protect themselves.

Evaluations of school programs on sexual abuse support the notion that, like the ESPACE program, they increase awareness of sexual abuse among children, and most investigators report positive results. However, according to a critical review by Topping and Barron (2009), not all programs have yielded positive results and there is only limited evidence of the maintenance of these positive effects. And research is still needed to show that the knowledge

Frederick M. Brown/Getty Images

In contrast to the lighthearted persona he portrays on television, Drew Carey, comedian and host of the TV show *The Price Is Right*, disclosed in his autobiography that he was sexually abused as a child, has suffered from depression, and had attempted suicide on two occasions. R. A. Dickey, who won the Cy Young Award in 2012 for being the best pitcher in Major League Baseball's National League and was then traded to the Toronto Blue Jays, is also well-known for his openness about the sexual abuse he endured when he was eight years old. Dickey revealed in his autobiography that he kept the abuse secret for decades before going public with it after receiving treatment as an adult.

(continued)

is actually put into use. Nevertheless, these programs seem to legitimize discussion of the problem at home (Wurtele & Miller-Perrin, 1987) and might therefore achieve one important goal: to increase the reporting of the crime by encouraging and empowering children to tell their parents or guardians that an adult has made a sexual overture to them.

Clearly, there is a need for broader solutions at the national level. Accordingly, in November 2010, a national think tank was convened with 22 participants (researchers, practitioners, and government officials) at the University of Western Ontario in London. They issued a call for and outlined a proposed national prevention strategy to address child sexual abuse (Centre for Research and Education on Violence Among Women and Children, 2010). This proposed strategy included 16 specific recommendations divided into universal strategies, selected strategies, and indicated strategies. Recommendations include identifying a ministry that assumes responsibility for protecting children, develop-

ing prevention programs for organizations, and developing more support services both for victims and for offenders and potential offenders. The next step was the 2011 publication of the Standing Senate Committee on Human Rights' report *The Sexual Exploitation of Children in Canada: The Need for National Action* (see Jaffer & Brazeau, 2011). This report noted that there are almost 9,000 reported sexual assaults against children in Canada each year, with 80% being against girls, and there is a particular problem with the incidence of sexual assaults among Aboriginal children and youth. Recommendations include establishing a national databank to assist people working in the field and creating a National Children's Commissioner who is dedicated to safeguarding all children in Canada.

Note that Canada does have a national strategy for the protection of children from sexual exploitation on the Internet. The Canadian government renewed and extended the funding for this strategy.

Student Perspectives 14.1

The Prevalence of Child Sexual Abuse Among Students

The issue of university students having been sexually abused as children became a broadly considered issue in North America when the Pennsylvania State University sex scandal became public in 2011. Jerry Sandusky (see photo) is now serving a lengthy prison sentence. Sandusky was an assistant football coach at Penn State who was convicted for having sex with eight underage boys either on university property or nearby. Key testimony was provided by Mike McQueary, another assistant coach, who described seeing an incident in 2001. He testified that he saw Sandusky rape a boy taking a shower in the Penn State football building. Sandusky was convicted on 45 of 48 charges of child sexual abuse and several school officials were suspended or fired for failing to act on their knowledge of what was going on.

While there were no allegations involving any university students on the Penn State campus, the Sandusky scandal shone a light on child sexual abuse that hit home for students. Obviously, anyone can experience sexual abuse during their childhood. How common is a history of child sexual abuse among university and college students? A study of 796 college students conducted over 30 years ago found that an astounding 19% of the women and nearly 9% of the men reported that they had been sexually abused as children. Of the abused women, 28% had had incestuous relations; of the men, 23% had (Finkelhor, 1979). A more recent survey by Finkelhor and associates (2014) of 17-year-olds found that the lifetime experience of sexual abuse and sexual violence was 26.6% for girls and 5.1% for boys. It was found that adults were the exclusive perpetrators for about 1 in 9 girls.

What is indicated by data in the broader community? A global assessment of people in general was conducted by a team of researchers from the Netherlands. Their meta-analysis is one of the largest ever conducted: it involved almost 10 million participants in over 300 studies (see Stoltenborgh, van Ijzendoorn, Euser, &

Patrick Smith/Stringer/Getty Images, Inc

Jerry Sandusky, previously a Penn State assistant football coach, was convicted on 45 counts of child molestation. Sandusky has maintained that he is innocent, both before and after his trial, and he launched legal proceedings in September 2013 in the hopes of getting a new trial. His appeal for a new trial was rejected soon after by a Pennsylvania court. University administrators were convicted of child endangerment charges in 2017 for their failure to alert the police when a student told them of Sandusky's actions.

Bakermans-Kranenburg, 2011). Overall, 127 people per 1,000 reported childhood sexual abuse, with girls almost 2.5 times more

(continued)

likely to be victims. Highest rates were found among girls in Australia and boys in Africa.

How do rates compare for students? Another meta-analysis compared students and people from the general population. This meta-analysis of 65 articles from 22 countries established that 7.9% of men and 19.7% of women had been sexually abused prior to age 18 (Pereda, Guilera, Forns, & Gomez-Benito, 2009). These prevalence rates are very similar to the numbers found over 30 years ago. The overall prevalence rate was 14.6% for people from the general population and 13.9% for students (about 1 in 7 students).

Students who have a history of childhood sexual abuse are at risk for subsequent adjustment difficulties (e.g., Futa, Nash, Hansen, & Garbin, 2003). One study, for instance, found higher levels of PTSD symptoms among students with a history of child sexual abuse vs. those who did not have this history (Canton-Cortes & Canton, 2010). Longitudinal research has also found that college students with a history of childhood sexual abuse tend to have higher dropout rates (Duncan, 2000). But it is important to realize that some students are quite resilient in coping with life challenges. Key mediating factors that result in a poorer outcome include having an avoidant coping style (Canton-Cortes & Canton, 2010). Other key factors that predict better or worse outcomes include feeling a sense of shame and self-blame and having other interpersonal difficulties (Whiffen & MacIntosh, 2005). Unfortunately, there is a tendency for people in general to blame themselves for uncontrollable events such as being a victim of child sexual abuse, but learning to be self-compassionate by being kind to oneself is an important element of resilience and one of the keys to having a better life.

A study by Studer et al. (2000) at the Alberta Hospital–Edmonton Site yielded evidence suggesting that risk assessments of incest offenders have substantially underestimated the threat they actually posed. First, it has generally been believed that incest offenders have a low likelihood of being a repeat incest offender (between 4 and 10%). Studer et al. (2000), however, found that 22% had prior incestuous offences and were, in fact, repeat offenders. Also, almost two-thirds of the incest offenders reported having non-incestuous victims as well, which suggests they are also pedophiles. Studer et al. (2000) concluded that for these men, the main issue is one of opportunity; they have a general sexual attraction to children that may indeed go beyond members of their own family.

Further empirical work by Rice and Harris (2002) indicates that daughter-only molesters have lower levels of psychopathy than incestuous fathers who also engage in extrafamilial offences. Although these daughter-only child molesters have less deviant sexual preferences and lower recidivism rates than molesters who commit offences inside and outside the family, their sexual preferences are still deviant overall and the recidivism risk is not low in absolute terms.

Data from penile plethysmography studies (see Figure 14.1 for an explanation of these measures) conducted in Canada confirm that men who molest children unrelated to them are sexually aroused by photographs of nude children. Men who molest children within their families show more arousal to adult heterosexual cues (Marshall, Barbaree, & Christophe, 1986).

One of the first rudimentary versions of the penile plethysmograph was developed by Kurt Freund, who developed his first device in Czechoslovakia. Freund then worked for several decades at the Clarke Institute of Psychiatry in Toronto (see Freund, 1967; Freund & Watson, 1991). Plethysmograph measures have been described as "phallometric tests," and they have been used to identify males—both adults (Laws, Hanson, Osborn, & Greenbaum, 2000) and adolescents (Seto, Lalumière, & Blanchard, 2000)—with pedophilic interests. Once established, phallometric testing results show little variance, indicating that it is very difficult to change sexual preferences (Lalumière & Quinsey, 1998).

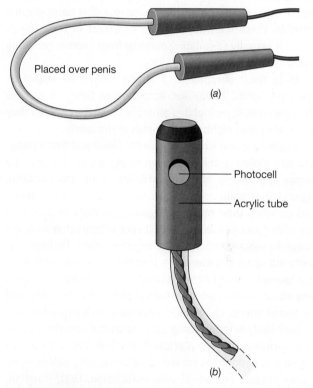

Placed over penis

(a)

Photocell

Acrylic tube

(b)

FIGURE 14.1 Behavioural researchers use two genital devices for measuring sexual arousal. Both are sensitive indicators of vasocongestion of the genitalia (i.e., the flooding of the veins with blood, a key physiological process in sexual arousal); both provide specific measurements of sexual excitement (e.g., Barlow et al., 1970; Heiman, Rowland, Hatch, & Gladue, 1991). (a) For men, the penile plethysmograph measures changes in the circumference of the penis by means of a strain gauge, consisting of a very thin rubber tube filled with mercury. As the penis is engorged with blood, the tube stretches, changing its electrical resistance, which can then be measured by a suitably configured polygraph. (b) For women, sexual arousal can be measured by a vaginal plethysmograph, such as the device invented by Sintchak and Geer (1975). Shaped like a menstrual tampon, this apparatus can be inserted into the vagina to provide direct measurement of the increased blood flow characteristic of female sexual arousal.

Although phallometric testing is used routinely with sex offenders, concerns have been raised about the reliability and validity of these measures (see Marshall & Fernandez, 2000). In particular, Marshall and Fernandez (2000) expressed concern about the demonstrated ability of some people to fake their responses when being measured.

It is generally believed that a history of exposure to pornography is a cause of sexual offending. However, in a review paper, a team of Canadian researchers concluded that pornography plays a role only among men who are already predisposed to sexually offend (Seto, Maric, & Barbaree, 2001); men who are not predisposed show little effect.

It is sometimes alleged that child pornography is a critical ingredient in motivating child molestation in predisposed people, but a clinical study of male pedophiles indicates that such materials may not even be necessary. These men could be aroused by media materials widely available, such as television ads and clothing catalogues picturing young children in underwear. In other words, rather than using explicitly pornographic materials, these men appeared to construct in their minds their own sexually stimulating material from sources generally viewed as innocuous (Howitt, 1995).

As in most paraphilias, a strong subjective attraction impels pedophilic behaviour. According to Gebhard and his colleagues (1965), pedophiles generally know the children they molest; they are neighbours or friends of the family.

Alcohol use and stress increase the likelihood that a pedophile will molest a child (Abracen et al., 2006). Research by Looman at the Regional Treatment Centre in Kingston, Ontario, suggests that child molesters have sexual fantasies about children when their mood is negative, perhaps as a way to cope with their unease; however, it also appears that having a pedophilic fantasy enhances the negative affect. Perhaps this downward spiral can eventually lead to the person's acting on the impulse to molest a child (Looman, 1995). Indeed, research using inmates from Canadian federal penitentiaries confirmed that sexual offenders, relative to non-sexual violent offenders, are more likely to report using consensual and non-consensual sex as a coping strategy (Cortoni & Marshall, 2001). Data also suggest that pedophiles are low in social maturity, self-esteem, impulse control, and social skills (Kalichman, 1991; Marshall, Cripps, Anderson, & Cortoni, 1999). Most older heterosexual pedophiles are or have been married.

One half of all child molestations, including those that take place within the family, are committed by adolescent males (Morenz & Becker, 1995). About 50% of adult offenders began their illegal behaviour in their early teens. These juveniles have typically experienced a chaotic and negative family life. Their homes often lack structure and positive support (Blaske, Borduin, Hengeler, & Mann, 1989). Research conducted in Canada by Worling (2001) as part of the Sexual Abuse: Family Education and Treatment (SAFE-T) Program has shown that many of these teenagers were themselves sexually abused as children. Thus, there was support for what is now known as the abused abuser hypothesis. Worling (2001) reported that 39% of his sample had experienced childhood sexual victimization

and 45% reported receiving abusive physical discipline from parents. A meta-analysis of the results of 17 studies confirmed that sex offenders, relative to non-sex offenders, are more likely to have a history of sexual abuse but not physical abuse (Jespersen, Lalumière, & Seto, 2009).

Overall, adolescents who engage in child molestation are more socially isolated and have poorer social skills than peers who are in trouble with the law for non-sexual crimes (Awad & Saunders, 1989). Social isolation is most characteristic of the unusual/isolated group identified by Worling (2001), who suggested that these adolescents are most likely to benefit from training in basic social skills, such as learning how to listen, how to start a conversation, and how to introduce oneself to someone else. Academic problems are also common (Becker & Hunter, 1997). In general, these young males (females are much less often found among the ranks of sex offenders) are what one would call juvenile delinquents, in frequent trouble with the police for a wide variety of lawbreaking. Not surprisingly, conduct disorder and substance abuse are frequent diagnoses made of these youths. Somewhat more surprisingly, depression and anxiety disorders are also common features (Galli et al., 1999).

Because overt physical force is seldom used in incest or pedophilia, the child molester often denies that he is actually forcing himself on his victim. Sometimes the molester rationalizes that he is doing something good for the child, despite the betrayal of trust that is inherent in child sexual abuse and despite the serious negative psychological consequences that can befall the abused child some years later.

Advances in the assessment of child molesters continue to emerge, and researchers based in Canada have played a substantial role. For instance, Seto and Lalumière (2001) developed a brief measure known as the Screening Scale for Pedophilic Interests (SSPI) and have shown that this screening instrument is quite successful in distinguishing pedophilic child molesters and non-child molesters who have abused older victims. This instrument was developed on the basis of earlier work that compared adult child molesters and molesters of adolescents (see Freund & Watson, 1991). Seto, Harris, Rice, and Barbaree (2004) administered the SSPI to two samples of adult male sex offenders with child victims. The SSPI was associated significantly with violent recidivism, sexual recidivism, and phallometrically measured sexual arousal from depictions of prepubescent children. The SSPI is now a widely used, accepted measure.

One SSPI item refers to whether an unrelated (extrafamilial) victim was involved. Greater pedophilic interest tends to be present when an unrelated victim is involved (Seto & Lalumière, 2001).

Voyeurism

Now and then, a man may by chance see a nude woman without her knowing he is watching her. If his sex life is primarily conventional, his act is voyeuristic, but he would not generally be considered a voyeur. Similarly, voyeuristic fantasies are quite common in men but do not by themselves warrant a diagnosis (Hanson & Harris, 1997). **Voyeurism** involves a marked preference for obtaining sexual gratification by watching others in a state of undress or having sexual relations. If it occurs by videotaping another person, it is called electronic voyeurism. For some men, voyeurism is the only sexual activity in which they engage; for others, it is preferred but not absolutely essential for sexual arousal (Kaplan & Kreuger, 1997). As with William in the Brief Case Example at the beginning of this chapter, the looking, often called peeping, is what helps the individual become sexually aroused. The voyeur's orgasm is achieved by masturbation, either while watching or later, remembering what he saw. Sometimes the voyeur fantasizes about having sexual contact with the observed person, but it remains a fantasy. In voyeurism, there is seldom contact between the observer and the observed.

A true voyeur, almost always a man, does not find it particularly exciting to watch a woman who is undressing for his special benefit. The element of risk seems important, for the voyeur is excited by the anticipation of how the woman would react if she knew he was watching. Some voyeurs derive special pleasure from secretly observing couples having sexual relations. As with all categories of behaviour that are against the law, frequencies of occurrence are difficult to assess, since the majority of all illegal activities go unnoticed by the police. Indeed, voyeurs are most often charged with loitering rather than with peeping itself (Kaplan & Kreuger, 1997).

Voyeurism typically begins in adolescence. It is thought that voyeurs are fearful of more direct sexual encounters with others, perhaps because they lack social skills. Their peeping serves as a substitute gratification and possibly gives them a sense of power over those watched. Voyeurs often have other paraphilias, but they do not seem to be otherwise disturbed.

In Denmark, following the lifting of all restrictions against the sale of pornographic materials to adults, a significant reduction in peeping, at least as reported to the police, was observed (Kutchinsky, 1970). It may be that the increased availability of completely frank pictorial and written material, typically used in masturbation, partially satisfied the needs that had made voyeurs of some men in the absence of other outlets. Perhaps the ready availability of pornography on the Internet will have a similar, but more global, effect.

Exhibitionism

Exhibitionism is a recurrent, marked preference for obtaining sexual gratification by exposing one's genitals to an unwilling stranger, sometimes a child. It typically begins in adolescence (Murphy, 1997). As with voyeurism, there is seldom an attempt to have actual contact with the stranger. Sexual arousal comes from fantasizing that one is exposing himself or from actually doing so, and the exhibitionist masturbates either while fantasizing or even during the actual exposure. In most cases, there is a desire to shock or embarrass the observer.

Historically, it has been assumed that the exhibitionist, or flasher, does not have actual contact with his or her victim. However, research conducted in Ottawa by Firestone, Kingston, Wexler, and Bradford (2006) led the authors to warn that exhibitionism "is not a benign act" (p. 358). They found that 39% of their sample of exhibitionists went on to commit other offences and 31% committed a sexual or violent act. Accordingly, they differentiated between "hands-off exhibitionists" and "hands-on exhibitionists."

Voyeurism and exhibitionism together account for a majority of all sexual offences that come to the attention of the police. The frequency of exhibitionism is much greater among men, who are often arrested for what is legally termed "indecent exposure." Other paraphilias are very common in exhibitionists, notably voyeurism and frotteurism (discussed in the section "Frotteurism") (Freund, 1990).

The urge to expose seems overwhelming and virtually uncontrollable to the exhibitionist, and is apparently triggered by anxiety and restlessness, as well as by sexual arousal. One exhibitionist persisted in his practices even after suffering a spinal cord injury that left him without sensation or movement from the waist down (DeFazio & Cunningham, 1987). Because of the compulsive nature of the urge, the exposures may be repeated rather frequently and even in the same place and at the same time of day.

The penile plethysmograph was used in a study of male exhibitionists in Alberta in an effort to determine whether they were sexually aroused by stimuli that do not arouse non-exhibitionists (Fedora, Reddon, & Yeudall, 1986). Compared with normal people and with sex offenders who had committed violent assaults, the exhibitionists showed significantly greater arousal in response to slides of fully clothed women in non-sexual situations, such as riding on an escalator or sitting in a park, but they showed similar levels of sexual interest in response to erotic and sexually explicit slides. These results are consistent with the hypothesis that exhibitionists misread cues in the courtship phase of sexual contact, in the sense that they construe certain situations as sexual that are judged non-erotic by non-exhibitionists.

Frotteurism

Frotteurism is the sexually oriented touching of an unsuspecting person. The frotteur may rub his penis against a woman's thighs or buttocks or fondle her breasts or genitals. These attacks typically occur in places that provide an easy means of escape, such as a crowded bus or sidewalk. Frotteurism has not been studied very extensively. It appears to begin in adolescence (American Psychiatric Association, 2000) and typically occurs along with other paraphilias (Kaplan & Kreuger, 1997).

A recent analysis concluded that frotteurism and exhibitionism occur often enough to be considered a significant concern. A survey of 459 undergraduate students found that 44% of them had experienced at least one act of either frotteurism or exhibitionism (Clark, Jeglic, Calkins, & Tartar, 2016). These events typically occurred near public transit sites, and most notably, about one-third of the students who experienced frotteurism reported lasting negative impact. This was the case for about 1 in 7 who experienced an act of exhibitionism.

Sexual Sadism and Sexual Masochism

A marked preference for obtaining or increasing sexual gratification by inflicting pain or psychological suffering (such as humiliation) on another is the key characteristic of **sexual sadism** (see photo). A marked preference for obtaining or increasing sexual gratification through subjecting oneself to pain or humiliation is the key characteristic of **sexual masochism**. While sexual sadism is often seen as motivated by the control over another person and overcoming their resistance and non-consent, data from Canada suggest that the overriding motivation is the actual violence or aggression (Seto, Lalumière, Harris, & Chivers, 2012).

Both these disorders are found in heterosexual and homosexual relationships, though it is estimated that upwards of 85% of people with these disorders are exclusively or predominantly heterosexual (Moser & Levitt, 1987). Some sadists and masochists are women; surveys have found that 20 to 30% of the members of sadomasochistic clubs are female (Moser & Levitt, 1987). The disorders seem to begin in early adulthood, and most sadists and masochists are relatively comfortable with their unconventional sexual practices (Spengler, 1977). The majority of sadists and masochists lead otherwise conventional lives, and there is some evidence that they are above average in income and education (Moser & Levitt, 1987; Spengler, 1977).

The majority of sadists establish relationships with masochists to derive mutual sexual gratification. From 5 to 10% of the population have engaged in some form of sadomasochistic activity, such as blindfolding one's partner, but few do so regularly, and even fewer prefer such activities during sex

(Baumeister & Butler, 1997). The sadist may derive full orgasmic pleasure by inflicting pain on his or her partner, and the masochist may be completely gratified by being subjected to pain. For other partners, sadistic and masochistic practices, such as spanking, are a prelude to or an aspect of sexual intercourse.

Although a great many people are switchable—that is, able to take both dominant and submissive roles—masochists outnumber sadists. For this reason, bondage-and-discipline services may constitute a considerable portion of the business of a house of prostitution. The manifestations of sexual masochism are varied. Examples include restraint (physical bondage), blindfolding (sensory bondage), spanking, whipping, electric shocks, cutting, humiliation (e.g., being urinated or defecated on, being forced to wear a collar and bark like a dog, or being put on display naked), and taking the role of slave and submitting to orders and commands. Themes of submission/domination seem as important as the infliction of physical pain. "Infantilism" is the desire to be treated like a helpless infant and clothed in diapers. One particularly dangerous form of masochism, called hypoxyphilia, involves sexual arousal by oxygen deprivation, which can be achieved using a noose, a plastic bag, chest compression, or a chemical that produces a temporary decrease in brain oxygenation by peripheral vasodilation (American Psychiatric Association, 1994).

Occasionally, sadists murder and mutilate; some are sex offenders who are imprisoned for torturing victims, mostly strangers, and deriving sexual satisfaction from doing so (Dietz, Hazelwood, & Warren, 1990). One well-known Canadian example is Paul Bernardo (see photo), who was described by the judge at sentencing as a sexually sadistic psychopath.

The sexual sadist obtains sexual gratification from inflicting pain or humiliation on another person, often a sexual masochist, who is aroused by being dominated or humiliated.

Paul Bernardo and Karla Homolka were involved in the death of Homolka's sister and in the murder of two teenaged girls in Ontario. Paul Bernardo was also the "Scarborough Rapist," who allegedly raped, brutalized, and terrorized more than two dozen women in Toronto. Bernardo claimed in 2008 that he is not a psychopath anymore and that he was driven by sexual performance anxiety (see Tyler, 2008).

Bernardo will soon be eligible for consideration for parole, but he has been deemed a dangerous offender because not only did he participate in the killing of at least three young women, he also was confirmed as the Scarborough Rapist via DNA testing conducted after he had been imprisoned. Bernardo was a classmate and friend of another convicted murderer and rapist, Colonel Russell Williams, when they were both students at the University of Toronto's Scarborough campus. Bernardo announced from the now-closed Kingston Penitentiary in 2008 that he used to be a psychopath but was no longer. At one point, Bernardo had an exceptionally high level of psychopathy, scoring 35 out of 40 on the PCL-R (see Chapter 13) (CBC News, 2014).

Sadists who commit acts of aggression against people have a different pattern of offences than that of non-sadistic sex offenders. Sadistic offenders are more likely to impersonate police officers, commit serial murders, tie up their victims, and conceal corpses (Gratzer & Bradford, 1995). One disconcerting finding is that in a forensic sample, two-thirds of those who were actually sexual sadists were misdiagnosed as non-sadistic sex offenders (Nitschke et al., 2009).

Other Specified Paraphilic Disorders

In addition to the paraphilias described above, there are several other specified paraphilic disorders. These include such disorders as necrophilia (sex with dead people), zoophilia (bestiality), telephone scatalogia (repeated urge to make obscene phone calls), coprophilia (the use of feces for sexual excitement), klismaphilia (enemas), and uruophilia (urine).

The high level of dysfunction that can be involved in these paraphilias is underscored by the report of a 54-year-old man incarcerated in a Canadian federal penitentiary (Earls & Lalumière, 2002). This man had been convicted four times for cruelty to animals. He was diagnosed with bestiality and an anti-social personality disorder. He had developed a sexual attraction to horses and killed a horse by puncturing its vaginal wall with his arm when he became jealous of the horse's interest in a stallion. Phallometric testing indicated that he was sexually aroused by horses and not at all sexually aroused by people.

Another compelling case study presented once again by Earls and Lalumière (2009) has led them to suggest that zoophilia may be more common than realized. This case also challenged the notion that it is more likely in rural areas among men with lower levels of intelligence. This case involved a medical researcher named "Possum" who developed an unfortunate affinity for horses. Another recently reported case involves a man with schizophrenia from Nigeria who developed an unnatural alliance with a goat. This person became a recidivist when the same problem resurfaced (see Amoo, Abayomio, & Olashore, 2012).

Etiology of the Paraphilias

Of the many theories and hypotheses about the etiology of the paraphilias, the principal ones come from psychodynamic and behavioural perspectives; others are from the biological perspective.

Psychodynamic Perspectives   The paraphilias are viewed by psychodynamic theorists as defensive in nature, protecting the ego from having to deal with repressed fears and memories and representing fixations at pregenital stages of psychosexual development. The person with a paraphilia is seen as someone who is fearful of conventional heterosexual relationships, even of heterosocial relationships that do not involve sex. His (less often, her) social and sexual development is immature, stunted, and inadequate for both social and heterosexual intercourse with the adult world (Lanyon, 1986). For example, the fetishist and the pedophile are viewed as men whose castration anxiety makes heterosexual sex with other adults too threatening. Castration anxiety leads the exhibitionist to reassure himself of his masculinity by showing his manhood (his genitals) to others; it results in the sadist dominating others.

Behavioural and Cognitive Perspectives   Some theorists operating within a behavioural paradigm hold the view that the paraphilias arise from classical conditioning that by chance has linked sexual arousal with classes of stimuli deemed by the culture to be inappropriate causes of sexual arousal (Kinsey, Pomeroy, & Martin, 1948; Kinsey, Pomeroy, Main, & Gebhard, 1953). For example, a young man may masturbate to pictures or images of women dressed in black leather boots. According to this theory, repetitions of these experiences endow boots with properties of sexual arousal. Similar proposals have been made for transvestism, pedophilia, voyeurism, and exhibitionism. Overall, this orgasm-conditioning hypothesis has very little empirical support (see O'Donohue & Plaud, 1994). However, as described later, some innovative therapeutic strategies have been developed based on this etiological speculation.

Most current behavioural and cognitive theories of the paraphilias are multi-dimensional and propose that a paraphilia results when a number of factors impinge on an individual. The childhood histories of individuals with paraphilias reveal that often they were subjected to physical and sexual abuse and grew up in a family in which the parent–child relationship was disturbed (Mason, 1997; Murphy, 1997). These early experiences may well contribute to the insecure attachment style usually found among sex offenders in general (Stirpe, Abracen, Stermac, & Wilson, 2006) and the low level of social skills, low self-esteem, loneliness, and lack of intimate relationships often seen among those with paraphilias (Kaplan & Kreuger, 1997; Marshall, Champagne, Sturgeon, & Bryce, 1997). A history of childhood sexual abuse (CSA) relates to risk of sexual recidivism. A study by Nunes and colleagues at Carleton University found among 462 male sexual offenders that CSA by a female abuser predicted higher rates of sexual recidivism. However, CSA by a male predicted more pedophilic interest (see Nunes, Hermann, Malcolm, & Lavoie, 2013).

Paraphilias such as exhibiting or peeping may thus be activities that substitute for more conventional relationships and sexual activity. Distorted parent–child relationships may also

Focus on Discovery 14.3

Neuroimaging, Neurobiology, and Brain Systems and Structures in Sexual Disorders

Neuroimaging has provided many new clues to the nature of normal and abnormal sexual responses. For instance, fMRI research has shown that sexually arousing visual stimuli create neuronal activity in the human reward system, including the centromedian hypothalamus (Maravilla & Yang, 2008). Men and women share many brain activation areas, but men show a greater degree of activation in the thalamus, hypothalamus, and amygdala (Maravilla & Yang, 2008). These differences are sometimes reflected in self-reported responses, but an important caveat was provided by Meredith Chivers from Queen's University and her colleagues (see Chivers et al., 2010). Their meta-analysis showed strong agreement between self-reports and genital measures for men ($r = .66$) but much less association for women ($r = .26$). Chivers (2008) concluded that sexual responses differ qualitatively for women and men. The genital responses of women are more nonspecific; they respond to preferred and non-preferred stimuli.

What about people with sexual disorders? A German study of male-to-female transsexuals found that relative to male control participants, the cerebral activation pattern while viewing erotic stimuli indicated a female-like form of cerebral processing (Gizewski et al., 2009). Extensive research is now using fMRI data to explore the neural responses of pedophiles. The overall picture is that pedophiles seem to have altered brain activity in the frontal brain areas and in the temporal lobe region. There are some indications that pedophilia involves the subcortical areas of the brain implicated in addicted, uncontrolled behaviour (Schiffer et al., 2008). Brain regions implicated when healthy individuals are presented with erotic stimuli evoke less activation when presented to pedophilic clients (Sartorius et al., 2008; Walter et al., 2007). However, when presented images of nude children, there is extensive activation among pedophiles (Schiffer, Krueger, et al., 2008; Schiffer, Paul, et al., 2008) and one study confirmed that the differences in brain activity strongly differentiated pedophiles from control participants independent of gender differences and differences in the stimuli they were presented with (see Ponseti et al., 2012).

Thus, there is growing support for the notion that those with sexual disorders have brains that are wired differently! The legal implications of these differences are explored in Chapter 18. It is suffice to say for now that some researchers have discussed that perhaps someday it may be possible using real-time fMRI measures to see whether neurofeedback can result in brain changes among people with sexual disorders (see Wiebking & Northoff, 2013).

---

create in an individual hostility or a general negative attitude and lack of empathy toward women, which may increase the chances of his victimizing a woman. Alcohol and negative affect are often triggers of incidents of pedophilia, voyeurism, and exhibitionism. Marshall (1996) reported that 50% of the sex offenders in his sample were intoxicated at the time of their offence.

Cognitive distortions also play a role in the paraphilias. A voyeur, for example, may believe that a woman who left her blinds up while undressing really wanted someone to look at her (Kaplan & Kreuger, 1997).

From an operant conditioning perspective, many paraphilias are considered an outcome of inadequate social skills or reinforcement of unconventionality by parents or relatives. Case histories of transvestites, for example, often refer to childhood incidents in which the little boy was praised and fussed over for looking cute in his mother's dresses.

Biological Perspectives As the overwhelming majority of people with paraphilias are male, there has been speculation that androgen, the principal male hormone, plays a role. Because the human fetus begins as a female, with maleness emerging from later hormonal influences, perhaps something can go wrong during fetal development. Findings of hormonal differences between normal people and people with paraphilias do not show elevated levels of testosterone among those with paraphilia (Stoléru, 2008).

As to differences in the brain, it has long been suspected that a dysfunction in the temporal lobe may be relevant to a minority of cases of sadism and exhibitionism (Mason, 1997; Murphy, 1997). The general role of brain functions and processes in sexual disorders is discussed in Focus on Discovery 14.3.

Therapies for the Paraphilias

Because most paraphilias are illegal, many people diagnosed with them are imprisoned and their treatment is ordered by the court. Outcomes for incarcerated adult sex offenders are highly variable; published success rates range from more than 90% to as low as 30% (Marshall et al., 1991). Juvenile sex offenders have also been the focus of some research, because most offenders begin in adolescence. The results, as with the findings on adults, are variable (Becker & Hunter, 1997). Published data are hard to interpret for several reasons. Experimental designs are not the rule here, because ethical considerations have led most researchers to conclude that control groups should not be used. Some programs select the most problematic prisoners for treatment, whereas others treat those with the most promising prognoses (e.g., first offenders). Some programs do not have follow-up sessions after release, whereas others do. Recidivism increases as the years go by, especially after two years have passed since termination of treatment (Marshall & Barbaree, 1990).

As we have seen with substance abusers, sex offenders often lack the motivation to try to change their illegal behaviour. Undermining their motivation for treatment are such factors as denial of the problem (see Marshall, Hamilton, & Fernandez, 2001), minimization of the seriousness of their problem, a belief that their victims will not be credible witnesses, and the confidence that they can control their behaviour without professional assistance. Denial is linked with other cognitive distortions (Nunes & Jung, 2013) in addition to negative perceptions of treatment (Jung & Nunes, 2012). Some blame the victim—even a child—for being overly seductive. Such people are frequently judged to be inappropriate for treatment programs, for when they do become involved, they frequently drop out. There are several methods to enhance their motivation to commit to treatment (Miller & Rollnick, 1991):

1. The therapist can empathize with the offender's reluctance to admit that he is an offender, thereby reducing the defensiveness and hostility.

2. The therapist can point out to the offender the treatments that might help him control his behaviour better and emphasize the negative consequences of refusing treatment (e.g., transfer to a less attractive incarceration setting if the person is already in custody) and of offending again (e.g., stiffer legal penalties).

3. Having elaborated on the possible benefits of treatment, the therapist can implement a paradoxical intervention by expressing doubt that the person is motivated to enter into or continue in treatment, thereby challenging him to prove wrong the therapist whom he has been resisting.

4. The therapist can explain that there will be a psychophysiological assessment of the client's sexual arousal, the implication being that the client's sexual proclivities can be revealed without his admitting to them (Garland & Dougher, 1991).

There is also the issue of what happens to motivation levels after the offender is released back into the community. A study conducted with sex offenders from Ontario showed that motivation to change sexually deviant behaviour increased substantially throughout the course of treatment but decreased significantly, relative to post-treatment levels, after conditional release to the community (Barrett, Wilson, & Long, 2003). Barrett et al. (2003) concluded that motivation is dynamic rather than static and that many clinicians in community settings will find it difficult to re-engage the offender in the treatment process. With the foregoing as background, we now describe treatments for the paraphilias.

Behavioural Techniques Behaviour therapists have been less interested in presumed deep-seated personality defects among people with paraphilias and more focused on the particular pattern of unconventional sexuality. Consequently, they have tried to develop therapeutic procedures for changing only the sexual aspect of the individual's makeup. Some successes have been achieved, especially when a variety of techniques are used in a broad-spectrum, multi-faceted treatment (Becker, 1990; Marshall et al., 1991).

In the earliest years of behaviour therapy, paraphilias were narrowly viewed as attractions to inappropriate objects and activities. Looking to experimental psychology for ways to reduce these attractions, researchers fixed on aversion therapy. Thus, a boot fetishist would be given shock (on the hands or feet) or an emetic (a drug that produces nausea) when looking at a boot, a transvestite when cross-dressing, a pedophile when gazing at a photograph of a nude child, and so on. Although aversion therapy may not completely eliminate the attraction, in some cases, it provides the client with a greater measure of control over the overt behaviour (McConaghy, 1990, 1994). Another method is called satiation; with this method, the man masturbates for a long time, typically after ejaculating, while fantasizing out loud about his deviant activity. There is reason to believe that both aversion therapy and satiation, especially when combined with other psychological interventions, such as social skills training, can have beneficial effects (Laws & Marshall, 1991; Marshall & Barbaree, 1990).

Orgasmic reorientation has been employed to help the client learn to become more aroused by conventional sexual stimuli. In this procedure, clients (again, most of whom are men) are confronted with a conventionally arousing stimulus (e.g., a photograph of a woman) while they are responding sexually for other, undesirable reasons. In the first clinical demonstration of this technique, Davison (1968) instructed a young man troubled by sadistic fantasies to masturbate at home in the following manner:

> "When assured of privacy in his dormitory room ... he was first to obtain an erection by whatever means possible—undoubtedly with a sadistic fantasy, as he indicated. He was then to begin to masturbate while looking at a picture of a sexy, nude woman (the target sexual stimulus) ... If he began losing his erection, he was to switch back to his sadistic fantasy until he could begin masturbating effectively again. Concentrating again on the ... picture, he was to continue masturbating, using the fantasy only to regain the erection. As orgasm was approaching, he was at all costs to focus on the ... picture."
>
> (p. 84)

The client was able to follow these instructions and, over a period of weeks, began to find conventional pictures, ideas, and images sexually arousing. However, the therapist had to complement the orgasmic procedure with some imaginal aversion therapy (e.g., imagining receiving a painful electric shock contingent on inappropriate thoughts) for the sadistic fantasies. The follow-up after a year and a half found the client capable of conventional arousal, although he apparently reverted at will to his sadistic fantasies every now and again. This dubious outcome has been reported for other instances of orgasmic reorientation. Behaviour therapists continue to explore its possibilities, despite no clear evidence of its effectiveness (Laws & Marshall, 1991).

In addition to the arousal-based procedures just described, several other techniques are in widespread use. Social skills training is often used because of the well-established fact that many individuals with paraphilias have social skills deficits. Another technique, alternative behavioural completion, entails imagining a typical deviant activity but changing its ending, such as in the following scenario:

> "As you drive home one night you notice an attractive woman driver on your right in a van. She can see right into your car. You slow down and drive parallel with her as you begin to get aroused. You want to rub your penis and take it out to show her. However, the urge this time is weaker and you drive past her quickly without exposing. You feel good about yourself for being able to exert control."

> (Maletzky, 1997, p. 57)

Cognitive Treatment

Cognitive procedures are often used to counter the distorted thinking of individuals with paraphilias. For example, an exhibitionist might claim that the girls he exposes himself to are too young to be harmed by it. The therapist would counter this distortion by pointing out that the younger the victim, the worse the harm will be (Maletzky, 1997). Training in empathy toward others is another cognitive technique. Teaching the offender to consider how his behaviour would affect someone else may lessen the sex offender's tendency to engage in such activities. Relapse prevention, modelled after the work on substance abuse described in Chapter 12, is also an important component of many treatment programs.

Cognitive and behavioural approaches have become more sophisticated and broader in scope since the 1960s, when the paraphilias were addressed almost exclusively in terms of sexual attraction to inappropriate environmental stimuli. In many instances, therapy is modelled on the approach of Masters and Johnson (1970) under the assumption that some paraphilias develop or are maintained as a result of unsatisfactory sexual relationships with consenting adults (Marshall & Barbaree, 1990). Overall, both institution-based and outpatient programs that follow a cognitive-behavioural model with sex offenders reduce recidivism to a greater degree than would be expected were no treatment at all attempted. These outcomes are much better for child molesters than for rapists. Although sex offenders generally evoke disgust and fear more than genuine interest, society tends to overlook the fact that even minimally effective efforts to treat such people not only are cost-effective but may protect others when the person is released from prison (Prentky & Burgess, 1990).

We have mentioned rape several times in our discussion of the paraphilias, especially in connection with pedophilia and incest. Forced sexual contact, however, occurs far more often between adults than between an adult and a child. We now examine the important topic of rape.

14.3   Rape

In legal terms, rape falls into two categories: forced and statutory. **Forced rape** is sexual intercourse with an unwilling partner. **Statutory rape** is sexual intercourse with a minor, someone under the age of consent. The age of consent in Canada is 14, and is decided by statutes. It is assumed that a person younger than the age of consent should not be held responsible for his or her sexual activity. A charge of statutory rape can be made even if it is proved that the person entered into the situation knowingly and willingly. Thus, statutory rape need not involve force, only consummated intercourse with a minor that is reported to the police. We focus in this section on forced rape.

The Crime

The specifics of rape cases vary widely. Some rapes are planned, and some are thought to be more impulsive, spur-of-the moment crimes. Up to 70% of rapes are associated with intoxication (Marshall & Barbaree, 1990). Some rapes seem motivated by a desire to control the other person. Others are more clearly sexually motivated, although many rapists experience erectile failure or fail to reach orgasm (Hudson & Ward, 1997). In what is sometimes termed "sadistic rape," the rapist severely injures the victim's body; for example, by inserting foreign objects into her vagina or pulling and burning her breasts. Some rapists also murder their victims. Little wonder, then, that rape is considered as much an act of violence, aggression, and domination as an act of sex. In many jurisdictions, the definition of rape includes oral and anal entry, as well as vaginal penetration. Although men can be victims of sexual assault—especially by other men in prison—our discussion focuses on women because rape is primarily an act committed by men against women.

Rape that occurs on dates is called **acquaintance rape**, or **date rape**. Rapes of this kind outnumber rapes by strangers by as much as 3 to 1 (Kilpatrick & Best, 1990). In general, the vast majority of rapes in Canada are committed by people who are known to the victim (Stermac, Du Mont, & Dunn, 1998; Stermac, Du Mont, & Kalemba, 1995), with one Canadian study finding that 81% of sexual assaults were perpetrated by men who were familiar to their victim (Canadian Panel on Violence against Women, 1993).

Unfortunately, many students are sexually assaulted. One study of 259 Canadian undergraduate women found that about one-third of those who dated had experienced physical, verbal, or psychological sexual coercion during the previous year (DeKeseredy, Schwartz, & Tait, 1993). In a subsequent survey of more than 3,600 female students at six Ontario universities, 15% reported being sexually assaulted (including 2% who reported date rape) and 24% reported being physically assaulted (Newton-Taylor, DeWit, & Gliksman, 1998). First-year students were more likely to be assaulted than were students in their second, third, or fourth years. A recent study of undergraduate women in attendance at historically Black colleges or universities found that 358 of 3,951 undergraduates (about 9%) had been sexually assaulted since beginning college (Lindquist et al., 2013). Most were assaulted by people they knew. Drinking usually took place on the part of the assailant and victim. Those who had been assaulted had more symptoms of PTSD and depression. Follow-up research found that most sexual assault survivors reported it to someone close to them but very few reported it to formal authorities (Lindquist et al., 2016). Non-reporting reflected privacy concerns. Survivors indicated a need for more survivor services and improved ways to protect the confidentiality of survivors who wish to report the assault.

A contemporary theme that is receiving long overdue attention is how colleges and universities respond when a student alleges that she or he has been the victim of a sexual assault. Much of the recent attention has been attributed to the case of Brock Turner, a Stanford University student and aspiring athlete, who was found guilty of sexually assaulting an unconscious woman but received only a six-month sentence. There have been extensive reports of sexual assaults of students taking place at various campuses throughout Canada (see Tamburri & Samson, 2014). It is now required by law that policies be put into place at all colleges and universities in Ontario and British Columbia. A task force was created at the University of British Columbia following the occurrence of six assaults over a six-month period in 2013. Students at various universities have been demanding immediate investigations and the development of procedures that convey trust and support to victims who are willing to come forward because there are concerns that complaints are not seriously treated (Chiose, 2016). Students alleged at UBC that the university did not address complaints received over an 18-month period about multiple acts allegedly committed by a 28-year-old graduate student who was eventually expelled from the university.

Of course, the act of being assaulted is highly traumatic, so the presence of PTSD symptoms is not surprising. Rape victims are usually traumatized by the attack, both physically and mentally (Resick, 1993). For weeks or months following the rape, many victims feel extremely tense and deeply humiliated. They feel guilty that they were unable to fight harder. Many have nightmares about the rape. Depression and loss of self-esteem are common. Some victims of rape develop phobias about being outdoors or indoors or in the dark, depending on where the rape took place. They may also fear being alone or in crowds or having anyone behind them. Unfortunately, some of these reactions are exacerbated by insensitivity on the part of police and other members of the legal system, and even friends and loved ones, some of whom may question the victim's complicity in what happened. Sometimes an unwanted pregnancy results from a rape, and justifiable concern about sexually transmitted diseases, including AIDS, adds to the trauma of the attack.

The nature and duration of what some call *rape trauma syndrome* (Burgess & Holmstrom, 1974) depend a great deal on the person's life both prior to and following the attack. Factors that can mitigate the negative aftermath of rape

include a supportive spouse and friends, as well as receiving therapy and counselling.

A contemporary development with regard to date rape is the use of the tranquilizer Rohypnol (i.e., the date rape drug). This drug is odourless and tasteless and can be easily slipped into a drink. If ingested, it causes the person to pass out and have little if any memory of what happens. Men have used Rohypnol to rape women when on a date. There have been unconfirmed reports of the increasing use of date rape drugs since the 1990s among people who have been drinking alcohol. Du Mont et al. (2009) investigated 184 cases in Ontario of suspected drug-facilitated sexual assaults. Total amnesia of the event was reported by 115 of the women (62.5%). Du Mont et al. (2009) concluded that date rape is both common and serious and this points to the need for easily conducted toxicological screening at hospitals and other facilities.

The Rapist

As documented some years ago in a classic book on the politics of rape, the fact that men with their generally superior strength can usually overpower women buttresses the view that rape has served in the past and still serves to control and intimidate women (Brownmiller, 1975).

Who is the rapist? Is the rapist primarily the psychopath who seeks the thrill of dominating and humiliating a woman through intimidation and often brutal assault? Is he an ordinarily unassertive man with a fragile ego who, feeling inadequate after disappointment and rejection in work or love, takes out his frustrations on an unwilling stranger? Is he an otherwise respectable, even honoured, man in authority who takes advantage of his position of power over a woman? Is he a teenager, provoked by a seductive and apparently available young woman who, it turns out, was not as interested as he in sexual intimacy? Is he a man whose inhibitions against expressing anger have been dissolved by alcohol? The best answer is that the rapist is all these men, often operating under a combination of several of these circumstances.

Research on rapists in Canada suggests that heterogeneity does exist and that one can make meaningful distinctions between types of rapists, such as psychopathic and non-psychopathic rapists (see Brown & Forth, 1997). However, what many rapists probably have in common is unusually high hostility toward women, arising from beliefs of having been betrayed, deceived, or demeaned by them or from exposure to parental violence and physical or sexual abuse during childhood (Lisak & Roth, 1990). A qualitative study by Beech, Ward, and Fisher (2006) of 41 rapists identified five implicit theories that dominate their thoughts: (1) the world is dangerous; (2) women are dangerous (accounting for some of the hostility toward women); (3) women are primarily sex objects; (4) the male sex drive is uncontrollable; and (5) they are entitled to do whatever they want. Thus, a clear element of narcissism seems to be operating here.

Rapists often lack social skills, have low self-esteem, and have demonstrably low levels of empathy for their victims

(Hudson & Ward, 1997; Marshall & Moulden, 2001). Follow-up research conducted in Kingston, Ontario, indicates that rapists may repress empathy toward their own victim rather than suffer from a general deficit in empathy (Fernandez & Marshall, 2003).

Therapy for Rapists and Rape Victims

Unlike most of the disorders discussed in this book, rape has the dubious distinction of presenting two different challenges to the mental health professional: treating the man who has committed the act and treating the woman who has been the victim.

Therapy for Rapists   Therapy programs for incarcerated rapists are typically multi-dimensional and are evaluated by following men after release from prison to determine recidivism rates. Among the components of these programs are cognitive techniques aimed at rapists' distorted beliefs (such as that women want to be raped) and inappropriate attitudes toward women, attempts to increase empathy with their victims, anger management, techniques to improve self-esteem, and efforts to reduce substance abuse. These methods are often implemented in confrontational group-therapy sessions that attempt to goad the rapist into taking responsibility for his aggressive behaviour and include an explicit focus on relapse prevention (Marshall, 1999). As with the paraphilias, this psychologically based therapy is sometimes supplemented with the use of biological treatments to reduce the rapist's sex drive. Although these programs typically have not had adequate control groups, meta-analyses have led to the conclusion that cognitive therapy and the biological interventions may lower recidivism somewhat, especially among men who complete the treatment programs (Hall, 1995; Hanson & Bussière, 1998). The meta-analysis technique is described in more detail in Canadian Perspectives 14.1.

Canadian Perspectives 14.1

Canadian Research on Sex Offender Recidivism

In Chapter 18 we examine the literature on risk assessment of sex offender recidivism in detail. According to Karl Hanson from Public Safety Canada, structured risk assessments that assign weights to key variables has supplanted the poor predictive utility of unstructured professional opinions, so there have been significant improvements in the ability to predict risk of reoffence among those who have been sex offenders (see Hanson, 2009). Still, the prediction of further risk is very difficult to determine.

Who is most likely to reoffend? A review conducted by Greenberg (1998) at the Royal Ottawa Hospital found that incest offenders, relative to extrafamilial offenders, are less likely to reoffend, while rapists and exhibitionists have higher levels of recidivism.

A meta-analysis conducted by Hanson and Bussière (1998) examined the factors associated with sexual recidivism in 61 follow-up studies. They found that demographic variables (e.g., being young and single) and criminal lifestyle variables (e.g., total number of prior offences) were reliable but modest predictors of sexual recidivism. Measures of psychological maladjustment had little predictive utility. Only anti-social personality disorder predicted sexual recidivism.

Recently, Hanson and Yates (2013) summarized known risk factors for sexual recidivism to make the key point that treatment interventions need to target these factors in order to reduce recidivism. Their comprehensive list of risk factors is in Table 14.2.

Subsequent research has clarified the role of psychopathy in sexual recidivism. A Canadian study found that men with elevated levels of psychopathy and deviant sexual arousal tended to recidivate sooner and at much higher rates than men low in these factors (Serin, Mailloux, & Malcolm, 2001). However, a later study showed that it was the sexual deviance component that predicted sexual recidivism; psychopathy did not predict sexual recidivism but did predict non-sexual recidivism (Olver & Wong, 2006). This finding fits with a widely cited meta-analysis of 82 studies of sex offenders that confirmed that sexual deviance was a predictor of sexual

TABLE 14.2	Established Risk Factors for Sexual Recidivism
Sexual deviance	
Any deviant sexual preference	
Sexual preference for children	
Sexualized violence	
Multiple paraphilias	
Sexual preoccupations	
Attitudes tolerant of sexual assault	
Lifestyle instability/criminality	
Childhood behaviour problems (e.g., running away, grade failure)	
Juvenile delinquency	
Any prior offences	
Lifestyle instability (reckless behaviour, employment instability)	
Personality disorder (anti-social, psychopathy)	
Grievance/hostility	
Social problems/intimacy deficits	
Single (never married)	
Conflicts with intimate partners	
Hostility toward women	
Emotional congruence with children	
Negative social influences	
Response to treatment/supervision	
Treatment dropout	
Non-compliance with supervision	
Violation of conditional release	
Poor cognitive problem-solving	
Age (young)	

Source: Adapted with kind permission from Springer Science + Business Media, Psychological treatment of sex offenders. *Current Psychiatry Reports*, 15(3), p. 348. Hanson, R. K., & Yates, P. M.

recidivism for both adult and adolescent sex offenders, while anti-social orientation predicted violent and general recidivism (Hanson & Morton-Bourgon, 2005). This meta-analysis found a relatively small association between scores on Hare's PCL-R and sexual recidivism. However, this analysis did not separately examine the PCL-R factors. An updated meta-analysis by Hawes, Boccaccini, and Murrie (2013) that took the PCL-R factors into account found a stronger association between psychopathy and sexual recidivism. These researchers also found that a combination of psychopathy and past sexual deviance was associated robustly with the likelihood of sexual reoffences.

While sexual deviance is better than psychopathy when it comes to predicting sexual recidivism, people who are characterized jointly by sexual deviance and psychopathy may engage in extreme forms of sex-related violence. This was underscored by a case description of a man with erotic violence syndrome (Litman, 2004). This person had a history of sexual assault, including an assault of an 82-year-old man! The offender was also diagnosed as a psychopath and he was evaluated as having a 100% likelihood of reoffending. Unfortunately, he raped a young woman shortly after being allowed more contact with the community. The offender threatened to kill this young woman if she informed the police, but to her credit, she was courageous and did indeed tell police about the sexual assault.

Research in Canada on the treatment of sexual offenders and levels of recidivism has yielded inconsistent findings, and a study conducted by Seto and Barbaree (1999) actually found that men rated as having more appropriate treatment behaviour while receiving group treatment (i.e., higher attendance, less disruptive interactions) actually were the most likely to reoffend. The authors concluded that offenders, particularly those high in psychopathy, may learn social skills in group treatment that enable them to gain access to and manipulate potential victims! However, an update investigation by Barbaree (2005) with a national police database did not replicate this troubling finding; treatment behaviour did not predict recidivism, and psychopathy did not mediate the link between treatment behaviour and recidivism. Still, we should be alert to the fact that some offenders may have ulterior motives for their seemingly good treatment response.

One review led to the conclusion that there is a positive treatment effect (see Schmucker & Losel, 2008). Overall, sexual recidivism was found for 17.5% of the untreated participants and 11.1% of the treated participants. Hormonal medication, castration, cognitive-behavioural therapy (CBT), and behavioural approaches were all effective; non-behavioural treatments were not effective. The issue of whether psychopathic sex offenders benefit from treatment remains open, however; a qualitative review by Doren and Yates (2008) found that studies tapping this issue have too many limitations to draw a conclusion.

Guidelines for conducting research on sexual offender treatment have been published by a group called the Collaborative Outcome Data Committee (CODC, 2007). This group is dedicated to improving the quality of treatment outcome research. It recognizes that many previous studies were actually program quality reviews and were not conducted according to the usual principles associated with scientific research.

Thinking Critically

1. On the basis of the available data, do you believe that treatment for sex offenders is essential? If yes, would you change your view if you knew the person was a psychopath?

2. When people learn that a former sex offender is now living in their community following release, they have often responded by harassing the offender until he leaves the area. Do you think communities have the right to do this? How would you respond upon learning that one of your new neighbours is a former sex offender who has responded well to treatment? How do you weigh the former offender's right to privacy against the possible risk of harm to the public?

Therapy For Rape Victims   Efforts to counsel rape victims have expanded considerably in recent years. Rape crisis centres and telephone hotlines have been established throughout North America (see photo). Some are associated with hospitals and clinics; others operate on their own.

Mental health professionals who attend to rape victims typically focus on the woman's ongoing relationships, which may be disrupted or negatively affected by the rape. Friends and family, especially spouses and lovers, will need help handling their own emotional turmoil so that they can provide the kind of non-judgemental support that rape victims need.

Much of the therapy for rape has a great deal in common with the treatment for PTSD, and although treatment is successful for the most part, approximately one-third of treatment participants either still met PTSD criteria at the end of treatment or drop out of treatment (Vickerman & Margolin, 2009). Exposure treatment is among the more effective treatments. The few studies testing CBT also seem effective (see Vickerman & Margolin, 2009).

Depression can be addressed by helping the woman re-evaluate her role in the rape, as many victims tend to see

Caro/Alamy

Sexual assault counsellors support a victim's decision to prosecute the perpetrator if she chooses to. There are crisis centres across the country that provide assistance to victims through services such as crisis lines and accompaniment and support services to police, hospitals, lawyers, and other social service resources.

themselves as at least partially responsible. A little-researched topic is the anger and rage many victims have toward their assailants; women are often afraid of expressing or are socialized not to express such feelings (Calhoun & Atkeson, 1991).

A cognitive-behavioural intervention that has been validated empirically is the cognitive processing therapy (CPT) of Patricia Resick (see Resick & Schnicke, 1993). It too has been acknowledged as effective (Vickerman & Margolin, 2009). This therapy combines exposure to memories of the trauma (as is done in other anxiety-reduction interventions) with the kind of cognitive restructuring found in the work of Ellis and Beck. For example, the rape victim is encouraged to dispute any tendency to attribute the blame to herself and to consider fully those aspects of the attack that were beyond her control. CPT is described as an evidence-based 12-session intervention that combines cognitive therapy and written narratives to reduce PTSD and other symptoms (Resick & Schnike, 1993). A key assumption of CPT reflects the Piagetian notions of **assimilation** and **accommodation**. Assimilation is the process of incorporating new information into existing schemas. Accommodation is the process of modifying existing schemas to incorporate new events. Resick and Schnike (1993) maintain that traumatized rape victims suffer as a result of overassimilated and overaccommodated beliefs about trauma. For instance, they alter their control schema by coming to believe that people either have total control or no control over events (overaccommodation) or they assimilate a sense that victims are partly responsible for events into their pre-existing belief in a just and fair world to reflect the notion that victims are at least partly responsible (overassimilation). Similarly, they can come to believe that people are totally responsible or not responsible at all for events. A major CPT emphasis is to develop accommodated, balanced views of events. CPT has proven effective in reducing guilt-related thoughts (Resick et al., 2002) as well as shame, PTSD symptoms, and cognitive distortions (Resick et al., 2008). Data suggest that CPT reduces overaccommodation and overassimilation (Sobel, Resick, & Rabalais, 2009).

Social attitudes and support systems encourage the victim to report rape and pursue the prosecution of the alleged rapist, but the legal situation is still problematic. Interviews with half a million women indicated three reasons for reluctance to report rape:

1. They consider the rape a private matter.
2. They fear reprisals from the rapist or his family or friends.
3. They believe that the police would be inefficient or insensitive (Wright, 1991).

Unfortunately, only a small percentage of rapists are ultimately convicted of their crimes. A study of sexual assaults reported to B.C. Women's Sexual Assault Services found that charges were filed in only about one-third of the cases and a conviction occurred in only about 1 in 10 filed cases (McGregor, Du Mont, & Myhr, 2002). Key factors that facilitated filing a charge included greater severity of injury and the receipt of physical evidence via forensic sampling. Ideally, today, med-

ico-legal evidence is obtained via a **medical forensic examination** (MFE). An Ontario study found that although MFE is optional, several women who had been sexually assaulted were instructed to undergo MFE. Many women reported that the stress of undergoing the MFE procedures was balanced by "a sense of doing something" about the assault and MFE helped them feel that other people were recognizing that they had been assaulted (see Du Mont, White, & McGregor, 2009).

There is no denying that going to trial is very stressful. Any familiarity of the victim with her assailant argues strongly against conviction, and the victim's role in her own assault is almost always examined by defence lawyers. Society must be attentive and active to ensure that the legal system defends the victim's rights.

14.4 Sexual Dysfunctions

Having discussed the unconventional patterns of the sexual behaviour of a small minority of the population, we turn now to sexual problems that interfere with conventional sexual enjoyment during the course of many people's lives. Our concern here is with **sexual dysfunctions**, the range of problems considered to represent inhibitions in the normal sexual response cycle.

What is defined as normal and desirable in human sexual behaviour varies with time and place. The contemporary view that inhibitions of sexual expression underlie abnormality can be contrasted with views held during the nineteenth and early twentieth centuries in the Western world, when excess was regarded as the culprit. We must keep these varying temporal and cultural norms in mind as we study human sexual dysfunctions.

Psychological problems have consequences not only for the people who experience them but also for those with whom the people are involved. This aspect of human emotional problems is especially important in our consideration of sexual dysfunctions, which usually occur in the context of intimate personal relationships. A marriage is bound to suffer if one of the partners fears sex. And most of us, for better or for worse, base part of our self-concept on our sexuality. Do we please the people we love, do we gratify ourselves, or, more simply, are we able to enjoy the fulfillment and relaxation that can come from a pleasurable sexual experience? Sexual dysfunctions can be so severe that human tenderness itself is lost, let alone the more intense satisfaction of sexual activity.

We look first at the human sexual response cycle as it normally functions. With that as context, we examine the several sexual dysfunctions. Then we discuss etiologies and therapies for these problems.

Sexual Dysfunctions and the Human Sexual Response Cycle

As indicated in Table 14.1, sexual dysfunctions are divided into several categories: sexual desire disorders, sexual arousal

Bettmann/Getty Images

The pioneering work of the sex therapists William H. Masters and Virginia Johnson helped launch a candid and scientific appraisal of human sexuality. Their work and their lives were depicted on the TV show "Masters of Sex."

disorders, orgasmic disorders, and sexual pain disorders. The difficulty should be persistent and recurrent, and should cause marked distress or interpersonal problems. A diagnosis of sexual dysfunction is not made if the disorder is believed to be due entirely to a medical illness (such as advanced diabetes, which can cause erectile problems in men) or if it is due to another disorder (such as major depression).

Most contemporary conceptualizations of the sexual response cycle are a distillation of proposals by Masters and Johnson (1966) and Kaplan (1974). More than 40 years ago, the work of Masters and Johnson (see photo) signalled a revolution in the nature and intensity of research in and clinical attention to human sexuality. These researchers extended the earlier interview-based breakthroughs of the Kinsey group (Kinsey et al., 1948, 1953) by making direct observations and physiological measurements of people masturbating and having sexual intercourse. Four phases in the human sexual response cycle are typically identified; they are considered quite similar in men and women:

1. Appetitive. Introduced by Kaplan (1974), this stage involves sexual interest or desire, often associated with sexually arousing fantasies.

2. Excitement. In this phase, originally Masters and Johnson's first stage, a subjective experience of sexual pleasure is associated with physiological changes brought about by increased blood flow to the genitalia and, in women, also to the breasts. This tumescence, the flow of blood into tissues, shows up in men as erection of the penis and in women as enlargement of the breasts and changes in the vagina, such as increased lubrication.

3. Orgasm. In this phase, sexual pleasure peaks in ways that have fascinated poets and the rest of us ordinary people for thousands of years. In men, ejaculation feels inevitable

and indeed almost always occurs. In women, the walls of the outer third of the vagina contract. In both sexes, there is general muscle tension and involuntary pelvic thrusting.

4. Resolution. This last of Masters and Johnson's stages refers to the relaxation and well-being that usually follow an orgasm. In men, there is an associated refractory period, during which further erection and arousal are not possible. Women may be able to respond again with sexual excitement almost immediately, a capability that permits multiple orgasms.

This four-stage view is one of many conceivable ways to organize and discuss the relevant body of information (Gagnon, 1977; Kuhn, 1962). We are about to see how the *DSM* uses this scheme to describe sexual dysfunctions.

Descriptions and Etiology of Sexual Dysfunctions

The prevalence of occasional disturbances in sexual functioning is quite high. Table 14.3 presents data from a survey of more than 3,000 men and women who were asked whether they had experienced various symptoms of sexual dysfunction in the past 12 months (Laumann, Paik, & Rosen, 1999). The overall prevalence of symptoms of sexual dysfunction was 43% for women and 31% for men. Because these symptoms are so common, people should not assume that they need treatment if they sometimes experience one or more of the problems described in this section. In the diagnostic criteria for each sexual dysfunction, the phrase "persistent or recurrent" is used to underscore the fact that a problem must be serious indeed for the diagnosis to be made. In addition, there is a fair amount of comorbidity among the sexual dysfunctions. For example, almost half of both men and women diagnosed with hypoactive sexual disorder (low sexual desire) also have at least one other dysfunction (Segraves & Segraves, 1991). As we review the various disorders, their interconnectedness will become evident.

TABLE 14.3	Self-Reported Rates of Experiencing Various Sexual Problems in the Past 12 Months	
Problem	**Men**	**Women**
Lacked interest in sex	13–17%	27–32%
Unable to achieve orgasm	7–9%	22–28%
Climax too early	28–32%	N/A
Sex not pleasurable	6–8%	17–24%
Trouble maintaining/achieving erection	11–18%	N/A
Trouble lubricating	N/A	18–27%
Pain during sex	N/A	8–15%

Note: The ranges reflect the fact that rates vary according to age.
Source: After Laumann et al., 1999.

Sexual Desire Disorders   **Hypoactive sexual desire disorder** involves deficient or absent sexual fantasies. A more extreme form, known as **sexual aversion disorder**, has been removed from *DSM-5* because it is rarely diagnosed. Here the person actively avoids nearly all genital contact with another person. Consider the following case excerpt:

> *"A 51-year-old secretary explained that she had had a wonderful sexual life with her husband until she humorously asked whether he had ever had an affair during their 20-year marriage. He shocked her by confessing a past 'insignificant' one. As she thought about this over a week, she became increasingly enraged and asked him to leave the home. Several weeks later, he came back after constant phone contact and in response to her coming down with a flu-like illness. When their sexual behavior resumed two months later, she became the 'ice queen'—unable to stand his touches. Her aversion lasted six months. Four years later when she discovered that he was having an affair, she redeveloped her aversion, adding that she felt that he was raping her when he touched her and that she could not stand his saliva or semen. She did everything she could to avoid sex. Her second period of aversion lasted four years before she was referred by her gynecologist for psychotherapy. At this time, she saw no relationship between her discoveries of his infidelity and her sexual aversion state."*

> *(From Levine, in Tasman, Kay, & Lieberman, 2003, p. 1475)*

Clearly, the lack of sexual contact signals that this is an example of sexual aversion disorder.

The diagnosis of sexual desire disorders, often colloquially referred to as low sex drive, seems particularly problematic. How frequently should a person want sex? And with what intensity or urgency? The reason a person goes to a clinician in the first place and ends up with this diagnosis is probably that someone else is dissatisfied with that person's interest in sex. The hypoactive desire category appeared for the first time in *DSM-III* in 1980, under the title of "inhibited sexual desire," and may owe its existence to the high expectations some people have about being sexual. It is striking that entire books—for example, Leiblum and Rosen (1988)—have been written about a disorder that 40 years ago was hardly mentioned in professional sexology circles. Data attest to the significance of subjective factors in the extent to which a person believes he or she has a low sex drive; for example, hypoactive sexual desire disorder was reported more often by American men than by British men (Hawton, Catalan, Martin, & Fagg, 1986).

We know little about the causes of hypoactive sexual desire. Among the causes of low sex drive in people seen clinically are religious orthodoxy, trying to have sex with a partner of the non-preferred sex, fear of loss of control, fear of pregnancy, depression, side effects from such medications as antihypertensives and tranquilizers, and lack of attraction resulting from such factors as poor personal hygiene in the partner (LoPiccolo & Friedman, 1988).

Several potential factors have been identified (for a comprehensive review, see West, Vinikoor, & Zolnoun, 2004). Relationship factors may be part of the picture, as women with sexual desire disorder report that their communication with their husband is poor and that they are unhappy with the way conflicts are resolved. Other possible causes include a history of sexual trauma, such as rape or childhood sexual abuse, and fears of contracting sexually transmitted diseases, such as AIDS. Two empirical studies indicate that anger is a major factor in reducing sexual desire in both men and women, though it has a smaller role for women (Beck & Bozman, 1995; Bozman & Beck, 1991). Sexual desire is lower when people complain of high levels of everyday stress (see West et al., 2004). There are also data pointing to the importance of testosterone levels in men—the lower the levels, the lower the sexual desire (Bancroft, 1988).

Sexual Arousal Disorders   Some people have little or no trouble experiencing sexual desire but do have difficulty attaining or maintaining sexual arousal, the next stage of the sexual response cycle described by Masters and Johnson. The subcategories of arousal disorders are **female sexual interest/ arousal disorder** and **male erectile disorder**. The former used to be called frigidity, and the latter, impotence.

Replacing the words "impotence" and "frigidity" with the phrase "sexual interest/arousal disorder" can be considered an advance. Impotence implies that the man is not potent, in control, or truly masculine, and negatively supports the macho conception of masculinity that many people today challenge. Frigidity implies that the woman is emotionally cold, distant, unsympathetic, and unfeeling. Both terms are derogatory and encourage a search for causes within the person rather than focus attention on the relationship, a domain that many contemporary investigators explore for answers and solutions.

The diagnosis of arousal disorder is made for a woman when there is consistently inadequate vaginal lubrication for comfortable completion of intercourse. It occurs for a man when there is persistent failure to attain or maintain an erection through completion of the sexual activity.

How many women suffer from female sexual dysfunction? A comprehensive meta-analysis of premenopausal women considered various problems (i.e., hypoactive sexual desire disorder, sexual aversion disorder, female sexual arousal disorder, female orgasmic disorders, pain disorders, and lubrication difficulties). It was based on data from 135 studies. The overall prevalence of female sexual dysfunction was 40.9% (about 2 out of 5 women). The most prevalent problem was hypoactive sexual desire disorder at 28.2% (see McCool et al., in press).

For male erectile disorder, prevalence is estimated at between 3 and 9% (e.g., Ard, 1977; Frank, Anderson, & Rubenstein, 1978). It increases greatly in older adults (Feldman et al., 1994; Kinsey et al., 1948). Some men suffer jointly from erectile dysfunction and premature ejaculation, and the presence of premature ejaculation elevates the risk of erectile dysfunction. Predictors of this combination include anxiety, depression, and advanced age (Corona et al., 2015).

As many as two-thirds of erectile problems have some biological basis, usually in combination with psychological factors (LoPiccolo, 2002). In general, any disease, drug, or hormonal imbalance that can affect the nerve pathways or blood supply to the penis can contribute to erectile problems. Examples are certain drugs, such as Thorazine, Prozac, and some antihypertensive medications, and illnesses, such as diabetes, kidney problems, and chronic alcoholism. As indicated, though, somatic factors usually interact with psychological factors to produce and maintain erectile difficulties. For example, anxiety and depression are common among men with erectile disorder (Araujo et al., 1998). Research using a measure of sexual self-efficacy developed by researchers in Quebec (Libman, Rothenberg, Fichten, & Amsel, 1985) shows that men with erectile dysfunction often have low levels of sexual self-efficacy and that depression is linked closely with this sense of inefficacy (see Fichten, Libman, Takefman, & Brender, 1988; Holden, 1999; Libman et al., 1985). Once the disorder has begun, fears of sexual failure arise and could certainly inhibit subsequent sexual responding (Rowland, Cooper, & Slob, 1996).

Before we focus specifically on disorders experienced by women, note that a major shortcoming of *DSM-5* is its failure to include a disorder that has been described as **hypersexual disorder** (see Kafka, 2010). This applies to individuals who are compelled and seemingly addicted to sex. Kafka (2013) describes hypersexual disorder as "a sexual desire disorder with an impulsivity component." According to Bradford and Fedoroff (2009), Kinsey was aware of this condition and wanted to measure it with an index he described as "The Total Sexual Outlet," which was defined as the number of orgasms experienced in a seven-day period.

We often hear about people, including celebrities, who are described as "sex addicts." Speculation had surfaced that golfer Tiger Woods may have suffered from this, and in May 2010, Woods's former coach Hank Haney confirmed that Woods did indeed receive treatment for "sex addiction." Comedian Russell Brand and actor David Duchovny (see photo) are other public figures with an acknowledged sex addiction.

Given the prevalence of people with hypersexual disorder and that it makes sense that some people can develop a compulsion, it is hard to fathom why it was not included in the *DSM-5*. Kafka (2014) noted that there were concerns that its inclusion would pathologize normal tendencies and the diagnosis would be cited strategically by lawyers seeking to exonerate their clients. Still, he also noted that large surveys have found that 1 to 2% of men indicate compulsive sexual tendencies that often resulted in treatment and there are over four decades of research and accounts of people requiring treatment. Moreover, its inclusion is supported by the results of a favourable *DSM* field trial (see Reid et al., 2012). Because hypersexual disorder was considered by the professionals revising the addiction section of the *DSM-5*, extensive discus-

Actor David Duchovny, who has starred in the *X-Files*, admitted suffering from sex addiction in 2009. Ironically, his character on the HBO show *Californication*, Hank Moody, also displays many of the symptoms of sex addiction.

sion has focused on whether compulsive sexual behaviour qualifies as an addiction according to established criteria; some key gaps in knowledge limit the conclusions that can be drawn here (see Kraus, Voon, & Potenza, in press). It is more than a conceptual topic for debate when the clinician is faced with someone suffering from significant impairment due to a sex addiction. Krueger (in press) noted that a diagnosis is still possible using another international classification system that is the most widely used worldwide (i.e., the ICD-10). He also noted that it is possible to apply a more obscure *DSM-5* category, a generic one for "other specified sexual dysfunction."

Orgasmic Disorders

Various sexual dysfunctions are listed in *DSM-5*. Three kinds of orgasmic disorders are described in *DSM-5*: one found in women and two in men.

Female orgasmic disorder   Formerly called inhibited female orgasm, **female orgasmic disorder** is the absence of orgasm after a period of normal sexual excitement. According to a recent review, this is the second most common problem among women, surpassed only by hypoactive sexual desire disorder. Prevalence rates vary widely from 16% to 46%, with higher rates of prevalence being found in Asia (Laan, Rellini, & Barnes, 2013). Female orgasmic disorder is the problem that most often brings women into therapy (Kaplan, 1974; Spector & Carey, 1990). Failure to achieve orgasm is not only a problem for women, it is also an important aspect of sex for their partners, who may come to believe that they are unskilled or insensitive lovers. This last point probably accounts for the fact that up to 61% of women report faking an orgasm on occasion (Ellsworth & Bailey, 2013).

There is an important distinction between problems a woman may have in becoming sexually aroused and those she may have in reaching an orgasm. Although as many as 10% of adult women have never experienced an orgasm (Andersen, 1983), far fewer are believed to remain unaroused during sexual activity. Indeed, laboratory research has shown that women with orgasmic disorder are as responsive to erotic stimuli as are women in a control group (Meston & Gorzalka, 1996).

Numerous reasons have been put forward to explain the problem. Perhaps many women, unlike men, have to learn to become orgasmic; that is, the capacity to have an orgasm may not be innate in females as it is in males. In men, ejaculation, which almost always is accompanied by orgasm, is necessary for reproduction. Survey findings indicate that women who masturbated little or not at all before they began to have intercourse were much more likely to be non-orgasmic than those who had masturbated to orgasm before becoming sexually active with a partner (Hoon & Hoon, 1978; Kinsey et al., 1953). These are, of course, correlational data; some third factor may be responsible both for infrequent masturbation and for diminished ability to have orgasms. Lack of sexual knowledge also appears to play a role, according to clinical data. Many non-orgasmic women, as well as those who experience little excitement during sexual stimulation, are unaware of their own genital anatomy and therefore have trouble knowing what their needs are and communicating them to a partner. Chronic use of alcohol may be a somatic factor in orgasmic dysfunction in women (Wilsnak, 1984).

Another factor is that women have different thresholds for orgasm. Although some have orgasms quickly and without much clitoral stimulation, others seem to need intense and prolonged stimulation during foreplay or intercourse. A man may conclude that he and his penis are inadequate if the female asks for or provides manual stimulation of her clitoris herself during intercourse, and his reaction can contribute to the problem.

Another possibility arose from research examining the sexual responses of non-orgasmic women to erotic films (Meston & Gorzalka, 1996). One feature of this study was determining whether activation of the sympathetic nervous system (achieved by riding a stationary bicycle) would increase genital responding to erotic films. It did in normal women but not in those with orgasmic dysfunction. Meston and Gorzalka speculate that women with orgasmic dysfunction may have a lower threshold for optimal sympathetic activation. Among normal women, low to moderate levels of sympathetic activation (as was induced by bicycle riding in their study) augment vaginal responses to erotic stimuli, but higher levels of sympathetic arousal inhibit sexual responding. Women with an orgasmic disorder may not be able to tolerate even moderate levels of sympathetic arousal and respond to it in a way that interferes with sexual response.

Yet another factor may be fear of losing control. The French have an expression for orgasm: *la petite mort*, "the little death."

Some women fear that they will scream uncontrollably, make fools of themselves, or faint. A related source of inhibition is a belief, perhaps poorly articulated, that to let go and allow the body to take over from the conscious, controlling mind is somehow unseemly.

Delayed ejaculation and premature ejaculation

Delayed ejaculation and premature ejaculation are the two orgasmic disorders of men in *DSM-5*. Delayed ejaculation is relatively rare, occurring in 3 to 8% of clients in treatment (Spector & Carey, 1990). Causes that have been put forth include fear of impregnating a female partner, withholding love, expressing hostility, and, as with female orgasmic problems, fear of letting go. In some instances, the problem may be traced to a physical source, such as spinal cord injury or certain tranquilizers (Rosen, 1991).

Premature ejaculation (PE) is probably the most prevalent sexual dysfunction among males. It is also known as early ejaculation. Sometimes premature ejaculation occurs even before the penis enters the vagina, but it more usually occurs within a few seconds of intromission. Premature ejaculation is generally associated with considerable anxiety. Data from the Canadian Male Sexual Health Council Survey found that PE is a very common medical condition that influences 16–27% of Canadian men depending on how PE is defined, and this is comparable with results found in other countries. PE was confirmed as the most common form of sexual complaint experienced by Canadian men. It was more common in British Columbia and the Atlantic provinces. PE had a negative impact on overall quality of life and sexual quality of life as reported both by the men themselves and their partners (see Brock et al., 2009). Relationship problems and a sexually dysfunctional partner can play a role (Metz et al., 1997).

There is some laboratory-based evidence that men who have premature ejaculation problems are more sexually responsive to tactile stimulation (a vibrator) than men who don't have this problem (Rowland et al., 1996). Perhaps, then, their penises are very sensitive, causing them to ejaculate more quickly. Men with premature ejaculation also have longer periods of abstinence from climactic sex than do men who are not premature ejaculators (Spiess, Geer, & O'Donohue, 1984). Learning has also been proposed as a factor (i.e., exposure to situations that promote and reinforce short ejaculation latency). For example, a man may acquire the tendency to ejaculate quickly as a result of having hurried sex because of not being in a private place and fearing detection (Metz et al., 1997).

Sexual Pain Disorders

Pain disorders associated with sex are now listed in the *DSM-5* as genito-pelvic pain/penetration disorder. There are four symptoms, any one of which is enough to warrant a diagnosis if it is linked with significant distress or impairment.

The first symptom is persistent or recurrent difficulties with vaginal penetration during intercourse. The second symptom involves persistent or recurrent pain during sexual intercourse or during penetration attempts. This has been called **dyspareunia**.

Dyspareunia is linked with alterations of all aspects of the sexual response cycle, including lower sexual desire, lower arousal, and greater dissatisfaction, resulting in less sexual intercourse and strained interpersonal relationships (Smith, Pukall, & Boyer, 2009).

The third symptom is marked fear or anxiety about vulvovaginal or pelvic pain. The final symptom is marked by involuntary spasms of the outer third of the vagina to a degree that makes intercourse impossible. This condition has been called **vaginismus**. Despite not being able to have intercourse, women with vaginismus have normal sexual arousal and have orgasms from manual or oral stimulation that does not involve penetration. According to Reissing (2009) from the University of Ottawa, it is difficult, if not impossible, to differentiate between vaginismus and dyspareunia because vaginal penetration problems apply to both.

General Theories of Sexual Dysfunctions

Having reviewed descriptions of the sexual dysfunctions and some of the causes believed to underlie each, we turn now to a consideration of general theoretical perspectives.

At one time, sexual dysfunctions were generally viewed as a result of moral degeneracy. As reviewed by LoPiccolo (2002), excessive masturbation in childhood was widely believed to lead to sexual problems in adulthood. Von Krafft-Ebing (1902) and Ellis (1910) postulated that early masturbation damaged the sexual organs and exhausted a finite reservoir of sexual energy, resulting in lessened abilities to function sexually in adulthood. Even in adulthood, excessive sexual activity was thought to underlie such problems as erectile failure. The general Victorian view was that dangerous sexual appetite had to be restrained. To discourage handling of the genitals by children, metal mittens were promoted, and to distract adults from too much sex, outdoor exercise and a bland diet were recommended. In fact, Kellogg's Corn Flakes and graham crackers were developed as foods that would lessen sexual interest. They didn't.

Psychoanalytic views have assumed that sexual dysfunctions are symptoms of underlying repressed conflicts. The analyst considers the symbolic meaning of the symptom both to understand its etiology and to guide treatment. Since sexual dysfunctions bring discomfort and psychological pain to the individual and to his or her partner, and since unimpaired sexuality is inherently pleasurable, the theme of repressed anger and aggression competing with the gratification of sexual needs pervades psychoanalytic writings. Thus, a man who ejaculates so quickly that he frustrates his female partner may be expressing repressed hostility toward women, who remind him unconsciously of his mother. A woman with vaginismus may be expressing her hostility toward men, perhaps as a result of childhood sexual abuse or more directly because of her husband's overbearing manner.

Many contemporary psychoanalysts supplement their therapy with cognitive-behavioural techniques (LoPiccolo, 1977). The spirit of rapprochement has also affected cognitive-behavioural approaches to the treatment of sexual dysfunctions, as these therapists are coming to appreciate the role of psychodynamic themes in what used to be straightforward behavioural treatments.

The most comprehensive account of the etiology of human sexual dysfunctions was offered by Masters and Johnson in their widely acclaimed book *Human Sexual Inadequacy* (1970), based on case studies from their practice. We will first examine their suggestions and then consider subsequent modifications and extensions of their ideas.

Masters and Johnson (1970) used a two-tier model of current and historical causes to conceptualize the etiology of human sexual inadequacy (Figure 14.2).

Current Causes

The current or proximal causes can be distilled down to two: fears about performance and the adoption of a spectator role. **Fear of performance** is being overly concerned with how one is performing during sex. The **spectator role** is being an observer rather than a true participant in a sexual experience. Both involve a pattern of behaviour in which the individual's focus on and concern for sexual performance impedes his or her natural sexual responses.

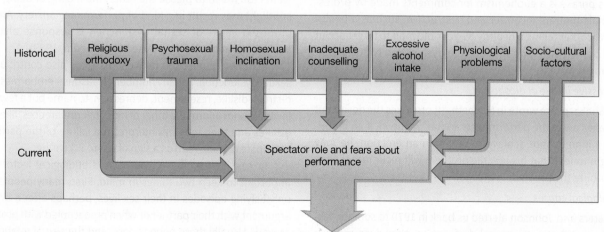

FIGURE 14.2   Historical and current causes of human sexual inadequacies, according to Masters and Johnson.

We have no conclusive evidence, however, that these factors are the causal agents in sexual dysfunctions. This is because of the directionality problem, discussed first in Chapter 4 and again in many places throughout this book. Researchers have consistently shown that performance fears do exist in people with sexual dysfunctions, but the data do not show that the fear preceded and caused the dysfunction. Someone with an erectile dysfunction, for example, may well become fearful that he will not attain an erection in a sexual encounter, and that anxiety may ensure that he is unable to become erect. But the anxiety may be functioning here as a factor that is maintaining the disorder, not one that caused it in the first place.

Historical Causes

In the Masters and Johnson model, the current, or proximal, reasons for sexual dysfunctions were hypothesized to have one or more historical antecedents:

- *Religious orthodoxy*

  Some conservative religious upbringing styles look askance at sexuality for the sake of pleasure, particularly outside marriage. Masters and Johnson found that many of their sexually dysfunctional participants had negative views of sexuality as a consequence. One female client, for example, had been taught as she was growing up not to look at herself naked in the mirror and that intercourse was reserved for marriage and then only to be endured for purposes of having children.

- *Psychosexual trauma*

  Some dysfunctions can be traced to rape or other degrading encounters. One young male client of Masters and Johnson's was told by a prostitute that he would never be able to "get the job done" with other women if he didn't "get it done here and now with a pro."

- *Homosexual inclination*

  Sexual enjoyment is understandably less if a person with homosexual inclinations tries to engage in heterosexual sex.

- *Inadequate counselling*

  This phrase is a euphemism for comments made by professionals that are incorrect and destructive, such as a health care worker telling a healthy 65-year-old man to forget about sex or a cleric saying that erectile dysfunction is God's punishment for sins.

- *Excessive intake of alcohol*

  As Shakespeare wrote in Macbeth, "It provokes the desire but it takes away the performance" (Act II, Scene 3). If an inebriated man cannot achieve or maintain an erection, he may begin to fear that his erectile problem will recur rather than attribute the problem to alcohol.

- *Biological causes*

  Masters and Johnson alerted us back in 1970 to somatic factors contributing to sexual dysfunction. Now even more is known about such factors; we have reviewed this information in our discussions of the individual dysfunctions.

- *Socio-cultural factors*

  Expectations and concerns differ between women and men and as a function of social class. For example, men have the blessing, even demand, of society to develop sexual expressiveness and to take the initiative. Despite the changes that have resulted from the feminist movement of the past 50 years, it remains questionable whether this holds true for women.

Other Views   Masters and Johnson considered sexual dysfunctions as problems in and of themselves that could be treated directly, rather than as symptoms of other intrapsychic or non-sexual interpersonal difficulties. The couples whose treatment formed the basis of their book *Human Sexual Inadequacy* (1970) had marriages that, in spite of sexual problems, were marked by caring and closeness. But as the Masters and Johnson therapy techniques became widespread and as the social milieu changed to allow more people to feel comfortable seeking help, sex therapists began to see people whose relationships were seriously impaired. In such situations, by the time a therapist is consulted, it is impossible to know whether the hostility between the two people caused the sexual problem or vice versa.

The working assumption of most sex therapists is that sexually dysfunctional couples have both sexual and interpersonal problems (Rosen & Leiblum, 1995). It is unrealistic to expect a satisfying sexual encounter when, for example, the man is angry with the woman for spending more and more time outside the home or the woman resents the man's insensitive dealings with their children. Such negative thoughts and emotions can intrude into the sexual situation and thereby inhibit whatever arousal and pleasure might otherwise be found.

Many other causes of sexual dysfunction have been identified. As mentioned earlier, people who have sexual problems are often found to lack knowledge and skill (LoPiccolo & Hogan, 1979). Sometimes their partners may have deficiencies; for example, the husbands of non-orgasmic women are often reported to be awkward lovers (Kaplan, 1974; LoPiccolo, 1977). Simply caring for the partner may not be enough to establish a mutually satisfying sexual relationship. In fact, Kaplan (1974) suggested that inhibiting anxiety can arise when one partner wants too much to please the other; the feeling of being in the spotlight may result in a kind of performance anxiety. Another proposed cause of sexual dysfunction is response anxiety— anxiety about not being aroused (Apfelbaum, 1989).

Poor communication between partners also contributes to sexual dysfunction. For any number of reasons—embarrassment, distrust, dislike, resentment, depression, to name but a few—one lover may not inform the other of his or her preferences, likes, and dislikes and then may misinterpret the failure of the partner to anticipate or mind read as a sign of not really caring.

In considering these hypothesized etiological factors, it is important to keep two things in mind. First, many people have unsatisfying episodes in their sex lives, perhaps after a bruising argument with their partner or when preoccupied with problems at work. Usually these periods pass, and the sexual relationship returns to normal. Second, many people who currently have in their lives or had in the past one or more of the pathogenic factors discussed do not develop persistent sexual dysfunctions. Although to date there is little real understanding of this phenomenon, there is speculation that other variables, such as an unusually supportive network of friends or a particularly understanding sexual partner, must be operating in these people's present lives to mitigate the putative negative effects of the pathogenic factors.

Therapies for Sexual Dysfunctions

One of the most important challenges in treating sexual dysfunctions is getting the afflicted individual to seek professional help. A five-nation survey that included Canadian data found that many men and women had experienced sexual dysfunction, but relatively few actually sought help. Overall, 75% of those with a sexual dysfunction did not seek medical assistance (Nicolosi et al., 2006).

The treatment of sexual dysfunctions was pioneered by Masters and Johnson (1970), who virtually created the sex-therapy movement. With some variations, their approach is still followed by many practitioners conducting therapy for sexual dysfunctions (LoPiccolo, 2002). The overall aim of Masters and Johnson was to reduce or eliminate fears of performance and to take the participants out of the maladaptive spectator role. They hoped that these steps would enable the couple to enjoy sex freely and spontaneously.

In this approach, assessment interviews took place over the first few days. These interviews placed considerable focus on the so-called **sexual value system**, the ideas of each partner about what was acceptable and needed in a sexual relationship. Sometimes the sexual value system of one or both partners had to be changed before sexual functioning could improve. For example, if one partner persisted in regarding sexuality as ugly and unacceptable, even the most powerful therapy would not be likely to help the partner enjoy sex.

On the third day, the therapists began to offer interpretations about why problems had arisen and why they were continuing. In all cases, the emphasis was on the problems in the relationship, not on individual difficulties of either partner. A basic premise of the Masters and Johnson therapy was that "there is no such thing as an uninvolved partner in any marriage in which there is some form of sexual inadequacy" (1970, p. 2). Whatever the problem, the couple was encouraged to see it as their mutual responsibility. At this time, the clients were introduced to the idea of the spectator role. They were told, for example, that a male with erectile problems—and often his partner as well—usually worries about how well or poorly he is doing rather than participating freely, and that this pattern of observing the state of the erection, although totally understandable in context, blocks his natural responses and greatly interferes with sexual enjoyment.

At the end of the third day an all-important assignment was given to the couple, namely, to engage in **sensate focus**. The couple was instructed to choose a time when both partners felt "a natural sense of warmth, unit compatibility . . . or even a shared sense of gamesmanship" (Masters & Johnson, 1970, p. 71). They were to undress and give each other pleasure by touching each other's bodies. The co-therapists appointed one marital partner to do the first pleasuring, or giving; the partner who was "getting" was simply to be allowed to enjoy being touched. The one being touched was not required to feel a sexual response and was responsible for immediately telling the partner if something became distracting or uncomfortable. Then the roles were to be switched. Attempts at intercourse were still forbidden. To Masters and Johnson, this approach was a way of breaking up the frantic groping common among these couples. The sensate-focus assignment usually promoted contact where none had existed for years, constituting a first step toward gradually re-establishing sexual intimacy. Once this sense of intimacy was established, couples received explicit instructions involving specific techniques.

Over the past 30 years, therapists and researchers have devised new procedures for the clinicians who seek to improve the sexual lives of dysfunctional clients. We will describe several strategies and procedures that extend Masters and Johnson's work. A therapist may choose only one technique for a given case, but the complex and multi-faceted nature of sexual dysfunctions usually demands several. Note that because psychological issues are reflected in sexual behaviours, this is one area of dysfunction where the behavioural element of CBT may be more prominent than it is in other disorders. As is the case with most other disorders, CBT can be quite effective, and this was the conclusion reached in an evaluation of the usefulness of CBT in treating female sexual pain disorders (see LoFrisco, 2011).

Anxiety Reduction Well before the publication of the Masters and Johnson therapy program, behaviour therapists appreciated that their dysfunctional clients needed gradual and systematic exposure to anxiety-provoking aspects of the sexual situation. Wolpe's systematic desensitization and in vivo desensitization (desensitization by real-life encounters) have been employed with high degrees of success (see Andersen, 1983), especially when combined with skills training. Specific interventions may include relaxation training or in vivo desensitization.

Directed Masturbation We have previously mentioned that women with orgasmic disorder frequently lack knowledge of their own sexual anatomy. Directed masturbation, devised by LoPiccolo and Lobitz (1972), is a multi-step program that supplements the Masters and Johnson program. The first step is for the woman to carefully examine her nude body, including her genitals, and identify various areas with the aid of diagrams. Next, she is instructed to touch her genitals and locate areas that produce pleasure. With this accomplished, she then increases the intensity of masturbation using erotic fantasies. If orgasm has not been achieved by this time, she is instructed to buy a vibrator and use it in her masturbation. Finally, her partner enters the picture, first watching his mate masturbate, then doing for her what she has been doing for herself, and finally having intercourse in a position that allows him to stimulate the woman's genitals manually or with a vibrator. Directed masturbation appears to add significantly to the effectiveness of treatment of orgasmic disorder (O'Donohue, Dopke, & Swingen, 1997).

Procedures to Change Attitudes and Thoughts

In what are called sensory-awareness procedures, clients are encouraged to tune in to the pleasant sensations that accompany even incipient sexual arousal. The sensate-focus exercises described by Masters and Johnson, for example, are a way of opening the individual to truly sensual and sexual feelings. Rational-emotive behaviour therapy tries to substitute less self-demanding thoughts for "musturbation," the "I must" thoughts that often cause problems for people with sexual dysfunctions. A therapist might try to reduce the pressure a man with erectile dysfunction feels by challenging his belief that intercourse is the only true form of sexual activity. Kaplan (1997) recommends several procedures to try to increase the attractiveness of sex. She has clients engage in erotic fantasies and gives them courtship and dating assignments, such as getting away for a weekend.

Skills and Communication Training

To improve sexual skills and communication, therapists assign written materials, show clients videotapes and films demonstrating explicit sexual techniques, and discuss techniques (McMullen & Rosen, 1979). Of particular importance for a range of sexual dysfunctions is encouraging partners to communicate their likes and dislikes to each other (Hawton, Catalan, & Fagg, 1992; Rosen, Leiblum, & Spector, 1994). Taken together, skills and communication training also expose clients to anxiety-provoking material—such as seeing one's partner naked—which allows for a desensitizing effect. Telling one's partner one's preferences in sex is often made more difficult by tensions that go beyond the sexual relationship, which leads us to the next strategy.

Couples Therapy

Sexual dysfunctions are often embedded in a distressed marital or other close relationship, and troubled couples usually need special training in non-sexual communication skills and other ways of relating to each other (see McCarthy & Thestrup, 2008a, 2008b). Concerns have been expressed recently that in actual practice, marital therapists do not focus enough attention on sexual matters. Indeed, writings on sex therapy emphasize the need for a systems perspective and for the therapist to appreciate that a sexual problem is embedded in a complex network of relationship factors (Wylie, 1997).

Regardless of whether couples therapy takes place, it is clear that the partner can play a key role. Research on erectile dysfunction shows quite clearly that the partner plays a key support role and incorporating the partner is key in treatment adherence, promoting realistic expectancies, and achieving positive long-term outcomes (see Dean et al., 2008). It is unfortunate, then, that men who receive treatment for erectile dysfunction often go by themselves for treatment.

Medical and Physical Procedures

As more discoveries are made about biological factors in sexual dysfunctions, it becomes increasingly important for therapists to consider whether underlying somatic problems are contributing to the dysfunction (LoPiccolo, 1992; Rosen & Leiblum,

1995). Consideration of possible somatic factors is especially important for the disorders of dyspareunia and complete erectile dysfunction. An acknowledged trend is to combine medical and other types of treatment with psychological interventions in order to enhance treatment effectiveness (see Meana & Jones, 2011).

Dyspareunia in postmenopausal women can be improved by estrogen treatments, which can reduce the thinning of vaginal tissue and improve vaginal lubrication (Walling, Anderson, & Johnson, 1990). When depression, along with severely diminished sex drive, is part of the clinical picture, antidepressant drugs can be helpful. Tranquilizers are also used as an adjunct to anxiety-reduction techniques. However, a complicating factor is that some of these psychoactive drugs themselves interfere with sexual responsiveness.

Surgical procedures are also available. A semi-rigid silicone rod can be implanted in a chronically flaccid penis, or a device can be implanted in the penis that can be stiffened with fluid from a reservoir and a small pump that is implanted in the scrotum. However, long-term follow-ups of men who have had such operations indicate that poor sexual functioning continues in many cases (Tiefer, Pedersen, & Melman, 1988). If the psychological components of the problem are not addressed, men with rod implants may continue to have sexual problems, but with a penis that is never flaccid. (With a rod, sexual interest and arousal are not necessary for intercourse, and this situation is usually not favourable for long-term psychological adjustment.) Vascular surgery involves correction of problems with blood inflow via arteries or outflow via veins in the penis. Results are mixed at best (Melman & Rossman, 1989), but the possibility exists for restoration of normal functioning because, unlike the case with implants, erection will occur only with desire and arousal (Wincze & Carey, 1991).

Several drugs have been used in the treatment of sexual dysfunctions. It is now estimated that up to 150 million men worldwide suffer from erectile dysfunction (Dean et al., 2008). Viagra (sildenafil) is now widely accepted as drug treatment for erectile dysfunction (see photo). It was first approved by the U.S. Food and Drug Administration in March 1998 and, in its first three months, was prescribed more than 3 million times. Viagra relaxes smooth muscles and thereby allows blood to flow into the penis during sexual stimulation, creating an erection. It is taken one hour before sex, and its effects last about four hours, thus allowing an erection to be maintained for a substantial period. Thus far, research indicates that 7 out of 10 men who take Viagra report improvement, whether the cause of their erectile dysfunction is biological (e.g., diabetes) or psychological (Lamberg, 1998). Generally, Viagra produces modest side effects, such as headaches. Relative to men who ingest a placebo, those taking Viagra report a much greater frequency of side effects, including headaches, flushing, dyspepsia, and visual disturbances (Tsertsvadze et al., 2009). Moreover, Viagra may be dangerous for men with cardiovascular disease, in part because erectile dysfunction and cardiovascular disease often co-exist in men (see Byrne et al., 2011).

In all instances of medical intervention, consideration of psychosocial factors remains important, for sexual

The Canadian Press/Graham Hughes

Montreal Canadiens hockey legend Guy Lafleur became the spokesperson for the first Canadian campaign for the erectile dysfunction wonder drug Viagra.

dysfunctions are almost always embedded in a complex set of interpersonal and intrapsychic conflicts. How important is the need for a broader perspective? In an intriguing paper titled "Viagra: The little blue pill with big repercussions,"

Barnett, Robleda-Gomez, and Pachana (2012) concluded that the psychological and interpersonal issues accompanying the widespread use of Viagra have been largely ignored at the societal and individual levels in a way that is simply unacceptable. The use of Viagra has interpersonal repercussions for partners and it has changed the aging process so that diminished sex interest with aging, which was previously seen as normal, now may be more likely to be seen as a problem and a deficit. Similarly, the current trend toward viewing sexual dysfunctions as medical or biological problems may divert the attention of therapists and clients from the inherently interpersonal nature of these problems, giving rise to a quick-fix mentality that is probably ill-advised (Rosen & Leiblum, 1995). Indeed, the need for a complex and integrated approach was highlighted by an international consortium of more than 200 experts from 60 countries. The Psychological and Interpersonal Committee of Sexual Function and Dysfunction concluded that the biopsychosocial model should be adopted (see Althof et al., 2005). As such, these experts advised that no single type of intervention (pharmacotherapy or marital therapy, for instance) will be sufficient for most couples experiencing sexual dysfunction and both physical and psychological factors and interventions deserve consideration.

Summary

14.1 Gender identity disorder (GID) is no longer considered a disorder according to *DSM-5*. Changes reflect comparable cultural beliefs about transgender people. The focus is now on gender dysphoria and the distress that many people feel when they have the deep and persistent conviction that there is a discrepancy between their anatomic sexual makeup and the psychological sense of self as man, woman, boy, or girl. For a time, the only kind of help available to people with gender identity issues was sex-reassignment surgery to bring certain bodily features into line with their gender identity. This procedure is no longer a highly controversial one.

14.2 In the paraphilias, unusual imagery and acts are persistent and necessary for sexual excitement or gratification. Principal paraphilias include fetishism, reliance on inanimate objects for sexual arousal; voyeurism, a marked preference for watching others in a state of undress or in sexual situations; exhibitionism, obtaining sexual gratification by exposing oneself to unwilling strangers; frotteurism, obtaining sexual contact by rubbing against or fondling women in public places; sexual sadism, a reliance on inflicting pain and humiliation on another person to obtain or increase sexual gratification; and sexual masochism, obtaining or enhancing sexual gratification through being subjected to pain, usually from a sadist. Psychoanalytic theories generally hold that paraphilias are defensive in nature, protecting the person from repressed conflicts and representing fixations at immature stages of psychosexual development. Behavioural and cognitive theorists focus more directly on the sexual behaviour itself. One view is that a fetishistic attraction to objects, such as boots, arises from accidental classical conditioning of sexual arousal. Another behavioural hypothesis posits social-skills deficiencies that make it difficult for the person to interact normally with other adults. Cognitive distortions appear to be involved, as voyeurs may claim that the women they viewed wanted to be seen.

14.3 Rape is a pattern of behaviour that results in considerable social and psychological trauma for the victim. The inclusion of rape in a discussion of human sexuality is a matter of some controversy, as many theorists regard rape as an act of aggression and violence rather than of sex. Victims of rape often do not report the incident for many reasons including the nature of the process involved in reporting it. There is substantial heterogeneity among rapists so it is really a misnomer to refer to "the rapist." Recidivism is predicted by a range of factors including the nature of the sexual deviance, lifestyle factors, social problems, deficits in problem-solving ability, and responses to treatment and supervision.

14.4 Few emotional problems are of greater interest to people than the sexual dysfunctions. These disruptions in the normal sexual response cycle are often caused by inhibitions, and they rob many people of sexual enjoyment. Disturbances include sexual desire disorders, sexual arousal disorders, orgasmic disorders, and sexual pain disorders. Although not recognized by the *DSM-5*, hypersexual arousal can also be a sexual dysfunction. The disorders can vary in severity, chronicity, and pervasiveness, and occur generally or only with certain partners and in particular situations. In no instance should a person believe that he or she has a sexual dysfunction unless the difficulty is persistent and recurrent; most people normally experience sexual problems on an intermittent basis throughout their lives. Although biological factors must be considered, especially for dyspareunia and erectile failure, the etiology of the disorders usually lies in a combination of unfavourable attitudes, difficult early experiences, fears of performance, assumption of a spectator role, relationship problems, and lack of specific knowledge and skills. Accordingly, therapies now often combine medical and psychological interventions. Controlled data suggest there is good reason to be optimistic about the ultimate ability of the mental health professions to help many people achieve at least some relief from sexual problems.

Key Terms

accommodation
acquaintance (date) rape
assimilation
child sexual abuse
delayed ejaculation
dyspareunia
exhibitionism
fear of performance
female orgasmic disorder
female sexual interest/arousal
    disorder

fetishism
forced rape
frotteurism
gender dysphoria
gender identity disorder
hypersexual disorder
hypoactive sexual desire
    disorder
incest
male erectile disorder
medical forensic examination

orgasmic reorientation
paraphilias
pedophilia
premature ejaculation
sensate focus
sensory-awareness
    procedures
sex-reassignment surgery
sexual aversion disorder
sexual dysfunctions
sexual masochism

sexual sadism
sexual value system
spectator role
statutory rape
transsexualism
transvestic disorder
vaginismus
voyeurism

Reflections: Past, Present, and Future

1. Given changes that are reflected by our contemporary society, do you think that gender identity disorder should be regarded as a disorder? Why or why not?

2. Tragically for the victims, it appears that high intelligence also contributes to "successful" multiple rapes, murders, and serial killing. Paul Bernardo, Clifford Olson, Russell Williams, Jeffrey Dahmer, and Ted Bundy are (or were) endowed with above average, even superior, intelligence. Why would intelligence be a critical consideration in our understanding of some multiple and serial rapists and killers? What role would narcissism play in the case of Paul Bernardo (and possibly in other cases, too)?

3. During the development of *DSM-III*, experts considered including "rape" in the list of sexual disorders. The specific disorder to be included was to be called something like "paraphilic coercive disorder." Why do you think the decision was made not to include the proposed disorder in the 1980 and subsequent revisions of the manual? Should rape, or some specific subtype of rape, be included in the next revision of the *DSM*? Why or why not?

4. Suppose that you specialize in sex therapy. A couple has initiated therapy with you because they are concerned that the male partner is unable to maintain an erection. What would you need to focus on during your initial meeting? Would it be important for you to make a referral to a physician? How will your conceptualization of the case influence the treatment plan that you develop?

Disorders of Childhood

LEARNING OBJECTIVES

1. Provide the two main reasons why there is a mental health crisis among young people.

2. Explain the difference between undercontrolled and overcontrolled behaviour and why typical behaviour has to be taken into account when classifying childhood disorders.

3. List the similarities and differences between two types of disorders of undercontrolled behaviour: attention-deficit/hyperactivity disorder and conduct disorder.

4. List various types of learning disorders and explain their etiology in terms of intellectual disability.

5. Describes the characteristic tendencies of autistic behaviour and research findings that help illuminate the etiology of autism.

6. List various types of anxiety disorders found among children and the factors that contribute to the development of these disorders.

Brief Case Example

Missing out on the Game

"ERIC. ERIC? ERIC!!" His teacher's voice and the laughter of his classmates roused the boy from his reverie. Glancing at the book of the girl sitting next to him, he noticed that the class was pages ahead of him. He was supposed to be answering a question about the Confederation of Canada, but he had been lost in thought about what seats he and his father would have for the baseball game they'd be attending that evening. A tall, lanky 12-year-old, Eric had just begun Grade 7. His history teacher had already warned him about being late for class and not paying attention, but Eric just couldn't seem to get from one class to the next without stopping for drinks of water or investigating an altercation between classmates. In class, he was rarely prepared to answer when the teacher called on him, and he usually forgot to write down the homework assignment. He already had a reputation among his peers as a "space cadet."

Eric's relief at the sound of the bell was quickly replaced by anxiety as he reached the playground for his physical education class. Despite his speed and physical strength, Eric was always picked last for baseball teams. His team was up to bat first, and Eric sat down to wait his turn. Absorbed in studying a pile of pebbles at his feet, he failed to notice his team's third out and missed the change of innings. The other team had already come in from the outfield before Eric realized that his team was out in the field—too

late to avoid the irate yells of his P.E. teacher to take his place at third base. Resolved to watch for his chance to field the ball, Eric nonetheless found himself without his glove on when a sharply hit ball rocketed his way; he had taken it off to toss it in the air in the middle of the pitch.

At home, Eric's father told him he had to finish his homework before they could go to the Blue Jays game. He had only one page of math problems and was determined to finish them quickly. Thirty minutes later, his father emerged from the shower to find Eric building an elaborate Lego structure on the floor of his room; the math homework was half done. In exasperation, Eric's father left for the game without him.

By bedtime, frustrated and discouraged, Eric was unable to sleep. He often lay awake for what seemed like hours, reviewing the disappointments of the day and berating himself for his failures. On this night, he ruminated about his lack of friends, his teachers' disappointment in him, and his parents' exhortations to pay attention and "get with the program." Feeling that it was hopeless to do better despite his daily resolve, Eric found himself thinking—as he often did—of suicide. Tonight he reviewed his fantasy of wandering out into the street in front of a passing car. Although Eric had never acted on his suicidal thoughts, he frequently replayed in his mind his parents' sorrow and remorse, his classmates' irritation with him, and the concern of his teachers.

The difficulty for Eric in the Brief Case Example in focusing his attention is characteristic of attention-deficit/hyperactivity disorder (ADHD)—just one of the disorders clinicians encounter when they work with children. The clinical problems loosely characterized as disorders of childhood cover a wide range of difficulties, from an attentional problem such as that suffered by Eric to depression, fear, the sometimes serious intellectual deficits found in mental retardation, the gross and sometimes callous disregard for the rights of others found in conduct disorder, and the social isolation of autism spectrum disorder. The extreme dependency of troubled children on their parents and guardians adds to the sense of responsibility these people feel and to their guilt, justified or not. Whether such children receive professional attention usually depends on the adults in their lives—parents, teachers, and school counsellors.

Chapter 15 provides an overview of disorders in childhood and adolescence and the various mental health difficulties and issues experienced by children and adolescents. Specific disorders that may exist in adulthood but that emerge primarily in childhood and adolescence are the main focus of this chapter.

15.1 The Mental Health Crisis Among Children and Adolescents

This chapter is timely in two key respects. First, there is growing evidence of an alarming epidemic of mental health issues among younger people in Canada and elsewhere. It is now estimated in Canada that at any one time, 14% of children aged 4 to 17 years (more than 800,000 children in Canada) have clinically important disorders that cause significant distress and impairment at home, at school, and in the community, with anxiety disorders being most prevalent (see Waddell et al., 2005; Waddell, 2007). A meta-analysis of data from 27 countries suggests that the worldwide estimate of mental disorders among children and adolescents is 13.4% (see Polanczyk et al., 2015). Concerns have been raised in Canada based on analyses of data from 2002 to 2014 suggesting that levels of symptoms of anxiety and depression are increasing among girls, while staying relatively stable among boys (Gariepy & Elgar, in press).

According to Waddell (2007), mental health problems are arguably the leading health problems that Canadian children face after infancy. Fewer than 25% of children with psychological disorders receive specialized treatment. Comorbidity adds to the burden since more than 50% of children with a disorder have two or more disorders at the same time (Waddell et al., 2002). According to the Early Years Study 2 (McCain, Mustard, & Shanker, 2007), it is estimated that in Ontario alone, the cost of

behavioural and mental health problems in early childhood is $30 billion per year.

Data gathered in the United States paint a particularly stark picture. Merikangas and associates have produced several reports based on the results of The National Comorbidity Survey—Adolescent Supplement (NCS-A). This study involved conducting an in-person survey of over 10,000 adolescents between the ages of 13 and 18. Diagnoses were made based on a modified version of a diagnostic interview developed by the World Health Organization. Overall, it was found that 22.2% (2 out of 9) of adolescents had a disorder with severe impairment and/or distress. The most prevalent disorders were anxiety disorders, with almost 1 in 3 having a diagnosable anxiety disorder of varying levels of impairment. A specific phobia was most common and was found in about 1 in 5 adolescents. Girls were much more likely to have anxiety disorders. The median age of onset for disorder classes was earliest for anxiety (6 years), followed by 11 years for behavioural disorders, 13 years for mood disorders, and 15 years for substance use disorders (Merikangas et al., 2010).

Flett and Hewitt (2013) advanced the argument that as alarming as current statistics are, they may actually underestimate the number of children and adolescents who need treatment. Why? Two factors were suggested. First, there are many young people who do not meet thresholds for the various diagnoses but nevertheless experience significant distress and impairment. Thus, while an official diagnosis is not warranted, the cost in suffering still warrants intervention. Second, Flett and Hewitt (2013) argued that due to self-presentational concerns and related concerns about shame and stigma, many young people are "flying under the radar" and they hide their distress behind a mask or facade. All too often, this style results in suicides or attempted suicides that occur "without warning" by young people who appeared on the surface to be highly functioning.

Second, there is a crisis in Canada because young people do not have timely access to mental health services. Quite simply, child and adolescent mental health services are inadequate in Canada (Kutcher, Hampton, & Wilson, 2010). Wait-list times in many instances are considered by many to be unacceptable and this is often exacerbated when a young person lives in a more remote area of Canada that is particularly underserviced or she or he lives in a densely populated area where service resources are outstripped by the demand. The bottom line is that far too many children and youth who need it do not receive any form of treatment or they eventually receive treatment that was needed much sooner.

To illustrate this point in general, we revisit the work of Merikangas and associates. Follow-up analyses by this research team confirmed that only a small proportion of adolescents in the United States who need some form of intervention actually receive it. Merikangas et al. (2011) conducted a more fine-grained analysis of service utilization for lifetime mental disorders based on data from over 6,000 adolescents. They found that only about one-third (36.2%) of adolescents with an identifiable mental disorder actually received service for their disorder. More severe forms of disorder were more likely to be addressed by psychological treatments, but even among those with severe impairment, only half of the adolescents requiring treatment actually received it. The highest levels of intervention were found for more observable forms of disorder, with 59.8% of adolescents with ADHD receiving treatment and 45.4% of adolescents with behavioural disorders receiving treatment. In contrast, fewer than 1 in 5 adolescents with an anxiety disorder, eating disorder, or substance abuse disorder received any form of treatment. These data accord with accounts and suggestions that internalizing problems (e.g., depression, anxiety), relative to more overt behavioural problems, are much less observable and much less likely to garner therapeutic intervention. Very similar findings were reported when this research team restricted their focus to the 12 months prior to the diagnostic interview (see Costello et al., 2014). It was determined that 45% of adolescents with psychiatric disorders received some form of professional help but fewer than 1 in 4 received specialized mental health treatment. It is estimated that specialized treatment is being received by only 31% of the children and adolescents in Canada who require it (Waddell, Shepherd, Schwartz, & Barican, 2014).

The notion that young people with internalizing symptoms are less likely to receive treatment is in keeping with the findings of a recent study conducted in Ontario, which involved an analysis of all 370 adolescent suicides that took place between 2000 and 2006 (Soor et al., 2012). Analyses were based on data obtained from the Office of the Chief Coroner of Ontario. This study found that only 66 of the 370 adolescents who took their lives had previously received psychological treatment of any kind.

Former Senator Michael Kirby observed astutely that our National Mental Health Strategy emphasizes that "child and youth mental health services must be given the highest priority in a transformed mental health service" (Kirby, 2013, p. 3) and he pointed to two reasons for this claim. First, he noted that 70% of the adults with mental health problems have symptom onset prior to the age of 20. Second, he cited some other statistics indicating that perhaps only 20% of the young people who need treatment actually get it.

The extent of the mental health problems among young people has provided the impetus for some unprecedented developments in Canada. For example, reflecting the role of schools in mental health assessment and prevention, in Canada we now have the School-Based Mental Health and Substance Abuse Consortium, a national group of Canadian researchers, policymakers, and practitioners (see Manion, Short, & Ferguson, 2013). A key role for this group is to share information with governments and school boards in order to enhance the delivery of mental health services.

Another national initiative, TRAM, was introduced in 2013. TRAM stands for a partnership in Transformational Research in Adolescent Mental Health and the goal is to establish a national network focused on adolescent mental health. This initiative was put in place to increase the early detection of mental health problems and earlier access of children and adolescents to treatment. It has led to ACCESS Canada, a pan-Canadian research network focused on enhancing early identification of disorders and improved access to appropriate treatment. Hopefully, this type of initiative will serve as a catalyst for a dramatic expansion of the number of therapists and counsellors trained in Canada. That is, better access to treatment will occur only to the extent that more trained professionals are available.

Attempts to resolve this mental health crisis need to be informed by a clear understanding of the disorders experienced and expressed by children and adolescents. Accordingly, much of this chapter is focused on the classification of disorders and descriptions of various types of disorders, along with research developments that help illuminate the nature of these disorders.

15.2 Classification of Childhood Disorders

Conceptualizations of psychopathology and other adjustment problems among children and adolescents first have to consider what is normal or typical for a particular age. The diagnosis for a child who lies on the floor kicking and screaming when they don't get their way must take into account whether the child is 2 years old or 7. The field of developmental psychopathology (see Cicchetti & Toth, 2009) involves disorders of childhood within the context of normal lifespan development, enabling us to identify behaviours that are appropriate at one stage but considered disturbed at another. A basic theme is that "because all psychopathology can be conceived as a distortion, disturbance, or degeneration of normal functioning, it follows that, if one wishes to comprehend psychopathology more fully, then one must understand the normal functioning with which psychopathology is compared" (Cicchetti & Toth, 2009, p. 17). The approach is consistent with a biopsychosocial paradigm, a multiple levels of analysis perspective, and an interdisciplinary approach.

The issue of what is typical and normal for a child has been receiving great consideration recently because of the controversial inclusion in *DSM-5* of disruptive mood dysregulation disorder, which some critics have mocked as "the temper tantrum disorder." The severe recurrent temper outbursts qualify as a disorder only if the temper outbursts occur three or more times a week and if they are inconsistent with the child's developmental level (American Psychiatric Association, 2013). Obviously, diagnosticians may vary in their subjective perception of what is appropriate at a particular developmental level.

When adjustment problems do exist, they can reflect **externalizing problems** (i.e., overt behavioural problems that are visibly expressed and on display) or **internalizing problems** (i.e., symptoms that are primarily experienced inside the person and not as noticeable, such as anxiety and depression). Children and adolescents may have externalized symptoms, internalized symptoms, or both (e.g., the angry, depressed child who acts out). A related distinction involves undercontrolled behaviours vs. overcontrolled behaviours. Undercontrolled behaviour is characterized by excess, including extreme aggressiveness. In contrast, children who are overcontrolled may seem docile, passive, and emotionally inhibited or restricted. Children and adolescents may exhibit symptoms from both extremes, as Eric did in the Brief Case Example.

The distinction between externalizing and internalizing problems is reflected in the top problems found among adolescents. Analyses of responses to a widely used measure known as the Child Behavior Checklist (CBCL; Achenbach & Rescorla, 2001) show that undercontrolled and overcontrolled behaviours are abundant. The CBCL lists over 100 problems that children may experience across multiple areas (e.g., social problems, attention problems, thought problems, conduct problems). There are parent and teacher rating versions of the CBCL as well as a youth self-report version. A comprehensive analysis of problems was conducted by examining the ratings provided by over 55,000 parents from 31 societies (see Rescorla, Achenbach, Almqvist, et al., 2007). An equally comprehensive analysis was conducted of child ratings (see Rescorla, Achenbach, Ivanova, et al., 2007). It was found that the top 10 problems reported by youths included several that reflect undercontrolled tendencies (e.g., "I argue a lot. I swear or use dirty language. I daydream a lot. I have trouble concentrating or paying attention") and overcontrolled tendencies (e.g., "I am too shy or timid. I am secretive or keep things to myself") (see Rescorla et al., 2007b). The pervasive pressure that young people experience was also clearly evident; analyses of self-reports and parent ratings showed that feeling a pressure to be perfect was among the top 10 problems listed both by youths and parents. This pressure to be perfect was included due to its link with anxiety and depression.

Chapter 15 is divided into segments that reflect disorders involving undercontrolled behaviours (e.g., conduct disorders, ADHD) vs. disorders that primarily involve overcontrolled behaviours (e.g., anxiety, depression). However, it is important to recognize that a substantial proportion of children and adolescents diagnosed with undercontrolled disorders also have problems with anxiety and depression. This has been illustrated effectively by work in the field of autism spectrum disorder that focuses on those autistic children who suffer from comorbid anxiety. In other words, children and adolescents with disorders can have the same adjustment and mental health problems experienced by other children. Jonathan Weiss from York University holds a CIHR Chair in Autism Spectrum Disorders Treatment and Care Research and he has been instrumental in drawing attention to the broader psychological needs of these children and adolescents by developing a blog that provides an impressive summary of new mental health research focused on people with autism spectrum disorders (see http://asdmentalhealth.blog.yorku.ca).

Early-onset, undercontrol problems such as autism spectrum disorder and conduct disorders are consistently found more often among boys, whereas adolescent-onset, overcontrol problems are more often found among girls across cultures (e.g., Zahn-Waxler, Shirtcliff, & Marceau, 2008). Problems of undercontrol and overcontrol can lead to significant distress in children and their families, often at great cost to society. Thus, in 1994, Canada initiated an important research study—the National Longitudinal Survey of Children and Youth (NLSCY)—to establish a national database on the characteristics and experiences of children and youth in Canada as they grow up. This ongoing study is the subject of Canadian Perspectives 15.1.

15.3 Disorders of Undercontrolled Behaviour

The child who is undercontrolled does not behave in a given setting in a way that is expected or is appropriate to his or her age. Eric, for example, should be able to follow his teacher's lessons as well as his team's progress at bat. The undercontrolled child is frequently an annoyance to adults and peers and usually gets the attention of parents and teachers more often than children who are overcontrolled. Two general categories of undercontrolled behaviour are typically differentiated: ADHD and conduct disorder.

Attention-Deficit/Hyperactivity Disorder

The term "hyperactive" is familiar to most people, especially parents and teachers. The child who is constantly in motion, tapping fingers, jiggling legs, poking others for no apparent reason, talking out of turn, and fidgeting is often called hyperactive. These children also have difficulty concentrating on the task at hand for an appropriate period of time. The current diagnostic term is **attention-deficit/hyperactivity disorder (ADHD)**.

Virginia Douglas, a professor emerita of the McGill University Department of Psychology, played an instrumental role in refining our understanding of ADHD in the 1970s. Until that time, hyperactive children were identified as having "minimal brain damage" or "minimal brain dysfunction" because of apparent similarities between their hyperactive behaviours and the behaviours expressed by certain children with brain damage. Because brain damage could not be detected, more emphasis was placed on the hyperactivity, and the disorder came to be known as "hyperactive child syndrome" and "hyperkinetic reaction of childhood." Douglas (1972) is credited with being the first researcher to note the attentional problems in ADHD.

Canadian Perspectives 15.1

The National Longitudinal Survey of Children and Youth (NLSCY)

The National Longitudinal Survey of Children and Youth (NLSCY) involves approximately 23,000 children from 13,439 households with at least one child, in all 10 Canadian provinces. The children ranged from birth to 11 years old at the outset of the study in 1994 and are being studied prospectively, every two years, throughout their childhood into adulthood (age 25). Complete longitudinal data from ages 0 to 24 was to be available in 2018. The project has yielded many illuminating findings, some of which were first described in the initial report *Growing Up in Canada* (Human Resources Development Canada and Statistics Canada, 1996), including the following: (1) low birth weight is associated with numerous childhood health problems and is more likely if a mother smokes during pregnancy; and (2) children with difficult temperaments have parents characterized by greater hostility.

Numerous research reports involve findings from the NLSCY. We mention a few specific studies to illustrate the rich findings from this "gold mine" of data:

- Immigrant children actually had better adjustment overall than children born in Canada! New immigrant children had lower prevalence rates of hyperactivity, emotional disorders, and conduct disorders. Poor immigrant families seem to provide a supportive environment that fosters a greater sense of resilience than the poor families of children born in Canada (Beiser, Hou, Hyman, & Tousignant, 1998).

- The problems of aggressive girls were quite similar to those experienced by aggressive boys. Aggressive girls (relative to nonaggressive girls) suffered in terms of interpersonal relationships, low self-esteem, difficult behaviour, and academic problems (Pepler & Sedighdeilami, 1998).

- Exposure to a depressed mother predicted a child's problems involving aggression and hyperactivity; however, emotional problems in the child were associated with subsequent depression in the mother. Thus, bi-directional influences were apparent (Elgar et al., 2003). Moreover, adolescents exposed to maternal depression during middle childhood were subsequently more likely to use substances (alcohol, cigarettes, marijuana) and engage in violent and nonviolent delinquent behaviour (Wickham et al., 2015).

- Children age 10 and over were followed until they were 16 to 17 years of age to determine factors related to drug use. Parental rejection was a positive predictor of initial drug use, whereas warmth was a negative predictor over time and appears to be most important in minimizing later drug use. Deviant peer affiliations were a positive predictor of drug use (Pires & Jenkins, 2007).

- Neighbourhood poverty and child hunger are associated with suicidal thoughts and adolescence. The associations were not explained by various other risk factors (Dupere, Leventhal, & Lacourse, 2009; McIntyre, Williams, Lavorato, & Patten, 2013). The prevalence of child hunger was 5.7% (McIntyre et al., 2013).

- Functional impairment in children is associated with increased internalizing symptoms at baseline but is not related to developmental trajectories in internalizing symptoms. The association between functional impairment and internalizing symptoms is constant, linear, and similar for girls and boys. However, internalizing symptoms in girls increased from ages 10 to 15, while it declined for boys (Cleverley, Bennett, & Duku, 2013).

Thinking Critically

Assume that you are the NLSCY project director and that the initial findings point to some interventions that could improve the well-being of children in the study. From an ethical perspective, should you implement the interventions, even though it will mean that the study will be compromised? Can you justify holding off on interventions for some children in the interest of approved research design?

Children with ADHD seem to have particular difficulty controlling their activity in situations that call for sitting still, such as in the classroom or at mealtimes. They appear unable to stop moving or talking when asked to be quiet. They are disorganized, erratic, tactless, obstinate, and bossy. Their activities and movements seem haphazard. They smash their toys and exhaust their family and teachers. ADHD children have difficulty in adjusting to a typical classroom environment (Barkley, DuPaul, & McMurray, 1990).

These children often encounter problems in social interactions with peers and are confronted with peer rejection and social isolation (de Boo & Prins, 2007). Their behaviour is often aggressive and annoying to others. They tend to miss subtle social cues, such as noticing when playmates are tiring of their constant jiggling. They frequently misinterpret the wishes and intentions of their peers and make inadvertent social mistakes, such as reacting aggressively because they assume that a neutral action by a peer was meant to be aggressive. (Such cognitive misattributions are also found in some children with conduct disorder.) Children with ADHD can know what the socially correct action is in hypothetical situations but be unable to translate this knowledge into appropriate behaviour in real-life social interactions (Whalen & Henker, 1999). Nevertheless, despite these deficits, some evidence suggests that boys with ADHD may have an illusory bias that sees them overestimate the actual quality of their social behaviours (see Hoza et al., 2000).

About 15 to 30% of children with ADHD have a learning disability (e.g., Casey, Rourke, & Del Dotto, 1996). Children diagnosed with ADHD and mathematical and reading disorders are more severely impaired and attain lower IQ (intelligent quotient), language, and academic scores relative to those with ADHD alone (Capano et al., 2008). Approximately 25% of children with ADHD exhibit comorbidity with anxiety disorders (Jarrett & Ollendick, 2008).

The ADHD diagnosis does not properly apply to youngsters who are rambunctious, active, or slightly distractible, for in the early school years children are often so. It would be a misuse of the term simply because a child is livelier and more difficult to control than a parent or teacher prefers. The diagnosis is reserved for truly extreme and persistent cases. The symptoms of ADHD are varied; some children primarily have poor attention while other children have difficulties primarily due to hyperactive-impulsive behaviour, but most children have both sets of symptoms (see Levy, Hay, Bennett, & McStephen, 2005).

New longitudinal data provide some evidence indicating that the two sets of symptoms may not emerge at the same time, with hyperactivity-impulsivity contributing to the subsequent emergence over time of inattentiveness (Greven, Asherson, Rijsdijk, & Plomin, 2011). This inattentiveness often confers significant cost. Breslau et al. (2010) reported that increases in teacher-rated attention problems from age 6 to 11 were followed by declines in academic achievement in math and reading from age 11 to 17. Similarly, Galera et al. (2009) conducted a longitudinal study and found a link between childhood ADHD symptoms and negative academic outcomes eight years later.

Children with both attentional problems and hyperactivity are more likely to develop conduct problems and oppositional behaviour, to be placed in special classes for behaviour-disordered children, and to have peer difficulties (Faraone, Biederman, Weber, & Russell, 1998; Beauchaine, Hinshaw, & Pang, 2010). Children with ADHD typically use long-term support from public sector services, with high rates of contact with schools, educational professionals, and the criminal justice system (see Ford et al., 2008). This link between ADHD and oppositional behaviour was the impetus for recent research that evaluated whether an early years intervention created initially for children prone to oppositional problems could reduce levels of externalizing problems, interpersonal problems, and attentional problems in 4- to 6-year-olds with ADHD. This program involved six months of treatment that included both child and parent training components. Initial results are quite favourable and suggest that the substantial reductions in externalizing symptoms, hyperactivity, and inattentiveness are maintained at one-year follow-up (see Webster-Stratton, Reid, & Beauchaine, 2013).

The prevalence of ADHD has been difficult to establish because of varied definitions of the disorder over time and differences in the populations sampled. A systematic review of 102 studies comprising over 170,000 participants from all world regions estimated the worldwide-pooled prevalence was 5.29% (Polanczyk et al., 2007). It is generally believed that the disorder is more common in boys than in girls, but the sex difference may be overestimated because boys are more likely to

be referred to clinics because of a higher likelihood of aggressive and anti-social behaviour. However, a comparative study in Toronto showed that ADHD girls, relative to ADHD boys and control participants, have significantly greater impairment on a wide range of measures (Rucklidge & Tannock, 2001).

A recent investigation suggests that there may be racial and ethnic disparities in the diagnosis of ADHD. This study involved a re-analysis of data from the Early Childhood Longitudinal Study conducted in the United States and it confirmed that children who were African-American, Hispanic, or a member of some other minority group, compared with Caucasian participants, were less likely to receive a diagnosis (Morgan et al., 2013) and this was seen as underdiagnosis. One factor that decreased the likelihood of receiving a diagnosis was not having health insurance. Factors associated with increased risk of being diagnosed were being a boy, being raised by an older mother, displaying more externalized problem behaviours, and being raised in an English-speaking house.

It was once thought that hyperactivity simply went away by adolescence. This belief was challenged by numerous longitudinal studies (e.g., Biederman et al., 1996). Although most people with childhood ADHD no longer satisfy the full criteria for ADHD by the age of 30 or 40 years, about 50% will exhibit ongoing psychosocial impairment (Gerlach, 2009). As a result of the growing awareness of ADHD that persists in adults, *DSM-5* has symptom descriptions that have been altered slightly to facilitate their application across the lifespan (see American Psychiatric Association, 2013) and a symptom cut-off for adults has been added (five or more symptoms vs. the six or more symptoms required among children and adolescents).

The first large population-based longitudinal study of adult ADHD has recently been completed and it yielded several new insights. This study was sponsored by the prestigious Mayo Clinic and involved following all children in Rochester, Minnesota, born between 1976 and 1982. They were followed throughout adulthood until about 27 years of age and it was found that among those with ADHD in childhood, the disorder persisted into adulthood in 29.3% of the cases. Overall, among adults with ADHD, about 4 out of 5 had at least one other disorder. ADHD was also associated with higher mortality risk (Barbaresi et al., 2013). The authors concluded that there is a need to take a chronic disease approach to ADHD.

The National Comorbidity Survey Replication (Kessler et al., 2006) indicated that the overall prevalence of adult ADHD is 4.4%. In 2009, Major League Baseball granted "therapeutic use" drug exemptions to 108 players for the use of otherwise banned stimulants because the players were diagnosed with ADHD (Campbell, 2009). This is noteworthy because it translates into a prevalence rate of approximately 11.7%, given that there were 926 players at that time. Some have suggested that the apparent epidemic of adult ADHD among baseball players is overestimated and was simply fuelled by attempts to benefit from drugs used to increase attention.

The expression of ADHD in adults vs. children has more emphasis placed on inattention symptoms and less emphasis on impulsivity and hyperactivity (Bonvicini, Faraone, & Scassellati, 2016). Studies of ADHD in adulthood suggest that affective, anxiety, substance abuse, and anti-social disorders are common comorbidities (see Antshel et al., 2009 for review). While most adults with ADHD are employed and financially independent, these individuals generally reach a lower socio-economic level and change jobs more frequently than would normally be expected. One study (Kessler, Lane, Stang, & Van Brunt, 2009) reported that adult ADHD employees of a large manufacturing firm showed a 4–5% reduction in work performance and relatively more sickness absence and workplace accidents and injuries. Only a small minority of these workers were in therapy. A study in Montreal found that family and marital functioning was impaired in families with an ADHD adult (Minde et al., 2003). An earlier study of adult women with ADHD in Toronto found that they had impairments in social functioning, reduced self-esteem, elevated stress, and a self-blaming attributional style (Rucklidge & Kaplan, 1997).

Biological Theories of ADHD   The search for causes of ADHD is complicated by the heterogeneity of children given this diagnosis; any factor found to be associated with the syndrome is perhaps linked with only some of the diagnosed cases. At present, according to Thapar, Cooper, Eyre, and Langley (2013), the main conclusion that can be reached is that "no single risk factor explains ADHD" (p. 3).

Next we provide an overview of factors believed to be involved in the etiology of ADHD. It is helpful to consider these factors within the context of some very insightful comments by Nigg (2012) about future directions in etiology research. First, in light of mounting evidence for the role of genetic factors (see the section "Genetic factors"), Nigg (2012) cautioned that future research is likely to highlight the role of early experiences, including prenatal events that influence genetic expression. He predicts that increasing attention will be given to the possible role of environmental causality and the role of the gene by environment interaction. Second, current neurological research will only be meaningful if there is an expanded focus that reflects cultural variations and rapid changes in social factors and technology use by children and adolescents. Regarding race and cultural differences, Nigg (2012) noted that the structure of ADHD is similar around the world and there is evidence of universality (see Bauermeister, Canino, Planczyk, & Rohde, 2012). However, whereas ADHD was previously under-represented in African-American children vs. Caucasian children, this is no longer the case and it is important to understand why this shift has occurred, as well as why African-American children with ADHD seem to have more behavioural problems than Caucasian children with ADHD (see Miller, Nigg, & Miller, 2009). Finally, Nigg (2012) highlighted the need for more work on the phenotype for ADHD symptoms to assess whether the structure is dimensional or categorical.

Genetic factors   Research suggests a genetic predisposition toward ADHD, with estimates of heritability at approximately 75% (Biederman & Farone, 2005). Overall, ADHD is viewed as having one of the most heritable phenotypes (see Nigg, 2012). Recall in Chapter 11 that work by the Cross-Disorder Group of the Psychiatric Genomics Consortium (2013) examining several specific genetic variations that apply to all five disorders indicate that all five disorders, which include ADHD, involve single-nucleotide polymorphisms in regions on chromosomes 3p21 and 10q24, and in two calcium subunits: CACNA1C and CANB2 (Cross-Disorder Group of the Psychiatric Genomics Consortium, 2013). What remains to be determined is how the same genetic vulnerability develops into ADHD instead of some other disorder such as schizophrenia or depression. Some insights have emerged from a study of genetic effects in adult ADHD. Initial indications are that the gene BAIAP2 is implicated in ADHD susceptibility among adults (Bonvicini et al., 2016).

Overall, however, research on genetic risk factors has yielded only small effect sizes (Thapar et al., 2013). Moreover, exactly what is inherited in ADHD also needs more inquiry, but some studies point to differences in brain function and structure. As noted in Chapter 2 in Focus on Discovery 2.1 on the neuroscience of ADHD, evidence implicates frontal striatal circuitry in ADHD, reductions in volume throughout the cerebrum and cerebellum, and delays in cortical maturation, and the hypothesis that ADHD is due to a dopamine deficit (see Poissant et al., 2008; Shaw et al., 2007; Vaidya & Stollstorff, 2008).

Goos, Crosbie, Payne, and Schachar (2009) proposed motor response inhibition as a prime marker of underlying liability (endophenotype) in ADHD. They studied inhibitory control in children with ADHD, unaffected siblings, and their biological parents to determine covariation in inhibitory control within families. Children with ADHD manifested an inhibitory control deficit, as did their parents, and this deficit was independent of symptom severity in both generations. This deficit in children was predicted by the ability of their parents, particularly their fathers. Goos et al. (2009) concluded that the findings "indicate that an inhibitory control deficit is a cognitive marker of genetic risk shared by parents and offspring" (p. 711).

Environmental toxins   Popular theories of ADHD have involved the role of environmental toxins. A biochemical theory put forth by Feingold (1973) proposed that food additives upset the central nervous system (CNS) of hyperactive children, and he prescribed a diet free of such additives. Well-controlled studies of the Feingold diet found that very few ADHD children respond positively to it (Goyette & Conners, 1977). Similarly, the once-popular view that refined sugar can cause ADHD has not been supported (Wolraich, Wilson, & White, 1995). More recent data have linked higher hyperactivity scores at age 7 with excessive exposure early in life to traffic-related air pollution (Newman et al., 2013).

While there is some evidence for lead exposure being linked with ADHD, research on certain environmental risk factors still is in its early stages and these factors can only be regarded as possibilities worth exploring (see Thapar et al., 2013). Methodologically sound research in this area is only beginning to emerge, according to Thapar et al. (2013).

TABLE 15.1 **Possible Environmental Risk Factors in ADHD**

Pre- and Perinatal Factors	Environmental Toxins	Dietary Factors	Psychosocial Adversity
Maternal smoking, alcohol, and substance misuse	Organophosphate pesticides	Nutritional deficiencies; e.g., zinc, magnesium, polyunsaturated fatty acids	Family adversity and low income
Risk but not proven causal risk factor	*Risk but not proven causal risk factor*	*Correlate not yet proven risk factor*	*Correlate not yet proven risk factor*
Maternal stress	Polychlorinated biphenyls	Nutritional surpluses; e.g., sugar, artificial food colourings	Conflict/parent–child hostility
Risk but not proven causal risk factor	*Risk but not proven causal risk factor*	*Correlate not yet proven risk factor*	*Correlate not yet proven risk factor*
Low birth weight and prematurity	Lead	Low/high IgG foods	Severe early deprivation
Risk but not proven causal risk factor	*Risk but not proven causal risk factor*	*Correlate not yet proven risk factor*	*Risk, likely causal risk factor*

Source: Thapar, A., Cooper, M., Eyre, O., & Langley, K. (2013). What have we learnt about the causes of ADHD? *Journal of Child Psychology and Psychiatry, 54*, 3–16. Reprinted with permission from John Wiley & Sons, Inc. Note that IgG refers to the antibody Immunoglobulin G.

Table 15.1 summarizes environmental risk factors that have been explored and what the evidence seems to indicate. This table includes but goes beyond environmental toxins. One possibility is that there are multiple pathways and that environmental toxins play a role in some proportion of ADHD cases. Note that in Table 15.1, the environmental factor seen as most likely implicated is severe early deprivation, which is a condition implicated in a wide range of disorders.

Psychological Theories of ADHD

The child psychoanalyst Bruno Bettelheim (1973) proposed a diathesis–stress theory, suggesting that hyperactivity develops when a predisposition to ADHD is coupled with an authoritarian upbringing. Or, as Ross and Ross (1982) suggested, hyperactivity may be modelled on the behaviour of parents and siblings. However, such psychological theories have not been supported by research. Neurological and genetic factors have far greater research support. In any event, the parent–child relationship is bidirectional. Just as parents of hyperactive children give their offspring more commands and have negative interactions with them, so hyperactive children have been found to be less compliant and more negative in interactions with parents (Barkley, Karlsson, & Pollard, 1985). Stimulant medication reduces hyperactivity and increases compliance in ADHD children. When such medication is used, the parents' commands and negative behaviour decrease (see Barkley, 1990), suggesting that it is the child's behaviour that negatively affects the parents rather than the reverse.

Treatment of ADHD

In 2002, a consensus statement on ADHD by leading experts indicated that fewer than half of those with ADHD receive treatment. The need for treatment is underscored by the fact that those with ADHD, relative to normal people, are more likely to drop out of school, have no or few friends, engage in anti-social activities, use tobacco or illicit drugs, contract a sexually transmitted disease, and drive at excessive speeds and have multiple car accidents (Barkley, 2002).

An international team, led by Stan Kutcher from Dalhousie University, concluded that the optimal treatment for ADHD is to "combine pharmacotherapy, which addresses core biological symptoms, with psychosocial intervention, which focuses on the youngsters' and families' attitudes and life strategies" (Kutcher et al., 2004, p. 19).

Stimulant drugs Stimulant drugs, in particular methylphenidate, or Ritalin, have been prescribed for ADHD since the early 1960s (Sprague & Gadow, 1976). One perception that has emerged is that ADHD is overdiagnosed and overtreated. These concerns were fuelled by dramatic increases in the 1990s in the use of Ritalin to treat ADHD. Canadian surveys indicate that there was almost no change in the use of Ritalin between 1983 and 1990 but that use between 1990 and 1996 increased by 3 to 4.5 times the previous levels of use (Miller et al., 1998). A rising number of Canadian children aged 2 to 4 years were prescribed methylphenidate (see Romano et al., 2002). In 2012, the *Globe and Mail* posed the question "Are we medicating a disorder or treating boyhood as a disease?" when the newspaper obtained data indicating that prescriptions for Ritalin and related drugs had increased dramatically—by 2.9 million in 2009, representing a four-year increase of 43% (Abraham, 2012).

Meanwhile, in the United States, a 10-year study from 2000 to 2010 found that the diagnosis of ADHD increased by two-thirds and accounted for 10.4 million visits for treatment by 2010. Data analyses indicated a changing trend in treatment providers, with an increasing proportion of treatment being provided by psychiatrists. It was also the case that in 3 out of 4 instances of people receiving treatment, they were males (Garfield et al., 2012). Does this apparent epidemic simply reflect more lax prescribing practices? This issue needs to be closely examined in the coming years.

Psychological treatment Other than medication, the most effective treatments for ADHD children involve parent training and changes in classroom management based on operant-conditioning principles. The children are monitored

Point systems and star charts, which are common in classrooms, are particularly useful in the treatment of ADHD.

at home and in school and are reinforced for behaving appropriately; for example, for remaining in their seats and working on assignments. Point systems and star charts are typical components of these programs (see photo). Youngsters earn points and younger children earn stars for behaving in certain ways; the children can then spend their earnings for rewards. The focus is on improving academic work, completing household tasks, or learning specific social skills, not on reducing signs of hyperactivity, such as running around or jiggling.

School interventions for children with ADHD include training teachers to understand the unique needs of these children and to apply operant techniques in the classroom, initiating peer tutoring in academic skills, and having teachers provide daily reports to parents about in-school behaviour, with follow-up rewards and consequences at home. Certain classroom structures have a favourable impact on children with ADHD. In the ideal classroom environment, teachers vary the presentation format and the materials used for tasks, keep assignments brief, provide immediate feedback on accuracy, have an enthusiastic and task-focused style, provide breaks for physical exercise, use computer-assisted drill programs, and schedule academic work during the morning hours. Such environmental changes are designed to accommodate the limitations imposed by this disorder rather than to change the disorder itself (Pfiffner & Barkley, 1998).

A meta-analysis of 174 studies of behavioural treatments for ADHD (Fabiano et al., 2009) led to the conclusion that "there is strong and consistent evidence that behavioral treatments are effective for treating ADHD" (p. 129). Nonetheless, not all treatments are equally effective and some may not be considered "evidence based." For example, de Boo and Prins (2007) reviewed the research on the outcome of social skills training for social incompetence in children with ADHD, including mediators (e.g., social cognitive skills) and moderators (e.g., comorbidity). They concluded that there is now sufficient evidence and knowledge to adapt the social skills paradigm and to guide research toward making it a more effective, established intervention for ADHD children who are confronted with peer rejection and social isolation. Toplak et al. (2008) from York

University identified 26 studies of cognitive-behavioural, cognitive, and "neural-based" intervention approaches that are not currently considered evidence-based practice. Although some of these methods show promise in the treatment of ADHD, their analysis indicated that further research is needed to determine the efficacy of these approaches.

Stimulant medication vs. psychological treatment

The MTA Cooperative Group Study (MTA; 1999) comparison of Ritalin with an operant intervention indicated better outcomes with the drug alone than with the behaviour therapy program alone. Although a treatment combining the two was not superior to the drug alone, it did show an advantage of not requiring as high a dosage of Ritalin to reduce ADHD symptoms. Further, the combined treatment improved positive functioning, such as social skills, more than the drug alone. This study deserves additional discussion because it was the first of its kind in treatment research on children. MTA refers to the Multimodal Treatment Study of Children with ADHD. It involved six collaborating academic sites, including one site in Canada. Multi-site studies have seldom been conducted on childhood disorders. More importantly, this study was the largest and most methodologically rigorous study conducted thus far (Schachar, 1999). This lends credence to its main finding that a carefully managed medication approach is superior to behavioural treatment and routine community care in treating ADHD symptoms, but that more general areas of functioning (i.e., social skills and academic performance) were enhanced by a combined form of medication and behavioural treatment (see Jensen et al., 1999). Secondary analyses confirmed the benefits of the combined treatment, which have come to be referred to as "the multimodality superiority effect" (Swanson et al., 2001). The multimodality superiority effect is reduced among families who have a child with extreme ADHD symptoms and at least one depressed parent (Owens et al., 2003).

More recently, van der Oord, Prins, Oosterlaan, and Emmelkamp (2008) conducted a meta-analysis that compared effect sizes of methylphenidate, psychosocial treatments, and their combination on ADHD, concurrent oppositional or conduct symptoms, social behaviours, and academic functioning. Stringent inclusion criteria were used, including a formal diagnosis of ADHD, aged 6 to 12 years, a randomized controlled trial (RCT) design, efficacy established with parent and teacher rating scales, behavioural or cognitive-behavioural psychosocial treatment, short-acting methylphenidate treatment, and treatment conducted in a clinical setting. The reviewers concluded that both methylphenidate and psychosocial treatments are effective; however, psychosocial treatments were less effective than both other treatment conditions. It was concluded that psychosocial treatment had no additional value to methylphenidate, at least for the reduction of ADHD and teacher-rated oppositional and conduct symptoms. Note, however, that for social behaviour and parent-rated oppositional defiant disorder, all three treatment strategies were equally effective. Unfortunately, for improvement of academic functioning, van der Oord et al. (2008) concluded that none of the treatments was effective.

Laura Dwight/Reuters - ImagesArtist

Student Perspectives 15.1

Using Adderal as a Study Aid: Prevalence and Motivation

"The benefits are overblown, the risks are underplayed, and frankly, there's no really good reason to do this."

—Dr. Paul Herbert, Editor-in-Chief of the Canadian Medical Association Journal, *discussing the misuse of Ritalin and Adderal by students (see Abma, 2011)*

One of the most pressing problems on university and college campuses is the number of students who are misusing Adderal and Ritalin as study aids. Why the misuse and just how widespread is this problem? These drugs are included among a class of drugs that have been labelled as "smart pills" and there is some limited evidence that their use is linked with enhancements in some aspects of memory, such as declarative memory, but the overall evidence of benefits is not extensive (see Smith & Farah, 2011). Indeed, a recent study of almost 900 college students found no evidence of use resulting in higher grade point averages (Arria et al., in press). Nevertheless, the perceived benefits are cited by students. For instance, a CBC News report in April 2013 quoted a University of Manitoba student who admitted that he had purchased Adderal XR from a friend. He told the CBC that "I have five of them on me here . . . I feel it's helping me concentrate and focus on schoolwork . . . (It's) much easier than without it" (CBC News, 2013, April 18).

Reliable estimates for the amount of misuse are not readily available, but a study conducted with 3,400 students from Duke University and UNC-Greensboro found that 5.4% of students admitted to the nonmedical use of these drugs in the previous six months. The main reason given is that it enhanced their ability to study. By and large, students perceived it as a benefit despite the health risks involved (see Rabiner et al., 2009).

Estimates of the amount of use vary across studies, however. Another recent investigation is noteworthy because it followed students across four years. Overall, 61.8% of students reported being offered these drugs by their fourth year, with 31% indicating some use (Garnier-Dykstra et al., 2012). Usage was predicted by having a lower grade point average and also having a cannabis or alcohol abuse disorder. Different surveys confirmed that the vast majority of students indicated that their primary motivation for use was studying.

Programmatic research on this topic is being conducted by DeSantis and colleagues. Their study of 1,811 undergraduates yielded higher estimates, with 34% of students (about 1 in 3)

reporting illegal use of ADHD stimulants because it was not prescribed for them (DeSantis, Webb, & Noar, 2008). This estimate is comparable to the one provided by Garnier-Dyskstra et al. (2012). Not surprisingly, students reported that they were more likely to use ADHD stimulants during periods of high academic stress and they were taken in order to reduce fatigue. DeSantis and colleagues have recently turned their attention to who supplies these drugs. Drugs are often obtained from students who are not taking their own prescribed medication. Indeed, having a friend with a prescription is the most common form of access (Garnier-Dykstra et al., 2012). These "distributors" are more likely to be a member of a fraternity and belong to "at-risk" peer groups (DeSantis, Anthony, & Cohen, 2013). Assessment of the distributors further indicated that they have misguided subjective perceptions, as reflected by their overestimates of the percentage of students misusing these drugs.

Other research indicates that the use of these drugs is more common among students suffering from cognitive forms of test anxiety (Sattler & Wiegel, 2013). Other predictors of higher usage levels include being a member of a fraternity or sorority and having higher levels of anxiety, stress, impulsivity, and restlessness (Dussault & Weyandt, 2013). Students are substantially more likely to use these drugs if they also engage in various forms of academic dishonesty (Gallucci, Martin, Hackman, & Hutcheson, in press).

Students opting to use ADHD stimulants have likely engaged in their own cost-benefit analysis but the chief problem according to Ragan, Bard, and Singh (2013) is that even though the risks are well-documented, they are poorly appreciated by students. The health risks were outlined in a 2011 editorial in the *Canadian Medical Association Journal (CMAJ)* (see Rosenfeld et al., 2011). The risks include possible death, hypertension, cardiac arrhythmias, dependence, and depression. Of course, there are also the risks of engaging in illegal behaviour. Another issue identified by Ragan et al. (2013) is that some of the drugs being purchased are obtained via the Internet and there is no real control or knowledge of exactly what is in the pills being purchased.

This problem is so great that Duke University declared in 2012 that the use of these drugs is a form of cheating that will be treated like other academic offences. There is no doubt that other universities and colleges will follow suit. But this does not necessarily result in less use and it is clear that information sessions and interventions are needed given the inherent dangers of using these drugs in this manner. Indeed, as part of their editorial, the *CMAJ* editors noted that failure to address the problem could constitute significant liability for university and college administrators (see Rosenfeld et al., 2011).

Although there is extensive evidence of treatment-related improvements, significant treatment challenges remain. As part of their general endorsement of the promise of neurofeedback training as a way to treat ADHD, Lofthouse et al. (2012) noted that fine-grained analyses of the MTA study indicate that many children do not respond to drug treatment, with treatment success being only about 50%. In addition, they noted that there is a large proportion of parents who will simply not allow medication to be administered to their children. Why? One reason is that stimulant medication has side effects, including transient loss of appetite and sleep problems. There

has been considerable controversy about possible adverse effects of stimulants on brain development, but Shaw, Sharp, & Morrison (2009) determined from two neuroanatomic MRI scans (at 12.5 years and 16.4 years on average) that stimulant treatment for ADHD was not associated with differences in the development of the cerebral cortex during adolescence.

Concerns have also been raised about the safety of stimulant medications and a possible association between stimulant use for ADHD treatment and serious cardiovascular events, including sudden death. Although the events are very rare, Gould et al. (2009) concluded that there is, in fact, an association between the use of stimulants and sudden unexplained death among both children and adolescents. Although this finding needs to be considered in the context of the evidence for the benefits of stimulants, it will no doubt fuel further debate over clinical recommendations for physicians and families. Although there has been some concern that stimulant treatment, especially early exposure, increases susceptibility to subsequent substance use disorders, a 10-year prospective follow-up study (Biederman et al., 2008) found no evidence that stimulant treatment affects the risk for substance use disorders in children and adolescents with ADHD followed into young adulthood.

More generally, one risky side effect of the widespread prescription of stimulants has clearly emerged. *Newsweek* magazine was among the first sources to report that children are using Ritalin and other stimulants obtained from their siblings or friends as recreational drugs (Leland, 1995). Its use also spread among high school and college students not suffering from ADHD who found that snorting it like cocaine helped them focus better on their schoolwork and ward off fatigue (Tennant, 1999). This issue of growing importance is addressed in Student Perspectives 15.1.

Conduct Disorder

The term **conduct disorder** encompasses a wide variety of undercontrolled behaviour. *DSM-5* focuses on behaviours that violate the basic rights of others and major societal norms. Nearly all such behaviour is illegal. The types of behaviour considered symptomatic of conduct disorder include being aggressive and cruel toward people or animals, damaging property, lying, and stealing (see photo). Conduct disorder denotes a frequency and severity of acts that go beyond the mischief and pranks common among children and adolescents. Often the behaviour is marked by callousness, viciousness, and lack of remorse, making conduct disorder one of the criteria for anti-social personality disorder. A distinguishing element according to *DSM-5* is limited prosocial emotions. The *DSM-5* criteria for conduct disorder are reproduced in Table 15.2.

A related but lesser-known category in the *DSM* is **oppositional defiant disorder (ODD)**. There is a debate as to whether ODD is distinct from conduct disorder, a precursor to it, or merely an earlier manifestation of it (Loeber et al., 1993). Historically, ODD could be diagnosed if a child did not meet the criteria for conduct disorder, but this exclusion criterion

---

TABLE 15.2   *DSM-5* **Diagnostic Criteria for Conduct Disorder**

A. A repetitive and persistent pattern of behavior in which the basic rights of others or major age-appropriate societal norms or rules are violated, as manifested by the presence of at least three of the following 15 criteria in the past 12 months from any of the categories below, with at least one criterion in the past 6 months:

Aggression to People and Animals

1. Often bullies, threatens, or intimidates others.

2. Often initiates physical fights.

3. Has used a weapon that can cause serious physical harm to others (e.g., a bat, brick, broken bottle, knife, gun).

4. Has been physically cruel to people.

5. Has been physically cruel to animals.

6. Has stolen while confronting a victim (e.g., mugging, purse snatching, extortion, armed robbery).

7. Has forced someone into sexual activity.

Destruction of Property

8. Has deliberately engaged in fire setting with the intention of causing serious damage.

9. Has deliberately destroyed others' property (other than by fire setting).

Deceitfulness or Theft

10. Has broken into someone else's house, building, or car.

11. Often lies to obtain goods or favors or to avoid obligations (i.e., "cons" others).

12. Has stolen items of nontrivial value without confronting a victim (e.g., shoplifting, but without breaking and entering; forgery).

Serious Violations of Rules

13. Often stays out at night despite parental prohibitions, beginning before age 13 years.

14. Has run away from home overnight at least twice while living in the parental or parental surrogate home, or once without returning for a lengthy period.

15. Is often truant from school, beginning before age 13 years.

B. The disturbance in behavior causes clinically significant impairment in social, academic, or occupational functioning.

C. If the individual is age 18 years or older, criteria are not met for anti-social personality disorder.

The Canadian Press/Ryan Remiorz

Conduct disorder is diagnosed among those who act aggressively, steal, lie, and vandalize property.

was dropped in *DSM-5*. ODD would be indicated if a child exhibits such behaviours as losing his or her temper; arguing with adults; repeatedly refusing to comply with requests from adults; deliberately doing things to annoy others; and being angry, spiteful, touchy, or vindictive. Diagnostic criteria reflect three themes: (1) angry/irritable mood; (2) argumentative/defiant behaviour; and (3) vindictiveness. Most who go on to be diagnosed with conduct disorder have had a prior ODD diagnosis, but ODD typically does not lead to conduct disorder.

According to the international consensus statement, comorbidity is the norm rather than the exception for children with ODD, conduct disorder, and ADHD (Kutcher et al., 2004). Still, ODD differs from ADHD in that the defiant behaviour is not thought to arise from attentional deficits or sheer impulsiveness. This difference is evident in the tendency of children with ODD to be more deliberate in their obstreperousness than ADHD children.

Frick and Nigg (2012) reviewed the history of ODD and noted that this diagnostic category has often been questioned because it is so comorbid with other disorders and the symptoms of this disorder are quite common among children, especially during certain periods in their life. However, Frick and Nigg (2012) went on to summarize extensive evidence showing that ODD has extensive incremental validity in predicting outcomes beyond the variance attributable to disorders such as ADHD. They concluded that ODD should be regarded as "a separate clinical entity" (p. 90).

Still, our primary focus here is on the more serious and less questioned diagnosis of conduct disorder. Perhaps more than any other childhood disorder, conduct disorder is defined by the impact of the child's behaviour on people and surroundings. Schools, parents, peers, and the criminal justice system usually determine which undercontrolled behaviour constitutes unacceptable conduct. Preadolescents and adolescents are often identified as conduct problems by legal authorities, in which case they might be considered juvenile delinquents—a legal, not a psychological, term.

Many children with conduct disorder display other problems as well. A Quebec study (Toupin et al., 2000) showed that

even after controlling for ADHD symptoms, children with conduct disorder revealed significant cognitive deficits on attentional tests of executive functioning. Investigators from the Pittsburgh Youth Study, a longitudinal study of conduct problems in boys, found a strong association between substance use and delinquent acts (van Kammen, Loeber, & Stouthamer-Loeber, 1991). For example, among Grade 7 students who reported having tried marijuana, more than 30% had attacked someone with a weapon and 43% admitted breaking and entering; fewer than 5% of children who reported no substance use had committed these acts.

Population-based studies indicate that conduct disorder is fairly common. A study comparing prevalence rates across countries based on 25 studies concluded that about 3.2% of children meet diagnostic criteria. Similarly, the prevalence of oppositional defiant disorder was 3.3%. Rates did not vary significantly as a function of geographic location (Canino et al., 2010).

When it comes to the prognosis for children with conduct disorder, Moffitt (1993, 2003) theorized that two different courses of conduct problems should be distinguished. Some individuals show a "life-course-persistent" pattern of anti-social behaviour, beginning their conduct problems by age 3 and continuing with serious transgressions into adulthood. Others are "adolescence-limited." These people had normal childhoods, engaged in high levels of anti-social behaviour during adolescence, and returned to non-problematic lifestyles in adulthood. *DSM-5* recognizes different onsets of conduct disorder: childhood-onset type (defined by the onset of at least one criterion characteristic prior to age 10), and adolescent-onset type (defined by the absence of any criteria prior to age 10). The childhood-onset type is presumed to be more persistent and more likely to develop into adult anti-social personality disorder. Recent data, however, suggest that early-onset and late-onset conduct disorder may be more similar than they are different in terms of shared etiological factors, including both having a large, substantial genetic influence (Silberg, Moore, & Rutter, 2015). However, this study did clearly establish that the persistence of anti-social behaviours is largely a reflection of having early ADHD and parental dysfunction (i.e., having at least one parent with anti-social personality disorder and/or alcohol abuse).

The diagnostic criteria also currently include three levels of severity (mild, moderate, severe) based primarily on the number of conduct problems present. There is a large male preponderance in conduct disorder that begins in childhood and is life-course-persistent. The consensus is that biological factors are major influences on the difference (see Eme, 2007, for review).

Canadian research by Tremblay and his colleagues (see Canadian Contributions 15.1) found that there is much more heterogeneity than previously believed in the developmental trajectories associated with conduct disorder and violent behaviour. The term "developmental trajectory" refers to changing or stable behavioural patterns and characteristics that emerge when individuals are studied in longitudinal research designs. Research conducted in Montreal, studying boys from kindergarten through to the age of 17 years, identified as many as six different developmental trajectories in

Canadian Contributions 15.1

Richard Tremblay and the GRIP Research Unit

"Aggression does not suddenly erupt in our teens or when conflicts arise in a couple. All humans make spontaneous use of physical aggression very early in life — and it is then that we learn to control our violent reactions. Unfortunately, those who don't learn alternatives to physical aggression tend to use it later against their parents and partners."

—Richard Tremblay

Richard Tremblay was identified by *Time* magazine (Blumstein, 2003) as one of the most innovative researchers in Canada (see photo). A professor of pediatrics, psychiatry, and psychology at the Université de Montréal, he holds a Canada Research Chair in child development. Tremblay is also the former director of the Groupe de recherche sur l'inadaptation psychosociale chez l'enfant (GRIP; Research Unit on Children's Psychosocial Maladjustment) and is affiliated with University College, Dublin, Ireland, and the International Laboratory for Child and Adolescent Mental Health Development, Paris, France. A fellow of the Royal Society of Canada, he was honoured in 2003 with the Innis-Gerin Medal for distinguished and sustained contribution to the literature of the social sciences. In 2002, Tremblay won the Jacques-Rousseau Interdisciplinary Research Award.

Tremblay is known for his involvement in the Montreal Longitudinal-Experimental Study designed to help prevent anti-social behaviour in boys who were disruptive in kindergarten (see Tremblay et al., 1992). The study tested the hypothesis that poor parental management and deficits in social skills contribute to the development of anti-social behaviour. The results after two years of treatment (when the children were 7 and 8) and after three years of follow-up were encouraging: disruptive boys were less physically aggressive, more often in an age-appropriate regular classroom, had less serious school-adjustment problems, and engaged in fewer delinquent behaviours.

Courtesy of Richard Tremblay

Richard E. Tremblay, former director of the Groupe de recherche sur l'inadaptation psychosociale chez l'enfant (GRIP; Research Unit on Children's Psychosocial Maladjustment).

The LaCourse et al. (2002) longitudinal study in Montreal of developmental trajectories, just mentioned, also included a preventive component. Recall that this study tracked boys from kindergarten until they were 17 years old. A subset of participants received an intervention that consisted of social skills training for the at-risk boys, as well as parent training. Boys who received the intervention were more likely to follow the lowest level trajectory and were less likely to follow the high-level trajectory of aggressive and violent behaviour. This is the first intervention program with a long-term follow-up component to demonstrate a significant impact on the developmental course of physical aggression. It represents solid evidence that well-designed and well-timed interventions can make a difference!

Recent supplementary analyses have been conducted to identify protective factors that mitigate engaging in violent delinquency among males from low socio-economic backgrounds (Fontaine, Brendgen, Vitaro, & Tremblay, 2016). Key protective factors included the perceived legitimacy of legal authorities, parental supervision, and school engagement. The authors noted that large benefits should follow from preventive interventions started during early elementary school that are designed to enhance not only parental supervision and school engagement, but also bonds in the community. However, they noted that for young males in the high aggressive-high disruptive group, average prevention efforts won't work; rather, intense levels of prevention are needed.

The longitudinal study also focused on the causes and correlates of developmental trajectories of aggression. Tremblay and Vitaro were part of an international multi-site team that examined the developmental course of physical aggression in childhood (see Broidy et al., 2003). This study found that a small but identifiable number of boys and girls chronically exhibit aggression throughout childhood and that, for boys (but not girls), this chronic physical aggression predicted later violent delinquency as well as non-violent offending.

Additional research themes address the biological and physical correlates and predictors of physical aggression. Examples include the following:

- Obstetrical complications predict the risk of violence at 6 and 17 years of age in boys (Arseneault, Tremblay, Boulerice, & Saucier, 2002).

- High levels of harsh, reactive parenting predict a preschool trajectory of high/chronic peer victimization. Insufficient parent income and child physical aggression also predicted this trajectory (Barker et al., 2008).

- A longitudinal study (ages 5 to 74 months) examined prenatal and postnatal risk factors for a chronic (4.3% of children) trajectory of "disregard for rules" (an important dimension of conduct disorder). In addition to male sex, the strongest predictors were a mother's history of anti-social behaviour and depressive symptoms manifested by the mother and the father. Children's difficult temperament and parenting at 5 months did not predict chronic disregard for rules (Petitclerc et al., 2009).

Tremblay and his associates have also examined the NLSCY data set. Developmental trajectories of physical aggression from

(continued)

toddlerhood to pre-adolescence were modelled in more than 10,000 children followed for over 6 years. Three groups with distinct developmental trajectories between 2 and 11 years of age were identified. A high stable trajectory of physical aggression was found in 16.6% of the children. What risk factors distinguished the different developmental patterns? Children in the high physical aggression trajectory group were more likely to be boys, from low-income families, from families where the mother had not completed high school, and who reported using hostile/ineffective parenting strategies (Côté et al., 2006).

The research findings identified by Tremblay and his colleagues have important societal implications, and certain findings have already led to positive changes in "the real world." After showing empirically that aggressive boys who become violent teenagers tend to have poor, uneducated mothers who gave birth as teenagers (Nagin & Tremblay, 2001), Tremblay convinced the provincial government to develop a prenatal care and parenting-skills program for at-risk mothers.

anti-social behaviour (see LaCourse et al., 2002). Only 11.4% of participants were on a rising trajectory of physical aggression. This finding is inconsistent with the "age crime curve hypothesis," which maintains that there is a substantial increase in physical violence during adolescence. In fact, most boys were either on a low-level anti-social behaviour trajectory or a declining trajectory that was especially apparent when they were between the ages of 11 and 17.

It is becoming increasingly clear that a conduct disorder diagnosis is associated with many long-term consequences. A new meta-analysis of both conduct disorder and ADHD determined on the basis of 98 eligible studies that conduct disorder is associated longitudinally with negative academic achievement outcomes (e.g., failure to complete high school), criminality, and other disorders, including substance use disorders (Erskine et al., 2016). ADHD was also associated with negative achievement outcomes, such as failure to complete high school, unemployment, greater criminality, and other disorders, including substance use disorders.

Lahey et al. (1995) found that boys with conduct disorder were much more likely to persist in their anti-social behaviour if they had a parent with anti-social personality disorder or if they had low verbal intelligence. Boys with higher verbal IQs and no anti-social parent apparently had a more transient form of the disorder.

Recall our discussion about the childhood roots of psychopathy (see Chapter 13). As noted by Frick and Moffitt (2010), in a proposal to the *DSM-5* childhood disorders and the ADHD and disruptive behaviour disorders work groups, a significant body of recent research refined how key features of psychopathy can be expressed in children and demonstrated the importance of using these features to designate a subgroup of anti-social youths. This research led to the February 2010 proposal (see American Psychiatric Association, 2010) of a specifier/subtype to the diagnosis of conduct disorder based on the presence of "callous-unemotional" traits. This recommendation was adopted in *DSM-5*; children receive this diagnosis if they meet the full criteria for conduct disorder and show two or more of the following characteristics over at least 12 months: lack of remorse or guilt, callous lack of empathy, no concern for performance, and shallow or deficient affect. These tendencies are evaluated as to whether they are mild, moderate, or severe and they must be confirmed by informant reports (American Psychiatric Association, 2013).

There is a strong evidence base supporting this specifier. For example, numerous studies showed a predictive

relationship (as long as 10 years) between callous-unemotional traits and more severe, stable, and pervasive aggressive, anti-social, or delinquent behaviour, including premeditated and instrumental (i.e., for gain) aggression. This resulted in more police contacts, and poorer treatment outcomes to currently available modes of treatment, including in children aged 4 to 9 (see Frick, 2012; and Frick & Moffitt, 2010 for reviews).

Longitudinal research has also isolated the callous-unemotional subtype in young girls. These girls consistently are distinguished throughout childhood and early adolescence by more conduct disorder symptoms, more severe aggression, greater academic problems and global impairment, but lower levels of anxiety (Pardini et al., 2012).

Children in the current childhood-onset group show higher rates of callous-unemotional traits than those in the adolescent-onset group. Further, it is impulsive and anti-social youth who also show callous-unemotional traits who are most likely to show emotional (e.g., less recognition of signs of fear in others), cognitive (e.g., less sensitive to punishment cues), and personality (e.g., more fearless or thrill-seeking behaviour) characteristics similar to those seen in psychopathic adults (see Frick & Moffitt, 2010). The association between callous-unemotional traits and the more severe pattern of aggressive/anti-social behaviour cannot be accounted for by higher levels of impulsivity or diagnoses of ADHD (Frick, 2009, 2012).

Etiology of Conduct Disorder   Numerous proposals have been put forward for the causes of conduct disorder, including biological, psychological, and sociological factors.

Biological factors   Evidence from twin studies indicates that aggressive behaviour (e.g., cruelty to animals, fighting) is clearly heritable, whereas other delinquent behaviour (e.g., stealing, running away, truancy) may not be (Edelbrock, Rende, Plomin, & Thompson, 1995). In a large sample of 7-year-old twins, Viding and colleagues (Viding, Blair, Moffitt, & Plomin, 2005) found that conduct problems in children with callous and unemotional traits were under strong genetic influence (heritability of .81) with little influence of shared environment. The findings were replicated when the children were 9 years old (Viding et al., 2008). The genetic contribution remained when controlling for ADHD symptoms. Another recent twin study found that conduct disorder and oppositional defiant disorder have shared genetic influences as well as familial environmental effects (Knopik et al., 2014).

Neuropsychological deficits have been implicated in the childhood profiles of children with conduct disorder (e.g., Moffitt, Lynam, & Silva, 1994), including poor verbal skills, difficulty with executive functioning (the ability to anticipate, plan, use self control, and solve problems), and problems with memory. Catherine Cappadocia and her colleagues at York University (Cappadocia, Desrocher, Pepler, & Schroeder, 2009) reviewed the neurological and neurochemical correlates of conduct disorder. The evidence suggests that neurological profiles of children with conduct disorder are characterized by (1) reduced p300 brain wave amplitude, (2) deactivation of the anterior cingulated cortex and reduced activation in the left amygdala in response to negative stimuli, and (3) reduced right temporal lobe volume. Neurochemical correlates included reduced serotonin and cortisol levels (i.e., decreased hypothalamic-pituitary-adrenal axis function) and attenuated autonomic nervous system functioning. The authors suggested that emotion dysregulation theory provides a framework for understanding the neurobiological aspects of conduct disorder.

Findings from brain imaging studies show promise in uncovering the neurological bases to the cognitive and affective deficits found in anti-social youths with callous and unemotional traits. Thus, Jones et al. (2009) and Marsh et al. (2008) found support for the hypothesis that children with these traits and conduct problems show amygdala hyporeactivity to other peoples' distress. Marsh et al. (2008) also reported that a reduction in amygdala-ventromedial prefrontal cortex connectivity, which plays a role in fear affect processing, was associated with callous-unemotional symptom severity. Gao and colleagues (2010) used poor fear conditioning as a proxy for amygdala dysfunction. They measured classically emotional responses at age 3 in a large birth cohort, followed up after 20 years, and concluded that poor fear conditioning predisposes to crime at age 23. Unfortunately, callous-unemotional traits were not assessed. Much more research on the neurological correlates of callous-unemotional traits is needed.

Psychological factors Lax, inadequate, inconsistent, harsh, coercive, and hostile parental discipline coupled with parental adjustment difficulties appear to contribute to conduct-disordered behaviour (e.g., Moffitt, 2003; Patterson, 1982; Snyder, Reid, & Patterson, 2003; Verlaan & Schwartzman, 2002). Indeed, analyses of the NLSCY (Benzies, Keown, & Magill-Evans, 2009) determined that hostile/ineffective parenting had a sustained effect on physical aggression that carried forward across time from birth up to 6 years of age, suggesting that hostile/ineffective parenting has an effect prior to any evidence of aggressive behaviour in the child. The study also found that being a boy, having a mother with less education, and living in a lone-parent family with siblings also contributed to aggression.

Bandura and Walters (1963) were among the first researchers to appreciate the significance of the fact that children can learn aggressiveness from parents who behave aggressively. Children may also imitate aggressive acts they see elsewhere,

such as on television. Since aggression is an effective, albeit unpleasant, means of achieving a goal, it is likely to be reinforced. Thus, once imitated, aggressive acts will probably be maintained. This social mimicry may at least partially explain the dramatic surge in delinquent behaviour in adolescents who had not previously shown conduct problems. Moffitt (1993) proposed that these adolescents imitate the behaviour of persistently anti-social peers because they see them as enjoying high-status possessions and sexual opportunities.

Ferguson, San Miguel, and Hartley (2009) concluded that exposure to violent television or video games were not predictive of youth (ages 10–14 years) violence and aggression. More recent research has failed to consistently establish a link between violent game exposure and higher levels of anti-social behaviours (see Ferguson & Colwell, in press), despite the advisory statement from the American Psychological Association (2015) warning about the possibility that violent games can influence children in harmful ways. Perhaps a more differentiated view is needed that focuses on how violent games affect certain children (i.e., some children some of the time) based on their other characteristics.

While it seems that exposure to violent games has an uncertain impact, other recent research shows longitudinally that viewing relational aggression on television is linked with future relational aggression (Coyne, 2016). Fortunately, there is also evidence that exposure to prosocial television content promotes empathic concern and is associated prospectively with less likelihood of engaging in aggressive behaviour (Padilla-Walker, Coyne, Collier, & Nielson, 2015).

Childhood maltreatment can contribute to externalizing difficulties, especially children's aggression toward peers (see Cullerton-Sen et al., 2008 for review). Cullerton-Sen et al. (2008) examined patterns of association between maltreatment and aggression using a gender-informed developmental approach. They reported that maltreatment is associated with physical aggression for boys and relational aggression in girls. Consistent with Bandura and Walters (1963), physical abuse was associated with physically aggressive behaviours. However, sexual abuse predicted relational aggression for girls only. The combination of child abuse and genetic risk appears to put children at higher risk for the development of conduct-disordered and aggressive behaviour than either risk factor alone (e.g., Jaffee et al., 2005).

A cognitive perspective on aggressive behaviour comes from the work of Kenneth Dodge and his associates. Dodge and Frame (1982) found that the cognitive processes of aggressive children had a particular bias; these youngsters interpreted ambiguous acts, such as being bumped in line, as evidence of hostile intent. Perceptions like this may lead such children to retaliate aggressively for actions that may not have been intended to be provocative. Subsequently, their peers, remembering these aggressive behaviours, may tend to treat them more aggressively, further angering the already aggressive children and continuing a cycle of rejection and aggression.

Dodge's cognitive theory is now incorporated into a comprehensive biopsychosocial model of the development of conduct disorder (Dodge & Pettit, 2003). According to this model,

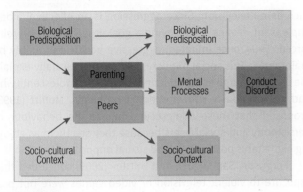

FIGURE 15.1 A biopsychosocial model of the development of conduct disorder.

biological predisposition and socio-cultural context operate both as distal factors (i.e., more remote influences) and as proximal factors (see Figure 15.1). Socio-cultural context factors include the influence of neighbourhood and classroom environments. In addition to the acknowledged roles played by life experiences that the child has with parents and peers, the child's mental processes (i.e., cognitive factors) play a central role in this model because it is the cognitive and emotional mental factors that are the final determinants of how distal factors eventually get translated into anti-social behaviour. Thus, malevolent cognitions still play an important role, but biological and socio-cultural factors are also recognized.

The research on children with early-onset conduct disorder who have callous-unemotional traits is consistent with the notion that there are several distinct developmental pathways to severe anti-social and aggressive behaviour (see Frick, 2009). The child with callous-unemotional traits has a temperamental style characterized by a lack of responsivity to distress in others, abnormalities in responsivity to rewards and punishment, and a preference for novel and dangerous activities that could influence the development of appropriate levels of guilt and empathy. This child could be less sensitive to typical parental socialization practices (see Frick, 2009) and there is growing evidence for differences in dysfunctional parenting for children with or without traits of callousness (Frick, 2012). One pattern that has emerged is that among children high in callousness but not among those lower in callousness, parental warmth is strongly and negatively linked with conduct problems, and this holds for both boys and girls (Kroneman et al., 2011; Pasalich, Dadds, Hawes, & Brennan, 2011). However, it is important to note that even among children with multiple risk factors, "such a trajectory is not immutable, and some children with this temperamental style may develop appropriate levels of guilt and empathy, if they experience certain corrective environments" (Frick, 2009, p. 809).

Treatment of Conduct Disorder   The management of conduct disorder poses a formidable challenge, and working to influence the multiple systems involved in the life of a youngster (family, peers, school, neighbourhood) may be critical to the success of treatment efforts.

Some young people with conduct disorder, particularly those who have a childhood onset that is characterized by

callous-unemotional traits, are probably the psychopaths of tomorrow. And like psychopaths, young people who commit violent and anti-social acts with little remorse or emotional involvement are extraordinarily difficult to reach. Incarceration, release, and recidivism are typically the rule. An enduring societal problem is how to deal with people whose social consciences appear grossly underdeveloped. According to a review by Canadian researchers, interventions for younger children are generally more effective than interventions for adolescents (Moretti et al., 1997).

Harsh discipline, whether imposed by government or by parents, appears to contribute in a major way to further delinquency and criminal activity in adulthood (e.g., Laub & Sampson, 1995; Steinberg, 2009). Nonetheless, the current zeitgeist in Canada is to consider dealing with children who engage in criminal activity in a more stringent manner. The federal government originally enacted the Youth Criminal Justice Act in 2003 to provide a better balance between punishment and rehabilitation.

Family interventions   Many approaches to treating conduct disorder involve intervening with the parents or families of the anti-social child. Gerald Patterson and his colleagues have worked for over three decades on a behavioural program of parental management training in which parents are taught to modify their responses to their children so that prosocial rather than anti-social behaviour is consistently rewarded. Parents are taught to use techniques such as positive reinforcement when the child exhibits positive behaviours and time-out and loss of privileges for aggressive or anti-social behaviours. Parents' and teachers' reports of children's behaviour and direct observation of behaviour at home and at school both supported the program's effectiveness (Patterson, 1982). Parental management training has also been shown to improve the behaviour of siblings and reduce depression in mothers involved in the program (Kazdin, 1985). A study of chronic adolescent offenders by Patterson's group (Bank et al., 1991) found that both parent training and court-provided family treatment reduced rates of criminal offence; however, the parent-training approach led to more rapid improvement. More recent evaluations have concluded that behavioural parent training can be effective in reducing maladaptive behaviour in conduct-disordered children (e.g., Kazdin, 2005) and the benefits of parent training are generalizable and can be detected in "real world" clinical settings (see Michelson et al., 2013).

What about parent training for callous-unemotional trait children? Given that these children manifest conduct problems early in their development, it is important to intervene early in the parent-child relationship if at all possible. Such interventions could include teaching parents to attempt to foster empathic concern in their young child (see Frick, 2009). Children with callous-unemotional traits generally do poorly in treatment programs relative to other anti-social children (e.g., Waschbusch et al., 2007). Hawes and Dadds (2005) reported that boys aged 4 to 9 years with conduct problems and callous-unemotional traits were less responsive to a parenting intervention than boys low on these traits, despite apparent initial improvements when the training was first implemented.

Frick (2009) noted that with certain children it is necessary to develop comprehensive interventions that are tailored to the unique needs of each child. Multisystemic treatment is a widely used comprehensive strategy.

Multisystemic treatment Henggeler's multisystemic treatment (MST; Henggeler et al., 1998) involves delivering intensive and comprehensive therapy services in the community—targeting the adolescent, the family, the school, and in some cases, the peer group. MST interventions reflect the view that conduct problems are influenced by multiple contexts within the family and between the family and other social systems. The strategies used by MST therapists incorporate behavioural, cognitive, family-systems, and case-management techniques. A major implication of MST is that youths receive treatment in their homes and stay in their communities rather than be incarcerated. This approach may result in reduced financial costs to society, and it recognizes that real changes must also occur in the troubled youth's environment.

As described by Henggeler and Schaeffer (2010), MST is not based on a rigid and proscriptive manualized treatment approach. Instead, it is based on nine treatment principles (see Table 15.3). It involves highly integrated treatment components implemented by a single therapist "who understands and responds to the needs of family members and external stakeholders" (p. 154). The therapy's uniqueness and perhaps its effectiveness (see Henggeler et al., 1998) lie in its emphasizing individual and family strengths, identifying the context for the conduct problems, using present-focused and action-oriented interventions, and using interventions that require daily or weekly efforts by family members. Treatment is provided in "ecologically valid" settings, such as the home, school, or local recreational centre, to maximize generalization of therapeutic changes.

The need to consider multiple systems and influences on the youth was underscored in a case excerpt concerning a troubled youth named Paul. Henggeler and Schaeffer (2010) described the following:

> "Paul, aged 16 years, was referred to the MST program after two separate assault charges (e.g., police were called to the home to disrupt physical altercations between he and his mother) and one arrest for smoking marijuana on school grounds. After conversations with Paul, his mother and father, his older brother (who attended college nearby), several of Paul's teachers, and his probation officer, evidence emerged that Paul's assaults against his mother all occurred when she was attempting to set limits and discipline him, and that his marijuana use largely occurred in the context of his association with a group of peers with reputations at school for using drugs."
>
> (pp. 154–155)

The next step is that the parents agreed to a behaviour plan for Paul, but this was ultimately undermined by Paul's father,

TABLE 15.3   MST Treatment Principles

1. The primary purpose of assessment is to understand the "fit" between the identified problem and their broader systemic context.

2. Therapeutic contacts should emphasize the positive and use systemic strengths as levers for change.

3. Interventions should be designed to promote responsible behaviour and decrease irresponsible behaviour among family members.

4. Interventions should be present-focused and action-oriented, targeting specific and well-defined problems.

5. Interventions should target sequences of behaviour within and between multiple systems.

6. Interventions should be developmentally appropriate and fit the developmental needs of the youth.

7. Interventions should be designed to require daily or weekly effort by family members.

8. Intervention efficacy should be evaluated continuously from multiple perspectives.

9. Interventions should be designed to promote treatment generalization and long-term maintenance of therapeutic change.

Adapted from Henggeler and Schaeffer, 2010, p. 152. Reprinted with permission from John Wiley & Sons, Inc.

who gave Paul money and allowed him to do things that went against his wife's prior decisions. The therapist discovered that much of the problem was rooted in conflict and marital dissatisfaction between Paul's mother and father, so the therapist provided marital therapy in recognition of the role that family systems was playing in Paul's behaviour.

How effective is MST? Henggeler et al. (1998) compared the results for an MST group with those for a control group that received an equivalent number of sessions (about 25) of traditional individual therapy in an office setting. Adolescents in the MST group showed reduced behaviour problems and far fewer arrests over the following four years; 70% of adolescents receiving traditional therapy were arrested in the four years following treatment, while only 22% of those completing MST were arrested. Parents who were involved in MST showed reductions in psychiatric symptoms, and MST families showed improved supportiveness and decreased conflict and hostility. In contrast, the quality of interactions in the families of the adolescents receiving traditional individual therapy deteriorated following treatment. In an RCT with long-term follow-up, Huey, Henggeler, Brondino, and Pickrel (2000) examined the specific MST mechanisms of change that led to the improvements: the therapist's adherence to the MST protocol facilitated a sequence in which improved family functioning decreased the adolescents' affiliation with delinquent peers, which in turn decreased their delinquent behaviour. Another long-term 25-year follow-up focused on siblings of violent juvenile offenders found that relative to those who received individual therapy, those who received MST were much less likely to be arrested and sentenced to incarceration, thus establishing that MST can help address risk among family members (Wagner, Borduin, Sawyer, & Dopp, 2014).

Canadian Perspectives 15.2

Multisystemic Treatment in Ontario and Alternative Canadian Approaches to the Rehabilitation of Young Offenders

A team of researchers led by Allan Leschied (see photo) and Alison Cunningham implemented MST in Ontario in a project started in 1997 (see Cunningham, 2002; Leschied & Cunningham, 2000; Leschied, Cunningham, & Hawkins, 2000). This project, known as The Clinical Trials of Multisystemic Therapy in Ontario, involved coordination with agencies located in London, Mississauga, Ottawa, and Simcoe County. MST was seen as a cost-efficient community alternative to custodial residential placement for high-risk Ontario youth. Participants were eligible for the study if they had a history of criminal offences and a high level of risk for reoffending. The study has high ecological validity in terms of the generalizability to life settings because the 409 youths in the study were identified as providing the greatest challenge for local agencies.

Half the participants received MST and half continued with the usual services in the local system. The key research question asked whether the group that received MST would receive lower levels of criminal conviction relative to a group that was randomly assigned to existing services in Ontario. The sample was 73.6% males, 13.2% self-identified as Aboriginal, and 6.6% under 12 years of age at referral. Two-thirds of the youth had a history of at least one prior conviction at referral. Unfortunately, although some early findings appeared to favour the MST participants, the interim results (Cunningham, 2002) and final results reported in 2006 based on a follow-up that ended in 2004 (see www.lfcc.on.ca/mst_final_results.html) indicated that the MST group and the treatment-as-usual group did not differ significantly on any outcome measure. These measures include rate of conviction throughout the three-year follow-up, days to reconviction, sentenced to custody during follow-up, days to first custody admission, average days in sentenced custody, number of convictions, and number of offences. For example, 68.2% of the MST group had at least one conviction after three years, in contrast to 66.5% for the control group. The final results corroborate Cunningham's (2002) preliminary conclusion that "it is not possible to recommend the adoption of MST in Canada" (p. 27). It would have been easy to reach the wrong conclusion if a less rigorous methodology had been used.

It is not clear why the MST study in Ontario did not work. As noted above, subsequent studies conducted elsewhere have

Alan Leschied from Western University in London, Ontario, is one of Canada's top advocates for youth at risk and he has been involved extensively in research on youth justice issues and children's mental health. In 2004, he received a lifetime achievement award through the Criminal Justice Section of the Canadian Psychology Association.

continued to point to the treatment success of this approach, and it is interesting to note that proponents of MST, including Henggeler, often fail to cite the work by Leschied and Cunningham when summarizing and evaluating the past literature (see for instance, Henggeler & Schaeffer, 2010; Henggeler, 2011). This omission is difficult to fathom given the large magnitude of the Ontario study and the attention that it received. Obviously, advances in clinical psychology are best served when non-significant findings are considered and a more balanced view of the existing literature is provided.

Thinking Critically

1. Would a program such as MST be more effective with children identified as "at risk" at a very young age? Could it work with childhood-onset conduct-disordered children who also manifest callous-unemotional traits, or are these youth untreatable?

2. Does the best hope for the future lie in the development of early intervention and prevention programs? Why or why not? Why do relatively few government prevention programs exist for conduct-disordered children, even though such programs could probably play a critical role in reducing dysfunction and distress?

Canadian Perspectives 15.2 illustrates an application of MST in Ontario, and provides examples of other approaches in several provinces. This study conducted in Ontario did not find evidence that MST is effective, but subsequent research has continued to attest to its usefulness (see Henggeler, 2011) and Henggeler and Schaeffer (2016) noted that the results from over 100 studies indicate that MST has yielded almost uniformly positive results for youths and their families. There is some indication that whether MST is effective depends on the outcome measure. An investigation conducted in the Netherlands found that MST, compared with treatment as usual, decreased

externalizing behaviour, oppositional defiance disorder, conduct disorder, and property offences, but did not reduce violence (Asscher et al., 2013). Other research has attested to the complexities involved here. A qualitative study of 21 families affirmed the importance of the therapeutic intervention but also showed that a range of positive outcomes are experienced (e.g., improved family relationships, greater aspirations of the youth) despite mixed behavioural outcomes. In this investigation, families reported benefits of MST to family members even when the youth reoffended (Tighe et al., 2012). This study illustrates that it is important to evaluate a broad range of outcome variables when determining whether and how an intervention was successful.

Cognitive approaches   Although research by Patterson's and Henggeler's groups suggests that intervention with parents and families is a critical component of success, such treatment is expensive and time-consuming (though clearly less so than incarceration). Indeed, some families may not be able or willing to become involved in it. Moretti et al. (1997) observed that the parents of youths with conduct disorder have often disengaged by the time their children come into contact with the mental health system, and thus, if parental involvement is not forthcoming, these youths will be excluded from treatment research that has a parental component.

However, individual cognitive therapy with some conduct-disordered children can improve their behaviour even without family involvement. For example, in anger-control training, aggressive children are taught self control in anger-provoking situations. To withstand verbal attacks without responding aggressively, they learn to use distracting techniques such as humming a tune, saying calming things to themselves, or turning away. The children then apply these self-control methods while a peer provokes and insults them (e.g., Lochman & Wells, 1996).

Another strategy involves focusing on the deficient moral development of conduct-disordered children. The teaching of moral-reasoning skills to groups of behaviour-disordered adolescents in school has achieved success (Arbuthnot & Gordon, 1986). Adolescents who were identified by their teachers as having behaviour problems (e.g., stealing and vandalism) participated in groups at school that encouraged higher levels of moral reasoning. Compared with a control group, adolescents participating in the groups showed improvement in moral-reasoning skills and school grades, as well as reductions in tardiness, referrals to the principal for behaviour problems, and contacts with police or juvenile courts.

Unfortunately, behavioural changes produced by altering cognitive patterns may yield only short-term gains—improvements that may be lost when the youngsters return to their familiar, "bad" neighbourhoods. Environmental contingencies—the communities in which people live—need to be considered when dealing with the complexities of aggression (Guerra & Slaby, 1990).

Prevention of Conduct and Related Disorders

"Psychiatry needs to place much more attention on the origin, early development, and prevention of DBDs [disruptive behaviour disorders] if it seriously intends to prevent at-risk children from living a life of misery."

—Petitclerc and Tremblay, 2009, p. 229

Few prevention programs for anti-social behaviour and conduct disorder have proven to be effective. Perhaps interventions would be more effective if initiated at a young age (toddler and early preschool periods) with "early starter" children who go on to manifest the most chronic and severe forms

of anti-social behaviour (e.g., Moffitt et al., 2002). Consistent with this idea, Barker and Maughan (2009) used data from a large longitudinal population-based cohort of children from the prenatal period to age 13 in order to differentiate early-onset persistent vs. childhood-limited conduct problem youth. They identified robust predictors of the early-onset persistent trajectory: maternal anxiety during pregnancy, partner cruelty to the mother, harsh parenting, and higher levels of child undercontrolled temperament. Barker and Maughan (2009) concluded that there is a need for interventions that focus on prenatal risks in mothers and early postnatal risks in mothers and their young children.

Petitclerc and Tremblay (2009) from the Université de Montréal reviewed preventive studies of disruptive behaviour disorders (DBDs): conduct disorder, ODD, and ADHD. Consistent with an "early starter" hypothesis, they argued that prevention needs to begin before children are aged 3 years. They first drew on the results of longitudinal studies of children beginning in infancy to determine the onset, development, and risk factors for DBD symptoms. They then reviewed RCTs of preventive interventions provided to families before the child is 3 years old that included outcome measures of DBD symptoms at follow-up.

Petitclerc and Tremblay (2009) reported that children who manifest high levels of DBD symptoms begin to do so in the first two years of life. Further, they have risk factors that can be identified in the mother during pregnancy or earlier, and soon after the child's birth. These factors, primarily based on multivariate analyses of the Canadian NLSCY, included maternal anti-social behaviour, young age of the mother when she had her first child, smoking during pregnancy, and maternal depression soon after the child's birth. Other factors were hostile parenting practices, and, as would be expected, being male. A high physical aggression trajectory was further predicted by low income, low maternal education, family dysfunction, and the presence of other young siblings.

15.4 | Learning Disorders

"These are people who suffer in silence because there's such a stigma—... children who feel they are dumb, adults who've always been told they should shake their heads and get over it."

—Judy Kerr, executive director of the Learning Disabilities Association of Canada and mother of twin 13-year-old sons with learning disabilities, quoted in Girard (2007, A6)

Several years ago, a young man in an undergraduate course showed an unusual pattern of strengths and difficulties. His oral comments in class were exemplary, but his handwriting and spelling were sometimes indecipherable. After the instructor had noted these problems on the student's mid-term examination, the undergraduate came to see him and explained that he was dyslexic and that it took him longer to complete the weekly reading assignments and to write papers and exams. The instructor decided to accord him additional time for preparing written work. The student was obviously of superior intelligence and highly motivated to excel. Excel he did, earning an A in the seminar and on graduation being admitted to a leading law school.

Unfortunately, the outcomes of a learning disability are not always, or even generally, so positive. On March 26, 2007, the Learning Disabilities Association of Canada released a groundbreaking, federally funded research study entitled Putting a Canadian Face on Learning Disabilities (PACFOLD), the first-ever "snapshot" of the impact of living with a learning disability in Canada. The study reported that learning problems early in childhood compound with age and affect school, work, and relationships and can lead to depression and chronic illness. The problems aren't typically detected until children are already in Grade 5. The study called for a broader societal approach to dealing with learning disabilities, including mandatory early screening for children aged 4 to 8, publicly funded support, awareness and training among professionals, and greater employer awareness to offer accommodations to workers. The study is available online at www.pacfold.ca. An earlier report for the association (Crawford, 2002) estimated the incremental direct (e.g., services of doctors) and indirect (e.g., reduced earnings) costs of learning disabilities to individuals, families, and society. The present value (i.e., incorporating future costs in terms of today's dollars) of the incremental cost from birth to retirement (age 65) in year 2000 dollars was conservatively estimated to be over $450,000 per person with a learning disability. Assuming a prevalence rate of 5%, the present value cost to all individuals with a learning disability, their families, and to public and private programs in Canada was estimated to be $707 billion in year 2000 dollars.

Learning disabilities signify inadequate development in a specific area of academic, language, speech, or motor skills that is not due to mental retardation, autism spectrum disorder, a demonstrable physical disorder, or deficient educational opportunities. Children with these disorders are usually of average or above-average intelligence but have difficulty learning some specific skill (e.g., arithmetic or reading), and thus their progress in school is impeded.

The term *learning disabilities* is not used by *DSM-5* but is used by most health professionals to group together three disorders that do appear in the DSM: learning disorders, communication disorders, and motor skills disorder. Any of these disorders may apply to a child who fails to develop to the degree expected of his or her intellectual level in a specific academic, language, or motor skill area.

Specific Learning Disorders

DSM-IV-TR divided **learning disorders** into three categories: reading disorder, disorder of written expression, and mathematics disorder. *DSM-5* now groups these specific disorders into the category of **specific learning disorder** and deficits of a particular kind are classified as separate specifiers. No diagnosis is appropriate if the disability can be accounted for by a sensory deficit, such as a visual or auditory problem. Specific learning disorder is defined as difficulties learning and using academic skills with symptoms that persist six months or more despite interventions targeting these difficulties (American Psychiatric Association, 2013).

- Children with a specific learning disorder involving **reading disorder** have a condition that other diagnostic systems refer to with a more well-known term: **dyslexia**. People with dyslexia have significant difficulty with word recognition, reading comprehension, and typically written spelling as well. When reading out loud, they omit, add, or distort the pronunciation of words to an extent unusual for their age. In adulthood, problems with reading, comprehension, and written spelling persist though the stories of well-known celebrities (see photo of Anderson Cooper) underscore the resilience and ability to overcome challenges such as dyslexia. Clearly, this disorder does not preclude great achievements. The *DSM-5* work group recommended a name change to "dyslexia" to be consistent with international use but *DSM-5* did not make this change.

- Children with a specific learning disorder known previously as **mathematics disorder** may have difficulty

Monica Schipper/WireImage/Getty Images

TV personality Anderson Cooper had dyslexia at an early age and was able to overcome his tendency to see some letters backwards through his love of reading. He is an advocate for early intervention. Other celebrities acknowledging dyslexia include Canadian actor Keanu Reeves, Pirates of the Caribbean actor Keira Knightley, Lord of the Rings actor Orlando Bloom, and movie producer Steven Spielberg.

rapidly and accurately recalling arithmetic facts, counting objects correctly and quickly, or aligning numbers in columns. The *DSM-5* work group recommended a name change to "dyscalculia" to be consistent with international use.

- **Disorder of written expression** describes an impairment in the ability to compose the written word (including spelling errors, errors in grammar, or very poor handwriting). The *DSM-5* work group recommended removing disorder of written expression due to lack of evidence that it occurs independently of dyslexia or communication disorders.

Numerous studies confirm that children with learning disabilities can experience considerable psychosocial dysfunction. For example, a Norwegian study (Undheim & Sund, 2008) examined a representative sample of adolescents aged 12–15 years and found that 7.8% reported reading difficulties. Relative to classmates without reading problems, the children with reading difficulties reported higher levels of depressive symptoms, more school stress and worry about attending school, lower school grades, and lower attachment to parents. They also scored lower on measures of self-worth and social acceptance, showed poorer psychological functioning during the previous year, and had received more help and had used more medication for mental health problems. The life history of Jacques Demers further illustrates how learning disabilities may be accompanied by other adjustment challenges (see photo).

Communication Disorders

Several categories of communication disorders have been distinguished:

- In **language disorder**, the child has difficulty expressing himself or herself in speech. The youngster may seem eager to communicate but have inordinate difficulty finding the right words; for example, he or she may be unable to come up with the word "car" when pointing to a car passing by on the street. By age 4, this child speaks only in short phrases. Old words are forgotten when new ones are learned, and the use of grammatical structures is considerably below age level.

- Children with the communication disorder known formerly as **phonological disorder** (see photo) comprehend and are able to use a substantial vocabulary, but their speech sounds like that of Elmer Fudd; "blue" comes out "bu", and "rabbit" sounds like "wabbit," for example. They have not learned articulation of the later-acquired speech sounds, such as r, sh, th, f, z, l, and ch. With speech therapy, complete recovery occurs in most cases and milder cases may recover spontaneously by age 8.

- Also included under communication disorders is **stuttering** (now referred to in *DSM-5* as childhood onset fluency disorder), which is a disturbance in verbal fluency characterized by one or more of the following speech patterns: frequent repetitions or prolongations of sounds, long pauses between words, substituting easy words for those that are difficult to articulate (e.g., words beginning with certain consonants), and repeating whole words (e.g., saying "go-go-go-go" instead of just a single "go"). Sometimes bodily twitching and eye blinking accompany the verbal dysfluencies. Stuttering can interfere with academic, social, and occupational functioning and can prevent otherwise capable people from fulfilling their potential. About three times as many males as females have

The Canadian Press/Paul Chiasson

Former head coach of the Montreal Canadiens, Jacques Demers, who took the team to its last Stanley Cup victory in 1993, became an advocate for literacy. He revealed in 2005 that he has a learning disability and could sign his name but couldn't read most sentences. He was appointed to the Canadian Senate on August 27, 2009. Demers described a childhood characterized by chronic insomnia and anxiety due to being raised in a home with an abusive father and being ridiculed and bullied at school because of his learning problems. He has overcome many challenges and perhaps this will assist him in recovering from the stroke that Demers had in October 2016.

Hattie Young/Science Source

A speech therapist works with a child with phonological disorder by having him practise the sounds he finds difficult.

the problem, which usually shows up at around age 5. The *DSM-5* estimates that 65 to 85% of stutterers recover, with the severity of the disorder at age 8 predicting who will recover.

- **Social (pragmatic) communication disorder** is newly added to *DSM-5*. This disorder involves persistent difficulties in the social use of either verbal or non-verbal forms of communication (American Psychiatric Association, 2013).

A Canadian study highlights the serious dysfunction and impairment that tends to accompany language difficulties. Cohen et al. (2000) compared functioning in ADHD children with no language impairment with functioning in ADHD children with language impairment and in psychiatric control groups composed of children with or without impairment. Children with language impairment were the most disadvantaged, regardless of their diagnosis. In fact, when it came to predicting executive functioning, language impairment was a stronger predictor than having an ADHD diagnosis.

Beitchman et al. (2001) undertook a 14-year prospective study of the outcomes experienced by language-impaired children and found that there is a link between language problems in early childhood and psychiatric disorders years later. Thus, early remediation of language problems is an important goal. By age 19, the language-impaired boys had greater symptoms of delinquency based on parental reports and higher rates of arrests and convictions (Brownlie et al., 2004).

Motor Disorder

In **developmental coordination disorder**, which falls under the general classification **motor disorder**, children show marked impairment in the development of motor coordination that is not explainable by mental retardation or a known physical disorder such as cerebral palsy. The young child may have difficulty tying shoelaces and buttoning shirts and, when older, building models, playing ball, and printing or handwriting. The diagnosis is made only if the impairment interferes significantly with academic achievement or with the activities of daily living.

Other *DSM-5* motor disorders include stereotypic movement disorder and tic disorder. One thing they have in common is repetitive movements.

Etiology of Learning Disorders and Communication Disorders

Most research on learning disorders specifically concerns one learning disorder: dyslexia, perhaps because it is the most prevalent of this group of disorders. Although studies on other specific learning disorders (e.g., mathematics) have emerged, the literature has advanced more slowly in this area. The high comorbidity among learning disorders is the result of a complex interplay between both general and disorder-specific causal factors (Landerl & Moll, 2010).

Although no single causal factor has been identified in the development of learning disorders (e.g., Plomin & Kovas, 2005), genetic and biological factors as well as ineffective learning strategies can lead to greater risk. There is frequently a family history of learning disorders in children identified as having a learning disorder (e.g., Plomin & Kovas, 2005), and there is a higher concordance rate for learning disorders in monozygotic twins, relative to dizygotic twins. A gene mutation and/or chromosomal abnormalities may also be involved (Galaburda, 2005). For example, chromosome 13 (13q21) appears to be directly implicated as a dyslexia phenotype (Bartlett et al., 2002). Other evidence continues to suggest that brain abnormalities, possibly heritable, may be responsible for dyslexia and other learning disorders (see Gilger & Kaplan, 2001, for review). As noted by Grigorenko (2009), the common forms of speech and language disorders are probably associated with variability in the function of multiple genes. Further, children with learning disabilities are more likely to have experienced prenatal and perinatal complications (e.g., Watson & Westby, 2003).

Multivariate genetic analyses have determined that there is substantial overlap between learning abilities, between cognitive abilities, and between learning and cognitive abilities (see Haworth et al., 2009). This finding has been referred to as the "generalist genes hypothesis": the genes that affect one ability are much the same genes that affect a different ability, even though there are also some genetic effects that are specific to each ability. Haworth et al. (2009) conducted a multivariate genetic analysis of low performance in reading, mathematics, language, and general cognitive ability in a sample of 8,000 12-year-old twins. The generalist genes hypothesis held for language and general cognitive disabilities, as well as reading and mathematics disabilities. There was a strong degree of overlap in genetic influences on these diverse traits; however, non-shared environmental influences were primarily specific to each trait, accounting for phenotypic differentiation of traits. Recent data continue to support the generalist genes hypothesis by showing that the general effects of genes can be detected among Chinese twins, thus indicating that the general effects of genes may be universal across languages (Chow et al., 2013). Other data implicate the *SNAP25* gene, a presynaptic plasma membrane protein, that contributes to widespread variation in the normal range and also in the lower extreme of intellectual ability (Rizzi et al., 2012).

Biological factors may be related to the development of a learning disability. Possibilities include deficits in perceptual systems, perceptual-motor functioning, oculomotor functioning, and neurological organization that could lead to abnormal cognitive processing (see Ahonen et al., 2004). For example, past psychological theories focused on perceptual deficits as the basis for dyslexia; however, findings have not supported simple perceptual deficits as characterizing dyslexia (Wolff & Melngailis, 1996). Most children make letter reversals when first learning to read, but even dyslexic individuals very rarely make letter reversals after age 9 or 10.

Other research points to one or more problems in language processing that might arise from a deficit in the brain structures that are used to process stimuli rapidly (Eden & Zeffiro, 1996).

PET scans made of dyslexic and normal children as they performed a variety of cognitive tasks revealed that the left temporoparietal cortex was activated in the normal children but not in the dyslexic children (Rumsey et al., 1994). The temporoparietal cortex is important in an aspect of language processing called *phonological awareness*, believed to be critical to the development of reading skills (Voeller, 2004). Children with phonological awareness deficits have diminished ability to "notice, think about, or manipulate sounds in words" (Lyon & Cutting, 1998, p. 481). When a task demands more phonological awareness, children with a learning disability show greater deficits (Voeller, 2004).

Neuroimaging studies have yielded evidence of structural anomalies and anomalous activation in critical language areas in the temporal and frontal lobes of people with dyslexia (see Shaywitz & Shaywitz, 2005, for review). Specht et al. (2009) conducted an fMRI study of 6-year-old children considered at risk for dyslexia, compared with a matched control group, to examine differences in brain activation when the children were presented with visual stimuli that differed in demands for literacy processing. Brain responses distinguished between presentation conditions as a function of group within numerous cortical areas but particularly in the left angular gyrus and inferior occipitotemporal regions. The authors concluded that, "Since similar patterns are reported in adult dyslexics when processing written words, it appears that sensitivity to the cortical differentiation of reading networks is established prior to formal literacy training" (p. 79).

The family history of learning disorders might put a child at risk for developing a learning disability due to environmental factors (in addition to genetic factors). For example, the parent with a learning disorder might not be able to assist the child with school projects. Rashid, Morris, and Sevcik (2005) reported that children whose parents don't read to them regularly often have high rates of reading disorders.

Since there are no clear causal factors that lead consistently to the development of a learning disability, it is probable that these disorders develop from a complex interaction among variables.

Treatment of Learning Disorders

The anxiety of parents whose otherwise normal child lags behind in reading or cannot speak effectively and normally for his or her age cannot be underestimated. Professional attempts to remedy learning disabilities have been subject to somatic, educational, and psychological fads—from using stimulants and tranquillizers to training the child in motor activities (such as crawling) believed to have been inadequately mastered at a younger age—in the hope of reorganizing neuronal connections in the brain. For example, although Ritalin can be effective in reducing some maladaptive behaviours in ADHD children, it has limited effectiveness in raising achievement scores in children diagnosed with both a learning disability and ADHD (Brown, Carpenter, & Simerly, 2005).

Most treatment for learning disorders occurs within special-education programs in the public schools. An individualized program should be implemented for a child diagnosed with a learning disorder (Siegel, 2006). That is, there should be a match between the needs of the child and the services provided to the child within the school system. Ideally, schools will employ evidence-based strategies. Because of mainstreaming, there is currently an emphasis on keeping children with special needs in regular classrooms as much as possible.

Although efficacy and effectiveness studies are limited, there is some evidence that special-education services can facilitate overcoming learning disabilities in children and adolescents (e.g., Alexander & Slinger-Constant, 2004). Special-education services typically incorporate some of the following interventions (adapted from Phares, 2008):

- Instructional interventions (e.g., using teaching methods that maximize ability to learn)
- School-home notes (e.g., sending notes home to communicate about what needs to be done)
- Performance feedback (e.g., providing direct feedback about performance)
- Self-management (e.g., helping children learn how to manage time)
- Contingency management interventions (e.g., providing reinforcement to increase on-task behaviour)
- Cognitive-based interventions (e.g., self-instructional training to increase self-control)
- Peer tutoring (e.g., peers helping peers on academic tasks)
- Group contingencies (e.g., rewarding the entire class for maximal efforts)
- Co-operative learning (e.g., working together in teams to maximize learning of group members)
- Phonological training (e.g., techniques such as word identification training to facilitate reading and writing development)

A meta-analysis of five types of special-education strategies (Kavale & Forness, 1999) found that applied behaviour analysis was the only intervention to achieve a large mean effect size. Perceptual-motor training was apparently not effective despite the fact it had been evaluated in 180 studies. Phonological training programs are now widely used and are effective in helping children with reading disorders (Calhoon, 2005). Longer periods of training are especially helpful with children who have severe reading difficulties (Alexander & Slinger-Constant, 2004).

Most children with learning disabilities experience frustration and failure, which erodes their motivation and confidence. Whatever their design, education programs should provide opportunities for children to experience feelings of mastery and self-efficacy and include strategies to address the secondary social and emotional adjustment problems they experience. A meta-analysis concluded that learning-disabled children with poor self-concepts can be helped at school by cognitive-behavioural therapy (CBT) interventions (Elbaum & Vaughn, 2003).

Parental involvement in the educational process has been linked to fewer learning disabilities for children and to better academic outcomes (e.g., Pantin et al., 2003).

Individuals with dyslexia or other learning disorders often can succeed in university or college with the aid of instructional supports, such as recorded lectures, tutors, editorial assistance, and untimed tests (e.g., Bruck, 1986). Most universities and colleges have special services to help such students.

Intellectual Disability Disorder

The term "intellectual disability disorder" in *DSM-5* primarily refers to people with mental retardation. *DSM-5* work group members recommended in February 2010 (see www.dsm5.org) that the diagnostic term "mental retardation" be changed to "intellectual disability" to align the *DSM* terminology and criteria with those of other disciplines, organizations, and international opinion. Historically, coding of severity has focused on IQ that level but the emphasis in *DSM-5* is on varying levels of adaptive functioning.

In October 2004, Montreal hosted the Pan-American Health Organization and World Health Organization Conference on Intellectual Disability (Lecomte & Mercier, 2007). The Montreal Declaration on Intellectual Disabilities, a consensus result, emphasizes three fundamental rights of people with an intellectual disability—equality, non-discrimination, and self-determination—and is intended to guide international organizations and civil and public authorities in attempts "to ensure full and complete citizenship to persons with intellectual disabilities" (Lecomte & Mercier, 2007, p. 66).

Traditional and Contemporary Criteria for Intellectual Disability

Intelligence-Test Scores   The original DSM definition required a judgement of intelligence. As discussed in Chapter 3, approximately two-thirds of the population achieve IQ test scores between 85 and 115. Those with a score below 70 to 75, two standard deviations below the mean of the population, meet the criterion of "significant subaverage general intellectual functioning." Approximately 3% of the population fall within this category.

The determination of IQ should be based on tests administered by a competent, well-trained professional. Interpretation of scores must take into account cultural, linguistic, and sensory or motor limitations that may affect performance. For example, a child who speaks Farsi at home and English at school cannot be tested in a valid way using only English-language measures.

Adaptive Functioning   Adaptive functioning is the mastering of childhood skills such as toileting and dressing; understanding the concepts of time and money; being able to use tools, to shop, and to travel by public transportation;

and becoming socially responsive. An adolescent, for example, is expected to be able to apply academic skills, reasoning, and judgement to daily living and to participate in group activities. An adult is expected to be self-supporting and to assume social responsibilities. Thus, adaptive behaviour is the collection of skills that we all learn in order to function in our daily lives.

DSM-5 focused on deficits in adaptive functioning in three domains: the conceptual (academic) domain, the social domain, and the practical domain (American Psychiatric Association, 2013). The practical domain essentially taps all key aspects of daily life requirements. These domains form the basis of the Diagnostic Adaptive Behavior Scale (DABS), which was released by the American Association on Intellectual and Developmental Disabilities (AAIDD) in 2010. The DABS provides a comprehensive, standardized assessment of adaptive behaviour designed for use with people ages 4 to 21 years. The scale "provides precise diagnostic information around the cutoff point where an individual is deemed to have 'significant limitations' in adaptive behavior" (see www.aaidd.org). The DABS measures three domains of adaptive behaviour: conceptual skills (e.g., literacy, self-direction); social skills (e.g., social problem solving, following rules); and practical skills (e.g., activities of daily living, schedules, and routine).

A final definitional criterion is that intellectual disability be manifest before age 18, to rule out classifying as mental retardation any deficits in intelligence and adaptive behaviour from traumatic accidents or illnesses occurring later in life. Children with severe impairments are usually diagnosed during infancy. Most children considered mentally retarded, however, are not identified as such until they enter school, despite the fact that differences in children with more subtle forms of mental retardation can be perceived as early as 1 year of age (Osterling, Dawson, & Munson, 2002).

Classification of Intellectual Disability

Four levels of intellectual disability are recognized by *DSM-5*: mild, moderate, severe, and profound. Previously, these four categories were used, but they were defined primarily by IQ scores:

- *Mild mental retardation* (50–55 to 70 IQ). About 85% of all those with IQs less than 70 are classified as having **mild mental retardation**.

- *Moderate mental retardation* (35–40 to 50–55 IQ). About 10% of those with IQs less than 70 are classified as having **moderate mental retardation**.

- *Severe mental retardation* (20–25 to 35–40 IQ). Of those people with IQs less than 70, about 3 to 4% come under the category of **severe mental retardation**.

- *Profound mental retardation* (below 20–25 IQ). About 1 to 2% of people with mental retardation are classified as having **profound mental retardation**, requiring total supervision and often nursing care all their lives.

A Canadian study of adolescents established that the overall prevalence of mental retardation is 7.2 per 1,000, with the prevalence of severe mental retardation being 3.6 per 1,000 (Bradley, Thompson, & Bryson, 2002). The prevalence estimate is comparable with the estimated prevalence worldwide. Boys are considerably more likely to be diagnosed with intellectual disability than girls. The ratio of boys to girls is about 1.6:1 (American Psychiatric Association, 2000). There are high rates of comorbidity with psychological disorders (e.g., autism spectrum disorder). Indeed, a wide range of psychological, behavioural, and social problems are common in children and adolescents with mental retardation (see Phares, 2008, for review).

The Approach of the American Association of Intellectual and Developmental Disabilities

"AAIDD is committed to setting aside labels and instead focus on creating and supporting the services people with intellectual disability need to function fully in our society. AAIDD is committed to including the people with intellectual disability within every aspect of our lives whether they ride the bus with us, work in the same offices or play with our children."

—*AAIDD news release, September 14, 2009*

We turn now to a very different approach to mental retardation. In the ninth edition of its classification system, the American Association of Mental Retardation (AAMR, 1992), now the AAIDD, shifted its focus from identifying severity of disability to determining what remedial supports are necessary to facilitate higher functioning. Professionals were now encouraged to identify an individual's strengths and weaknesses on psychological, physical, and environmental dimensions with a view toward determining the kinds and intensities of environmental supports needed to enhance a person's functioning in different domains. This approach abandons a deficit model approach and instead encourages a more individualized assessment of a person's skills and needs and focuses more on what people can do. More attention is placed on how best to make positive changes in the person's life.

Consider Roger, a 24-year-old man with an IQ of 45 who has attended a special program for mentally retarded children since he was 6. A deficit approach would highlight his difficulties and emphasize that he would not be expected to be able to live independently, get around on his own, or progress beyond Grade 2. The AAIDD classification system, however, would emphasize what is needed to maximize Roger's functioning. A clinician might discover that Roger can use the bus system if he takes a route familiar to him, and thus he might be able to go to a movie by himself from time to time. And although he cannot prepare complicated meals, he might be able to learn to prepare frozen entrées in a microwave oven. The assumption

is that Roger will make more progress and have a better life by concentrating and building on what he can do.

In 2010, the AAIDD issued the 11th edition of its definitive manual (*Intellectual Disability: Classification, Definition, and Systems of Support*). This book synthesizes current information and "best practices," including uniform criteria to be used to diagnose intellectual disability. Individualized supports remain the cornerstone of the system in order to reduce any mismatch between the capabilities and skills of a person with an intellectual disability and what is necessary to participate in all aspects of daily living in the community and workplace.

Etiology of Intellectual Disability

The causes of mental retardation may be primarily biological, psychosocial, or a combination of both. The major predisposing factors, as recognized by the American Psychiatric Association (2000), are summarized here.

No Clear Etiology (Approximately 30–40% of Cases)   Although many possible causes account for mental retardation, at this time between 30 and 40% of cases have no known risk factor or genetic marker that can explain its occurrence despite extensive evaluation (American Psychiatric Association, 2000).

Hereditary Disorders (5%)   Hereditary disorders include inborn errors of metabolism inherited mostly through autosomal recessive mechanisms (e.g., phenylketonuria, Tay-Sachs disease), other single-gene abnormalities with variable expression (e.g., tuberous sclerosis), and chromosomal aberrations (e.g., fragile X syndrome).

Several hundred recessive-gene diseases have been identified, and many of them cause mental retardation. Here we discuss one recessive-gene disease, phenylketonuria. In **phenylketonuria** (PKU), the infant, born normal, soon suffers from a deficiency of a liver enzyme, phenylalanine hydroxylase. This enzyme is needed to convert phenylalanine, an amino acid found in protein, to tyrosine, an amino acid essential for the development of such hormones as epinephrine. Because of this enzyme deficiency, phenylalanine and its derivative phenylpyruvic acid are not broken down and instead build up in the body's fluids. This buildup eventually causes irreversible brain damage because the unmetabolized amino acid interferes with the process of myelination, the sheathing of neuron axons, which is essential for the rapid transmittal of impulses and thus of information. The neurons of the frontal lobes, the site of many important mental functions, are particularly affected, and thus mental retardation is profound.

Although PKU is rare, with an incidence of about 1 in 14,000 live births, it is estimated that 1 person in 70 is a carrier of the recessive gene. A blood test is available for prospective parents who have reason to suspect that they might be carriers. After the newborn with PKU has consumed milk for several days, an excess amount of unconverted phenylalanine can be detected in the blood. If the test is positive, parents should provide the infant with a diet low in phenylalanine as early as possible.

Early Alterations of Embryonic Development (Approximately 30%)

About 30% of cases of mental retardation are caused by early alterations of embryonic development. These factors include chromosomal changes (e.g., Down's syndrome due to trisomy 21) or prenatal damage due to toxins (e.g., maternal alcohol consumption, infections).

Most of these cases can be prevented through prenatal genetic testing or prevention of substance abuse during pregnancy. Perhaps the best-known example is **Down's syndrome**, or **trisomy 21** (see photo). People with Down's syndrome have moderate to severe retardation, as well as several distinctive physical signs (e.g., short and stocky stature; oval, upward-slanting eyes). Although there is a shortened life expectancy for people with Down's syndrome, it has increased steadily over the past century and they now live past 60 on average (Bittles & Glasson, 2004). Beacher et al. (2009) demonstrated that volume reductions of the hippocampus and caudate nucleus, as measured by volumetric MRI, are seen in Down's syndrome individuals with Alzheimer's disease and suggested that these reductions might provide markers of Alzheimer's disease.

Down's syndrome is named after the British physician Langdon Down, who first described its clinical signs in 1866. In 1959, the French geneticist Jerome Lejeune and his colleagues identified its genetic basis. Human beings normally possess 46 chromosomes, inheriting 23 from each parent. Individuals with Down's syndrome almost always have 47 chromosomes instead of 46. During maturation of the egg, the two chromosomes of pair 21, the smallest ones, fail to separate. If the egg unites with a sperm, there will be three of chromosome 21, thus the technical term trisomy 21. Down's syndrome is found in about 1 in 800 to 1,200 live births.

While in utero, the fetus is at increased risk of mental retardation resulting from maternal infectious diseases such as rubella (German measles). The consequences of these diseases are most serious during the first trimester of pregnancy, when the fetus has no detectable immunological response. Cytomegalovirus, toxoplasmosis, rubella, herpes simplex, and syphilis are all maternal infections that may cause both physical deformities and mental retardation in the fetus. The mother may experience slight or no symptoms from the infection, but the effects on the developing fetus can be devastating. Pregnant women who go to prenatal clinics are given a blood test for syphilis. Women can also have their blood tested to determine whether they are immune to rubella; nearly 85% of North American women are. Women who are not immune should be vaccinated six months before becoming pregnant. If a fetus contracts rubella from the mother, the child is likely to be born with brain lesions that cause mental retardation.

Later Pregnancy and Perinatal Problems (Approximately 10%)

Problems in later pregnancy and perinatal problems are thought to account for about 10% of mental retardation cases. Factors include fetal malnutrition, placental insufficiency, prematurity, hypoxia, low birth weight, intracranial hemorrhage, trauma, and viral and other infections. All of these can be responsible for diminished intellectual functioning.

Medical Conditions Acquired During Childhood and Accidents (Approximately 5%)

Factors such as infections, traumas, and poisoning (see photo) account for about 5% of cases. For example, infectious diseases can also affect a child's developing brain after birth. Encephalitis and meningococcal meningitis may cause irreversible brain damage and even death if contracted in infancy or early childhood. There are several forms of childhood meningitis, a disease

Child with Down's syndrome.

Although lead-based paint is now illegal, it can still be found in older homes. Eating these paint chips can cause lead poisoning and mental retardation.

in which the protective membranes of the brain are acutely inflamed and fever is very high. Some children who survive without severe retardation may become mildly to moderately retarded. Other disabling after-effects are deafness, paralysis, and epilepsy.

Environmental toxins can cause intellectual, developmental, behavioural, and learning problems (Hodapp & Dykens, 2005). For example, lead poisoning can cause kidney and brain damage, as well as anemia, mental retardation, seizures, and death. Falls, near drowning, and automobile accidents are among the most common mishaps in early childhood, causing varying degrees of head injuries and mental retardation. Laws mandating that children riding in automobiles wear seat belts and protective helmets when bicycling could play a major role in reducing the incidence of mental retardation in children.

Environmental Influences and Other Mental Disorders (Approximately 15–20%)

Factors that include deprivation of nurturance and of social, linguistic, and other stimulation, as well as severe mental disorders (e.g., autism spectrum disorder), account for another 15 to 20% of cases of mental retardation.

People with mild or moderate mental retardation do not appear to have an identifiable brain defect. And while individuals whose mental retardation is associated with identifiable biological impairments are found in much the same percentages throughout all socio-economic, ethnic, and racial groups, those with mild or moderate mental retardation are overrepresented in the lower socio-economic classes, suggesting that certain social conditions of deprivation are major factors in retarding their intellectual and behavioural development. Several variables might act in concert to produce milder forms of mental retardation.

Prevention and Treatment of Intellectual Disability

In the early part of the twentieth century, many large institutions were built in Canada and the United States to house retarded individuals apart from the rest of the population. Many were no more than warehouses for anyone unfortunate enough to do poorly on newly constructed intelligence tests. The majority of residents were recently arrived immigrants, members of ethnic or racial minorities, children with physical disabilities, and indigents.

This forced segregation did not stop couples within institutions from bearing children. The first mandatory sterilization law for women with mental retardation in the United States was passed in Indiana in 1907. By 1930, 28 states had these laws. Although its constitutionality was questioned, forced sterilization—especially for undereducated minority and immigrant groups—continued to be practised in many institutions through the 1950s. In the 1960s, safeguards were passed to protect the rights of individuals with mental retardation to marry and bear children. The extent of this deplorable sterilization program recently came to light following an analysis of records from California. There were over 19,000 sterilization recommendations

over a 33-year period with many documented cases of sterilization occurring against the wishes of family members. Moreover, among those operated upon it is estimated that about 831 people (with an average age of 87.9 years) were still alive in 2016 in California (see Stern et al., 2017).

Unfortunately, Canada's track record in this area was equally deplorable. Canadian Perspectives 15.3 features the situation in Alberta and the tragic case of Leilani Muir.

Current workers in the field promote the right of adults with intellectual disability to freedom of sexual expression, as well as to marry and have children.

Unfortunately, intellectually disabled children are still warehoused in many parts of the world. In Russia, for example, the old Soviet ideal of "perfect children" still encourages parents to give up their disabled children to the care—actually neglect—of state-run institutions (Bennett, 1997). The cruelty and neglect experienced by children in Russian orphanages was documented in a December 1998 report by the organization Human Rights Watch (see www.hrw.org).

Environmental Interventions and Enrichment Programs

There has been a concerted effort to bring people with intellectual disability into the mainstream (Zucker, Perras, Gartin, & Fidler, 2005), including finding suitable treatment facilities, group homes, and community living arrangements (Breedlove et al., 2005), and having them participate in competitive activities, such as the Special Olympics (see photo). Further, the consensus today is that children with developmental disabilities should be included in public educational systems whenever possible. "Mainstreaming" is important because intellectually handicapped people, both children and adults, who live in the mainstream of society and receive services there show greater educational attainment and improvement in psychological functioning than those who are more confined (e.g., Kavale, 2002).

Behavioural Interventions Based on Operant Conditioning

Early-intervention programs have been developed to improve the level of functioning of individuals with more serious intellectual disability. Projects have intervened with children during infancy and early childhood in an attempt to improve their functioning. These programs typically include systematic home- and treatment centre- or school-based instruction in language skills, fine and gross motor skills, self-care, and social development. Specific behavioural objectives are defined, and in an operant fashion, children are taught skills in small, sequential steps. Children with severe intellectual disability usually need intensive instruction to be able to feed, toilet, and groom themselves. This **applied behaviour analysis**, or ABA, approach is also used to reduce inappropriate and self-injurious behaviour. Studies of these programs indicate consistent improvements in fine motor skills, acceptance by others, self-help skills, communication skills, social skills, and vocational techniques (e.g., Zucker et al., 2005). Being able to act more normally increases the

Canadian Perspectives 15.3

Eugenics and the Sexual Sterilization of Canadians with Intellectual Disability

"Nobody has the right to play God. Nobody."

—Leilani Muir (Nemeth, 1995), who was sexually sterilized as an adolescent without her knowledge or consent, under the Sexual Sterilization Act in Alberta

In Chapter 1, we referred to C.M. Hincks and his support of the sexual sterilization of mentally ill Canadians. Throughout the twentieth century, Canadians with intellectual disability were often the targets of the eugenics movement. According to the proponents, elimination of the possibility that mentally retarded people would reproduce was one way of "perfecting" the gene pool.

Alberta and British Columbia were particularly active in the number of sexual sterilizations performed (Park & Radford, 1998; Woodill, 1992). The Sexual Sterilization Act was approved initially in Alberta in 1928 and modified in 1937 so that any form of consent was no longer required. Overall, 2,822 people were sexually sterilized in Alberta before the act was finally repealed in 1972 (Woodill, 1992); this included 2,102 people identified as "mental defectives" and 370 psychotics (Park & Radford, 1998). British Columbia was the only other province that put a sterilization law into place, in 1933 (McLaren, 1986). Sterilizations were also performed in other parts of Canada, even without similar laws. For instance, there are reports of mentally retarded children being sterilized at the request of their parents, and one of the authors of this text received clinical training at a site where sterilizations took place in Ontario.

Dickin and Ryan (1983) provided a cogent summary of the arguments made both for and against the sexual sterilization of mentally retarded Canadians. They outlined the three main arguments put forth by those in favour of non-consensual sterilization (essentially that sterilization serves the well-being of the handicapped individual, the well-being of potential children, and the well-being of society). In response, four arguments have been raised by those vehemently opposed to sterilization:

1. Evidence for the genetic inheritance of intellectual disability is not strong, and genetic theory and research does not support the unmitigated sterilization of mentally retarded people.

2. Serious human rights violations are involved, including the right to equal treatment under the law.

3. Negative psychological consequences involving the loss of self-esteem may ensue from being sterilized and being degraded and treated as less human than other people.

4. The practice of sterilization is open to bias and discrimination such that those people who are considered "unfit" actually are fit and may not receive fair and impartial treatment.

The fourth point applies to the case of Leilani Muir (see photo). Muir's story is depicted in the National Film Board of Canada documentary *The Sterilization of Leilani Muir* (National Film Board of Canada, 1996). Muir grew up on a farm in Alberta. She had an abusive mother who beat her, starved her, and locked her away. In 1955, at the age of 11, her mother left her at the Provincial Training School for Mental Defectives in Red Deer (which is now called the Michener Centre). Muir's mother lied about her daughter's true

mental abilities and Muir was confined improperly for 10 years. The only IQ test she received while at the training school was administered in 1957, and she scored a 65, thereby obtaining the label "moron."

Muir was sterilized surgically in 1957 at the age of 14. She was told that she was going to have her appendix out. According to Wahlsten (1997), the order for Muir's sterilization was signed by John MacEachran, founder of the Department of Philosophy and Psychology at the University of Alberta and chair of the Eugenics Board from 1929 to 1965. The Board was a four-person committee that listened briefly to the youths deemed suitable for sexual sterilization and then made their decision.

Muir left the training school at the age of 21; however, having been institutionalized for so long, she had difficulty functioning in the outside world. Later, she dated and married the first man she met. When she was in her mid-twenties, a medical examination determined that she had been sterilized earlier and that her "insides looked like they had been through a slaughterhouse" (National Film Board of Canada, 1996).

Muir and her first husband eventually divorced. She remarried, and she and her second husband considered the possibility of adoption, but that fell through. He turned to alcohol and Muir experienced depression and considered suicide. Meanwhile, her IQ was retested several times and was always found to be in the normal range (i.e., it varied from 90 to 101).

Muir pursued legal action against the Alberta government and was awarded approximately $740,000 in 1996 and an additional $230,000 in legal costs. She became a symbol for all people who were affected by the Sexual Sterilization Act. In 1996, hundreds of other people began comparable legal action that would lead to settlements of over $140 million. The Leilani Muir Graduate Research Scholarship was established at the University of Alberta "in honour of the historical legal victory won by Leilani Muir and hundreds of victims of sterilization."

In 2013, the Michener Centre was slated to close. According to *The Globe and Mail* (see Wingrove, 2013), this meant that only Manitoba, Quebec, and Nova Scotia still operated large-scale

Leilani Muir was a tireless advocate for the rights of children with disabilities after being sexually sterilized while an adolescent without her consent. Premier Rachel Notley described Muir as a hero after Muir passed away in March 2016. Muir's life experiences are described in her 2014 memoir "A Whisper Past -- Childless After Eugenic Sterilization in Alberta."

institutions for people with mental disabilities. The article showed that opinions varied substantially on whether the Michener Centre should close since it housed 125 voluntary residents. However, Leilani Muir, then at the age of 68, was quite clear about how she felt. She stated, "I will try to be the one there to bulldoze those buildings down . . . There's a lot of ghosts in those buildings. And they're not good. They're not good" (Wingrove, 2013, p. A12).

Leilani Muir died in March 2016 at the age of 71. She had come along way since being put in the Provincial Training School for Mental Defectives some 60 years earlier.

Thinking Critically

1. The rights of people with intellectual disability are now protected under the Charter of Rights and Freedoms. Many people felt that Muir's family was to blame for her institutionalization and that the government should not be held accountable. Were these settlements against the government justified? Is the government responsible?

2. Why do you think that Muir's first IQ test showed that she had an IQ of 65 while at least one subsequent test showed that she had an IQ of 101? What factors could account for the discrepancy?

Eunice Kennedy Shriver (1921–2009) founded the Special Olympics, with the help of eminent Canadian Frank Hayden, an Officer of the Order of Canada. It was launched in 1968 with 1,000 competitors from Canada and the United States. Today, 3 million athletes from more than 180 countries vie to compete. Eunice Shriver, sister of President John F. Kennedy, was perhaps the 20th century's most notable advocate for people with developmental challenges. In 1984, she was awarded the Presidential Medal of Freedom and in 2006 she received a papal knighthood.

chances of interacting meaningfully with others. Moreover, the self-esteem that comes from learning to take better care of oneself is extremely bolstering. Strategies are also available to assist families who are coping with the challenges of having a loved one with a developmental disability (Blacher, Neece, & Paczkowski, 2005).

Cognitive Interventions   Many children with intellectual disability fail to use strategies in solving problems, and when they do have strategies, they often apply them ineffectively. **Self-instructional training**, first developed by Meichenbaum and Goodman in 1971, teaches these children to guide their problem-solving efforts through speech. Self-

instructional training has been employed to teach these children self-control, as well as how to pay attention and how to master academic tasks, and then how to generalize the strategy to new tasks (Hughes & Agran, 1993). Children with severe disability can effectively master self-help skills through this technique. Hughes, Hugo, and Blatt (1996), for example, taught high school students with IQs below 40 to make their own buttered toast and clean up after themselves. Further, researchers in Kingston, Ontario, demonstrated that self-instructional manuals are effective in teaching child care skills to mothers with mild intellectual disability (Feldman, Ducharme, & Case, 1999).

15.5 Autism Spectrum Disorder

A psychology student walks into a special-education classroom. She is taking a course on child disabilities, and one requirement is to volunteer some time in this class. As several children rise to greet her, she becomes aware of their minor or major physical characteristics. One child has slanted eyes and a flat nose, typical of Down's syndrome. Another makes spastic movements, a sign of cerebral palsy. A third child calls to her from a wheelchair with grunting noises and communicates with a combination of hand gestures and pictures. Then this psychology student notices a fourth child in the room, standing in front of the fish tank. She approaches him and notices his graceful, deft movements and the dreamy, remote look in his eyes. She wonders if he is a visitor to the class. She starts talking to him about the fish. Instead of acknowledging her comment or even her presence, he begins rocking back and forth while continuing to smile, as if enjoying a private joke. When the teacher enters the room, she tells the psychology student that he is autistic.

Characteristics of Autism Spectrum Disorder

From the time it was first distinguished, **autism spectrum disorder** has had a somewhat mystical aura. The syndrome was identified in 1943 by a Harvard psychiatrist, Leo Kanner, who noticed in his clinical work that 11 disturbed children behaved in ways that were uncommon in children with mental retardation or schizophrenia. He named the syndrome early infantile autism because he noted that "there is from the start an extreme autistic aloneness that, whenever possible, disregards, ignores, shuts out anything that comes to the child from the outside" (Kanner, 1943). Kanner considered autistic aloneness the most fundamental symptom. He also found that these children had been unable from the beginning of life to relate to people in the ordinary way. They were severely limited in language and had a strong obsessive desire for everything about them to remain exactly the same. Despite its early description by Kanner and others, the disorder was not accepted into official diagnostic nomenclature until the publication of *DSM-III* in 1980.

The evidence seems to indicate that childhood-onset schizophrenia and autism spectrum disorder are separate disorders. Nonetheless, contemporary research suggests that childhood-onset schizophrenia is preceded by and comorbid with autism spectrum disorder in 30 to 50% of cases (Rapoport et al., 2009). Further, a growing number of risk genes and rare chromosomal variants appear to be shared by both disorders.

In part to clarify the differentiation of autism spectrum disorder from schizophrenia, *DSM-III* introduced (and *DSM-III-R*, *DSM-IV*, and *DSM-IV-TR* retained) the term **pervasive developmental disorders**. This term emphasized that autism spectrum disorder involves a serious abnormality in the developmental process itself. In *DSM-IV-TR*, autistic disorder was but one of several pervasive developmental disorders:

- Rett's disorder is very rare and is found only in girls. Development is entirely normal until the first or second year of life, when the child's head growth decelerates. She loses the ability to use her hands for purposeful movements, instead engaging in stereotyped movements such as hand-wringing or handwashing; walks in an uncoordinated manner; learns only poorly to speak and understand others; and is profoundly retarded. The child relates poorly to others, though this may improve later in life.

- Childhood disintegrative disorder occurs in children who have had normal development in the first two years of life but then suffer significant loss of social, play, language, and motor skills. Abnormalities in social interaction and communication and the presence of stereotyped behaviour are very similar to those in autism spectrum disorder.

- Asperger's syndrome is often regarded as a mild form of autism. Social relationships are poor and stereotyped behaviour is intense and rigid, but language and intelligence are intact. Extensive research on Asperger's syndrome has been conducted by Canadian researcher Peter Szatmari and his team (see Focus on Discovery 15.1).

As noted in Chapter 3, in February 2010, the *DSM-5* work group proposed a new name for the category, autism spectrum disorder (ASD), which includes autistic disorder (autism), and subsumes Asperger's syndrome, childhood disintegrative disorder, and pervasive developmental disorder not otherwise specified (PDD-NOS). The work group provided a detailed rationale for representing autism as a single

diagnostic category with clinical specifiers (e.g., severity, verbal abilities) and associated features (e.g., known genetic disorders, epilepsy, intellectual disability). It was noted that "distinctions among disorders have been found to be inconsistent over time, variable across sites and often associated with severity, language level or intelligence rather than features of the disorder. . . .previously, the criteria were equivalent to trying to 'cleave meatloaf at the joints'" (see American Psychiatric Association, 2010). The *DSM-5* criteria for ASD are reproduced in Table 15.4.

It was also noted that there were concerns that children and adolescents with milder levels of impairment might no longer meet diagnostic criteria with the changes that were put in place. The new criteria do seem to have had a substantial impact. A review of 25 studies that compared the *DSM-IV-TR* and *DSM-5* criteria found that between 50 and 75% maintained their diagnoses (see Smith, Reichow, & Volkmar, 2015); this range of disorders was attributed to differences in assessment and research methods. However, it was typically the case that 1 out of 4 or more children or adolescents no longer met diagnostic criteria. This most likely happened when there was a diagnosis of PDD-NOS or Asperger's disorder, or an IQ greater than 70. The majority of these children and adolescents no longer meet criteria for a diagnosis. The authors noted that their higher level of functioning should not be confused with high functioning and their lack of access to services could deny them the chance of ultimately achieving their optimal level of functioning.

ASD begins in early childhood and can be evident in the first months of life. The popular press sometimes cites an "epidemic of autism." Thus, while the prevalence was held to be 4 in 10,000 in the 1970s and 1980s, current estimates indicate that, in the general population, based on studies conducted globally since the turn of this century, autism occurs in 17 infants in 10,000, or 0.17% of births (Elsabbagh et al., 2012). The prevalence rises to 62 per 10,000 when all autistic spectrum disorders are included (Elsabbagh et al., 2012). What factors account for the increase in incidence? According to one team of authors, about two-thirds of the increase is attributable to earlier age of diagnosis and a gradual broadening of the diagnostic criteria (Scott, Duhig, Hamlyn, & Norman, 2013); the other one-third of the increase is due to unknown factors but possible environmental contributors.

About 4.3 times more boys than girls have ASD (Fombonne, 2003) and the ratio is 7:1 when it comes to high-functioning autism (Fombonne, 2005). According to a contemporary analysis by De Rubeis and Buxbaum (2015), tests of whether this difference is due to increased male vulnerability (i.e., the presence of male specific factors) vs. a "female protective effect" (i.e., females having to have a higher "etiological load" in order to have ASD) favour the female protective effect explanation, especially in terms of the role of genetic factors.

Comorbidity is high, with depression, anxiety, and ADHD being common (Tidmarsh & Volkmar, 2003). Anxiety may worsen during adolescence in the face of a more complex social milieu and an awareness of being different and having

TABLE 15.4 *DSM-5* Criteria for Autism Spectrum Disorder

A. Persistent deficits in social communication and social interaction across multiple contexts, as manifested by the following, currently or by history (examples are illustrative, not exhaustive, see text):

1. Deficits in social-emotional reciprocity, ranging, for example, from abnormal social approach and failure of normal back-and-forth conversation; to reduced sharing of interests, emotions, or affect; to failure to initiate or respond to social interactions.

2. Deficits in nonverbal communicative behaviors used for social interaction, ranging, for example, from poorly integrated verbal and nonverbal communication, to abnormalities in eye contact and body language or deficits in understanding and use of gestures; to a total lack of facial expressions and nonverbal communication.

3. Deficits in developing, maintaining, and understanding relationships, ranging, for example, from difficulties adjusting behavior to suit various social contexts; to difficulties in sharing imaginative play or in making friends; to absence of interest in peers.

B. Restricted, repetitive patterns of behavior, interests, or activities, as manifested by at least two of the following, currently or by history (examples are illustrative, not exhaustive, see text):

1. Stereotyped or repetitive minor movements, use of objects, or speech (e.g., simple motor stereotypes, lining up toys or flipping objects, echolalia, idiosyncratic phrases).

2. Insistence on sameness, inflexible adherence to routines, or ritualized patterns of verbal or nonverbal behavior (e.g., extreme distress at small changes, difficulties with transitions, rigid thinking patterns, greeting rituals, need to take same route or eat same food every day).

3. Highly restricted, fixated interests that are abnormal in intensity or focus (e.g., strong attachment to or preoccupation with unusual objects, excessively circumscribed or perseverative interests).

4. Hyper- or hyporeactivity to sensory input or unusual interest in sensory aspects of the environment (e.g., apparent indifference to pain/temperature, adverse response to specific sounds or textures, excessive smelling or touching of objects, visual fascination with lights or movement).

C. Symptoms must be present in the early developmental period (but may not become fully manifest until social demands exceed limited capacities, or may be masked by learning strategies in later life).

D. Symptoms cause clinically significant improvement in social, occupational, or other important areas of current functioning.

E. These disturbances are not better explained by intellectual disability (intellectual developmental disorder) or global developmental delay. Intellectual disability and autism spectrum disorder frequently co-occur; to make comorbid diagnoses of autism spectrum disorder and intellectual disability, social communication should be below that expected for general developmental level.

Reprinted with permission from the *Diagnostic and Statistical Manual of Mental Disorders, Fifth Edition*, Copyright 2013. American Psychiatric Association.

interpersonal problems (White, Oswald, Ollendick, & Scahill, 2009). ASD is found in all socio-economic classes and in all ethnic and racial groups.

Autism and Intellectual Disability

Historically, approximately 80% of autistic children scored below 70 on standardized IQ tests, and it is sometimes difficult to differentiate ASD and intellectual disability. However, although children with intellectual disability usually score poorly on all parts of an intelligence test, generally, children with ASD do worse on tasks requiring abstract thought, symbolism, or sequential logic, all of which may be associated with their language deficits (Carpentieri & Morgan, 1994). They usually obtain better scores on items requiring visual-spatial skills. In addition, a few may have isolated skills that reflect great talent and have exceptional long-term memory. Sensorimotor development is the area of greatest relative strength among children with ASD. These children, who may show severe or profound deficits in cognitive abilities, can be quite graceful and adept at swinging, climbing, or balancing, whereas children with mental retardation are much more delayed in areas of gross-motor development (e.g., learning to walk).

Extreme Autistic Aloneness

In a sense, autistic children do not withdraw from society—they never joined it to begin with. Normally infants show signs of attachment as early as three months of age. In children with ASD, this early attachment is less pronounced. Parents of autistic children must work harder to make contact and share affection with their babies. Autistic children rarely try to engage their parents in play, and they do not point to, show, or share objects of play with others. Children with ASD rarely approach others and may look through or past people or turn their backs on them (e.g., Volkmar, Cohen, & Paul, 1986). Autistic children rarely offer a spontaneous greeting or farewell, either verbally or through smiling, making eye contact, or gesturing (Hobson & Lee, 1998). Physical play, such as tickling and wrestling, may be enjoyable. Observations of their spontaneous play reveal that they spend much less of their time engaged in symbolic play, such as pretending that a block is a car, than do either mentally retarded or normal children of comparable mental age (Sigman et al., 1986). Autistic children are more likely to twirl a favourite block continually for hours on end.

Few children with autism initiate play with other children, and they are usually unresponsive to any who may approach them. Children with autism do make eye contact, but their gaze has a different quality. Normal children gaze to gain someone's attention or to direct the other person's attention to an object; autistic children generally do not (Mirenda, Donnellan, & Yoder, 1983)—they just stare. Some autistic children appear not to recognize or distinguish one person from another.

They become preoccupied with and form strong attachments to inanimate objects (e.g., keys, rocks, light switches) and to mechanical objects (e.g., refrigerators, vacuum cleaners).

It may be that the autistic child's social isolation is the source of his or her retarded development in other areas, such as language (Kanner, 1943). On the other hand, the core deficit may be an inability to process certain kinds of sensory input, leaving the child incapable of understanding and responding to the world around him or her (Ornitz, 1989). Some researchers have proposed that a deficiency in the autistic child's **theory of mind** represents the core deficit and leads to the kinds of social dysfunctions we have described here (e.g., Sigman, 1994). Theory of mind is our understanding that other people have desires, beliefs, intentions, and emotions that may be different from our own. Children with autism seem unable to understand others' perspectives and emotional reactions; they lack empathy. Although high-functioning autistic children can learn to understand emotional experiences, they "answer questions about . . . emotional experiences like normal children answer difficult arithmetic questions" (Sigman, 1994, p. 15); that is, with concentrated cognitive effort. Although intriguing, there has been limited empirical support for the theory of mind hypothesis (e.g., Klinger, Dawson, & Renner, 2003).

Communication Deficits
Even before they acquire language, autistic children show deficits in communication. Babbling, the utterances of infants before they actually begin to use words, is less frequent in infants with ASD and conveys less information than it does in other infants. By two years of age, most normally developing children use words to represent objects in their surroundings and construct one- and two-word sentences to express more complex thoughts, such as "Mommy go" or "Me juice." The speech of autistic children who learn to speak includes various peculiarities.

One such feature is **echolalia**, in which the child echoes, usually with remarkable fidelity, what he or she has heard another person say. The teacher may ask an autistic child, "Do you want a cookie?" The child's response may be "Do you want a cookie?" Mute autistic children who later acquire some functional speech through training usually first pass through a stage of echolalia.

Another abnormality common in the speech of autistic children is **pronoun reversal**. Children refer to themselves as "he," "she," or "you" or by their own proper names. Pronoun reversal is closely linked to echolalia. Since autistic children often use echolalic speech, they refer to themselves as they have heard others speak of them. For example:

Parent:	What are you doing, Johnny?
Child:	He's here.
Parent:	Are you having a good time?
Child:	He knows it.

If speech continues to develop more normally, this pronoun reversal might disappear. In most instances, however, it is highly resistant to change.

Neologisms, made-up words or words used in unusual ways, are another characteristic of the speech of autistic children. A two-year-old autistic child might refer to milk as "moyee" and continue to do so well beyond the time when a normal child has learned to say "milk."

Children with ASD are very literal in their use of words. For example, a child may say, "Do not drop the cat" to mean "no," because his or her mother had used these emphatic words when the child was about to drop the family feline.

Even after they learn to speak, people with ASD often lack verbal spontaneity, are sparse in their verbal expression, and do not always use language appropriately.

Obsessive-Compulsive and Ritualistic Acts
Children with ASD become extremely upset over changes in their daily routines and surroundings. An offer of milk in a different drinking cup or a rearrangement of furniture may make them cry or precipitate a temper tantrum. One child had to be greeted with the set phrase "Good morning, Lily, I am very, very glad to see you." If any word, even one "very," was omitted, or another added, the child would begin to scream (Diamond, Baldwin, & Diamond, 1963). In their play, they may continually line up toys or construct intricate patterns with household objects. As they grow older, they may become preoccupied with train schedules and number sequences.

Children with ASD are also given to stereotypical behaviour, peculiar ritualistic hand movements (see photo), and other rhythmic movements, such as endless body rocking, hand flapping, and walking on tiptoe. They spin and twirl string, crayons, sticks, and plates, twiddle their fingers in front of their eyes, and stare at fans and spinning things. These are often described as self-stimulatory activities. They may become preoccupied with manipulating a mechanical object and be very upset when interrupted.

Prognosis for Autism Spectrum Disorder
What happens to such severely disturbed children when they reach adulthood? Early follow-up studies painted a generally gloomy picture of adults with ASD. From his review of all published studies, Lotter (1978) concluded that only 5 to 17%

Nancy J. Pierce/Science Source

Autistic children frequently engage in stereotyped behaviour, such as ritualistic hand movements.

of autistic children had made a relatively good adjustment in adulthood, leading independent lives but with some residual problems, such as social awkwardness. Most of the others led limited lives, and about half were institutionalized.

Similar outcomes were found in population-based, follow-up studies (e.g., von Knorring & Hagglof, 1993). Generally, children with higher IQs who learned to speak before age 6 had the best outcome, and a few of them functioned nearly normally in adulthood. Follow-up studies focusing on non-mentally retarded, high-functioning autistic individuals indicated that most did not require residential care and some even attended college and supported themselves through employment (Yirmiya & Sigman, 1991). Optimal outcome is extremely difficult to predict at a young age. Sutera et al. (2007) found that of 73 2-year-old children diagnosed with ASD, 13 "lost the diagnosis" by age 4, at which time they scored within the normal range on standardized tests of cognitive and adaptive functioning. Surprisingly, symptom severity, socialization, and communication had little predictive power in determining outcome. However, children with pervasive developmental disorder not otherwise specified were more likely than those with full autistic disorder to lose the diagnosis.

The United States passed the Developmentally Disabled Assistance and Bill of Rights Act in 1975 and similar laws were passed in Canada at about the same time. (See Bowlby & Wootton Regan, 1998, for a discussion of federal [e.g., the 1982 Canadian Charter of Rights and Freedoms] and provincial human rights legislation, and Bowlby, Peters, & MacKinnon, 2001, for a discussion of special-education laws for "exceptional" children.) Prior to that time, children with autism (and other children with special needs) were often excluded from educational programs in the public schools. Thus, most of the autistic children followed into adulthood had not had the benefit of intensive educational interventions or behavioural programs. In contrast, newer studies involving early, intensive interventions paint a considerably more promising picture.

After reviewing several new studies on early detection and early interventions, often in school settings, a group of Canadian authors (Bryson, Rogers, & Fombonne, 2003) indicated that they share the conclusion reached by several international groups: American Academy of Pediatrics recommendations advise that all 18- and 24-month-olds be screened for ASD (see Zwaigenbaum et al., 2009).

> *"[It seems that] outcomes for children with autism can be significantly enhanced by offering many hours weekly of targeted and individualized teaching that is carefully planned, delivered, and monitored. . . . It seems clear that we must leave behind several truisms about autism, including the assumptions that 50% of affected children will not speak, and 75% will have mental retardation. These older findings need to be considered as reflecting untreated children with autism, rather than as the expected course and outcome for children with autism today."*
>
> *(p. 511)*

Etiology of Autism Spectrum Disorder

The earliest theorizing about the etiology of autism spectrum disorder was that psychological factors were responsible for its development. This narrow perspective has been replaced by evidence supporting the importance of biological factors, some of them genetic, in the etiology of this puzzling syndrome.

Psychological Bases   Early theorists discounted the importance of biological factors. Both Bettelheim (1967) from a psychoanalytic perspective and Ferster (1961) from a behavioural perspective stated that parents play the crucial role in the etiology of autism. Kanner described the parents as cold, insensitive, meticulous, introverted, distant, and highly intellectual (Kanner & Eisenberg, 1955). Systematic investigations, however, failed to confirm these clinical impressions (e.g., Cantwell, Baker, & Rutter, 1978); moreover, such "refrigerator" parents raise other normal and healthy siblings. Further, any deviant parental behaviour could be a reaction to the child's abnormality rather than the other way around. Unfortunately, over the years, a tremendous emotional burden has been placed on parents who have been told that they are at fault.

Biological Bases   The very early onset of ASD, along with an accumulation of genetic and neurological evidence, strongly implicates a biological basis for this disorder.

Genetic factors   According to Nicolson and Szatmari (2003), autism is the most heritable psychiatric disorder, with heritability estimates that are even higher than those for schizophrenia and bipolar disorder. Studies following twins and families with an autistic member suggest that ASD is linked genetically to a broader spectrum of deficits in communicative and social areas (e.g., Bailey et al., 1995). For example, the non-autistic identical twin of an autistic adult is almost always unable to live independently or maintain a confiding relationship. In addition, most of these non-autistic identical twins show (or have) communication deficits, as well as severe social deficits. In contrast, the non-identical twin of an autistic child is almost always normal in social and language development and marries and lives independently in adulthood (Le Couteur et al., 1996).

The autism spectrum disorders probably have a variety of etiologies and the exact genetic background is still unclear, but important new advances have occurred. De Rubeis and Buxbaum (2015) summarized recent advances by concluding that there has been enormous progress made but it is also evident that autism reflects exceedingly complex genetic variation, with potentially more than 1,000 genes being involved.

Genome-wide linkage scans for autism susceptibility loci have identified chromosomal regions 2q, 7q, and 17q, with 7q yielding the most consistently positive results, and substantial evidence suggests that chromosomal abnormalities contribute to autism risk, although the exact prevalence is unclear (see Autism Genome Project Consortium, 2007). Focus on Discovery 15.1 summarizes an exciting discovery in the molecular genetics of ASD with a Canadian connection.

Focus on Discovery 15.1

Mapping Autism Risk Loci Using Genetic Linkage and Chromosomal Rearrangements

"Not only have we found which haystack the needle is in, we now know where in the haystack that needle is located. This is a major breakthrough in our efforts to better understand the disorder and improve diagnosis and treatment for patients and their families" (Cecil, 2007).

—Dr. Peter Szatmari

Researchers at the Offord Centre for Child Studies at McMaster University, led by Dr. Peter Szatmari (see photo), and Sick Children's Hospital in Toronto, led by Dr. Stephen Scherer, were leaders in an international consortium—The Autism Genome Project Consortium—that discovered one gene and a previously unidentified region of another chromosome as the location of an additional gene that possibly contributes to risk for an ASD. The consortium is made up of more than 120 scientists from 50 centres in North America and Europe who agreed in 2002 to share data, samples,

and expertise in order to accelerate the process of identifying the susceptibility genes that heighten the risk for autism.

In the consortium's model for autism, combinations of multiple loci that possibly interact and microscopic or sub-microscopic chromosomal abnormalities contribute to risk, complicating the detection of individual loci. Increasing the likelihood of detecting loci requires analyzing a large sample of multiplex families (i.e., families with two or more affected individuals), thereby enhancing the power of linkage analysis and controlling sources of etiologic heterogeneity (Autism Genome Project Consortium, 2007).

The findings of this massive international effort, reported in the March 2007 issue of the journal *Nature Genetics*, are based on genetic samples from 1,168 families with two or more children diagnosed with an ASD. The strategy unleashed unprecedented statistical power, which allowed the scientists to perform the largest linkage scan to date and to analyze copy number variation in these families. The results implicate a previously unidentified region of chromosome 11 and neurexins among other candidate loci in the genome. The neurexin finding especially highlights a unique group of neurons, called glutamate neurons, and the genes that affect their development and function. This discovery suggests that the neurexins may play a critical role in ASD.

The consortium is now focusing on mapping the specific genes that cause autism. Ultimately, the research could revolutionize how autism is both detected and treated. One recent finding reported by Stephen Scherer on behalf of the collaborators is that whole-genome sequencing of 32 families established that genetic causes were implicated in 50% of autism. Previously, it was believed that genetic causes were implicated clearly in only about 1 in 5 cases (see Jiang et al., 2013).

Rene Johnston/Toronto Star/Getty Images

While based previously in Hamilton, Ontario, Dr. Peter Szatmari is currently based in Toronto, where he is the Chief of the Child and Youth Mental Health Collaborative linking CAMH, the Hospital for Sick Children, and the University of Toronto.

Source: Adapted from the Offord website: www.offordcentre.com/asd/study_genetics/genstudy_ld.html, The Autism Genome Project Consortium (2007).

A collaborative research team connected more pieces of the autism "puzzle" with the publication in *Nature* of two major studies. In total the team analyzed DNA from 12,834 participants. One study (Wang et al., 2009) pinpointed a gene region, 5p14.1, that has gene variants that could possibly account for about 15% of autism cases (usually referred to as the "population-attributed risk" of the variant). The region is located between two genes, cadherin 9 (CDH9) and cadherin 10 (CDH10). These genes carry codes to produce neuronal cell-adhesion molecules, which affect how nerve cells communicate, thought to be an underlying problem in ASD. The other study (Glessner et al., 2009) identified missing or duplicated stretches of DNA (copy number variations) along two crucial gene pathways or networks that play critical roles in the development of neuronal activity expressed within the CNS that may

also contribute to the genetic susceptibility of ASD. The study leader, Hakon Hakonarson, noted that the gene discoveries converge with evidence from fMRI imaging that autistic children might have reduced connectivity among neural cells, and with anatomy studies that have found abnormal development in the frontal lobes of autistic people (see www.autismspeaks.org). Future research must determine the exact mechanisms by which genetic variations cause autistic disorder. Further, other genes will no doubt be discovered.

Neurological factors and environmental risks

Most researchers assume that a fundamental disturbance of the CNS is involved in ASD. In adolescence, 30% of those who have severe autistic symptoms as children begin having epileptic seizures, a sign that a neurological dysfunction

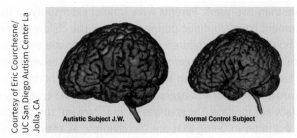

Courtesy of Eric Courchesne/
UC San Diego Autism Center La
Jolla, CA

A case of extreme macroencephaly. The 3D MRI image of 3.4-year-old autistic subject J.W. (left) is compared with that of a normal male child whose brain volume was scaled to equal normal average size (right). J.W.'s brain volume (1816 ml) was much larger than the normal average (1162 ml) for his age.

is involved in the disorder (Fombonne, 1999). Neuroimaging studies indicate that a variety of structural and functional deficits occur in ASD. For example, MRI studies show that autistic people have larger brains than normal people (e.g., Sparks et al., 2002), especially in the frontal lobe, perhaps due to the late development of this region (see Mitchell et al., 2009, for review) (see illustration). As noted by Nicolson and Szatmari (2003), this is unique to autism, as other neurodevelopmental disorders and mental retardation are associated with reduced brain volume.

Further evidence supporting the possibility of brain dysfunction derives from 16 MRI and autopsy studies from nine independent research groups, all finding abnormalities in the cerebellum of autistic children (Haas et al., 1996). Other specific regions found to be altered include the amygdala and corpus callosum (see Mitchell et al., 2009). Variability in findings is most likely attributable to the heterogeneity of autism. Mitchell and colleagues (2009) used MRI to investigate brain regions of interest in monozygotic twins who differed in degree of phenotypic discordance for autism narrowly defined. Relative to comparison children, they found alterations in the prefrontal cortex, corpus callosum, and posterior vermis in the autistic children. Further, in children with narrowly defined autism only, dorsolateral prefrontal cortex, amygdala, and posterior vermis volumes were associated with severity of autism. Although the exact nature of all the deficits remains unclear, MRI research leads to the conclusion that abnormalities in brain anatomy contribute to the metabolic differences and behavioural phenotype in ASD (McAlonan et al., 2005).

Although, as indicated above, genetic factors clearly play a role in the neurological dysfunction seen in ASD, environmental risks possibly also play a role in establishing a deficit in CNS structure and function. Indeed, it is possible that autism is already established in the fetus by about 32 weeks of gestation (Beversdorf et al., 2005). Mothers of children with autism reported higher levels of prenatal stressors from 25 to 28 weeks of gestation compared with mothers with Down's syndrome or mothers without known disorders. The timing of these stressors is consistent with the period for brain development that is abnormal in children with ASD. A subsequent meta-analysis that examined 50 prenatal factors concluded that there was insufficient evidence to establish a causal role in etiology, but

The Moncton Times & Transcript- Greg Agnew/The Canadian Press

Jenna Flanagan, a child with autism, experiences the Snoezelen Room at Magnetic Hill School in Moncton, N.B. The room has soft, soothing lights that shift colours continually, and various tactile-oriented surfaces.

several prenatal factors were linked with autism risk, including advanced parental age at birth, maternal prenatal medication use, gestational diabetes, and having a mother born abroad (Gardener, Spiegelman, & Buka, 2009). Evidence continues to accumulate for the possible roles of maternal infections, drugs, and toxicants as well as metabolic and nutritional factors, especially during the prenatal period (Matelski & Van de Water, 2016). It will be important in future research to gain a better understanding of gene–environment interactions in the etiology of autism.

In 2009, a network of leading autism researchers launched the Early Autism Risk Longitudinal Investigation (EARLI), the most comprehensive study thus far of the earliest possible causes of autism (www.earlistudy.org). EARLI will follow approximately 1,200 pregnant women who already have a child with autism in an effort to discover biological markers and environmental risk factors for autism. The research team will study possible environmental exposures, ranging from suspected neurotoxicants, like persistent organic pollutants, to medications taken during pregnancy, and their interplay with genetic susceptibility during the prenatal, neonatal, and early postnatal (36 months) periods.

Treatment of Autism Spectrum Disorder

Because their isolation is so moving and their symptoms so pronounced, a great deal of attention has been given to trying to improve the condition of children with an ASD. Sadly, there are many scientifically questionable treatments (see Lilienfeld, 2005; Vismara & Rogers, 2010), including facilitated communication, sensory integration therapy, and dolphin-assisted therapy. Treatments usually try to reduce unusual behaviour and improve communication and social skills.

Sometimes an eagerly sought-after goal for a family is simply to be able to take their autistic child to a restaurant or market without attracting negative attention. Today, the preferred interventions employ the scientific teaching principles of applied behaviour analysis (ABA). Indeed, the evidence-based treatment of choice is a long-term, comprehensive ABA intervention initiated at a very young age (see Virues-Ortega, 2010). This approach is alternatively referred to as intensive behavioural intervention (IBI).

Special Problems in Treating Children with ASD

As noted by Reiss (2009), the heterogeneity of autistic individuals diagnosed by *DSM* criteria makes it difficult for investigators to develop effective, etiology-specific interventions. Further, children with autism have several characteristics that make teaching them difficult:

1. They do not adjust well to changes in routine, yet change is the essence of treatment.

2. Their isolation and self-stimulatory movements may interfere with effective teaching.

3. It is particularly difficult to find ways to motivate them.

4. Their overselectivity of attention (i.e., when the child's attention becomes focused on one particular aspect of a task or situation, other properties, including relevant ones, may not be noticed) makes it especially difficult for the children to generalize or apply their learning to other areas.

In spite of these problems, educational programs for students with autism have achieved positive results.

Behavioural Treatment of Children with ASD

Ivar Lovaas, a leading clinical researcher at the University of California at Los Angeles (see photo), conducted a landmark intensive operant program with very young (under four years old) autistic children (Lovaas, 1987). Therapy encompassed all aspects of the children's lives for more than 40 hours a week over

more than two years. Parents were trained extensively so that treatment could continue during almost all the children's waking hours. Nineteen children receiving this intensive treatment were compared with 40 control youngsters who received a similar treatment for less than 10 hours per week. All children were rewarded for being less aggressive, more compliant, and more socially appropriate. The goal was to "mainstream" the children, the assumption being that autistic children, as they improve, benefit more from being with normal peers than from remaining by themselves or with other seriously disturbed children.

The results were dramatic and encouraging for the intensive-therapy group. Their measured IQs averaged 83 in Grade 1 (after about two years in the intensive therapy), compared with about 55 for the control children; 12 of the 19 reached the normal range, compared with only 2 (of 40) in the control group. Furthermore, 9 of the 19 in the intensive-therapy group were promoted to Grade 2 in a regular public school, whereas only 1 of the much larger control group achieved this level of normal functioning. A follow-up four years later indicated that the intensive-treatment group maintained their gains in IQ, adaptive behaviour, and grade promotions in school (McEachin, Smith, & Lovaas, 1993). Although critics have pointed out weaknesses in the study's methodology and outcome measures (Schopler, Short, & Mesibov, 1989), this ambitious program confirms the benefits of the heavy involvement of both professionals and parents in dealing with the extreme challenge of autistic disorder. The effectiveness of the Lovaas approach was confirmed in an RCT published by Smith, Groen, and Wynn (2000).

A more contemporary study (Ben-Itzchak & Zachor, 2007) illustrates the importance of early intensive behavioural intervention (EIBI) and the value of pre-intervention cognitive and social interaction levels for predicting outcome. Autistic children (20–32 months) enrolled in EIBI were divided into two groups based on IQ scores and severity of social interaction and communication deficits. Significant progress was noted in six developmental-behavioural domains after one year of intervention: imitation, receptive language, expressive language, non-verbal communication skills, play skills, and stereotyped behaviours. The children with higher initial cognitive levels and children with fewer early social interaction deficits demonstrated better acquisition of skills in language and play.

More recently, a rigorous RCT of a program called the Early Start Denver Model (ESDM; Dawson et al., 2010) demonstrated that two years of treatment vastly improved symptoms in toddlers as young as 18 months. ESDM uses a developmental profile model to create individually tailored interventions in each of the domains (e.g., social skills) affected by ASD in the child. The program is novel because it combines ABA teaching methods with play-based routines that focus on building a relationship with the child. The children received 15 hours weekly of one-on-one treatment from home-trained therapists and 16 hours per week from parents. Relative to the control group (which received standard community-based treatments), the ESDM group showed improvements in receptive and expressive language, communication, daily living, and motor skills. IQ

Photo by Susan Oliver Young. Courtesy of Ivar Lovaas

Ivar Lovaas is noted for his operant-conditioning treatment of autistic children.

increased, on average, by almost 18 points, relative to an increase of 7 points in the control group. Most of the change was due to improvements in receptive and expressive language. Nonetheless, all children in both groups continued to have some type of ASD diagnosis when the children were, on average, 52 months old.

Two comprehensive reviews (Virues-Ortega, 2010; Vismara & Rogers, 2010) concluded that ABA or EIBI interventions are effective for children with ASD, especially if delivered before age 5 years and implemented intensively (20 hours or more per week for two or more years). Interventions are preferably initiated under the age of 2 (see Zwaigenbaum et al., 2009). Vismara and Rogers (2010) noted, however, that "ESDM needs to be independently replicated before it can be considered to be an empirically supported treatment for early ASD" (p. 7). Virues-Ortega (2010) concluded that long-term, comprehensive ABA intervention leads to positive effects in terms of intellectual functioning, language development, acquisition of daily living skills, and social functioning. However, Vismara and Rogers (2010) noted that additional evidence on the long-term effects of both comprehensive and skills-based programs is needed. They also proposed that the required next step is to determine if earlier interventions result in more normal patterns of brain function and organization.

Finally, it must be understood that some autistic and other severely disturbed children can be adequately cared for only in a hospital or in a group home staffed by mental health professionals. Moreover, the circumstances of some families preclude the home care of a seriously disturbed child. That effective treatments can be implemented by parents does not mean that this is the appropriate course for all families. Caring for an autistic child is clearly associated with high levels of parenting stress (see Schieve et al., 2007).

Drug Treatment of Children with Autism

Currently, no available medication treats the full range of core symptoms of ASD. The current strategy is to employ drugs that target specific symptoms or clusters of symptoms. For example, antipsychotic medications such as haloperidol and risperidone are commonly used to reduce maladaptive behaviour, such as self-mutilation and aggression (e.g., DuPaul, McGoey, & Mautone, 2003). Many autistic children do not respond positively to these drugs, however, and they have potentially serious side effects. Efforts to substitute olanzapine, an atypical neuroleptic, showed it to have fewer side effects, but it was less effective in symptom improvement (Kemner et al., 2002). Further, the combination of behavioural treatments and medication appear to be superior to medication alone in controlling severe aggression in autistic children (e.g., Brown et al., 2005). Antidepressants that reduce the action of serotonin such as clomipramine and the selective serotonin reuptake inhibitors (SSRIs) such as fluoxetine are used to treat stereotypic and repetitive behaviours (e.g., Hollander et al., 2005). Stimulant drugs such as Ritalin have shown some effectiveness in reducing inattentiveness and hyperactivity (e.g., Research Units on Pediatric Psychopharmacology Network, 2005). There is, as yet, no drug of proven effectiveness for improving the social impairments or language abilities that are the hallmarks of ASD (DuPaul et al., 2003). Unfortunately, the use of medication increases as autistic children grow into adulthood, despite the fact that there are few studies of the efficacy of medication (e.g., Seltzer, Shattuck, Abbeduto, & Greenberg, 2004).

Although outcomes are variable and specific characteristics and symptoms can change over time, a majority of ASD children remain within the spectrum as adults. They usually continue to experience problems related to mental health, social relationships, and employment (see Myers & Johnson, 2007).

15.6 Disorders of Overcontrolled Behaviour

This chapter began by highlighting the distinction between undercontrolled and overcontrolled behaviour. We conclude by examining overcontrolled or internalizing behaviour in the form of anxiety disorders in children and adolescents. Considerable evidence supports the study of anxiety and depressive symptoms jointly during childhood (see Côté et al., 2009, for review). Colman, Wadsworth, Croudace, and Jones (2007), using data from an English national birth cohort, reported that about 70% of adolescents who had an internalizing disorder (primarily anxiety or depression) at both ages 13 and 15 had a mental disorder at age 36, 43, or 53, relative to approximately 25% in a control group of mentally healthy adolescents. Sadly, the long-term outcome for children with persistent or recurrent internalizing disorders can be poor.

At the outset we can state that both genetic and environmental factors play a role in the development of internalizing disorders. Hicks, DiRago, Iacono, and McGrue (2009) conducted a comprehensive analysis with over 1,300 adolescent twin pairs that examined multiple environmental risk factors (stressful life events, parent–child relationship problems, anti-social and prosocial peer affiliation, and academic achievement and engagement) in order to delineate general mechanisms of gene–environment influence in the development of internalizing disorders. They detected significant moderation effects between each environmental risk factor and internalizing disorders: in the context of greater environmental adversity, non-shared environmental factors became more important in causing internalizing symptoms. These findings are consistent with an interpretation that environmental risk factors play a causative role in the emergence of internalizing disorders. Hicks et al. (2009) concluded that there is "a general mechanism of environmental influence" on internalizing disorders irrespective of the specific form of environmental risk (p. 1309).

Côté et al. (2009) modelled the developmental trajectories of anxiety and depressive symptoms during early childhood in a large population sample of infants in Quebec who were followed yearly from 5 to 60 months of age. They found that for most children, anxiety and depression symptoms increased over the first 5 years of life. Three distinct trajectory groups were identified. A substantial minority (about 15%) exhibited high frequency at 1.5 years and a sharper increase with age relative to the other groups, leading the authors to conclude that "an atypically high propensity to evince DAS [depressive and anxiety symptoms] can be identified very early in life" (p. 1205). The investigators sought to identify early risk factors for depressive and anxiety symptoms. The impact of children's difficult temperament at five months was the most important vulnerability predictor of depression and anxiety in the atypical high-rising trajectory. Lifetime maternal depression was the second most important predictor, even after controlling for other maternal risk factors (e.g., maternal anti-social behaviours and low education).

Childhood Fears and Anxiety Disorders

Most children experience fears and worries as part of the normal course of development. Common fears, most of which are outgrown, include fear of the dark and of imaginary creatures (in children under 5) and fear of being separated from parents (in children under 10). A comparative survey of children from five countries, including Canada (see Phipps, 1999), found that more than one-third of Canadian children between the ages of 4 and 11 were rated by their parents as too fearful or anxious, and that Canadian children were three times more anxious and fearful than children from Norway. For fears and worries to be classified as disorders, children's functioning must be impaired; unlike adults, however, children might not regard their fear as excessive or unreasonable, as they sometimes lack the insight to make such judgements. Using this definition, about 10 to 15% of children and adolescents have an anxiety disorder, making these the most common disorders of childhood (Cohen et al., 1993).

In general, as with adults, fears and phobias are reported more often for girls than for boys (e.g., Burnham, Lomax, & Hooper, 2013), though this sex difference may be due at least in part to social pressures against boys' admitting that they are afraid of things. Although most unrealistic childhood fears dissipate over time, many anxious adults trace their problems back to childhood. The seriousness of some childhood anxiety problems should therefore not be underestimated. Surprisingly, a majority of children who develop anxiety disorders are not referred for treatment (Klein, 2009). Klein (2009) recommends interventions to allow identification and treatment of children with anxiety in schools and primary care settings.

Murray, Creswell, and Cooper (2009) conducted an integrative review of the development of child anxiety. Murray et al. noted that anxiety disorders in children and adolescents are common and disabling, often run a chronic course, and can be comorbid with depression, conduct disorder, and ADHD. There is an extensive focus on family factors given that "[i]t is now widely accepted that anxiety disorders run in families" (Drake & Ginsburg, 2012, p. 144). Murray et al. (2009) concluded that (1) family aggregation and genetic studies confirm increased vulnerability to anxiety in offspring of adults with an anxiety disorder (e.g., the temperamental style of behavioural inhibition or biases in information processing), and (2) important environmental factors include negative life events and exposure to modelling or negative information. Parental factors linked with anxiety in children include parental overcontrol, lack of parental warmth, and exposure to parental criticism (for a review, see Drake & Ginsburg, 2012). Longitudinal research is needed because parenting behaviours (e.g., overprotection) may be elicited by child vulnerabilities. Indeed, Murray et al. (2009) also highlighted the potential bi-directionality of child and parental influences.

In another review, Klein (2009) reported that parental anxiety disorders, particularly when coupled with depression, are documented risks for child anxiety disorders. However, there is little specificity of concordance between parental and offspring anxiety disorders.

According to their review of anxiety disorders in children and adolescents from an epidemiological perspective, Costello et al. (2011) concluded there is now extensive evidence that the anxiety disorders that exist among adults also exist among younger people and the various disorders are distinguishable in terms of certain distinctive correlates. How many young people have a diagnosable anxiety disorder? Costello et al. (2011) summarized data from several comprehensive studies including work conducted by Costello and associates on the Great Smoky Mountains Study and found that the mean prevalence of any anxiety disorder based on 26 datasets is 11.0%. Most common is specific phobia (6.0%) and social phobia (5.0%), with others being 2.3% for separation anxiety disorder, 1.9% for generalized anxiety disorder, and 1.1% for panic disorder. The median age of onset was 8 years old, with panic disorder most likely to emerge during mid-adolescence or later.

Below we examine in more detail two specific disorders: separation anxiety disorder and social phobia. We then consider research on the treatment and prevention of anxiety disorders in children and adolescents.

Separation Anxiety

Separation anxiety is the unrealistic concern about separation from major attachment figures. As noted in Chapter 5, separation anxiety disorder was once considered to be specific to childhood and adolescence, and *DSM-IV-TR* diagnostic criteria stipulated that the symptoms apply to individuals under the age of 18. However, in February 2010, the *DSM-5* work group (see American Psychiatric Association, 2010) announced that it was considering rewording the criteria to be suitable for adults as well as children, and indeed, the publication of *DSM-5* removed the criterion of onset before age 18 years. We still consider it here due to separation anxiety being much more prevalent among children. Note that the *DSM-5* added the stipulation that adults must have the symptoms for six months or more so that occasional fears are not deemed to reflect a clinical disorder.

The *DSM-5* description of separation anxiety disorder emphasizes that the eight symptoms must be experienced for at least four weeks in children and they usually cause clinically significant distress. These symptoms include unrealistic and persistent worries about harm to major attachment figures along with fears of abandonment, refusal to attend school owing to a need to stay close to an attachment figure, an avoidance of being alone, the experience of nightmares involving separation themes, and the experience of physical complaints in anticipation of being separated from attachment figures.

The experience of separation anxiety is a natural reaction among very young children. Levels may reach their peak when toddlers are 18 months of age (Wachtel & Strauss, 1995). It appears to be the most common individual anxiety diagnosis in children below 12 years of age (Cartwright-Hatton, McNicol, & Doubleday, 2006).

Important insights about separation anxiety disorder have come from a recent Canadian longitudinal study that is remarkable because it is the first to examine varying developmental trajectories of levels of separation anxiety (see Battaglia et al., 2016). This research examined children from 1,933 families when these children were 1.5 to 6 years old. Four groups were identified. The majority of children were in the persistently low separation anxiety disorder group. There was also a low increasing group (22.1% of the sample), a high increasing group (6.9%), and a high decreasing group (10.8%). The high increasing group participants were the ones deemed to have clinical levels of dysfunction. They were uniquely distinguished by exposure to elevated maternal depression, maternal smoking during pregnancy, and parental unemployment.

Much of our understanding of separation anxiety comes from the seminal work of attachment theorists such as Ainsworth and Bowlby. An "anxious attachment style" among infants predicts subsequent anxiety disorders. Canadian Contributions 15.2 focuses on Ainsworth's work. This description makes reference to the Strange Situation in which the child's reaction to a stranger is evaluated once the mother leaves the room. A similar situation was used (having the mother leave) to compare the responses of three groups: children with separation anxiety disorder, children with another anxiety disorder, and healthy controls. The children with separation anxiety disorder not only had higher subjectively reported anxiety, they also exhibited heightened physiological reactivity across cardiovascular, respiratory, and electrodermal measures (see Kossowsky, Wilhelm, Roth, & Schneider, 2012). These data illustrate the distinctiveness of separation anxiety vs. other types of disorder.

Canadian Contributions 15.2

Mary Ainsworth, Attachment Styles, and Distress

Mary Ainsworth was one of the top psychologists produced in Canada. She spent most of her childhood in Toronto and completed her undergraduate and graduate work at the University of Toronto. She obtained her Ph.D. in 1939. She was a research fellow at the Institute of Child Study at the University of Toronto from 1946 to 1950. In 1950, she married and moved to England, where she began her lifelong research collaboration with attachment-style theorist John Bowlby.

Ainsworth is known primarily for her work on infant attachment styles(see photo). She developed a paradigm known as **the Strange Situation**, in which an infant was left in a room for a brief period with a stranger, the mother having left the room. Observational data indicated that three distinct types of infants reflect the differences between secure attachment and anxious attachment (Ainsworth, Blehar, Waters, & Wall, 1978). A **securely attached** infant shows little distress and interacts quite willingly with the stranger, secure in the knowledge that his or her mother will return. This pattern of behaviour contrasts with the pattern expressed by two types of insecurely attached infants. An **anxiously attached** infant becomes very distressed when his or her mother leaves the room. These infants have been described as "clingy" and are at risk of being overly dependent and prone to feelings of separation anxiety. When mothers of anxiously attached infants return to the room, their babies tend to express their upset by making a fuss as a form of protest, as if they are saying, "Don't do that to me again." In contrast, an infant with an **avoidant attachment style** displays little emotion when the mother leaves the room and shows little reaction upon her return, almost as if an attachment bond has

Psychologist Mary Ainsworth was a pioneer in the field of infant–caregiver attachment styles. See if you can clearly identify babies in this photograph that seem to be exhibiting the anxiety or lack of engagement associated with attachment insecurity.

never been formed in the first place. Avoidantly attached infants can become withdrawn and socially isolated.

Insecure forms of attachment are likely to develop when a child is exposed to harsh or inconsistent parenting (see Ainsworth, 1984). Secure attachment emerges when the parent responds to the infant's needs in a warm and predictable manner, so that the infant comes to believe that the parent will be available as a source of comfort on a regular basis. A fourth attachment style has since been identified. The **disorganized attachment style** is evident in infants who seem totally confused by their surroundings. This style results from being exposed to chaotic and abusive environments.

(continued)

It is possible to distinguish older children, adolescents, and adults in terms of whether they have a secure or insecure style. What are the early experiences and related factors that contribute to insecure attachment? A meta-analytic study conducted by researchers in Canada concluded that maternal mental health variables are associated with degree of attachment security (Atkinson et al., 2000). Significant correlates of attachment security included the amount of social support available to the mother, marital satisfaction, maternal stress, and maternal depression.

Forms of insecure attachment have been linked with adjustment problems in children and adolescents. One longitudinal study assessed children exposed to the Strange Situation at 1 year of age and then used interviews 18 years later to determine which children had developed an anxiety disorder (Warren, Huston, Egeland,

& Sroufe, 1997). An anxious attachment style among infants predicted subsequent anxiety disorders, while an avoidant attachment style predicted other types of psychiatric disorders. Another study conducted by researchers from Simon Fraser University found that fearful, insecure attachment in adolescents was associated with the severity of suicide risk in a clinical sample (Lessard & Moretti, 1998). More recently, a meta-analysis involving data from 60 studies with over 5,000 participating families confirmed a small to moderate association between avoidant attachment and internalizing behaviour in early childhood (Madigan, Atkinson, Laurin, & Benoit, 2013).

Ainsworth received numerous awards, including the American Psychological Association Gold Medal Award in 1998 for "Lifetime Achievement in the Science of Psychology." Mary Ainsworth died in 1999. Her work will be valued for many generations.

Social Phobia

Recall our discussion of social phobia (also known as social anxiety) in Chapter 5. Most classrooms include at least one or two children who are extremely quiet and shy. Often these children will play only with family members or familiar peers, avoiding strangers both young and old. Their shyness may prevent them from acquiring skills and participating in a variety of activities enjoyed by most of their age-mates, for they avoid playgrounds and games played by neighbourhood children. Although some shy youngsters may simply be slow to warm up, withdrawn children never do, even after prolonged exposure to new people.

Extremely shy children may refuse to speak at all in unfamiliar social circumstances; this condition is called **selective mutism** (see Viana, Beidel, & Rabian, 2009). In crowded rooms, they cling and whisper to their parents, hide behind the furniture, cower in corners, and may even have tantrums. At home, they ask their parents endless questions about situations that worry them. Withdrawn children usually have warm and satisfying relationships with family members and family friends, and they show a desire for affection and acceptance. Selective mutism was included as a new disorder in the *DSM-5*, and a recent review by Muris and Ollendick (2015) resulted in the conclusion that it was justified to treat selective mutism as an anxiety disorder based on its symptoms and the associated factors and etiological indicators that overlap substantially with those found with other anxiety disorders in children. However, they did note that it is important that clinicians treating this disorder do not focus exclusively on the anxiety elements of selective mutism and ignore other features of selective mutism (i.e., oppositional tendencies, and language and other developmental problems).

Theories of the etiology of social phobia in children are not well developed. However, individual differences in behavioural inhibition (introduced in Chapter 5) certainly play a role. Behavioural inhibition is a persistent tendency to show extreme reticence, fearfulness, or avoidance in novel situations, or with unfamiliar people (see Hirshfeld-Becker et al.,

2008). In her discussion of established risk factors for child anxiety disorders, Klein (2009) noted that, "The most consistent and heuristic finding in developmental psychopathology is the role of behavioural inhibition as a risk for social phobia" (p. 157). The importance of this relation is supported by findings of amygdala overreactivity to novelty in adolescents who manifested behavioural inhibition at an early age and by evidence of gene–environment interaction in the prediction of shyness at age 7 (see Fox, Henderson, et al., 2005; Fox, Nichols, et al., 2005). Behavioural inhibition likely contributes vulnerability to anxiety disorders in general and not just social phobia. A new longitudinal investigation that examined predictors of anxiety disorder found that behavioural inhibition, parental anxiety, low social skills, and peer victimization as assessed at 4 years of age all predicted subsequent anxiety disorders in Norwegian children (Wichstrom, Belsky, & Berg-Nielsen, 2013).

Essex and colleagues (2010) sought to determine developmental pathways to chronic high inhibition among school-age children in a community sample followed from birth to age 9. They assessed four early risk factors: female gender; exposure to maternal stress; and at age 4.5 years, early signs of inhibition and elevated afternoon salivary cortisol levels. All of the risk factors predicted chronic high inhibition via two developmental pathways: (1) in girls, partially mediated by early evidence of behavioural inhibition and elevated cortisol levels; and (2) began with exposure to early maternal stress, partially mediated by cortisol levels. Most important, by Grade 9, chronic high behavioural inhibition was associated with social anxiety disorder.

It has also been suggested that anxiety interferes with social interaction, causing the child to avoid social situations and thus not to get much practice at social skills. Another suggestion is that withdrawn children may simply not have the social know-how that facilitates interaction with their age-mates. The finding that isolated children make fewer attempts to make friends and are less imaginative in their play may indicate a deficiency in social skills. Finally, isolated children may have become so because they have spent most of their time with adults. Having a parent with social phobia may also play a role. A study by Mancini and her associates in Hamilton, Ontario, found that among children who had a parent with social phobia, 49% had at least one anxiety disorder diagnosis (Mancini et al., 1996). Overall, 23% of the children were diagnosed with social phobia, and 19% with separation anxiety disorder. The specific processes and mechanisms in social phobia can involve social learning (i.e., imitation of the parent), exposure to an overly anxious parenting style, and increased risk due to genetic factors.

Social anxiety disorder was found to be a valid diagnosis in children and adolescents by a *DSM-5* work group (see Bogels et al., 2010).

Treatment of Childhood Fears and Anxiety Disorders

How are childhood fears overcome? Many simply dissipate with time and maturation. However, without treatment many anxiety disorders in children and adolescents follow a chronic course and can be associated with comorbid psychopathology in adulthood, including anxiety, depression, and substance use (see Beesdo, Knappe, & Pine, 2010). For the most part, treatment of anxiety disorders in children is similar to that employed with adults using CBT (e.g., exposure, relaxation training, role playing, and cognitive strategies), with suitable modifications to accommodate the different abilities and circumstances of childhood (see Klein, 2009). The typical treatment goals are to teach children to recognize signs of anxiety and to use these signs as cues to initiate anxiety management strategies.

Summaries of psychotherapy for anxiety in children and adolescents continue to support the effectiveness of CBT. A meta-analysis by Reynolds, Wilson, Austin, and Hooper (2012) of 55 studies involving RCT designs led to the conclusion that psychotherapy is moderately effective overall, but effect sizes were small to moderate compared with control conditions. Effect sizes were significant for CBT but were non-significant for non-CBT interventions. One caveat was that treatment was more successful when it targeted a specific anxiety disorder rather than a range of disorders. Another recent meta-analysis showed that the effectiveness of therapy held across the age range and CBT was effective for both children and adolescents (Bennett et al., 2013). Finally, a comparative study in Australia found that online CBT was just as effective as face-to-face CBT in treating anxiety disorders in adolescents, with about 4 out of 5 participants showing lasting improvement 12 months after completing treatment (Spence et al., 2011).

Katharina Manassis (2013) from the Hospital for Sick Children in Toronto (see photo) summarized the current status of the field by providing a blunt and insightful contemporary assessment that acknowledged the apparent superiority of CBT but also the gaps in knowledge that need to be addressed as well as directions for improvement. Specifically, this researcher and clinician, one of Canada's leading authorities in the field, noted the following:

Courtesy of Hospital for Sick Children, Creative Services Studio

Katharina Manassis from the Hospital for Sick Children is one of the leading authorities on the treatment and prevention of anxiety disorders in children and adolescents.

> *"When students ask me to summarize empirically supported treatments for childhood anxiety disorders, I often answer with a simplistic formula: CBT ± SSRI. In other words, cognitive behavioural therapy (CBT) with or without concurrent use of a medication targeting serotonin (selective serotonin reuptake inhibitor or SSRI). There is some truth to this rather facetious answer: but it obscures some of the complexities of the literature. While it is true that there is more empirical support for CBT than for any psychosocial treatment in this population, not all children respond to it, the strength of the evidence varies among disorders, mechanisms of action for CBT in children are poorly understood, and CBT's optimal integration with other treatment has received only limited study. Therefore, there is a role for critical examination of all psychosocial treatments that may benefit anxious children."*

> *(Manassis, 2013, p. 207)*

One of the key points raised by Manassis (2013) is that CBT does not work for everyone. More information is needed to illuminate why only some children respond and when they do respond, what factors act as mediators and moderators of treatment response. Kendall, Settipani, and Cummings (2012) have called for more emphasis on individualized, tailored treatments that take into account the unique factors that contribute and maintain dysfunctional anxiety. Work of this nature needs to consider a range of factors that can become complicating issues for some people. As one illustration, because links have been established between perfectionism and anxiety in young people (Affrunti & Woodruff-Borden, 2014) and there is general evidence that perfectionism can undermine treatment for people of various ages, Manassis and her team have followed up on earlier research linking perfectionism with childhood anxiety (see Essau et al., 2008) by exploring the role of perfectionism as a factor that mitigates the effectiveness of interventions for anxiety and depression (Nobel, Manassis, & Wilansky-Trainor, 2012). A school-based program designed to lower levels of anxiety and depression among at-risk students did indeed reduce levels of anxiety, depression, and perfectionism, but among those who still had elevated self-oriented perfectionism at post-test, there was still an association with depression (but not anxiety). A subsequent study of clinically anxious children found that self-oriented perfectionism predicted poorer outcomes following group CBT even though there were significant reductions in levels of perfectionism as a result of treatment (Mitchell, Newall, Broeren, & Hudson, 2013). These investigations did not include an explicit multi-faceted emphasis on perfectionism and this may be what is needed for the anxious child or adolescent who is highly focused on making mistakes and is highly attentive to threatening cues involving negative social evaluations.

One of the most popular methods for helping children overcome fears, employed by millions of parents, is to expose them gradually to the feared object, often while simultaneously performing some action to inhibit their anxiety. If a little girl fears strangers, a parent takes her by the hand and walks her slowly toward the new person. Contemporary therapists and reviewers generally agree that exposure is the most effective way of eliminating fear and avoidance (see Klein, 2009). Modelling has also proven effective. Another child—for example, someone the fearful child is likely to imitate—could be asked to demonstrate fearless behaviour. Offering rewards for moving closer to a feared object or situation can also help a fearful child. Both modelling and operant treatments involve exposure to what is feared. When the fear and avoidance of a child are very great and of long duration, the child may require desensitization through direct, graduated exposure plus operant shaping. Some shy children lack specific social skills needed for peer interaction. Skills such as asking questions, giving compliments, and starting conversations with age-mates may be taught.

Manassis and Monga (2001) noted that parents may contribute to the etiology of anxiety disorders by being anxious themselves and providing a model that can be imitated. This fits with Hiller et al.'s (2016) observation that anxious children typically respond less well to treatment if one or more parents has an anxiety disorder. They identified several factors involving the parents of anxious children that are possible contributing factors. These factors include a tendency for parents to respond to children in ways that exacerbate and maintain the child's anxiety, such as using a "helicopter parenting style" that is intrusive and keeps the child on edge while expressing catastrophic predictions about threats that await the child in the outside world. Hiller et al. (2016) also documented that these parents had a reduced ability to tolerate the child's negative emotions.

Anxiety in the child can also be a response, at least in part, to being the target of parental frustration; high levels of parental frustration can undermine treatment gains (see Liashko &

Manassis, 2003). A follow-up investigation of adolescents who had received CBT seven years earlier attested to the long-term effectiveness of treatment for the majority of participants with a previous anxiety disorder. Manassis, Avery, Butalia, and Mendlowitz (2004) found that almost all of the adolescents still experienced some anxiety-related impairment, but 70% required no further treatment. However, these data were based on telephone surveys and did not involve actual diagnostic interviews. More recently, Saavedra et al. (2010) reported that successful exposure-based CBT for childhood phobic anxiety disorders extended into the transition years of young adulthood (8–13 years post-treatment).

Comprehensive manualized programs developed by Kendall and his associates, among others, include between 16 and 20 sessions (see Kendall & Hedtke, 2006a, 2006b) and have been translated into numerous languages. The first part of treatment involves training the child to recognize physiological signs of anxiety, to challenge and change cognitions and internal dialogue, and to learn new problem-solving and coping plans. The last half of treatment involves having the child implement these new skills when exposed to anxiety-provoking situations. The final session typically requires the child to make a videotaped commercial describing the steps of CBT and how they are used to combat anxiety (for a detailed description, see Kazdin, 2003). Variations on Kendall's approach include group and family treatment (see Crawley et al., 2010).

The use of antidepressants (SSRIs and venlafaxine) in children with anxiety disorders (see Pine & Kline, 2008 for review) followed reports of efficacy in adults with anxiety disorders; however, in contrast to CBT, there are apparently no specific diagnostic indications in children. One trial (Biedel et al., 2007) compared group exposure therapy and fluoxetine in the treatment of social phobic adolescents and found that both were more effective than a placebo. However, exposure was superior to medication and it also significantly enhanced social skills. Meta-analytic findings from studies that compared CBT and pharmacological treatment for obsessive-compulsive disorder in children indicate that both serotonin reuptake inhibitors and CBT are effective but CBT was more effective (see Ost, Riise, Wergeland, Hansen, & Kvale, 2015).

Prevention of Anxiety Disorders

We conclude this chapter by noting that there are some encouraging prevention studies for children with high anxiety in selected settings (e.g., Rapee, Schniering, & Hudson, 2009). These preventive efforts are fuelled by the early onset of anxiety disorders and the sheer number of young people who are vulnerable to anxiety disorders. Australia is one of the leading nations in making innovative efforts to prevent internalizing disorders, including anxiety. Another recent study in Australia by Rapee (2013) of preschool children showed that a brief, cost-effective intervention program delivered to parents yielded lasting benefits in terms of fewer internalizing disorders and anxiety symptoms when the participants were

15 years old. One caveat, however, is that this positive intervention was limited to girls, in part because boys were simply less susceptible to anxiety problems over time.

Neil and Christensen (2009) evaluated the efficacy and effectiveness of 20 individual, primarily CBT, school-based prevention and early intervention programs and concluded that most are effective in reducing symptoms of anxiety in children and adolescents. Most programs focused on reducing the symptoms of non-specific anxiety. However, Neil and Christensen also indicated a need for longer-term follow-up, the use of attention control conditions, and evaluations of teacher delivery. A follow-up meta-analysis confirmed the role of prevention programs in reducing not only anxiety but also depression in adolescents, but it was also noted that the overall effectiveness of these programs was limited and there is a need to build in some other elements to make them more effective (see Corrieri et al., 2014).

What are the components of existing programs? The well-known FRIENDS program (Barrett & Turner, 2001) is a combination of cognitive-behavioural principles, coping strategies, and homework activities. Other elements that can be added include relaxation training and social problem-solving skills. At the heart of these programs is developing a sense of self-control and emotional self-regulation, setting reasonable goals and standards, and fostering a more positive view of the self as capable in achievement and social situations.

Summary

15.1 There is a mental health crisis among children and adolescents in terms of the prevalence of disorders and the difficulties in gaining timely access to qualified treatment providers. Estimates suggest that about 1 in 6 children and adolescents has some form of diagnosable disorder, but it has been suggested that estimates may be underestimated due to the tendency for some young people to hide their distress and experience significant distress and impairment even though their characteristics may not meet diagnostic criteria.

15.2 Disorders among children and adolescents are differentiated in terms of whether they reflect undercontrolled behaviours (i.e., unable to restrain maladaptive tendencies) or overcontrolled behaviours (i.e., constrained behaviours that typically reflect anxiety or depression). A primary difficulty is determining whether the behaviour expressed by children is typical and a reflection of the child's developmental stage or whether it is atypical.

15.3 Attention-deficit/hyperactivity disorder and conduct disorder are marked by undercontrolled behaviour. ADHD is a persistent pattern of inattention and/or impulsivity that is judged to be more frequent and more severe than what is typically observed in youngsters of a given age. There is growing evidence for genetic and neurological factors in its etiology, but parents can be helpful in improving the behaviour of children with ADHD. Conduct disorder is often a precursor to anti-social personality disorder in adulthood, although many children carrying the diagnosis do not progress to that extreme. It is characterized by high and widespread levels of aggression, lying, theft, vandalism, cruelty to other people and to animals, and other acts that violate laws and social norms. Among the apparent etiological factors are a genetic predisposition, inadequate learning of moral awareness, modelling and direct reinforcement of anti-social behaviour, and living in impoverished and crime-ridden areas.

15.4 Learning disorders are diagnosed when a child fails to develop to the degree expected by his or her intellectual level in a specific academic, language, or motor skill area. These disorders are usually identified and treated within the school system rather than through mental health clinics. There is mounting evidence that the most widely studied of the learning disorders, dyslexia, has genetic and other biological components. Mental retardation is now referred to as "intellectual disability disorder." The more severe forms of intellectual disability have a biological basis, such as the chromosomal trisomy that causes Down's syndrome. Certain infectious diseases in the pregnant mother (e.g., HIV, rubella, and syphilis) and illnesses that affect the child directly (e.g., encephalitis) can stunt cognitive and social development, as can malnutrition, severe falls, and automobile accidents that injure the brain. Environmental factors are considered the principal causes of mild retardation. Thus far, no brain damage has been detected in people with mild retardation, who often are from lower-class homes and live in an environment of social and educational deprivation.

15.5 Characteristics of autism include (1) extreme autistic aloneness, a failure to relate to other people; (2) communication problems consisting of either a failure to learn any language or speech irregularities, such as echolalia and pronoun reversal; and (3) preservation of sameness, an obsessive desire to keep daily routines and surroundings exactly the same. A biological cause is suspected for a number of reasons: its onset is very early, family and twin studies give compelling evidence of a genetic predisposition, and abnormalities have been found in the brains of autistic children.

15.6 Some children and adolescents experience difficulties that involve overcontrolled behaviours. Anxiety disorders and related fears in children reflect overcontrolled tendencies. These disorders include separation anxiety disorder and social phobia. Theorists seeking to account for the etiology of these disorders are increasingly focusing on the role of attachment style, first described by theorists such as Ainsworth and Bowlby. Family factors are also seen as important in the etiology and treatment of anxiety disorders in children and adolescents.

Key Terms

anxiously attached

applied behaviour analysis

attention-deficit/hyperactivity disorder (ADHD)

autism spectrum disorder

avoidant attachment style

conduct disorder
developmental coordination disorder
   (motor disorder)
disorder of written expression
disorganized attachment style
Down's syndrome (trisomy 21)
echolalia
externalizing problems
internalizing problems
language disorder
learning disabilities

learning disorders
mathematics disorder
mild mental retardation
moderate mental retardation
oppositional defiant disorder (ODD)
pervasive developmental disorders
phenylketonuria
phonological disorder
profound mental retardation
pronoun reversal
reading disorder (dyslexia)

securely attached
selective mutism
self-instructional training
separation anxiety
severe mental retardation
social (pragmatic) communication disorder
specific learning disorder
the Strange Situation
stuttering
theory of mind

Reflections: Past, Present, and Future

1. Effective early intervention programs for children at risk for developing conduct disorder probably require the co-operation of multiple social service and mental health agencies that employ "individualized care" or "wraparound" services involving interdisciplinary teams that develop individualized and comprehensive plans. Such programs would employ multiple-component, flexible treatments that would involve the child, the family, and the school. Do you think that in some cases multiple interventions will be required throughout the youngster's life, including into adulthood? Do you think anything can be done preventively to alter the tendencies and behaviour of an Eric Harris or a Dylan Klebold (the teenagers responsible for the massacre at Columbine High School in April 1999)?

2. With respect to learning disabilities, it is often stated that in contemporary society, learning disabilities are determined when there is a discrepancy between the child's level of achievement and her or his potential. Do you think reliable and valid assessments of achievement can be obtained when young children are involved? What would you do to determine whether an under-performing child in Ontario who has English as a second language has a learning disability (versus language-related issues)? How concerned should we be about a child being labelled as having a disability versus just needing more time to adjust?

3. We all should treat intellectually challenged children and adults with decency and dignity and facilitate their participation in our communities. What could you do that would help them develop a sense of purpose, pride, and self-esteem?

4. Many children with ASD also have an anxiety or mood disorder. What are the implications for the treatment of autistic children? Design a comprehensive treatment program for autistic children with comorbid anxiety and depression.

5. An anxious attachment style among infants seems to be a risk factor for the subsequent development of anxiety disorders. Do you think that a prevention program will be developed in the future that will target such high-risk infants at a very early age? What form would such an intervention take? What other risk factors should be targeted?

CHAPTER 16

Aging and Psychological Disorders

LEARNING OBJECTIVES

1. Explain the challenges involved in interpreting the nature of age differences and how age is also a consideration from an assessment perspective.

2. Differentiate the two main brain disorders found among aging people.

3. List the psychological disorders that are prominent among older people and describe how their features and presumed causes can differ from the disorders experienced by younger people.

4. Describe the issues specific to older adults that often mean they are less likely than younger people to receive adequate psychological treatment and care.

5. State the obligations that psychologists have in tailoring psychological treatment to the needs of older people.

Brief Case Example

Frozen Memories

THE STORY of Brendan Shanahan, the retired Canadian NHL hockey player who is now the president of the NHL's Toronto Maple Leafs, and his father, Donal Shanahan, illustrates with poignancy the symptoms and difficulties associated with disorders related to aging.

Brendan's father never played hockey himself, but being a hockey dad, he was just as fascinated as his son with this truly Canadian sport. "My father was always there for me, driving me to practices and games religiously."

Brendan was barely 14 when he started noticing a change in his father's behaviour; the year was 1983. Early on, his father showed signs of confusion that gradually became worse. A full year went by before Donal Shanahan was diagnosed with Alzheimer's disease at age 52. During this time, Brendan recalls feeling frustrated and impatient. "I didn't know what was happening and couldn't understand. I never heard of Alzheimer's until my dad was diagnosed with it—even then, the whole thing was foreign to me."

The symptoms appeared gradually as the disease took its course. Often, simple tasks became big challenges. Brendan

remembers his father being puzzled by a pen. "He had forgotten how to use a pen and would hold it the wrong way. Driving was also a problem and he was no longer confident driving me to the games. Sometimes he would get lost getting to or from the game—other times he didn't know where to insert the car keys. On my 16th birthday, we drove to the licensing bureau to get my driving permit. It was the last time my father drove a car; he was 54" (see www.alzheimer.ca).

Donal Shanahan passed away in 1991 when Brendan was 21. Brendan Shanahan has worked extensively and been an active fundraiser for research on Alzheimer's disease.

Shanahan provided a poignant account in 1997 of becoming a Stanley Cup champion and taking the Stanley Cup with him to his father's gravesite near Toronto. Shanahan recounted, "It was about 5 o'clock on a beautiful Sunday afternoon. . . The whole cemetery was empty. And I just sat there at my father's grave and said, 'Look. Look what I brought you. . .' I just wanted to share it with my dad. It made me feel better" (Zoomer.com, 1997). Shanahan went on to be inducted in the Hockey Hall of Fame in 2013. In 2017, he was included among the top 100 NHL players of all time in the NHL's centennial year.

If you are fortunate, you will grow old one day. As you do, physiological changes are inevitable, and there may be many emotional and mental changes as well. Are aged people at higher risk for mental disorders than young people? Are earlier emotional problems, such as anxiety and depression, likely to become worse in old age? Do these emotional problems develop in people who did not have them when younger?

Most segments of North American society tend to have certain assumptions about old age. We fear that we will become doddering and befuddled—maybe even develop Alzheimer's disease like Brendan Shanahan's father in the Brief Case Example. We worry that our sex lives will become unsatisfying. This chapter examines such issues and considers whether some therapies are better suited than others to deal with the psychological problems of older adults. We shall consider also whether, as life expectancy extends well into the seventies and beyond, society is devoting enough intellectual and monetary resources to studying aging and helping older adults.

In contrast to the esteem in which they are held in most Asian countries, older adults are generally not treated very well in North America, and numerous myths abound. The process of growing old, although inevitable for us all, is resented, even abhorred, by many. The presence of negative aging stereotypes may account for the fact that most people, including older people, report that they feel younger than they actually are (see Teuscher, 2009). This tendency is called the **subjective age bias**. Younger subjective age is linked with greater life satisfaction and a host of other positive outcomes (Teuscher, 2009). A study from British Columbia found that positive health experiences and greater health satisfaction are linked with lower subjective age (Hubley & Russell, 2009). Clearly, the tendency to apply negative aging stereotypes to oneself can have severe consequences. A longitudinal study found that application of negative aging stereotypes to oneself predicts a greater likelihood of experiencing subsequent cardiovascular events and related health problems (Levy, Zonderman, Slade, Ferrucci, 2009). Other longitudinal research suggests that negative perceptions of aging predict actual cognitive declines based on objective tests (Robertson, King-Kallimanis, & Kenny, 2016); this was especially the case for negative perceptions of control and anticipated consequences (e.g., "Slowing down with age is not something I can control.") Longitudinal results from the Baltimore Longitudinal Study of Aging showed that endorsing aging stereotypes decades earlier predicts physiological changes in Alzheimer's disease markers (e.g., steeper loss of hippocampal volume and greater accumulation of brain plaques) (see Levy, Zonderman, Slade, Ferrucci, 2016). So, it is better to feel younger than you are, and you should not believe negative aging stereotypes, nor should you apply them to yourself.

The general public endorses many mistaken beliefs about the elderly. For instance, considerable mythology has surrounded sexuality and aging, the principal assumption being that at the age of 65 sex becomes improper, unsatisfying, and even impossible. Evidence indicates otherwise.

Rene Johnston/Toronto Star/Getty Images

Advancing age need not lead to a curtailment of activities. Hazel McCallion, the longstanding mayor of Mississauga, Ontario, celebrated her 95th birthday in 2016. She is one of Canada's most active citizens. Mayor McCallion, one of Canada's most famous and longest-serving mayors, left office when she decided against running for re-election in 2014. She is the first and current Chancellor of Sheridan College in Oakville, Ontario.

Barring serious physical disability, older people, well into their eighties and beyond, are capable of deriving enjoyment from sexual intercourse and other kinds of lovemaking. Some remarkable older people such as recently deceased astronaut John Glenn and former Mississauga mayor Hazel McCallion help combat mistaken societal beliefs about older people (see photo).

The social problems of aging may be especially severe for women. Even with the consciousness-raising of the past four decades, our society does not readily accept in women the wrinkles and sagging that become more and more prominent with advancing years. Although grey hair at the temples and even a bald head are often considered distinguished in a man, signs of aging in women are not valued in society. The cosmetics and plastic-surgery industries make billions of dollars each year exploiting the fear inculcated in women about looking their age.

The physical realities of aging are complicated by **ageism**, which can be defined as discrimination against any person, young or old, based on chronological age. Ageism can be seen when a professor in his or her sixties is considered too old to continue teaching at a university or seen as unworthy of a long-term research award or when a person over 75 is ignored in a social gathering on the assumption that he or she has nothing to contribute to the conversation. Like any prejudice, ageism ignores the diversity among people in favour of employing stereotypes (Gatz & Pearson, 1988).

Mental health professionals have until recently paid little attention to the psychological problems of older adults. This situation is now changing, as illustrated by the formation in 2002 of the Canadian Coalition for Seniors' Mental Health (see www.ccsmh.ca). This group is playing a vitally important role in providing key resources to the Canadian public. Grants from the Public Health Agency of Canada have enabled coalition members to provide a series of guides available for download from their website. The four guides compiled thus far focus on the following issues among older adults: delirium, depression, suicide prevention, and mental health issues for those in long-term care homes.

Another important initiative with mental health implications is the Canadian Longitudinal Study on Aging (CLSA), launched in 2004. The CLSA has provided a wealth of basic information about healthy aging, health care use, and risk factors for diseases and disabilities. Its goals include preventive interventions and cost-efficient treatments. Hébert (2003) has indicated that this nationwide research initiative is vital in light of what he refers to as "The Big Boom," which is the impact that Canada's baby boomers will have on the country's health system when they become senior citizens en masse in less than a decade from now.

In the past, mental health professionals operated under the popular misconceptions that intellectual deterioration is prevalent and inevitable, that depression among old people is widespread and untreatable, and that sex is a lost cause. Although those who provide mental health services are probably not extremely ageist (Gatz & Pearson, 1988), their attitudes and practices merit special attention because of the influence they have on policies that affect the lives of older adults. Since the 1980s, many schools and universities that prepare people for the health professions have added research and training in gerontology to their curricula, yet there is still a dearth of professionals committed primarily to serving the needs of older adults (Knight, 2004). The need for greater understanding is underscored by a survey conducted in Kingston, Ontario, that showed that family physicians feel less prepared to identify older patients with psychological problems than younger patients with psychological problems (Mackenzie, Gekoski, & Knox, 1999). They also reported that they were much less likely to treat or to refer older patients for treatment, and they rated psychotherapy as less effective with older people. These findings are disturbing because while elderly people seldom seek help for psychological problems, when they do, they are most likely to turn to their physicians.

The "old" are usually defined as those over the age of 65. The decision to use this age was set largely by social policies, not because age 65 is some critical point at which the physiological and psychological processes of aging suddenly begin. To have some rough demarcation points, gerontologists usually divide people over age 65 into three groups: the young-old, those aged 65 to 74; the old-old, those aged 75 to 84; and the

oldest-old, those over age 85. The health of these groups differs in important ways. According to a report by the National Advisory Council on Aging (1999), in 1998 about 3.7 million Canadians (12.3% of the population) were 65 or older. This number is expected to jump to about 10 million by 2041. Statistics gathered in 2011 indicated that Canada reached the 5-million mark for seniors (or 14.8% of the population) (see Joanette, 2013). A report by Statistics Canada (2005) based on national and provincial data suggested a rapid increase in the proportion of senior citizens; it is now estimated that, for the first time in Canada, the number of senior citizens is greater than the number of children.

The changes in Canada reflect a worldwide trend. At present, it is estimated that there are over 600 million people in the world who are 60 years of age or older. It is projected that by the year 2050, that figure will grow to almost 2 billion, so that about 21% of the world's population—roughly 1 in 5 people—will be 60 or older (Sowers & Rowe, 2007). Thus, it is important to examine what we know about the psychological and neuropsychological issues facing older adults and to expose some of our misconceptions about aging. The global challenges facing us are becoming increasingly apparent. For instance, the initial results from the China Health and Retirement Longitudinal Study (CHARLS) indicate that approximately 40% of the elderly people in China report elevated symptoms of depression (32% of men and 48% of women). This amounts to over 74 million elderly people in China potentially requiring treatment and social services (CHARLS Research Team, 2013).

It is also important to ensure that we have adequate services and access to psychological treatment for elderly people suffering from mental illness. Unfortunately, Canada seems exceptionally underprepared in this regard. A 2009 survey of clinical and counselling programs conducted by researchers at the University of Calgary found no program in Canada with a formal concentration on geropsychology (Konnert, Dobson, & Watt, 2009). Training activities, when they exist, focus on diagnosis and assessment of older people rather than therapeutic intervention; however, Konnert et al. (2009) concluded that the overall breadth and depth of exposure to aging content is quite superficial when it does exist. A comparative analysis was conducted by surveying graduate students from Canada, the United States, Australia, and New Zealand, which found that there are much fewer geropsychology training opportunities in Canada (Woodhead et al., 2013). Another analysis found that Canadian students, relative to students from the United States, were less likely to anticipate working some day in a specialization that includes older adults (Woodhead et al., 2015). This situation does not bode well given the anticipated needs of our growing and aging population; the lack of available services would make it far too easy for an older adult in Canada who is avoidant but who needs help to fail to seek it out.

This problem does not exist just in Canada and calls have been issued globally for psychologists to increase their competencies in treating older adults (see Karel, Gatz, & Smyer, 2012). Clearly, much more is needed in the years to come in order to make certain that our mentally ill elderly have access to treatment.

In this chapter, we review some general concepts and topics critical to the study of aging. We look next at brain disorders of old age. Then, we examine psychological disorders—most of which were discussed in earlier chapters—focusing especially on how these disorders are manifested in old age. Finally, we discuss general issues of treatment and care for older adults.

16.1   Issues, Concepts, and Methods in the Study of Older Adults

Theory and research bearing on older adults require an understanding of several specialized issues, ranging from diversity among old people to problems unique to old age.

Diversity in Older Adults

The word "diversity" is well suited to the older population. Not only are older people different from one another, but they are more different from one another than are individuals in any other age group. People tend to become less alike as they grow older. That all old people are alike is a prejudice held by many people. The many differences among people who are 65 and older will become increasingly evident as you read this chapter.

Age, Cohort, and Time-of-Measurement Effects

Chronological age is not as simple a variable in psychological research as it might seem. Because other factors associated with age may be at work, we must be cautious when we attribute differences in age groups solely to aging. In the field of aging, as in studies of earlier development, a distinction is made among three kinds of effects (see Table 16.1):

- **Age effects** are the consequences of being a given chronological age.

- **Cohort effects** are the consequences of having been born in a given year and having grown up during a particular time period with its own unique pressures, problems, challenges, and opportunities. For instance, the 1991 Canadian Study of Health and Aging is a national cohort study that investigated the prevalence and characteristics of dementia and Alzheimer's disease in a sample of more than 9,000 people who were aged 65 or older when assessed in 1991 (see Canadian Perspectives 16.1 for more information). A cohort effect exists if these people have some factor that distinguishes them from people who turned 65 or older at an earlier date (e.g., in 1965) or a later date (e.g., 2005).

- **Time-of-measurement effects** are confounds that arise because events at an exact point in time can have a specific effect on a variable being studied over time (Schaie & Hertzog, 1982). For example, time of measurement could affect the results of studies assessing post-traumatic stress disorder in Holocaust survivors if one of the assessments occurred shortly after the terrorist attacks in the United States on 9/11.

TABLE 16.1   Age, Cohort, and Time-of-Measurement Effects

Age Effects	Cohort Effects	Time-of-Measurement Effects
The consequences of being a chronological age (e.g., Jewish boys are bar mitzvahed at age 13).	The consequences of having been born in a given year and having grown up during a time (e.g., people who invested money in the stock market in the late 1990s viewed investments in equities as a reasonably safe and very lucrative place to put their money—unlike people who lost a lot of money in the bear markets of the 1930s or late 1960s).	The consequences of the effects that a particular factor can have at a particular time period (e.g., people responding in the 1990s to surveys about their sexual behaviour were more likely to be frank than people responding to the same questions in the 1950s because public discussions of sex were much more the norm in the 1990s).

Canadian Perspectives 16.1

The Canadian Study of Health and Aging and The Canadian Longitudinal Study on Aging

The Canadian Study of Health and Aging (CSHA) began in February 1991 and the first phase of data collection ended in May 1992. Data were collected at two other time points (1995–1996 and 2001–2002). This nationwide project was coordinated by the University of Ottawa and Health Canada's Division of Aging and Seniors. Initially, it involved researchers from at least 18 universities throughout Canada and 9,008 seniors aged 65 or older drawn from 36 communities, as well as 1,255 elderly people living in institutions. Participants were selected by random sampling with stratification by area. They underwent interviews and medical examinations as part of being in this study. The 45-minute interview focused on gathering demographic data and information on daily living and health status. Participants were also administered the modified version of the Mini-Mental State Examination (MMSE). The medical examination focused on confirming whether dementia was evident. It included neuropsychological testing and a structured interview with an examination. The test battery assessed memory, abstract thinking, judgement, language, recognition of familiar objects, attention, and psychomotor speed (CSHA Working Group, 1994a).

The CSHA website listed the four main goals of this massive project:

1. to use a common research protocol to estimate prevalence of dementia in Canadians aged 65 and older

2. to identify risk factors associated with Alzheimer's disease

3. to examine patterns of caring for Canadians with dementia

4. to develop a uniform database for subsequent longitudinal investigations

Several noteworthy findings from this investigation are described in other parts of this chapter. Other noteworthy results include the following:

1. The prevalence of Alzheimer's disease and other forms of dementia is 8% in Canada among people who are 65 or older. Furthermore, another 17% of Canadians who are 65 or over have some cognitive impairment but no dementia, with many of these people having circumscribed memory loss (see Graham et al., 1997). Cognitive impairment in the absence of dementia (i.e., subclinical dementia) predicts negative outcomes such as death, dementia, and institutionalization (St. John, Montgomery, Kristjansson, & McDowell, 2002; Tuokko et al., 2003).

2. The onset of dementia is usually gradual. A study of 1,132 CSHA participants with dementia found that only 11.5% had dementia with an acute, sudden onset. A more sudden onset was associated with less chance of institutionalization but greater vascular risk and reduced survival rates (King, Devichand, & Rockwood, 2005). Importantly, various predictor variables (e.g., poor cognition, health history, socio-demographic history) assessed during the first phase of CSHA data collection have been used to develop an algorithm that is effective in predicting which Canadian seniors are most likely to develop dementia (Meng, D'Arcy, Morgan, & Mousseau, 2013).

3. Most primary caregivers are female and married. Most informal caregivers (i.e., family member or friend) for seniors in the community are wives, while adult daughters are most likely to be the informal caregiver for institutionalized seniors (CSHA Working Group, 1994a).

4. A re-evaluation in 1996 of the original participants revealed that there are more than 60,000 new cases of dementia per year in Canada (CSHA Working Group, 2000).

5. Deficits identified via neuropsychological tests (e.g., short delayed verbal recall) predicted subsequent Alzheimer's disease 5 and 10 years later (Tierney, Yao, Kiss, & McDowell, 2005).

6. Physical frailty is associated with greater levels of psychiatric illness, while older age, in and of itself, is not associated with greater odds of psychiatric illness (Andrew & Rockwood, 2007). Frailty is defined as having multiple, interacting illnesses. A history of heavy smoking is one of the most reliable predictors of physical frailty (Hubbard, Searle, Mitnitski, & Rockwood, 2009).

7. Among elderly people with some cognitive impairment but not dementia, hypertension is associated with increased likelihood of progressing to dementia (Oveisgharan & Hachinski, 2010).

The success of this study paved the way for the subsequent 2006 launch of the Canadian Longitudinal Study on Aging. This new study was the subject of an entire special issue of the *Canadian Journal on Aging* in September 2009. This new investigation involves 51,000 Canadians aged 45 to 85 years of age. They are measured every three years and will be followed for at least 20 years. At least 30,000 participants have provided biological specimens (see Raina et al., 2009). A steady stream of new findings should soon start to emerge because it was announced in April 2016 that the data have been released and researchers can begin exploring key longitudinal research issues.

Thinking Critically

1. The cause or causes of Alzheimer's disease have received increased attention from clinical scientists in the last few years. Do you think this disorder is one of the most pressing problems in Canadian society? What are the implications of the findings thus far from the Canadian Study of Health and Aging?

2. Would you be prepared to make "eldercare" one of your responsibilities in the future should a loved one develop dementia? Would you put your own life on hold in order to care for a loved one? Or, do you think that this is the government's responsibility?

The two major research designs used to assess developmental change, the cross-sectional and the longitudinal, clarify these terms. In **cross-sectional studies**, the investigator compares different age groups at the same moment in time on the variable of interest. Suppose that in 1995 we took a poll and found that many interviewees over age 80 spoke with a European accent, whereas those in their forties and fifties did not. Could we conclude that as people grow older, they develop European accents? Hardly! Cross-sectional studies do not examine the same people over time; consequently, they allow us to make statements only about age effects in a particular study or experiment, not about age changes over time.

In **longitudinal studies**, the researcher selects one cohort—say, the graduating class of 2002—and periodically retests it using the same measure over a number of years. This design allows researchers to trace individual patterns of consistency or change over time—cohort effects—and to analyze how behaviour in early life relates to behaviour in old age (see photo).

Cohort effects refer to the fact that people of the same chronological age may differ considerably depending on when they were born.

However, because each cohort is unique, conclusions drawn from longitudinal studies are restricted to the cohort chosen. If members of a cohort studied from 1956 to 1996 are found to decline in sexual activity as they enter their sixties, we cannot conclude that the sexuality of those in a cohort studied from 1996 to 2036 will decline when they reach the same age.

An additional problem with longitudinal studies is that participants often drop out as the studies proceed, creating a bias commonly called **selective mortality**. The least-able people are the most likely to drop out, leaving a non-representative group of people who are usually healthier than the general population. Thus, findings based on longitudinal studies may be overly optimistic about the rate of decline of a variable such as sexual activity over the lifespan.

Diagnosing and Assessing Psychopathology in Later Life

The diagnostic criteria for older adults are basically the same as those for younger adults. The nature and manifestations of mental disorders are usually assumed to be the same in adulthood and old age, even though little research supports this assumption (Gatz, Kasl-Godley, & Karel, 1996; LaRue, Dessonville, & Jarvik, 1985). We often do not know what certain symptoms in older adults mean because we have few specifics about psychopathology in old age. For example, somatic symptoms are generally more prevalent in late life, but they are also evident in depression in older adults. Are the somatic symptoms of a depressed older adult necessarily a part of depression, or might they reflect physical changes?

Accurate assessment of elderly people for the purposes of establishing diagnoses and conducting research requires assessment measures tailored to elderly people. A measure of cognitive functioning is often included as standard practice in research to determine whether the elderly respondent has experienced declines in cognitive ability. Researchers often assess cognitive functioning with the Mini-Mental State Examination (MMSE; Folstein, Folstein, & McHugh, 1975) in its original or modified form (i.e., the Modified Mini-Mental State Exam). The MMSE is a brief measure of an individual's cognitive state, assessing "orientation, memory, and attention, . . . ability to name, follow

verbal and written commands, write a sentence spontaneously, and copy a complex polygon" (Folstein et al., 1975, p. 190).

Because some elderly people will have diminished attention spans, one goal is to develop short but reliable measures suitable for screening purposes. A relatively simple measure used to detect dementia and Alzheimer's disease is the clock-drawing subtest of the Clock Test. The Clock Test was developed by Holly Tuokko of the University of Victoria and her associates (Tuokko, Hadjistavropoulos, Miller, & Beattie, 1992; Tuokko, Kristjansson, & Miller, 1995). Respondents are presented with a previously drawn circle (7 cm in diameter) and are asked to imagine that the circle is the face of a clock and to put the numbers on the clock and then draw the hand placement for the time of 11:10. Up to 25 different types of errors can occur, including omissions, perseverations (i.e., repetitions), rotations, misplacements, distortions, substitutions, and additions. This simple test has been found to be reliable and valid, though results vary depending on the scoring system used (see Tuokko, Hadjistavropoulos, Rae, & O'Rourke, 2000).

Another assessment goal is to create measures whose item content is tailored directly to the concerns and symptoms reported by elderly people, not to those of younger respondents. One well-known measure crafted for the elderly is the Geriatric Depression Scale (GDS; Yesavage et al., 1983), a true-false self-report measure. The GDS has acceptable psychometric characteristics and is regarded as the standard measure for assessing depression in the elderly. The Geriatric Suicide Ideation Scale (GSIS) is a 31-item measure that is the first measure of suicide ideation created specifically for the elderly (see Heisel & Flett, 2006, 2016). The GSIS has a 10-item suicide ideation scale, as well as three other subscales tapping death ideation, loss of personal and social work, and the perceived meaning in life. Heisel and Flett (2008) reported that higher GSIS scores were associated with depression and health problems and lower scores in various domains of well-being, including positive relations with others and self-acceptance. Subsequent research with a community sample attested to the psychometric features of the GSIS and its subscales, and it established that higher GSIS scores are associated with higher levels of loneliness and social hopelessness and lower levels of social support and well-being (Heisel & Flett, 2016).

Range of Problems

We know that mental health may be tied to the problems in a person's life. As a group, no other people have more of these problems than the aged. They have them all: physical decline and disabilities, sensory and neurological deficits, loss of loved ones, the cumulative effects of a lifetime of many unfortunate experiences, and social stresses such as ageism. One concern expressed by the World Health Organization (WHO, 2002) is that elderly people with a mental disorder may suffer from "double jeopardy"; that is, they suffer the stigmas associated with being older and being mentally ill. Unfortunately, almost no research has explored stigma associated with mental illness among older adults (WHO, 2002).

It is important to remember that in addition to a lifetime of exposure to losses and to other stressors, older adults have many positive life experiences, coping mechanisms, and wisdom on which to draw. Moreover, older adults who belong to groups that provide meaningful, strong roles for them seem to have an easier time adjusting to growing old (Keith, 1982).

16.2 Old Age and Brain Disorders

Although the majority of older people do not have brain disorders, these problems account for more admissions and hospital inpatient days than any other geriatric condition (Christie, 1982). We will examine two principal types of brain disorders: dementia and delirium. Their *DSM-5* descriptions are found in the chapter titled "Neurocognitive Disorders." This chapter was previously titled "Dementia, Delirium, Amnestic, and Other Cognitive Disorders." According to the *DSM-5*, the preferred term instead of "dementia" is "neurocognitive disorder," but the term "dementia" was retained in the interests of continuity and the tendency for "dementia" to be used in settings where doctors and patients are familiar with the term (see APA, 2013). The neurocognitive disorders are grouped into the diagnostic categories of delirium, mild neurocognitive disorder, and major neurocognitive disorder. Minor neurocognitive disorder is indicated by minor levels of decline as reflected primarily by cognitive deficits. Neurocognitive disorder, major or minor, can be due to Alzheimer's disease, but it could also be due to medical conditions (e.g., Parkinson's disease) or traumatic brain injury. A person is evaluated in terms of whether the disorder is major or minor; with traumatic brain injury, for instance, someone would have major neurocognitive disorder or mild neurocognitive disorder due to traumatic brain injury, thus enabling differentiation of severe vs. less disabling disorders. Unlike other *DSM-5* segments, disorders in this area often stem from known physical factors.

Dementia

"With an aging population, dementia will be a huge burden on the population as time goes by. The cost will be unbelievable 15 to 20 years from now."

—Dr. Alain Beaudet, president of the Canadian Institutes of Health Research (2009, E36)

"The predicted surge in dementia cases will certainly overwhelm Canada's health care system unless specific and targeted action is taken now. Canada must act now."

—Richard Nakoneczny, Volunteer President, Alzheimer Society of Canada (2010, p. 2)

Dementia—which laypeople sometimes call "senility"—is a general descriptive term for gradual deterioration of intellectual abilities to the point that social and occupational functions are impaired. Difficulty remembering things, especially recent events, is the most prominent symptom, and reported memory problems in people who objectively have normal cognition predict subsequent dementia (St. John & Montgomery, 2002). People with dementia may leave tasks unfinished because they forget to return to them after an interruption. The person who had started to fill a teakettle at the sink leaves the water running; a parent is unable to remember the name of a daughter or son. Hygiene may be poor and appearance slovenly because the person forgets to bathe or how to dress. People with dementia also get lost, even in familiar settings.

Judgement may become faulty, and the person may have difficulty comprehending situations and making plans or decisions. People with dementia relinquish their standards and lose control of their impulses; they may use coarse language, tell inappropriate jokes, or shoplift. The ability to deal with abstract ideas deteriorates, and disturbances in emotions are common, including symptoms of depression, flatness of affect, and sporadic emotional outbursts. People with dementia are likely to show language disturbances as well, such as vague patterns of speech. Although the motor system is intact, they may have difficulty carrying out motor activities, such as those involved in brushing teeth or dressing themselves. They may also have trouble recognizing familiar surroundings or naming common objects. Episodes of delirium, a state of great mental confusion (discussed in detail in the section "Delirium"), may also occur. These should be distinguished from **paraphrenia**, the term used to describe schizophrenia that has its onset during old age.

The course of dementia may be progressive, static, or remitting, depending on the cause. Many people with progressive dementia eventually become withdrawn and apathetic. In the terminal phase of the illness, the personality loses its sparkle and integrity. Relatives and friends say that the person is just not himself or herself anymore. Social involvement with others keeps narrowing. Finally, the person is oblivious to his or her surroundings.

The prevalence of dementia increases with advancing age. One U.S. study found a prevalence of 13.9% for people 71 and older and a 9.7% prevalence of Alzheimer's disease. The prevalence of dementia was 5.0% for those aged 71–79 years old, but 37.4% for those aged 90 years and older (Plassman et al., 2007). This same team of investigators estimated later that another 22.2% of those aged 71 years or older have some form of cognitive impairment without dementia (Plassman et al., 2008).

Types and Causes of Dementia
Dementias are typically classified into three types. Alzheimer's disease is the most common. Then, there are the frontal-temporal and frontal-subcortical dementias, which are defined by the areas of the brain that are most affected.

Alzheimer's disease   **Alzheimer's disease** was described in the Brief Case Example that began this chapter. It accounts for about 50% of dementia in older people. According to a 2010 report called *Rising Tide: The Impact of Dementia on Canadian Society* (see the Alzheimer Society of Canada, 2010), approximately 480,600 people in Canada had some form of dementia (1.5% of the population) and this will rise to 1,125,000 people by 2038 (2.8% of the population). A recent analysis by the Alzheimer Society examined available data and estimated that 564,000 Canadians have dementia, with women accounting for about two-thirds of the cases (Alzheimer Society of Canada, 2016). The estimated 2008 costs for dementia care in Canada were $15 billion, accounting for 231 million hours spent by Canadians who provided informal care. The projected 2038 costs for dementia care in Canada are $153 billion, accounting for 756 million hours spent by Canadians providing informal care. About 1 in 13 Canadians over the age of 65 has Alzheimer's disease or a related dementia. As a result of these projections and in recognition of people in Canada who are afflicted at present, calls have been issued for a multi-faceted national dementia strategy (see Collier, 2009). As of 2016, in contrast to many other countries, Canada has not committed to a national dementia strategy.

Current projections for the future prevalence of Alzheimer's disease later in this century are beyond alarming! It is estimated that 46 million people in the world have dementia and this will rise to 131.5 million by 2050 (Prince et al., 2015).

In Alzheimer's disease, initially described by the German neurologist Alois Alzheimer in 1906, the brain tissue deteriorates irreversibly, and death usually occurs 10 or 12 years after the onset of symptoms. The median survival time is 3.1 years for Canadians with Alzheimer's disease and 3.3 years for Canadians with vascular dementia (Wolfson et al., 2001). Gender is a factor. Women with Alzheimer's disease live longer than men with Alzheimer's disease, but more women than men die as a result of this disease (Alloul et al., 1998).

The person may at first have difficulties only in concentration and in memory for newly learned material, and may appear absent-minded and irritable, shortcomings that can be overlooked for several years but that eventually interfere with daily living. Indeed, well before the onset of any clinical symptoms, subtle deficits in learning and memory are revealed by neuropsychological tests in people who will later develop the disease (Linn et al., 1995). As the disease develops, the person often blames others for personal failings and may have delusions of being persecuted. Memory continues to deteriorate, and the person becomes increasingly disoriented and agitated. A study at the University of Victoria found that people are wholly unaware of the extent of their memory decline (Correa, Graves, & Costa, 1996). However, imaging of brain changes show clear signs of decline that are often beyond a person's awareness (see photo).

The main physiological change in the brain, evident at autopsy, is an atrophy (wasting away) of the cerebral cortex, first the entorhinal cortex and the hippocampus and later the frontal, temporal, and parietal lobes. As neurons and synapses are lost, the fissures widen and the ridges become narrower and flatter. The ventricles also become enlarged. **Plaques**—small,

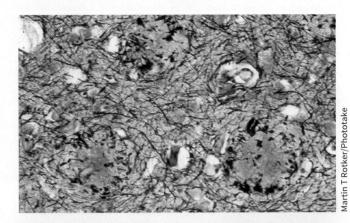

Martin T Rotker/Phototake

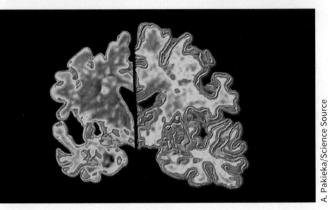

A. Pakieka/Science Source

In the photograph above of brain tissue from a patient with Alzheimer's disease, the plaque shows up as areas of dark pink. Below are computer-generated images of a brain of a patient with Alzheimer's disease (left) and a normal brain. Note that the patient's brain has shrunk considerably owing to the loss of nerve cells.

round areas making up the remnants of the lost neurons and b-amyloid, a waxy protein deposit—are scattered throughout the cortex. Tangled, abnormal protein filaments—**neurofibrillary tangles**—accumulate within the cell bodies of neurons. These plaques and tangles are present throughout the cerebral cortex and the hippocampus.

A quantitative review of neuroimaging studies involving 3,411 patients led Toronto researchers to conclude that, in terms of structural imaging, volume loss within the hippocampus (and episodic memory impairment) best discriminated people in the early stages of Alzheimer's disease from control participants. However, volume loss within the medial temporal lobes (and associated naming deficits) was the most sensitive measure when identifying patients with Alzheimer's disease for four or more years (Zakzanis, Graham, & Campbell, 2003). Further clarification was provided by a subsequent meta-analysis of 40 studies focused on people with early Alzheimer's and those with mild cognitive impairment in the prodromal stage (see Schroeter, Stein, Maslowski, & Neumann, 2009). It was found that early Alzheimer's disease has a structural effect on the (trans-)entorhinal and hippocampal regions, and functionally, it impacted the inferior parietal lobules and precuneus. Schroeter et al. (2009) further noted that the most reliable predictor of progression from mild cognitive impairment to Alzheimer's disease was not changes in the posterior cingulate cortex and precuneus. Rather, it was atrophy in the (trans-)entorhinal area in the hippocampus and hypometabolism/hypoperfusion in the inferior parietal lobules.

The cerebellum, spinal cord, and motor and sensory areas of the cortex are less affected, which is why Alzheimer's sufferers do not appear to have anything physically wrong with them until late in the disease process. For some time, people are able to walk around normally, and their over-learned habits, such as making small talk, remain intact, so that in short encounters, strangers may not notice anything amiss.

There is very strong evidence for a genetic basis for Alzheimer's. Several recent advances show quite conclusively that Alzheimer's disease is highly heritable but genetically, it is quite complex. According to one review (see Hollingworth et al., 2011), three large genome studies have traced vulnerability to individual variants in four genes—CLU, PICALM, CR1, and BIN1. The role of genetic factors was the main focus of the MIRAGE (Multi-Institutional Research in Alzheimer Genetic Epidemiology) Project that examined predictors at 13 centres in Canada, Germany, and the United States. This project found that by the time they reach the age of 80, children of parents who both developed Alzheimer's disease will themselves have a cumulative risk of 54%, which is 1.5 times the level of risk for children with one parent who developed the disease and five times the level of risk for children whose parents did not (Lautenschlager et al., 1996).

In other research, analyses conducted by a team led by researchers from the University of Waterloo used cumulative data from the famous Nun Study (see Focus on Discovery 16.1). The risk of dementia increased with age for those with low educational level, and the presence of the E4 allele increased the risk by 400% (see Tyas et al., 2007).

Focus on Discovery 16.1

The Nun Study: Unlocking the Secrets of Alzheimer's?

"It's the day after Easter, and the first crocus shoots have ventured tentatively above the ground at the convent on good Counsel Hill. This is Minnesota, however; the temperature is 23 F and the wind chill makes it feel far colder. Yet even though she's wearing only a skirt and sweater, Sister Ada, 91, wants to go outside. She wants to feed the pigs.

But the pigs she and the other nuns once cared for have been gone for 30 years. Sister Ada simply can't keep that straight. In recent years, her brain, like a time machine gone awry, has been wrenching her back and forth between the present and the past, depositing her without warning into the days when she taught primary schoolchildren in Minnesota or to the years when she was a college student in St. Paul. Or to the times when she and the sisters had to feed the pigs several times a day."

Lemonick and Park (2001)

The Nun Study is arguably one of the most remarkable research investigations in recent years. David Snowdon, who retired recently, had been studying 678 Catholic nuns from the American School Sisters of Notre Dame since 1986. The sisters have allowed Snowdon and colleagues to research their personal and medical histories, and they have undergone cognitive testing on an annual basis. They also agreed to donate their brains for analysis via autopsies after they die. Snowdon (Mortimer, 2012) contends that this is the first ever cohort study to follow a well-defined group of people, some of whom go on to develop dementia, and all participants' brains are available for study upon their deaths.

This study continues to provide insight from a long-term perspective on the factors associated with the development of Alzheimer's disease and other forms of dementia. For instance, the nuns had written autobiographies in the weeks preceding their religious vows. These autobiographies were analyzed for their grammatical complexity and idea density, concepts related to general knowledge, vocabulary skills, and other cognitive abilities. The key variable is idea density (see Mortimer, 2012). Excerpts from two sisters illustrate the differences in linguistic ability that were found:

Low linguistic ability: *I was born in Eau Claire, Wis. on May, 24, 1913 and was baptized in St. James church.* High linguistic ability: *The happiest day of my life so far was my First Communion Day which was in June nineteen hundred and twenty when I was but eight years of age, and four years later I was confirmed by Bishop D. D.*

(Snowdon et al., 1996, p. 530)

Low linguistic ability was found in 90% of those who developed Alzheimer's disease and in only 13% of those who didn't (Snowdon et al., 1996). Supplementary analyses continue to show that high levels of linguistic ability predict less cognitive impairment and fewer neuropathological indicators of Alzheimer's disease (Riley, Snowdon, Desrosiers, & Markesberry, 2005).

Danner, Snowdon, and Friesen (2001) also investigated the expression of positive and negative emotions in the previous writings of 180 nuns. Nuns who expressed more positive emotions lived longer, and nuns who eventually succumbed to Alzheimer's disease gradually expressed fewer positive emotions prior to the disease's onset. A related analysis of language samples taken over 60 years used a grammatical complexity measure to confirm earlier findings suggesting that reduced language ability was a precursor for dementia (Kemper et al., 2001).

Mortimer (2012) has summarized some of the key findings that emerged thus far, in addition to the importance of idea density, which was described earlier:

1. About one-third of those who fulfill Alzheimer's disease (AD) neuropathologic criteria at the physical level do not display signs of dementia at the times of their death.

2. Brain infarcts in isolation have little impact on cognitive status but they increase the risk of dementia among those with AD pathology.

3. Hippocampal volume in the brain has a strong positive correlation with Braak neurofibrillary stage, among those with normal or abnormal cognitive functioning.

(continued)

An intriguing follow-up analysis of the brains of 523 nuns showed that having Alzheimer's disease at the physical level but not showing the signs (i.e., asymptomatic Alzheimer's) showed that nuns who seemed protected from fully experiencing the disease had higher levels of education and higher allelic frequencies of the APOE gene. This outcome supports past suggestions that this gene plays a protective role (Iacono et al., 2015).

One drawback of the Nun Study is that even though it is longitudinal, and several factors can be controlled statistically, it still does not enable the researchers to make definitive cause and effect statements about the factors of importance in aging and Alzheimer's disease. The generalizability of the results to other people also needs to be considered. Nevertheless, this study is remarkable, not only because of the extreme co-operation that the nuns have given in the name of science, but also because the nuns have all experienced a common environment and have similar experiences, which reduces the likelihood that other factors have biased the results.

How, exactly, does the gene increase the risk for Alzheimer's disease? While the answer is not certain, the gene appears to be related to the development of both plaques and tangles, and it seems to increase the likelihood that the brain will incur damage from free radicals (unstable molecules derived from oxygen that attack proteins and DNA).

Finally, the environment is likely to play a role in most cases of Alzheimer's, as demonstrated by reports of long-lived MZ twins who are discordant for the disorder. A study of the Swedish Twin Registry found that non-shared environmental factors played a substantial role in susceptibility to Alzheimer's disease (Gatz et al., 2006). This study is the largest conducted thus far; it tested almost 12,000 twin pairs, with 392 pairs having at least one member with Alzheimer's disease. Gatz et al. (2006) confirmed the role of environmental factors; recognition of these modifiable factors is important for those seeking to lessen the incidence and prevalence of Alzheimer's disease. Nevertheless, their main finding was that the heritability of Alzheimer's disease was very high (79%), with it being quite similar for men and women.

General research on cognitive decline in the elderly supports the phrase "Use it or lose it!" As part of the Victoria Longitudinal Study, Hultsch, Hertzog, Small, and Dixon (1999) tested 250 middle-aged and older adults over a six-year period and showed a link between undergoing changes in intellectually related activities and changes in cognitive functioning. That is, remaining active at the cognitive level may buffer or protect an individual in terms of the degree of cognitive decline experienced.

A review conducted by Canadian investigators continues to support the use it or lose it principle. The review by Milgram et al. (2006) supported three conclusions: (1) cognitive activity helps preserve cognitive functioning, (2) cognitive activity helps crystallized intelligence more than fluid intelligence, and (3) there is support for the cognitive reserve hypothesis. The act of cognitive compensation creates a cognitive reserve. The **cognitive reserve hypothesis** is the notion that high education levels delay the clinical expression of dementia because the brain develops backup or reserve neural structures as a form of neuroplasticity.

Recent analyses continue to support the role of cognitive activity, but protective benefits are enhanced further if cognitive activity is combined with physical activity. Both forms of activity have resulted in significant improvements as assessed via neuroimaging (Bamidis et al., 2014) and a recent meta-analysis concluded that physical exercise and brain fitness exercises produced nearly identical cognitive benefits (Smith, 2016). In light of these findings, it has even been suggested that engaging in behaviours that combine physical and cognitive activity (e.g., learning a new dance) are most beneficial (Bamidis et al., 2014).

A related protective factor is being bilingual. Innovative research that has received global attention by Ellen Bialystok from York University and Fergus Craik from the Rotman Research Institute and their colleagues indicates that being bilingual protects against the negative effects of aging on cognitive control (Bialystok, Craik, Klein, & Viswanathan, 2004). Tests of older adults showed that bilingual participants responded much more quickly, relative to unilingual participants, in experimental conditions that placed heavy demands on working memory. Follow-up research has established that lifelong bilingualism attenuates the negative cognitive changes leading to dementia (Craik, Bialystok, & Freedman, 2010) and bilingualism confers advantages in executive functioning and working memory among both younger and older participants (Bialystok, Poarch, Luo, & Craik, 2014). In keeping with the cognitive reserve hypothesis, it is believed generally that bilingual people engage in more stimulating mental activities and more extensive cognitive practice that contribute to a cognitive reserve that becomes ultimately reflected in brain plasticity. Recent research is examining specific processes and mechanisms. Experimental research indicates that executive functioning advantages reflect improved cognitive flexibility in task switching (Wiseheart, Viswanathan, & Bialystok, 2016) and "lapsed bilinguals" (i.e., bilinguals who have reverted to being monolinguals) show fewer advantages and have only slightly better working memory than monolingual individuals (Bogulski, Rakoczy, Goodman, & Bialystok, 2015). Brain research indicates that bilingual people have preserved frontal and temporal lobe functioning in aging in ways that should be protective from dementia (Olsen et al., 2015) and bilingualism is associated with better cognitive outcomes after experiencing a stroke (Alladi et al., 2016).

New insights about protective factors should emerge from unique research being conducted by Emily Rogalski and her colleagues on "super agers," a group of remarkable elderly people who show no evidence of cognitive decline, and, in some instances, show elevated cognitive functioning. According to one account, these people include "an octogenarian attorney, a 96-year-old retired neuroscientist, a 92-year-old Holocaust survivor and an 81-year-old pack a day smoker who drinks a nightly martini" (Tanner, 2013, B2). These people have been characterized as having episodic memory functioning that is equal to or better than the functioning of people who are 20 to 30 years younger (Gefen et al., 2015). Initial research by Rogalski et al. (2013) linked these advanced cognitive abilities with denser cortical thickness in the brain, but what is unclear at present is whether brain-related changes occurred throughout life or whether these super agers were born with this apparent physiological advantage. Gefen et al. (2015) established, based on autopsies of super agers who have died, that the brains of these individuals show less evidence of Alzheimer-related pathology than other people of the same age. MRI analyses of living super agers showed further that they had structural advantages in the anterior cingulate cortex in the right hemisphere (Gefen et al., 2015).

Charles Eshelman/FilmMagic/Getty Images

Canadian actor Michael J. Fox has Parkinson's disease. Fox has been instrumental in promoting research and awareness of Parkinson's disease and noted in 2016 that predictions he would be disabled by then have yet to come true.

Frontal-temporal dementias

This type of dementia accounts for 10 to 15% of cases. It typically begins in a person's late fifties. In addition to the usual cognitive impairments of a dementia, frontal-temporal dementias are marked by extreme behavioural and personality changes. Sometimes people are very apathetic and unresponsive to their environment; at other times, they show an opposite pattern of euphoria, overactivity, and impulsivity (Levy et al., 1996). Unlike Alzheimer's disease, frontal-temporal dementias are not closely linked to loss of cholinergic neurons. Serotonin neurons are most affected, and there is widespread loss of neurons in the frontal and temporal lobes.

Pick's disease is one cause of frontal-temporal dementia. Like Alzheimer's disease, Pick's disease is a degenerative disorder in which neurons are lost. It is also characterized by the presence of Pick bodies, spherical inclusions within neurons. Frontal-temporal dementias have a strong genetic component (Usman, 1997).

Frontal-subcortical dementias

Because these dementias affect subcortical brain areas, which are involved in the control of motor movements, both cognition and motor activity are affected. Types of frontal-subcortical dementias include the following:

- *Huntington's chorea*, now referred to more commonly as Huntington's disease, is caused by a single dominant gene located on chromosome 4 and is diagnosed principally by neurologists on the basis of genetic testing. Its major behavioural feature is the presence of writhing (choreiform) movements. The best-known person with this disease is the late folk songwriter and singer Woody Guthrie. Huntington's disease was the first disease identified and located on the human genome as part of the Human Genome Project (Huntington's Disease Collaborative Research Group, 1993).

- *Parkinson's disease* is marked by muscle tremors, muscular rigidity, and akinesia (an inability to initiate movement),

and can lead to dementia. Canadian Michael J. Fox has Parkinson's disease (see photo).

- *Vascular dementia* is the second most common type, next to Alzheimer's disease. Vascular dementia is now referred to in the *DSM-5* as "major or mild neurocognitive disorder." It is diagnosed when a patient with dementia has neurological signs, such as weakness in an arm or abnormal reflexes, or when brain scans show evidence of cerebrovascular disease. Most commonly, the patient had a series of strokes in which a clot formed, impairing circulation and causing cell death. Genetic factors appear to be of no importance (Bergem, Engedal, & Kringlen, 1997), and risk for vascular dementia increases with the same risk factors generally associated with cardiovascular disease—for example, a high level of "bad" cholesterol (Moroney et al., 1999).

Other causes of dementia

A number of infectious diseases can produce irreversible dementia. Encephalitis, a generic term for any inflammation of brain tissue, is caused by viruses that enter the brain either from other parts of the body (such as the sinuses or ears) or from the bites of mosquitoes or ticks. Meningitis, an inflammation of the membranes covering the outer brain, is usually caused by a bacterial infection. The organism that produces the venereal disease syphilis *(Treponema pallidum)* can invade the brain and cause dementia.

Finally, head traumas, brain tumours, nutritional deficiencies (especially of B-complex vitamins), kidney or liver failure, and endocrine-gland problems such as hyperthyroidism can result in dementia. Exposure to toxins, such as lead or mercury, as well as chronic use of drugs, including alcohol, are additional causes.

Treatment of Dementia   If the dementia has a reversible cause, appropriate medical treatment (such as correcting a hormonal imbalance) can be beneficial. Despite numerous investigations, no clinically significant treatment has been found that can halt or reverse Alzheimer's disease, although some drugs, as described here, show promise in effecting modest improvement in certain cognitive functions for a short period of time.

Biological treatments of Alzheimer's disease

Because Alzheimer's disease involves the death of brain cells that secrete acetylcholine, various studies have attempted to increase the levels of this neurotransmitter. Research using choline (a precursor of the enzyme that catalyzes the reaction that produces acetylcholine) and physostigmine (a drug that prevents the breakdown of acetylcholine) has been disappointing. Tetrahydroaminoacridine (tacrine, brand name Cognex), which inhibits the enzyme that breaks down acetylcholine, produces mild improvement or slows the progression of cognitive decline (Qizilbash et al., 1998). Tacrine cannot be used in high doses, however, because it has severe side effects; for example, it is toxic to the liver. Donepezil (Aricept) is similar to tacrine in its method of action and results but produces fewer side effects (Rogers et al., 1998).

Gauthier and Scheltens (2009) provided a cogent update of biological treatments. Five drugs have been approved for use thus far: tacrine, donepezil, rivastigmine, galantamine, and memantine. They also reported that questions have been raised by critics about the cost effectiveness of these treatments from a societal perspective. Moreover, these drugs have not stopped progression of Alzheimer's disease though they may slow down the progression of symptoms.

Psychosocial treatments of Alzheimer's disease for the individual and the family

Although effective medical treatment for Alzheimer's is not yet available, patients and their families can be helped to deal with the effects of the disease. The general psychological approach is supportive. The overall goal is to minimize the disruption caused by the person's behavioural changes. Health workers achieved this by allowing the person and the family the opportunity to discuss the illness and its consequences, providing accurate information about it, helping family members care for the person in the home, and encouraging a realistic attitude in dealing with the disease's specific challenges (Knight, 2004; Zarit, 1980).

Counselling the person with Alzheimer's is difficult. Because of cognitive losses, psychotherapy provides little long-term benefit for those with severe deterioration. However, some patients seem to enjoy and be reassured by occasional conversations with professionals and with others not directly involved in their lives—in both individual and group settings. Interventions employed with normally functioning older adults, like Butler's life review (discussed further in the section "Treatment of Depression"), can also be useful for early- to mid-stage Alzheimer's sufferers whose cognitive abilities have not markedly deteriorated (Kasl-Godley & Gatz, 2000). In contrast to approaches taken with other psychological problems, denial may be the best coping mechanism available rather than being forced to acknowledge problems (Zarit, 1980).

For every institutionalized individual with a severely disabling dementia, there are at least two individuals with dementia living in the community, usually supported by a spouse, daughter, or other family member. It is estimated that families provide 75% or more of the long-term care to older adults (Thomas & Applebaum, 2015). A national survey in the United States found that caregivers are most likely to be female (60%) and the caregivers have an average age of 49.2 years (AARP and National Alliance for Caregiving, 2015). Given the extent to which family members are relied on and the stressors and challenges facing families, Qualls (2016) issued a call for much greater recognition of the roles played by families and greater integration of families into social systems and the removal of practice and policy barriers that limit the support that families receive from psychologists.

Not surprisingly, caring for a person with Alzheimer's has been shown to be extremely stressful and distressing. Analyses reported by the Canadian Study of Health and Aging Working Group (1994b) indicate that depression is twice as evident among caregivers as among non-caregivers. This CSHA study is important because it is one of the few caregiver studies that began with a nationally representative sample of individuals suffering from dementia and their caregivers.

Follow-up analyses of the CSHA data by Chappell and Penning (1996) indicate that depression and feelings of being burdened are highly correlated among caregivers. Caregivers were especially likely to feel burdened in response to apathy and an apparent lack of interest on the part of the patient, despite the best efforts of the caregiver. What forms do burden take? An analysis of caregiver burden came out of the Canadian Alzheimer's Disease Caregiver Survey (see Black et al., 2010). This study focused on 221 baby boomer caregivers (ages 44 to 64) taking care of an afflicted individual. Four significant areas of burden were identified: emotional burden, physical burden, financial burden, and employment burden due to needing to change one's own employment status (71% indicated some form of work disruption). Further complicating the situation were other physical health problems among some of those requiring care; for instance, about one-quarter of those with Alzheimer's disease also had diabetes. Similarly, about one-quarter had heart disease and 36% had unacceptably high blood pressure.

Objective and subjective indicators of burden predict caregivers' psychological distress (Chappell & Reid, 2002; Provencher, Perreault, St-Onge, & Rousseau, 2003). Moreover, longitudinal data indicate that perceived burden predicts subsequent depression, but the opposite temporal sequence (depression predicts subsequent perceptions of burden) is not supported (O'Rourke & Tuokko, 2004). Finally, the link between role-specific demands of caregiving and burden are mitigated by resilience; resilience promotes well-being among caregivers experiencing significant burden (Chappell & Dujela, 2008). Optimism in the caregiver is also protective (Gottlieb & Rooney, 2004).

Caregivers are also more likely than non-caregivers to experience chronic health problems, especially if they have experienced caregiver strain, burden, and difficulty providing care. Problems are experienced in terms of self-reported health but also in terms of a host of physiological indicators (e.g., cortisol production, stress markers, and neurohormonal and inflammatory processes) (see Chappell & Funk, 2011).

Some resources are available to assist caregivers. In Canada, the Alzheimer Society of Canada has an online caregivers' forum that enables caregivers to share their experiences via the Internet and seek support and comfort from others (see www.alzheimer.ca). Expressing one's concerns online is a compelling way to achieve a better understanding within society of the challenges faced by caregivers. Indeed, a study of Chinese-Canadian caregivers taking care of relatives with Alzheimer's disease found lower reported levels of burden among frequent users of an Internet-based caregiver support service (Chiu et al., 2009).

Caregivers of people with dementia can also benefit from participating in psychoeducation groups. Hébert et al. (2003) found that participants in weekly sessions on stress appraisal and coping reported significant improvements in their reactions to the behavioural problems of care receivers. A meta-analysis that included a test of 14 psychoeducation studies found that there was substantial effectiveness for skill training programs with three elements: behaviour management, depression management, and anger management (Gallagher-Thompson & Coon, 2007). Combinations of individual treatment and support groups also seemed to be effective.

Because the family members are affected so powerfully, it is often recommended that they be given respites from their task. The patient may be hospitalized for a week, or a health care worker may take over and give the family a much-needed break. Unfortunately, a review of respite programs in Canada by Gottlieb and Johnson (2000) concluded that the phrase "too little too late" can be applied; when respites are used, which is infrequently, the use occurs quite late and the pattern of use is not intense or protracted in time. Typically, up to half of caregivers do not take advantage of available programs, and when they do participate, it is only after they have already been in the caregiver role for two to four years.

As we will see in our subsequent discussion of home care, perhaps the most wrenching decision facing caregivers is whether to institutionalize the person with dementia. A qualitative study of caregivers in Northern Canada suggested that feelings of guilt among caregivers are intense when a loved one is institutionalized, but their most predominant emotion is worry (Loos & Bowd, 1997). One wife who had assumed the caregiver role stated, "Putting him in the institution, even though the care is good, is like putting him in jail. It haunts you" (Loos & Bowd, 1997, p. 510). The conflicts people face when making this decision are considerable. A review by Alloul et al. (1998) concluded that the three best predictors of making the difficult decision to institutionalize a loved one are the elderly person's level of aggression, incontinence, and the presence of psychiatric disturbances.

Delirium

The term **delirium** is derived from the Latin words "de," meaning "from" or "out of," and "lira," meaning "furrow" or "track." The term implies being off track or deviating from the usual state (Wells & Duncan, 1980). Delirium is typically described as "a clouded state of consciousness." The patient, sometimes rather suddenly, has great trouble concentrating and focusing attention and cannot maintain a coherent and directed stream of thought. In the early stages, the person with delirium is frequently restless, particularly at night. The sleep–waking cycle becomes disturbed, so that the person is drowsy during the day and awake, restless, and agitated during the night. Vivid dreams and nightmares are common.

Delirious people may be impossible to engage in conversation because of their wandering attention and fragmented thinking. In severe delirium, speech is rambling and incoherent. Bewildered and confused, some delirious individuals lose their sense of time and place. They are often so inattentive that they cannot be questioned about orientation. Memory impairment, especially for recent events, is common. In the course of a 24-hour period, however, delirious people have lucid intervals and become alert and coherent. These daily fluctuations help distinguish delirium from other syndromes, especially Alzheimer's disease.

Perceptual disturbances are frequent. Individuals mistake the unfamiliar for the familiar, stating, for example, that they are at home instead of in a hospital. Although illusions and hallucinations are common, particularly visual and mixed visual–auditory ones, they are not always present. Paranoid delusions have been noted in 40 to 70% of delirious older adults. These delusions tend to be poorly worked out, fleeting, and changeable.

Swings in activity and mood accompany disordered thoughts and perceptions. Delirious people can be erratic, ripping their clothes one moment and sitting lethargically the next. They are in great emotional turmoil and may shift rapidly from one emotion to another—depression, fright, anger, euphoria, and irritability. Fever, flushed face, dilated pupils, tremors, rapid heartbeat, elevated blood pressure, and incontinence are common. If the delirium proceeds, the person will completely lose touch with reality and may become stuporous (Lipowski, 1983).

Although delirium is one of the most frequent biological mental disorders in older adults, it has been neglected in research and, like dementia, is often misdiagnosed (Knight, 2004). It is often the case that delirium is simply not detected (Zarit & Zarit, 1998). Cameron et al. (1987) assessed 133 consecutive admissions to an acute medical ward. They found 15 cases of delirium, only one of which had been detected by the admitting physician. Older adults are frequently misdiagnosed as having an irreversible dementia.

Independent research in Montreal has confirmed that delirium is a risk factor for mortality, as well as for functional status and cognitive difficulties in the 12 months following hospital admission (McCusker et al., 2001, 2002). A 2010 meta-analysis established that delirium in older people is associated with very poor outcomes and prognosis and this finding holds after controlling for age, comorbid illness, illness severity, and baseline dementia (Witlox et al., 2010).

The following is a typical example of delirium in an acute care facility. An older woman found in a filthy apartment with no food was believed by a poorly informed physician to have dementia and was given routine custodial care in a nursing home. A professional knowledgeable about delirium learned that she had become depressed over the loss of a loved one and had neglected her diet. Once this was recognized, appropriate attention was given to her nutritional deficiencies, and her condition improved such that she was discharged to her own home after one month (Zarit, 1980).

Causes of Delirium

The causes of delirium in older adults can be grouped into several general classes: drug intoxications and drug-withdrawal reactions, metabolic and nutritional imbalances (as in uncontrolled diabetes and thyroid dysfunction), infections or fevers, neurological disorders, and the stress of a change in the person's surroundings (Knight, 2004). Delirium may also occur following major surgery, most commonly hip surgery (Zarit & Zarit, 1998); during withdrawal from psychoactive substances; and following head trauma or seizures. Common physical illnesses that cause delirium in older adults include congestive heart failure; pneumonia; urinary tract infection; cancer, kidney, or liver failure; malnutrition; and cerebrovascular accidents or strokes. Probably the most frequent cause of delirium in this age group is intoxication with prescription drugs (Besdine, 1980; Lipowski, 1983). However, delirium usually has more than one cause. A contemporary review of the existing literature conducted by Canadian researchers (see Elie, Cole, Primeau, & Bellavance, 1998) concluded that the top five correlates of delirium among elderly hospitalized patients are dementia, being on medication, medical illness, age, and male gender.

Although delirium usually develops swiftly (within a matter of hours or days), the exact mode of onset depends on the underlying cause. Delirium resulting from a toxic reaction or concussion has an abrupt onset; when infection or metabolic disturbance underlies delirium, the onset of symptoms is more gradual.

Why are older adults especially vulnerable to delirium? Many explanations have been offered: the physical declines of aging, the increased general susceptibility to chronic diseases, the many medications prescribed for older people, the greater sensitivity to drugs, and vulnerability to stress. One other factor, brain damage, increases the risk of delirium. A retrospective review of 100 hospital admissions of people with delirium revealed that 44% had delirium superimposed on another brain condition (Purdie, Honigman, & Rosen, 1981).

Treatment of Delirium

Complete recovery from delirium is possible if the syndrome is identified correctly and

TABLE 16.2	Comparative Features of Dementia and Delirium
Dementia	**Delirium**
Gradual deterioration of intellectual abilities, especially memory for recent events	Trouble concentrating and staying with a train of thought
	Restlessness at night, nightmares
Difficulties in everyday problem-solving	Frequent lucid intervals
Periods of depression	Hallucinations; sometimes loss of contact with reality
Problems naming common objects	Large swings in mood and activity
Faulty orientation to time (e.g., day of week), place (e.g., location), and person (e.g., who the self is or others are)	Usually reversible but potentially fatal if cause (e.g., malnutrition) not treated
Usually progressive and irreversible	Prevalence high in the very young as well as the old
Increased prevalence with age	

the underlying cause promptly treated. It generally takes one to four weeks for the condition to clear; it takes longer in older vs. younger people. If the underlying cause is not treated, however, permanent brain damage and death can ensue.

Primary prevention strategies appear to reduce the high rates of delirium, as well as the duration of delirium episodes in hospitalized older adults (Inouye et al., 1999). The intervention addresses such risk factors for delirium as sleep deprivation, immobility, dehydration, visual and hearing impairment, and cognitive impairment.

One often-neglected aspect of the management of delirium is educating the family of a person with dementia to distinguish the manifestations of dementia and delirium. Table 16.2 compares the features of dementia and delirium, and serves as a useful summary of the nature of delirium.

16.3 Old Age and Psychological Disorders

Although a psychological disorder at any age may have at least a partial physical explanation, this explanation can be misleading, since much psychopathology found in older adults has not been linked directly to the physiological processes of aging. Indeed, the maladaptive personality traits and inadequate coping skills that the person brings into old age play a role in psychological disturbances, as do health, genetic predisposition, and life stressors.

We look first at the prevalence of mental disorders in late life and then survey a number of them, paying specific attention to their characteristics in older adults.

Overall Prevalence of Mental Disorders in Late Life

Is age itself a contributing factor to emotional and mental malfunction? Do more old people than young people have mental disorders?

It is not entirely clear whether mental disorders become more prevalent with age, partly because of the methodological and conceptual difficulties we have already discussed. An extensive cross-sectional study conducted by the U.S. National Institute of Mental Health (NIMH) yielded valuable data on mental disorders in all age groups, including the old (Myers et al., 1984; Regier et al., 1988).

Current prevalence data indicate that persons over age 65 have the lowest overall rates of mental disorder of all age groups when the various disorders are grouped together. The primary problem detected was cognitive impairment, not as a separate *DSM* category but as an important characteristic of more than one disorder (e.g., depression, dementia, delirium). Rates for mild cognitive impairment were about 14% for older men and women; for severe cognitive impairment, rates were 5.5% for older men and 4.7% for older women.

The majority of persons 65 years of age and older are free from serious psychopathology, but 10 to 20% do have psychological problems severe enough to warrant professional attention (Gatz et al., 1996; Gurland, 1991).

Depression

One consistent finding that was confirmed in a global study conducted by the World Health Organization is that major depression is less prevalent among adults aged 65 and older, relative to younger people (Kessler et al., 2010). However, this was found only among the eight developed countries included in this study and the age difference was not found in the 10 developing countries. Results from the Canadian Community Health Survey confirmed that elderly Canadians, vs. those in the 50–64 years age group and the 20–49 years age group, had lower rates of depression, anxiety, and alcohol abuse/dependence, and lower rates of service use in terms of conducting their doctors and other health providers (Mosier et al., 2010). However, depression and other disorders are still quite evident among the elderly. One study involved physician ratings of 12 symptoms of depression as part of a clinical interview. This survey of 2,341 elderly Canadians found that 2.6% had major depression (five or more symptoms) and 4.9% had minor depression (two to four symptoms). Greater prevalence of depression was associated with female gender, the presence of dementia, and the presence of physical health problems (Ostbye et al., 2005).

One review concluded that at least half of the depressed older adults are experiencing depression for the first time, a phenomenon known as "late-onset depression" (see Fiske et al., 2009). Those with early-onset depression are more likely to have a family history of depression and personality

dysfunction that renders them vulnerable. Data indicate that people with early-onset depression have comparatively greater depression and less social support than people with late-onset depression and have more severe cognitive and neurological changes (Sachs-Ericsson et al., 2013). People with late-onset depression who commit suicide tend to have a high frequency of negative life events. They also have less history of alcohol misuse and self-harm behaviours (Voshaar et al., 2011).

Women have more periods of depression than men for most of their lives. An epidemiological study in Edmonton showed that elderly women have substantially higher rates of depression regardless of whether they are between 65 and 74 years old or 85 years old and older (Newman, Bland, & Orn, 1998).

The use of standard diagnostic criteria may lead to the underdiagnosis of depression in older adults. Older adults are less likely to demonstrate impaired social and occupational functioning as a result of their depression because they are less likely than younger people to be working, but they have higher risk due to relatively less engagement in daily activities (Fiske, Wetherell, & Gatz, 2009). Some researchers (e.g., Newman et al., 1998) have described a subtype of depression more commonly seen in older adults, called depletion syndrome, which is also known as depression without sadness. This syndrome is characterized chiefly by loss of pleasure, vitality, and appetite, as well as hopelessness and somatic symptoms; self-blame, guilt, and dysphoric mood are either absent or less prominent.

Causes of Depression in Older Adults   Recently, Fiske et al. (2009) posited a new model that focuses on depression in older adults due to decreased involvement in daily activities and depression that is maintained by self-critical thoughts. Both of these factors have been implicated in depression among younger people, however.

Many elderly people in poor physical health are depressed and it is often difficult to ascertain whether the health problems came first or were as a result of being depressed. A survey of 900 older adults in the community found that 44% with depressive symptoms were medically ill (Blazer & Williams, 1980). Many physicians who care for older people are insensitive to the likelihood of depression coexisting with physical illnesses. More often than not they do not diagnose, and therefore do not treat, the psychological condition (Rapp, Parisi, Walsh, & Wallace, 1988). This oversight can lead to the worsening of the depression and the medical condition. By the same token, psychotherapists who are focusing on the treatment of depression also need to be cognizant of chronic health conditions that will likely complicate treatment when depression is the primary emphasis. Laidlaw and Pachana (2009) have echoed concerns about the growing number of elderly people who will require treatment in the years to come and the certainty that the majority of these people will also have co-occurring physical comorbidities.

As we grow older, we almost inevitably experience a number of life events that could cause depression. Bereavement after the loss of a loved one has been hypothesized to be the most important risk factor for depression in the elderly (see Vinkers et al., 2004). Bereavement also contributes to poorer prognosis in elderly people already suffering from depression (Denihan et al., 2000). The predictiveness of bereavement was also confirmed in a meta-analysis conducted by researchers from McGill University (Cole & Dendukuri, 2003). Significant risk factors for depression across 20 prospective studies were bereavement, sleep disturbance, disability, prior depression, and female gender.

Longitudinal research on bereavement suggests that while bereavement contributes in general to depression, the extent of its effect depends on the nature of the loss and the timing of assessment. For instance, in a well-designed prospective study, Carnelley, Wortman, and Kessler (1999) found that widowed women reported more depression than control participants up to two years following the loss. However, widowed women whose husbands were ill when the study started did not experience more depression when their husbands died. Carnelley et al. (1999) suggest that there is a timing effect in being forewarned; women with ill husbands anticipate the loss and may become depressed prior to their spouse's death.

Clearly, there is a link between bereavement and depression and, as noted in Chapter 3, this topic has received extensive attention in *DSM-5* following the removal of the bereavement exclusion that previously meant that people who were bereaved and depressed would not qualify for a depression diagnosis. Although opinions vary, several authors have suggested that diagnostic systems should be substantially revised to include a separate category for the pathological grief experienced by people who suffer a prolonged reaction to bereavement (see Bonanno & Kaltman, 2001; Stroebe, Schut, & Finkehauer, 2001), and indeed, a diagnostic category called "persistent complex bereavement disorder" is listed in the *DSM-5* as a condition for further study. Calls for a separate category are based on evidence that grief-stricken individuals have grief-related symptoms that are distinguishable from existing definitions of depression (see Stroebe et al., 2001). A key issue is how to distinguish between normal and abnormal grief reactions.

Given the different reactions to bereavement, researchers have identified factors associated with resilient reactions to the death of one's spouse. Prem Fry at Trinity Western University in British Columbia has found that existential factors are quite important. For instance, a study of widows and widowers between the ages of 65 and 87 found that people who were optimistic and found meaning in their lives had better psychological adjustment than people lacking these attributes (Fry, 2001). An involvement in organized religion was also associated with better adjustment.

Numerous findings point to the importance of social support as a stress buffer for elderly people faced with life challenges (e.g., Cappeliez, 1993; Fry, 1993). Ostbye, Steenhuis, Walton, and Cairney (2000) examined the correlates of dysphoria in elderly Canadians living in the community who did not have dementia. Correlates of dysphoria included lower perceived social support, chronic pain, poor health, and functional dependency. While support is typically protective, a more recent longitudinal Canadian study suggests a more complicated picture, with some forms of social support having little protective role (i.e., tangible support) and some forms of social support (i.e., affectionate support) being associated with higher psychological distress (Robitalle, Orpana, & McIntosh, 2012). When support seems to "backfire" in this manner, it could reflect that the person has become too needy or resents a loss of autonomy.

Although retirement has been assumed to have negative consequences, research does not generally support this assumption (George, 1980). Any ill effects of retirement may have more to do with the poor health and low incomes of some retirees and less with retirement per se (Pahkala, 1990). Retirement often ushers in a satisfying period of life.

Each older person brings to late life a developmental history that makes his or her reactions to common problems unique. Each person's coping skills and personality determine how effectively that individual will respond to new life events. Overall, adaptation rather than depression is the more common reaction to stress in late life.

Treatment of Depression
A substantial proportion of older people who suffer from depression have persistent forms of depression. Meta-analytic reviews conducted by researchers in Montreal indicate that depression in elderly people is associated with a poor prognosis and is undertreated (Cole & Bellavance, 1997; Cole, Bellavance, & Mansour, 1999). One meta-analysis of studies that examined the course of depression found that only 33% of the participants recovered, while another 33% were still depressed and 21% had died (Cole et al., 1999). A one-year follow-up study conducted in Montreal of a sample of elderly people with depression found that fewer than half of the depressed elderly in the study were improved; this study showed that major depression superimposed on dysthymic disorder (i.e., double depression) was especially persistent (see Fenton, Cole, Engelsmann, & Mansouri, 1997). The low remission rate of depression was attributed to lack of treatment intervention.

Although clinical lore holds that depressions in older people are more resistant to treatment than the depressions in younger people, we have known for some time that these claims are not substantiated (Small & Jarvik, 1982). Rather, there is considerable evidence that depressed older adults can be helped by both psychological and pharmacological interventions, but there must be access to treatment.

Gallagher and Thompson (1982, 1983) compared cognitive, behavioural, and brief psychodynamic psychotherapies for older individuals with depression. These three methods were found equally effective, and in subsequent studies (Gallagher-Thompson & Thompson, 1995a, 1995b; Thompson, Gallagher, & Breckenridge, 1987), about three-quarters of the clients were judged either completely cured or markedly improved. These rates compare very favourably with the outcomes of psychotherapy in younger people with depression. A meta-analysis that included subsequent studies also attested to the effectiveness of cognitive-behavioural therapy (CBT) vs. treatment as usual or being on a waiting list but CBT was not more effective than other treatments (Gould, Coulson, & Howard, 2012).

A study with depressed elderly people from Ottawa showed that they responded quite well to cognitive therapy, with decreases in depressive symptoms comparable with those obtained in other research investigations (Cappeliez, 2000). However, as is often the case with younger participants, depressed elders had a less positive response to treatment if they had more severe levels of depression to begin with. It was also found that depressed elders with negative self-views had less positive responses to the cognitive interventions.

Another treatment study compared cognitive therapy and bibliotherapy (the reading of a self-help book) as treatments for the depressed elderly (Floyd et al., 2004). Both these therapies were superior to delayed treatment in a control group. Finally, a more recent study compared individualized CBT with treatment as usual and this randomized control trial confirmed that CBT was more effective in reducing levels of depression as assessed by the Beck Depression Inventory-2 (Serfaty et al., 2009).

Interpersonal psychotherapy (IPT) has also been used successfully to treat depression in older adults. IPT is a short-term psychotherapy that addresses themes such as role loss, role transition, and interpersonal disputes, which are problem areas prominent in the lives of many older adults. Existing evidence attests to the efficacy of IPT as an established treatment. A meta-analysis of nine existing studies with adults of various ages concluded that IPT was superior to CBT for treating depression in adults in general (de Mello et al., 2005). One study with the elderly found that IPT was particularly effective if it focused on role conflict and it was less effective if it focused on abnormal grief experiences (Miller et al., 2003). Recent data suggest that a modified 16-week form of IPT for suicidal elderly people has promise as an effective intervention (see Heisel et al., 2009). This study needs to be replicated because it was based on a small sample ($n = 12$) and it did not include a control group; nevertheless, IPT did significantly reduce levels of suicide ideation.

A form of treatment known as reminiscence therapy can also be effective for treating depression in the elderly, and numerous studies of reminiscence therapy have emerged in recent years (see photo). Reminiscence therapy is also known as life review therapy. It is a cognitive process that requires individuals to reflect on previous negative events and address any remaining conflicts; it also requires that they strive to find life's meaning while examining the present situation and the past. One focus here is to re-examine the role of the self in events in an attempt to achieve a sense of self-acceptance and reduced self-blame. For instance, a self-critical perfectionist could dredge up previous mistakes from the past and re-examine his or her role, working toward the ultimate goal of achieving a less self-critical interpretation.

iStock.com/ebstock

Reminiscence (or life review) therapy for depression requires individuals to reflect on their past and present situation to help achieve a sense of self-acceptance and reduce self-blame.

Life review was proposed by Butler (1963) as a psychotherapeutic approach uniquely suitable for older adults. This approach reflects the influence of Erik Erikson's (1950, 1968) lifespan developmental theory, which postulates stages of conflict and growth extending well into the senior years. Life review facilitates what appears to be a natural tendency of older adults to reflect on their lives and to try to make sense of what has happened to them. In Eriksonian terms, it helps the person address the conflict between ego integrity and despair. Ego integrity is the process of finding meaning in the way one has led one's life, and despair reflects the discouragement that can come from unreached goals and unmet desires. Life-review methods include having the patient bring in old photographs, travel to a childhood home, and write an autobiography.

A meta-analysis of 20 studies showed that reminiscence and life review had both statistical and clinical significance in terms of reducing depression in elderly people (Bohlmeijer, Smit, & Cuijpers, 2003). The treatment effect was comparable with those obtained with pharmacotherapy and other psychological treatments. More recently, a randomized control trial found that life review was again effective in reducing symptoms, but participation in the no-treatment control group was also effective (see Pot et al., 2010). Life review seems useful, but not necessarily better than other forms of treatment. Another recent meta-analysis of 128 studies found that reminiscence interventions yielded improvements not only in terms of reduced depression, but also in terms of higher levels of purpose in life, positive well-being, mastery, and social integration (Pinquart & Forstmeier, 2012).

According to Watt and Cappeliez (2000), the type of reminiscence involved determines the effectiveness of reminiscence therapy. Clearly, reflecting on the past is maladaptive if it involves obsessively ruminating about past shortcomings or problems. Indeed a "negative self-form" of reminiscence (i.e., doing it to alleviate boredom or reawakening old feelings of bitterness) is maladaptive

(Cappeliez & O'Rourke, 2006), but reminiscence therapy can be particularly effective if it takes the form of integrative or instrumental reminiscence (see Watt & Cappeliez, 2000). Integrative reminiscence is a non-judgemental way of looking back that emphasizes cognitive reattribution and the consideration of realistic causes of life events that go beyond the self. It focuses on establishing a sense of purpose and meaning in life. To provide an example of integrative reminiscence, Watt and Cappeliez (2000) described a woman who, through integrative reminiscence, learned to attribute her failure to obtain a teaching degree in the 1930s to the economic depression of the era rather than to personal failings. Instrumental reminiscence is remembering past coping responses, such as the plans that were used to address challenging situations, goal-directed activities, and recalling when goals were met. For instance, remembering what you did to fix a flooded basement would reflect instrumental reminiscence.

Emerging evidence suggests that certain antidepressants can be somewhat useful. A longitudinal study conducted over a four-year period in Toronto found that antidepressant medication was highly effective and that 70% of the depressed elderly receiving treatment did not experience a recurrence of their depressions (Flint & Rifat, 2000). Another current treatment investigation found that if antidepressant treatment lasted for 24 months rather than the more typical six to 12 months, only 37% of those taking antidepressants experienced a relapse vs. 68% of those receiving interpersonal therapy (Reynolds et al., 2006). This study suggests that protracted drug treatment may be even more effective. Overall, a contemporary meta-analysis found that antidepressants are more effective than placebos. However, treatment improvements are modest at best and quite varied across studies (Nelson, Delucchi, & Schneider, 2008).

Electroconvulsive therapy (ECT) is back in favour among many geriatric psychiatrists (Hay, 1991), particularly for patients who had an earlier favourable response to it (Janicak, Davis, Preskorn, & Ayd, 1993). ECT does, however, carry significant risks, and it should be considered only when other treatments have not been effective or are contraindicated, or when a rapid response (such as in the case of an acutely suicidal patient) is needed (Zarit & Zarit, 1998).

We now turn to a discussion of anxiety disorders in the elderly. Although depression and anxiety are discussed separately, they are often correlated and comorbid in older people, as they are in younger people. A mixed subtype of depression and anxiety in certain elderly individuals is associated with poor treatment response and higher relapse rates (Flint & Rifat, 1996, 1997; Lynch et al., 2000).

Anxiety Disorders

Anxiety disorders are more prevalent than depression among older adults (Gatz et al., 1996; Wetherell, Gatz, & Craske,

2003). Anxiety disorders in old age can be a continuation or re-emergence of problems experienced earlier in life, or they can develop for the first time in the senior years. Analyses suggest that most anxiety disorders are chronic and developed earlier in life but some older adults develop generalized anxiety disorder and agoraphobia later in life (Andreescu & Varon, 2015). It has been suggested that like depression, *DSM*-defined anxiety disorders appear to be less prevalent among older than among younger adults (Flint, 1994; Kessler et al., 1994). Fuentes and Cox (1997) argued that earlier estimates are too low because they are based on criteria and measures that do not represent core aspects of anxiety in older adults, including the tendency to express anxiety through somatic symptoms. This counterclaim is supported by more recent estimates from a U.S. national study, which found that 7% of adults aged 65 or older met criteria for an anxiety disorder in the previous 12 months (Gum, King-Kallimanis, & Kohn, 2009). Wolitzky-Taylor et al. (2010) concluded that anxiety disorders are relatively common among elderly people with the caveat that they are more prevalent among younger people. Significant risk factors for anxiety disorders in older people include being female, having several chronic medical conditions, not being married, having lower levels of education, having had adverse early childhood experiences, and having elevated neuroticism (Wolitzky-Taylor et al., 2010).

The factors contributing to anxiety in older people are believed to differ and reflect physical differences (i.e., age-related neuropathology) as well as changes in living conditions (i.e., losses and greater isolation) (Andreescu & Varon, 2015). The need to consider how anxiety might be expressed differently among older people is supported by apparent age-related differences in the symptom expression of generalized anxiety disorder. Stanley and Novy (2000) identified a number of differences. First, elderly people report more worries about health and fewer worries about work-related issues than younger people do; worry about health matters was confirmed as the predominant focus in a study of older adults from Quebec (Doucet, Ladouceur, Freeston, & Dugas, 1998), followed by worries about relationships with family members and friends. Second, differences exist in the structure of affect, with elderly people placing less emphasis on feelings of guilt and self-blame. Third, elderly people tend to emphasize the somatic aspects of anxiety rather than the cognitive aspects. Finally, symptoms of anxiety in the elderly may be more closely intertwined with symptoms reflecting sleep difficulties and declines in cognitive capabilities (see Skarborn & Nicki, 1996).

In terms of overall level of worry, a study of worry content across the lifespan assessed participants between the ages of 16 and 74, and the number of worries declined with age (Lindesay et al., 2006). However, worry may fluctuate over time among the elderly. A seven-year longitudinal investigation not only confirmed that the oldest-old (85 years or older) worry mostly about health issues and memory loss, but also found a dramatic age-related increase in the content, frequency, and severity of worry as these people got older (Jenn, Dunkle, & Roberts, 2006).

Scoggin (1998) remarked that post-traumatic stress disorder (PTSD) and acute stress disorder may be especially relevant to the lives of older adults, but have received scant attention from researchers. We noted in Chapter 9 that Beal's (1995) study revealed long-term PTSD in Canadian veterans of the Dieppe raid. PTSD has also been observed in older patients following such trauma as major health crises (Scoggin, 1998). One of the few prevalence studies conducted thus far found PTSD in 0.9% of the elderly and subthreshold PTSD in 13.1%. The strongest predictors of both forms of PTSD were neuroticism and adverse events in early childhood (van Zelst et al., 2003). Another recent study found negligible rates of PTSD in the elderly, but 10% reported re-experiencing trauma symptoms (Creamer & Parslow, 2008).

In general, research on reactions to traumatic stressors tends to yield findings comparable with those obtained with younger people. For instance, when assessed on their reactions to the July 2005 London transit bombings just 11 days after they occurred, the percentage of people aged 65 or older who reported substantial stress (32%) was virtually identical to the proportion of younger people who reported still experiencing substantial stress (31%) (Rubin et al., 2005).

The results from the Canadian Community Health Survey—Mental Health and Well-Being found that Canadian adults who are 55 years or older are relatively less likely to use mental health services. It was found that 20.8% of older adults with an anxiety disorder used services in the previous year vs. 43.1% of older adults with a mood disorder (Scott, Mackenzie, Chipperfield, & Sareen, 2010). The level of mental health service use is even lower among older adults who have an anxiety disorder and a comorbid physical condition (e.g., gastrointestinal disease) (see El-Gabalawy, Mackenzie, & Sareen, 2016).

But when older adults do seek treatment, how do they respond? It seems older adults with anxiety problems respond to the same kinds of psychological treatments found useful with younger adults. For instance, accumulating evidence attests to the value of cognitive behaviour therapy (CBT) in the treatment of generalized anxiety disorder in elderly adults (Ayers, Sorrell, Thorp, & Wetherell, 2007; Stanley et al., 2003; Wetherell, Gatz, & Craske, 2003). CBT consisting of three main components (relaxation training, cognitive therapy, and exposure-based procedures), according to Stanley et al. (2003), is useful for older adults because it is time-limited, symptom-focused, and collaborative.

Because the physician usually hears the psychological complaints of older adults, psychoactive medications are in widespread use. However, potentially dangerous interactions with other drugs, along with the elderly's increased sensitivity to any drug, make anti-anxiety medication a risky intervention (Fisher & Noll, 1996).

Substance-Related Disorders

Substance abuse is less prevalent in today's cohorts of older adults than among younger adults, but it is a problem nonetheless. One reason for the lower prevalence may be increased mortality among those who have abused drugs in the past (Gilhooly & McDonach, 2003). However, many researchers (e.g., Gomberg & Zucker, 1998; Zarit & Zarit, 1998) have predicted all along that as successive cohorts enter old age, the prevalence of substance abuse and dependence in older adults will begin to rise. As we will see below, this seems to be the case. Indeed, alcohol and drug use among older adults is becoming an increasing public health concern (see Satre, 2015).

Alcohol Abuse and Dependence   Historically, it has been assumed that alcohol abuse is less prevalent in older than in younger cohorts, but there are growing indications that problem drinking among older people has been under-recognized. An investigation compared elderly people from the United States and from England; it was found that alcohol misuse is quite prevalent among the elderly and there are cross-nation differences. Lang, Guralnik, Wallace, and Melzer (2007) found in their study of more than 13,000 seniors that 10.8% of U.S. men and 28.6% of English men had more drinks per day than was recommended. Overall, 2.9% of U.S. women and 10.3% of English women exceeded the prescribed threshold. Another team of investigators found that 4.1% of the almost 25,000 older adults assessed were at-risk drinkers (8 to 14 drinks per week) and another 4.5% were heavy drinkers or binge drinkers with 15 or more drinks per week (Kirchner et al., 2007). Heavy drinking was linked with depression, anxiety, and health problems. Another investigation found that 14% of men and 3% of women aged 65 or older reported binge drinking, and binge drinking was associated with the use of tobacco and illicit drugs. In addition, binge drinking among men was linked with being separated, divorced, or widowed (see Blazer & Wu, 2009). A more recent study of alcohol consumption among Canadians aged 55 and older found age-cohort period effects when data gathered in 1994 and 2004 were compared; higher rates of drinking and binge drinking were found among the participants assessed in 2004 (see Moriconi, Nadeau, & Demers, 2012). Binge drinking rates for men and women in 2004 were 44.1% and 15.7% vs. 33.4% and 8.8%, respectively, in 1994. Fortunately, given these percentages, the reported rate of binge drinking was less than once per month.

It might be assumed that problem drinking in older adults is always a continuation of a pattern established earlier in life, but this is not the case. Many problem drinkers begin having alcohol-related problems after the age of 60—so-called late-onset alcoholism. Estimates vary widely, but a review of the literature concluded that between one-third and one-half of those who have drinking problems in old age began their problem drinking after the age of 60 (Liberto, Oslin, & Ruskin, 1996).

As noted, tolerance for alcohol diminishes with age, in part because the ratio of body water to body mass decreases with age, resulting in higher blood-alcohol concentration per unit of alcohol imbibed (Morse, 1988). In addition, older people metabolize alcohol more slowly. Thus, the drug may cause greater changes in brain chemistry and more readily bring on toxic effects, such as delirium, in older people. Several neuropsychological studies have shown that cognitive deficits associated with alcohol abuse, such as memory problems, are likely to be more pronounced in the aged alcoholic than in younger individuals with comparable drinking histories (Brandt, Buffers, Ryan, & Bayoz, 1983). In addition, data indicate that there are age-alcoholism interactions and that a history of alcoholism interacts with older age; MRI tests revealed deficits in the macrostructure and the microstructure of the corpus callosums of elderly people with a history of alcoholism even though they had been abstinent from drinking for at least three months (Pfefferbaum, Adalsteinsson, & Sullivan, 2006). Thus, residual cognitive effects may remain long after the older person has stopped drinking.

Medication Misuse

The misuse of prescription and over-the-counter medicines is a much greater problem than drug or alcohol abuse in the aged population (LaRue et al., 1985) (see photo). Elderly people have a higher overall rate of legal drug intake than any other group; although they constitute only 13% of the population, they consume about one-third of all prescribed medications (Weber, 1996). Older patients use more anti-anxiety medications than any other age group. Rates of benzodiazepine use among community-dwelling older adults have been estimated at 14 to 37%,

Over-the-counter sleep aids can have serious side effects.

Keith Homan/Alamy Stock Photo

while rates among nursing-home residents are thought to be even higher (Wetherell, 1998). Some of this use reflects serious drug abuse. These and other concerns have resulted in the Canadian Pharmacists Association calling for greater involvement of home support workers, since much of the medication misuse occurs in the home. Home support workers can serve as "medication mentors" (Canadian Pharmacists Association, 2004).

Abuse of prescription or legal drugs is often inadvertent but can be deliberate. Some people obtain medications from a number of sources; for example, by going to more than one physician, filling their prescriptions at different pharmacies, and paying cash instead of using credit cards to reduce the chances that their multiple prescriptions will be discovered (Weber, 1996). One study of 141 well-functioning, middle-class older adults living in their own homes found that almost half reported having misused prescription or over-the-counter drugs at least once over a period of six months (Folkman, Bernstein, & Lazarus, 1987).

Older adults may abuse tranquilizers, antidepressants, or sleep aids (see photo) to deal with postoperative pain or the grief and anxiety of losing a loved one. These drugs often create physical as well as psychological dependency. However, because older adults tend not to go to work regularly and may sometimes not even be seen in public for days or weeks at a time, they can hide their abuse for years. The slurred speech and memory problems caused by drugs may be attributed by others to old age and dementia (LaRue et al., 1985), another example of how popular stereotypes can interfere with proper diagnosis and treatment. Said one addiction specialist, "They're not like a 25-year-old mixing it up to get high. . . . They're trying to make a lonely, miserable life less miserable" (Weber, 1996, p. A37). A former Valium addict and now a leader of Pills Anonymous in California stated the problem this way: "Closet junkies, that's what we call them here. They're at home. They're alone. They're afraid. They're just hiding. Their drug pusher is their doctor" (Weber, 1996, p. A37).

Since the current cohort of older adults is not as acculturated as younger people to seeking help for psychological

Radius Images/Getty Images, Inc

Medication misuse, whether deliberate or inadvertent, is a serious problem among older patients and can cause delirium.

problems, including drug problems, many make unsupervised efforts to abstain, sometimes going cold turkey. Doing so can be very dangerous, even life-threatening, because withdrawal reactions place great demands on the cardiovascular system.

Some older addicts end up in places where one doesn't expect to find an older adult.

> *"Her skin itched as if an invisible case of hives were creeping across her flesh. She would shiver, then sweat. She felt suffocated by despair.*
>
> *She was 65, a doctor's wife, a proud grandma with a purseful of photographs. But there she was, curled in a ball like any other junkie at the . . . drug treatment center, sobbing as her body withdrew from a diet of painkillers and tranquilizers.*
>
> *She couldn't believe it had come to this.*
>
> *People her age, the woman said, 'don't associate themselves with the lowlifes [who] sneak into doorways to shoot up. No, they sneak into the bathroom for a pill.'"*
>
> (Weber, 1996, p. A1)

Sleep Disorders

Insomnia is a frequent complaint among older adults. While insomnia can be experienced by people in any age group, we consider it in this chapter because evidence indicates that at least 1 in 5 people aged 65 or older experience insomnia and this is double the rate experienced by younger people (Ohayan, 2002). Indeed, according to Belanger, LeBlanc, and Morin (2012), the prevalence of insomnia goes up steadily as age increases and this was concerned in an epidemiological study conducted with 2,000 Canadians (Morin et al., 2011). Overall, insomnia in the elderly (especially in very late life) is both more frequent and severe than in younger people and is associated with more complications (Lichstein & Morin, 2000). One concern that applies to people of all ages is that the 2011 Canadian survey by Morin et al. (2011) found that while about 1 in 7 Canadians meet all criteria for insomnia (i.e., at least one insomnia symptom for three nights or more per week for at least a month, along with distress and daytime impairment), relatively few people seek professional help. The need for help is indicated by insomnia being linked with lower self-reported levels of physical health and psychological health (Morin et al., 2011).

The most common sleep problems experienced by older adults are waking often at night, frequent early-morning awakenings, difficulty falling asleep, and daytime fatigue (Miles & Dement, 1980). Older adults sleep somewhat less or the same amount of time as younger adults do, but their sleep is also more often spontaneously interrupted; in addition, they take longer to fall back to sleep after awakening (Webb & Campbell, 1980). Thus, older people generally sleep less in relation to the total time they spend in bed at nighttime; they tend to make up for this loss with daytime naps.

Older adults also spend less absolute time in a phase known as rapid eye movement (REM) sleep, and stage 4 sleep—the deepest stage—is virtually absent. Instead, older adults spend more time in light sleep (i.e., stage 1). Older men generally experience more disturbances of their sleep than older women do, a gender difference found to a lesser extent in young adults (Dement, Laughton, & Carskadon, 1981). The sleep problems of older adults must be treated seriously, as the symptoms of chronic insomnia have been found to be associated with higher rates of morbidity and mortality (Neckelmann, 1996).

Causes of Sleep Disorders   In addition to the changes associated with aging, various illnesses, medications, caffeine, stress, anxiety, depression, lack of activity, and poor sleep habits may make insomniacs of older adults. Depressed mood has been shown to be related to sleep disturbances in older adults, especially early-morning awakening (Rodin, McAvay, & Timko, 1988). However, not all geriatric sleep problems should be attributed to depression.

Whatever the cause of insomnia at any age, it is worsened by self-defeating actions such as ruminating over it and counting the number of hours slept and those spent waiting to fall asleep. Sleeping problems can also be worsened by medications that are taken to deal with them.

Sleep apnea is a respiratory disorder in which breathing ceases repeatedly for a period of a few seconds to as long as two minutes as the person sleeps. It seriously disrupts normal sleep and can lead to fatigue, muscle aches, and elevation in blood pressure over a period of time. The disruption in normal breathing is usually due to markedly reduced airflow caused by relaxation-produced obstruction from excess tissue at the back of the throat. These interruptions in breathing can occur upwards of 200 times an hour! Both snoring and sleep apnea increase as people get older (Bliwise, Carskadon, Carey, & Dement, 1984). Reliable diagnosis of sleep apnea requires the person to spend a night in a sleep lab, where various parameters of sleep (e.g., eye movements, respiration, muscle tension) are monitored.

Treatment of Sleep Disorders   Pharmacotherapy is the most common form of treatment for sleep disorders for people of all ages, but this is especially true for the elderly, who receive one-third of the sedatives and hypnotics that are used (Morin, Bastien, Brink, & Brown, 2003). Yet sleep drugs rapidly lose their effectiveness and, with continuous use, may make sleep light and fragmented. REM rebound sleep, an increase in REM sleep after prolonged reliance on drugs, is fitful (Bootzin et al., 2002). Medications can even bring about what is called a drug-dependent insomnia. These so-called aids can also give people drug hangovers and increase respiratory difficulties, which in older adults is a great hazard.

According to a recent review by Morin and Benca (2012), there is strong empirical evidence supporting the use of benzodiazepine-receptor agonists, which they characterized as readily available, and effective in the short term, but long-term management requires more than drug treatment. Indeed, evidence indicates that CBT is an effective long-term treatment for insomnia. Additional information about the influential work of Charles Morin and associates is profiled in Canadian Contributions 16.1.

There is considerable evidence that tranquilizers are not the appropriate treatment for people of any age with chronic insomnia, and particularly not for older people with insomnia. Side effects of tranquilizers such as the benzodiazepines (e.g., Valium) include problems in learning new information and serious difficulties in thinking clearly the day after taking the medication (Ghoneim & Mewaldt, 1990). Nonetheless, historically, tranquilizers have been prescribed for most nursing-home residents, and in many instances, they were administered daily, even sometimes without evidence of a sleep disturbance (Bootzin et al., 1996). Contemporary evidence suggests wide variability among nursing home physicians in attitudes toward these medications, with some indications that there is not enough consideration of risks associated with drug use (see Flick, Garms-Homolova, & Rohnsch, 2012).

Melatonin, a hormone secreted by the pineal gland, plays an important role in regulating sleep and is known to decrease with aging. Thus, it is not surprising that it has been used to treat sleep disorders in older adults and has had some success. Other recommended pharmacological treatments besides melatonin receptor agonists include benzodiazepines and benzodiazepine receptor agonists (see Taylor & Weiss, 2009).

Suicide

Several factors put people in general at especially high risk for suicide: serious physical illness, feelings of hopelessness, social isolation, loss of loved ones, dire financial circumstances, and depression. Because these problems are widespread among older adults, it should not be surprising that adults aged 70 and up have the highest suicide rates in most regions throughout the world (World Health Organization, 2014). According to cohort research by Phillips (2014), these rates of suicide are likely to escalate because there are heightened risk factors among baby boomers and later cohorts.

Older persons are less likely than younger persons to communicate their intentions to commit suicide, and they make fewer attempts (Conwell, 2001). When older people attempt suicide, they use more lethal methods and more often kill themselves (Heisel & Duberstein, 2005; Koponen et al., 2007; Van Orden & Conwell, 2016), so the ratio of attempted to completed suicides for elderly people tends to be much lower than for younger people. According to Pearson and Brown (2000), the ratio of attempted suicides to completed suicides is about 4 to 1 for elderly people, but ranges between 8 to 1 and 20 to 1 for the overall population.

Several factors contribute to this difference. Conwell (2001) mentions such factors as vunerable elderly people having fewer physical reserves (e.g., diminished strength and energy), so they are less likely to survive self-inflicted damage. Also, elderly people are often more socially isolated and less likely to be rescued prior to death. Finally, the suicide acts themselves are more planned and determined in older people and are less impulsive (Heisel, 2006; Heisel & Duberstein, 2005). Unfortunately, the statistics are probably underestimates. Older adults have many opportunities to give up on living, such as by neglecting their diet or medications, thus killing themselves in a more passive fashion. As more and more people live longer, the number of suicides in people over age 65 is almost certain to increase (see Conwell, 2001).

Numerous factors play a role in suicide among the elderly. Conwell (2001) alluded to the role of psychosocial factors. Individual differences in loneliness and feelings of isolation predicted suicide ideation in the elderly in Canadian studies (Mireault & DeMan, 1996; Stravynski & Boyer, 2001).

Heisel, Flett, and Besser (2002) showed that poor cognitive functioning, depression, general hopelessness, and interpersonal hopelessness were predictors of suicide ideation in a sample of seniors from the Toronto area, and they presented a model in which depression and hopelessness mediated the link between poor cognitive functioning and suicide ideation.

Subsequent work led by Marnin Heisel from the University of Western Ontario (see photo) has focused on the possible role of protective factors and has shown that meaning in life is protective against suicide ideation (Heisel & Flett, 2014). Elderly people are also at lower risk to the extent that they endorse more reasons for living; both reasons for living and meaning in life are protective and meaning in life is a factor that mediates the association between reasons for living and reduced suicide ideation (Heisel, Neufeld, & Flett, 2016).

Data also point to completed suicides being tied to feeling like life itself had become a burden and to a palpable sense of loss of self (i.e., no longer feeling like the person you used to be) (see Kjølseth, Ekeberg, & Steihaug, 2010). Interestingly, feeling like a burden tends to have a negative impact on protective factors such as meaning in life (see Van Orden, Bamonti, King, & Duberstein, 2012). Other potential factors of importance such

Canadian Contributions 16.1

Charles Morin and the Treatment of Insomnia in Older Adults

Charles Morin is a professor in the Department of Psychology at Université Laval in Quebec City (see photo). He is the director of the Sleep Disorders Research Centre and he has also served as the president of the Canadian Sleep Society (www.canadiansleepsociety.ca). In 1995, Morin received the American Psychological Association's Distinguished Award for Early Career Contributions in the field of health psychology and he was awarded the Sleep Research Society Distinguished Scientist Award in 2016. Since the late 1980s, Morin and his colleagues have been engaged in a comprehensive program of research on all aspects of sleep disorders. Much of what we know about the nature and psychological treatment of insomnia in elderly adults is due to the impressive efforts of Morin and his colleagues. Most recently, for instance, Morin, Bélanger, et al. (2009) reported the results of a three-year study of adults described as having a diagnosis of insomnia, symptoms of insomnia, or good sleep. Almost half of those with sleep problems had insomnia throughout the entire three-year study. Persistent insomnia was found among those with more severe initial insomnia, among older persons, and among women. In another investigation, Daley, Morin, LeBlanc, Grégoire, and Savard (2009) projected that the annual economic costs of insomnia in Quebec alone totalled $6.6 billion! About $5 billion of the cost came in the form of insomnia-related productivity losses.

In one of their first studies, Morin and Gramling (1989) compared the sleep characteristics and associated factors for older adults with insomnia and without insomnia. The main sleep variable that distinguished those with insomnia from those without was the amount of time awake after sleep onset. This was in keeping with the general situation of older poor sleepers having trouble staying asleep, and with younger poor sleepers having trouble getting to sleep in the first place. Morin and Gramling (1989) also established that poor sleepers had substantially elevated levels of depression and anxiety. The extent of physical illness and medication usage did not distinguish the two groups.

Courtesy of Dr. Charles Morin

Charles Morin of Université Laval has helped uncover much of what we know about the nature and psychological treatment of insomnia in older adults.

Research has focused on pharmacological and psychological treatments for chronic insomnia in older adults. Morin and associates provided incontrovertible evidence that older adults can benefit greatly from behavioural treatment or CBT for their sleep difficulties (Morin et al., 1999; Morin, Vallières, et al., 2009). In fact, these interventions may, in the long run, be superior to drug therapies; medication should be reduced and even eliminated eventually so that improvement is not attributed to the drug (Morin et al., 1999). If so, clients may not invest as much time and energy in the behavioural treatment.

Follow-up analyses of the 1999 data examined predictors of treatment response (see Gagné & Morin, 2001). Treatment response was assessed with subjective self-reports of sleep quality and objective physiological recordings of sleep quality (i.e., polysomnography) based on three nights of laboratory assessment. Poorer treatment outcome was associated with more advanced age and longer duration and greater severity of insomnia.

Morin, Blais, and Savard (2002) also showed that CBT resulted in reductions in dysfunctional attitudes about sleep and that these reductions were linked directly with improvements in sleep efficiency (i.e., the ratio of total sleep time to total time spent in bed) as assessed by daily sleep diaries and polysomnography (e.g., electroencephalographic monitoring). Dysfunctional attitudes were assessed with Morin's (1993) Dysfunctional Beliefs and Attitudes about Sleep (DBAS) Scale. The DBAS assesses five themes: (1) misconceptions about causes of insomnia (e.g., "I believe that insomnia is essentially the result of aging and there isn't much that can be done about this problem"); (2) diminished perception of control and predictability of sleep (e.g., "When I sleep poorly on one night, I know it will disturb my sleep schedule for the whole week"); (3) unrealistic sleep expectations (e.g., "I must get eight hours of sleep to feel refreshed and function well during the day"); (4) misattribution or amplification of the consequences of insomnia (e.g., "I am concerned that chronic insomnia may have serious consequences on my physical health"); and (5) faulty beliefs about sleep-promoting practices (e.g., "When I have trouble sleeping, I should stay in bed and try harder").

Many conclusions about the positive effects of interventions were confirmed by the results of a meta-analytic review by Morin et al. (2006). This analysis surveyed the results of 37 treatment studies between 1998 and 2004. Morin et al. concluded that "psychological and behavioural therapies predict reliable changes in several sleep parameters" (p. 1398) and they suggested that behavioural approaches should be tried first. Overall, they established that five treatments met criteria as empirically supported treatments: cognitive-behavioural therapy, stimulus control therapy, relaxation, paradoxical intention, and sleep restriction.

What's next for Morin? He has an ongoing role in the evaluation of SHUTI, an online CBT intervention for insomnia called "Sleep Healthy Using the Internet" (see Ritterband et al., 2009). He also played a key role as a member of the DSM-5 Work Group for the Sleep Disorders Section. Morin is continuing his personal mission to disseminate therapies and reach those people who have insomnia but have not accessed treatment that can help them with their sleep problems. Morin recognizes the need to translate and share knowledge that contributes to people's lives.

as feelings of mattering to others still need to be explored; the loss of a sense of mattering is likely a core theme for some vulnerable individuals.

Brown, Bongar, and Cleary (2004) asked a sample of 681 practising psychologists with expertise on aging to rate the importance of 36 potential suicide risk factors. Factors deemed of critical importance for suicides by elderly people included a history of suicide attempts, severe hopelessness, the seriousness of previous suicide attempts, depression, isolation, losses and separations, and a family history of suicide.

What about the role of health problems? Several investigators have confirmed a link between physical illness and suicide among the elderly (Duberstein et al., 2004; Erlangsen, Vach, & Jeune, 2005; Koponen et al., 2007). Erlangsen et al. (2005) found that two-thirds of the oldest old had at least one medical hospitalization within the previous two years and medical hospitalization was particularly evident among women who killed themselves. A 15-year study of suicide in Finland confirmed that suicides among the elderly were associated with more violent means of committing suicide and that alcohol was more likely to be involved. In addition, they found that the suicidal elders, relative to younger people, had a higher prevalence of physical illness and depressive episodes.

Unfortunately, only a small number of suicidal elderly people actually seek help from a mental health professional. About 70% of those who commit suicide had visited their physician sometime during the month prior to committing suicide, but their profound depression and despair often goes undetected (see Pearson & Brown, 2000). A Quebec study found that 53% of those who committed suicide had visited their physician in the two weeks prior to their suicide (see Preville et al., 2005). As a result, it has been strongly suggested that, in primary care settings, doctors should conduct routine screenings for depression and suicidal tendencies when assessing their elderly patients. The utility of screening and intervention at the primary care level was illustrated by the substantial reductions in suicide ideation and depression among elderly medical patients who took part in a comprehensive study known as the PROSPECT Study (see Alexopoulos et al., 2009). In part, the greater benefits were simply the result of having greater access to psychotherapy and antidepressants compared with those who received care as usual.

Clearly, the elderly are neglected when it comes to suicide prevention, and in their review paper, Heisel and Duberstein (2005) were critical of the lack of training and knowledge in general, but especially when it comes to suicide in the elderly. One approach being evaluated is an initiative led by Marnin Heisel that is funded by the Movember Canada Mental Health Fund. Men facing retirement participate weekly in meaning-centred men's groups to discuss common issues and increase their social connectedness in ways that should enhance levels of personal resilience (Heisel & the Meaning-Centered Men's Group Project Team, 2016).

16.4 Treatment and Care of Older Adults

Older people in Canada are typically less likely than younger adults to receive adequate psychological treatment and care. We now explore the various factors that contribute to this unfortunate situation.

Treatment of Older Adults

Older adults sometimes go to mental health centres or seek private psychotherapy through referrals. Yet older people are less likely than younger adults to be referred (Knight, 2004), which could be a reflection of the attitudes uncovered in the Kingston, Ontario study described at the start of this chapter. One problem is that general practitioners usually fail to detect depression in older patients (Bowers, Jorm, Henderson, & Harris, 1990). This situation may be due in part to inadequate geriatric training for medical professionals.

Clinicians tend to expect less success in treating older people than in treating young people (Knight, 2004; Settin, 1982). In one study, therapists in Canada and the United States were provided with descriptions of people of various ages with personality disorders requiring treatment (Zivian et al., 1992). The results showed that therapists overwhelmingly preferred to provide treatment to middle-aged and younger adults than to the elderly. Psychotherapists were less likely to respond this way if they themselves were older, had taken three or more professional courses focusing on older adults, or had practices in which at least 1 in 10 of their clients was 65 or older.

The views of psychotherapists are paralleled by equally negative views of the elderly endorsed by people in the general population. The same team of researchers assessed public opinions of psychotherapy for the elderly in a large sample of visitors to the Ontario Science Centre in Toronto (see Zivian et al., 1994). The respondents were presented with the same scenarios used in the previous study and were asked to evaluate the value of psychotherapy if provided to the target people in the scenarios. Zivian et al. found that older people were seen as less likely to benefit from psychotherapy; they also found that this negative view was especially pronounced among the older people in the sample.

These findings have emerged even though, as we noted earlier, research does not show that psychotherapy is less successful for older clients (Gallagher-Thompson & Thompson, 1995a, 1995b; Knight, 2004; Knight, Kelly, & Gatz, 1992; Scoggin & McElreath, 1994). If older clients are viewed as having limited possibilities for improvement, they may not be treated. Admissions of older adults to mental hospitals and to psychiatric units of general hospitals have decreased substantially in recent years owing to changes in mental health policy in most provinces and territories.

Nursing and Home Care

Older people needing mental health treatment typically live in nursing homes or receive community-based care. There have been significant and ongoing concerns about the quality of care in nursing homes and this has been exacerbated by some horrific stories of abuse and neglect of elderly people, including a number of recent cases in Canada (see photo).

Many older people wish to stay at home as long as possible. The Health Council of Canada (2012) reported that 93% of Canadian seniors live at home and want to stay there as long as they can. According to a recent report compiled for Statistics Canada, in 2012, about 2.2 million people (about 8% of Canadians who are 15 years or older) received help at home for a long-term condition (typically a health condition) but there were another 461,000 individuals who had a need for home care but did not receive it at all and 15% of those who did receive home care only received partial care (Turcotte, 2014). This report also established that those people with partially or totally unmet needs have elevated levels of stress, distress, and loneliness.

Nursing homes play a major role in the institutional care of the aged. They have often been criticized for the poor care they provide, as well as for the lack of stimulation in the environment.

Home care is essential for a certain portion of our elderly population. It is discussed in more detail in Canadian Perspectives 16.2.

Canadian Perspectives 16.2

Home Care in Canada

In a policy statement, the Canadian Association on Gerontology (CAG, 1999) decried the fact that Canada does not have a universally accessible, comprehensive home care policy or program. Each province has a different approach to home care delivery (see Romanow & Marchildon, 2003; Woodward, Abelson, Tedford, & Hutchison, 2004). Should home care be a vital part of a comprehensive health care system? Home care is more affordable than residential care at all levels of need (Hollander & Chappell, 2007). A strong case has been made for the benefits of integrated care that would include home care supplemented by some facility care (see Hollander et al., 2009). Roy Romanow, who led the Commission on the Future of Health Care in Canada, concluded that integrated home care should definitely be expanded to include mental health services (Romanow & Marchildon, 2003).

A key group in this effort is the Canadian Association of Retired Persons (CARP), a national, non-partisan organization for Canadians aged 50 or older (www.carp.ca). CARP conducted a national survey of 300 organizations involved in home care. The results were summarized in the report *Home Care by Default, Not by Design* (Parent & Anderson, 2001). CARP's "report card" concluded that home care in Canada is a system by default, and the organization reiterated previous calls for a national strategy, national standards, and a common national definition of home care. Failure to do so means that many Canadians simply cannot cope. This became evident when, as part of the release of a 2012 Health Council of Canada report, Judy Southon went public with her story by participating in a podcast with other caregivers (www.healthcouncilcanada.ca/rpt_det_gen.php?id=348) (see photo). She tried for two years to take care of her husband Vic, who was diagnosed with dementia in 2007, while trying to keep her contract job at a bank in Toronto. She eventually had to put her husband in a long-term care facility, where he died

Since this life journey of caring for her husband, Judy Southon is now a Licensed Spiritual Practitioner and an Officiant at Memorial Services. She is asked to speak to families and volunteers about person-centred dementia care. This photo was taken at a Toronto Long Term Care Home where she is still a volunteer years after her husband passed away.

in September 2012. When her husband was at home, Judy received a couple of hours of help per week from caregivers. What toll did it take on Judy? She recounted that, "My evenings, my weekends, and all those other times when the caregivers weren't there, they were all devoted to him. . . It was work and then take care of him. I felt trapped. . . I felt inconsolably sad for him, but it had to be done or I would fall sick too" (McIlroy & Baluja, 2012, A7).

The Health Council of Canada (2012) concluded that many seniors with complex needs are not receiving the extent of home care that they need. Specifically, one-third of home care recipients have high needs but receive only a few extra hours of care per week, relative to people with less severe needs. And the result, according to the Health Council of Canada, is that family caregivers

(continued)

of high-needs seniors are at "the breaking point," as illustrated by Judy Southon's story.

So, who is most likely to receive home care? Results from the Canadian Community Health Survey show that women were more likely than men to receive home care (Carrière, 2003). Home care was more likely for those who lived alone, who were almost two times more likely to receive home care than those who lived with another person. Those who lived alone were also more likely to have been hospitalized within the previous year and they more often had a chronic medical condition. Home care also increased with age, with 42% of those 85 years or older receiving home care (vs. 8% of those 65 to 74 years old and 20% of those 75 to 84 years old) (also see Martens et al. 2007).

A recent study conducted in Ontario found once again that women were more likely than men to receive home care, but, as a group, the men who received home care were much more in need. Men were more likely to have chronic conditions and experience impairment. Women who were caregivers for their husbands reported distress twice as often as men who were caregivers for their wives (Gruneir et al., 2013).

Will Canada commit the resources needed to enhance the degree and quality of home care? Going forward, the Health Council of Canada (2012) made several key recommendations as part of its report:

- Recognize that home care has become an integral cornerstone of the health system.
- Provide ongoing support for family caregivers and immediate relief for those in distress.
- Adapt or expand what is already working.
- Consider new home care options before making new investments in long-term care facilities.

Thinking Critically

1. Do you think that home care should be available as part of medicare in Canada? Should every citizen have access?

2. What criteria should be used to determine access? Would all elderly people with dementia be eligible? Would adults with intellectual disability living in their own homes receive home care? What about people with chronic schizophrenia living on their own?

3. Should means testing and cost sharing (to require financial contributions from those who can afford them) be a part of the home care system everywhere in Canada? Should all services be privatized?

Alternative Living Settings

Recently, the United States and Canada have seen a dramatic rise in assisted-living or retirement homes, a viable alternative to placement in nursing homes for many older adults who require assistance of one sort or another. The American Association of Retired Persons (AARP) reports that assisted living is the fastest-growing category of housing for older adults in the United States (AARP, 1999). In contrast to nursing homes, assisted-living facilities resemble hotels, with separate rooms and suites for the residents, as well as dining rooms and on-site amenities such as beauty and barber shops. The philosophy of assisted living stresses autonomy, independence, dignity, and privacy (AARP, 1999). Many such residences are quite luxurious, with attentive staff, nursing and medical assistance readily available, daily activities such as bingo and movies, and other services all designed to provide assisted care for older adults too infirm to live on their own but not so infirm as to require a nursing home. However, as with nursing homes, there is a great deal of variability in the quality of care.

16.5   Issues Specific to Therapy with Older Adults

Treatment interventions for the elderly need to recognize the special needs and unique challenges encountered by elderly people and how these may change with development throughout the aging process. The need to acknowledge

the unique challenges was shown formally in 2003 when the American Psychological Association (2003) outlined 20 guidelines in its document *Guidelines for Psychological Practice with Older Adults.* Guidelines were agreed upon in six distinct areas: (1) attitudes; (2) general knowledge about adult development, aging, and older adults; (3) clinical issues; (4) assessment; (5) intervention, consultation, and other service provision; and (6) education. In other words, unique issues need to be considered in terms of all aspects of the treatment process. In Canada, national guidelines for the assessment and treatment of seniors' mental health were published in 2006 in the *Canadian Journal of Geriatrics.* These guidelines were put together by the Canadian Coalition for Seniors' Mental Health. The initial series of guidelines for seniors' mental health address (1) the assessment and treatment of delirium, (2) the assessment and treatment of depression, (3) the assessment of suicide risk and the prevention of suicide, and (4) the assessment and treatment of mental health issues in long-term care homes.

The list of guidelines from the APA is too lengthy to reproduce in its entirety due to space limitations. Table 16.3 provides illustrative guidelines in each of the six areas outlined above.

It is important that we consider in more detail some other issues concerning the conduct of therapy for older people. They can be divided into issues of content and issues of process (Zarit, 1980).

Content of Therapy

The incidence of brain disorders increases with age, but other mental health problems of older adults are not that different

TABLE 16.3	Illustrative Guidelines Provided by the American Psychological Association for Psychological Practice with Older Adults

Guideline 2—Psychologists are encouraged to recognize how their attitudes and beliefs about aging and about older individuals may be relevant to their assessment and treatment of older adults, and to seek consultation or further education about these issues when indicated.

Guideline 6—Psychologists strive to be familiar with current information about biological and health-related aspects of aging.

Guideline 9—Psychologists strive to be knowledgeable about psychopathology within the aging population and cognizant of the prevalence and nature of that psychopathology when providing services to older adults.

Guideline 10—Psychologists strive to be familiar with the theory, research, and practice of various methods of assessment with older adults, and knowledgeable of assessment instruments that are psychometrically suitable for use with them.

Guideline 14—Psychologists strive to be familiar with and develop skills in applying specific psychotherapeutic interventions and environmental modifications with older adults and their families, including adapting interventions for use with this age group.

Guideline 20—Psychologists are encouraged to increase their knowledge, understanding, and skills with respect to working with older adults through continuing education, training, supervision, and consultation.

from those experienced earlier in life. Although clinicians should appreciate how physical incapacities and medications may intensify psychological problems, they should also note the importance of consistency and continuity from earlier decades of the older person's life.

For older people, medical illnesses can create irreversible difficulties in walking, seeing, and hearing. Finances may be a problem. Therapists treating psychological distress in older adults must bear in mind that much of it is an understandable response to real-life challenges rather than a sign of psychopathology. Professional intervention, however, may still be helpful.

Therapy with older adults must take into account the social contexts in which they live, something that cannot be accomplished merely by reading the professional literature. The therapist who, for example, urges a lonely widower to seek companionship in a neighbourhood recreation centre for senior citizens may be misguided if the centre is not suited to the particular patient (Knight, 2004); this could make the patient feel even lonelier. All social organizations, even those as loosely structured as a senior centre, develop their own local mores and practices, or what social scientists have come to call social ecology. Some organizations may be tolerant of physical frailty, others not. Mental health care workers need to know and understand the social environments in which their older patients live. We take this need for granted when dealing with younger patients but, Knight points out, often neglect to consider it with older adults.

The social needs of older people often differ from those of younger people. The widespread concern that old people are socially isolated and need to be encouraged to interact more with others appears to be ill-founded. There is no link between level of social activity and psychological well-being among old people (Carstensen, 1996). As we age, our interests shift away from seeking new social interactions to cultivating those few social relationships that really matter to us, such as those with family and with close friends and associates.

Death and dying figure prominently in therapy with older people. They may need help dealing with the fear of facing death or an illness that requires life support. It may be helpful to counsel some older clients to examine their lives from a philosophical or a religious perspective. These perspectives may help them transcend the limitations that aging imposes on human existence. When the person is dying, discussions of the meaning of the individual's life can facilitate self-disclosure and enhance his or her sense of well-being and personal growth (see the previous discussions of life review). The person's loved ones may also benefit from such discussions.

Process of Therapy

We have already indicated that traditional individual, group, family, and marital therapies are effective with older adults (Gatz, Popkin, Pino, & VandenBos, 1985). Some clinicians adapt these therapies to here-and-now practical problems. They hold that therapy with older people needs to be more active and directive, and thus they provide information and take the initiative in seeking out agencies for necessary services.

Some characteristics of aging may mean that therapy will proceed differently (Knight, 2004). Certain kinds of thinking simply take longer for many older people. Older people also tend to experience some diminution in the number of things that can be held in mind at any one time. Therapists may find that it helps to move with greater deliberation when seeing an older adult. Explanations may have to be more elaborate and conversation more extended.

The very process of being in therapy can foster dependency. Older adults, whether institutionalized or living at home with caregivers, often receive much more social reinforcement (attention, praise) for dependent behaviours, such as asking for help or being concerned about the opinion of their therapist, than for instances of independent functioning (Baltes, 1988). The growing specialization of behavioural gerontology (Nemeroff & Karoly, 1991) emphasizes helping older people to enhance their self-esteem by focusing on specific, deceptively minor behaviours, such as controlling their toileting better, increasing their self-care and mobility, and improving their telephone conversational skills in order to enhance social contacts. One development, though hardly a formal therapy, involves teaching older adults computer skills so that they can access the Internet and expand their social contacts (Cody, Dunn, Hoppin, & Wendt, 1999) (see photo).

Being able to use a computer and access the Internet is one way older adults can increase their social contacts.

All therapists must be able to interpret the facial expressions of their clients and thereby understand the meaning of their words or reactions and appreciate their phenomenological experience of the world. Research on emotional changes over the lifespan suggests real potential for error when the therapist is younger than the client (Knight, 2004). Knight has maintained that his older clients are less emotionally expressive and they use more subtle forms of emotional expression. To what extent will a younger therapist be sensitive to these emotional cues?

We will conclude with a statement on the overall amount and quality of care available to seniors in Canada. This statement was made several years ago but still seems to apply. In its position paper on the delivery of mental health services to elderly people, the Canadian Association on Gerontology (CAG) (2000) stated: "The current range of community services are inadequate and insufficient to meet the needs of older mental health clients, but no money to expand or improve community services seems immediately forthcoming." In particular, there is a lack of focus on prevention, and too much of the current funding and available treatment is medically driven, even though, as the CAG notes, many issues facing the elderly are non-medical in nature. Given the increasing proportion of the population that will be elderly in the years to come, this is a problem deserving of more attention at the national level. It is also important to conduct rigorous scientific evaluations of preventive and treatment programs (see Canadian Perspectives 16.3).

Canadian Perspectives 16.3

PRISMA: An Integrated Preventive Project for the Frail Elderly at Risk of Functional Decline

The province of Quebec is the location of an innovative project designed to promote the well-being and autonomy of frail elderly. This program is known as PRISMA (Program of Research to Integrate the Services for the Maintenance of Autonomy). It is a clear example of how clinical resources can be combined for maximum impact and be evaluated by research that determines the impact of clinical interventions. It is in keeping with increasing calls for integrated care (e.g., Hollander et al., 2009). PRISMA has been led by Dr. Réjean Hébert, who heads a team of 14 other researchers. Hébert is the founding scientific director of the Canadian Institutes of Health Research — Institute of Aging. Hébert is also the public spokesperson for PRISMA (see Health Council of Canada podcast; http://healthcouncilcanada.ca/rpt_det.php?id=352).

What is unique about PRISMA? According to MacAdam (2015), PRISMA is "the only evaluated international model of a coordination approach to integration and one of the few, if not the only, integration model to have been adopted at the system level by policy-makers" (p. 1).

In an earlier study, Hébert and his colleagues determined that the annual incidence of functional decline in individuals over 75 years of age who are living at home is almost 12% (Hébert, Brayne, & Spiegelhalter, 1997). The prevalence of disabilities is approximately 80% in people in Quebec over age 85 (Saucier, 1992). Can early detection of elderly individuals at risk of losing their autonomy and the application of an assessment and surveillance program prevent or delay functional decline?

The PRISMA project is an integrated, client-centred effort that relies on extraordinary coordination of services (see Hébert, Durand, Dubuc, Tourigny, & The PRISMA Group, 2003). It is based on an integrated service delivery model. PRISMA is composed of four integrated care mechanisms and two assessment tools. The PRISMA model is outlined in Figure 16.1. The four care mechanisms are (1) coordination between decision-makers at the regional and local levels, (2) a single entry point for accessing the services, (3) a case management process, and (4) individualized service plans. Service plans stem from the overall assessment of the person. It is formulated by the case manager in consultation with all other parties involved in the older person's care.

The two tools are (1) an assessment instrument that is combined with a management system to measure a person's functional autonomy and (2) a computerized clinical chart to keep track of progress and ease communication between institutions and treatment providers. The assessment instrument is a universally recognized measure that was created by Hébert. The Functional Autonomy Measurement System is a 29-item rating scale based on how disabilities are described by the World Health Organization. It taps the elderly person's ability to function in five categories: (1) activities of daily living, (2) mobility, (3) communication, (4) mental functions, and (5) instrumental activities of daily living.

Results from the PRISMA project are promising. Hébert et al. (2010) analyzed the results for more than 1,500 people at risk of functional decline, half of whom were part of PRISMA. Overall, the involvement in PRISMA was successful and resulted not only in higher levels of satisfaction and empowerment, but also 137 fewer cases of functional decline per 1,000 people.

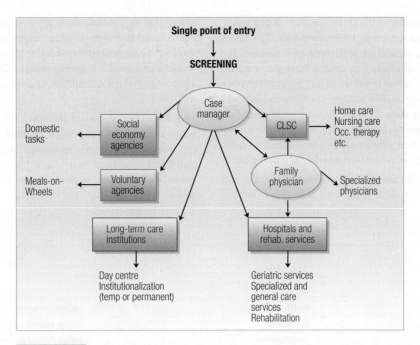

FIGURE 16.1 The PRISMA model of an integrated service delivery system. A CLSC is a "Centre local de services communautaires" (community service centre).

Comment

The PRISMA project is obviously unique in several respects. It was included here not only because it is novel and was developed in Canada, but also because it illustrates the benefits of an expanded approach that includes a range of clinical resources that are located at several sites but integrated in the treatment of a particular person.

The members of the PRISMA project have noted that this endeavour is unusual because it involves an extraordinary degree of contact and coordination among the various members. Is this integrated service delivery model realistic in areas that lack financial resources and necessary sources of "human capital"? On the surface, PRISMA seems to represent a model of how resources should be combined to maximize the well-being of individuals, but

it remains to be determined whether similar programs can be put together in other jurisdictions.

Just how effective is PRISMA? A recent independent evaluation was conducted and the reviewers concluded that it is effective in that it decreases clients' levels of functional decline and it improves client satisfaction and feelings of health care empowerment. It was concluded that similar "programs of integrated care should be strongly considered by governments and policy-makers" (Stewart, Georgiou, & Westbrook, 2013, p.11). However, MacAdam (2015) has noted that there is still room for improvement and that future challenges include reducing the unmet needs for case management and home care services, and finding more incentives so that a greater number of physicians will participate in planning care for patients.

Summary

16.1 Until recently, the psychological problems of older people were neglected by mental health researchers and professionals. When age differences are found, interpretation can be complex because researchers must consider whether the differences are due to age or cohort differences. The approach to assessment must be nuanced, and ideally, levels of cognitive functioning should be assessed and measures designed specifically for older people should be used whenever possible.

16.2 Serious brain disorders affect a small minority of older people—fewer than 10%. Two principal disorders have been distinguished: dementia and delirium. In dementia, the person's intellectual functioning declines; memory, abstract thinking, and judgement deteriorate. If the dementia is progressive, as most cases are, the individual seems another person altogether and is, in the end, oblivious to his

or her surroundings. A variety of diseases can cause this deterioration. The most important is Alzheimer's disease, a progressive, irreversible illness in which cortical cells waste away. Genes figure prominently in the etiology of Alzheimer's, particularly the early-onset forms. Head injury and depression are also risk factors. In delirium, there is sudden clouding of consciousness and other problems in thinking, feeling, and behaving—fragmented and undirected thought, incoherent speech, inability to sustain attention, hallucinations, illusions, disorientation, lethargy or hyperactivity, and mood swings. The condition is reversible, provided that the underlying cause is self-limiting or adequately treated. Brain cells malfunction but are not necessarily destroyed. Causes include overmedication, infection of brain tissue, high fevers, malnutrition, dehydration, endocrine disorders, head trauma, cerebrovascular problems, and surgery.

16.3 Older people may experience the entire spectrum of psychological disorders, in many instances brought with them from their earlier years. Yet it appears that, overall, the prevalence of depression and anxiety is lower among older adults than among those younger than 65. The newer cognitive behaviour therapies as well as various psychodynamic therapies are being applied to depression in older patients, and results are encouraging. More of the suicide attempts of old people result in death than do those of younger people. Mental health professionals may assume that people who are old and debilitated have nothing to live for. This attitude may reflect their own fear of growing old.

16.4 Many older people can benefit from psychotherapy, but several issues specific to treating older adults need to be kept in mind to ensure that they receive adequate psychological treatment and care. The emotional distress of older adults is often realistic in content. Many have experienced irreplaceable losses and face real medical and financial problems. It is unwise always to attribute their complaints to a psychopathological condition. Death can be a more salient issue as well.

16.5 As for the process of therapy, clinicians should sometimes be active and directive, providing information and seeking out the agencies that provide the services needed by their clients. Therapy should also foster a sense of control and hope and should help the older patient elucidate a sense of meaning as he or she approaches the end of life.

Key Terms

age effects	delirium	selective mortality
ageism	dementia	sleep apnea
Alzheimer's disease	longitudinal studies	subjective age bias
cognitive reserve hypothesis	neurofibrillary tangles	time-of-measurement effects
cohort effects	paraphrenia	
cross-sectional studies	plaques	

Reflections: Past, Present, and Future

1. Are Canada's economic, social, and medical resources sufficient to provide for the coming dramatic increase in the population of elderly people? Are we facing a caregiving crisis in the future? What can the people of Canada and different levels of government do to prepare for the aging of the Canadian population?

2. If you were consulted by the federal, provincial, and territorial governments about how they might best cope with the increase in disorders of the elderly owing to the aging of the Canadian population, what would you advise them to do? Why?

3. A leading American neurologist and ethicist, Dr. Ron Crawford, has suggested that people with Alzheimer's disease should have the right to choose to die rather than be required to live with the possibility that they will become a burden on their families (Vienneau, 1999). However, Dr. Margaret Somerville, director of McGill University's Centre for Medicine, Ethics and Law, is appalled by Crawford's ideas: "Despite its overlay of empathy, it is a 'gene machine' approach to human life. It focuses on cognitive, neural processes as identifying us as human . . . and when these are absent we should be disposed of" (Vienneau, 1999, p. L8). Crawford believes that his own position is ahead of its time and "pushes the moral envelope," but he believes that it is "the reality of what we are going to have to face" in the future (Vienneau, 1999, p. L8). What is your own position on this controversial issue? Refer to Chapter 8 if you need more background information on the right to die issue.

4. In 1999, the year dedicated to the elderly by the United Nations, Pope John Paul II, who suffered from Parkinson's disease, decried the fact that some cultures cherished the elderly, whereas other cultures seemed to dismiss them as disposable items (Reuters, 1999). What is the situation in your own culture? Are the elderly "cherished" or "disposable"?

CHAPTER 17

Outcomes and Issues in Psychological Intervention

LEARNING OBJECTIVES

1. Describe client factors, therapist factors, and client–therapist relationship factors that influence psychotherapy outcomes.

2. Explain the general issues in evaluating psychotherapy research.

3. Describe and evaluate behavioural and cognitive therapies.

4. Describe and evaluate psychoanalytic therapies.

5. Describe and evaluate client-centred therapy.

6. Describe and evaluate couples therapy.

7. Describe the different forms of psychotherapy integration.

8. Explain how contemporary developments in treatment and intervention are intended to address challenges in providing psychological services.

Brief Case Example

Confronting the Past

THERAPY FOCUSED on a client with multiple presenting concerns, including major depression, anxiety disorder, and interpersonal problems overcoming her core maladaptive fear by accessing her sadness at loss and anger at violation, and mobilizing her current abilities to protect herself. . . . Having spent the first three sessions establishing an empathic bond the therapy first focused on her primary fear of her abusive parents and her fear of her dependence/weakness and vulnerability. Her frequent experiences of shame and embarrassment in therapy were often mixed with her fear. Her parents had disciplined her with harsh criticism and ridicule, as well as physical abuse, and she stated that her greatest pain was that "they never believed in me." She was called stupid, crazy, a whore, and a slut and grew up utterly paralyzed in interpersonal relationships. Interventions were aimed at [her] becoming aware of and accessing her fear and shame in the session by talking about her childhood. This led to [her] experiencing and reprocessing these emotions and to a strengthening of her sense of self.

One of her earliest memories was of her father forcing her and her siblings to watch him drown a litter of kittens. This was to "teach her a lesson about life" and the client believed he enjoyed it. The client accessed a core self-organization, which included her "suppressed scream of horror" from this experience. While [she] imaginally reliv[ed] this scene in therapy the therapist guided her attention to the expression of disgust in her mouth while she was feeling afraid. This mobilized this sub-dominant adaptive emotion as a resource to begin building a stronger sense of self. Rather than feeling afraid she accessed her alternate emotions of disgust and anger, which she actively expressed toward her father in an empty chair. She mobilized her adaptive needs to not be violated by her father and to be protected by her mother and expressed these to her parent in the empty chair dialogues. Expression and exploration of her vulnerability (fear and sadness) took place, not to the imagined father, but in the affirming and safe dialogue with the therapist. . . . These imaginary confrontations with the father evoked her fear and her painful memories of childhood beatings, of being told she was bad, and of being aware

(continued)

of nothing but her desperate need to escape. . . . Her anger undid her fear and the therapist supported the client's newfound sense of power, heightening her awareness of her strengths. This motivated further assertion and self-validation. The client acknowledged that she was worthy and had deserved more than

she got from her parents. She began to create a new identity narrative, one in which she was worthy and had unfairly suffered abuse at the hands of cruel parents. She also began to feel that it would be possible to need love and she was now open to learn love. (Greenberg, 2004, pp. 13–14)

The Brief Case Example illustrates how people requiring treatment often have very complex concerns and idiosyncratic experiences that require an equally complex and multi-faceted intervention in a supportive therapeutic environment. The client described in this example received emotion-focused therapy, a form of treatment described later in this chapter.

Chapter 17 opens with a discussion of key themes and issues that contribute to these complexities. We discuss such issues as the key roles played by the client's expectations and motives, as well as the need to consider differences among clients in their personality styles. Differences related to the therapist are also discussed as well as how the therapeutic relationship influences the quality of the bond between the therapist and client.

Next, we evaluate the effectiveness of various therapies. In Chapter 2, we outlined the major approaches to therapeutic intervention, and in Chapters 5 through 16, we reviewed how these approaches have treated various psychopathologies. A major component of this chapter is a critical appraisal of a number of psychological interventions. We discuss the research on their effectiveness as well as offer some general comments and identify some key issues and themes that should further enrich your understanding of the complexities of psychotherapy. Chapter 17 concludes with a discussion of contemporary developments in the delivery of services. We focus our attention primarily on the use of technology in the delivery of psychotherapy.

how to structure and frame treatment. Clients differ not only in terms of their personal histories and types of dysfunction, but also in other key ways related to their expectancies, goals, and motives and associated personality styles. Failure to take these differences into account could arguably undermine the potential effectiveness of whatever therapeutic orientation is implemented.

Client Therapy Outcome Expectations

Frank and Frank (1985) advanced the **demoralization hypothesis** as an explanation for when clients will seek therapy. They suggested that clients seek help not just because of their symptoms. The symptoms are accompanied by a state of demoralization that includes feelings of alienation, helplessness, hopelessness, loss of self-esteem, and subjective feelings of incompetence. Frank (1974) has argued that the key therapeutic task is to restore a sense of morale by instilling a renewed sense of mastery. Once a sense of mastery is in place, then hope will follow.

Kuyken (2004) established the importance of outcome expectancies by showing in a naturalistic study of 122 people diagnosed with major depression that non-responsiveness hopelessness predicted negative therapy outcomes following cognitive-behavioural therapy (CBT). In keeping with the views of Frank (1974), Kuyken identified "remoralization" as a key first step in improvement, for it was those who were able to become lower in hopelessness who improved.

The opposite of hopelessness, of course, is hope. Snyder and his associates have outlined a two-factor theory of hope reflecting their contention that hope is the key to the success of CBT interventions (see Snyder, Ilardi, Michael, & Cheavens, 2000). The two components—agency (i.e., the will or belief

17.1   Client, Therapist, and Client–Therapist Factors That Influence Therapy Outcome

We begin with a discussion of some factors that often influence the course and the effectiveness of treatment. The various types of factors are summarized in Table 17.1. Here we can see that the range of factors includes client factors (including the role of certain types of disorder and dysfunction), therapist factors, and factors involving the client–therapist relationship.

Client Factors That Influence Therapy Outcomes

Regarding the client factors, clearly, any therapist must remain cognizant of the client's unique features when determining

TABLE 17.1   Predictors of Therapy Outcome
Client Factors
Therapy outcome beliefs (i.e., hope vs. hopelessness)
Client personality (e.g., secure vs. insecure attachment style)
Motivation for change
Type and severity of dysfunction
Therapist Factors
Personal qualities of the therapist (e.g., therapist attachment style)
Therapist experience, training, and competence
Client–Therapist Relationship Factors
Match between the client and therapist (e.g., personality compatibility, goals and expectations)
Therapeutic working alliance

component) and pathways (i.e., specific ways to make the hoped-for outcomes be realized)—are both key elements of hope therapy. Support for this conceptualization was provided by Irving et al. (2004). They assigned clients to either a wait-list control group or motivational orientation group and then all clients received 12 weeks of individual therapy. Higher hope at the start of the study was associated subsequently with greater well-being, fewer symptoms, and better functioning and coping. Also, clients with higher levels of hope in the motivational group rated the group as much more helpful. Another investigation of more than 3,000 adolescents tracked levels of hopefulness and confirmed that adolescents who reported greater hopefulness over time had fewer problems and greater adaptive functioning at follow-up (Weis & Ash, 2009).

An intriguing qualitative study conducted in Alberta by Larsen and Stege (2012) examined client accounts of hope in order to illuminate the various ways that hope can contribute to positive therapy outcomes. Key factors associated with hope included developing a hopeful self-identity and fostering a new self-awareness and a greater sense of self-acceptance. Hope also promoted a more salient future focus and recognition of future possibilities, and also contributed positively to cognitive reappraisal and cognitive reframing. Consider, for instance, how reframing changed one client's view of retirement. His therapist talked about life issues using the metaphor of being in the third quarter of a football game and there is still the fourth quarter to play. This resulted in the following enthusiastic client response:

> "That's hope. Hope. She's giving me hope. It's not the end of the world for God's sake. There's still a lot of work ahead of us, that we can still do. . . and that's inspirational, hopeful. . . I will have a different attitude because of that."
>
> (Larsen & Stege, 2012, p. 51)

The instillation of such hope is most likely to be beneficial when it leads to a generalized improvement in outlook such as would be the case in this instance.

An interesting ethical issue arises: Should psychotherapists provide hope when clients have tried several treatments unsuccessfully? Dembo and Clemens (2013) reviewed the ethics. In general, in medicine, it is not ethical to provide hope to patients if their medical situation does not warrant it. In other words, it is not acceptable to provide false hope. However, Dembo and Clemens (2013) concluded that psychiatric care is an exception; it is ethical to encourage hope, given that encouraging hope may lead to better outcomes. This conclusion has been supported by recent data on treatment-resistant depression. Abel, Hayes, Henley, and Kuyken (in press) had raters review video files of client sessions and rate them on levels of client hope. They used the following definition: "Hope is the extent to which the person expresses a commitment to change and an expectation that the future will be better and that progress can be made on problem areas" (Abel et al., in press, p. 4). Greater hope early

on, as observed and rated by the coders when watching the sessions, was related to less depression at follow-up.

Although the link between hope and outcome is strongly supported, even in cases of treatment-resistant depression, there are instances of unrealistic hope that can arise in psychotherapy. Returning to the work of Larsen and colleagues in Alberta (Larsen, Stege, Edey, & Ewasiw, 2014), they outline ways to work with unrealistic hope, which they prefer to call unshared hope. For example, they suggest using the CBT strategy of examining the evidence for and against hopeful thinking.

The role of positive expectancies is now widely acknowledged (see Greenberg, Constantino, & Bruce, 2006). More fine-grained analyses are being conducted by Constantino and his colleagues to identify client characteristics that influence positive vs. negative expectations of psychotherapeutic change (see Constantino, Ametrano, & Greenberg, 2012; Constantino, Penek, Bernecker, & Overtree, 2014).

Moreover, the importance of addressing outcome expectancies explicitly has been increasing (Constantino, 2012; Swift & Derthick, 2013). Swift and Derthick (2013) outlined five techniques for increasing treatment expectancies among clients:

1. Present a strong treatment rationale early on in therapy (i.e., share with the client why the therapy will be helpful for his/her symptoms).

2. Increase the client's belief in the skills and competencies of the therapist.

3. Express confidence in the client's ability to complete the therapy.

4. Share research outcomes (i.e., tell clients what we know about others who have undergone a similar therapy so they know what to expect).

5. Review progress and compare it with expectations.

We will say more about some of these factors when we review therapist factors.

Client Personality   The role of personality factors in treatment has been discussed in previous chapters. Most notably, Chapter 8 includes an overview of the role of personality factors such as perfectionism in the treatment of depression, and Chapter 12 describes the attempt to differentiate treatment according to personality factors as part of the Project Match initiative. Chapter 13 outlined how certain personality disorders have a negative impact on treatment outcome. How important are personality factors? Lambert (1992) reviewed the literature and concluded that personal attributes of the client, including personality differences, may account for as much as 40% of the variability in therapy outcomes and that these factors outweigh differences attributable to specific types of treatment. Given the relevance of personality factors, it is clear that personality factors are assessed not only to determine whether a prospective client has significant personality dysfunction, but also to identify personality orientations that influence the treatment course and treatment outcome.

As one illustration, individual differences in attachment style are receiving a great deal of attention regarding their role in therapy outcome and processes. Recall that attachment styles were discussed at length in Chapter 15. An investigation conducted by a team of Canadian researchers yielded more evidence indicating that clients with insecure attachment have less favourable treatment outcomes (see Joyce, Ogrodniczuk, Piper, & Sheptycki, 2010). This study of clients with complicated grief found that attachment style was "a strong predictor of psychotherapy outcome" (p. 122) and it replicated a previous finding by this same research team. A fearful attachment style was linked with negative outcomes. Joyce et al. (2010) concluded that people with this style would, in all likelihood, be quite fearful in interpersonal interactions. More generally, meta-analyses indicate small but significant links between attachment styles and both poorer therapy outcomes and poorer client–therapist working alliances (Bernecker, Levy, & Ellison, 2014; Levy, Ellison, Scott, & Bernecker, 2011).

Giorgio Tasca at the University of Ottawa reviewed the link between attachment and eating disorders, including therapy outcomes (Tasca & Balfour, 2014). It was found that avoidant and anxious attachment styles were linked to dropping out of therapy and poorer treatment outcomes, respectively. There are similar findings in the personality disorder field, but one promising avenue is recent research showing that for clients with personality disorders, psychotherapy can lead to positive shifts in attachment (e.g., moving from insecure to secure attachment styles) (Levy et al., 2015). Attachment style was also thought to influence which type of treatment would best suit a client (CBT vs. interpersonal therapy—IPT), but a recent study failed to replicate earlier findings (Bernecker et al., 2016).

Client Goals and the Motivation to Change

Common sense would suggest that clients who are highly motivated and ready to change will actually be more likely to improve due to treatment. Indeed, a review conducted many years ago assessed 91 potential predictors of the outcome of psychotherapy, and client motivation was identified as one of the most significant factors in treatment outcomes (Luborsky et al., 1971). The importance of the motivation to change was illustrated in a novel study of how depressed adolescents responded to treatment (see Lewis et al., 2009). Adolescents who endorsed items on the Stages of Change Questionnaire such as "I'm not the one with the problem," "It doesn't make much sense for me to be here," and "Being here is pretty much a waste of time for me because problems don't have to do with me" were more depressed and responded more poorly to treatment regardless of the modality of treatment than those adolescents who seemed more self-motivated and disagreed with these questionnaire items.

Self-report measures such as the Stages of Change Questionnaire require some degree of insight. Levels of self-insight may be quite variable. Some clients may be consciously aware of their desire and need to change, while others may be ready

and not quite realize it. Motivational interviewing may be required to make people aware of their desire for change.

Motivational interviewing (MI), which was described briefly in Chapter 12, is often incorporated within CBT or offered prior to CBT to enhance engagement in CBT (Westra, Constantino, & Antony, in press). Miller and Rollnick (2002) have outlined how MI is client-centred in the tradition of Carl Rogers, but it is directive rather than non-directive. MI is described in greater detail in Focus on Discovery 17.1.

Type and Severity of Dysfunction

The degree of clinical dysfunction and impairment is an individual difference factor that varies among clients and its importance cannot be discounted. It is generally accepted that for people with complex clinical presentations, even the best possible therapist will be highly challenged. For instance, it was noted in Chapter 13 that people with borderline personality disorder can be particularly difficult to treat, and this is also the case with people suffering from extreme levels of narcissism or psychopathy.

Typically, in any sample of clients requiring treatment, those with the more extreme levels of dysfunction and distress at baseline prior to treatment are the ones who may demonstrate significant clinical improvement, but they are likely to still have residual symptoms following treatment and they may not fully recover, even if the treatment is successful to some degree. For example, those with greater pre-treatment symptoms of personality dysfunction tend to achieve the greatest symptom reduction (Barnicot et al., 2012) but progress often does not equate with full recovery.

The other key factor is the complexity of dysfunction, with elevated levels of comorbidity typically being linked with less positive outcomes. It has been established, for instance, that comorbidity undermines the success of CBT for depression (Kuyken & Tsivirkos, 2009). It is particularly challenging when a person is suffering from depression or anxiety that is complicated by the presence of one or more personality disorders or a problem with substance abuse.

Finally, it is important to consider that these client factors do not operate in isolation—they interact with one another. For example, the type of dysfunction was found to correlate with treatment expectancy (Constantino et al., 2014). Greater symptoms of mania or psychosis were associated with more hopefulness, whereas greater symptoms of personality dysfunction or substance abuse were associated with lower expectations regarding therapy.

Therapist Factors That Influence Therapy Outcomes

The role of therapist factors must also be acknowledged. In addition to the differences associated with variability among therapists according to their therapeutic allegiance, there are several factors that differentiate therapists in ways that are related to therapy outcome. These factors are also listed in Table 17.1 and they are discussed briefly below.

Focus on Discovery 17.1

Motivational Interviewing

Motivational interviewing (MI) reflects the fact that some people are highly threatened by change and are very ambivalent about engaging in therapy. MI helps clients to develop a readiness for change by enabling them to explore and incorporate their own personal motives and issues and resolve feelings of ambivalence and resistance (Hettema, Steele, & Miller, 2005). Therapists try to facilitate the client's own development according to their personal wishes, values, and goals.

Initially, we discuss MI in the context of a case study of Carol, a woman suffering from generalized anxiety disorder. Angus and Kagan (2009) described her in the following manner:

> "Carol was a 50-year-old divorced woman when she sought therapy for severe GAD at York University. The MI therapist was a seasoned clinical psychologist who completed an MI training course. Carol described a chronic pattern of worrying, never being relaxed, having 'no peace or happiness,' and feeling constantly busy and rushed. She further complained of chronic tiredness and exhaustion; however, she was puzzled because 'there's nothing major going on, yet my mind is busy all the time.' ... Carol reported worrying about everything, especially her relationships with other people and the well-being of her family members. She stated that worry caused her distress and reported difficulties with insomnia, tension, and inability to concentrate. In fact, Carol had to take a leave from her job due to the severe concentration problems associated with her worry. She described herself as a 'lifelong worrier' and had previously been treated with psychotherapy and antidepressant medication with little improvement."

> (pp. 1158–1159)

Carol participated in four MI sessions. She responded well to therapist empathy and she showed no ambivalence in "opening up" (i.e., discussing painful personal memories) despite a history of being non-expressive and covering up personal difficulties and concern. As a result of her MI treatment, Carol also took pride in doing something for herself and gaining a sense of mastery. Her experience not only lowered her level of worry, it further increased her readiness for additional change.

Carol was ready for change, but this is not the case with everyone. Even when experiencing great distress and engaging in self-defeating behaviour, some clients resist change and focus on the benefits of their dysfunctional behaviours. For instance, West (2004) described the case of Ms. C, who suffered from generalized social anxiety disorder and recurring depression. Ms. C was ambivalent about homework activities and the possibility of change. When asked to list the benefits of her disorder, she readily named a variety of perks. She indicated that avoiding others "keeps me from getting hurt," "saves energy because it is exhausting to be around others," and means that "[I] don't have to deal with the dissatisfaction I have with my marriage" (p. 172). A central component of MI is using CBT techniques to challenge these perceived benefits, but within the context of an empathic relationship with the therapist. The focus is on changing the value of negative behaviours and increasing the value of positive, adaptive behaviours.

MI was designed initially for use in the treatment of people who are ambivalent about giving up their addictions and it is within this context that most research has been conducted. A meta-analysis of 30 treatment studies by Burke, Arkowitz, and Menchola (2003) found that MI, relative to no treatment control and placebo conditions, yielded treatment improvements. The overall effect size of MI was deemed to be moderate. It is now generally concluded that some of the strongest support for the benefits of MI come from substance abuse interventions (see Moyers & Houck, 2011). The COMBINE Research Project (Moyers & Houck, 2011) is an illustration of how MI combines effectively with CBT to produce positive outcomes.

In recent years, various authors have sought to extend the range of MI's applicability by using it with other disorders. Westra, Constantino, and Antony (in press) showed that clients with severe generalized anxiety disorder who received MI prior to CBT were five times more likely to no longer meet diagnostic criteria for GAD a year later, compared with those clients who received CBT without MI. Importantly, they were also less likely to drop out of treatment.

An influential book edited by Arkowitz, Westra, Miller, and Rollnick (2007) has played an important role in further extending the applicability of MI. This volume contains chapters on the use of MI in the treatment of a wide range of disorders, including post-traumatic stress disorder (PTSD), obsessive-compulsive disorder (OCD), depression, schizophrenia, and pathological gambling.

Personal Qualities of the Therapist   We have more positive reactions to some people than others, and this is largely a function of the personal qualities that differentiate among these people. This is also the case with therapists. This was underscored by a qualitative analysis that was undertaken with 10 clients who were successfully treated and who were then later interviewed about what led to their improvement. The therapists' theoretical orientations did not seem to matter but what did matter was having a warm therapist who made it easier for them to communicate and reveal intimate aspects about themselves. These therapists brought a sense of stability in a relationship that contrasted with the chaotic and often distressing relationships that contributed to the clients' original need for treatment (see Binder, Holgersen, & Nielsen, 2009). The personal qualities of the therapist can typically be traced to personality traits and personality styles that represent very salient differences among therapists.

One factor of significance is whether the therapist has a secure attachment style. Just as attachment insecurities are problematic among clients, therapists with an insecure attachment style tend to be linked with less favourable therapy outcomes and greater difficulties in establishing positive therapist–client relationships (Mikulincer, Shaver, & Berant, 2013). In light of the evidence linking attachment style of the therapist and client outcome, Degnan and colleagues concluded that "therapists do need to be sensitive to their own attachment experiences and how these play out when delivering therapy" (Degnan, Seymour-Hyde, Harris, & Berry, 2016, p. 63).

Other factors can influence how warm a therapist appears. In a recent study, participants were presented with information about clinicians as biologically oriented or psychosocial in orientation (Lebowitz, Ahn, & Oltman, 2015). Those described as biologically oriented were rated as less warm than those described as psychosocial. Participants were also asked to rate competence: if the condition presented was more biological, then the biologically oriented clinician was rated as more competent; otherwise, there were no differences in competence ratings. We consider therapist competence next.

Therapist Experience, Training, and Competence

Not surprisingly, the extent to which the therapist is experienced is a factor that makes a difference in the success of therapy. A recent analysis of variability in the outcomes of couples therapy found, for instance, that differences among the 18 therapists studied accounted for a significant 8% of the variance in outcome, with more instances of better outcomes being reported by couples whose therapists have greater experience in conducting couples therapy. Therapist variability also accounted for 10% of the variability in working alliance scores (Owen et al., 2014).

An obvious consideration is that therapists differ in their quality and competence, as is the case with people in any profession. Training requirements stipulate that standards must be reached in order for a clinical psychologist to provide treatment, but some are more capable and skilled than others in terms of core competencies—the essential skills needed by a therapist. Core competencies include the ability to engage in relationships and the ability to communicate. They also involve cultural competencies for those therapists with diverse clients.

Westra, Constantino, Arkowitz, and Dozois (2011) found in their longitudinal study that, despite no initial baseline differences in expectations for anxiety change, more effective therapists had clients with anxiety disorder who developed higher outcome expectancies following CBT. Westra et al. (2009) were able to show quite clearly that different therapists regularly produced different therapy outcomes and that those therapists who were linked with better outcomes demonstrated elevated levels of CBT competence. Competence was assessed by the Cognitive Therapy Scale (CTS; Young & Beck, 1980), a measure that requires trained observers to make seven-point ratings of therapists across 11 dimensions. The dimensions are grouped into three general therapeutic skills (collaboration, understanding, and interpersonal effectiveness)

and three specific cognitive therapy skills (focusing on key cognitions, strategy for change, and use of cognitive-behavioural techniques). According to the dimensional ratings on the CTS, the lowest rating means the therapist does not at all select cognitive-behavioural techniques; in contrast, the highest rating is attained when the therapist has a consistent and promising strategy for change that incorporates several CBT techniques. Psychometric analyses indicate that these 11 dimensions combine to form an overarching single construct tapping therapist competence (Dobson, Shaw, & Vallis, 1985).

Other research in CBT treatment of depression has linked greater therapist competence with better outcomes (Kuyken & Tsivrikos, 2009). While there is little doubt that the competency factor can make a considerable difference, research evidence in this field is surprisingly quite limited. A meta-analysis found that therapist competence did not make a significant difference, except in research such as the study by Kuyken and Tsivrikos (2009) mentioned above that targeted depression (Webb, DeRubeis, & Barber, 2010). However, this is one issue where a nuanced approach is needed in future research, as was the case in the Westra et al. (2009) study; perhaps therapist competence becomes more important as clinical cases become much more complex. It is also likely the case that the results vary here depending on how therapist competence is assessed.

Although the CTS was developed several decades ago, how best to assess therapist competence is still being debated (Muse & McManus, 2016). In their qualitative analysis of experienced CBT therapists, Muse and McManus (2016) warned of the danger in focusing too strongly on scales such as the CTS when training student therapists. Muse and McManus offered the following participant quote: "students sometimes are more concerned with getting a good CTS score than they are with doing a good CBT session" (p. 251).

Branson, Shafran, and Myles (2015) examined the link between CBT competence (using a revised version of the CTS) and outcome in a large sample: they had data from 43 therapists treating 1,247 clients. They did not find a general association between competence and outcome, but they did find that the most competent therapists were more likely to have clients who improved reliably compared with the least competent therapists. It may be that reaching an average level of competence is sufficient for most clients to change.

Client–Therapist Relationship Factors That Influence Therapy Outcomes

Several aspects of the client–therapist relationship can play a role. As is the case with any dyadic relationship, the client and therapist can be quite compatible and "hit it off" or they can seem to be at odds with each other. There can also be a discrepancy in their expectations and goals. Most of the work in this area has focused on the working alliance, which we describe below.

The term **therapeutic**, or **working**, **alliance** (see Horvath & Greenberg, 1994) refers to rapport and trust and to a sense that the therapist and the client are working together to achieve mutually agreed-upon goals.

Reviews of studies conducted over two decades confirm that the stronger the therapeutic relationship, or alliance, the better the outcome (see Horvath, 2001) and contemporary research continues to support the benefits of having a stronger therapeutic alliance (e.g., Barnicot et al., 2012) (see photo). Horvath (2001) observed that the most clinically useful indicator may be the client's report of the early alliance.

There are different views on how a good working alliance works (Henry, Strupp, Schacht, & Gaston, 1994). It might have a direct therapeutic effect, or it might have an indirect effect by making the therapist's interpretations more effective. Research on therapist factors indicates that the therapist's skills and personal characteristics are both key factors, while the therapist's level of training is relatively inconsequential (see Horvath, 2001). Nevertheless, Adam Horvath (2001) allows for the realistic possibility that therapists need more extensive training to be able to form a good alliance with a client suffering from extreme psychopathology.

Another issue to consider is the fact that the working alliance is multi-faceted, and one or more of its aspects may be involved in a given case. Horvath and Greenberg (1989) developed the Working Alliance Inventory to assess three components of the alliance: (1) the bond between the client and therapist, (2) agreement on the goals of treatment, and (3) agreement on the tasks of therapy.

Several findings have clarified the nature and importance of the therapeutic alliance:

1. The correlation between the ratings of the working alliance by clients and their therapists is only moderate at best, as shown across several measures of the working alliance (see Fenton et al., 2001).

2. As treatment progresses, the differences in how the working alliance is viewed by the client and therapist do not lessen substantially (Fitzpatrick, Iwakabe, & Stalikas, 2005).

A strong relationship between therapist and client is widely regarded as essential for implementing therapy procedures.

Brad Killer/E+/Getty Images, Inc.

3. A positive treatment outcome is much better predicted by the client's view of the working alliance than it is by the therapist's view of the working alliance (Horvath & Bedi, 2002). This emphasizes the importance of the client's unique phenomenological perspective.

Alexandra Bachelor (2013) from Université Laval examined the similarities and differences between client and therapist reports of alliance using the Working Alliance Inventory, among other measures. This work reinforced the point that therapists should not assume that their views of alliance are in line with their clients' views. Other key messages were that therapists should emphasize to the client that client views and work are strongly valued. Finally, continuously linking therapy work to the client's desired changes is critical.

Zilcha-Mano and colleagues (in press) also examined alliance from both a client and therapist perspective. They assessed alliance and outcome at each session, allowing for a very detailed look at the relationship between alliance and outcome across therapy. Increases in alliance as reported by the clients were a stronger predictor of outcome than increases in alliance as reported by the therapists.

Horvath (2006) pinpointed several key challenges that remain. These challenges include the need to develop a clearer and more extensive definition of the alliance and to more clearly specify the role and purpose of the alliance at various points in the treatment process. Further, research in this area should not rule out the possibility that a strong working alliance is the result, rather than the cause, of therapeutic change; clients might feel better about their relationship with their therapist if they have improved. In the context of binge eating symptoms, a recent study found support that it is in fact alliance that leads to symptom change, rather than the other way around (Tasca, Compare, Zarbo, & Brugnera, 2016). The researchers measured alliance and binge eating symptoms at every session. Higher alliance change in an earlier session predicted less binge eating in future sessions.

Compared with research with adults, where the evidence for the relationship between alliance and outcome is strong, there is only limited evidence of the benefits of the alliance in youth psychotherapy outcomes (McLeod, 2011). There may be other factors at play. For example, a recent study examined the role of attachment style among adolescents and young adults (Zack et al., 2015). For those with secure attachment histories, alliance was not related to how well they did in therapy. However, for those with poor attachment histories, working alliance was strongly related to outcome.

Finally, how should alliance be taught? In a qualitative study, Constantino and colleagues (2013) held discussions with 10 alliance researchers. They generally agreed that current training in alliance is unstructured but that a structured approach may be preferable. Clinical training programs are quite full but given the consistent research findings of alliance as a significant predictor of outcome, room should clearly be made for enhancing therapists' ability to build strong working alliances with their clients.

17.2 General Issues in Evaluating Psychotherapy Research

Our analysis of the effectiveness of various therapies follows. First, however, we begin with a few general issues that will inform our understanding and appreciation of research in psychotherapy.

Therapy as researched vs. Therapy As practised

Beutler (2009) has referred to the "chasm" that exists between science and practice. Below is an illuminating quote from Parry et al. (2010) in which it is suggested that the gap between psychotherapy research and practice may be a gulf rather than a gap.

> "That there is a gap, possibly a gulf, between research and practice in psychological therapies has long been acknowledged. Most therapists base their practice on the theoretical orientation in which they trained and their own clinical experience rather than on research findings. Much experimental clinical research in psychology is designed to answer questions of little direct interest to clinicians, using methods which mitigate against clinical realism."
>
> (Parry, Castonguay, Borkovec, & Wolf, 2010, p. 311)

What is the essence of this discrepancy? Therapist manuals are detailed guides on how to conduct a particular therapy, stipulating specific procedures to be followed at different stages of treatment. The use of such manuals has become the norm in psychotherapy research (e.g., Nathan & Gorman, 1998). Indeed, it is impossible nowadays to obtain funding to study the outcome of psychotherapy without first explicitly defining the independent variables via a manual that the therapists in the study must follow as closely as possible.

The use of therapist manuals began with the earliest controlled studies on Wolpe's technique of systematic desensitization (e.g., Paul & Shannon, 1966). In contrast, in earlier psychotherapy research of the 1940s and 1950s, the activity of the therapist was, for the most part, described only in terms of his or her theoretical orientation (psychodynamic, client-centred, etc.). But what therapists actually do in the consulting room is often difficult to know based on what they say they do and their allegiance to a particular orientation. Specifying via manuals what therapists are to do in a controlled study and then monitoring what they actually do in their sessions with clients has thus been hailed as a significant advance in the scientific study of therapeutic interventions (see Hunsley & Rumstein-McKean, 1999). It allows someone reading a psycho-

Courtesy of John Hunsley

John Hunsley from the University of Ottawa is a leader in the field of clinical psychology and a strong advocate of the use of treatment manuals and empirically supported treatments.

therapy study to know what actually happened to clients in a given experimental condition.

Treatment manuals continue to be advocated by leading psychologists such as John Hunsley (see photo). Hunsley and Rumstein-McKean (1999) endorsed the use of treatment manuals as an adjunct to research involving randomized clinical trials, a controlled experimental procedure in which participants are assigned randomly to experimental conditions. At the same time, they acknowledged that several concerns involving some treatment manuals need to be addressed. The most common criticism is that manuals are too unwieldy for actual clinical practice, with some situations requiring a more specific approach and others requiring a more general approach. They also expressed concern that "many manuals inadvertently promote rule-governed behaviour that may not be appropriate in all instances" (p. 1511), and noted that more attention needs to be given to contextual factors, including timing issues, such as advice on when a particular technique is appropriate. This latter issue reflects the more general concern that treatment manuals lose sight of the individuality of people because they are based on abstract representations of the typical client, and therapists may thus have to rely on their own clinical judgement to deal with the unique and complex issues facing certain clients (see Nathan, Stuart, & Dolan, 2000). Finally, Hunsley and Rumstein-McKean (1999) pointed to an urgent need for research that examines the extent to which treatment manuals, accompanied by little or no supervision, do indeed result

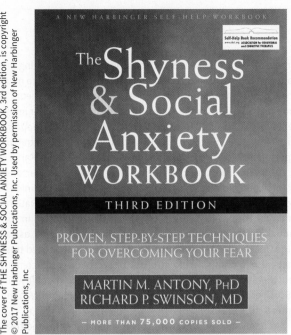

Workbooks such as this are designed for clients and are commonly used in conjunction with a manual that guides the therapist in treating the client.

in treatments that are accurate and effective. These concerns notwithstanding, they suggested that, for treatments supported by randomized clinical trials, "working knowledge of the treatment manual would be essential to practitioners" (p. 1510). Further, workbooks, developed for clients, can be used in conjunction with a therapist manual (see photo for an example of a CBT workbook for social anxiety).

Although the use of manuals buys us greater internal validity—results obtained can be attributed with some confidence to the action of the independent variable—what about external validity? Do the results obtained from manual-based studies generalize to the actual practice of psychotherapy outside the constraints of a controlled study? There is perhaps no more important and more hotly debated topic in psychotherapy than this (e.g., Beutler, 1999). A decade later, Beutler (2009) still maintains that the onus is on scientists because they have failed to provide a workable model of how to integrate science and instead had "an unwarranted devotion to a limited number of scientific methods" (p. 301).

We know that most therapists seldom behave strictly in line with a particular theoretical orientation, whether psychoanalytic, client-centred, or cognitive-behavioural. Therefore, the kinds of controlled studies emphasized in this chapter and earlier in the book are limited in what they can tell us about the effectiveness of the psychotherapy available to clients who are not participants in research studies. This situation is ironic, for it is these controlled studies that provide the evidence used by proponents of particular techniques or general theoretical approaches to support their positions!

A common characteristic of today's controlled studies is the exclusion of people on various grounds. For example, people

may be excluded from a study if they have problems in addition to the one being studied (the comorbidity issue). Moreover, studies rely on people who are willing to be seen in a highly structured treatment protocol. In short, the clients who volunteer and are accepted as participants in controlled studies are different from many—and perhaps the vast majority of—clients in psychotherapy. This point was underscored by the results of a provocative study that compared psychotherapy research participants in randomized controlled trials (RCTs) with general community outpatients (Stirman, DeRubeis, Crits-Cristoph, & Brody, 2003). This study found that 58% of the community sample had primary diagnoses that had never been studied in RCTs, indicating that some diagnoses are common but not represented in psychotherapy research. Common diagnoses overlooked in research studies included adjustment disorder and milder but chronic forms of depression. Clearly, it is quite risky to generalize from controlled studies to the actual practice of psychotherapy and the people receiving this psychotherapy.

The concerns about the gap or gulf between research and practice were illustrated by the results of a Canadian survey of practitioners who provide group psychotherapy (see Ogrodniczuket al., 2010). Overall, most of the 55 respondents expressed high appreciation for research and acknowledged reading an average of three new articles each month and attending two conferences per year. While this study suggested research was valued to a greater degree, significant concerns were still noted, with 60% or more participants in the Ogrodniczuk et al. (2010) survey endorsing the following:

1. Psychotherapy research studies do not capture the complexities of group psychotherapy.
2. Research procedures distort or disrupt the typical therapeutic process.
3. Therapists, clients, and settings used in research studies do not represent typical clinical practice.
4. Not enough attention is given to qualitative studies of group therapy or systematized case studies.
5. Randomized control trials are overemphasized.
6. Researchers are too often dismissive of relationship variables in favour of specific treatment techniques.

In short, therapy as practised in the real world is not reflected in research, in part because therapy as actually practised does take a more idiographic approach; it is tailored to the particular needs and characteristics of a particular client, including the personality factors that were described earlier. When they are working in clinical settings, therapists make continual adjustments that are not constrained by the demands of a scientific study. In contrast, the very essence of treatment manuals is to minimize the tailoring of intervention to individual clients. It remains a challenge to researchers and clinicians alike to reconcile the seemingly incompatible needs of these two approaches (e.g., Fishman, 1999).

There are other factors that influence what therapies are put into practice. It is particularly important to consider

---

Focus on Discovery 17.2

Research vs. Practice in PTSD Treatment: Why a Gap Exists and How it is Being Addressed

The gap or lack of correspondence between therapy research and therapy practice is not just an academic issue. If therapeutic approaches deemed to be effective in laboratory research are not being translated into clinical practice, the inevitable conclusion can be drawn that some people are simply not receiving the kind and quality of treatment they deserve.

One clear illustration of this failure to put knowledge into practice is the treatment received by military personnel with PTSD. Edna Foa and her colleagues have been instrumental in heightening awareness of the fact that successful evidence-based exposure treatments are infrequently used, including by therapists working for the U.S. Department of Veterans Affairs who treat military personnel with PTSD (Foa, Gillihan, & Bryant, 2013).

Rather than simply noting that the gap exists, the researchers and clinicians in the PTSD field went further by posing and addressing two key questions: (1) Why is research not translating into actual clinical practice? and (2) What can be done to resolve this situation? Regarding the first question, extensive research was sought to identify why research is not being put into practice. According to Foa et al. (2013), these factors range from therapists being influenced by former mentors who did not use exposure techniques to not feeling competent enough to implement new techniques while also being hesitant to expose already traumatized people to stimuli (e.g., reminders of war) that can add to their distress.

So, what has been done to bridge the gap between research and practice? The availability of vast resources (including the number of trained personnel) as well as legislation mandating that more effective treatments be implemented has resulted in a much broader implementation of empirically supported treatments to combat PTSD in the United States. To a large extent, greater implementation has resulted from providing extensive training opportunities of high quality to therapists who may not have had training opportunities (for discussions, see Karlin & Agarwal, 2013; Karlin et al., 2010). As of February 2016, the U.S. Veterans Affairs department had provided prolonged exposure training to over 1,800 clinicians and cognitive processing therapy to over 7,700 clinicians (National Center for PTSD, 2016). This training has been implicated in substantial clinical improvements (see Karlin et al., 2010). Also, as part of the U.S. Veterans Affairs dissemination of evidence-based treatments, it has committed to a rollout of acceptance and commitment therapy (ACT) for depression, due to its high comorbidity with PTSD. Over 650 clinicians have received the ACT training (National Center for PTSD, 2016).

In Canada, exposure therapy is recommended for the treatment of PTSD, but extensive federal training opportunities are not available. Although more funding has been devoted to mental health care over the last decade, veterans continue to encounter many obstacles, including long wait times for treatments. There has also been a disturbing rate of suicide among veterans following the Afghanistan mission (54 veterans committed suicide post-war; a total of 158 died in the mission, D'Aliesio, 2016).

The message here is that barriers exist to implementing a therapeutic technique even when it is well-supported by empirical findings. If these findings are to become incorporated into clinical practice, resources are needed to promote dissemination and implementation efforts.

---

real-world barriers to implementation. For instance, a recent survey of 19 clinicians examined issues that limited the implementation of dialectical behaviour therapy (see Chapter 13) in the public health system in northern California. Significant barriers mentioned by eight or more clinicians (42% or greater) were time commitment, lack of administrative support, and the amount of training required, which is a problem that is exacerbated by staff turnover (Carmel, Rose, & Fruzzetti, 2014). In Focus on Discovery 17.2, we discuss this issue in detail with respect to the treatment of PTSD in combat veterans, but barriers exist across various contexts.

Treatment Efficacy vs. Treatment Effectiveness

Regarding the issue of therapy in laboratory studies vs. in actual clinical settings, psychotherapy researchers do make an important distinction between efficacy and effectiveness. The **efficacy** of an intervention is its impact as determined from a controlled outcome study, typically conducted in an academic research setting. The **effectiveness** of an intervention is its impact when offered to and received by people in the everyday world. According to Dobson and Hamilton (2002), efficacy researchers emphasize maximizing the internal validity of research, often conducted in controlled laboratory settings, while effectiveness researchers hope to optimize the external validity or generalizability of the intervention. The elimination of observable, well-defined problems, such as a person with agoraphobia being unable to venture far from his or her home, is the usual focus of efficacy studies. In contrast, effectiveness is usually judged subjectively by clients themselves based on more global criteria, such as their level of satisfaction with their therapy, how much they believe they have been helped, and how much the quality of their life has improved (cf. *Consumer Reports*, 1995; Seligman, 1995).

The efficacy of treatments is often well-established but evidence of effectiveness lags well behind. This is not always the case, however. Stewart and Chambless (2009) reported a meta-analysis of effectiveness studies of CBT for adult anxiety disorders in actual clinical practice. Large effect sizes were found, suggesting that CBT can be effective in "clinically representative conditions" (p. 595). Secondary analyses indicating that there was greater evidence of effectiveness when clients were not assigned randomly to experimental conditions and medication for anxiety management was permitted. Not surprisingly, factors that decreased effectiveness included lack of therapist training, failure to use treatment manuals, and a lack of ongoing monitoring of treatment.

The efficacy–effectiveness distinction continues to be a topic of lively debate in the field. The *Consumer Reports* study (1995) is cited widely as a clear example of research that examines the effectiveness of treatment rather than its efficacy. A survey was mailed to 180,000 of the magazine's readers and 22,000 answered; about 7,000 gave responses to the mental health questions, and 4,100 of these people said that they received assistance from some combination of mental health professionals, doctors, and support groups. The main conclusions were summarized by Seligman (1995):

1. The treatment usually worked; in fact, of the 786 people who said they felt poor at the outset, 92% reported feeling very good, good, or so-so after treatment.

2. Long-term treatment was associated with more improvement than short-term treatment.

3. There was no benefit to psychotherapy plus medication vs. psychotherapy alone in terms of perceived effectiveness.

4. Family doctors were just as effective as mental health professionals in the short term, but mental health professionals were much more effective in the long term.

5. Alcoholics Anonymous fared especially well and was rated as doing substantially better than mental health professionals.

6. Active participants had better outcomes than more passive recipients.

7. Comparisons among the various psychotherapies showed that no particular type of treatment had superior effectiveness.

Controlled follow-up studies are needed to confirm the *Consumer Reports* findings. One of the most glaring shortcomings of this report was the absence of a control group (for a discussion, see Nathan et al., 2000). This factor and other limitations led Nathan et al. (2000) to conclude that although this study reached an encouraging conclusion about the effectiveness of treatment, it should be regarded as a consumer survey rather than a research study per se, and as such, it tells us little about efficacy.

Although this study is not without its flaws, it did reach some conclusions that replicated other research findings, including confirmation of the **dodo bird effect**. The dodo bird effect is the tendency for various therapies to achieve similar results. The term was coined by Rosenzweig (1936), who adapted it from *Alice in Wonderland*. In this famous book, a dodo bird judges the outcome of a race and concludes that everyone has won. Indeed, a "meta-meta analysis" of 17 meta-analyses concluded that differences in the outcomes of therapies are small and not statistically significant (Luborsky et al., 2002). While there is strong evidence of the dodo bird effect and evidence continues to grow (see Baardseth et al., 2013), note that there is an opposing view. Budd and Hughes (2009) concluded that there is also evidence that specific therapies are more effective for certain diagnoses. They suggested that support for the dodo bird effect may be overstated, in part, due to an overreliance in research studies on randomized control designs that constrain key factors that operate in therapy as practised.

The dodo bird effect is but one of several beliefs and principles shared by many psychotherapy researchers. Other consensus beliefs are outlined in Focus on Discovery 17.3.

Lambert and Ogles (2004) concluded that about 75% of people entering psychotherapy achieve at least some improvement, and these effects seem to be more powerful than support

Focus on Discovery 17.3

Consensus Beliefs Involving Psychotherapy Research

A study by Boisvert and Faust (2003) involved discovering the beliefs of an international group of 12 experts who conduct psychotherapy research. Each researcher was asked to indicate his or her degree of agreement with 20 statements about psychotherapy, based on existing research. The experts demonstrated strong agreement that research supported the following claims:

1. Therapy is helpful to the majority of clients.

2. Most people achieve some change relatively quickly in therapy.

3. In general, therapies achieve similar outcomes (i.e., the dodo bird effect).

4. People change more because of "common factors" than because of "specific factors" associated with therapies.

5. The client–therapist relationship is the best predictor of treatment change.

6. Most therapists learn more about effective therapy techniques from their experience than from research.

7. About 10% of clients get worse as a result of therapy.

Boisvert and Faust (2003) observed that, given the researchers' acceptance of the view that a small proportion of clients actually get worse as a result of treatment, perhaps informed-consent procedures should be modified so that potential clients are made aware of the potential risk, as well as the potential benefits, of treatment. Do you agree?

Troubled people may talk about their problems with friends or seek professional therapy. Therapy is typically sought by those for whom the advice and support of family or friends have not provided relief.

from family and friends and the mere passage of time (see photo). Further, the positive effects exceed those of placebo treatments or no treatment for a wide variety of psychological problems and disorders (e.g., Westen, Novotny, & Thompson-Brenner, 2004).

Practising clinicians and other mental health service providers must make daily decisions about how to treat their clients. In some settings, they now use a stepped care approach in making treatment decisions (see Haaga, 2000). The approach offers guidelines for both efficient and effective delivery of psychological services and does this at both the individual and the community service level (Sobell & Sobell, 2000). Focus on Discovery 17.4 presents a brief summary and evaluation of the stepped care approach.

The Challenge of Managed Care

No doubt you have heard of managed care. In the United States, health care is most often provided to people via an insurance company that attempts to control costs (and maximize profits) by requiring prior approval of the nature and extent of treatment and by reducing the amount of payment provided to hospitals, clinics, and medical and psychological personnel.

Run for the most part by businesspeople rather than by health care providers, managed-care organizations (MCOs) have indeed brought down the costs of care in the United States over the past few decades. They have also demanded increased accountability from providers. MCOs look to scientific evidence to justify the procedures used by health professionals. Surgical, dental, and medical procedures are justified by scientific evidence. Drugs approved by the Food and Drug Administration for use in the United States are judged from controlled research to be safe and effective for particular conditions. More recently, these standards have been applied to assessments and treatments of mental disorders. The scrutiny that physicians and

dentists have been accustomed to for many years is now being brought to bear on mental health professionals.

The situation is considerably different in Canada owing to our universal health care system, where there is an expectation that every citizen will have equal opportunity to receive the best care available (e.g., Romanow & Marchildon, 2003). Nonetheless, in recent years, there has been considerable pressure on governments at the federal, provincial and territorial, and local levels to increase the efficiency of our system, to reduce costs, and to be accountable for the use of tax dollars. Of course, as in the United States, some services, such as private psychotherapy sessions provided by psychologists, usually require personal payment or reimbursement by insurance providers.

In Chapter 1, we introduced the issue of evidence-based treatment or **empirically supported therapies (ESTs)** (e.g., Hunsley & Johnston, 2000). These treatments have been demonstrated to be effective in research studies with appropriate scientific controls in a specific population, such as people diagnosed with major depression (Chambless & Ollendick, 2001).

In 2015, the American Psychological Association's Division 12 (Society for Clinical Psychology) began updating its list of ESTs for various disorders based on criteria set out by Tolin, McKay, Forman, Klonsky, and Thombs (2015). It will be a long process. At time of writing, 80 treatment packages were listed, with 16 having new content. The new criteria involve the use of systematic reviews of all available research evidence for any given treatment being evaluated (step 1). Following the systematic review, a committee-based evidence review takes place where the treatment is graded as very strong, strong, or weak (step 2). As outlined by Tolin and colleagues (2015), there are many questions and issues in this large undertaking, including:

- Why do we continue to focus on a list of ESTs rather than mechanisms of change? Instead of having lists of empirically supported treatment packages for each disorder, it may be beneficial to have empirically supported processes of change. For example, rather than state that a whole CBT package is effective for depression, stating the elements of that package (e.g., behavioural activation) that lead to change would be more desirable. Tolin and colleagues (2015) argue that the field is not yet ready for that type of detailed analysis.

- What if there is conflicting evidence? There are often inconsistencies in the literature, with some research being strongly supportive of a particular treatment, while other research is not. In such cases, taking all of the evidence into account and arriving at a decision is the approach advocated by Tolin and colleagues (2015).

- Is short-term change sufficient or should there be evidence of long-term change? Many studies evaluate outcome following 12 weeks of treatment, for example. Some may conduct follow-up assessments a few months later or a year later, others five years later. How much follow-up data are required? Tolin

Focus on Discovery 17.4

Stepped Care Models and the Treatment Process: Can We Do More with Less?

The concept of **stepped care** involves the notion that clinicians should match the level of the required treatment to the seriousness of the adjustment problem being addressed, but they should begin with less involved and less costly interventions, followed by more complex interventions if the initial interventions are not successful. Lower cost is seen by many as the guiding principle in stepped care (see Haaga, 2000), but it has been suggested by Sobell and Sobell (2000) that the preferred treatment option is the one that is least restrictive for the individual. In this context, "restrictive" refers to such considerations as physical effects of treatment, as well as issues involving lifestyle restrictions and economic considerations. Sobell and Sobell (2000) also suggest that treatment must be individualized to reflect the client's beliefs and resources and that the tailoring of treatment to the individual must be consistent with the current research literature.

Figure 17.1 is a diagram of the stepped care approach as conceptualized by Sobell and Sobell (2000). The left-hand portion of the figure shows how the intensity of treatment increases in response to negative treatment outcomes when more basic interventions are used. The usefulness of a stepped care approach will vary depending on the problem in question. Wilson, Vitousek, and Loeb (2000) observed that a low-intensity solution is not well suited to such situations as someone with anorexia nervosa being close to starving to death. In such a potentially life-threatening situation, unless other complications need to be considered, high-intensity treatments designed to provide immediate relief should begin immediately.

Another qualifying condition was identified by Otto, Pollack, and Maki (2000) in the course of their evaluation of the usefulness of stepped care to treat panic disorder. They observed that a substantial proportion of people with panic disorder receive medical treatment before psychological treatment is considered and approximately half of these individuals prefer this kind of treatment and likely would not participate in a stepped care program.

Recent research evaluating the use of stepped care models has demonstrated mixed findings for anxiety and depression. Nordgreen et al. (2016) found similar outcomes in a stepped care model, compared with a direct face-to-face CBT approach, for clients with panic disorder or social anxiety disorder. The stepped care model began with psychoeducation, then guided Internet treatment, and ended with face-to-face CBT. There was one caveat: attrition was higher in the stepped care model. Using data from the same client participants, Haug and colleagues (2015) examined possible predictors of outcome from the two approaches to treatment. Clients with the most impairment had the poorest outcomes, but

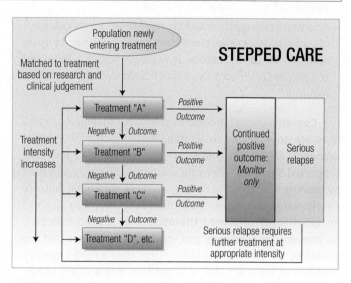

FIGURE 17.1 A stepped care approach to the delivery of health care services.

Source: Adapted from Sobell, M. B., & Sobell, L. C. Stepped care as a heuristic approach to the treatment of alcohol problems. *Journal of Consulting and Clinical Psychology, 68*, 573–579. American Psychological Association.

there were few differences across conditions. A meta-analysis on the use of stepped care for depression led to the following conclusion: "Although many guidelines recommend stepped care, there is currently only limited evidence to suggest that it should be the dominant model of treatment organization compared with alternative systems" (van Straten, Hill, Richards, & Cuijpers, 2015, p. 243). They found only a modest effect size for reductions in depression and noted different definitions of stepped care across the 14 studies they evaluated (e.g., different steps, different durations of steps, different treatment components). There was preliminary support for cost-effectiveness but several caveats were noted, namely that stepped care has not been directly compared with high-intensity care. In another recent study, Goorden et al. (2014) concluded that, compared with care as usual, stepped care was cost-effective for panic disorder and generalized anxiety disorder.

Although there may be benefits to a stepped care approach, future research is needed to address a number of issues, including high rates of attrition, lack of consensus on steps, and the actual degree of cost savings with a stepped care approach. One final concern with a stepped care model is that some clients may stop at a first step believing they have received sufficient care, when they may have gained more from a more intensive approach (Goorden et al., 2014).

and colleagues (2015) argue that both short-term and long-term data are important.

- If the focus is on results from research settings, how does that apply to the real world? We already discussed how evidence from research settings may not be perfectly generalizable to community settings. How much evidence must there be from

the community to determine that a treatment should be on the list? Tolin and colleagues (2015) indicate that both types of studies should be considered.

- Should cost-effectiveness be taken into account? Some treatments are more costly than others. Tolin and colleagues (2015) concluded that criteria for determining whether a treatment is cost-effective do not exist. Therefore, the panel of reviewers should take cost into account and "update or downgrade a treatment" accordingly.

- How much change is enough change? There are various ways of evaluating how effective a treatment is, with just as many opinions on which method is the best method. Tolin and colleagues (2015) concluded that human decision-making is required.

Concerns about randomized controlled trial methods and ESTs are summarized in Westen, Novotny, and Thompson-Brenner's (2004) insightful, critical review of empirically supported therapies. They concluded that ESTs are well suited to treating some disorders (e.g., anxiety disorders) but are poorly suited to treating other disorders. They issued a call for **empirically informed therapies** that are more focused on intervention strategies and for change processes that are guided by the clinician's insights rather than a rigidly invoked manualized approach that may not take into account important factors such as the personality characteristics of the client, the presence of comorbid disorders, and so on. As noted by Goldfried and Eubanks-Carter (2004), when it comes to more complex cases, there is a widening gap between clinical practice and the EST-driven outcome research that has high internal validity but questionable external validity.

As described by Hunsley and Johnston (2000), rather than redeveloping lists of empirically supported therapies (as was done in the United States), the Canadian Psychological Association Task Force focused on promoting **evidence-based practice** in Canada, promoting collaboration among stakeholders, and providing information about the limitations of current empirical knowledge. The American Psychological Association has also developed an evidence-based practice policy statement (APA Presidential Task Force on Evidence-Based Practice, 2006).

The most recent update from the Canadian Psychological Association Task Force on Evidence-Based Practice was published in 2012 (Canadian Psychological Association Task Force, 2012). The Task Force provided the following definition of evidence-based practice: "Evidence-based practice of psychological treatments involves the conscientious, explicit and judicious use of the best available research evidence to inform each stage of clinical decision-making and service delivery." Basically, the presenting problems and issues that clients present vary widely; it is the psychologist's responsibility to stay up to date on the literature and apply the current research base in diagnosis and treatment. Rather than list treatment packages for each disorder, this report outlines the process by which psychologists should operate. The report contains many examples of presenting problems and how a psychologist would apply evidence-based practice.

Although empirically supported treatments and evidence-based practice sound similar, these terms are not identical. Empirically supported treatments have been tested as a package in randomized controlled trials and have data attesting to their efficacy (see above for more details on the current

American Psychological Association procedures for determining EST status; Tolin et al., 2015). Evidence-based practice encourages psychologists to use the current evidence base as it applies to the presenting client, making informed decisions regarding assessment and treatment at every step.

The Canadian Psychological Association also commissioned a report on the efficacy and effectiveness of psychological treatments, reviewing the current evidence for many treatments for the most common presenting problems (Hunsley, Elliott, & Therrien, 2013). The main conclusion of the report is that psychotherapy works. In the authors' words:

> "There is extensive evidence demonstrating that psychotherapy can be an efficacious and effective health care service for a wide range of commonly experienced mental health and health conditions. This conclusion applies across the lifespan and is based on many hundreds of studies, including both randomized controlled trials and studies examining the impact of evidence-based psychological treatments delivered in typical clinical settings."
>
> (Hunsley et al., 2013, p. 3)

Given that some approaches currently have more empirical support than others, how is evidence-based treatment practised in the real world? Rowa et al. (2000) sought to determine the extent to which empirically supported psychological and pharmacological treatments were used in Canada for people with panic disorder, social phobia, or obsessive-compulsive disorder. They found that the types of pharmacological treatment received by clients were consistent with findings from the empirical literature. In contrast, empirically validated cognitive and behavioural treatments had been tried by fewer than one half of the participants. This result is consistent with other more recent studies that report a preference on the part of psychiatrists and many psychologists for traditional but non-validated treatments, such as psychodynamic approaches. Rowa et al. (2000) also reported that the most frequently used psychological intervention for the anxiety disorders was "supportive" therapy. Why is there a discrepancy between treatments identified as effective and treatments actually received by clients in clinical practice? Rowa et al. observed that

> ". . . these numbers are a cause for concern. It is possible that these results can be explained in part by the fact that psychiatric services in Canada are government funded and thus are more accessible, and that training for psychiatrists has traditionally focused on psychodynamic approaches."
>
> (Rowa et al., 2000, p. 97)

Rowa et al. (2000) recommended improving efforts to educate people about empirically supported treatments, improving the training of mental health professionals in all fields in methods of cognitive-behavioural therapy, and finding ways to make cognitive-behavioural treatments more available and affordable.

We conclude this part of our discussion by introducing another issue that needs to be taken into account: the role of demand characteristics in influencing the extent to which laboratory research generalizes to real-world contexts. An intriguing study by Gibbons, Stirman, DeRubeis, Newman, and Beck (2013) suffers to some degree because it was based on a relatively small sample of only 41 depressed adults, but the results offer a cautionary tale. This study involved randomly assigning people to treatment in an outpatient clinic or a large RCT study. The same therapists were involved in each group so this factor was held constant. The results showed that there was a very large difference involving treatment setting, with the people in the research trial showing up to three times more improvement. Importantly, the results did not simply reflect pre-existing differences between the groups of participants in intake characteristics. So, why did the people in the research study do much better? Were they more motivated? Did they misrepresent their improvement? Did they have more positive expectations? Whatever the case, if this result is replicated, it will cast severe doubt on the replicability of laboratory-based psychotherapy research in real-world settings.

With these general observations and considerations and the consensus beliefs of psychotherapy experts as background, we turn now to an evaluation of several therapeutic approaches, both the data on their effectiveness and some issues pertaining to them.

17.3 Review of Behavioural and Cognitive Therapies

Behavioural and cognitive therapies attempt to use the investigative methods of experimental psychology to study, develop, and evaluate specific therapeutic interventions. Many principles were drawn initially from animal research on classical and operant conditioning, but the more recent cognitive trends understandably rely on research and theory with humans. Because the techniques vary greatly, we provide summary details of several behavioural and cognitive therapies in the separate sections devoted to evaluating each one. There are many more variations in the CBT family that we do not have the space for here (e.g., acceptance and commitment therapy, dialectical behaviour therapy). Also, we focus here on individual treatment, but discuss the effective use of CBT interventions for couples in the "Review of Couples Therapy" section of this chapter.

Evaluation of Counterconditioning and Exposure Methods

Clinicians have treated many different anxiety-related problems by systematic desensitization, an approach developed by Joseph Wolpe in the 1950s. The original technique involves having a deeply relaxed person imagine a hierarchy of situations that he or she finds unduly fear-provoking in real life. As with any therapy for people in emotional distress, its proper application is a complicated affair. The clinician must first determine that the situations eliciting the client's anxious reactions do not warrant such reactions. If a person is anxious because he or she lacks the skills to deal with a given set of circumstances, then desensitization or actual exposure is inappropriate. Desensitization is appropriate, however, if a person seems to be inhibited by anxiety from behaving in customary and known ways. The applicability of desensitization depends largely on the therapist's ingenuity in discovering the source of the anxiety underlying a client's problems (Goldfried & Davison, 1994).

It has been well documented that exposing fearful people to what they are frightened of or uneasy about—whether in imagination, as in Wolpe's technique, or in real life, as is usually done today—usually leads to marked reductions in their unrealistic fears. The demonstrated importance of exposure has benefited people with a wide variety of anxiety disorders. However, behaviour change can be difficult to sustain. In reviewing basic behaviour change principles, relevant to counterconditioning as well as other methods (e.g., operant methods), Bouton (2014) highlights the importance of context. Bouton notes how the original behaviour has not been erased, but rather, has been inhibited in certain contexts. Therefore, the therapist should pay close attention to the context in which behaviour change occurs, and work to expand that context.

In terms of actual use, we discussed concerns about the limited use of exposure therapy in clinical practice and efforts undertaken in the United States to increase the use of exposure therapy for military personnel suffering from PTSD. As with all the techniques we describe, exposure is very rarely used exclusively. A person fearful of social interactions might be given training in conversational and other social skills in addition to undergoing exposure.

Evaluation of Operant Methods

Operant methods have proved successful with a wide range of behavioural problems. Systematically rewarding desirable behaviour and extinguishing undesirable behaviour have been particularly successful in the treatment of many childhood problems, as reviewed in Chapter 15.

Treatment of Childhood Problems   Perhaps one reason operant conditioning behaviour therapy has been so effective with children is that much of their behaviour is subject to the control of others. Children tend more than adults to be under continual supervision. At school their behaviour is scrutinized by teachers, and at home their parents often oversee their play and other social activities. The behaviour therapist works with the parents and teachers in an effort to change the ways in which they reward and punish children. It is assumed that altering the reinforcement practices of the adults in a child's life will ultimately change the child's behaviour.

The range of childhood problems dealt with through operant conditioning is broad, including bedwetting, thumb-sucking, nail-biting, aggression, tantrums, hyperactivity, disruptive classroom behaviour, poor school performance, language deficiency, extreme social withdrawal, and asthmatic attacks (Kazdin & Weisz, 1998). Self-mutilation has also been treated effectively with punishment procedures, sometimes involving the response-contingent application of painful electric shock to the hands or feet. Such extreme measures should be used only when less drastic interventions are ineffective and problem behaviours are life-threatening (e.g., Sandler& Steele, 1991).

Before applying operant techniques, the therapist must determine that the problem behaviour is, in fact, operant behaviour that can be controlled by a contingent reinforcer. A child who is crying because of physical pain, for example, should be attended to. Encouraging results have been achieved by applying operant techniques to therapy with children with intellectual disability and autism. Therapists who apply operant-conditioning techniques have challenged assumptions about the limited trainability of such children, much to the benefit of these children.

Generalization and Maintenance of Treatment Effects

A problem that is common to all treatments but perhaps especially to the behavioural and, to a lesser extent, the cognitive therapies, is that of generalizing to real life and maintaining whatever gains have been achieved while the client is in regular contact with the therapist. Brian Shaw, a well-known cognitive therapist and researcher from Toronto, observed that perhaps the most disappointing and challenging problem today is that the confidence placed in the effectiveness of treatment is not accompanied by concerns about sustaining treatment effects over time and the narrow range of clients included in clinical trials (see Shaw, 1999).

Therapists have different views on how treatment effects will be maintained, largely dependent on their orientation. Insight therapists assume that therapeutic effects are enduring because of the restructuring of the personality. In contrast, behaviour therapists, who look a good deal to the environment for factors that affect people, wonder how therapeutic changes can be made to last once clients return to their everyday situations, often assumed to have been instrumental in creating their problems in the first place. This challenge has been addressed by behaviourists in several ways.

Intermittent and naturalistic reinforcement Intermittent reinforcement—rewarding a response only some of the times it appears—makes new behaviour more enduring. Thus, many operant programs take care to move away from continuous schedules of reinforcement once desired behaviour is occurring with satisfactory regularity. For example, if a teacher has succeeded in helping a disruptive child spend more time sitting down by praising the child generously for each arithmetic problem finished while seated, the teacher will gradually reward the child for every other success and, ultimately, only infrequently. Another strategy is to move from artificial reinforcers to those that occur naturally in the social environment. A token program might be maintained only long enough to encourage certain desired behaviour, after which the person is weaned to naturally occurring reinforcers, such as praise from peers.

Environmental modification Another approach to bringing about generalization takes the therapist into the province of community psychology. Behaviour therapists manipulate surroundings, or attempt to do so, to support changes brought about in treatment. For example, Lovaas and his colleagues (Lovaas, Newsom, & Hickman, 1987; McEachin, Smith, & Lovaas, 1993) found that the gains painstakingly achieved in therapy for autistic children were sustained only when their parents continued to reinforce their good behaviour.

Eliminating secondary gain Most behaviour therapists assign their clients homework tasks to do between sessions. However, clients sometimes fail to follow through consistently. Many clients are so resistant to doing on their own what they consciously and rationally agree is in their best interest that therapists sometimes invoke as an explanation the psychoanalytic concept of secondary gain, the notion that clients can derive benefit from their problem. For complex and poorly understood reasons, people sometimes act as though they unconsciously wish to keep their symptoms. Therapists, whatever their persuasion, may have to examine a client's interpersonal relationships for clues that might explain why he or she seems to prefer to hold on to a problem that causes distress.

Attribution to self A person who has terminated therapy might attribute improvement in behaviour to an external cause, the therapist, and could relapse once that attributed factor is no longer present. Since behaviour therapy, especially therapy relying on operant manipulation, attributes much improvement to environmental forces, it might be wise for behaviour therapists to help their clients feel more responsible. By encouraging an "I did it" attitude, perhaps by motivating them to practise new skills and expose themselves to challenging situations, therapists may help their clients depend less on therapy and the therapist and better maintain their treatment gains.

Evaluation of Cognitive-Behavioural Therapy

The core assumption of all cognitive therapies is that the way people construe their world is a major—if not the major—determinant of their feelings and behaviour. Our examination of CBT focuses on the rational-emotive behaviour therapy (REBT) inspired by Ellis and on Beck's cognitive therapy (CT). We also include a more extensive discussion of Young's schema therapy.

Ellis's Rational-Emotive Behaviour Therapy

The basic premise of REBT is that emotional suffering is due primarily to the often unverbalized assumptions and demands that people carry around with them as they negotiate their way in life. Demanding perfection from oneself and from others, Ellis hypothesizes, is a principal cause of emotional distress. Expecting that one has to be approved of by everyone and for everything one does is another belief that Ellis regards as irrational and that other writers (e.g., Goldfried & Davison, 1994) have called unproductive or self-defeating. The REBT therapist challenges these assumptions and persuades the client that living a life without imposing on oneself unattainable demands and goals will be less stressful and more satisfying. Irrational beliefs must be disputed and replaced by new rational beliefs. Meanwhile, the process of challenging irrational beliefs continues in order to reduce the likelihood of previous problems recurring at a later date (see Dryden, David, & Ellis, 2010).

While there is a body of research supporting the effectiveness of REBT for various forms of psychopathology, including depression and anxiety, as well as helping emotionally healthy people cope better with everyday stress (for a review, see David, Szentagotai, Kallay, & Macavei, 2005), we are currently in an era where there have been few empirical attempts to compare REBT with other forms of treatment. Thus, in comparative terms, there is a growing disparity between the amount of research support for classical REBT vs. the degree of support for CBT. Still, REBT principles can be useful in many contexts. For instance, REBT principles formed the basis of a seemingly successful resilience boosting intervention for soldiers deployed during Operation Iraqi Freedom called "warrior resilience and thriving" (see Jarrett, 2013). Also, REBT appears to achieve its effects through a reduction in the irrationality of thought. The importance of the support that REBT gives clients to confront what they fear and to take risks with new, more adaptive behaviour should not be underestimated. Further, in actual practice, REBT is typically integrated with other interventions within the CBT family (e.g., Beck's cognitive therapy, exposure therapy), rather than used as a stand-alone treatment (DiGiuseppe & David, 2015).

Beck's Cognitive Therapy

Like Ellis, Beck hypothesizes that people in emotional distress operate with assumptions—he calls them schemas—that are impossible to live with, such as believing that one has to be a perfect parent or student. But in contrast to Ellis, Beck focuses a great deal on the lack of objective evidence that depressed and anxious people have for maintaining their maladaptive schemas. Beck engages the client in a process very much like a scientific investigation, asking such questions as what evidence the client has for believing that he or she is totally inept and worthless. A principal focus is on cognitive biases: errors in information processing, such as selective abstraction and overgeneralization, that filter experience in a way that contributes to negative beliefs about oneself and the world.

The effectiveness of Beck's CT has been under intensive study for more than 30 years. Numerous studies attest to the favourable impact it has on depression (e.g., Clark, Beck, & Alford, 1999; Dobson & Hamilton, 2002), and an earlier meta-analysis of outcome studies of diverse therapies for depression concluded that Beck's therapy achieves greater short-term improvement than wait-list controls, drug therapies, non–cognitive-behavioural treatments, and a heterogeneous group of other psychotherapies (Dobson, 1989). CT may also be better than drug treatment at preventing future episodes, a consideration of major importance in light of the oft-observed tendency for depressive episodes to recur (e.g., Hollon, DeRubeis, & Evans, 1996). Perhaps CT clients acquire some useful skills that they are able to use following termination of therapy. As seen in Chapter 16, because older clients can be extremely sensitive to medications and can also have medical problems that contraindicate prescribing psychoactive drugs, nonpharmacological interventions are especially appropriate for them.

The great interest in CT led to the widely publicized comparative outcome study sponsored by the National Institute of Mental Health (Elkin, Parloff, Hadley, & Autry, 1985), a study that did not find CT superior to a drug therapy or to IPT but nonetheless supported the utility of Beck's approach to the treatment of depression. Further, a task force of the clinical division of the American Psychological Association concluded that Beck's CT is an effective treatment for panic disorder, generalized anxiety disorder, social phobia, chronic pain, irritable bowel syndrome, and bulimia nervosa, and that it often fares better than medications alone (Chambless et al., 1996).

As originally hypothesized by Beck, CT helps clients change their cognitions. Predictable changes in cognitions do occur in CT (e.g., Hollon et al., 1996), but such changes are found as well in successful treatment of depression by drugs (e.g., Rush et al., 1982). Cognitive change may therefore be the consequence of change produced by other means (Jacobson et al., 1996). Or, at least with depression (the disorder in which CT has been most researched), cognitive change may be the mediator of therapeutic improvement brought about by any therapy, including Beck's CT, IPT, and pharmacotherapy.

Evidence in support of CBT has been cited in several chapters of this book, including chapters focused on anxiety, depression, and schizophrenia. An important paper by Hofmann, Asmundson, and Beck (2013) titled "The Science of Cognitive Therapy" provides an up-to-date overview of the voluminous evidence and they argue that cognitive therapy has moved beyond a specific treatment model and now represents "a scientific approach that incorporates a wide variety of disorder-specific interventions and treatment techniques" (p. 199). Hofmann et al. (2013) included a description of research linking changes stemming from CBT with brain-related changes. Overall, their conclusion seems to be quite reasonable, but some caveats are in order.

First, evidence for the superiority of CBT vs. other forms of treatment fails to provide consistent evidence that CBT is superior. This was demonstrated most recently in a review of CBT for depression in adults that CBT is an effective treatment for depression but it is not demonstrably superior to other psychotherapies or pharmacotherapy (Cuijpers et al., 2013). Another meta-analysis that appeared at about the same time found no comparative superiority of CBT in both anxiety and depression treatment studies (Baardseth et al., 2013). More recently, Honyashiki and colleagues (2014), using a newer multiple treatments meta-analysis approach, concluded that CBT was more effective than no treatment controls, but in comparison with other psychological treatments, although CBT had higher effect sizes, it was not significantly better. The authors pointed out that when CBT was given for a longer period of time, there was greater evidence of a specific effect and that future research may support specificity for CBT.

Second, it remains to be established that CBT is effective in addressing certain deeply ingrained personality styles unless treatment is tailored specifically to key themes. For instance, Hewitt, Flett, and Mikail (2017) argue that people suffering from perfectionism often have developed perfectionism in response to unmet interpersonal needs and they require treatment components that address not only their perfectionism but also key interpersonal issues.

Other caveats were raised by Dobson (2013), who agreed with the general conclusions reached by Hofmann et al. (2013) about the strong empirical support for CBT. However, he cautioned that research is still needed to provide further insights into establishing how the specific components and mechanisms leading to improvement actually work. Dobson (2013) also predicted that in future years, there will be an increasing emphasis on meta-cognitive processes in CBT. His emphasis on a "meta-cognitive model of change" is in recognition of emerging approaches such as acceptance and commitment therapy (ACT; Hayes, 2004) that are less interested in change because the focus of these approaches is to acknowledge and accept difficult situations and self-realities. As summarized by Dobson (2013), "an alternative metacognition may be to accept that things are difficult, and then choose to do something different in any event" (p. 226).

Research on CBT for depression has sought to identify the specific treatment components that are most effective. A general statement endorsed by many in the field is that we know that CBT works, but we need more insight into the specific factors and processes that operate when it does work. Initially, this research indicates that it is the behavioural interventions rather than the cognitive interventions that are most beneficial, both in the short term (Jacobson et al., 1996) and in the longer term (Gortner, Gollan, Dobson, & Jacobson, 1998). Contemporary research emphasizes fine-grained "component analyses." For instance, one study found that social skills development and problem solving may be key CBT elements for treating depression in adolescents (Kennard et al., 2009).

Beck and his colleagues believe that additional research into the mechanisms of CT might be even more important to the future of CT than research into its efficacy.

"In order to serve our patients better, and to assure that the progress of cognitive therapy keeps pace with that of alternative treatments, clinical researchers need to improve and refine cognitive therapy and the training of cognitive therapists, so that more patients can benefit from it. To do so, we need first to understand better how cognitive therapy achieves its effects."

(DeRubeis, Tang, & Beck, 2001, p. 386)

According to Bieling and Kuyken (2003), even though CT seems to be effective, until research on the validity of cognitive case formulation is conducted, "researchers cannot conclude that cognitive therapy is effective because its statements about etiology and the mechanisms of change are correct" (p. 53). The ultimate goal is to move from a descriptive approach toward a more explanatory approach by identifying and testing specific, hypothesized cognitive mechanisms that contribute to the presentation of problems and by identifying and testing the distal and proximal factors believed to be involved when a person begins to develop dysfunctional beliefs and cognitive styles.

As an example, Gellatly and Beck (2016) argue that catastrophic thinking is a process relevant across various psychological disorders, with unique content depending on the specific disorder. For example, a client with social anxiety disorder may catastrophize the meaning of showing visible symptoms of anxiety (e.g., "if others notice me blush, they won't want to hang out with me in the future"). In therapy, strategies aimed at decatastrophizing should lead to symptom change. Future research is necessary to empirically validate catastrophic thinking as such a process.

Finally, there are many other issues to be addressed in future research, such as a greater focus on the effectiveness of CBT delivered in the real world and improved dissemination to reach the many clients who currently do not have access (McMain, Newman, Segal, & DeRubeis, 2015). Finally, in this section we focused on the main unique aspects of CBT, but we would be remiss not to recognize that therapeutic alliance is important for successful CBT (Weck et al., 2015).

Young's Schema-Focused Therapy

The approaches advocated by Ellis and Beck have one thing in common. They both convey the message that people can change their psychological predicaments by thinking differently. They emphasize that how a person construes himself or herself and the world is a major determinant of the kind of person he or she will be, and that people have choices in how they construe things. They assert that people can, sometimes with great effort, choose to think, feel, and behave differently. Unlike behaviour therapists, who are not cognitive, but like the humanists and existentialists, Beck and Ellis believe that new behaviour is important primarily for the evidence it can provide about how the person looks at himself or herself and the world. Thus, their focus remains on the cognitive dimension of humankind and on the abiding belief that people's minds can be set free and that their thinking is the key to positive psychological change.

Jeffrey Young has taken these approaches a significant step further in his schema-focused therapy. Recall that schema-focused therapy (also known as schema therapy) was introduced in Chapter 13. A focus on core themes or constructs is at the root of his schema therapy (see Young, 1999; Young, Klosko, & Weishaar, 2003). Schema therapy is designed for people with personality disorders suffering from complex forms of dysfunction. It uses cognitive techniques but also borrows from other approaches, such as interpersonal treatment. According to Martin and Young (2010), schema therapy can not only be used to treat personality disorders or other specific individual difficulties (e.g., depression) but can also be amended to treat couples. The focus is on early maladaptive schemas that represent the key themes addressed with CBT techniques. Schemas exist at a deep level and attempts to identify and change them are called "schema work" (DeRubeis, Webb, Tang, & Beck, 2010).

Is schema therapy effective? An initial review of 12 treatment studies that met inclusion criteria led to the conclusion that schema therapy yields significant clinical improvements. However, the researchers also concluded that more comparative research is needed, especially involving clients with complex cases (Masley, Gillanders, Simpson, & Taylor, 2012).

As noted by Jacob and Arntz (2013), most existing research testing the value of schema therapy has focused on its use in treating borderline personality disorder, but variations on schema therapy have been developed for most of the recognized personality disorders. Jacob and Arntz (2013) cautioned that research on the use of schema therapy to address other personality disorders is still in its infancy, but nevertheless, the existing data suggest this approach is promising. However, they also noted the need to expand the application of schema therapy to both group and individual therapy and as a treatment approach for episodic disorders such as depression.

17.4 Review of Psychoanalytic Therapies

Before we evaluate several psychoanalytic psychotherapies, it will be good to review and summarize their core features and contrast this with contemporary versions of psychodynamic treatment. Information on the whole range of psychotherapy was presented in greater detail in Chapter 2.

Basic Concepts and Techniques in Classical Psychoanalysis vs. Contemporary Psychodynamic Treatment

"Undergraduate textbooks too often equate psychoanalytic or psychodynamic therapies with some of the more outlandish and inaccessible speculations made by Sigmund Freud roughly a century ago, rarely presenting mainstream psychodynamic concepts as understood and practised today."

(Shedler, 2010, p. 98)

At the heart of classical psychoanalysis is the therapeutic attempt to remove repressions that have prevented the ego from helping the individual grow into a healthy adult. Psychopathology is assumed to develop when people remain unaware of their true motivations and fears. They can be restored to healthy functioning only by becoming conscious of what has been repressed. When people can understand what is motivating their actions, they have a greater number of choices. Where id is, let there ego be, to paraphrase a maxim of psychoanalysis. The ego—the primarily conscious, deliberating, choosing portion of the personality—can better guide the individual in rational, realistic directions if repressions are minimal.

As described in Chapter 2, psychoanalysts employ a variety of techniques to achieve the goal of insight into repressed conflicts. Among these are:

- free association, in which the client, reclining on a couch, is encouraged to give free rein to thoughts and feelings and to verbalize whatever comes to mind;

- the analysis of dreams, in which the therapist guides the client in remembering and later analyzing his or her dreams, the assumption being that during sleep the ego defences are lowered, allowing repressed material to come forth, usually in disguised form; and

- interpretation, whereby the therapist helps the person finally face the emotionally loaded conflict that was previously repressed; at the right time, the analyst begins to point out the client's defences and the underlying meaning of his or her dreams, feelings, thoughts, and actions.

The concept of transference is of particular importance to psychoanalysts. Freud noted that his clients sometimes acted toward him in an emotion-charged and unrealistic way. For example, a client much older than Freud would behave in a childish manner during a therapy session. Although these reactions were often positive and loving, they could also be negative and hostile. Since these feelings seemed out of character with the ongoing therapy relationship, Freud assumed that they were relics of attitudes transferred to him from those held in the past toward important people in the client's childhood, most often parents. In other words, Freud felt that clients responded to him as though he were one of the important people in their past. Freud used this transference of attitudes, which he came to consider an inevitable aspect of psychoanalysis, as a means of explaining to clients the childhood origin of many of their concerns and fears. This revelation and explanation, he believed, tended also to help lift repressions and allow the client to confront buried impulses. In psychoanalysis, transference is regarded as essential to a complete cure. It is precisely when analysts notice transference developing

Contemporary psychodynamic therapists contend that this form of therapy is just as effective as other types of treatment.

that they take hope that the important repressed conflict from childhood is getting closer to the surface.

Those who have modified classical psychoanalysis to make it more efficient—generally referred to as *psychodynamic therapists*—are more oriented toward the present than was Freud (see photo). However, they still emphasize unconscious motivation and the need for clients to understand the hidden reasons for their current feelings and behaviour.

Brief therapy, or brief psychodynamic therapy, focuses more on practical, real-life problems, still within the general framework of psychoanalysis. The different forms of brief therapy share several common elements (Koss & Shiang, 1994):

- Assessment tends to be rapid and early.
- It is made clear right away that therapy will be limited and that improvement is expected within a small number of sessions, from six to 25.
- Goals are concrete and focused on the amelioration of the client's worst symptoms, on helping the client understand what is going on in his or her life, and on enabling the client to cope better in the future.
- Interpretations are directed more toward present life circumstances, interpersonal experiences, and client behaviour than on the historical significance of feelings.
- Development of transference is not encouraged, but some positive transference to the therapist is fostered to encourage the client to follow the therapist's suggestions and advice.
- There is a general understanding that psychotherapy does not cure, but that it can help troubled individuals learn to deal better with life's inevitable stressors.

What are the elements that distinguish short-term psychodynamic interpersonal psychotherapy from CBT? A very useful

summary was provided by Blagys and Hilsenroth (2000). They identified the following seven distinguishing features:

1. a focus on affect and the expression of emotion;
2. the exploration of attempts to avoid thoughts and feelings that create distress;
3. the identification of recurring themes and patterns that are expressed in thoughts, feelings, experiences, or relationships;
4. an emphasis on past experiences and how they relate to current experiences;
5. a focus on interpersonal relationships;
6. an emphasis on the therapy relationship; and
7. the exploration of the clients' wishes, dreams, and fantasies.

It is important to note that these distinguishing attributes were identified on the basis of empirical articles that described the key elements of contemporary psychodynamic interventions.

According to Messer and Abbass (2010), contemporary psychodynamic treatment of personality disorders has three primary emphases in addressing personality dysfunction: (1) *defensive restructuring* to address hidden and repressed themes; (2) *affective restructuring* to facilitate the tolerance of distress; and (3) *cognitive restructuring* of beliefs and schemas while bolstering coping skills. The emphasis on cognitive restructuring suggests that although there are differences, there is significant overlap with CBT.

Evaluation of Psychodynamic Psychotherapy Outcomes of Research

The time involved means that there are relatively few outcome studies of long-term psychoanalytic treatment. In fact, there is a limited number of trials that evaluate long-term outcome based on any form of psychotherapy (Steinert, Kruse, & Leichsenring, 2016). One of the most ambitious early attempts to evaluate the effectiveness of psychoanalysis that deserves mention was the Menninger Foundation Psychotherapy Research Project, which began in the mid-1960s. In this study, 42 participants—mostly white clients with anxiety, depression, or both (what used to be referred to as "garden-variety neuroses")—were seen in either psychoanalysis (22) or short-term psychodynamic psychotherapy (20). In both groups, about 60% of the clients improved. There were no significant differences between the two groups either immediately after treatment or at follow-ups of two to three years (Wallerstein, 1989).

A review by de Maat, de Jonghe, Schoevers, and Dekker (2009) was quite illuminating. Their review was based on 27 studies since 1970, of which 19 met quality control criteria. The criterion of long-term treatment was 50 sessions or more. Overall, the studies collectively involved more than 5,000 participants. The mean number of sessions for those receiving psychoanalysis was 500 over an average period of 3.6 years (i.e., 140 sessions per year). The mean number of sessions for those receiving psychotherapy was 150 over an average period of 2.5 years (i.e., 60 sessions per year). It was concluded that long-term psychotherapy was quite effective, but this conclusion needs to be qualified in at least three respects. First, significantly greater effectiveness was found for symptom reduction rather than personality change, but moderate personality change did occur. Second, most studies focused on moderate pathology and only three studies focused on severe pathology; thus, follow-up research on severe pathology is needed. Finally, only one study used a randomized control trial design and two others had control groups. Thus, statements about the comparative effectiveness of long-term psychodynamic treatment had to be made with significant caution.

More recently, Smit et al. (2012) conducted a meta-analytic summary of 11 clinical RCT investigations. The conclusion that emerged from this study was that the rate of recovery following long-term psychoanalytic psychotherapy was relatively equal to the recovery rate found with other interventions. Most importantly, substantial evidence was found of variability in the results across studies and this led Smit et al. (2012) to conclude that, at present, there is only limited and conflicting support for the effectiveness of long-term psychoanalytic psychotherapy. Finally, Knekt and colleagues (2016) randomly assigned 326 clients to short-term psychodynamic psychotherapy, solution-focused therapy, or long-term psychodynamic psychotherapy. Across 10 years of follow-up, the authors found little benefit to the long-term approach, but they noted that about half of clients in the short-term groups and a third of clients in the long-term group sought out other therapies during the follow-up period.

The picture emerging from outcome studies on brief psychodynamic therapy is generally positive. A comprehensive meta-analysis of 23 studies of over 1,300 participants found that brief psychodynamic therapy is effective (Driessen et al., 2010). Short-term psychodynamic psychotherapy yielded large treatment changes in depression level and these changes were maintained at one-year follow-up. Initially, other forms of treatment were deemed to be slightly more effective at post-treatment, but this superiority was not maintained at one-year follow-up. Similar results have been found in more recent meta-analyses (see Abbass, Town, & Driessen, 2012; Leichsenring et al., 2015), although there is a call for more research on some disorders (e.g., PTSD, OCD; Leichsenring et al., 2015). On the basis of these and other findings, some authors have argued vociferously for the effectiveness of contemporary versions of short-term psychodynamic psychotherapy (Leichsenring & Klein, 2014).

17.5 | Review of Client-Centred Therapy

We turn now to client-centred therapy, developed by the influential psychologist Carl Rogers.

Basic Concepts and Techniques of Client-Centred Therapy

Usually regarded as a humanistic psychotherapy, Rogers's client-centred therapy rests on the basic premise that people can be understood only in terms of their own phenomenology—the immediate experience that they have of themselves and their world—and that they become disordered when they fail to attend to their own inner nature and instead guide their behaviour according to what others wish. Client-centred therapy places great emphasis on people's freedom to choose and on the responsibility that comes from having that freedom. We are what we make of ourselves, according to Rogerian and other humanistic and existential therapists.

The therapist's principal role is to create conditions in therapy that are totally accepting and non-judgemental, and the therapist should accomplish this by being empathic rather than directive. The result is that clients gradually come to better understand their own wishes, needs, fears, and aspirations and gain the courage to pursue their own goals rather than the goals that others have set.

Evaluation of Client-Centred Therapy

Many efforts have been made to evaluate client-centred therapy, largely because of Rogers's insistence that the outcome and process of therapy be carefully scrutinized and empirically validated. Indeed, Rogers is rightfully credited with originating the field of psychotherapy research. He and his students deserve the distinction of being the first to remove the mystique and excessive privacy of the consulting room. For example, they pioneered the tape-recording of therapy sessions for subsequent analysis by researchers.

A meta-analysis of studies on client-centred therapy from 1978 to 1992 conducted by Les Greenberg at York University and his colleagues concluded clients were better off after the intervention than about 80% of comparable people who had not received any professional therapy (see Greenberg, Elliot, & Lietaer, 1994). Although not bad, this outcome is no better than that achieved by comparison therapies, such as brief psychodynamic treatment, with people who are not severely disturbed. Of the 35 studies in the meta-analysis, only eight had a control group.

Most research on Rogerian therapy has focused principally on relating outcome to the personal qualities of therapists. While some results have been inconsistent, a meta-analysis of data from 3,599 clients in 59 independent samples found that therapist empathy was a moderately strong predictor (mean weighted $r = .31$) of positive therapy outcomes and this pattern held across therapists with different theoretical orientations (Elliott, Bohart, Watson, & Greenberg, 2011). Further, a recent qualitative meta-analysis involving 109 studies suggested the importance of enhancing therapists' understanding of client experiences and that clients are their own agents of change (Levitt, Pomerville, & Surace, 2016). Thus, it makes sense to

Adam Horvath of Simon Fraser University has done extensive work examining the client–therapist relationship and the efficacy of the therapeutic alliance.

continue emphasizing these qualities in the training of clinicians, as such qualities are likely to help create an atmosphere of trust and safety and increase the client's sense of mattering to key other people.

According to a historical review of developments involving the client–therapist relationship by Adam Horvath (2000) from Simon Fraser University (see photo), one finding that was not anticipated by Rogers is entirely in keeping with his emphasis on subjective, phenomenological experiences; that is, the client's perception of the therapist's behaviour is more important in predicting therapy outcome than the therapist's actual behaviour in the therapeutic relationship. Thus, the client's cognitive appraisals are quite important.

Rogers's emphasis on subjective experience raises epistemological problems, for the therapist must be able to make accurate inferences about what the client is feeling or thinking. Validity is a real issue. Rogers relied on what the client said, yet he also asserted that clients can be unaware of their true feelings; it is this lack of awareness that brings most of them into therapy in the first place.

The exclusive use of self-descriptive measures of outcome in the earliest research on client-centred therapy was later supplemented with more direct assessment of how well the client functions in daily life, such as how adequately he or she performs social roles. An associated trend is the use of multiple methods to assess therapeutic change, as investigators have come to appreciate the complex nature of behaviour and the need to assess it along many dimensions (e.g., Lambert, Shapiro, & Bergin, 1986). Client self-reports, for example, can be supplemented by physiological measures, as well as by reports from significant others (e.g., spouses).

Rogers may be criticized for assuming that self-actualization is the principal human motivation. He inferred this motive from his observation that people seek out situations offering fulfillment, but then he proposed the self-actualization tendency as an explanation for the search for these situations—an example of circular reasoning (i.e., a tautology). Rogers assumed both that the psychologically healthy person makes choices to satisfy self-actualizing tendencies and that people are by their very natures good. But how do we explain people who engage in abhorrent behaviour that injures or kills others? Are these people basically good?

It may be that the problem of extreme unreasonableness was not adequately addressed by Rogers because he and his colleagues concentrated on people who were only mildly disturbed. As a way to help unhappy but not severely disturbed people understand themselves better (and perhaps even to behave differently), client-centred therapy may be appropriate and effective.

Extension of Client-Centred Therapy: Compassion-Focused Therapy

The views of Rogers have had an enormous impact in several ways, including how certain concepts such as empathy and being able to explore emotions in a safe and warm atmosphere contribute to higher levels of functioning. One impact is that the principles underscoring client-centred therapy have helped pave the way for related theoretical approaches. Indeed, in the next segment of this chapter, we discuss emotion-focused therapy mostly as a form of couples therapy. **Compassion-focused therapy** is another therapeutic approach rooted in a Rogerian approach. Paul Gilbert and his associates have developed a therapy designed specifically for people who are highly self-critical and who seem to have never developed the capacity for self-compassion and self-acceptance. A key element of the process here is the therapist being a model of empathy and displaying a compassionate approach both to the client and to himself or herself (Gilbert, 2014). In short, the therapist provides the kind of non-judgemental, safe space that enables people to begin to address their self-criticism and the issues and negative emotions they have avoided or repressed. According to Gilbert (2014), self-compassion training has an evolutionary basis and it has biological underpinnings because he maintains that learning to be self-compassionate can elicit the same neurological responses that people experience when they have been treated in warm and supportive ways by other people.

Early research focusing on case studies yielded a variety of interesting findings. A case series by Mayhew and Gilbert (2008) of three people with psychotic features involving hallucinations of experiencing malevolent voices showed that compassion-focused therapy can be used effectively with more severe forms of psychopathology. A case excerpt for a 26-year-old student (referred to as Participant 2) indicated the following:

> "Participant 2 had concealed his psychotic symptoms for three years prior to being diagnosed with schizophrenia. Many of his self-critical thoughts related to previous sexual encounters that he felt were shameful. He kept his illness hidden from others as he felt ashamed of his diagnosis and felt that people would reject him if they found out. He also felt ashamed of his weight gain since commencing psychotropic medication. He tended to keep people at a distance from him as it felt safer and had difficulty trusting others as he felt they

could read his mind. He had a history of self-harming by cutting, which he used to regulate his emotions. He felt that the function of his malevolent voices was to remind him of the 'bad things' he had experienced in life."

(p. 125)

Compassion-focused therapy increased his spontaneous self-compassionate thoughts and resulted in substantial overall improvement.

Case studies have also been used to show that compassion-focused therapy can result in treatment gains among people who were previously treated unsuccessfully with CBT. One case involved a young woman named Jenny who suffered a traumatic brain injury. CBT had a limited impact on her low self-esteem and difficulties interacting with other people, but subsequent treatment with compassion-focused therapy yielded improvements in self-esteem and general mental health functioning across a range of indicators (Ashworth, Gracey, & Gilbert, 2011).

Compassion-focused therapy is beginning to be studied extensively and evidence is accumulating for its usefulness. For instance, a study conducted in Canada by Kelly and associates showed that compassion-focused therapy was effective in reducing levels of smoking, especially among those smokers who were high in trait self-criticism and low in readiness to change (Kelly, Zuroff, Foa, & Gilbert, 2010).

Research is also beginning to show that compassion-focused therapy can be incorporated into existing treatment programs. One study showed that compassion-focused therapy as part of standard CBT for eating disorders yielded clinically significant improvement for 73% of the clients with bulimia nervosa. However, people with anorexia or eating disorder not otherwise specified showed less improvement, with only about 1 in 4 experiencing clinically significant improvement (Gale, Gilbert, Read, & Goss, 2014).

Two recent reviews concluded that compassion-focused therapy shows promise but more high-quality trials are required: one review was based on 12 studies (Beaumont & Hollins-Martin, 2015) and the other was based on 14 studies (Leaviss & Uttley, 2015). Additionally, given that some of the research combined compassion-focused therapy with other interventions, it is hard to draw conclusions specific to the efficacy of compassion-focused therapy (Beaumont & Hollins-Martin, 2015). Further, compassion-focused therapy may be particularly helpful for highly self-critical clients, the people for which it was designed (Leaviss & Uttley, 2015).

17.6 Review of Couples Therapy

The issues and problems facing individuals seeking treatment are often complicated because the person is often impacted by

iStock.com/asiseeit

When a problem involves a couple, therapy is most effective if the couple is seen together.

and impacting on dysfunctional relationships. Johnson and Lebow (2000) noted, "Distress in an intimate relationship is recognized as the single most frequent presenting problem in psychotherapy" (p. 23). Couples therapy is often the preferred mode of treatment (see photo).

It is interesting from a historical perspective that some of the classic approaches to treatment of individuals were rooted initially in treatments geared toward couples. Most notably, a recent overview paper noted that REBT really began with Ellis as a form of marital therapy and that this topic fascinated Ellis from the beginning of his career (McMahon & DiGiuseppe, 2013). These same authors also noted that Ellis himself had several failed marriages, so this likely fuelled his interest. Beck also applied cognitive therapy to marital conflict. His views and recommendations are outlined in a book titled *Love Is Never Enough* (Beck, 1988). He outlined in this book how negative thinking can potentiate and prolong relationship conflict.

Clearly, marital conflict can have a profound negative impact on the well-being of family members. Marital adjustment is closely linked with life satisfaction (Be, Whisman, & Uebelacker, 2013). The relationship is bidirectional: the higher the marital adjustment people reported, the more satisfied people reported they were with their lives two years later, and vice versa. Moreover, in another study, marital disruption was associated with shorter salivary telomere length, an indication of advanced cellular aging (Whisman, Robustelli, & Sbarra, 2016). Given the negative impact marital conflict has, it is important to examine how best to treat it, but first we consider whether some conflict in relationships is to be expected.

The Normality of Conflict

There is almost universal agreement among couples therapists and researchers, regardless of theoretical orientation, that conflict is inevitable in a marriage or in any other long-term relationship. Evidence attests to the fact that most marriages are characterized from the beginning by a high level of relationship satisfaction, but couples differ because there are substantially different patterns of relationship change as measured by change trajectories (see Lavner & Bradbury, 2010). The aura of the honeymoon can pass quickly for some couples or gradually when the couple makes unromantic decisions about where to live, where to seek employment, and how to budget money. How couples deal with such inherent conflicts often determines the quality and duration of their relationship.

Lavner and colleagues (2014) examined changes in marital problems over the course of the first four years of marriage. Not surprisingly, marital satisfaction decreased, on average across the four years, but marital problems tended to stay stable. They questioned the couples every six months about 19 problems in a marriage (e.g., money management, trust, in-laws, sex) and their responses were similar across time. Perhaps the commonly held belief that marital problems increase over time is not true, at least not across the early years of marriage. Couples were less satisfied with their marriage, but had the same problems as when they were first married.

The Approaches to Couples Therapy

The term "couples therapy" does not denote a set procedure. It tells us that therapeutic focus is on two people in a relationship, but it leaves undefined such issues as how the therapist views the nature and causes of the problem, what techniques are chosen to alleviate it, and how often clients are seen.

Couples therapy shares some theoretical frameworks with individual therapy. Psychoanalytic marital therapists, for example, focus on how a person seeks or avoids a partner who resembles, to his or her unconscious, the opposite-sexed parent (Segraves, 1990). Transference is explored, but in analytic couples therapy, it is the transference between the two partners rather than between the client and the therapist that is usually the focus. We now describe some of the more commonly researched approaches to couples therapy.

The Mental Research Institute Tradition
Couples and family therapy seems to have begun in the 1950s at the Mental Research Institute (MRI) in California, where the focus was on faulty communication patterns, uneasy relationships, and inflexibility. Family members were shown how their behaviour affected their relations with others. They were then persuaded to make specific changes, such as making their needs and dislikes more clearly known to others. Few family therapists who identify themselves with the MRI approach are concerned with history. Their focus is on how current problems are being maintained and how they might be changed. Whatever the problem, the family therapist takes a family systems approach, a general view of etiology and treatment that focuses on the complex interrelationships within families.

Cognitive-Behavioural Approaches   Distressed couples do not react very positively toward each other, and this antagonism is usually evident in the very first session. In a pioneering treatise on behavioural marital therapy, Jacobson and Margolin (1979) recommended that the therapist attend to

this problem of antagonism as a first step in helping partners improve their marriage. One strategy is the "caring days" idea of Richard Stuart (1976), which applies an operant strategy to the couple's conflict. The husband, for example, is cajoled into agreeing to devote himself to doing nice things for his wife all day on a given day, without expecting anything in return. The agreement is that the wife will do the same for him the next day. If successful, this strategy accomplishes at least two important things: first, it breaks the cycle of distance, suspicion, and aversive control of each other; and second, it shows the giving partner that he or she is able to affect the spouse in a positive way. This enhanced sense of positive control is achieved simply by pleasing the partner. The improved atmosphere that develops as a consequence of their doing nice things for each other and having nice things done for them in return helps each of them become motivated to please the other on future occasions.

Behavioural marital or couples therapy shares with other approaches a focus on enhancing communication skills between the partners, but the emphasis is more on increasing the ability of each partner to please the other. Behavioural couples therapists generally adopt Thibaut and Kelley's (1959) exchange theory of interaction. According to this view, people value others if they receive from them a high ratio of benefits to costs; that is, if they see themselves getting at least as much from the other person as they give. Furthermore, people are assumed to be more disposed to continue a given relationship if other alternatives are less attractive to them, promising fewer benefits and costing more. Therapists therefore try to encourage a mutual dispensing of rewards by partner A and partner B. Distressed couples differ from non-distressed couples in that they have lower frequencies of positive exchanges and higher frequencies of unsatisfying exchanges.

Behavioural couples therapists have become increasingly interested in cognitive components of relationships and relationship distress, a reflection of the cognitive trend in behaviour therapy as a whole (Baucom, Epstein, & Rankin, 1995). As Camper et al. (1988) found, spouses in distressed marriages view negative behaviour on the part of their partners as global and stable—"There is nothing I can do to please him, and it's never going to change"—whereas they construe positive behaviour as less so—"Well, he was happy with me today, but it's not going to last." The interest in cognition in couples therapy can also be traced to the influence of attribution theory in social psychology (the study of how people explain the reasons for their own and others' behaviour) and the overlap between marital distress and depression. As a result of adding this cognitive component and broadening its treatment strategies, behavioural marital therapy is now frequently referred to as cognitive-behavioural marital therapy (CBMT). CBMT focuses on each person's attributions; for example, paying close attention to whether one partner decides that the other is responsible or blameworthy for an event that was actually not under anyone's control.

Integrative Behavioural Couples Therapy
Integrative behavioural couples therapy (IBCT) was developed by Andrew Christensen and Neil S. Jacobson (Christensen,

Jacobson, & Babcock, 1995). IBCT uses reinforcement principles as well as the behavioural exchange and communication training strategies just described, but it also incorporates the Rogerian notion of acceptance and provides a series of procedures designed to foster emotional acceptance in couples (Cordova & Jacobson, 1993). IBCT, relative to traditional behavioural couples therapy (TBCT), recognizes that the actions and inactions of partners are important but even more important is the emotional reactivity that one has to the actions and inactions.

How does IBCT fare vs. TBCT? A large clinical trial of couples therapy for maritally distressed people was conducted by Christensen et al. (2004). The initial results indicated that both types of treatment resulted in significant clinical improvements, but the improvement was more consistent with IBCT. The long-term follow-up investigation reported by Christensen, Atkins, Baucom, and Yi (2010) found that 50.0% of the IBCT couples and 45.9% of the TBCT couples showed clinically significant improvement five years later. Also, 25.7% of the IBCT couples were separated or divorced, while 27.9% of the TBCT couples were separated or divorced. These differences were not statistically significant but the divorce rates were substantially lower than in other couples therapy studies, where divorce rates have ranged from 38 to 70%. Thus, it seemed that both IBCT and TBCT worked.

Recent research has focused on identifying mechanisms of change. One study evaluated positive and negative spouse behaviours during IBCT and TBCT (Sevier, Atkins, Doss, & Christensen, 2015). They found different patterns of change for constructive behaviours (more positive behaviours, less negative behaviours) for the two treatments. Couples who responded to IBCT seemed to decrease in constructive behaviours early on but increase later. Couples who responded to TBCT were found to have the opposite pattern: increasing in constructive behaviours early but decreasing later. Another study found that following TBCT, couples were rated to have better communication at post-therapy than those who received IBCT, but couples who underwent IBCT had better communication at a two-year follow-up (Baucom, Baucom, & Christensen, 2015). Although the outcomes seem similar for the two treatments, there appear to be some differences in the patterns of change.

Can we predict who will do better with which treatment? Having a longer marriage and higher levels of commitment predicted lower rates of divorce and separation for both therapies (TBCT and IBCT) (Baucom, Atkins, Rowe, Doss, & Christensen, 2015). There was one distinguishing feature: for moderately distressed couples, higher wife-desired closeness was related to better outcomes for IBCT but worse outcomes for TBCT. The authors speculated that this result may be due to the greater emphasis placed on emotional acceptance in IBCT compared with TBCT.

Emotion-Focused Therapy The approach to conjoint treatment known as emotion-focused therapy (EFT) (e.g., Johnson, 2007; Johnson & Greenberg, 1987) contains psychodynamic elements, but its humanistic emphasis on feelings strikes us as more salient. There is an even stronger focus on emotion than in IBCT. See Canadian Perspectives 17.1 for a detailed description and evaluation of this therapy.

Canadian Perspectives 17.1

Emotion-Focused Couples Therapy

Emotion-focused therapy (EFT) was developed by Les Greenberg of York University and Susan Johnson (see photo), now at the University of Ottawa (e.g., Bradley & Johnson, 2005; Greenberg & Johnson, 1988; Johnson, 2007; Woolley & Johnson, 2006). EFT can be applied to individuals but is also used extensively with couples.

The essence of EFT for couples is that marital distress stems from maladaptive and distressed forms of emotion in the marital context and the destructive interactions that follow from this maladaptive emotion. This focus on negative emotions is consonant with the humanistic, experiential approach adopted originally by Greenberg and Johnson, as well as with findings indicating that the emotional processing in therapy is associated with improvements in psychological functioning (e.g., Pos, Greenberg, Goldman, & Korman, 2003; Watson & Bedard, 2006). Although the focus is on negative emotions such as guilt, anger, and shame, couples must also establish more constructive ways of relating via the processing and expression of positive emotions as well (see Greenberg & Goldman, 2008).

EFT incorporates a focus on adult attachment styles in relationships (Johnson, 2002; Johnson & Whiffen, 2003), integrating

Courtesy of Susan Johnson

Susan Johnson, Professor Emeritus, University of Ottawa and Distinguished Research Professor, Alliant International University, founded emotion-focused couples therapy. She was appointed to the Order of Canada in 2016, one of Canada's highest honours.

(continued)

WENN/Newscom

Sandra Bullock filed for divorce from her husband Jesse James after it was revealed that James had carried on multiple extramarital affairs. Such betrayals can cause attachment injuries, especially when a public humiliation is involved.

components from attachment theory (Bartholomew & Horowitz, 1991). From this vantage point, relationship distress occurs when the attachment needs have not been met and the relationship does not provide a secure base for one or both partners. In extreme forms, one partner may experience an attachment injury. This injury would follow betrayals of trust or abandonment at a key time. A publicly known betrayal of trust such as that experienced by actress Sandra Bullock when her husband's infidelities became known should result in an extreme attachment injury (see photo).

Typically, EFT involves 12 to 15 sessions. The process of change is broken down into three general phases that span nine steps altogether (see Johnson, 2000; Johnson, Hunsley, Greenberg, & Schindler, 1999). The goal of the first phase is to de-escalate the maladaptive cycle by: (1) assessing the current conflicts experienced by the couple and fostering an alliance; (2) identifying the problematic interaction cycle that is maintaining problems in the relationship; (3) accessing underlying emotions; and (4) trying to reframe the problem in terms of associated emotions and attachment needs.

The goal of the second phase is to change interactional positions by: (1) helping the couple to identify needs and aspects of the self that have been denied and incorporate these into the relationship; (2) learning to accept the partner's new emotional experience and related responses; and (3) learning to express specific needs and developing a sense of positive emotional engagement.

The goal of the third phase is consolidation and integration and this involves two main steps: (1) attempts are made to arrive at new solutions to old problems; and (2) new positions and new cycles of attachment behaviour must be consolidated.

Empirical evaluations suggest that EFT is effective. Johnson et al. (1999) reported the results of a meta-analysis of seven studies that assessed EFT and marital distress. The majority of couples reported clinical improvement, and 70 to 73% had recovered from marital distress. Further, Dessaulles, Johnson, and Denton (2003) found support for EFT as a treatment for couples experiencing marital distress where the female partner meets critieria for depression.

Recent research has focused on processes of change and predictors of outcome for EFT. Those who present for couples therapy are often high in emotional control and low in emotional self-awareness. EFT was shown to be effective for this presentation; these couples were still able to engage in the deep emotional experiencing characteristic of EFT (McRae et al., 2014). Further, individuals with higher levels of emotional control and higher attachment anxiety were actually found to show greater change in marital satisfaction (Dalgleish et al., 2015). Lastly, in an examination of warmth (Schade et al., 2015), it was found that how warm a therapist was toward the husband was strongly related to how warm the husband was toward his wife across therapy. However, therapist warmth toward the wife was not related to how warm the wife was toward her husband.

There is also growing evidence for the role of EFT in fostering forgiveness in couples where one member has been emotionally injured by the other member. One study documented gains in forgiveness among 17 of 20 couples undergoing EFT to repair emotional injuries (Greenberg, Warwar, & Malcolm, 2008) and another study found that greater trust and forgiveness lasted for three years following EFT for an attachment injury (Halchuk, Makinen, & Johnson, 2010). Finally, a recent study focused on the relationship between shame and forgiveness (Meneses & Greenberg, 2014). Shame predicted forgiveness, and decreases in marital distress were strongly related to the ability of the injured spouse to accept the shame of their partner.

EFT can be modified and tailored to address specific issues and specific adjustment problems. Johnson (2007) makes the point that EFT has a focus on universal emotions from the person's idiosyncratic viewpoint and, as such, it is well-suited for use with different kinds of people from different cultures.

Thinking Critically

1. Theorists have discussed the suitability of using couples treatment to address disorders that are experienced by individuals but may not yet involve a marital component (e.g., a depressed spouse). Do you think EFT could be used to address disorders experienced by individuals?

2. It is usually suggested that men are low in emotional expression. Do you think that men, relative to women, will benefit more, less, or the same from EFT? Explain.

It should be reiterated that emotion-focused therapy consists of principles and processes that can also be used to treat individuals. In 2012, Les Greenberg from York University was awarded the American Psychological Association Award for Distinguished Professional Contributions to Applied Research for his pioneering work on EFT. Greenberg (2012)

used this occasion to update his views on the role of emotion. He made the important point that because emotional experience often occurs prior to and independently of cognition, an exclusive emphasis on the cognitive level of processing is not likely to produce lasting emotional change. Greenberg (2012) also delineated six "empirically based principles of emotional

TABLE 17.2	Principles of Emotional Change in Emotion-Focused Therapy
Principle	**Description**
Emotional awareness	The most fundamental principle: people must come to know what they feel in order to reconnect to their needs
Expression	Displaying emotions, including physical movements and sensations, within the relative safety of the therapy context
Regulation	Identifying, labelling, allowing negative emotions while engaging in self-soothing and increasing positive emotions
Reflection	Contemplating emotional experiences in order to make greater sense of them and incorporate them into the self-narrative
Transformation	Changing primary maladaptive emotions through activating other adaptive emotions
Corrective experience	Changing an emotion by taking part in a new experience that changes the original emotion (e.g., having a successful experience that mitigates previous feelings of failure)

Source: Adapted from Greenberg (2012).

change" (p. 703) that are central to EFT-based improvements. These principles, which can also be considered mechanisms of change, are listed and described briefly in Table 17.2. The case study described at the beginning of this chapter illustrates a number of these key principles.

General Features of All Couples Therapy

In all forms of couples therapy, each partner is trained to listen empathically to the other and to state clearly to the partner what he or she understands is being said and what feelings underlie those remarks. A principal focus is improving communication between partners so that personal needs can be met without sacrificing the needs and wishes of others.

An interaction pattern known as the demand-withdraw cycle is recognized as particularly destructive for couples. First described by researchers at MRI (Watzlawick, Beavin, & Jackson, 1967; see also Christensen & Pasch, 1993), the demand-withdraw pattern is characterized by one partner attempting to discuss a problem and the other avoiding or withdrawing from such efforts. This withdrawal generates more demands from the first spouse, who tries harder and harder to engage the other, only to be met with more avoidance. And so the cycle escalates. Christensen and Heavey (1990) suggest that there are sex differences in this pattern: women tend to assume the demanding role whereas men usually withdraw. Although some couples engage in demand-withdraw behaviour more than others (Baucom, Dickenson, et al., 2015), this pattern has been linked to relationship quality for both heterosexual and same-sex relationships (Baucom, McFarland, & Christensen, 2010).

Couples and family therapy have for years made creative use of video recording equipment. A couple can be given a problem to solve during part of a therapy session, such as where to

go on vacation, and can be recorded while they attempt to solve it. The ways in which they push forward their own wishes—or fail to—and the ways in which they accommodate the other's wishes—or fail to—are but two aspects of their communication patterns that a therapist can come to understand from later viewing the video, often with the couple watching also.

Another common practice among family therapists is to give couples specific homework assignments so that they can practise the new patterns of interaction they have learned during sessions and begin the important process of generalizing change from the therapy room to their everyday lives. Couples may be asked to practise paraphrasing each other's sentences for a specified time period, such as a half hour after dinner, as part of an active listening assignment.

There is great variety within couples therapy—from psychoanalytic to behavioural to emotion-focused. The techniques employed reflect the therapist's particular theoretical orientation. What all couples therapies have in common is the view that conflicts and tensions are inevitable when people live together and that the best way to address these problems is to involve both partners.

Ethical Issues and Special Considerations

The severity and nature of marital dysfunction treated by therapists vary considerably. Couples therapy is further complicated when one or more elements of abuse (physical, sexual, and emotional) is present. The therapist must consider what effect saving the relationship may have on the abused spouse and possibly on the abused children, for when there is spousal abuse there is a high likelihood of child abuse, as well. Regardless of who the identified client is, the therapist must be sensitive to the needs of all those whose lives are affected by the relationship (Kadis & McClendon, 1998; see Karakurt et al., 2016 for a recent review and meta-analysis).

Other ethical considerations in couples therapy include how to deal with the disclosure of secrets by one spouse when the other spouse is not present. Some therapists handle this at the outset of treatment by telling the couple that nothing that is told to the therapist by one of the partners will be kept secret from the other. Other therapists feel that this policy may keep them from obtaining valuable information (Kadis & McClendon, 1998).

While the theoretical orientations used in individual therapy often transfer and can be used in couples therapy, it is important to acknowledge the additional complexities involved in couples therapy. For instance, as noted by Davis, Lebow, and Sprenkle (2012), it is often the case that one member of a couple is motivated and committed to change while the other member is not. Also, the couples therapist has to develop a working alliance with each member of the dyad as well as a working alliance with the couple as a whole. A **split alliance** occurs when the therapist has a stronger alliance with one member of the couple than with the other member.

Evaluation of Couples Therapy

A meta-analysis of 20 carefully selected outcome studies meeting stringent methodological standards concluded that, overall, couples therapy has beneficial effects for many relationship problems (Hazelrigg, Cooper, & Borduin, 1987). Subsequent reviews have reached similar conclusions (e.g., Stratton et al., 2015). According to Halford et al. (2012), about half of the couples receiving empirically supported couples therapy tend to improve so that they no longer have clinical problems in relationship dissatisfaction. About 1 in 5 couples show no improvement whatsoever and up to 30% show improvement but still have significant problems.

The obvious next question is "What factors differentiate those couples who improve vs. those who do not improve?" Couples therapy is typically less effective for those couples with more severe forms of relationship distress and dissatisfaction as well as couples where at least one member of the dyad has a co-existing psychological disorder (Halford & Snyder, 2012). This second factor illustrates how research may not relate to practice because laboratory studies testing the efficacy of couples therapy often exclude couples where one or more members has a serious adjustment problem (see Halford & Snyder, 2012).

Halford and Doss (2016) review several trends in couples therapy, including a trend for treating individual forms of psychopathology with couples therapy (see also Baucom et al., 2014). Even in a happy relationship, including a partner in therapy can help to use that partner in a helpful way, rather than have that partner behave in ways that may maintain symptoms or even make them worse (Baucom et al., 2014).

One example of the use of couples therapy for individual psychopathology is that of a multi-site gambling study done in Ontario and Alberta (Lee & Awosoga, 2015). Rather than just focusing on treating problem gamblers individually, problem gamblers and their spouses took part in couples therapy aimed at the problem gambling behaviour. There were significant improvements in gambling symptoms, distress, and family functioning.

Couples therapy can also be highly effective for alcohol abuse and drug dependence (McCrady et al., in press). A meta-analytic review of 12 randomized control trials found that behavioural couples treatment was superior to individualized therapies (Powers, Vedel, & Emmelkamp, 2008). Significant improvements were found in several domains, including frequency of drug use, consequences of use and abuse, and relationship functioning.

A final example concerns depression. Brief problem-focused couples therapy was conducted with couples in which there was a depressed wife (Cohen, O'Leary, & Foran, 2010). Two-thirds of the depressed women experienced improved depressive symptoms vs. only 17% in a control group. Treatment also contributed to improvements in other domains including marital satisfaction, depression in husbands, and in the understanding and acceptance of depression in depressed women and their partners.

Another trend relates to monitoring progress across sessions (Halford & Doss, 2016). Using a measure of relationship satisfaction, by the fourth session of therapy, researchers were able to predict how 70% of couples would fare at the end of therapy (Pepping, Halford, & Doss, 2015). Future research is needed to determine whether feedback given to couples as therapy progresses can enhance outcomes.

As reviewed by researchers at McGill University, relationship satisfaction is typically the outcome measure used in most studies of couples therapy; however, there is a trend to include other outcome measures, including measures of individual well-being (MacIntosh & Butters, 2014). These are positive changes when you consider that in many cases a therapy can be successful even if a marriage ends. For example, in cases where distressed couples are navigating their way through a separation, decreased distress may be the most important outcome.

Of importance, the large effect sizes seen in efficacy trials are not usually seen in effectiveness studies; typically only small to moderate effect sizes are found in actual clinical practice studies (Halford, Pepping, & Petch, 2016). Figure 17.2 shows the differences in effect sizes for efficacy vs. effectiveness trials and Figure 17.3 shows the differences in recovery rates. As a reminder, common features of efficacy studies include that they are done in research settings, have rigid inclusion and exclusion criteria, and often advertise to find participants. Effectiveness studies are done in routine clinical settings with typical clients seeking treatment.

As one possible explanation for the different results obtained with efficacy vs. effectiveness studies, Halford and colleagues (2016) note that efficacy trials often contain mostly couples who wish to enhance their relationship. However, effectiveness studies typically contain a greater mix of clients who wish to enhance their relationship and clients who are considering terminating their relationship. Other conclusions and recommendations reached by Halford and colleagues (2016) include:

- The importance of assessing whether couples are seeking to improve their relationship or instead are focused on determining whether or not to stay in the relationship.

- When working with couples, therapists should use appropriate measures to assess the relationship as well as the functioning of the individual partners. This information should be shared with the couple and used to determine therapy goals.

- Therapists should embark on further assessments throughout therapy to monitor progress and alliance, and discuss with the couple.

- Research does not generally support one form of couples therapy over another.

- There is significant room for future research, including studies comparing efficacy and effectiveness trials, studies comparing the various forms of couples therapy, and longitudinal studies.

We will conclude with some comments about the need for greater diversity in couples therapy research. Despite the growing use of "couples" rather than "marital" therapy, little

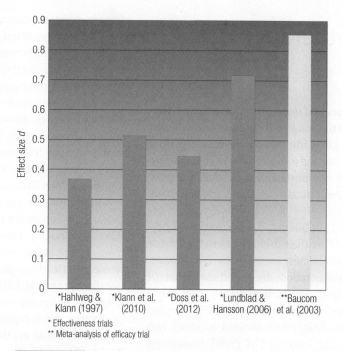

FIGURE 17.2 Effect size of pre-therapy to post-therapy changes in efficacy and effectiveness trials of couple therapy.

research has been done on same-sex or unmarried heterosexual couples. There are more and more cohabiting couples in Canada and other Western nations, but there is very little research comparing couples therapy with cohabiting vs. married couples (Halford et al., 2016). Also, as noted by Johnson and Lebow (2000), there is increasing recognition of the need

for research that incorporates a focus on cultural diversity; much of the field has focused on white, middle-class couples. There are over 200 ethnicities in Canada, and many newcomers, often arriving from difficult circumstances (such as war). The research in this area has not been done with such populations (McLuckie, Allan, & Ungar, 2013).

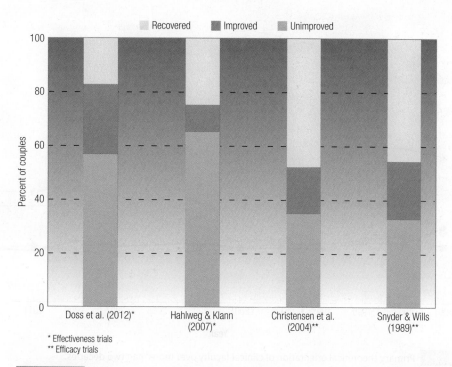

FIGURE 17.3 Comparison of variability and clinical significance of change immediately after therapy in efficacy and effectiveness trials.

17.7 Psychotherapy Integration

Having reviewed the theory and research on the major psychological interventions, we turn now to the question of whether useful connections can be made among them and general questions about eclecticism and integration in psychotherapy. Before we do, however, it is important to note some emerging trends in psychologists' theoretical orientations and in psychotherapy training.

As noted in Chapter 2, in Quebec, the percentage of psychologists who chose CBT as their primary orientation more than doubled in 20 years (Jaimes, Larose-Hébert, & Moreau, 2015). Numbers for other orientations decreased somewhat. Of the psychologists surveyed, 38% selected CBT, 22% chose existential-humanistic approaches, and another 22% selected psychodynamic-psychoanalytic. When allowed to select two orientations, more than half selected CBT (56%). Comparing Quebec psychologists with those of the rest of Canada yields some differences (Tasca, 2015). Compared with the rest of

Canada, fewer psychologists in Quebec report CBT as their primary orientation whereas more Quebec psychologists report emotion-focused/humanistic/existential and psychodynamic-psychoanalytic. Further, in an attempt to bridge the gap between what clinicians want to see researchers focus on and what researchers are actually doing, they were asked to rate a number of topics. Among the topics of greatest interest were alliance, client factors, therapist factors, and mechanisms of change. Among the lowest ranked topics were barriers to treatment access, client-treatment matching, technology, progress monitoring, and therapy manuals.

Recently, two separate analyses by different teams of researchers concluded that the cognitive-behavioural orientation is dominating clinical training programs to the degree that it may not be in the best interests of the clients or the field as a whole (see Heatherington et al., 2012; Levy & Anderson, 2013). Heatherington et al. (2012) found that 4 out of 5 clinical science programs designate themselves as CBT programs, and they stated that this is problematic because CBT is not superior to treatments based in other theoretical orientations. Figure 17.4 depicts the results of a multi-year survey that tracked the theoretical orientation of clinical faculty (see Levy & Anderson, 2013).

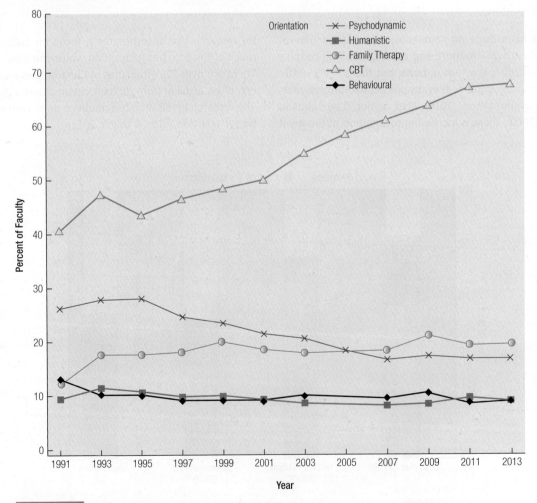

FIGURE 17.4   Primary theoretical orientation of clinical faculty over more than two decades.

Source: From page 212 of Levy & Anderson, 2013. *Clinical Psychology: Science and Practice,* 20, 211–220. This material is reproduced with permission of John Wiley & Sons, Inc.

Here the extreme predominance of CBT is shown, relative to the 10% of those who endorse a humanistic orientation or a purely behavioural orientation. Fortunately, this figure is focused on the main theoretical affiliation and does not preclude the possibility of embracing an integrated approach. Approaches to theoretical integration are discussed in the section "Eclecticism and Theoretical Integration in Psychotherapy."

Eclecticism and Theoretical Integration In Psychotherapy

How much integration is there at present? The answer to this question depends largely on whom you ask and when you ask.

A 2009 survey of 201 doctoral-level practitioners in the United States examined the use of 127 techniques reflecting eight major theories of psychotherapy (Thoma & Cecero, 2009). The survey found extensive evidence of use of techniques outside of one's primary theoretical orientation. Therapists from the humanistic, CBT, and psychodynamic orientations all reported using more techniques from outside of their orientation than from inside their orientation. Overall, 23 techniques out of the 127 were endorsed by respondents from all therapist groups. The top five techniques that were acknowledged universally were (1) trying to understand the world from the client's point of view, (2) providing unconditional positive regard, (3) challenging maladaptive or distorted beliefs, (4) being congruent and genuine, and (5) reflecting feeling.

Another investigation of 24 expert psychotherapists (with a mean of 32 years of clinical experience) found stronger allegiance to their main theoretical orientation (Hickman, Arnkoff, Glass, & Schottenbauer, 2009). However, most therapists still reported some degree of influence by all four orientations assessed (i.e., humanistic, CBT, psychodynamic, and family systems).

Treatment orientations and associated conceptualizations often reflect this emphasis on integration. For instance, although Young's schema-focused therapy was included in the section on CBT, a distinguishing element of Young's schema therapy is that it is an integration (see Edwards & Arntz, 2012) and it combines cognitive therapy relational perspectives rooted in classic accounts provided by the object relations theorist and seminal interpersonal theory as espoused by such luminaries as John Bowlby and Harry Stack Sullivan. Indeed, many schemas implicated in psychopathology, while clearly cognitive entities, are, in fact, relationship schemas. On a similar note, as part of his address given to the American Psychological Association, Greenberg (2012) concluded by issuing a call for integration so that emotion-focused therapy would be linked inextricably with CBT in a complex integration.

Four Types of Psychotherapy Integration

Distinctions have been drawn among four modes of psychotherapy integration: technical eclecticism, common factorism, theoretical integration, and assimilative integration. In technical eclecticism, exemplified in Lazarus's multimodal approach and in Beutler's prescriptive psychotherapy (Beutler & Harwood, 1995), the therapist works within a particular theoretical framework (e.g., CBT), but sometimes imports from other orientations techniques deemed effective, though without subscribing to the theories that spawned them. "Use whatever works" is the operating principle of the technical eclectic, but one should rationalize the use of a technique from one's own framework.

Common factorism (e.g., Frank, 1961; Goldfried, 1991; Schofield, 1964) seeks strategies that all therapy schools might share, such as alliance, empathy, hope, and unconditional positive regard. An approach that could be considered common factorism was outlined in a book on treatment planning by Sheila Woody and associates (see Woody, Detweiler-Bedeil, Teachman, & O'Hearn, 2003). Woody, located at the University of British Columbia, was a member of the APA Division 12 Task Force on empirically supported treatments (ESTs). Woody et al. (2003) outlined an eclectic treatment planning system that favours evidence-based approaches. They described a phase approach to treatment planning that includes steps toward identifying problems, establishing clear treatment goals and aims, and measuring treatment progress after implementing ESTs. It represents common factorism because, other than a general preference for ESTs, no single theoretical orientation is imposed and therapists are free to adopt techniques and conceptualizations from various approaches. Researchers at McGill University sought to determine which factors are most important, as perceived by expert psychologists (Stamoulos et al., in press). They found that most of their expert psychologist participants viewed therapeutic alliance as the most important common factor, followed by therapist empathy (Stamoulos et al., in press).

The third approach, theoretical integration, tries to synthesize not only techniques but also theories. Wachtel's efforts to justify and make sense of assertion training within a modified psychoanalytic framework is a prime example of an effort toward theoretical integration. The resulting theory is itself something different because of the blending of psychoanalytic and behavioural elements. As another example, the recent integration of mindfulness meditation techniques with traditional CBT, as seen in mindfulness-based cognitive therapy and dialectical behaviour therapy, challenges therapists to integrate acceptance and change-based strategies (see Lau & McMain, 2005). Hayes (2002) describes the integration of Eastern spiritual practices, particularly mindfulness meditation, with CBT as the third epoch in the evolution of behaviourally informed therapies. A group in Quebec developed a manual for combining CBT with acceptance and commitment therapy for depression (Hallis, Cameli, Dionne, & Knauper, 2016).

The fourth approach, assimilative integration, is the newest form of integration; the psychologist stays primarily within one orientation, but concepts and techniques from other orientations are assimilated in a cohesive manner (Castonguay et al., 2015). As described by McWilliams (in press), based on her personal perspective of therapists, including herself (a psychoanalyst): "Specifically, most of us are assimilative integrators, trained in one main language but then subsequently motivated to become at least literate in others."

How popular are the four types of psychotherapy integration? The Society for the Exploration of Psychotherapy Integration conducted a survey of its members and found that 29% preferred assimilative integration, 29% theoretical integration, 26% common factors, 10% technical eclecticism, and 6% endorsed other (Norcross, Nolan, Kosman, & Fernandez-Alvarez, in press).

Castonguay and colleagues (2015) summarized the past quarter century of research on integrationist perspectives. They note that many providers identify as integrative, but not many researchers focus on psychotherapy integration. They suggest greater collaboration between psychologists identifying as integrationists and psychotherapy researchers. McWilliams (in press) echoed that plea for greater collaboration across clinician and researcher camps. Boswell (in press) summarizes the integration movement as follows: "In my view, the core focus of the psychotherapy integration movement has always been the integration of research, theory, and practice, with the ultimate goal of improving the effectiveness of psychotherapy for individual patients." (p. 1).

17.8 Contemporary Developments in Treatment and Intervention

"We know now from improved and more comprehensive epidemiological research that the burdens of mental illness are enormous, that our well-developed evidence-based treatments are not reaching individuals in need and that merely extending our evidence-based needs to clinical practice with the dominant model currently in use will not have the needed impact."

(Kazdin & Rabbit, 2013, p. 185)

This conclusion from Kazdin and Rabbit (2013) is an extension of the conclusions and arguments advanced in an earlier paper by Kazdin and Blase (2011) in which they illustrated that the demand and need for services for people in need tends to dramatically exceed the services that are available and actually delivered. They make the point that this is especially true in developing countries where there is a paucity of resources, but it is also true in countries such as Canada and the United States, where more resources exist but are accessed by a relatively small proportion of the population. The papers by Kazdin and Blase (2011) and by Kazdin and Rabbit (2013)

outline extended modes and models of service delivery that are designed to extend the range of interventions provided to people.

Similarly, Parikh (2015) began a guest editorial in the *Canadian Journal of Psychiatry* by noting, "Psychotherapy works well, but our mental health care system does not" (p. 242). He summarized the evidence showing that most clients are not able to access psychotherapy in Canada, largely due to lack of funding. He also suggested ways to improve access without need for more funds, largely through stepped care models involving self-help and technology. The final segment of this chapter explores some of the innovations that have been developed to try to address this challenge. We have already discussed the role of new technology in psychological interventions in earlier chapters; most notably, the role of virtual reality was explored in terms of treatment of PTSD, and building resilience in soldiers going into combat was described at length in Chapter 9. Here we will focus on other innovative technological advances, but also discuss some of the complex issues that arise from the use of these technologies.

A recent overview paper by Maheu, Pulier, McMenamin, and Posen (2012) discussed at length the practical and ethical issues that accompany these new technologies and emphasized the need to have an increased focus on technology and related issues in graduate education, training, and supervision. The new term emerging for these innovations is **psychotechnologies**. This general term can refer to the delivery of psychotherapy and related services involving Skype, Twitter, Facebook, and various other alternatives such as mobile phones. There are also more secure telehealth apps, such as VSee, that are compliant with Canadian privacy laws. Mobile phones can be used for assessment purposes (e.g., self-monitoring) or for sending texted reminders to engage in positive self-management practices (e.g., engage in self-reward, be self-compassionate by directing a random act of kindness at yourself). Technologies that are used in treatment typically can also be used in prevention as well (see Proudfoot, 2013). Clough and Casey (2011) see technological advances as a useful adjunct to face-to-face therapy.

One avenue that continues to show promise is Internet-based delivery. Some versions are solely Internet-based, while others involve therapist support, possibly in the form of infrequent face-to-face sessions (either individually or in groups), telephone calls, and/or email check-ins. For example, Andersson et al. (2006) conducted a randomized control trial of a nine-week, Internet-delivered CBT self-help program for social anxiety disorder that was combined with two group exposure sessions in real life and minimal therapist contact via e-mail. Relative to waiting list controls, treated participants showed significant improvement on most measured dimensions, which were maintained at one-year follow-up. Importantly, recent data suggest that online therapist-assisted CBT can be effective not only in clinical trials but also in routine clinical practice. The reported level of client satisfaction was high, with reliable improvement in symptom functioning found among about 7 in 10 participants and full recovery sustained in slightly more than half of the participants (Ruwaard et al., 2012).

Studies on the use of Internet-based CBT have been growing and several meta-analyses have been published recently. A meta-analysis of Internet-based CBT for PTSD found moderate to large effect sizes compared with passive control conditions such as wait-list control groups (Kuester, Niemeyer, & Knaevelsrud, 2016). However, Internet-based CBT was not superior to active control conditions (e.g., psychoeducation) and no studies compared Internet-based CBT with face-to-face CBT. Another meta-analysis for PTSD had similar conclusions with respect to comparisons with passive control conditions, and also raised the lack of comparisons with face-to-face CBT, but they found a trend for superiority of Internet-based CBT over active control conditions (Sijbrandij, Kunovski, & Cuijpers, in press). These minor differences are likely due to different criteria for study inclusion in the two meta-analyses. With respect to OCD, a meta-analysis supported that technology-based CBT was superior to control conditions, but there was a trend toward face-to-face interventions yielding better outcomes (Dèttore, Pozza, & Andersson, 2015).

Availability of CBT is also limited for children and technology may represent a means to reach more children with mental health problems. Rooksby and colleagues (2015) conducted a review and meta-analysis on the use of the Internet in the delivery of CBT for treating anxiety in children. Ages across the seven studies ranged from 7 to 16, and the interventions included one stand-alone online therapy and three computer-assisted CBT programs. Overall, the evidence supported CBT interventions that included computerized delivery for childhood anxiety, but there were suggestions for improvements in this area of research. There is a need for more data on treatment completion and compliance, more follow-up assessments, more studies on younger children, and there are currently no published data on cost savings.

In the *Canadian Medical Association Journal*, Gratzer and Khalid-Khan (2016) reviewed the use of CBT delivered via the Internet for anxiety and depression, as well as psychological distress related to physical illness. For example, they cited an online therapy for patients in Saskatchewan who are experiencing anxiety and/or depression after completing cancer treatment. Overall, they found evidence for the efficacy of the programs they reviewed and ended with several challenges for implementation, including how to blend online CBT with other treatments (e.g., medication, therapist support), having a sufficient number of clinicians to support it, and increasing awareness.

Although results for online therapy are promising across a range of disorders, some caution is warranted. As Stangier (2016) notes, in the case of social anxiety disorder, much of the research has been conducted by the groups that developed the Internet-based therapies. Further, for some areas, results have not yet been compared with face-to-face delivery (e.g., PTSD;

Kuester et al., 2016). Finally, online therapies are typically not recommended for clients with a high level of severity. Prior to Internet-based therapies, videoconferencing has been used to address the problem of geographical distances in the delivery of services. The Alberta Mental Health Board developed a "telemental health service" that has been in existence since 1996. The service uses videoconferences to make psychiatric consultations available to health practitioners in rural parts of the province. There are videoconference sites throughout Alberta, including Drumheller, Slave Lake, Peace River, and Fort Chipewyan. Published studies indicate that the program is quite effective (e.g., Simpson et al., 2001a, 2001b). For instance, 96.2% of rural physicians indicate that they are satisfied or very satisfied with the telemental health service, and 80.8% indicate that they are satisfied with the mental health improvement of clients they have referred for service. Surveys indicate that approximately 9 out of 10 people were satisfied with their sessions, felt that the doctor listened to them, felt supported and encouraged, and felt that the sessions could provide the same information that would have been presented in person. Importantly, 9 out of 10 also felt that they would rather use telepsychiatry than have to spend time on a waiting list to obtain treatment. Still, assessment showed that about 50% of clients would have preferred a face-to-face session over telepsychiatry (Simpson et al., 2001b).

In one specific case, telehealth technology was used to deliver family therapy to family members who remained in their rural Ontario home while an adolescent female member of the family with anorexia was being treated in an urban hospital (Goldfried & Boachie, 2003). The family members were highly satisfied with telehealth and had no concerns about confidentiality issues.

How do these results compare with overall research patterns? A review conducted by Richardson et al. (2009) showed that with respect to the small number of randomized controlled studies conducted thus far, telemental health has been found to have equivalent efficacy in a variety of settings compared with face-to-face care. However, Richardson et al. (2009) further observed that methodologically flawed investigations are the norm and this has limited further research and adoption of telemental health approaches.

Bouchard and associates at the Université du Québec have conducted research on virtual reality exposure therapy. Klinger et al. (2005) conducted a pilot study of virtual reality therapy for social anxiety disorder that entailed 12 sessions of traditional group CBT with in vivo exposure vs. individual CBT with in virtuo exposure. "In virtuo" is a relatively new technique that has emerged only in recent years with the development of virtual reality therapy. Both experimental conditions resulted in significant improvements and it seems that in virtuo exposure is a useful alternative to existing treatments for social anxiety disorder. However, this experiment lacked a wait-list control group, so conclusions must be qualified. Bouchard et al. (2006) demonstrated the effectiveness of virtual reality exposure in the treatment of arachnophobia using 3D games. A review of

39 studies of virtual reality therapy for phobias concluded that in virtuo exposure treatment is an effective alternative to in vivo exposure treatment (Côté & Bouchard, 2008).

One innovation that is receiving an increasing amount of attention is computerized CBT (cCBT). Typically, this involves developing a standardized program that can be used in conjunction with treatment as usual. Student Perspectives 17.1 examines the results of a cCBT intervention implemented by researchers based at Harvard University. General evaluations suggest that cCBT can be effective, but dropouts tend to be higher in this form of treatment and substantial staff time is still involved when this option is employed (Waller & Gilbody, 2009).

Aboujaoude, Salame, and Naim (2015) conducted a broad review of the use of technology in the delivery of mental health treatment. They reviewed computerized CBT (cCBT), Internet-based CBT (iCBT), virtual reality exposure therapy (VRET), and mobile therapy. Overall, they found the most support for cCBT and iCBT, but concluded that VRET and mobile therapy were promising despite having less research to date. One challenge highlighted was the need for clients to have computers as well as the requisite computer skills. Other concerns raised were high rates of attrition and concerns regarding alliance. Notwithstanding these issues, the advantages of increased client access, increased efficiency of treatment delivery, and possibly reduced stigma are significant and warrant further investigation and dissemination efforts.

As technology advances and the need for therapeutic services increases, it is likely that more and more people will avail themselves of these technologically based forms of treatment. Regulatory bodies are continuously working on ethics and standards protocols for the therapeutic services often delivered through the Internet. Key issues to consider include ways to safeguard the client's confidentiality and right to anonymity, as well as to maximize the safety of these individuals.

An examination of the use of various self-help strategies in Canada, using data from the Canadian Community Health Survey—Mental Health (CCHSMH, 2012), found that very few Canadians are actually using the Internet to obtain mental health treatment (MacKenzie & Kocovski, 2016). Of those with a perceived need for help with their emotions, mental health, and or alcohol/drug use, about 25% turned to the Internet. Of those respondents who went online, the majority did so to learn about symptoms (77%); only 5% were taking part in online therapy. Perhaps more efforts aimed at public education and dissemination would be worthwhile.

Student Perspectives 17.1

Computerized CBT for Depressed and Anxious Students

Most university and college counselling centres have lengthy waiting lists as the year progresses because of the number of students who require some form of treatment. This is despite the fact that only a relatively small proportion of students in need actually seek this kind of help. Innovations that would increase the number of students able to access psychotherapy would be very welcome. What does this unaddressed service need look like at present?

Some useful insights were provided by a recent study by Santucci et al. (2014). Students suffering from depression and/or anxiety and who were deemed by trained personnel to be suitable were offered treatment with a cCBT program known as "Beating the Blues." This well-known program consists of eight 50-minute sessions offered over an eight-week period. Traditional CBT strategies used include the identification and challenge of negative automatic thoughts, beliefs, and negative attributions; exposure; problem-solving training; and sleep management. Homework assignments between sessions are also given.

Unfortunately, the program saw mixed results in terms of its usefulness. Those participants who completed the program reported significant improvement in their symptoms and their functional improvement. For instance, the initial mean score on the Beck Depression Inventory was 24.59 and this dropped to 16.59 at post-treatment and 14.16 at follow-up. The problem, however, was that there was a low rate of session completion. Only 12% of the participants completed all eight sessions, and only 3.2 sessions were completed on average. Moreover, reminders did not improve retention.

Nevertheless, participants indicated that they had moderate to high satisfaction with this cCBT program and the researchers concluded that the study illustrated the feasibility and effectiveness of this form of psychotherapy.

Thinking Critically

1. Do you agree with the researchers' conclusion that cCBT can be effective? Why do you think that most students completed fewer than four sessions?

2. If you had this option available and were feeling depressed or anxious, would you opt to see a personal therapist or try the cCBT option? Are there certain personal characteristics that would make some students more likely to select the cCBT option?

3. One argument in its favour is that cCBT can be accessed 7 days a week and 24 hours a day. Another recent study found that unhelpful aspects of cCBT reported by students included burden of work, time and pace, issues with the actual content of the program and its delivery, and "technical difficulties" running the program (see Richards & Timulak, 2012). What would you tell a fellow student who is conducting their own cost-benefit analysis about the potential benefits?

Summary

17.1 Research on the effectiveness of various forms of psychotherapy has been conducted for many decades, with sometimes complicated and inconsistent results. The evaluation of the effects of psychotherapy has grown in significance as increased demands for accountability are being imposed. Client factors, such as degree of hope and motivation for change, are related to outcome, as are therapist factors (e.g., therapist attachment style, experience). The relationship between the client and therapist, or the therapeutic alliance, is also important.

17.2 There are vast differences between the way therapies have been examined in experimental settings and the way they are actually practised by clinicians. Recent research has employed treatment manuals that specify what experimenters are to do when applying given therapies to research participants. Although this practice enhances the internal validity of psychotherapy research, the contrast with therapy as practised—making adjustments depending on the needs of the individual client—limits the external validity of such research. There is a gap or even a chasm between therapy as studied experimentally and therapy as delivered and practised.

17.3 The cognitive and behavioural therapies attempt to apply the methodologies and principles of experimental psychology to the alleviation of psychological distress. Because of their emphasis on research, the various behavioural and cognitive-behavioural therapies account for the lion's share of both process and outcome research in psychotherapy. Evidence attests to the efficacy of counterconditioning, exposure, operant, and cognitive-behavioural interventions in alleviating a wide range of disorders. However, the fact that high end-state functioning is often not achieved even by clients whose improvement is significant highlights the fact that much remains to be learned. Cognitive therapies, such as Ellis's rational-emotive behaviour therapy and Beck's cognitive therapy, alter the thoughts that are believed to underlie emotional disorders. They reflect the increasing importance of cognition in experimentally based psychological interventions. Research is now focusing increasingly on identifying the components of treatment that account for improvement. While CBT is effective in treating various forms of disorder, its superiority in terms of treatment effectiveness relative to other treatment options has not been clearly established. Of particular importance for the cognitive and behavioural therapies, as well as for other approaches, is the generalization of treatment effects once the client is no longer seeing the therapist on a regular basis.

17.4 Classical psychoanalysis tries to uncover childhood repressions which have prevented the individual from growing into a healthy adult. Brief psychodynamic therapy puts more emphasis on the client's need and ability to achieve greater control over both the environment and instinctual gratification. It is a time-limited therapy in which expectations are set for fewer than two dozen sessions. There is a focus on setting concrete goals and learning ways to cope with life's inevitable stressors, forsaking the goal of psychoanalysis to obtain a personality overhaul through analysis of the transference neurosis. Research on psychoanalytic and brief psychodynamic therapies suggests that they can be useful for a variety of anxiety and depressive disorders.

17.5 Rogers trusted the basic goodness of the drive to self-actualize, and he proposed the creation of non-judgemental conditions in therapy. Through empathy and unconditional positive regard, client-centred therapists help their clients view themselves more accurately and trust their own instincts for self-actualization. Research on client-centred therapy has investigated whether such factors as empathy and genuineness on the part of the therapist are associated with good outcomes. Compassion-focused therapies are derived in part from client-centred approaches and focus on increasing self-compassion among clients who are highly self-critical.

17.6 Marital or couples therapy helps distressed couples resolve the conflicts inevitable in any ongoing relationship of two adults living together. Behavioural and some insight-oriented therapies show promise in easing the stress that many couples experience. There is an increasing trend to use couples therapy to treat individual psychopathology of one partner.

17.7 Often clinicians identify with more than one theoretical orientation and may see themselves as eclectic. Integration in psychotherapy represents a trend that reflects growing awareness on the part of many clinicians and researchers of the limitations of their respective theoretical approaches. The four approaches to psychotherapy integration are technical eclecticism, common factorism, theoretical integration, and assimilative integration. There are risks, however, in integrating diverse theoretical perspectives, such as glossing over differences that might be better examined and evaluated.

17.8 Dissemination of effective therapies remains an important issue to be addressed. Although effective interventions exist, many people are not able to access them for various reasons (e.g., geographical location, cost). One promising development is the use of technology to deliver empirically supported interventions.

Key Terms

assimilative integration
common factorism
compassion-focused therapy
core competencies
demoralization hypothesis
dodo bird effect

effectiveness
efficacy
empirically informed therapies
empirically supported therapies (ESTs)
evidence-based practice
psychotechnologies

split alliance
stepped care
technical eclecticism
theoretical integration
therapeutic (working) alliance

Reflections: Past, Present, and Future

1. What do you think is most important in determining the success or failure of psychological treatment? Do you place more emphasis on client factors, therapist factors, or the relationship between the client and the therapist? Which client factors would you see as most important if this was the choice you made?

2. We discussed recent approaches that employ technology to make mental health services available in the remote and rural areas of Canada. At different points in this book, we have focused on the plight of many of Canada's Aboriginal people and, in particular, on rampant substance abuse, suicide, and child abuse. Do you think that some of the technology-based strategies described in this chapter could be adapted for use with Aboriginal people? How would you go about doing this? Would you develop approaches that would be run by the Aboriginal people themselves? Could this approach be helpful in reducing the devastating consequences of alcohol abuse in adults and gasoline sniffing in children, or is it more essential to focus on developing on-site programs? Would telemental health services be useful adjuncts to, or provide helpful support for, community programs?

3. Reflect on the different approaches to psychotherapy that we have discussed in this book and evaluated in the current chapter. If you were asked to choose the approach that had the most personal meaning for you, the one that would best fit into your own life narrative, which treatment would you select and why?

4. The issue of psychotherapy integration is controversial. While some theorists and researchers embrace it, others eschew it. We recognize that there are some risks in integration but that there also seems to be a trend toward it. Where do you stand on issues of eclecticism and integration? Is integration feasible or desirable?

CHAPTER 18

Legal and Ethical Issues

LEARNING OBJECTIVES

1. Explain the nature of criminal commitment and the legal options that are available and ethical issues that occur when someone who is mentally ill has committed a criminal act.

2. Describe the nature of civil commitment and the process involved when someone who is mentally ill needs to be protected.

3. Identify the ethical dilemmas and issues that can complicate clinical therapy and research.

Section 1—Guarantee of Rights and Freedoms. The Canadian Charter of Rights and Freedoms guarantees the rights and freedoms set out in it subject only to such reasonable limits prescribed by law as can be demonstrably justified in a free and democratic society.

Section 2—Fundamental Freedoms. Everyone has the following fundamental freedoms: 1. freedom of conscience and religion; 2. freedom of thought, belief, opinion and expression, including freedom of the press and other media of communication; 3. freedom of peaceful assembly; and 4. freedom of association.

Section 7—Legal Rights. Everyone has the right to life, liberty, and security of the person and the right not to be deprived thereof except in accordance with the principles of fundamental justice.

Section 8—Everyone has the right to be secure against unreasonable search or seizure.

Section 9—Everyone has the right not to be arbitrarily detained or imprisoned.

Section 12—Everyone has the right not to be subjected to any cruel and unusual treatment or punishment.

Section 15—Equality before and under law and equal protection and benefit of law. Every individual is equal before and under the law and has the right to equal protection and benefits of the law without discrimination, and, in particular, without discrimination based on race, national, or

ethnic origin, colour, religion, sex, age or mental or physical disability.

Source: Canadian Charter of Rights and Freedoms (1982).

We open our final chapter in this way, with sections of the Canadian Charter of Rights and Freedoms (1982), for two reasons. First, the legal and mental health systems collaborate continually, although often subtly, to deny a substantial proportion of the Canadian population their basic civil rights. With the best of intentions, judges, tribunals, governing boards of hospitals, bar associations, and professional mental health groups have worked over the years to protect society at large from the actions of people regarded as mentally ill or mentally disordered and considered dangerous to themselves or to others. However, in so doing, they have denied many thousands of people their basic civil rights.

Second, Section 15 (1) of the Charter of Rights and Freedoms (i.e., Equality before and under law) is especially significant because it extends the right of equality to mentally ill people. According to Eaves, Lamb, and Tien (2000), Canada "is one of the few countries in the world that explicitly extends the general rights found in our constitution to people who are mentally ill" (p. 615). The rights of mentally ill people are covered under provisions for the rights of disabled people.

A continuing concern in Canadian society is the extent to which mentally ill people are subject to discrimination in the workplace. Focus on Discovery 18.1 delves into this issue by summarizing extant concerns and cases that have surfaced in Canada.

Focus on Discovery 18.1

The Stigma of Mental Illness and Employment Discrimination

Imagine that you have suffered from persistent depression but a good job in your field becomes available. Do you apply for the job? And do you mention your depression when the interviewer asks why you quit your previous job and you haven't worked in the past six months? Because of concerns about stigma, you probably won't mention your bouts of depression. Indeed, Dr. Heather Stuart (2006b) from Queen's University in Kingston, Ontario, has identified stigma as both a proximal factor and a distal factor in workplace discrimination. Proximal, direct discrimination would be in the form of stereotypes and prejudice emanating from employers and co-workers, while distal influences include the historical disadvantage of mentally ill people in the workplace and failures to proactively monitor and implement policies.

Unfortunately, the Canadian Human Rights Commission (CHRC) reports many settlement cases every year and the inescapable conclusion is that workplace discrimination is pervasive for mentally ill people in Canada. Its website documents 10 cases in 2006 of settlements for people suffering from depression who alleged workplace discrimination (see www.chrc-ccdp.ca/). The allegations include outright termination due to depression, while in other cases, problems included being disciplined for not meeting deadlines and being passed over for promotions. As a result of the growing number of cases, in October 2008, the CHRC addressed the workplace and employment issues by crafting its Policy and Procedural Guideline on the Accommodation of Mental Illness. More recently, the CSA Group, in collaboration with the Mental Health Commission of Canada, has developed a tool titled "Psychological Health and Safety in the Workplace" that helps to establish guidelines and appropriate procedures for employers and their employees (CSA Group, 2013).

A compelling 2008 case outlines the consequences for employers who engage or appear to engage in discrimination. The Ontario Divisional Court upheld a previous discrimination ruling by the Human Rights Tribunal of Ontario in the Ottawa case of Lane v. ADGA Group Consultants Inc. (2007). Paul Lane, a quality assurance analyst, was fired in October 2001 just eight days into the job after requesting accommodation for his bipolar depression. In its defence, the employer, the ADGA Group, maintained that Lane was not fired due to discrimination; rather, they deemed that he could not perform essential job functions and he had been untruthful in response to interview questions asked prior to the decision to hire him. However, the Court ruled that the employer displayed a dismissive attitude and disregard for Lane because of his bipolar depression. Documents indicate that following his job loss, Lane went into a state of full-blown mania and was hospitalized for several days. This was part of a downward spiral that led eventually to marital problems and the loss of the family home. The employer was deemed to have demonstrated an egregious lack of awareness of employer responsibilities and Lane was awarded $35,000 as general damages, $10,000 for mental anguish, and another $34,278.75 in special damages. Moreover, the employer was given three months to develop a written, comprehensive anti-discrimination policy.

While there is a duty to accommodate workers with physical and mental disabilities, a 2008 decision by the Supreme Court of Canada placed limits on how far this goes. This case involved a woman who was working for Hydro-Québec. Collectively, the woman missed over 900 days of work in 7.5 years of employment due to physical problems (hyperthyroidism, hypertension), episodes of depression, and a mixed form of personality disorder with borderline and dependent features. She was also described as having deficient coping mechanisms and difficult relationships with supervisors and co-workers. The employer dismissed her. When lower courts ruled in her favour, the employer appealed. The Supreme Court upheld the organization's appeal on the grounds that it had taken extensive lengths to rearrange the workplace and job duties (see Hydro-Québec v. Syndicat des employées de techniques professionnelles et de bureau d'Hydro-Québec, section locale 2000 (SCFP-FTQ), 2008). The highest court ruled that an organization can terminate someone if it is established that any further accommodations of their disabilities would constitute "undue hardship" for the employer.

The Canadian Mental Health Association continues to maintain that among all people with disabilities, people with a mental illness face the greatest degree of discrimination and stigmatization. Sadly, the case of Paul Lane outlined above suggests that this problem is far from being resolved and there is no doubt that much work remains to be done. This is also the conclusion that was reached as part of a study led by the Ontario Human Rights Commission (2012) that involved interviews with 1,500 individuals and organizations. Its report, titled Minds That Matter, outlined several instances of discrimination toward people with mental illness, including particularly troubling accounts of Ontario health care workers engaging in discrimination and withholding timely treatment to people with mental health or addiction problems. As a result, the Human Rights Commission launched a public appeal for extensive training and education of workers in health care settings and throughout the public sector.

It is up to each province to formulate and implement laws that are in keeping with the Charter of Rights and Freedoms. Although all provinces share the same Charter-driven principles in their legislation, differences exist in how these principles are realized. Another possible source of differences between the provinces is the "notwithstanding clause," which permits provinces to opt out of the Charter if they perceive a conflict between their goals and values and the overall goals and values of the nation.

Although mentally ill people are extended rights under the equality provision, there are situations in which other principles come into effect. Specifically, the Charter of Rights and Freedoms also includes provisions that allow for some people to be removed from society if they act in a way that infringes on the rights of other people to a free and democratic society. In other words, at times, the needs of the society as a whole may outweigh the needs of any one individual. Mentally ill individuals who have broken the law, or who are alleged to have done so, may be subject to a loss of liberty where their mental disorder becomes relevant to the criminal prosecution because of either concerns regarding fitness to stand trial or criminal responsibility. In other words, they may be subject to **criminal commitment**, a procedure that may confine a person in a mental institution either for determination of competency to stand trial or after a verdict of not criminally responsible on account of mental disorder. Part XX.1 of the Criminal Code of Canada provides a "mini-code" that sets out the procedures for dealing with mentally disordered individuals who find themselves before the criminal courts. **Civil commitment**, provided for in provincial statutes, is a procedure by which a mentally ill and dangerous person who may not have broken a law can be deprived of liberty and incarcerated in a psychiatric hospital. Both committal procedures—one federal, the other provincial—may result in a loss of liberty as a result of mental disorder. In this chapter, we look at these legal procedures in depth. We then turn to an examination of some important ethical issues as they relate to therapy and research.

18.1 Criminal Commitment

Historically, much of Canadian law has derived from English common law, reflecting the British influence in Canada. The exception is Quebec, where Napoleonic law has been incorporated into civil statutes. In Canada, criminal law is a matter of federal statute and is therefore the same in every province. Matters of health law, however, are determined at the provincial level and can differ from province to province. Our criminal code was first enacted in 1892, when we adopted a draft British code that was never enacted in Britain. Britain, to this day, has no criminal code. Almost as early as the concept of *mens rea*, or "guilty mind," and the rule "No crime without an evil intent" had begun to be accepted in English common law, "insanity" had to be taken into consideration, for a disordered mind may be regarded as unable to formulate and carry out a criminal purpose (Morse, 1992). In other words, a disordered mind cannot be a guilty mind; only a guilty mind can engender culpable actions.

Initially, insanity was not a trial defence, but in England, the Crown sometimes granted pardons to people who had been convicted of homicide if they were judged completely

and totally "mad" (Morris, 1968). By the reign of Edward I (1272–1307), the concept of insanity had begun to be argued in court and could lessen punishment. It became the rule of law during the course of the fourteenth century that a person proven to be wholly and continually mad could be defended against a criminal charge.

In today's courts, judges and lawyers call on psychiatrists and clinical psychologists for assistance in dealing with criminal acts thought to result from the accused person's disordered mental state rather than from free will. Are such emotionally disturbed perpetrators less criminally responsible than those who are not distraught but commit the same crimes? Should such individuals even be brought to trial for transgressions against society's laws? Although efforts to excuse or protect an accused person by invoking the insanity defence or by judging him or her unfit to stand trial are undoubtedly well intentioned, invoking these doctrines can often subject those accused to a greater denial of liberty than they would otherwise experience.

The Not Criminally Responsible Defence

The cases described in the Brief Case Example all involved high-profile situations in which defendants in Canadian courts were found **not criminally responsible** for their acts on account of mental disorder (NCRMD). The so-called **insanity defence**, NCRMD involves the legal argument that a defendant should not be held responsible for an otherwise illegal act if it is attributable to mental illness that interferes with rationality or that results in some other excusing circumstance, such as not knowing right from wrong. Mental disorder may operate to negate the requisite mental element (*mens rea*), or it may operate to render the act (*actus reus*) involuntary. Or, it may operate to provide a supervening defence even where the requisite mental element and act have been proven. For example, an accused may specifically intend to kill his neighbour, believing him to be an alien sent to destroy the world. Here, the court may find that, notwithstanding the requisite elements having been proven, the accused did not appreciate the nature and consequences of his act or know it to be wrong. A staggering amount of material has been written on this defence, and public outcries continue to emerge in prominent cases in which the defendant is found not criminally responsible.

Brief Case Example

Tragic Cases of Crimes and Mental Illness

IN HAMILTON, Ontario, Lucia Piovesan had been diagnosed as having had paranoid schizophrenia for over 20 years, but she received minimal treatment because she did not take her antipsychotic drugs. Moreover, she resisted family requests to get additional treatment. Her neighbours, Tony Antidormi and his wife, Lori Triano-Antidormi (a former graduate student in psychology at York

University), tried unsuccessfully on several occasions to convince police that Piovesan was dangerous. In March 1997, Piovesan stabbed to death the Antidormis' two-year-old son, Zachary, after becoming convinced that he was the soul of her dead son and was asking for release (see Honywill, 1998). Piovesan was found not criminally responsible because of her paranoid schizophrenia.

Dorothy Joudrie, a wealthy Calgary socialite, apparently endured years of abuse from her former husband, Earl Joudrie, and

(continued)

as a result, developed a problem with alcoholism. The situation escalated in January 1995 when Joudrie shot her former husband six times and was arrested for attempted murder. Her lawyer argued that, at the time of the crime, Joudrie was in a dissociative, trance-like state (a condition known as automatism) and had no recollection of her actions. In May 1996, a jury found her not criminally responsible owing to a mental disorder, and she was confined at the Alberta Hospital in Edmonton for five months. Joudrie's mental state improved greatly over time, and she received an absolute discharge on October 20, 1998 (Martin, 2012). Until her death in 2002, she acted as an advocate for the rights of mentally ill people.

On May 28, 1998, two teenagers from British Columbia were killed when struck by a car driven by Julia Campagna of Seattle, Washington. Campagna's car was speeding and smashed into the back of the teenagers' car at the Canadian border crossing. The driver was charged with dangerous driving causing death, but on September 3, 1999, a B.C. court ruled that Campagna was not criminally responsible on account of mental disorder. The accident occurred while Campagna was in a psychotic state. She had symptoms of psychosis after taking the diet drug Xenadrine to lose weight for a marathon running race. Campagna thought that she was in an airplane rather than a car and that she was hearing the voice of Canadian NHL hockey player Joe Nieuwendyk on her radio. She was following the voice's instructions, believing she was on her way to a rendezvous with Nieuwendyk to conceive a child with him.

Because her symptoms were deemed to be due to the pills she was taking (a finding that was confirmed by a B.C. Children's Commission investigation ([R. v. Campagna, 1999]), Campagna was released and allowed to go free, having been found not criminally responsible. The court ruled that Campagna posed no risk to the public and could not be held. Julie Campagna subsequently launched a civil lawsuit against the drug manufacturer and other parties, and the families of the deceased launched civil lawsuits against Campagna and the drug manufacturer (see the CBC News, 2000).

Public concern about such cases escalated in March 2009 when Vincent Li was found not criminally responsible due to men-

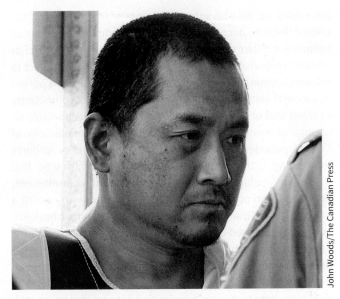

John Woods/The Canadian Press

Vincent Li was found not criminally responsible in 2009 for killing Tim McLean in 2008. Reports indicate that Li was acting in accordance with commands from God to remove a demon or face his own execution. The Li case has helped spark pending legislation and a national debate about how to address the situation of people who are not criminally responsible due to mental illness but who have engaged in a violent act while suffering profoundly from mental illness.

tal disorder (see photo). Li was accused of the gruesome murder of Tim McLean, a fellow passenger on a Greyhound bus who was not known to Li and was simply in the wrong place at the wrong time. The incident occurred in July 2008 in Manitoba on the Trans-Canada Highway. It was deemed that Li was experiencing a psychotic episode related to his schizophrenia. He believed that he had been commanded by God to act. Not surprisingly, the verdict of not criminally responsible provides little comfort to family members who have lost a loved one, such as McLean's relatives.

Concerns abound even though a review conducted by Canadian researchers (see Lymburner & Roesch, 1999) confirmed past findings suggesting that (1) the insanity defence is very rare; (2) it is usually only successful when applied to severely disordered individuals; and (3) people deemed insane are still typically detained for long periods of time that may greatly exceed the otherwise appropriate sentence. Note that being found not criminally responsible does not result in an acquittal.

This issue was recently in the news in Canada due to federal changes in the treatment of people deemed NCRMD. The new law under Bill C-54 was introduced by the Harper Government and came into effect in July 2014 (see the Not Criminally Responsible Reform Act). The new legislation makes it possible for certain people deemed high risk to possibly be detained indefinitely until a judge has been able to determine that the high-risk NCRMD offenders are no longer a threat to the general public. Two high-profile cases seem to have provided the impetus for these proposed changes: the Vincent Li case described above and the case of Allan Schoenborn, who killed his three children in Merritt, British Columbia.

Several eminent judges have expressed their objections and concerns. Justice Richard Schneider, the Alternate Chair of the Ontario Review Board and the Nunavut Review Board, has argued that the chances of people such as Vincent Li and Allan Schoenborn actually reoffending is so low, it is unlikely that they would be candidates for this new high-risk designation. Schneider further noted that there is no evidence that the current system is not working (Mackrael, 2013).

The Chief Justice of Canada's Supreme Court, Beverley McLachlin, also weighed in on this issue (see photo). Chief Justice McLachlin, the first female Chief Justice and now Canada's longest serving Chief Justice, expressed her reservations and observed that she is not aware of problems or deficiencies in the current law or the review-board system. She is quoted as saying, "Actually, my understanding is that it has worked quite well. Obviously, there are amendments being put forward and I'm not going to go into those, but it has served us well and it is looked at by other countries as a good model . . . The interesting thing is that the hearing process is staffed heavily by psychiatrists and I think it is well-supported by the medical side of things, by the police and by the judges" (Makin, 2013, pp. A10–A11).

Chief Justice Beverley McLachlin is noted for her extensive work on behalf of the rights of mentally ill people. McLachlin is Canada's longest serving Chief Justice. She has continually expressed her concern about the fates of mentally ill people in the justice system.

Over a period of many years, McLachlin has been a tireless advocate for the rights of mentally ill offenders. One of her continuing concerns is the tendency for mentally ill offenders to be "warehoused" in jails by police, and often released back on to the streets without receiving treatment.

Another person who spoke out against Bill C-54 is Dr. Lori Triano-Antidormi, the mother of the murdered boy, Zachary Antidormi. In her remarkable presentation to the Justice and Human Rights Committee, a federal parliamentary committee, Dr. Triano-Antidormi not only provided a compelling account of the day her son was lost and what this means to an individual and a family, she also expressed her grave concerns about how

Bill C-54 could promote stigma and how it reflects a misguided understanding of the nature of mental illness (see Triano-Antidormi, 2013).

Valuable information about the NCRMD designation is emerging from the National Trajectory Project of people with this designation, led by Anne Crocker and her colleagues (see Charette et al., 2015; Crocker, Nicholls, Seto, Charette, et al., 2015; Crocker, Nicholls, Seto, Côté, et al., 2015; Crocker, Charette, Seto, Nicholls, et al., 2015). This project is the first longitudinal cohort study that compares representative samples of NCRMD-accused people from three provinces (British Columbia, Ontario, and Quebec). Overall, more than 1,800 cases are included. Baillie (2015) summarized the advances in knowledge that have come from the first phase of this ongoing research. Key findings include the fact that 51% of the sample had no prior criminal convictions but 72% had at least one prior mental health hospitalization. Overall, about two-thirds of the cases (65%) involved acts against another person, with the majority being against a family member, followed by police and mental health workers. There are proportionally more cases in Quebec and the rate of NCRMD cases is increasing in Quebec and decreasing in British Columbia. The most common diagnosis found among those with an NCRMD designation was psychotic spectrum disorder and one-third of the sample had a co-occurring substance abuse problem. Finally, women had fewer identified risk factors for recidivism. The overall reconviction rate over a three-year follow-up period was 16.7% (i.e., 1 in 6 people).

Landmark Cases in Canada

In modern Anglo-American criminal law, several court rulings and established principles bear on the problems of legal responsibility and mental illness. Table 18.1 summarizes these rulings and principles.

TABLE 18.1 Landmark Cases and the Disposition of the Mentally ill in Canada

Case	Date	Significance
Rex v. Hadfield	1800	Led to changes where the mentally ill could be institutionalized rather than returned to prison or the community. The accused were held at "His or Her Majesty's Pleasure."
Regina v. M'Naghten	1843	Followed a reference to the House of Lords, setting a standard test for "insanity" that was subsequently adopted, with modifications, by much of the Western world. Is seen to mark the beginning of the modern insanity defence.
Regina v. Chaulk	1990	Specifies that "wrong" means morally wrong as well as legally wrong.
Regina v. Swain	1991	Led to the creation of Bill C-30 and establishes the jurisdiction of provincial review boards that can balance the individual's and the community's concerns; changes a verdict from "not guilty by reason of insanity" to "not criminally responsible on account of mental disorder."
Regina v. Oommen	1994	The accused must not only be able to know what is wrong but also be able to apply that knowledge at the time of the act.
Winko v. British Columbia	1999	If it cannot be determined whether a mentally disordered person is a significant threat to public safety, he or she must be discharged absolutely.
R. v. Conception	2014	Ruled that the court system could not refuse or delay the provision of treatment to mentally disordered people who are deemed unfit to stand trial. It overturned an Ontario court ruling that went in favour of the Centre for Addiction and Mental Health and the Mental Health Centre in Penetanguishene, which argued that they lacked the resources to provide immediate treatment to Brian Conception, who was sent to them by an Ontario judge who issued a treatment order. Conception was unfit to stand trial due to symptoms of schizophrenia.

According to Schneider et al. (2000), Canada's modern history with respect to the legal treatment of mentally disordered people began with the case of *Rex v. Hadfield* (1800; see Table 18.1). Hadfield fired a shot in the direction of King George III because he believed that the king's death would herald the end of the world and the second advent of Christ (Ogloff & Whittemore, 2001). Hadfield was found not guilty by reason of insanity. This case is noteworthy because the chief justice overseeing the case returned Hadfield to prison but remarked that neither the prison environment nor the community were proper alternatives. This case led the British Parliament to enact the Criminal Lunatics Act (1800), which provided the leeway for people to be sent to a place deemed fit by the court (i.e., a mental institution) rather than be incarcerated or set free. This provision was incorporated into a draft of the British criminal code and the first Criminal Code of Canada in 1892 (see Schneider et al., 2000, for a more complete description).

The well-known criteria, the **M'Naghten Rules**, were formulated in the aftermath of a murder trial in England in 1843. The accused, Daniel M'Naghten, had set out to kill the British prime minister, Sir Robert Peel, but had mistaken Peel's secretary, Sir Edward Drummond, for Peel. M'Naghten claimed that he had been instructed to kill Lord Peel by the "voice of God." As a result of a post-trial reference to the House of Lords, the M'Naghten Rules were articulated as follows: "to establish a defence of insanity, it must be clearly proved that, at the time of the committing of the act, the party accused was labouring under such a defect of reason, from disease of the mind, as not to know the nature and quality of the act he was doing; or if he did know it, that he did not know he was doing what was wrong."

The rules are unique in that they were never read as part of a court's ruling at the conclusion of the trial, and they were not part of any legislation. Nevertheless, the M'Naghten Rules have had an unprecedented impact, as they were adopted not only in Britain but throughout all of the Commonwealth and most American jurisdictions as the test to be met in an insanity defence. A key point to emphasize here is that the M'Naghten Rules apply to insanity at the time of the criminal act or omission.

The issue of being able to tell right from wrong as a component of the insanity defence has been the subject of some debate. According to Ogloff and Whittemore (2001), the Canadian legal system defined "wrong" in terms of legally wrong, but this was expanded by the Supreme Court of Canada in *Regina v. Chaulk* (1990) to include morally wrong, as well.

The case of *Regina v. Swain* (1991) led to the proclamation of Bill C-30 on February 4, 1992. Bill C-30 created the mini-code in Part XX.1 within the Criminal Code of Canada, dealing exclusively with the mentally disordered accused. The case involved a man who had acted in a threatening manner toward members of his family and was subsequently arrested for the crime of assault causing bodily harm. When the police arrived, they discovered that Swain "had swung his children over his head, scored a cross on his wife's chest, spoken about spirits, and fought with the air. At his arrest, he was speaking excitedly in religious themes" (Stuart, Arboleda-Florez, & Crisanti, 2001, p. 528). He later testified that he was trying to save his family from the devil.

Swain recovered after receiving drug treatment and had lived in the community for over a year without incident when the day of his trial finally came. The Crown raised the insanity defence over his objections. Swain was found to be not guilty by reason of insanity, but according to the Criminal Code provisions, he had to be held in "strict custody," even though he had been out on bail and was problem-free at the time of the verdict. The Supreme Court, in reviewing the legislative scheme, found that the failure of the provisions to set a maximum time within which the accused's status must be reviewed violated his Charter rights. The court noted that for many other similar situations, Parliament had set limits on the amount of time that could pass before an accused's status had to be reviewed. While the case turned on this narrow point, the court expressed "concern" with respect to other features of the legislative scheme. Accordingly, Parliament was given six months to bring the legislation into Charter compliance. This gave birth to Bill C-30.

Bill C-30 included a key change in terminology. The phrase "not guilty by reason of insanity" (NGRI) was altered to "not criminally responsible on account of mental disorder" (NCRMD). Another change concerned the party to be responsible for the individual found NCRMD. Previously, the mentally disordered individual had been kept at the "pleasure" of the lieutenant governor, but now legal authority was allocated to provincial review boards. Ogloff and Whittemore (2001) noted that, prior to changes made to the Criminal Code in 1992, people who were found NGRI were detained for an indeterminate length of time. However, as a result of *Regina v. Swain* (1991) and the subsequent proclamation of Bill C-30, review boards now determine the individual's fate within 45 days of the verdict and thereafter not less than annually. Review boards must weigh many factors, including the individual's current mental status and the risk to society posed by the individual. They can discharge the individual with or without conditions or, alternatively, they can order detention in a hospital setting.

Included in Bill C-30 is a list of issues for which assessments may be ordered. The issues include fitness to stand trial, criminal responsibility, infanticide, and, the least onerous, disposition. Specific time limits are set for the assessment of the various issues. It is presumed, for example, that a fitness assessment will be completed within five days, but the maximum period of assessment is set at 60 days for compelling situations. It is also presumed that all assessments will take place out of custody unless the Crown shows why this should not occur. Notwithstanding this presumption, most assessments take place on an in-patient basis because the subject of the assessment is often too unwell to be released into the community. While being assessed, an accused is not to be treated against his or her will. However, if the accused is found to be unfit to stand trial, the Crown may bring an application for the court to order that the accused be treated for up to 60 days in order to render him or her fit. This order, if the evidentiary hurdles are met, will be effected with or without the accused's consent.

Parenthetically, this process of what happens when someone is unfit to stand trial drew scrutiny with the case of Brian Conception (*R. v. Conception*, 2014; see Table 18.1). Conception was to stand trial for sexual assault but suffered from symptoms of schizophrenia (hearing voices). Conception was alleged to have sexually assaulted a staff member at the Centre for Addiction and Mental Health (CAMH) in Toronto. He was deemed unfit to stand trial and the judge ordered that Conception immediately receive treatment. Treatment at CAMH was deemed unsuitable, perhaps due to the nature of the alleged offence. He was eventually sent to the treatment facility in Penetanguishene where Conception was left in a hallway due to the lack of space (see Fraser, 2015). The facility balked due to lack of resources and appealed to the Ontario courts; this appeal was upheld but was subsequently overturned in 2014 by the Supreme Court of Canada. The highest court recognized that people had the right to treatment and the facility had to provide treatment. This Supreme Court decision was a response to the far too common tendency for mentally unfit violent offenders to be sent to jails instead of treatment facilities when no space is available in the treatment facility.

Initial research on the impact of Bill C-30 was conducted in British Columbia. A comparison of a cohort of people who had been found NGRI vs. a newer cohort of those found NCRMD uncovered a substantial increase in the number of cases following the enactment of Bill C-30, including cases involving people charged with less serious offences (Livingston, Wilson, Tien, & Bond, 2003). The average length of hospitalization for the NCRMD cohort (9.8 months) was much lower than for the NGRI cohort (47.7 months). Livingston et al. (2003) concluded, "The Bill C-30 provisions have made the NCRMD defence an attractive option for defendants and legal counsel" (p. 408). Available statistics indicate that the NCRMD defence is being used more frequently and for a broader range of offences. For instance, there were 177 cases in Quebec in 1992 vs. 360 cases in 2006 (Latimer, 2006; Schneider, Forestell, & MacGarvie, 2002).

Insanity and Mental Illness

In general, the insanity defence requires applying an abstract principle to specific life situations. As in all aspects of the law, terms can be interpreted in a number of ways—by defendants, defence lawyers, prosecutors, judges, and jurors—and testimony can be presented in a diverse fashion, depending on the skill of the interrogators and the intelligence of the witnesses. Furthermore, because the defendant's mental condition only at the time the crime was committed is in question, retrospective, often speculative, judgement on the part of lawyers, judges, jurors, and psychiatrists is required. And disagreement between defence and prosecution psychiatrists and psychologists is the rule.

A final point should be emphasized. There is an important difference between insanity and mental illness or defect. A person can be diagnosed as mentally ill and yet be held responsible for a crime. Insanity is a legal concept, not a psychiatric or psychological one. And, while the Criminal Code of Canada defines "mental disorder"—the legal term—to mean "disease of the mind," the presence of mental disorder is a necessary but not a sufficient condition to make the defence of insanity. This distinction, also a key concept in the U.S. legal system, was made vivid by the 1992 conviction of Jeffrey Dahmer in

Wisconsin. He admitted to butchering, cannibalizing, and having sex with the corpses of 15 boys and young men. Dahmer plead guilty but mentally ill, and his sanity was the sole focus of an unusual trial that had jurors listening to conflicting testimony from mental health experts about the defendant's state of mind during the serial killings to which he had confessed. They had to decide whether he had had a mental disease that prevented him from knowing right from wrong or from being able to control his actions. Even though there was no disagreement that he was mentally ill, diagnosable as having some sort of paraphilia, Dahmer was deemed sane and therefore legally responsible. He was sentenced to 15 consecutive life terms.

A more recent case is that of James Holmes, who went on a shooting rampage in a Colorado movie theatre on July 20, 2012, during the premiere of the Batman movie *The Dark Knight Rises* (see photo). Holmes killed 12 people and wounded 70 others and was charged with 160 counts of murder or attempted murder. In June 2013, the judge accepted Holmes's initial plea of not guilty by reason of insanity. After a trial by jury, in August 2015, Holmes was given 12 consecutive life sentences.

An interesting new development in the law and mental health is the introduction of neuroscientific data into the legal system. This is a rapidly growing practice that seems geared to reducing the severity of sentences rather than establishing innocence, at least at present. The field emerging here is called **neurolaw**, and it is a natural outgrowth of the emerging field of neuropsychiatry (see Silva, 2009). The primary argument is that the accused suffers from some form of brain dysfunction and related processing deficits, and, as such, he or she really couldn't help himself or herself. For instance, cases have been reported in which murder sentences have been reduced to manslaughter charges as a result of testimony involving

RJ Sangosti/The Denver Post via Getty Images

James Holmes, who killed 12 people and wounded 70 others in a Colorado movie theatre in July 2012, entered a plea of not guilty by reason of insanity. His mental status has been extensively evaluated. His trial did not take place until 2014 after he had entered a plea in 2013 of not guilty by reason of insanity. In 2015 he was given 12 consecutive life sentences.

neuroscientific data (Chen, 2009). Jones and Shen (2012) provided a detailed overview of current developments, including recent cases in the United States. For instance, they recounted the case of Grady Nelson, who was spared the death penalty after being found guilty in Florida for murdering his wife and raping a child. Later, jurors "revealed that, for some, the proffered neuroscientific evidence was a tipping point. As one juror remarked, 'the technology really swayed me . . . After seeing the brain scans, I was convinced that this guy had some sort of brain problem'" (Ovalle, 2010, p. 1, as cited in Jones & Shen, 2012, p. 351).

More generally, neurolaw can inform such issues as free will, responsibility, moral judgement, and punishment. However, it is also clear that there are many evidentiary issues that will need to be addressed (for a discussion, see Goodenough & Tucker, 2010).

Aharoni et al. (2008) have discussed how neuroscientific data can be used in the United States to contribute to the decision about whether someone is not guilty by reason of insanity. All that would need to be established is that neuroscientific data show that the person was unaware that what they did is wrong. Bennett (2008) has argued that the M'Naghten Rules need to be rewritten, given the precision of neuroscientific data. In particular, he highlighted the distinction between an irresistible impulse and the subsequent lack of self-control; apparently, irresistible impulses and a lack of self-control involve distinct activities in different brain structures and they are different capacities.

Fitness to Stand Trial

The insanity defence concerns the accused person's mental state at the time of the crime. A question that first arises is whether the person is competent or fit to stand trial at all. The mental fitness of individuals to stand trial must be decided before it can be determined whether they are responsible for the crime of which they are accused. The requirement that an accused be fit to stand trial was a refinement of the older principle that an accused had to be present before the state could proceed with its prosecution. The requirement of mere physical presence was expanded to require the accused to be "mentally present" as well. It is possible for a person to be judged competent to stand trial yet subsequently be deemed not criminally responsible by reason of mental disorder. In fact, that is the case for all accused raising the NCRMD defence because they must be fit prior to commencing their trial. Fitness has to do with the accused's present condition, not how he or she might have been functioning at the time of the alleged offence.

Decisions may be changed on appeal if the fitness of the defendant is in question and has not been adequately assessed. For instance, Schneider (2001) related a case in which the Ontario Court of Appeal overturned a conviction for attempted murder because of a judge's failure to assess the fitness of the defendant. In this case, although the Crown attorney suggested to the judge that fitness might be an issue, the judge simply asked the accused whether he felt fit to stand trial (Schneider, 2001). Obviously, fitness needs to be established by trained professionals. Canadian Perspectives 18.1 further examines the fitness to stand trial issue (as well as the use of the insanity defence) in the complex case of Louis Riel.

Rather than relying on subjective clinical judgements to determine an individual's fitness (or lack of fitness) to stand trial, another alternative is to adopt measures to assist with the

---

Canadian Perspectives 18.1

Louis Riel and the Issue of Fitness to Stand Trial

Louis Riel is one of the most controversial figures in the history of Canada (see illustration). Riel, of French-Canadian and Métis background, was executed for his role in the Métis uprising in 1885 known as the North-West Rebellion. This armed rebellion stemmed from political and land disputes in Western Canada between the Métis and the federal government, and involved the deaths of several North-West Mounted Police. Riel was executed for high treason after a jury found him guilty but recommended mercy.

One vexing question that remains to this day was whether Riel should have been deemed not criminally responsible due to mental disorder. An equally important and related issue is whether he was fit to stand trial. Riel had spent time in mental institutions on two separate occasions prior to the uprising. His lawyers based his defence on the insanity plea, after other options failed, despite his vehement protests that he did not support this strategy.

Was Riel insane at the time of the act or, at the very least, unfit to stand trial because of an inability to participate in his own

Bettmann/Getty Images

The trial of Louis Riel is one of the most well-known trials in Canadian history but the central issue is whether he was mentally fit to stand trial.

defence? Riel displayed many symptoms of megalomania (see Perr, 1992). He believed that he had been specially selected by the spirits to bring forth the message of the Métis. Similar tendencies to put aside one's personal identity and take on another identity (referred to as "misidentification of the self") have come to be described as "The Riel Phenomenon" (see Perr & Federoff, 1992).

The actual documents filed on Riel's behalf by his lawyer, François-Xavier Lemieux, and two psychiatrists contain vivid accounts of Riel's apparent deterioration (*Regina v. Louis Riel*, 1886). Lemieux noted the following in his declaration:

> "While he was speaking he suddenly stops showing me his hand. 'Do you see,' says he, 'blood flowing in the veins; the telegraph is operating actively, and I feel it, they are talking about me, and questioning authorities, in Ottawa, about me.' It is of similar fantastic visions he speaks with me every day. I am convinced that he is not acting a part, he speaks with a conviction and a sincerity which leave no doubt in my mind about the state of his mind, he has retracted his errors but he believes himself today to be a prophet and invested with a divine mission to reform the world on the day he has spoken to the Court and when I reprove him for his foolish and extravagant ideas, he answers that he submits, but that he cannot stifle the voice that speaks in him and the spirit that commands him to communicate to the world the revelations he receives. One must have the ferocious hatred of a fanatic or the stupidity of an idiot, to say that Riel is not a fool, because he is intelligent in other matters, as if history was not filled with such anomalies, among certain men who, remarkable in certain subjects, have lost the balance which contains intelligence within the limits from which it cannot escape

> without losing its privilege of guiding us or making us responsible for our own acts.

> ...The experience I have gained of this man by continual contact with him has only confirmed me more and more in the opinion I had already formed of him, that he is crazy and insane.... I have just been visiting him, and during an hour he spoke of extraordinary revelations made to him by the spirit the previous night, and that he has been ordered to communicate to me and to all the Catholic clergy: 'The great cause of sin in the world is the revolt of the body against the spirit, it is because we do not chew our food enough, and by this want of mastication it communicates animal life only to the body while by masticating and chewing it well, it spiritualizes the body.'"

> (*Regina v. Louis Riel*, p. 204)

The opinion offered by Lemieux was echoed by the two psychiatrists who concluded that Riel was insane and unable to discern right from wrong. However, the medical petition failed and Riel was eventually executed.

Thinking Critically

1. Was Riel not criminally responsible by reason of mental disorder, or was this simply a desperate attempt on the part of his defence team to avoid his execution? On the basis of your understanding of current legislation, do you think the same sentence and result would have been reached today?

2. Was it ethical of Riel's lawyers and psychiatrists to proceed with the insanity defence against their client's wishes? What would you have done? Note that Riel felt that to argue his insanity would, in effect, undermine the cause of his people and the strength of his views.

decision. One measure developed in Canada is the Fitness Interview Test-Revised (FIT-R; Roesch, Zapf, Eaves, & Webster, 1999). The three components of this interview-based measure assess whether the person (1) understands the nature and purpose of the legal proceedings; (2) understands the possible or likely consequences of the proceedings; and (3) is capable of communicating with his or her lawyer. The FIT-R appears to have an exceptional level of validity (see Zapf & Roesch, 1997) and when used carefully, it can be used to evaluate fitness among adolescent defendants (Viljoen, Vincent, & Roesch, 2006).

What role do psychologists play in fitness and criminal responsibility evaluations in Canada? According to Viljoen, Roesch, Ogloff, and Zapf (2003), psychologists are regarded as qualified to provide assessments under the Youth Criminal Justice Act and dangerous offender legislation, but only medical practitioners are qualified to provide court-ordered assessments of fitness and criminal responsibility. However, psychologists often assist physicians by conducting psychological evaluations when requested. Viljoen et al. (2003) predicted that, in time,

psychologists will play a larger role in fitness and criminality responsibility evaluations.

Judgements about the fitness to stand trial are still exceedingly difficult at times, and the possible influence of a dissociative state is an issue that further complicates the decision-making process. As noted earlier, in the Dorothy Joudrie case, the determination of a dissociative state was key to the court decision that she was not criminally responsible for shooting her husband.

18.2 | Civil Commitment

Historically, governments have had a duty to protect their citizens from harm. We take for granted the right and duty of government to set limits on our freedom for the sake of protecting us. Few drivers, for example, question the legitimacy of imposing limits on them by providing traffic signals that often make them stop when they would rather go. Government has a long-established right as well as an obligation to protect us both from ourselves—the *parens patriae*, "power of the state"—and from others—the police power of the state. Civil commitment is one further exercise of these powers.

In virtually all jurisdictions, a person can be committed to a psychiatric hospital against his or her will if a judgement is made that he or she is (1) mentally ill and (2) a danger to self (i.e., unable to provide for the basic physical needs of food, clothing, and shelter) or a danger to others (Perlin, 1994). (There is also a form of outpatient commitment, which we describe later.)

Specific commitment procedures generally fit into one of two categories: formal or informal. Formal or judicial commitment is by order of a court. It can be requested by any responsible citizen; usually the police, a relative, or a friend seeks the commitment. If the judge believes that there is a good reason to pursue the matter, he or she will order a mental health examination. The person has the right to object to these attempts to "certify" him or her, and a court hearing can be scheduled to allow the person to present evidence against commitment. In Canada, this procedure is covered by provincial legislation that permits an *ex parte* hearing before a justice of the peace. Generally, this legislation permits a justice of the peace to have an individual held against his or her will for a period of time (e.g., up to 72 hours in Ontario) for the purposes of assessment only. If, after that period of assessment, the individual meets the certification criteria, she or he may be held for longer periods, and most provinces have a process for subsequent involuntary treatment. Alternatively, where the prospective patient

is compliant, a person may be brought to a physician who may, where the individual is seen as a danger to himself or herself or to others, issue the same process. For example, in Ontario the form signed by the physician (Form 1) is in effect for seven days and is authority for a peace officer to take the individual to a psychiatric facility for assessment for up to 72 hours. If seven days elapse, and an order of a physician or justice of the peace has not been effected, it is no longer valid.

Informal, emergency commitment of mentally ill persons can be accomplished without initially involving the courts. For example, if a hospital administrative board believes that a voluntary patient requesting discharge is too disturbed and dangerous to be released, it can detain the patient with a temporary, informal commitment order.

Civil commitment affects far more people than criminal commitment. It is beyond the scope of this book to examine the intricacies of civil commitment laws. Our aim is to present an overview that will provide a basic understanding of the issues and current directions of change.

Table 18.2 provides an overview of the current Canadian criteria for involuntary admission for the provinces and territories (see Gray & O'Reilly, 2001). Inspection of this table reveals considerable differences among the provinces in the criteria used. One overarching difference is that some jurisdictions use a broad definition of mental disorder, while others use a specific definition. Douglas and Koch (2001) noted that provinces with a specific definition actually use a functional definition of mental illness that is quite detailed. The definition of mental disorder in Saskatchewan, for example, is "a disorder

TABLE 18.2   Canadian Criteria for Involuntary Admission by Jurisdiction

Jurisdiction	Definition of Mental Disorder	Harm Criterion	Deterioration as Alternative to Harm	Need for Treatment	Not Capable of Treatment Decision
British Columbia	Specific	Broad	Yes	Yes	No
Alberta	Specific	Physical	No	No	No
Saskatchewan	Specific	Broad	Yes	Yes	Yes
Manitoba	Specific	Broad	Yes	Yes	No
Ontario	Broad	Physical?	Yes	Yes and No[†]	No
Quebec	Broad	?	No	No	No
New Brunswick	Specific	Broad	No	Implied	No
Nova Scotia	Broad	?	No	Implied	No
Prince Edward Island	Specific	Broad	No	Implied	No
Newfoundland and Labrador	Broad	Broad	No	Implied	No
Yukon	Specific	Broad	No	No	No
Northwest Territories & Nunavut	Specific	Physical	No	No	No

[?]Not clear from the legislation or court cases how to classify.
[†]"Yes" for deterioration and "no" for bodily harm.

Source: Adapted from Gray J. E., O'Reilly R. L. Clinically significant differences among Canadian mental health acts. *Canadian Journal of Psychiatry*. 2001;46(4):315–321. Table 1. Criteria for involuntary admission by jurisdiction; p. 317. Reproduced with permission of the Canadian Psychiatric Association.

of thought, perceptions, feelings or behaviour that seriously impairs a person's judgment, capacity to recognize reality, ability to associate with others or ability to meet the ordinary demands of life, in which respect treatment is available" (Douglas & Koch, 2001, p. 355). In contrast, Ontario, Quebec, Nova Scotia, and Newfoundland and Labrador do not use such precise and detailed definitions of the impact of mental illness. In Ontario, mental disorder is defined simply as "a disease or disability of the mind" (see Douglas & Koch, 2001, p. 355).

The provinces and territories also differ in how they define harm to self or others. Ontario, Alberta, and the Northwest Territories and Nunavut focus on a definition that emphasizes the possibility of physical harm. Douglas and Koch (2001) state that Alberta is particularly stringent in its conceptualization of dangerousness. Other jurisdictions have an expanded definition of harm that includes the possibility of a wider range of harmful acts that may or may not involve direct physical damage to the self or others. Gray and O'Reilly (2001) note that four provinces include the additional criterion that the person is deemed likely to suffer further deterioration, either mental or physical.

The column on the far right of Table 18.2 shows that, at present, Saskatchewan is distinct in that even if other criteria are satisfied, individuals are not committed in this province if they are capable of making a treatment decision. Gray and O'Reilly (2001) indicated that this caveat exists to rule out situations in which a person is committed but then refuses the treatment needed in order to recover and eventually be discharged.

Who experiences civil commitment in Canada? Moss and Redelmeier (2010) analyzed 2,321 applicants to the Consent and Capacity Board in Ontario. These individuals were seeking to overturn their civil commitment. Overall, 18% were successful but follow-up indicated that once involuntary commitment was revoked, adverse subsequent events were common and nearly half sought outpatient treatment for suicidal thoughts within 100 days of being released. The prototypical person experiencing civil commitment was someone who was middle-aged, low income, living in an urban setting, and with a past diagnosis of schizophrenia or mood disorder. These individuals tended to have multiple prior contacts with outpatient services for suicide ideation and there was high comorbidity in terms of substance abuse and personality disorder.

Community Commitment: Community Treatment Orders

"I have patients who, if they weren't on CTOs, they would tell me 'I don't want to see you Doc.' They wouldn't turn up for their appointments. They wouldn't take their medications and there'd be nothing I could do about it."

—from Foot, 2007, May 26

One controversial issue that has arisen in Canada involves the concepts of involuntary **community commitment** and **community treatment orders** (CTOs). The latter, introduced in Chapter 1, can be characterized as a form of community commitment designed to ensure treatment compliance. In July 1995, Saskatchewan was the first province to implement CTOs (see Goering, Wasylenki, & Durbin, 2000; O'Reilly, Keegan, & Elias, 2000), followed by Ontario in 2000. Legislation for CTOs was enacted in Nova Scotia in 2007, in Newfoundland and Labrador in 2007, and in Alberta in 2010. CTOs are used throughout Canada with the exception of New Brunswick and the three territories (see Rynor, 2010).

A report indicates that 935 CTOs were issued in Toronto between 2000 and 2006. The majority (68%) involved people diagnosed with schizophrenia, while the other cases involved people with schizoaffective disorder, bipolar depression, or depression. Overall, 104 CTOs were terminated; 58 were due to an order of examination being issued because presumably it was deemed that the order was not being followed, but in other instances, it was because the person withdrew consent or needed to be placed in a long-term facility (Mfoafo–M'Carthy & Shera, 2012–2013).

Other provinces have conditional leave provisions in place. Conditional leaves are discussed below. CTOs stipulate that the individual will be released back into the community only if he or she adheres to recommended treatments. It is a controversial topic because this condition of release essentially forces people to be treated, regardless of their wishes. Foot (2007) outlines the story of Glen Race, a 26-year-old from Nova Scotia who was wanted for the murders of two men in Halifax and a third in New York state (see photo). His family, who stated that he had struggled with paranoid schizophrenia for six years, indicated that they tried everything to get additional treatment for him, but they were unsuccessful. After Race was captured in Texas in May 2007, family members issued a statement that his alleged killing spree could have been prevented if Nova Scotia had had CTOs at the time.

Andrew Vaughan/The Canadian Press

Glen Douglas Race from Nova Scotia apparently suffers from paranoid schizophrenia. His parents claimed that he wouldn't have killed three men in 2007 if Nova Scotia's CTO legislation had been in effect. In a public letter they stated that "we, too, have lost a loved one."

The right for jurisdictions to enact CTOs was the subject of an important 2013 court ruling in Ontario. A group called the Empowerment Council launched a challenge on behalf of Karlene Thompson. According to an account by André Picard (2013), Thompson, a former teacher, first developed schizophrenia, paranoid type, in 1973 and she was hospitalized 13 times by the year 2000. She was hospitalized again in December 2000. Thompson was described in court records as being "unable to adequately care for herself." She had been urinating and defecating into garbage bags and keeping them in her room, and would not touch anything that had touched the floor. She was not adequately dressed for winter. While fully oriented, she was obsessively counting her fingers and mumbling to herself, indicating that she might have been hearing voices. Thompson did not appear to be bothered by the overwhelming stench in her room. The discharge statement indicated that "her mental state [on admission] had deteriorated to the point that she was essentially nonfunctional"—the same as at her previous psychiatric admission. Thompson was admitted pursuant to a Form 1, deemed to be incapable of consenting to treatment and managing her property, and then admitted involuntarily (Form 3) (see *Thompson and Empowerment Council v. Ontario*, 2013).

Ultimately, Thompson's functioning improved upon receiving treatment and she was released on a CTO in 2000 that required her to take antipsychotic medication, but she deteriorated again in 2003 after experiencing delusions (see Picard, 2013). The court challenge launched on her behalf at this point was predicated on the argument that the CTO provisions in the Mental Health Act constitute a violation of the Charter of Rights provisions in Section 7 ensuring the right to life, liberty, and the security of the person. In September 2013, an Ontario court upheld the CTO provisions in this complex case (see *Thompson and Empowerment Council v. Ontario*, 2013). Picard (2013) described how this case was framed as a test of whether CTOs are in place for reasons of protecting public safety or the afflicted person's well-being. The judge upheld the notion of CTOs. He ruled that the role of CTOs is to protect the mentally ill person's well-being. He also explicitly rejected the community safety emphasis on the grounds that community safety is typically not an issue because the person is not violent or prone to violence. Justice Edward Belobaba also emphasized that the CTO provisions outlined a plan of community-based treatment deemed less restrictive than being detained in a treatment facility.

The inability of mentally ill people to make treatment decisions is often a key factor in CTOs. A study in Ottawa found that almost 3 out of 4 people who were issued a CTO lacked the basic capacity to make treatment decisions (O'Brien, Farrell, & Faulkner, 2009).

The Canadian Psychiatric Association, in its 2009 position paper, confirmed its support for mandatory outpatient treatment, stating that it has benefits in "certain clearly defined situations" and its use is supported "if specific legal rights and safeguards are in place" (see O'Reilly et al., 2009, p. 1). The association stated that mandatory outpatient treatment in the form of CTOs is especially called for when people suffer from persistent deficits in insight.

A survey of Saskatchewan psychiatrists found that 62% were satisfied or extremely satisfied with the effects of CTOs on their patients, while only 10% were dissatisfied or extremely dissatisfied. However, CTOs are issued for only three months in Saskatchewan (as opposed to six months in Ontario), and survey respondents felt that the three-month period was too short (see O'Reilly et al., 2000).

The law establishing CTOs in Ontario came into effect on December 1, 2000. It is named "Brian's Law" in memory of a popular Ottawa sportscaster who was killed by a man with paranoid schizophrenia who did not adhere to his prescribed treatment. Critics called it the "leash law" and some claimed that the police would soon drag the mentally ill away in handcuffs if they refused medication. The CTO criteria in Ontario differ slightly from those in Saskatchewan. A CTO may be issued if the person has two admissions or 30 cumulative days as an inpatient over a three-year period (see Gray & O'Reilly, 2001). Thus, the provinces differ in the specific CTO details. Although concerns have been raised about the coercive aspects of CTOs, it is interesting that the Province of Ontario, in describing the legislation, still maintains that all protections involving the issue of informed consent still exist. (This concept is discussed in the section "Informed Consent" below.) Also, according to this legislation (see Brian's Law [Mental Health Legislative Reform, 2000]), individuals subjected to a CTO retain a number of rights, including:

1. a right of review by the Consent and Capacity Board with appeal to the courts each time a CTO is issued or reviewed;

2. a mandatory review by the Consent and Capacity Board every second time a CTO is reviewed;

3. a right to request a re-examination by the issuing physician to determine if the CTO is still needed in order for the person to live in the community; and

4. a right of review of a finding of incapacity to consent to treatment.

In Ontario, the procedure should really be referred to as a "community treatment agreement" because the patient is free to withdraw his or her consent at any time. When that is done, the "order" comes to an end.

Richard O'Reilly (2004) from the University of Western Ontario concluded that few issues have so polarized the stakeholders in the mental health system as CTOs. Table 18.3 summarizes his analysis of the major arguments for and against CTOs.

Concerns about the coerciveness of CTOs continue to abound. Snow and Austin (2009) reviewed ethical concerns and the false notion that CTOs allow a degree of autonomy and self-determination because the person is still in his or her community. They noted that some have equated CTOs with "therapeutic stalking" and authors such as Thomas Szasz have described CTOs as a way of transforming "all of society into a kind of mental hospital" (Szasz, 2005, p. 81). However, they allowed for other considerations such as the need to

TABLE 18.3   Arguments Supporting and Opposing CTOs

Supporting CTOs

1. CTOs are a predictable and acceptable consequence of deinstitutionalization.

2. Society has a *parens patriae* obligation to care for citizens who cannot care for themselves.

3. Lack of awareness of mental illness is a persistent and pervasive symptom.

4. Offering services is often not enough when patients lack insight.

5. The assumption that physicians can safely manage patients by committing them just at the point when they become dangerous is mistaken.

6. CTOs are less restrictive than involuntary hospitalization.

7. Research confirms the effectiveness of CTOs.

8. No evidence indicates negative effects of CTOs.

Opposing CTOs

1. Society should never coerce individuals to take treatment.

2. CTOs extend coercion into the community.

3. It is more difficult to protect patients' rights in the community.

4. If we had sufficient services, we would not need CTOs.

5. Coercion will be used as an alternative to providing adequate service.

6. People should not be coerced to accept services when there are others willing to accept, but who cannot access, them.

7. People often refuse medications because of side effects or other bona fide reasons.

8. Research on CTOs is inconclusive.

9. CTOs will be used to sweep undesirable individuals off the streets.

10. Hospitals will fill up with nonadherent patients.

11. Coercion drives people away from the mental health system.

Source: Adapted from O'Reilly R. Why are community treatment orders controversial? *Canadian Journal of Psychiatry*. 2004; 49(9):579–534. Table 1 Arguments supporting community treatment orders (CTO); Table 2 Arguments against CTOs; p 580. Reproduced with permission of the Canadian Psychiatric Association.

also protect the safety and well-being of afflicted individuals. Clearly, a CTO can have benefits in addition to enhancing safety. A follow-up study of 84 people issued CTOs in Ottawa found that the most significant changes were greater engagement with community services and a shift toward more supportive housing arrangements (O'Brien et al., 2009).

What are the consequences of a patient's nonadherence to the conditions of a community treatment provision? As noted by Gray and O'Reilly (2005), the person can be either apprehended and examined involuntarily to determine if involuntary admission is warranted (e.g., Ontario) or returned directly to hospital without a re-examination of admissibility (e.g., British Columbia).

O'Reilly et al. (2006) conducted a qualitative study of 26 CTO cases from Regina and Saskatoon. The most predominant

diagnoses were schizophrenia and schizoaffective disorder, in keeping with the results reported for Toronto. This study involved interviews with patients, clinicians, family members, and community members. Patients were generally favourable but somewhat ambivalent; they resented the coercion but this wore off over time in most instances, and many patients recognized the need for structure and support that came as a result of the CTO. Still, a small subset of patients remained resentful of the coercion. Family members and clinicians were much less ambivalent; family members were very positive about the CTO and most clinicians saw the CTOs as helpful for most patients. However, they suggested that the three-month duration is too short and should be extended to at least six months. This suggestion fits with the results of an earlier American study that found that CTO treatment was more effective if treatment was maintained for at least 180 days with seven or more sessions per month (see Swartz et al., 2001).

Churchill, Owen, Singh, and Hotopf (2007) reviewed 72 empirical studies from six countries, including Canada, and concluded that it could not be determined one way or the other whether CTOs benefit or harm patients. Many questions remain unanswered in the CTO debate. As noted by Chaimowitz (2004), "the data, helpful as they may be, can be used selectively by both sides of the CTO debate" (p. 578). Less forceful alternatives, such as assertive community treatment teams, do exist. It will be important to demonstrate that CTOs are more effective than alternatives if their continued use is to be justified.

Clearly, simply issuing a CTO or conditional leave is not a solution. It must be followed through with the provision of high-quality care. This was illustrated in another tragic example. Seung Hui Cho killed 32 students and faculty members, and then himself, at Virginia Polytechnic Institute and State University on April 16, 2007 (see photo). Further examination revealed that a CTO was issued for Cho in 2005 after he stalked and harassed two students, and it was determined that he had suicidal and violent thoughts. Cho was ordered into outpatient

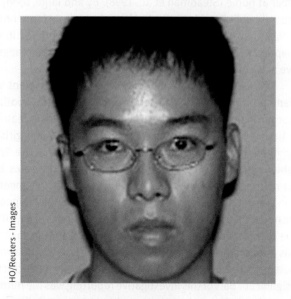

HO/Reuters - Images

Seung Hui Cho killed 32 students and faculty at Virginia Tech in 2007. Despite the fact that a CTO had been issued, he never received treatment.

community treatment after a judge deemed that he was an imminent danger to himself. However, Cho never received treatment because he was never contacted by community services. Accordingly, the gaps in psychiatric care were reviewed in hearings conducted by the Virginia House of Delegates (see Craig & Jenkins, 2007).

Preventive Detention and Problems in Risk Assessment

The perception is widespread that mentally ill people account for a significant proportion of the violence that besets contemporary society, but this is not the case (e.g., Bonta, Law, & Hanson, 1998; Monahan, 1992). Although the issue is complex, and the two constructs are positively related, "the relative contribution of mental illness to the overall rate of violence in society is quite small" (Norko & Baranoski, 2005, p. 21). Only about 3% of the violence in the United States is linked clearly to mental illness (Swanson, Holzer, Ganju, & Jono, 1990). Moreover, about 90% of people diagnosed as psychotic (primarily schizophrenic) are not violent (Swanson et al., 1990). Mentally ill persons—even allowing for their relatively small numbers—do not account for a large proportion of violent offenders, especially when compared with substance abusers and people who are in their teens and 20s, male, and poor (Mulvey, 1994). Large community-based studies indicate that mental disorders do increase violence risk when they co-occur with substance abuse (Monahan et al., 2001; Swanson et al., 1990). However, one study suggests that former mental health patients who are not substance abusers are no more likely to engage in violence than are non-mentally ill individuals who are not substance abusers. Thus, if substance abuse is not involved, mentally ill people are no more prone to violence than the average person. Also, when former patients do act aggressively, it is usually against family members or friends and the incidents tend to occur at home (Steadman et al., 1998). By and large, then, the general public is seldom affected by violence from former mental health patients. Thus, certain case studies outlined in this chapter are atypical because they involve violent and aggressive acts committed by people with mental disorders.

The extent to which mentally ill people are violent was made prominent by a 2016 series published by the Spotlight Team from the *Boston Globe*. This is the same team featured in the movie *Spotlight* about the abuse of boys and girls by members of the clergy, mentioned in Chapter 14. The Spotlight Team's more recent series of stories demonstrates that the mental health system in Massachusetts is badly in need of fixing and it seems evident that countless mentally ill people are not getting the care they receive (see Rezendes et al., 2016). The reporters concluded that the closing of ancient facilities was not accompanied by the creation of alternative treatment systems, so essentially people are "falling through the cracks." A significant part of this investigative reporting was the number of murders in Massachusetts committed by mentally ill people against mostly family members. This aspect of the story, while factual, led to complaints that the Spotlight Team was reinforcing the false belief that mental illness is associated with violence (see Massachusetts Association for Mental Health et al., 2016).

Nevertheless, there is a strong connection in the public mind between violence and mental illness, and this belief is central to society's justification of civil commitment (e.g., Steadman et al., 1998), as well as to the stigma attached to having been a patient in a psychiatric institution (e.g., Steadman et al., 1998). In fact, there is some evidence that mental disorder may sometimes contribute to violence, enough to justify preventive detention. In the Steadman et al. (1998) study, for example, substance abuse increased the chances of violent behaviour more among discharged mental health patients than among non-patient controls. There is also accumulating evidence that the effect of psychosis on risk of violence is much greater for women than for men. Skeem et al. (2006) conducted an intensive study of psychiatric emergency room patients at high risk for community violence based on an actuarial prediction model. The authors evaluated prospectively the temporal relation between symptoms and violence and reported that a high-risk patient with increased anger in one week is more likely to be involved in serious violence the following week. Violence was not related to anxiety, depression, or delusional beliefs. We now examine the issues and the evidence in greater detail.

The Prediction of Dangerousness

The likelihood of committing an act that is dangerous to the self or others is central to civil commitment. Historically, the focus of assessment has been on the prediction of dangerousness, but more contemporary approaches focus on the assessment of risk rather than the prediction of dangerousness (see Lyon, Hart, & Webster, 2001). Lyon et al. (2001) attribute the shift in emphasis to several factors, including results indicating that professionals tended to overestimate the incidence of violence when the institutionalized were released. Moreover, a focus on the dangerousness inherent in the individual promotes a tendency to attribute outcomes entirely to the dispositional traits of the individual and fails to take into account circumstantial and situational factors.

Regardless of which term is used, is dangerousness easily predicted or is risk easily assessed? Early studies examining the accuracy of predictions that a person would commit a dangerous act found that mental health professionals were poor at making this judgement (e.g., Kozol, Boucher, & Garofalo, 1972). Collectively, there is extensive literature on the limited validity of clinical judgements, including several studies conducted in Canada (e.g., Menzies & Webster, 1995). A meta-analytic, quantitative review by Hanson and Bussière (1998) found that clinicians' ability to predict recidivism among sex offenders is only slightly better than chance. The low validity of these judgements is a serious problem because of the weight given to such information. In fact, a Canadian study found that the senior clinician's testimony was the strongest predictor of the decision reached by tribunals in deciding whether to continue to detain forensic patients in maximum security (Hilton & Simmons, 2001).

One alternative is to make decisions on the basis of **actuarial prediction**. Actuarial prediction involves the use of statistical formulae composed of factors that are significant predictors of dangerousness. The factors are weighted statistically by their importance, based on the outcomes of previous studies. Several actuarial measures have been developed in Canada to assist decision-makers. The PCL-R (Hare, 1991), discussed in Chapter 13, is a consistent predictor of criminal recidivism (see Heilbrun, Ogloff, & Picarello, 1999) and is often included in risk assessment batteries, either as a stand-alone measure or as part of a broader assessment battery.

Lyon et al. (2001) summarized the strengths and criticisms of the actuarial approach. First, actuarial assessments are more likely than clinical ratings to use quantitative ratings and less likely to be influenced by subjective biases. Second, actuarial measures involve greater consistency because the creators of the measures have already specified with precision the information involved, the strategies for data coding, and required analyses. Also, actuarial decisions are easy for others to review. However, these same authors note that actuarial approaches may be too rigid and cannot be altered to take into account individual factors of potential importance. In addition, actuarial measures are derived from specific populations, so the generalizability of statistical formulae to other populations is always an issue.

Another alternative that is growing in popularity is to rely on more structured forms of clinical judgements instead of unstructured clinical judgements or actuarial approaches. The HCR-20 is a more structured assessment device developed in Canada (see Webster, Douglas, Eaves, & Hart, 1997). "HCR" refers to historical variables, clinical variables, and risk variables. Historical variables include such factors as previous violence, early maladjustment at home or at school, history of serious mental disorder, and other personality disorders. Current clinical variables include such indicators as being unresponsive to treatment, lacking insight, and acting in an impulsive manner. Finally, additional risk variables include consideration of such factors as lack of social support and experience of stressful events.

Quinsey, Harris, Rice, and Cormier (1998) criticized the HCR-20 on the grounds that it includes certain factors (e.g., a history of serious mental disorder) that have not been robust predictors of risk in previous studies. Moreover, they observed that the HCR-20 is not an actuarial measure in the truest sense because the checklist items were not selected on the basis of empirical links with outcomes. Still, as we see below, comparative data indicate that the HCR-20 fares as well as other measures and there is a wealth of evidence attesting to its usefulness (see Douglas & Reeves, 2010; Doyle & Dolan, 2006; Gray et al., 2003). The assessment package they advocate using is described in Canadian Contributions 18.1, which examines the contributions of Marnie Rice.

Canadian Contributions 18.1

Marnie Rice and Actuarial Risk Assessment

Marnie Rice was made a fellow of the Royal Society of Canada in 2003 (see photo). Rice died in 2015 but made numerous contributions throughout her career. She was a key member and former director of an effective research team based at the Oak Ridge Mental Health Centre in Penetanguishene, Ontario (which is now named the Waypoint Centre for Mental Health). Other team members included Grant Harris, Vernon Quinsey, Catherine Cormier, and Zoe Hilton. Her collaborative work has contributed greatly to our understanding of forensic patients and risk assessment, and in recognition of this, she was the 1995 recipient of the American Psychological Association Award for Contribution to Research in Public Policy. She was given the award for "pioneering the rigorous empirical evaluation of risk assessment and risk reduction in difficult forensic populations . . . . With her colleagues Grant Harris and Vernon Quinsey, she has established a remarkable program of cutting-edge research on the actuarial assessment of violence risk" (American Psychological Association, 1996, p. 342). She has also studied social skills deficits and clinical treatment, and she developed a program for preventing institutional violence.

Rice and her colleagues developed the Violence Risk Appraisal Guide (VRAG; Rice & Harris, 1995) for the purposes of actuarial assessments of risk; that is, the use of statistical models to predict the likelihood of violence. The construction and development of the VRAG is described at length in Quinsey et al. (1998). Rice and her

Marnie Rice furthered the actuarial approach to risk assessment.

associates sought to create an assessment tool that could predict over time which institutionalized offenders would incur another criminal charge from a violent act after being released. The 12 variables that compose the VRAG are displayed in Table 18.4. This table indicates that the two best predictors within the VRAG are scores

(continued)

TABLE 18.4 Violence Risk Appraisal Guide (Vrag) Variables and Pearson Correlations with Violent Recidivism

Revised Psychopathy Checklist score	.34
Elementary school maladjustment score	.31
Meets *DSM-III* criteria for any personality disorder	.26
Age at the time of the index offence	−.26
Separation from either parent (except death) under age 16	.25
Failure on prior conditional release	.24
Non-violent offence history score (using the Cormier-Lang scale)	.20
Never married (or equivalent)	.18
Meets *DSM-III* criteria for schizophrenia	−.17
Most serious victim injury (from the index offence)	−.16
Alcohol abuse score	.13
Female victim in the index offence	−.11

Source: Violent offenders: *Appraising and managing risk. The Law and public policy: Psychology and the social sciences series.* Quinsey, Vernon L.; Harris, Grant T.; Rice, Marnie E.; Cormier, Catherine A. Washington, DC, US: American Psychological Association. (1998). xviii, 356 pp. doi: 10.1037/10304-000

on the PCL-R (Hare, 1991) and a variable of elementary school maladjustment. The negative correlation between violent recidivism and age at the time of the index offence indicates that risk is higher to the extent that the offender was relatively young. Similarly, the negative correlation with schizophrenia indicates that it is associated with less risk (also see Rice & Harris, 1995) and underscores one of the main findings emerging from the work of Rice and her associates; namely, that mental disorder per se is not a risk factor. In fact, Rice (1997) concluded that "violent recidivism among mentally disordered individuals is related to the same variables as among non-mentally disordered individuals" (p. 420), so there is no basis for public perceptions that link mental disorder with the possibility of violence.

A comparative study found that the VRAG predicted general recidivism, as well as sexual and violent recidivism, thus supporting the actuarial approach (Barbaree, Seto, Langton, & Peacock, 2001). Prospective research involving a five-year follow-up of the original cohort of forensic patients found that the VRAG was a strong predictor of violent recidivism and a robust predictor of extreme violence (Harris, Rice, & Cormier, 2002). Comparative research of four actuarial measures found that the VRAG was comparable or superior to these measures in predicting violent recidivism and sexually motivated recidivism (Harris et al., 2003), and a new meta-analysis confirmed that the VRAG was a better predictor than comparable instruments of violent recidivism such as the HCR-20 (see Campbell, French, & Gendreau, 2009). Finally, in a very specific context, Rice and Harris (2003) found that the VRAG was a good predictor of violent and sexual recidivism by father–daughter child molesters, even though these child molesters had lower scores on the VRAG and lower rates of recidivism than non-familial child molesters.

A general finding that has emerged from research conducted in Canada is that it is the psychopaths among us who are especially

likely to reoffend in a violent manner (see Rice & Harris, 1995; Serin & Amos, 1995). For many years, Rice was distinguished by being quite pessimistic about the chances of treating and rehabilitating the psychopaths who have participated in her research investigations, in part because some findings indicate that treatment actually yields worse outcomes (see Rice, 1997). Rice and colleagues remained highly skeptical and argue that after 50 years of study, there was still no compelling evidence of rehabilitation and such evidence will only come from randomized control trials (see Rice & Harris, 2013). For these disturbed people, treatment is a chance to improve their social skills and increase their charm in order to further mislead unsuspecting victims. In contrast, others continue to maintain that treatment by highly capable therapists is effective and it may constitute an ethical violation that competent therapists are not more readily available (see Marshall & Marshall, 2013).

Rice's pessimism about treatment-related improvements was seemingly borne out by the details of the life and death of Peter Woodcock, a serial killer who was incarcerated for over 50 years, most of which were spent at the Oak Ridge Division of the Penetanguishene Mental Health Centre. Woodcock died in March 2010 (see Bourrie, 2010). Woodcock killed three children and molested countless others back in the 1950s, and he helped kill another person when he was let out on a day pass in 1991. Numerous treatments were tried, including a range of drug treatments that included LSD, but to no avail. Drug treatments were tried due to the attempted medicalization of interventions for psychopathy.

As a result of the inability to treat such psychopathic individuals, Rice concentrated her efforts on developing measures such as the VRAG that may be used to identify these people, so members of the court and review boards will be aware of whom they are evaluating. Recently, Rice and her colleagues responded to calls and revised the VRAG by creating the VRAG-R (see Rice, Harris, & Lang, 2013). The VRAG-R is shorter, easier to use, and comparable to the VRAG in its predictive utility.

Clearly, the VRAG is among the best actuarial tools for assessing dangerousness to date, and there have been great improvements in assessing risk over the years (for a review, see Hanson, 2009). The VRAG has even been shown useful beyond predictions of recidivism because it has also been used to predict institutional violence by violent in-patients (Hastings, Krishnan, Tangney, & Stuewig, 2011; Vitacco, Gonsalves, et al., 2012). Nevertheless, significant concerns still remain, and one meta-analysis of 73 studies led to serious questions about the usefulness of these measures in actual practice (see Fazel, Singh, Doll, & Grant, 2012). However, a recent analysis of decisions reached with 63 maximum-security patients in Ontario (i.e., transferred to a facility vs. discharged) yielded increasing evidence of the influence of the VRAG in risk assessment. Hilton, Simpson, and Ham (2016) reported that the psychiatrist's judgement was still the main factor in decisions reached but scores on the VRAG as well as Hare's PCL-R were correlated with these judgments.

However, we are still a long way from being able to use actuarial measures to determine levels of dangerousness with absolute certainty; predictive accuracy is based on statistical probabilities applied to complex individuals. The correlation between the VRAG and the outcome measure of violent recidivism is approximately $r = .44$ (see Rice, 1997), which means that almost four-fifths of the variance in this important outcome measure still remain to be predicted. Violence is a product of the individual's personal characteristics (including the consumption of drugs and/or alcohol) and the environment within which he or she is functioning. To make the point, you could take two clinically similar individuals with identical VRAG scores and place them in two very different environments: one will possibly reoffend, whereas the other possibly will not. Much of the variance in violent recidivism is accounted for by environmental factors that are probably not captured by instruments such as the VRAG.

A general criticism of the actuarial approach was provided by Rogers (2000), who noted that current measures are limited by their focus on negative predictors involving risk instead of protective factors that increase an offender's resilience when back in society. Rice et al. (2013) have responded to the collective concerns by acknowledging that yes, the VRAG and VRAG-R are not perfect, but the professional who is faced with making potentially life-and-death decisions needs to have something to aid in the decision and they feel that no other actuarial system is better than what they have provided. This point can be debated, however, in light of evidence suggesting that when nine different measures are compared, including the VRAG and the HCR-20, no measure is clearly superior and at best, they have "a moderate level of predictive accuracy" (Rice & Harris, 1995, p. 740).

Proponents of the HCR-20 believe that it is more suitable because it includes an assessment of dynamic, changing clinical risk factors. In addition, these researchers emphasize the importance of a multi-faceted approach that incorporates actuarial assessment within a model that also includes structured clinical judgements by trained professionals (Douglas, Ogloff, & Hart, 2003). A recent analysis of whether people deemed not criminally responsible were re-hospitalized or discharged led to the conclusion that dynamic factors including HCR-20 scores and recent salient behaviours (e.g., substance use or recent violence) played a substantial role in the ultimate decisions and that this information seems to be receiving strong weight from review boards (see Wilson et al., 2016).

The prediction of dangerousness remains a complicated and very difficult enterprise. Nevertheless, the work and contributions of Marnie Rice and her colleagues and other investigators in Canada and elsewhere has illustrated the potential usefulness of actuarial measures.

A court decision in the case of *Winko v. British Columbia* (see Table 18.1) further increases the importance of making accurate risk assessments. This case established that where there is uncertainty about whether an offender poses a risk, the onus is on the province in question to resolve this uncertainty, and if it cannot be resolved, the former offender must be released (see Schneider et al., 2000). In other words, unless the provincial review board can find affirmatively and *prove* that the accused poses a significant threat to public safety, he or she must be discharged absolutely. Previously, the interpretation of the law was that if there was uncertainty about risk, then the person in question would remain subject to the jurisdiction of the provincial review board. Analyses of decisions before and after the Winko decision have found few differences in terms of characteristics of the accused person and other details such as time elapsed between index offence and subsequent discharge (Desmarais, Hucker, Brink, & De Freitas, 2008). Desmarais et al. (2008) expressed surprise at the lack of differences and concluded that perhaps the need to prove significant threat to public safety had already been incorporated into decisions made about accused people prior to the Winko case.

Parenthetically, another aspect of this case involved the issue of "capping provisions" and setting a standard for the maximum amount of time that a person could be detained. The issue was whether Winko and three other offenders with similar appeals could be detained, perhaps indefinitely, if risk of dangerousness was still evident (see Schneider et al., 2000). The court ruled that these individuals could indeed still be held if there was a risk of dangerousness, with the caveat mentioned above that the risk of dangerousness had to be demonstrated.

Some researchers have gone so far as to argue that civil commitment for the purposes of preventive detention should be abolished. Reconsideration of earlier research suggests that greater accuracy can be achieved in predicting dangerousness in the longer term (e.g., Steadman et al., 1998). Violence

prediction becomes more accurate under the following conditions (note the role played by situational factors, sometimes in interaction with personality variables) (e.g., Campbell, Stefan, & Loder, 1994):

- If a person has been repeatedly violent in the recent past, it is reasonable to predict that he or she will be violent in the near future unless there have been major changes in the person's attitudes or environment. Thus, if a violent person is placed in a restrictive environment, such as a prison or high-security psychiatric hospital facility, he or she may well not be violent, given the markedly changed environment.

- If violence is in the person's distant past and constituted a single but very serious act, and if that person has been incarcerated for a period of time, then violence can be expected on release if there is reason to believe that the person's pre-detention personality and physical abilities have not changed and the person is going to return to the same environment in which he or she was previously violent.

- Even with no history of violence, violence can be predicted if the person is judged to be on the brink of a violent act; for example, if the person is pointing a loaded gun at an occupied building.

In addition, as stated earlier, the presence of substance abuse significantly raises the rate of violence (Steadman et al., 1998). This finding supports the inclusion of substance abuse among the factors to be considered when attempting to predict violence. (Substance abuse predicts violence also among non-mentally disordered individuals [Gendreau, Little, & Goggin, 1996].) Violence in discharged mental health patients is usually attributable to that small percentage of individuals who do not take their medication or, possibly, who self-medicate (Elbogen et al., 2006; Monahan, 1992). Outpatient commitment is one way to increase medication compliance.

For a detailed discussion of the responsibility of therapists to predict dangerousness and to warn people who may be in jeopardy, see Focus on Discovery 18.2. Another key point that deserves to be underscored is that there is a professional responsibility to not use measures for purposes they were not intended for. In this regard, in a comprehensive review paper, Vitacco, Erickson, Kurus, and Apple (2012) examined how the VRAG and HCR-20 have been used in actual cases in the United States. First, they noted that the measures are being used increasingly in actual cases. The two most common uses of these measures is in sexual commitment hearings followed by use of these measures to assess violence risk in individuals being considered for parole or conditional release. These uses are clearly appropriate. However, in other cases, the measures were used when it was not justified. This included cases where no norms exist and one instance when it was used in an argument about whether an offender should receive the death penalty. Vitacco et al. (2012) also expressed alarm about the use of these measures when determining the fate of juvenile offenders: a key concern is that actuarial systems are too static to reflect the dynamic changes in the lives of younger people and there is not enough weight placed on protective factors that would lower the overall level of risk.

Focus on Discovery 18.2

The Tarasoff Case—The Duty to Warn and to Protect

The client's right to **privileged communication**—the legal right to require that what goes on in therapy remain confidential—is an important protection, but it is not absolute. Society has long stipulated certain conditions in which confidentiality in a relationship should not be maintained because of harm that can befall others. A famous California court ruling in 1974 (*Tarasoff v. Regents of the University of California*, 1974) described circumstances in which a therapist not only may but must breach the sanctity of a client's communication. The facts in this case on the duty to protect the public are outlined below.

In 1968, Prosenjit Poddar, a graduate student from India studying at the University of California at Berkeley, met Tatiana (Tanya) Tarasoff at a folk dancing class (see photos). They saw each other weekly during the fall, and she kissed him on New Year's Eve. Poddar interpreted this act as a sign of formal engagement (as it might have been in India, where he was a member of the Harijam or "untouchable caste"). [But] Tanya told him that she was involved with other men, and indicated that she did not wish to have an intimate relationship with him.

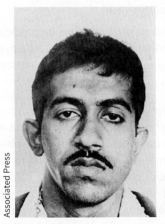

Prosenjit Poddar was convicted of manslaughter in the death of Tatiana Tarasoff. The court ruled that his therapist, who had become convinced Poddar might harm Tarasoff, should have warned her of the impending danger.

Poddar was depressed as a result of the rebuff, but he saw Tanya a few times during the spring (occasionally tape recording their conversations in an effort to understand why she did not love him). Tanya left for Brazil in the summer, and Poddar at the urging of a friend went to the student health facility where a psychiatrist referred him to a psychologist for psychotherapy. When Tanya returned in October 1969, Poddar discontinued therapy. Based in part on Poddar's stated intention to purchase a gun, the psychologist notified the campus police, both orally and in writing, that Poddar was dangerous and should be taken to a community mental health centre for psychiatric commitment.

The campus police interviewed Poddar, who seemed rational and promised to stay away from Tanya. They released him and notified the health service. No further efforts at commitment were made because the supervising psychiatrist apparently decided they were not needed and, as a matter of confidentiality, requested that the letter to the police and certain therapy records be destroyed.

On October 27, Poddar went to Tanya's home armed with a pellet gun and a kitchen knife. She refused to speak to him. He shot her with the pellet gun. She ran from the house, was pursued, caught, and repeatedly and fatally stabbed by him. Poddar was found guilty of voluntary manslaughter rather than first- or second-degree murder. The defence established with the aid of the expert testimony of three psychiatrists that Poddar's diminished mental capacity—paranoid schizophrenia—precluded the malice necessary for first- or second-degree murder. After his prison term, he returned to India, where, according to his own report, he is happily married. (Schwitzgebel & Schwitzgebel, 1980, p. 205)

Under the privileged communication statute of California, the counselling centre psychologist properly breached the confidentiality of the professional relationship and took steps to have Poddar civilly committed, for he judged Poddar to be an imminent danger. Poddar had stated that he intended to purchase a gun, and he had convinced the therapist that he was desperate enough to harm Tarasoff. What the psychologist did not do, and what the court decided he should have done, was to warn the likely victim, Tarasoff, that her former friend had bought a gun and might use it against her. Such a warning would have been consistent with previous court decisions requiring physicians to warn the public when they are treating people with contagious diseases and requiring mental institutions to warn others when a dangerous patient has escaped (Knapp & Vandecreek, 1982). The Tarasoff ruling (upheld in

1976 by a four-to-three majority of the California Supreme Court) is now being applied in other states as well (including *White v. United States*, 1986; *Soutear v. United States*, 1986; *Dunkle v. Food Services East Inc.*, 1990; and *People v. Clark*, 1990). The Tarasoff decision requires clinicians, in deciding when to violate confidentiality, to use the very imperfect skill of predicting dangerousness.

Extending Protection to Foreseeable Victims

A subsequent California court ruling (*Hedlund v. Superior Court*, 1983) held, by a bare majority, that foreseeable victims include those in close relationship with the identifiable victim. In this instance, a mother was hurt by a shotgun fired by a dangerous patient, and her seven-year-old son was present when the shooting took place. The boy later sued the psychologists for damages brought on by emotional trauma. Since a young child is likely to be in the company of his or her mother, the court concluded in this case that the Tarasoff ruling extended to the boy.

Chilling Effect of Tarasoff?

In the years since the Tarasoff ruling, professionals have wondered whether it would have a negative effect, perhaps even a chilling effect, on psychotherapists. If clients are informed of this limitation to confidentiality, they may become reluctant to express feelings of extreme anger to therapists for fear that therapists will notify the people with whom they are angry. Clients might become less open with their therapists, perhaps derive less benefit from therapy, and even become more likely to inflict harm if they have not disclosed their fury as a first step toward controlling it. The welfare of the people whom the Tarasoff decision intended to protect might be endangered by the very ruling itself!

The Tarasoff decision seems to have both immediate positive and negative effects depending on the therapist and the situation involved. A survey of psychologists and psychiatrists in California soon after Tarasoff became law indicated that the court decision was affecting their thinking and practices (Wise, 1978). On the plus side, one-third reported consulting more often with colleagues concerning cases in which violence was an issue. On the minus side, about 20% of the respondents indicated that they avoided asking their clients questions about violence, an ostrich-like stance that may keep the clinician from obtaining important information and yet reduces his or her legal liability should the client harm someone. A substantial number of therapists were keeping less detailed records, again in an effort to reduce legal liability. One troubling aspect is that a survey of 300 psychologists in four U.S. states found that 3 out of 4 participants were misinformed about their state laws, with it typically being the case that they had a duty to warn in situations where they did not have an established duty to do so. The authors of this study issued a call for better professional training (see Pabian, Welfel, & Beebe, 2009). At the same time, it is only fair to recognize that the decisions required are typically quite complex in reality and it is not always clear what the appropriate decision should be.

As an update to Tarasoff in California, in 2004, an appeals court ruled that a therapist has a duty to warn possible victims if the threat is reported to the therapist by a close member of the client's family (*Ewing v. Goldstein*, 2004).

It is important to emphasize that the duties involved here include the duty not only to warn but also to protect. As noted by Foellmi and Rosenfeld (2015), several jurisdictions in the United States require that the mental health professional take active steps to protect the potential target. Such measures would include alerting the authorities or taking other steps such as initiating psychiatric hospitalization for the potential perpetrator.

As for Canada, codes of ethics by professional organizations such as the Canadian Psychological Association stipulate clearly that psychologists must breach confidentiality when there is reason to suspect that a third party is at risk (see Ogloff, 1999). Thus, although confidentiality typically prevails in the therapeutic setting, certain circumstances can lead the therapist to inform others of the possible dangers. The duty to warn was clearly established in the *Wenden v. Trikha* case in 1993 (see Truscott & Crook, 1993), even though it was established that the mental health officials had no liability. In this case, the patient, Trikha, decided to elope and drove his car in the parking area of a mental hospital onto the street. He crashed through the parking exit and eventually hit a car driven by the plaintiff. Trikha was found not criminally responsible for his actions but lost a civil suit. But should his psychiatrists, also named in the lawsuit, be liable? It was deemed that they did not violate the duty to warn because they could not know specifically who was in danger. At the same time, the case established that the duty would apply if specific people in danger could have been identified.

In a Tarasoff situation, the clinician is seeing a client in a counselling capacity and comes to suspect that third persons may be at risk. What about the forensic context? The Supreme Court of Canada has visited this issue with results that are as chilling as the civil context of Tarasoff. According to Felthouse, O'Shaughnessy, Kuten, Francois-Purcell, & Medrano (2012), the definitive Canadian case is *Smith v. Jones* (1999). In this case, Jones (an alias) had been charged with a number of sexual assaults on prostitutes in the Vancouver area. Counsel for the accused retained the services of a psychiatrist—Smith (also an alias)—to conduct a psychiatric assessment of his client. This is a routine procedure for defence counsel and is usually perceived to be risk-free, as the psychiatrist's assessment would be privileged in that he or she is acting in the capacity of counsel's agent or, alternatively, under the umbrella of the "solicitor–client brief." In *Smith v. Jones*, the psychiatrist, Smith, contacted counsel for the accused to inquire when the trial was to commence. Counsel advised Smith repeatedly that he would not be needed (in that his report was quite negative). Smith persisted, indicating that Jones was very dangerous and prospective victims should be warned. Counsel continued to rebuff Smith. Finally, Smith retained counsel and sought to intervene. The case went to the B.C. Trial Division, Court of Appeal, and finally to the Supreme Court of Canada, where it was held that, notwithstanding the privilege that would normally be expected in a situation of this sort, where a mental health professional is retained by counsel to perform an assessment and as a result of that assessment the accused is seen as an imminent threat of serious bodily harm to an identifiable victim or class of victims, the clinician has an obligation to notify whomever, including the police, may be appropriate in the circumstances.

In this instance, Jones had outlined to Smith his detailed plans to kidnap and kill a small prostitute who could be physically overpowered. Jones planned to strangle the victim and dispose of her body in the bush near Hope, B.C. Jones had been diagnosed with multiple paraphilias, including sexual sadism, as well as drug abuse problems.

As a result of this decision, the defence bar is no longer able to rely upon the law of agency or the privilege that would attach

(*continued*)

to the gathering of information in anticipation of litigation—the solicitor–client brief. The frequency of referrals for assessments is anticipated to plummet, and ironically, it can be argued that the public safety concern driving the decision of the Supreme Court has actually been set back because now the prospectively dangerous accused will not be sent off for assessment by the defence bar unless the assessment is absolutely crucial. It is ironic because this is the clearest statement in Canada of a duty to warn and the decision is based on the principle that concerns about public safety outweigh the interest of doctor–patient confidentiality (Chaimowitz, Glancy, & Blackburn, 2000). The Canadian Psychiatric Association responded to the case of *Smith v. Jones* by concluding that the position about the duty to warn taken by the Supreme Court of Canada is to be accepted as a professional standard of practice (see Chaimowitz & Glancy, 2002).

A 2006 case in Ontario, *Ahmed v. Stefaniu*, has altered the situation in Canada. This case evaluated the duty of psychiatrists to warn and protect (see Glancy & Glancy, 2009) and resulted in the first-ever judgement against a mental health practitioner in Canada for failure to warn and protect. This case was launched by surviving relatives of Roslyn Knipe, including her two young daughters. It was deemed that Dr. Stefaniu, the psychiatrist who had treated Knipe's murderer, was deemed negligent and the plaintiffs were awarded $172,000.

The details of the case are as follows. A man named William Johannes was admitted involuntarily to Scarborough General Hospital in September 1996 after his bizarre behaviour was reported by his sister, Rosyln Knipe. Apparently, Johannes had threatened to harm his sister, whom he lived with, if she did not prove that she was on his side within two weeks. Johannes was admitted to hospital when it was deemed that he was potentially violent and lacked the capacity to consent to treatment. Tragically, Johannes did indeed kill his sister by stabbing her to death on January 24, 1997.

Johannes was under the care of Dr. Stefaniu and was a very difficult patient throughout his stay at the hospital. According to Glancy and Glancy (2009), physical restraints were used on him on 25 occasions. They reported that:

> "In mid-November, security records noted that he attempted to attack two patients. On December 2, 1996, the doctor assessed him and noted that he remained delusional and paranoid. A progress note on December 3, 1996, described him as very angry, loud, and intrusive, with threatening body language in a rigid posture. He was further described as extremely hostile, and on December 4, 1996, he threatened a nurse. It is reported that he became known as an extremely difficult patient. He wandered around naked and habitually sat next to the nursing station preaching loudly. At one point he incited a rebellion, encouraging other patients to refuse their medication."
>
> (pp. 250–251)

However, Dr. Stefaniu assessed Johannes on December 4 and found him to be much more co-operative and friendly. Johannes also indicated that he had staged his mental illness. He was released by Dr. Stefaniu the next day when he still appeared to be quite co-operative; however, Johannes refused the doctor's request to continue with voluntary treatment.

According to Glancy and Glancy (2009), when he killed his sister, Johannes appeared to be psychotic and had a delusional rage that included his belief that his sister was possessed by the devil. Later, Johannes was deemed not criminally responsible due to mental disorder and was sent to a maximum-security psychiatric hospital.

While the decision seems more than just, several concerns arise from this case. Most notably, advocates have noted that clinicians may now become overcautious. That is, people who have recovered to the point that they should be released may not be released.

Trends Toward Greater Protection

We turn now to a discussion of several issues and trends that revolve around the greater protections being provided to mental health patients in recent years: the right to treatment, the right to refuse treatment, and questions of free will in the law. We begin with a discussion of how to resolve complicated situations in which several themes may conflict in efforts to provide humane mental health treatment while respecting individual rights. Competing interests operate to create a complex and continually changing picture.

Choosing Among Ethical Principles   The ethical code prescribed by the American Psychological Association first appeared in 1953, and it was adopted and used for many years with minor changes by the Canadian Psychological Association and provincial associations (Sinclair, Poizner, Gilmour-Barrett, & Randall, 1987). One factor that provided the impetus for a separate code for Canadian psychologists was dissatisfaction with changes made to the American Psychological Association code in 1979 (see Sinclair, 1993). Specifically, Canadian psychologists were concerned about a change that loosened restrictions on advertising by psychologists. As a result, work was undertaken on a Canadian code of ethics in the 1980s, leading in 1986 to the first Canadian Code of Ethics for Psychologists. The third edition of this code was published in 2000 (Canadian Psychological Association, 2000).

A particularly useful aspect of the Canadian ethics code is that it assists psychologists who must make decisions in situations where various ethics may be in conflict (Sinclair et al., 1987). Psychologists were surveyed about how they would respond to hypothetical scenarios, and the four most relevant principles were identified and rank-ordered by their importance.

1. *Respect for the dignity of persons.* This principle is given the most weight, especially when there is the possibility that anyone will be exposed to physical danger.

2. *Responsible caring*. This provision includes the notion that responsible caring occurs only when it is provided by competent individuals who are able to respect the dignity of other people.

3. *Integrity in relationships*. This principle applies to all relationships, but it is noted in the code of ethics that there may be times when a need to be open and candid with an individual may conflict with the need to respect the dignity of others, and if so, the emphasis is on respecting the dignity of others.

4. *Responsibility to society*. The ranking of this ethical principle as the fourth consideration in no way suggests that this is not an important guideline. Rather, the Canadian code emphasizes that when there is a conflict between the needs of the individual and the needs of society, the need to preserve the dignity of the individual should prevail.

The notion of responsibility to society is important because it stipulates that psychologists have a general duty to promote the welfare of human beings and enhance our society. This principle was seen as particularly important by Dobson, Dobson, and Ritchie (1993). In their call for involvement, they observed the following:

> "[S]ustained advocacy by professional psychology on a range of issues linking psychological knowledge, expertise and practice with the public good is both an ethical requirement, particularly from the perspective of social responsibility, as well as a matter of enlightened self-interest. Although there have been some examples of political advocacy, there are other areas in which psychology has been mute or passively acquiescent. The profession requires a system to derive clear and defensible social policy positions as well as the ability to act upon these positions."
>
> (p. 451)

The importance of this approach is certainly evident to the many psychology students in Canada who embrace similar values and become actively involved as volunteers in their local communities.

Right to Treatment

An aspect of civil commitment that has received the attention of the courts is the so-called right to treatment, a principle first articulated by Birnbaum (1960). If a person is deprived of liberty because he or she is mentally ill and is a danger to self or others, is the state not required to provide treatment to alleviate these problems? Is it not unconstitutional (and even indecent) to incarcerate someone without then providing the required help? Olley, Nicholls, and Brink (2009) expressed their concerns about mentally ill inmates in Canada who are not receiving treatment for their mental illness. Inmates often suffer from profound symptoms of psychopathology and require treatment. Consider, for example, the following case excerpt from British Columbia:

> "Shortly before seeing the psychologist, the inmate was seen in his cell jumping off the side of the bed, appearing to be doing back flips, but landing on his head or back and seriously injuring himself. In response, the inmate was moved to an observation cell in the segregation area so that he could be more closely monitored. When assessed by the psychologist, the inmate was asked about his bruising, and stated that he was a Ninja and that he was practicing his moves. The psychologist referred the inmate to see the physician and suggested that a psychiatric consultation be arranged. After two days, the general practitioner (GP) examined the inmate, and recommended that he begin taking medication as a treatment for his condition. The inmate was unwilling to take the medication as he did not want it to interfere with his Ninja training . . . While waiting for bed space, the inmate continued to refuse medication, and engaged in impulsive, self-injurious behaviour. The inmate's personal hygiene became a concern when he began touching and sitting in his feces. At one point, the inmate was observed by a correctional officer to be holding a blanket over his head. The inmate claimed that he was 'astro-travelling' and needed to protect himself from flying debris, but in fact he was covered in pieces of feces and presented in an increasingly distraught state. The inmate's behaviours raised such concern that, while waiting for a transfer to a specialized forensic psychiatric hospital, the inmate was transferred to a local hospital. In the emergency department, he was assessed briefly and treated with antipsychotic medication. His head and back wounds were assessed and treated, and he was then discharged back to the correctional centre the same day. Once back in the centre, the inmate seemed stabilized temporarily, but he eventually resumed his 'Ninja training,' this time jumping off the toilet in his segregation cell, and his physical injuries worsened. The correctional centre's mental health professionals were extremely frustrated, as they did not have the authority to provide treatment without the inmate's consent. Their only option was to monitor the inmate's circumstances and work on helping him develop insight into the seriousness of his mental illness, a nearly impossible task under the circumstances."
>
> (Olley et al., 2009, p. 812)

Fortunately, according to Olley et al. (2009), an increasing proportion of mentally ill inmates in British Columbia have relatively short wait times and are more likely to access treatment due to co-operation and coordination among prison and mental health agencies, as well as provisions in the

B.C. Mental Health Act that allow for involuntary treatment for those deemed to require it, unlike in the case excerpt just described. Unfortunately, relatively quick access to treatment for inmates is likely the exception in Canada rather than the norm. However, Olley et al. (2009) noted the need to be careful in determining when treatment can occur against the inmate's will. The right to refuse treatment is another basic right that is discussed in the next section of this chapter. It has become an issue in British Columbia, which is regarded as the province where involuntary treatment is easiest to invoke. A civil challenge was submitted on September 12, 2016, to the Supreme Court of British Columbia by Mary Louise MacLaren and the Council of Canadians with Disabilities (Supreme Court of British Columbia Vancouver Registry, 2016). It was filed on behalf of MacLaren and an unknown 24-year-old male plaintiff who are arguing that their involuntary commitment violated their rights. MacLaren was a psychiatric nurse for 25 years. She was diagnosed with bipolar depression and forced to take treatment (psychotropic medications and electroconvulsive shock treatment) against her will. Her objection reflects, in part, her great fear of ECT and her wish to avoid the unpleasant side effects of her medication.

In *O'Connor v. Donaldson* (1975), a celebrated case in the United States that eventually went to the Supreme Court, a civilly committed mental patient sued two state hospital doctors for his release and for monetary damages on the grounds that he had been incarcerated against his will for 14 years without being treated and without being dangerous to himself or to others. In January 1957, at the age of 49, Kenneth Donaldson had been committed to a Florida state hospital on petition of his father, who felt that his son was delusional. A county judge had found that Donaldson had paranoid schizophrenia and committed him for "care, maintenance, and treatment." The Florida statute then in effect allowed for such commitment on the usual grounds of mental illness and dangerousness, the latter defined as inability to manage property and to protect oneself from being taken advantage of by others.

In 1971, Donaldson sued Dr. O'Connor, the hospital superintendent, and Dr. Gumanis, a hospital psychiatrist, for release. Evidence presented at the trial indicated that the hospital staff could have released Donaldson at any time following a determination that he was not a dangerous person. Testimony made it clear that at no time during his hospitalization had Donaldson's conduct posed any real danger to others or to himself. The evidence indicated that Donaldson received only custodial care during his hospitalization. No treatment that could conceivably alleviate or cure his assumed mental illness was undertaken. The original trial and a subsequent appeal concluded that Donaldson was not dangerous and had been denied his constitutional right to treatment. Throughout this litigation, Donaldson declared that he was neither dangerous nor mentally ill. But, said his claim, even if he were mentally ill, he should be released because he was not receiving treatment. The U.S. Supreme Court ruled on June 26, 1975, that, "a State cannot constitutionally confine . . . a nondangerous individual who is capable of surviving safely in freedom by himself or with the help of willing and responsible family members or friends." In 1977, Donaldson settled for $20,000 from Dr. Gumanis and the estate of Dr. O'Connor, who died during the appeals process.

The U.S. Supreme Court decision on *O'Connor v. Donaldson* created a stir when it was issued and has since given mental health professionals pause in detaining patients. Although this decision is often cited as an affirmation of the right to treatment, the Supreme Court did not, in fact, rule on the constitutionality of this doctrine. The Donaldson decision did say that a committed patient's status must be periodically reviewed, for the grounds on which a patient was committed cannot be assumed to continue in effect forever. In other words, people can change while in a mental hospital and may no longer require confinement. This position seems straightforward enough, yet it may still be overlooked.

Presumably, a situation such as that found in *O'Connor v. Donaldson* would not occur in Canada because a precondition to civil commitment is a finding of danger to self or others, which is reviewed every 90 days or upon the patient's request.

Right to Refuse Treatment   If a committed patient has the right to expect appropriate treatment, does he or she have the right to refuse treatment or a particular kind of treatment? The answer is yes, depending on the province in question.

The case of *Regina v. Rogers* (1991) in British Columbia reiterated that mentally disordered individuals have the right to refuse treatment, even if they were civilly committed against their personal wishes. Currently, the situation is more complicated when viewed from a national perspective. Douglas and Koch (2001) provided a summary of how the right to refuse treatment varies from province to province. Some provinces maintain the patient's right to refuse treatment (e.g., Nova Scotia, Quebec, Ontario, and Manitoba), while others have provisions that allow for treatment without the individual's consent (e.g., Prince Edward Island, Newfoundland and Labrador, New Brunswick, and British Columbia). The situation is more complicated in Alberta, where mental health officials have the opportunity to apply to a review panel in order to override the patient's right to refuse treatment (Douglas & Koch, 2001). Typically, when the patient's right to refuse treatment is circumvented, a substitute decision-maker (e.g., family member) is asked to provide consent.

One alternative in provinces where a person can be given treatment without his or her consent is to have the person outline his or her wishes during a time when he or she was of sounder mind. According to Simmie and Nunes (2001), this concept is known as establishing a person's **prior capable wish** and this wish has been ruled valid in court cases in both Canada and the United States.

In Ontario, patients can be treated against their will civilly only where they are determined to be incapable of consent. In such cases, a scheme exists whereby substitute consent to treatment may be obtained. A potentially more interesting question arises around patients who do consent to treatment.

Curiously, the issue of capacity to consent is rarely raised where the patient does consent to treatment. What percentage of those patients currently being treated "voluntarily" are actually incapable of consenting to their treatment?

In the case of *Starson v. Swayze* (2003), the Supreme Court of Canada confirmed the patient's right to refuse treatment. This remarkable case is the subject of Canadian Perspectives 18.2.

Canadian Perspectives 18.2

"A Beautiful Mind" in Canada? Scott Starson and the Right to Refuse Treatment

In some respects, Scott Starson is similar to John Nash, who was the subject of the book *A Beautiful Mind* by Sylvia Nasar and the subsequent Academy Award-winning movie starring Russell Crowe. Nash won a Nobel Prize in Economics for his contribution to game theory. He had a history of schizophrenia. Starson is a highly intelligent person with an abiding interest and expertise in physics as it pertains to the study of discrete anti-gravity and its implications for space travel (see photo).

Starson, who prefers to be referred to as Professor Starson, has authored some highly regarded articles in scientific journals despite not having any formal training in physics and not being an actual professor. Starson suffers from schizoaffective disorder, a condition that combines symptoms of schizophrenia and bipolar disorder. In 1998, he was found not criminally responsible on account of mental disorder after uttering death threats. Specifically, he phoned his work colleagues and informed them that he was in a phone booth with a rifle and was going to shoot the sales manager of a car dealership where he had been turned down for a lease or loan (Wente, 2003). He also threatened to kill his psychiatrist (Bailey, 2002).

Starson was an involuntary psychiatric patient who had been detained in psychiatric hospitals in Penetanguishene and Ottawa after experiencing mental difficulties as far back as 1985. There was no doubt that he suffered from mental illness. According to one interview account, he indicated that "Pope John Paul II works for me now." He also indicated that he had plans to wed comedian Joan Rivers, though he had never met her. He also believes that the late Prime Minister Pierre Elliott Trudeau was killed by an alien (see Bailey, 2003).

Starson gained notoriety for successfully winning a legal case in which his right to refuse treatment was upheld by the Supreme Court of Canada in a six-to-three decision. He argued that the medication was ineffective and would take away his mental faculties. In his statement to the Court of Appeal for Ontario, he observed:

> "Well, like all psychiatrists that I've met before them, they all think the same way, that the only thing they can do is to give you these chemicals—and I've been through these chemicals that they propose before—and I know the effects and what they want to achieve is slow down my brain, basically, and to slow down my brain which means I can't do what I've been trying to do—or what I have been doing for 30 years and will be successful at doing. And that would just be like worse than death."

> *(Starson v. Swayze, 2003, p. 99)*

The Supreme Court supported the ruling of two previous courts that had overturned the initial ruling of the Ontario Consent and Capacity Board (CCB), which ruled that Starson did not have the right to refuse treatment. The Supreme Court based its decision on the observation that the Ontario CCB based its initial ruling on what the board felt was in the best treatment interests of Starson rather than on a strict interpretation of his legal rights (see Brooks, O'Reilly, & Gray, 2003). It is still the case that patients have the right to refuse treatment if they are deemed to be capable of making this decision, but if it can be shown that they are incapacitated based on "a balance of probabilities," then treatment can be forced on them (Brooks et al., 2003).

Regardless of whether one agrees with the Supreme Court decision, it is hard not to feel sorry for Starson's mother, Jeanne Stevens. According to Bailey (2003), she wants her son to receive treatment and, in reaction to the court decision, she stated, "I'm devastated. I don't think what they did was a humane judgement. It's a disaster because they have destroyed his life and his dream."

Starson has acknowledged his mental problems, but he noted that he distrusts psychiatry, which he views as a religion. A year after winning the right to refuse treatment, Starson almost died. He became delusional and refused all offers of food and water due to his fear of being poisoned. According to a Canadian Press article (2006), Starson was granted a transfer to Toronto after finally agreeing to take his medication. Overall, Starson went seven years without treatment, and in an overview article, Gray and O'Reilly (2009) strongly criticized a legal situation that they characterized as incarcerating a person with a mental illness in a hospital because treatment could not be provided.

By the way, Starson's original surname is Schutzman. According to his mother, he changed it in 1993 because "he actually thought he was the son of the stars."

The evidence summarized by Gray and O'Reilly (2009) further illustrates the severe degree of mental illness experienced by Starson. He claimed at various times to be a world-class skier and arm wrestler, the creator of the CN Tower, and the greatest scientist in the world; he also claimed to be in regular communication with extraterrestrials.

What happened afterwards? Starson improved and was discharged in July 2007, but he deteriorated and was re-hospitalized in October 2007 and again in March 2008 (Gray & O'Reilly, 2009). He was again returned to the community, but in May 2009, he was in a secure unit at CAMH in Toronto (Tyler, 2009). An article in *The National Post* in February 2013 included an interview with Starson. He is now free but the conditions of his release stipulate that he must take his medication, which is a condition that Starson is fighting to escape. Starson will not acknowledge

(continued)

that he is mentally ill and he has particular views on psychiatry's role. He stated that, "The shrink profession is not scientific. It's not based on understanding and factual information and/or self-correctedness. Scientific processes self-correct when you find that you are wrong about something" (Brean, 2013, p. A3). Starson also predicted in the interview that the universe will reach its maximum size in 133 billion years and then another dimension will be added to the universe. He concluded "The universe is five-dimensional and I'm five dimensional . . . I'm going to get the world better and better more beautiful into the future" (Brean, 2013, p. A3).

Thinking Critically

1. Do you agree or disagree with the Supreme Court decision? Should Starson have the right to refuse treatment?

2. The decision was based on a strict interpretation of Starson's legal rights. What about the feelings and wishes of Starson's mother? Does she have any right to support forced treatment? Was the court's decision inhumane?

3. Are there any circumstances when it is in society's best interests for a person to be treated against his or her will? Do you think Starson should still have to take his medication?

Opponents of the right to refuse treatment are concerned that mental hospitals will revert to being warehouses of poorly treated patients. Psychiatrists fear that lawyers and judges will not accept that some people are too mentally ill to be believed, or too mentally disturbed to be able to make sound judgements about their treatment. In a book on what he calls America's mental health crisis, psychiatrist E. Fuller Torrey asserts that upwards of 90% of psychotic patients have no insight into their condition. Believing that they do not need any treatment, they subject themselves and loved ones to sometimes desperate and frightening situations by refusing medication or other modes of therapy, most of which involve hospitalization (Torrey, 1996).

Deinstitutionalization, Civil Liberties, and Mental Health

Recall in Chapter 1 our discussion of how since the 1960s, provinces throughout Canada have embarked on a policy of deinstitutionalization, discharging as many patients as possible from mental hospitals and discouraging admissions. The maxim is now "Treat them in the community," the assumption being that virtually anything is preferable to institutionalization.

Deinstitutionalization is a phenomenon that has taken place across Canada. Simmie and Nunes (2001) observed:

> "New Brunswick recently demolished its oldest psychiatric hospital, and former residents are now doing well in the community. Many of these people have spent years, even decades, on the inside. 'I never thought that some of the people coming out would make it,' says the director of a community mental health centre in Fredericton, 'but in fact their needs have declined.'"

> (p. 162)

But what is this community that former mental hospital patients are supposed to find more helpful to them on discharge? Facilities outside hospitals are often not prepared to cope with the influx of these patients. Some promising

programs were described in Chapter 11, but these are very much the exception, not the rule. Sadly, the state of affairs in many large metropolitan areas is an unrelenting social crisis.

The issues of deinstitutionalization and the conditions that some people find themselves in are worth revisiting in terms of concerns about legal rights and human rights. In late 2004, Ontario Superior Court Justice Robert Desmarais (see Rupert, 2005), in a landmark ruling intended to be binding on all Ontario courts, ruled there was no legal authority to jail mentally ill people pending in-custody forensic assessments and indicated that jailing them violated their Charter of Rights guarantees not to be arbitrarily detained. Although the Ontario health ministry announced an infusion of money to deal with these individuals, the government had not increased the beds within the six-month period ordered by the judge. Then-Health Minister George Smitherman admitted that there had been a 27% increase in the number of mentally ill people incarcerated in correctional facilities in Ontario between 1995 and 2005. Subsequently, at the Supreme Court of Canada, Chief Justice McLachlin lamented the fact that the courts and judges are facing a crisis because community-based care has never been properly funded (see Bailey & Bronskill, 2006). The Chief Justice was encouraged by steps such as the creation of mental health courts in Ontario and New Brunswick designed to divert the mentally ill from jail into treatment programs. However, Justice Richard Schneider, who presided over Canada's first mental health court at Old City Hall in Toronto (see photo), has stated that the government needs to involve fewer mentally ill people in the criminal justice system or provide more beds for assessment and treatment (*Toronto Star*, 2005). As we discussed in Chapter 1, the mentally ill are ending up in the criminal courts in unprecedented numbers. Schneider (2000) previously reported that across Canada the number of mentally disordered accused coming before provincial review boards has been increasing at a minimum of 10% per year since the early 1990s, while overall prosecution rates have been decreasing. It may be naive to expect that the community from which the mentally disordered individual came is the one best suited to provide support and treatment.

Many patients discharged from mental hospitals are eligible for social benefits, but a large number do not receive this

Courtesy of The Honourable Mr. Justice Richard D. Schneider

The Honourable Mr. Justice Richard D. Schneider presides as the judge at Canada's first mental health court in Toronto. He is also trained as a clinical psychologist. He is a tireless advocate for the psychiatric assessment and treatment of mentally ill people who come before the courts. Judge Schneider has questioned and expressed concerns about federal changes that allow judges to designate some mentally ill offenders as "high risk."

assistance. Homeless persons do not have fixed addresses and need help in establishing eligibility and residency for the purpose of receiving benefits.

It was noted earlier that there is now mounting evidence in Massachusetts that just because old institutions are closed does not mean that people will end up in better situations. In light of these observations and findings, do such challenging conditions justify reversing the policy of deinstitutionalization? In our view, they do not, because the problem lies with the failure of communities to provide suitable living and rehabilitation conditions, an issue discussed earlier in this book. In an interesting twist, it was reported in 2007 (see Fong, 2007) that the mayor of Vancouver wanted to re-institutionalize some former residents of Riverview Hospital in suburban Coquitlam who ended up in Vancouver's Downtown Eastside, where housing is generally unavailable and drugs are readily available. It is estimated that about 40% of the homeless people in B.C.'s Lower Mainland are mentally ill. Riverview once held about 5,000 patients, but, as a result of deinstitutionalization, the number dwindled to about 400 people. The mayor proposed new modern spaces that would provide support rather than a return to old-style locked wards.

Perhaps the best way to address the issues here is to find effects of reducing mental illness and promoting mental health. Canadian Perspectives 18.3 concludes this segment of the chapter by describing some recommended steps in addressing mental illness among Canadians.

Canadian Perspectives 18.3

Solutions for Mentally Ill People in Canada

"Whether it's a friend, a colleague or someone living in a bus shelter, there are really only eight kinds of people affected by mental health problems: Someone's mother, daughter, sister or wife; someone's father, husband, brother or son. People. Like me."

—Scott Simmie (October 10, 1998), author of the Atkinson Fellowship investigation into mental health, published as the eight-part "Out of Mind" series in the Toronto Star (October 3–10, 1998). Simmie has suffered from bipolar disorder.

In the spring of 1998, two investigative reporters for the *Toronto Star*, Donovan Vincent and Theresa Boyle, wrote a seven-part series (entitled "Madness") that was based on their investigations of the human tragedy of mental illness. Later, in the fall of 1998, Scott Simmie, winner of the Atkinson Fellowship in Public Policy, wrote an eight-part *Toronto Star* series (entitled "Out of Mind") that was based on his year-long exploration of mental health reform (see photo). More recently, in June 2008, an influential series on mental health issues and the mental health system in Canada called "Breakdown" appeared in *The Globe and Mail*. It featured the work of award-winning reporter André

Picard, whose contributions in highlighting key issues have been widely acknowledged (see photo). For instance, he was awarded the Humanitarian of the Year Award from the Canadian Psychological Association in 2009. Each series of articles concluded with long lists of recommendations and steps that should be taken for the benefit of people with serious and chronic mental illness. In our opinion, these series have covered the issues in a constructive, responsible, and fair way.

Steps to Take

Boyle and Vincent (1998) and Simmie (1998) listed steps that must be taken in Ontario to help people with serious and chronic mental health problems. Most of their recommendations can be applied right across Canada. Their recommendations include:

- Review of and changes to the *Mental Health Act* consistent with change from the old and outdated "institutional model" to a "community-oriented system" model.

- A variety of supportive housing, ranging from independent apartments to group homes, coupled with monitoring of standards and maintenance, particularly for boarding homes and rooming houses. At least 14,000 units are needed.

(continued)

Scott Simmie, author of the "Out of Mind" series about the plight of the mentally ill. His investigations led to many proposed and implemented solutions to the consequences of deinstitutionalization.

- An expanded home care program for people with serious mental disorders. (This recommendation is, of course, consistent with the recommendation of the Romanow Report and Kirby Report summarized in Chapter 1.)
- Community mental health centres as standard access points to the mental health "system" where people can receive on-site assistance and appropriate referrals. Consumer/survivor advocates would be a part of multidisciplinary teams.
- Development, evaluation, and implementation of risk assessment tools for forensic patients to facilitate the best use of resources and bed space.
- Opening of additional forensic beds for mentally ill offenders, to eliminate the problem of the mentally ill being incarcerated in jails.
- Diversion of the mentally ill from the criminal justice system if possible, as well as the hiring of additional mental health workers in jails.
- Community treatment orders as a last resort.
- Making available the most effective (but sometimes most expensive) medications for schizophrenia as "first-line" treatment.
- Increased emphasis on early detection and treatment of mental disorders in children. "Defragmenting" children's services as a high priority.
- More non-medical safe houses for people in crisis, patterned after Toronto's Gerstein Centre.

Sources: Boyle and Vincent (1998) and Simmie (1998).

- Government-established 24-hour information/crisis lines staffed by consumers/survivors who are trained to refer people to appropriate resources.
- Support for anti-stigma campaigns by the Ministry of Health or Health Canada, in consultation with the Canadian Mental Health Association.
- Support on the part of employers for employees with mental health problems.
- Increased training for the police in ways to deal with the mentally ill, including alternative "use of force" strategies to prevent the deaths of psychotic individuals.
- Appropriate contextual statements in all news stories linking violence and mental illness, since the seriously mentally ill are responsible for only 4% of the violence in society.

André Picard outlined a 12-step program that he prefaced with the observation that Canada's mental health system is not really a system; rather, it is a patchwork that has left up to 3 million afflicted Canadians "to the shadows" (Picard, 2008). Here are the 12 steps he proposed:

1. Commit to a national mental-health plan—now.
2. Conduct public education campaigns to combat stigma.
3. Create a $10-billion, national mental-health fund.
4. Set up community treatment programs in every health district.
5. Build tens of thousands of supportive housing units.
6. Double the amount Canada spends on research on mental health and mental illness.
7. Establish mental-health courts in every province.
8. Set up advisory groups to represent affected families in every district.
9. Implement early-intervention programs in all schools.
10. Push the business community to lead the way on workplace support.
11. Radically reduce wait times for both emergency and therapeutic care.
12. Invest in peer-support groups.

Picard and others at *The Globe and Mail* have continued to highlight mental health issues and the stories of people living with mental illness in Canada.

Thinking Critically

1. Some recommendations in this section have already been implemented, but the majority have not. Review the proposed steps and choose the five recommendations that you consider to be most critical. Explain why you chose them. Outline a plan for implementing your recommendations.

2. What steps do you believe will be most difficult to gain acceptance for—from politicians, practitioners, and possibly the consumers/survivors themselves?

3. What would you do to increase the number of qualified mental health practitioners in under-serviced regions of Canada?

18.3 Ethical Dilemmas in Therapy and Research

In this textbook, we have examined a variety of theories and a multitude of data that focus on what is and what is thought to be. Ethics and values, often embodied in laws, are a different order of discussion. They concern what ought to be, having sometimes little to do with what is. It is extremely important to recognize the difference.

Within a given scientific paradigm, we are able to examine what we believe is reality. As the study of philosophy and ethics reveals, however, the statements people have made for thousands of years about what should be are another matter. The Ten Commandments are such statements. They are prescriptions and proscriptions about human conduct.

The legal trends reviewed thus far place limits on the activities of mental health professionals. These legal constraints are important, for laws are one of society's strongest means of encouraging all of us to behave in certain ways. Mental health professionals also have professional and ethical constraints. All professional groups promulgate "shoulds" and "should nots," and by guidelines and mandates, they limit to some degree what therapists and researchers should do with their patients, clients, and research participants. Courts, too, have ruled on some of these questions. Most of the time what we believe is unethical is also illegal, but sometimes existing laws are in conflict with our moral sense of right and wrong. We examine now the ethics of making psychological inquiries and interventions into the lives of other human beings.

Ethical Restraints on Research

Basic to the nature of science is the saying "What can be done will usually be attempted." The most reprehensible ethical insensitivity was evidenced in the brutal experiments conducted by German physicians on concentration camp prisoners during the Second World War. One experiment, for example, investigated how long people lived when their heads were bashed repeatedly with a heavy stick. Even if important information might be obtained from this kind of experiment, such actions violate our sense of decency and morality. The Nuremberg Trials, conducted by the Allies following the war, brought these experiments and other barbarisms to light and meted out severe punishment to some of the soldiers, physicians, and Nazi officials who had engaged in or contributed to such actions, even when they claimed that they had merely been following orders (see photo). It would be reassuring to be able to say that such gross violations of human decency take place only during incredible and cruel epochs, such as the Third Reich, but unfortunately, this is not the case. Spurred on by a blind enthusiasm for their work, researchers have sometimes dealt with human subjects in reproachable ways.

Henry K. Beecher, a research professor at Harvard Medical School, surveyed medical research from 1946 to 1965 and

The Nuremberg Trials.

found that "many of the patients [used as subjects in experiments] never had the risk satisfactorily explained to them, and . . . further hundreds have not known that they were the subjects of an experiment although grave consequences have been suffered as the direct result" (Beecher, 1966, p. 1354). Half a century later, in January 1994, prompted by the work of Eileen Welsome, a journalist who won a Pulitzer Prize for her investigative reporting on the issue, the U.S. Energy Department began to publicize numerous experiments conducted in the 1950s through the 1970s that had exposed hundreds of people—usually without their informed consent or prior knowledge—to harmful doses of radiation. There was particular concern over the fact that the overwhelming majority were people of low socio-economic status, members of racial minorities, people with mental retardation, nursing home patients, or prisoners. The scientists, for the most part supported in their research with federal funds, clearly understood that the risks were great, even though relatively little was known about the harmful effects of radiation at the time, for, as was pointed out by a lawyer named Stanley Chesley who was arguing for compensation for some of the subjects, "they were doing it to poor and black people. You didn't see them doing it at the Mayo Clinic" (as quoted in Healy, 1994, p. A1). Some of these experiments involved giving women in the third trimester of pregnancy a radioactive tonic to determine safe levels of exposure and irradiating the testicles of prisoners to find out the degree of radiation that service personnel could endure without negative effects on sperm production. It is particularly troubling that these studies took place many years after the Nuremberg Trials.

The training of scientists equips them splendidly to pose interesting questions, sometimes even important ones, and to design research that is as free as possible of confounding elements. They have no special qualifications, however, for deciding whether a particular line of inquiry that involves humankind should be followed. Society needs knowledge, and a scientist has a right in a democracy to seek that knowledge. However, the ordinary citizens employed as participants in experiments must be protected from harm, risk, humiliation, and invasion of privacy.

Several international codes of ethics pertain to the conduct of scientific research: the Nuremberg Code formulated in 1947 in the aftermath of the Nazi war-crime trials, the 1964 Declaration of Helsinki, and statements from the British Medical Research Council. As for Canada, Young (1998) noted that medical research (including psychiatric investigations) in this country is governed by four documents: the Nuremberg Code, the Declaration of Helsinki, the Medical Research Council of Canada document *Guidelines on Research Involving Human Subjects* (1987), and the Tri-Council Working Group on Ethics (1997) document *Ethical Conduct for Research Involving Humans* (final report). The three councils that compose the Tri-Council Working Group are the Medical Research Council of Canada (MRC), the Natural Sciences and Engineering Research Council of Canada (NSERC), and the Social Sciences and Humanities Research Council of Canada (SSHRC).

In 1974, the U.S. Department of Health, Education, and Welfare began to issue guidelines and regulations governing scientific research that employs human and animal subjects. In addition, a blue-ribbon panel, the National Commission for the Protection of Human Subjects of Biomedical and Behavioral Research, issued a report in 1978 that arose from hearings and inquiries into restrictions that the U.S. government might impose on research performed with prisoners, children, and patients in psychiatric institutions. These various codes and principles are continually re-evaluated and revised as new challenges are posed to the research community.

For the past 30 years, the proposals of behavioural researchers, many of whom conduct experiments related to psychopathology and therapy, have been reviewed for safety and general ethical propriety by institutional review boards in hospitals, universities, and research institutes. Such committees—and this is significant—comprise not only behavioural scientists but also citizens from the community, lawyers, students, and specialists in a variety of disciplines, such as professors of English, history, and comparative religion. They are able to block any research proposal or require questionable aspects to be modified if, in their collective judgement, the research would put participants at too great a risk. Such committees also now pass judgement on the scientific merits of proposals, the rationale being that it is not ethical to recruit participants for studies that will not yield valid data (e.g., Capron, 1999).

Changes in the Declaration of Helsinki are being debated, driven by two developments in biomedical research. The first is an increase in research sponsored by for-profit organizations such as pharmaceutical companies. Faced with fierce competition and marketplace pressures to maximize profits, such companies may push for research that would not be approved by human subjects committees in non-profit organizations such as universities. This issue came to a head when the International Committee of Medical Journal Editors, a group that includes the *Canadian Medical Association Journal* (CMAJ), issued an extensive set of rules and new policies that will govern the publication of results in major journals (see CMAJ, 2001b). A CMAJ editorial on this issue stated:

"Henceforth, these 11 leading journals will require authors to attest that they 'had full access to all of the data in study and . . . take complete responsibility for the integrity of the data and the accuracy of the data analysis.' In addition, editors will retain the right to review the study protocol as well as funding contracts for the study before accepting the paper for publication. CMAJ will not accept reports on research that was conducted under a contractual arrangement that did not meet these ethical standards."

(CMAJ, 2001b, p. 733)

This position was reached in response to concerns that results could have been altered or even suppressed if the findings did not yield the results anticipated by the funding body.

The internationalization of research is a second factor in the possible attenuation of protection of human subjects. Developing countries are particularly eager for partnerships in research and do not always have the same historical commitment to individual informed consent and safety that is prevalent in more industrialized and democratic countries. A possible danger is that utilitarian standards (e.g., will the research yield generally useful results?) are becoming more important than the focus of the past half-century on the rights and safety of individual research participants.

In reaction to some ethical lapses in hospital-based research with mental health patients, the U.S. National Bioethics Advisory Commission recommended special precautions to ensure that research subjects with mental illness fully understand the risks and benefits of any research they are asked to participate in and that particular care be taken to make certain that they can decline or withdraw from research without feeling coerced. Specifically, instead of simply allowing a guardian or family member to make the decision for the patient, the commission proposed that a health professional who has nothing to do with the particular study make a judgement on whether a given patient can give informed consent. The commission recommended also that if a guardian is allowed to give consent on behalf of a patient judged incompetent to do so, then the guardian's own ability to give consent must be evaluated (Capron, 1999).

Informed Consent

This concern about conducting research with mental health patients underscores the all-important concept of **informed consent**. Just as committed mental health patients are gaining some right to refuse treatment, so may anyone refuse to be a participant in an experiment. The investigator must provide enough information to enable people to judge whether they want to accept any risks inherent in being a participant. Prospective participants must be legally capable of giving consent, and there must be no deceit or coercion in obtaining it. Furthermore, those who begin to participate as research subjects are free to withdraw at any time without fear of penalty.

Much research is relatively innocuous, but what if the experiment poses real risks, such as ingesting a drug, or what if a patient with schizophrenia whose condition has improved by taking a drug is withdrawn from it so that the investigator can assess the effects of "drug washout"? Or what if the prospective participant is a committed mental patient, or a child with mental retardation, unable to understand fully what is being asked? Such a person may not feel free or even be able to refuse participation. Although research shows that even committed patients with schizophrenia may be competent to understand and participate in treatment decisions, the degree of coercion that is part and parcel of being in a hospital setting must not be overlooked.

A further complication is that it is not always easy to demonstrate that a researcher has obtained informed consent. In an elaborate study, Stuart (1978) discovered that most college students could not accurately describe a simple experiment, even though it had just been explained to them and they had agreed to participate. A signature on a consent form is no assurance that informed consent has been obtained, which poses a challenge to investigators and members of review panels who are committed to upholding codes of ethics governing participation of human subjects in research.

Such problems are especially pronounced in clinical settings where patients may or may not understand the nature of antipsychotic medication. Irwin et al. (1985) found that although most patients said they understood the benefits and side effects of their drugs, only a quarter of them could actually demonstrate such understanding when queried specifically. Simply reading information to hospitalized patients—especially the more disturbed ones—is no guarantee that they fully comprehend; therefore, informed consent may not have been obtained. The report of the National Bioethics Advisory Commission pointed to many published experiments involving mental health patients in which no effort was made to determine whether the research participants had the decision-making capacity to give informed consent (Capron, 1999).

Still, as with the right to refuse treatment, there is recognition that being judged mentally ill—more specifically, being diagnosed with schizophrenia and being hospitalized—does not necessarily mean being incapable of giving informed consent. An experiment by Grisso and Appelbaum (1991) found that although patients with schizophrenia on average understood issues relating to treatment involving medication less well than non-psychiatric patients did, there was a wide range of understanding among the patients; in fact, the understanding of some was as good as that of non-psychiatric patients. These results suggest that it is important to examine each person individually for ability to give informed consent, rather than assume that a person is unable to do so by virtue of being hospitalized.

Confidentiality and Privileged Communication

When an individual consults a physician, psychiatrist, or clinical psychologist, he or she is assured by professional ethics codes that what goes on in the session will remain confidential. **Confidentiality** means that nothing will be revealed to a third party, except to other professionals and those intimately involved in the treatment, such as a nurse or medical secretary.

A privileged communication goes even further. It is communication between parties in a confidential relationship that is protected by law. The recipient of such a communication cannot legally be compelled to disclose it as a witness. The right of privileged communication is a major exception to the access that courts have to evidence in judicial proceedings. Society believes that in the long term the interests of people are best served if communications to a spouse and to certain professionals remain off limits to the prying eyes and ears of the police, judges, and prosecutors. The privilege applies to such relationships as those between husband and wife, physician and patient, pastor and penitent, attorney and client, and psychologist and patient. The legal expression is that the patient or client "holds the privilege," which means that only he or she may release the other person to disclose confidential information in a legal proceeding.

There are important limits to a client's right of privileged communication, however. For example, according to the current California psychology licensing law (similar elements are present in other state and provincial laws), this right is eliminated for any of the following reasons:

- The client has accused the therapist of malpractice. In such a case, the therapist can divulge information about the therapy in order to defend himself or herself in any legal action initiated by the client.

- The client is less than 16 years old and the therapist has reason to believe that the child has been a victim of a crime such as child abuse. In fact, the psychologist is required to report to the police or to a child welfare agency within 36 hours any suspicion he or she has that the child client has been physically abused, including any suspicion of sexual molestation.

- The client initiated therapy in hopes of evading the law for having committed a crime or for planning to do so.

- The therapist judges that the client is a danger to self or to others and disclosure of information is necessary to ward off such danger (recall Focus on Discovery 18.2 on Tarasoff).

In Canada, as seen in the Supreme Court of Canada's decision in *Smith v. Jones*, even formally privileged solicitor–client relationships may be pierced where an individual is seen by a consulting mental health practitioner to constitute an imminent risk of serious bodily harm to an identifiable person or class of persons.

Who is the Client or Patient?

Is it always clear to the clinician who the client is? In private therapy, when an adult pays a clinician a fee for help with a personal problem that has nothing to do with the legal system, the consulting individual is clearly the client. But an individual may be seen by a clinician for an evaluation of his or her competency to stand trial, or the clinician may be hired by an individual's family to assist in civil commitment proceedings. Perhaps the clinician is employed by a provincial psychiatric hospital as a regular staff member and sees a particular patient about problems in controlling aggressive impulses.

It should be clear, although it seldom is clear, that in these instances the clinician is serving more than one client. In addition to the patient, he or she serves the family or the province, and it is incumbent on the mental health professional to inform the patient that this is so. Simon Verdun-Jones (2000) from Simon Fraser University has written extensively on the conflict faced by clinicians who must be true to their clinical role and protect the client's rights while at the same time ensuring that the rights of the general public are also protected. This dual allegiance does not necessarily indicate that the patient's own interests will be sacrificed, but it does mean that discussions will not inevitably remain secret and that the clinician may in the future act in a way that displeases the individual.

Choice of Goals

Ideally, the client sets the goals for therapy, but in practice, it is naive to assume that some goals are not imposed by the therapist and may even go against the wishes of the client. For example, a school system may want to institute a program that will teach children to "be still, be quiet, be docile" (Winett & Winkler, 1972, p. 499). Many behaviour therapists have assumed that young children should be compliant, not only because the teacher can then run a more orderly class, but because children are assumed to learn better when they are so. But do we really know that the most efficient and most enjoyable learning takes place when children are forced to sit quietly in their seats? Some advocates of open classrooms believe that curiosity and initiative, even in the youngest elementary school pupil, are at least as important as the acquisition of academic skills.

As is generally the case in psychology, evidence is less plentiful than strongly held and vehemently defended opinions. But it is clear that any professionals consulted by a school system have to be mindful of their own personal biases with respect to goals and should be prepared to work toward different ones if the parents and school personnel so wish. Any therapist has the option of not working for a client whose goals and proposed means of attaining them are abhorrent in his or her view.

This question of goals is particularly complex in family and couples therapy (Margolin, 1982). If several people are clients simultaneously—inevitable in family treatment—an intervention that benefits one or more individuals may well work to the disadvantage of one or more others. This can happen if one partner in couples therapy really wants to end the relationship, but the other sees the therapy as a way to save it. Because people often do not openly express their real concerns and wishes at the very beginning of therapy, the therapist can already be deeply enmeshed in their lives before learning that the two partners have conflicting goals. For this reason, among others, couples and family therapy is particularly challenging.

The Right to Competent Treatment

Most readers of this text would assume that an important ethical principle that can almost go without saying is that people have a right to receive treatment from competent and highly trained individuals. Indeed, this provision is clearly stated in the ethical guidelines and standards of practice endorsed by the Canadian Psychological Association (2000). It is important to remain vigilant and ensure that the quality of care meets or exceeds expectations.

18.4 Concluding Comment

An underlying theme of this book concerns the nature of knowledge. How do we decide that we understand a phenomenon? The rules of science that govern our definition of and search for knowledge require theories that can be tested, studies that can be replicated, and data that are public. But given the complexity of abnormal behaviour and the vast areas of ignorance, which are far more extensive than the domains that have already been mapped by science as it is currently practised, we have great respect for theoreticians and clinicians, those inventive souls who make suppositions, offer hypotheses, follow hunches—all based on rather flimsy data, but holding some promise that scientific knowledge will be forthcoming.

This final chapter demonstrates again something emphasized at the very beginning of this book; namely, that the behavioural scientists and mental health professionals who conduct research and give treatment are only human beings. They suffer from the same foibles that sometimes plague non-specialists. They occasionally act with a certainty their evidence does not justify, and they sometimes fail to anticipate the moral and legal consequences of the ways in which they conduct research and apply the tentative findings of their young discipline. When society acts with great certainty on the basis of expert scientific opinion, particularly when that opinion denies to an individual the rights and respect accorded others, it may be good to let Szasz (1963) remind us that Sir Thomas Browne, a distinguished English physician, testified in an English court of law in 1664 that witches did indeed exist, "as everyone knew."

We hope that we have communicated in some measure our love for the subject matter and, more important, our commitment to the kind of questioning, doubting stance that wrests useful knowledge from nature and will yield more as new generations of scholars build on the achievements of their predecessors.

Summary

18.1 There are many legal and ethical issues related to treatment and research in psychopathology and intervention. Some civil liberties are rather routinely set aside when mental health professionals and the courts judge that mental illness has played a decisive role in determining an individual's behaviour. Criminal commitment sends a person to a hospital either before a trial for an alleged crime, because the person is deemed incompetent to stand trial, or after an acquittal by reason of not being criminally responsible on account of mental disorder. Several landmark cases in Canada and principles in Anglo-American law inform current thinking about the conditions under which a person who has committed a crime might be excused from legal responsibility for it. These decisions involve the notion that some people may not be able to distinguish between right and wrong (the M'Naghten Rules).

18.2 A person who is considered mentally ill and dangerous to him- or herself and to others, though he or she has not broken a law, can be civilly committed to an institution or be allowed to live outside of a hospital, although sometimes only under supervision and with restrictions placed on his or her activities. There is an important distinction between formal commitment that requires legal intervention and informal commitment in emergency situations when the person requires protection from himself or herself. It is important to acknowledge differences across jurisdictions in whether a person can experience civil commitment; there are definitional differences in what constitutes the risk of harming oneself or others.

18.3 There are a number of ethical issues concerning therapy and research: ethical restraints on what kinds of research are allowable, the duty of scientists to obtain informed consent from prospective human subjects, and the right of clients to confidentiality. These rights are just as important when the focus is on the ethics of treatment and the obligation to protect the client from harm and provide him or her with competent treatment.

Key Terms

actuarial prediction

civil commitment

community commitment

community treatment orders

confidentiality

criminal commitment

informed consent

insanity defence

M'Naghten Rules

neurolaw

not criminally responsible

prior capable wish

privileged communication

Reflections: Past, Present, and Future

1. Regarding the 2016 series by the *Boston Globe* Spotlight Team, if you worked for the newspaper, how would you have approached the information the reporters gathered that showed the number of murders committed by mentally ill people? Do you think they should have reported this information? What would you have done if you served as editor? Unfortunately, the concerns about how mental illness may be equated unfairly with violence tended to deflect attention away from how a highly regarded mental health system in Massachusetts has been allowed to deteriorate. What are your thoughts about what this says about contemporary society?

2. We reviewed recommended changes to the mental health "system" and the treatment of people with chronic mental health problems. What changes do you think will occur in the next 25 years? What reforms will be implemented? Will there be discoveries of new drugs that will act as "magic bullets" in the fight against disorders such as schizophrenia and bipolar disorder? Will there be breakthroughs in psychotherapy? What will it be like for the mentally ill in the next millennium? Will mental illness be all but eradicated, just as some illnesses such as leprosy or polio have been eliminated, at least in the Western world?

3. Do you think that we will ever get rid of the stigma associated with mental illness? Do you think that the goal of integrating people with serious and chronic mental health problems will ever become "reality rather than rhetoric" (Goering et al., 2000, p. 356)? Do you think that scarce dollars in the mental health area will be allocated to other priorities in health care as a consequence of the "baby boomer" generation developing physical health problems that put pressure on the health care system in Canada?

Abnormal behaviour Patterns of emotion, thought, and action deemed pathological for one or more of the following reasons: infrequent occurrence, violation of norms, personal distress, disability or dysfunction, and unexpectedness.

Accommodation The cognitive process of modifying existing schemas to incorporate new events and new information.

Accountability A requirement that Canada's health care system and provinces be held responsible for the quality of the care provided as part of a new Health Care Act, as recommended in the Romanow report.

Acquaintance (date) rape Forcible sex when the people involved know each other, sometimes occurring on a date.

Action (behavioural) therapies A term sometimes applied to behavioural therapies because they involve work on behaviour as opposed to work on dreams or transference, as occurs in psychodynamic therapies.

Actuarial prediction A prediction of dangerousness or risk. It involves the use of statistical formulae composed of factors that are weighted. Actuarial prediction is less influenced by subjective interpretive biases on the part of the person engaging in prediction.

Adoptees method Research method that studies children who were adopted and reared completely apart from their disordered parents, thereby eliminating the influence of being raised by disordered parents.

Age effects The consequences of being a given chronological age. Compare with *cohort effects*.

Ageism Discrimination against someone because of his or her age.

Agoraphobia A cluster of fears centring on being in open spaces and leaving the home. In the *DSM-5*, it is diagnosed separately from panic disorder, but it is still often linked to panic disorder.

Allostatic load A maladaptive condition based in neurochemical reactions that reflect prolonged exposure to unpredictable stressors.

Alogia A negative symptom in schizophrenia, marked by poverty of speech and of speech content.

Alternate-form reliability The extent to which scores on two forms of a test are consistent.

Altruistic suicide As defined by Durkheim, self-annihilation that the person feels will serve a social purpose, such as the self-immolations

practised by Buddhist monks during the Vietnam War.

Alzheimer's disease A dementia involving a progressive atrophy of cortical tissue and marked by memory impairment, involuntary movements of limbs, occasional convulsions, intellectual deterioration, and psychotic behaviour.

Amenorrhea Loss of menstrual period, which is sometimes caused by eating disorders.

Amphetamines A group of stimulating drugs that produce heightened levels of energy and, in large doses, nervousness, sleeplessness, and paranoid delusions.

Anaesthesia A form of conversion disorder in which the person experiences a loss of sensation or an impairment of sensation.

Analogue experiment An experimental study of a phenomenon different from but related to the actual interests of the investigator.

Anger-in theory The view that psychophysiological disorders, such as essential hypertension, arise from a person's not expressing anger or resentment.

Angina pectoris See *coronary heart disease*.

Anhedonia A negative symptom in schizophrenia in which the individual is unable to feel pleasure.

Anomic suicide As defined by Durkheim, self-annihilation triggered by a person's inability to cope with sudden and unfavourable change in a social situation.

Anorexia nervosa (AN) A disorder in which a person refuses to eat or to retain any food resulting in a significantly low body weight. The individual has an intense fear of becoming obese and feels fat even when emaciated.

Antabuse A biological drug treatment for drinking problems that causes a person to feel nauseated if he or she drinks alcohol.

Antipsychotic drugs Medications developed in the 1950s for the treatment of schizophrenia. Also called "neuroleptics."

Anti-social personality A disorder in which a person, also called a "psychopath" or a "sociopath," is superficially charming and a habitual liar, has no regard for others, shows no remorse after hurting others, has no shame for behaving in an outrageously objectionable manner, is unable to form relationships and take responsibility, and does not learn from punishment. See also *psychopathy*.

Anxiety An unpleasant feeling of fear and apprehension accompanied by increased physiological arousal. In learning theory, it is

considered a drive that mediates between a threatening situation and avoidance behaviour. Anxiety can be assessed by self-report, by measuring physiological arousal, and by observing overt behaviour.

Anxiety disorders Disorders in which fear or tension is overriding, including specific phobias, social anxiety disorder, panic disorder, agoraphobia, and generalized anxiety disorder. These disorders form a major category in the *DSM-5* and cover most of what used to be called the "neuroses."

Anxiety sensitivity A cognitive preoccupation that involves a fear of fear itself and thus contributes to a heightened sense of panic.

Anxiolytics Tranquilizers; drugs that reduce anxiety.

Anxiously attached An attachment orientation in which the infant expresses great distress when left alone by the caregiver, but perhaps still in the presence of a stranger.

Applied behaviour analysis The study of the antecedent conditions and reinforcement contingencies that control behaviour. See also *operant conditioning*.

Asociality A negative symptom of schizophrenia marked by an inability to form close relationships and to feel intimacy.

Asperger's syndrome A milder form of autism typically reflected in deficits in social functioning. It is no longer recognized as a separate disorder in the *DSM-5*.

Assertion training Behaviour therapy procedures that attempt to help a person more easily express thoughts, wishes, beliefs, and legitimate feelings of resentment or approval.

Assessment Finding out what is wrong with a person, what may have caused a problem or problems, and what steps may be taken to improve the person's condition.

Assimilation The cognitive process of incorporating new information and new events into existing schemas.

Assimilative integration A method of psychotherapy integration in which the clinician mostly identifies with one therapeutic orientation, but assimilates concepts and techniques from other orientations.

Asylums Refuges established in western Europe in the fifteenth century to confine and provide for the mentally ill; the forerunners of the mental hospital.

Attention-deficit/hyperactivity disorder (ADHD) A disorder in children marked by difficulties in focusing adaptively on the task at hand, by inappropriate fidgeting and anti-social behaviour, and by excessive non–goal-directed behaviour.

Attribution   The explanation a person has for his or her behaviour.

Atypical antipsychotics   A class of drugs (e.g., neuroleptics) used to treat schizophrenia and other disorders that were developed to elim- inate side effects, including problems with motor control.

Augmented reality (AR) exposure   A type of exposure that has been used in the treatment of small animal phobias. It uses a combination of virtual reality and the physical world.

Authoritarian parenting   A highly controlling and rigid form of parenting typically linked with substantial adjustment problems.

Authoritative parenting   A positive form of parenting style involving controlling, directive behaviour that is supported by a sound ration- ale. It is a style typically associated with positive adjustment.

Autism spectrum disorder   A pervasive devel- opmental disorder in which the child's world is one of profound aloneness. Speech is often absent, and the child has an obsessive need for everything to remain the same.

Autonomic lability   Tendency for the autonomic nervous system to be easily aroused.

Autonomic nervous system (ANS)   The divi- sion of the nervous system that regulates invol- untary functions; innervates endocrine glands, smooth muscle, and heart muscle; and initiates the physiological changes that are part of the expression of emotion. See also *parasympa- thetic* and *sympathetic nervous systems*.

Autonomy   A personality style associated with vulnerability to depression. It involves a need to work toward achievement goals while being free from constraints imposed by others.

Aversive conditioning   A process believed to underlie the effectiveness of aversion therapy.

Avoidant attachment style   An attachment orientation in which the infant is withdrawn and detached from the caregiver, almost as if no attachment bond were formed in the first place.

Avoidant personality   A disorder in which individuals have poor self-esteem and thus are extremely sensitive to potential rejection and remain aloof even though they very much desire affiliation and affection.

Avolition   A negative symptom in schizophrenia in which the individual lacks interest and drive.

Barbiturates   A class of synthetic sedative drugs that are addictive and in large doses can cause death by almost completely relaxing the diaphragm.

Bedlam   A scene or place involving a wild uproar or confusion. The term is derived from the scenes at Bethlehem Hospital in London, where unrestrained groups of mentally ill people interacted with each other.

Behaviour genetics   The study of individual differences in behaviour that are attributable to differences in genetic make up.

Behaviour modification   See *behaviour therapy*.

Behaviour therapy   A branch of psychother- apy narrowly conceived as the application of classical and operant conditioning to the alter- ation of clinical problems, but more broadly conceived as applied experimental psychol- ogy in a clinical context. Also called *behaviour modification*.

Behavioural medicine   An interdisciplinary field concerned with integrating knowledge from medicine and behavioural science to understand health and illness and to prevent as well as to treat psychophysiological disor- ders and other illnesses in which a person's psyche plays a role. See also *health psychology*.

Behavioural (learning) paradigm   An orienta- tion that is based on the notion that abnormal behaviour is acquired based on behaviours that receive reinforcement or punishment.

Behaviourism   The school of psychology associated with Watson, who proposed that observable behaviour, not consciousness, is the proper subject matter of psychology. Currently, many who consider themselves behaviourists do use mediational concepts, provided they are firmly anchored to observables.

Bilateral ECT   Electroconvulsive therapy in which electrodes are placed on each side of the forehead and an electrical current is passed between them through both hemispheres of the brain.

Binge eating disorder (BED)   Added officially as a new eating disorder diagnosis in the *DSM-5*; includes recurrent episodes of unrestrained eat- ing that can involve the ingestion of thousands of calories at one time.

Biofeedback   Procedures that provide an individual immediate information on minute changes in muscle activity, skin temperature, heart rate, blood pressure, and other somatic functions. It is assumed that voluntary control over these bodily processes can be achieved through this knowledge, thereby ameliorating to some extent certain psychophysiological disorders.

Biological paradigm   A broad theoretical view that holds that mental disorders are caused by some aberrant somatic process or defect.

Biopsychosocial paradigm   A paradigm that suggests that all normal and abnormal behav- iour is caused by an interaction of biological, psychological, and social factors.

Bipolar I disorder   A disorder in which people experience episodes of both mania and depres- sion or of mania alone.

Bipolar II disorder   A disorder in which peo- ple experience episodes of major depression followed by a type of manic phase that is less severe than in bipolar I disorder.

Body dysmorphic disorder (BDD)   A disor- der categorized in the *DSM-5* manual under obsessive-compulsive and related disorders. It is marked by preoccupation with an imagined or exaggerated defect in appearance; for exam- ple, facial wrinkles or excess facial or body hair.

Body-focused repetitive behaviours   Cat- egory of behaviours that includes excoriation (skin-picking disorder) and trichotillomania (hair-pulling disorder).

Body mass index   An index that reflects how heavy someone is as a function of their height. It is calculated by a set formula (i.e., body mass in kilograms divided by the square of the person's height). Also called "BMI."

Borderline personality   A disorder in which people are impulsive and unpredictable, with an uncertain self-image, intense and unstable social relationships, and extreme mood swings.

Brief therapy   Time-limited psychotherapy, usually ego-analytic in orientation and lasting no more than 25 sessions.

Brooding   A moody contemplation of depres- sive symptoms—"What am I doing to deserve this?"—that is more common in females than males.

Bulimia nervosa (BN)   A disorder character- ized by episodic uncontrollable eating binges followed by purging either by vomiting or by taking laxatives.

Canadian Mental Health Association   A national organization that provides information about mental illness and acts as an advocate for mentally ill people.

Cardiovascular disorders (CVDs)   Medical problems involving the heart and the blood circulation system, such as hypertension or coronary heart disease.

Cardiovascular reactivity   The extent to which blood pressure and heart rate increase in response to stress.

Case study   The collection of historical or biographical information on a single individ- ual, often including experiences in therapy.

Case validity   The extent to which the formu- lation of a case accurately encompasses the multiple influences that contribute to distress and dysfunction.

Catatonic immobility   A fixity of posture, sometimes grotesque, maintained for long periods, with accompanying muscular rigidity, trancelike state of consciousness, and waxy flexibility.

Catatonic schizophrenia A subtype of schizophrenia whose primary symptoms alternate between stuporous immobility and excited agitation.

Categorical classification An approach to assessment in which the basic decision is whether a person is or is not a member of a discrete grouping. Contrast with *dimensional classification*.

Cathartic method A therapeutic procedure introduced by Breuer and developed further by Freud in the late nineteenth century whereby a patient recalls and relives an earlier emotional catastrophe and re-experiences the tension and unhappiness, the goal being to relieve emotional suffering.

Child sexual abuse Sexual abuse of children that involves direct physical contact, such as pedophilia or incest.

Chronic traumatic encephalopathy (CTE) Atrophy of the brain, typically in response to a history of physical trauma to the head, as illustrated by the problems in aging reported by some professional athletes.

Civil commitment A procedure whereby a person can be legally certified as mentally ill and hospitalized, even against his or her will.

Classical conditioning A basic form of learning, also called "Pavlovian conditioning," in which a neutral stimulus is repeatedly paired with another stimulus (called the *unconditioned stimulus*, UCS) that naturally elicits a certain desired response (called the *unconditioned response*, UCR). After repeated trials the neutral stimulus becomes a *conditioned stimulus* (CS) and evokes the same or a similar response, now called the *conditioned response* (CR).

Classificatory variables The characteristics that people bring with them to scientific investigations, such as sex, age, and mental status; studied by correlational research and mixed designs.

Client-centred therapy A humanistic-existential insight therapy, developed by Rogers, which emphasizes the importance of the therapist's understanding the client's subjective experiences and assisting the client to gain more awareness of current motivations for behaviour. The goal is not only to reduce anxieties but also to foster actualization of the client's potential.

Clinical interview A conversation between a clinician and a client that is aimed at determining diagnosis, history, causes for problems, and possible treatment options.

Clinical psychologist An individual who has earned a Ph.D. degree in psychology or a Psy.D. and whose training has included an internship in a mental hospital or clinic.

Clinician A health professional authorized to provide services to people suffering from one or more pathologies.

Cocaine A pain-reducing, stimulating, and addictive alkaloid obtained from coca leaves, which increases mental powers, produces euphoria, heightens sexual desire, and in large doses causes paranoia and hallucinations.

Cognition The process of knowing; the thinking, judging, reasoning, and planning activities of the human mind. Behaviour is now often explained as depending on these processes.

Cognitive-behavioural case formulation A process in which a cognitive-behavioural therapist attempts to ascertain how the various problems experienced by a client are related in order to pick out the overt behaviours and underlying schemata that will become the focus of therapy.

Cognitive-behavioural therapy (CBT) Behaviour therapy that incorporates theory and research on cognitive processes such as thoughts, perceptions, judgements, self-statements, and tacit assumptions. A blend of both the cognitive and behavioural paradigms.

Cognitive enhancement therapy (CET) A treatment for schizophrenia that involves competence-based training in cognitive capacities and skills (e.g., attention, memory, and problem solving) and social-cognitive skills (e.g., conversing with someone).

Cognitive paradigm The general view that people can best be understood by studying how they perceive and structure their experiences.

Cognitive reserve hypothesis The theory that high education levels delay the clinical expression of dementia because the brain develops backup or reserve neural structures as a form of neuroplasticity.

Cognitive restructuring Any behaviour therapy procedure that attempts to alter the manner in which a client thinks about life so that he or she changes overt behaviour and emotions.

Cohort effects The consequences of having been born in a given year and having grown up during a particular time period with its own unique pressures, problems, challenges, and opportunities. Compare with *age effects*.

Common factorism A method that seeks therapeutic strategies that are common to all forms of psychotherapy (e.g., therapeutic or working alliance).

Community commitment A form of commitment in which a person is committed to involuntary treatment while still residing in the community, derived from community treatment orders.

Community psychology An approach to therapy that emphasizes prevention and the seeking out of potential difficulties rather than waiting for troubled individuals to initiate consultation. The location for professional activities tends

to be in the person's natural surroundings rather than in the therapist's office. See also *prevention*.

Community treatment order A legal tool that specifies the terms of treatment that must be adhered to in order for a mentally ill person to be released and live in the community. Recent court decisions emphasize the intent of protecting the mentally ill person.

Comorbidity The co-occurrence of two disorders, as when a person meets criteria for major depression and an anxiety disorder.

Compassion-focused therapy A new therapy developed by Gilbert from his evolutionary theory. It is centred on developing a sense of acceptance of oneself and others and fostering self-kindness to combat self-criticism.

Compulsion The irresistible impulse to repeat an irrational act over and over again.

Concordance As applied in behaviour genetics, the similarity in psychiatric diagnosis or in other traits within a pair of twins.

Conditioned response See *classical conditioning*.

Conditioned stimulus See *classical conditioning*.

Conditioning theory of tolerance The notion that tolerance and extinction are learned responses and that environmental cues become associated with addictive substances through Pavlovian conditioning.

Conduct disorder Patterns of extreme disobedience in youngsters, including theft, vandalism, bullying, and early drug use. It may be a precursor of anti-social personality disorder.

Confidentiality A principle observed by lawyers, doctors, pastors, psychologists, and psychiatrists that dictates that the goings-on in a professional and private relationship are not divulged to anyone else. See also *privileged communication*.

Confounds Variables whose effects are so intermixed that they cannot be measured separately, making the design of an experiment internally invalid and its results impossible to interpret.

Congruency hypothesis The prediction that people are likely to be depressed if they have a personality vulnerability that is matched by congruent life events (e.g., perfectionists who experience a failure to achieve). It is derived from research on personality, stress, and depression.

Construct validity The extent to which scores or ratings on an assessment instrument relate to other variables or behaviours according to some theory or hypothesis.

Content validity The extent to which a measure adequately samples the domain of interest.

Control group Those in an experiment for whom the independent variable is not manipulated, thus forming a baseline against which the effects of the manipulation of the experimental group can be evaluated.

Controlled drinking A pattern of alcohol consumption that is moderate and avoids the extremes of total abstinence and of inebriation.

Conversion disorder A somatoform disorder in which sensory or muscular functions are impaired, usually suggesting neurological disease, even though the bodily organs themselves are sound; anaesthesias and paralyses of limbs are examples. To be distinguished from *malingering*, in which actual impairment does not exist.

Coping The response that a person exhibits when faced with a controllable or uncontrollable problem or stressor.

Core competencies The key clinical skills and abilities needed to be an effective therapist, such as the ability to communicate and to relate well and in an empathic way toward others.

Coronary heart disease (CHD) Angina pectoris, chest pains caused by insufficient supply of blood and thus oxygen to the heart; and myocardial infarction, or heart attack, in which the blood and oxygen supply is reduced so much that heart muscles are damaged.

Correlation coefficient A statistic that measures the degree to which two variables are related.

Correlational method The research strategy used to establish whether two or more variables are related. Relationships may be positive—as values for one variable increase, those for the other do also, or negative—as values for one variable increase, those for the other decrease.

Counselling psychologist A doctoral-level mental health professional whose training is similar to that of a clinical psychologist, though usually with less emphasis on research and severe psychopathology.

Counterconditioning Relearning achieved by eliciting a new response in the presence of a particular stimulus.

Countertransference Feelings that the psychoanalyst unconsciously directs to the client, stemming from his or her own emotional vulnerabilities and unresolved conflicts.

Covert sensitization A form of aversion therapy in which the person is told to imagine undesirably attractive situations and activities while unpleasant feelings are being induced by imagery.

Criminal commitment A procedure whereby a person is confined in a mental institution either for determination of competency to stand trial or after acquittal by reason of insanity.

Criterion validity The extent to which a measure is associated in an expected way with some other measure (the criterion).

Cross-dependent Acting on the same receptors, as methadone does with heroin. See also *heroin substitutes*.

Cross-sectional studies Studies in which different age groups are compared at the same time. Compare with *longitudinal studies*.

CT scan Computerized axial tomography, a method of diagnosis in which X-rays are taken from different angles and then analyzed by computer to produce a representation of the part of the body in cross section; often used on the brain.

Cultural bias The degree to which assessment devices, such as intelligence tests, have content that is not representative and meaningful for individuals from various cultural backgrounds.

Cultural diversity The differences that exist in an area or region due to the heterogeneity and varying backgrounds of the members of that region.

Cultural Formulation Interview (CFI) A semi-structured interview approach developed as part of the *DSM-5*. The CFI assesses four themes: (1) cultural definition of the problem; (2) cultural perceptions of cause, context, and support; (3) cultural factors affecting self-coping and past help-seeking; and (4) cultural factors affecting current help-seeking.

Cumulative risk The combined susceptibility due to multiple risk or vulnerability factors.

Cyclothymic disorder Chronic swings between elation and depression not severe enough to warrant the diagnosis of bipolar disorder.

Daily hassles The relatively minor yet chronic and persistent life stressors that combine to have a strong, negative influence on personal well-being.

Dark tetrad A constellation of traits consisting of the dark triad plus the dimension of sadism.

Dark triad A constellation of traits consisting of the combination of narcissism, psychopathy, and Machiavellianism.

Deep brain stimulation A procedure used to treat various chronic mental health and health conditions that involves planting battery-operated electrodes in the brain that deliver low-level electrical impulses.

Defence mechanism In psychoanalytic theory, reality-distorting strategies unconsciously adopted to protect the ego from anxiety.

Deinstitutionalization The increasing tendency for treatment to take place in the community, perhaps on an outpatient basis, rather than having patients reside in a public institution, such as a provincial mental hospital.

Delayed ejaculation The difficulty for certain males to have an orgasm for several possible reasons (e.g., fear of impregnating one's partner).

Delirium A state of great mental confusion in which consciousness is clouded, attention cannot be sustained, and the stream of thought and speech is incoherent. The person is probably disoriented, emotionally erratic, restless, or lethargic, and often has illusions, delusions, and hallucinations.

Delirium tremens (DTs) An acute form of delirium caused by withdrawal from addictive substances. Also called "the shakes."

Delusional disorder A disorder in which the individual has persistent persecutory delusions or delusional jealousy and is very often contentious but has no thought disorder or hallucinations.

Delusional jealousy The unfounded conviction that one's mate is unfaithful. The individual may collect small bits of "evidence" to justify the delusion.

Delusions Beliefs contrary to reality, firmly held in spite of evidence to the contrary, common in paranoid disorders: of control, belief that one is being manipulated by some external force such as radar, television, or a creature from outer space; of grandeur, belief that one is an especially important or powerful person; of persecution, belief that one is being plotted against or oppressed by others.

Dementia Deterioration of mental faculties—memory, judgement, abstract thought, control of impulses, intellectual ability—that impairs social and occupational functioning and eventually changes the personality. See also *Alzheimer's disease*.

Dementia praecox An older term for "schizophrenia," chosen to describe what was believed to be an incurable and progressive deterioration of mental functioning beginning in adolescence.

Demonology The doctrine that a person's abnormal behaviour is caused by an autonomous evil spirit.

Demoralization hypothesis A hypothesis advanced by Jerome Frank that is based on the notion that people seek help when they experience a state of demoralization that includes feelings of alienation, helplessness, hopelessness, loss of self-esteem, and subjective feelings of incompetence.

Denial Defence mechanism in which a thought, feeling, or action is disavowed by the person.

Denormalization belief A belief that reflects widespread social disapproval (e.g., society's current lack of approval of smoking).

Dependence susceptibility The tendency for some people to be much more sensitive and prone to becoming addictive than are other people.

Dependency A personality style associated with vulnerability to depression. It involves excessive levels of dependency on others.

Dependent personality A disorder in which people lack self-confidence and passively allow others to run their lives and make no demands on them so as not to endanger these protective relationships.

Dependent variable In a psychological experiment, the behaviour that is measured and is expected to change with manipulation of the independent variable.

Depersonalization An alteration in perception of the self in which the individual loses a sense of reality and feels estranged from the self and perhaps separated from the body. It may be a temporary reaction to stress and fatigue or part of panic disorder, depersonalization disorder, or schizophrenia.

Depersonalization/derealization disorder A dissociative disorder in which the individual feels unreal and estranged from the self and surroundings enough to disrupt functioning. People with this disorder may feel that their extremities have changed in size or that they are watching themselves from a distance.

Depression A disorder marked by great sadness and apprehension, feelings of worthlessness and guilt, withdrawal from others, loss of sleep, appetite, sexual desire, loss of interest and pleasure in usual activities, and either lethargy or agitation. Called "major depression" in the *DSM-IV* and "unipolar depression" by others. It can be an associated symptom of other disorders.

Depressive paradox A cognitive tendency for depressed individuals to accept personal responsibility for negative outcomes despite feeling a lack of personal control.

Depressive predictive certainty The concept that people become prone to depression when they perceive that an anticipated state of helplessness is certain to occur. It is derived from the hopelessness theory of depression.

Derealization Loss of the sense that the surroundings are real; present in several psychological disorders, such as panic disorder, depersonalization disorder, and schizophrenia.

Detoxification The initial stage in weaning an addicted person from a drug. It involves medical supervision of the sometimes painful withdrawal.

Developmental coordination disorder (motor disorder) A learning disability characterized by marked impairment in the development of motor coordination that is not accounted for by mental retardation or a physical disorder such as cerebral palsy.

Developmental trajectories The age-related pattern of a specific behaviour over time. The trajectory remains constant when the behaviour stays about the same over time, or it may increase or decrease either slightly or substantially.

Diagnosis The determination that a patient's set of symptoms or problems indicates a particular disorder.

Diagnostic and Statistical Manual of Mental Disorders (DSM) A publication of the American Psychiatric Association that is an attempt to delineate specific and discrete syndromes or mental disorders. It has been through several revisions and the current one is the fifth edition (*DSM-5*).

Diagnostic crossover A tendency for people, over time, to shift their symptoms so that a new disorder now applies and the previous disorder no longer applies. This is usually used to refer to people with anorexia nervosa who then develop bulimia nervosa and vice versa.

Dialectical behaviour therapy A therapeutic approach to borderline personality disorder that combines client-centred empathy and acceptance with behavioural problem solving, social-skills training, and limit setting.

Diathesis–stress paradigm As applied in psychopathology, a view that assumes that individuals predisposed toward a particular mental disorder will be particularly affected by stress and will then manifest abnormal behaviour.

Differential susceptibility The tendency for the same factor to act as a vulnerability factor when experiencing stress and negative outcome experiences but also act as a protective factor when experiencing favourable conditions (e.g., interpersonal sensitivity is a risk factor when being criticized and a resilience factor when being praised).

Dimensional classification An approach to assessment according to which a person is placed on a continuum. Contrast with *categorical classification*.

Directionality problem A difficulty that arises in the correlational method of research when it is known that two variables are related but it is unclear which is causing the other.

Discriminative stimulus An event that informs an organism that if a particular response is made, reinforcement will follow.

Disease model See *medical model*.

Disorder of written expression Difficulties writing without errors in spelling, grammar, or punctuation.

Disorganized attachment style An attachment orientation in which the infant demonstrates a confused attachment style that emerges after being raised in a chaotic and abusive environment.

Disorganized schizophrenia A subtype of schizophrenia in which the person has diffuse and regressive symptoms. The individual is given to silliness, facial grimaces, and inconsequential rituals and has constantly changeable moods and poor hygiene. There are few significant remissions and eventually considerable deterioration. Formerly called "hebephrenia."

Disorganized speech (formal thought disorder) Problems in organizing ideas and in speaking so that a listener can understand.

Displacement A defence mechanism whereby an emotional response is unconsciously redirected from an object or concept perceived as dangerous to a substitute less threatening to the ego.

Disruptive mood dysregulation disorder (DMDD) A controversial disorder added in the *DSM-5* that reflects the link between hostile anger and depression. It is applied primarily to children who have three or more temper tantrums a week who might have previously received a diagnosis of bipolar mania.

Dissociative amnesia A dissociative disorder in which the person suddenly becomes unable to recall important personal information to an extent that cannot be explained by ordinary forgetfulness.

Dissociative disorders Disorders in which the normal integration of consciousness, memory, or identity is suddenly and temporarily altered; dissociative amnesia, dissociative fugue, dissociative identity disorder (multiple personality), and depersonalization disorder are examples.

Dissociative fugue A disorder in which the person experiences total amnesia, then moves and establishes a new identity.

Dissociative identity disorder (DID) A rare dissociative disorder in which two or more fairly distinct and separate personalities are present within the same individual, each with his or her own memories, relationships, and behaviour patterns, with only one of them dominant at any given time. Formerly called "multiple personality disorder."

Distress An emotional reaction that can involve a variety of negative feelings or emotional states, including anxiety and depression.

Dizygotic (DZ) twins Birth partners who have developed from separate fertilized eggs and who are only 50% alike genetically, no more so than siblings born from different pregnancies. Also called "fraternal twins." Contrast with *monozygotic (MZ) twins*.

Dodo bird effect The general finding that all forms of psychotherapies achieve similar outcomes.

Dopamine theory The view that schizophrenia arises from an increase in the number of dopamine receptors.

Double-blind procedure A method for reducing the biasing effects of the expectations of research participant and experimenter. Neither is allowed to know whether the independent variable of the experiment is being applied to the participant.

Down's syndrome (trisomy 21) A form of mental retardation generally caused by an extra chromosome. The child's IQ is usually less than 50, and the child has distinctive physical characteristics, most notably slanted eyes.

Dream analysis A key psychoanalytic technique in which the unconscious meanings of dream material are uncovered.

Drug-Stroop Task A task to assess implicit cognitions believed to be involved in vulnerability to addiction. The task assesses whether people respond slower when provided with words that they must colour identify (e.g., the word is "blue") but the word reflects drug-related content (e.g., "vodka").

DSM-5 The fifth edition of the *Diagnostic and Statistical Manual of Mental Disorders*, published in 2013.

DSM-5 V codes Life conditions or significant factors that are reflected in the diagnosis process because although they are not disorders *per se*, they can have a strong influence on treatment and well-being of self and others.

DSM-IV The fourth edition of the *Diagnostic and Statistical Manual of Mental Disorders* of the American Psychiatric Association.

DSM-IV-TR A text revision of *DSM-IV*. Some sections were rewritten to incorporate research findings and enhance clarity; however, there were few substantive changes.

Dysfunctional attitudes The negative cognitive attitudes identified in Beck's cognitive model of depression that are believed to confer risk for depression. An example is believing that a person must be perfect in order to be loved and admired.

Dyspareunia Painful or difficult sexual intercourse. The pain or difficulty is usually caused by infection or a physical injury, such as torn ligaments in the pelvic region.

Eating disorder not otherwise specified (EDNOS) The most common eating disorder diagnosis, characterized by heterogeneous symptoms and associated features that do not fit the symptoms of other eating disorders. This diagnosis is applied to between approximately 40 and 70% of diagnosed patients.

Echolalia The immediate repetition of the words of others, often found in autistic children. In delayed echolalia this inappropriate echoing takes place hours or weeks later.

Eclecticism In psychology, the view that more is to be gained by employing concepts and techniques from various theoretical systems than by restricting oneself to a single approach.

Ecstasy A relatively new hallucinogen that is chemically similar to mescaline and the amphetamines.

Effectiveness The impact of an intervention on clients' functioning outside the laboratory. Contrast with *efficacy*.

Efficacy The impact of an intervention as assessed in controlled and standardized clinical trials in research with participants who meet strict inclusion criteria for being in the study. Contrast with *effectiveness*.

Ego In psychoanalytic theory, the predominantly conscious part of the personality, responsible for decision-making and for dealing with reality.

Ego analysis An important set of modifications of classical psychoanalysis, based on a conception of the human being as having a stronger, more autonomous ego with gratifications independent of id satisfactions. Also called "ego psychology."

Egoistic suicide As defined by Durkheim, self-annihilation committed because the individual feels extreme alienation from others and from society.

Electrocardiogram A recording of the electrical activity of the heart, made with an electrocardiograph.

Electroconvulsive therapy (ECT) A treatment that produces a convulsion by passing electric current through the brain. Though an unpleasant and occasionally dangerous procedure, it can be useful in alleviating profound depression.

Electrodermal responding A recording of the minute electrical activity of the sweat glands on the skin, allowing the inference of an emotional state.

Electroencephalogram (EEG) A graphic recording of electrical activity of the brain, usually of the cerebral cortex, but sometimes of lower areas.

Emotional support A sense of being cared for and comforted by other people.

Empirically informed therapies Treatment approaches that have been based on processes and components shown to be effective via research.

Empirically supported therapies (ESTs) Treatments that have been shown via research to be effective when compared in controlled experimental research with other treatment approaches.

Epidemiology The study of the frequency and distribution of illness in a population.

Essential (or primary) hypertension A psychophysiological disorder characterized by high blood pressure that cannot be traced to an organic cause. Over the years it causes degeneration of small arteries, enlargement of the heart, and kidney damage.

Eustress Pleasant stress arising from environmental conditions, as coined by Selye.

Event-related potentials (ERPs) Brain wave potentials that can be used for cognitive assessments. ERPs are evaluated when a person is asked to perform a cognitive task.

Evidence-based assessment The selection of assessment measures based on research evidence attesting to the reliability and validity of the measures and reading level required. The concern is that many clinicians opt for measures that have less research support.

Evidence-based practice An approach advocated by the Canadian Psychological Association in which the best available research evidence is used in decision-making regarding assessment and treatment. It is an alternative to developing lists of empirically supported therapies.

Evidence-based treatment Treatments and interventions that have been shown to be effective according to controlled experimental research.

Excoriation (skin-picking disorder) A disorder new to *DSM-5*, part of the obsessive-compulsive and related disorders, characterized by excessive skin picking causing lesions.

Exhibitionism Marked preference for obtaining sexual gratification by exposing one's genitals to an unwilling observer.

Exorcism The casting out of evil spirits by ritualistic chanting or torture.

Experiment The most powerful research technique for determining causal relationships, requiring the manipulation of an independent variable, the measurement of a dependent variable, and the random assignment of participants to the several different conditions being investigated.

Experimental effect A statistically significant difference between two groups experiencing different manipulations of the independent variable.

Experimental hypothesis What the investigator assumes will happen in a scientific investigation if certain conditions are met or particular variables are manipulated.

Explicit cognition The controlled thought processes and beliefs that can be consciously deliberated upon in a person's awareness.

Exposure and response prevention (ERP) A behavioural treatment for OCD in which the person is exposed to the obsession (e.g., germs) and refrains from performing the compulsion (e.g., handwashing).

Expressed emotion (EE) In the literature on schizophrenia, the amount of hostility and criticism directed from other people to the client, usually within a family.

External validity The extent to which an experiment that yields phenomena and results in laboratory settings can be generalized beyond the immediate study.

Externalizing problems Visible symptoms of maladjustment that typically reflect anger, impulsivity, and conduct disorder symptoms.

Extinction The elimination of a classically conditioned response by omitting the unconditioned stimulus. In operant conditioning, the elimination of the conditioned response by omitting reinforcement.

Factitious disorder A disorder in which the individual's physical or psychological symptoms appear under voluntary control and are adopted merely to assume the role of a sick person. The disorder can also involve a parent producing a disorder in a child, which is then called "factitious disorder by proxy" or "Munchausen syndrome by proxy."

Faking bad The act of intentionally responding to assessment items in order to create a negative impression. Used in the mental health context to appear more distressed and disturbed than is actually the case. Certain measures include a response style subscale that assesses the degree of faking bad.

Family method A research strategy in behaviour genetics in which the frequency of a trait or of abnormal behaviour is determined in relatives who have varying percentages of shared genetic background.

Fat talk A process believed to be implicated in vulnerability to eating disorders that involves the tendency for friends, particularly female friends, to take turns criticizing and critiquing their bodies to each other.

Fear of performance Being overly concerned with one's behaviour during sexual contact with another, postulated by Masters and Johnson as a major factor in sexual dysfunction.

Feedforward mechanisms Regulatory responses made in anticipation of a drug that enables us to anticipate drug effects before they occur.

Female orgasmic disorder A recurrent and persistent delay or absence of orgasm in a woman during sexual activity adequate in focus, intensity, and duration. In many instances the woman may experience considerable sexual excitement.

Female sexual interest/arousal disorder The inability of a female to reach or maintain the lubrication–swelling stage of sexual excitement or to enjoy a subjective sense of pleasure or excitement during sexual activity. Formerly called "frigidity."

Fetal alcohol syndrome (FAS) Retarded growth of the developing fetus and infant; cranial, facial, and limb anomalies; and mental retardation caused by heavy consumption of alcohol by the mother during pregnancy.

Fetishism Reliance on an inanimate object for sexual arousal.

Flashbacks An unpredictable recurrence of psychedelic experiences from an earlier drug trip.

Flat affect A deviation in emotional response wherein virtually no emotion is expressed whatever the stimulus, emotional expressiveness is blunted, or a lack of expression and muscle tone is noted in the face.

Flooding A behaviour therapy procedure in which a fearful person is exposed to what is frightening, in reality or in the imagination, for extended periods of time and without opportunity for escape.

Forced rape The legal term for rape, forced sexual intercourse, or other sexual activity with another person. Statutory rape is sexual intercourse between an adult and someone who is under the age of consent, as fixed by local statute.

Free association A key psychoanalytic procedure in which the client is encouraged to give free rein to his or her thoughts and feelings, verbalizing whatever comes into the mind without monitoring its content. The assumption is that over time, repressed material will come forth for examination by the client and psychoanalyst.

Frotteurism A form of paraphilic disorder in which an individual receives sexual pleasure from rubbing against people in public places. It is called "frotteuristic disorder" in the *DSM-5*.

Functional magnetic resonance imaging (fMRI) Modification of magnetic resonance imaging (MRI), which allows researchers to take pictures of the brain so quickly that metabolic changes can be measured, resulting in a picture of the brain at work rather than of its structure alone.

Functional social support The quality of a person's relationships; for example, a good vs. a distressed marriage. Contrast with *structural social support*.

Gender dysphoria The distress that some people feel when they have the deep and persistent conviction that there is a discrepancy between their anatomic sexual makeup and their psychological sense of self as man, woman, boy, or girl. Diagnosis in *DSM-5*; the focus is on dysphoria, rather than gender identity, being the problem. See also *Gender Identity Disorder*.

Gender identity disorder A disorder in which there is a deeply felt incongruence between anatomic sex and the sensed gender. This disorder was dropped from the *DSM-5* because some people are not troubled by the incongruence and there is a sense that the disorder was adding to stigma.

Gene An ultramicroscopic area of the chromosome. The gene is the smallest physical unit of the DNA molecule that carries a piece of hereditary information.

General adaptation syndrome (GAS) Selye's model to describe the biological reaction of an organism to sustained and unrelenting stress. There are several stages, culminating in death in extreme circumstances.

General paresis Mental illness characterized by paralysis and "insanity" that typically led to death within five years. Now known to be caused by syphilis of the brain.

General personality disorder A new *DSM-5* category that reflects establishing whether a personality disorder first exists in general and then evaluating whether the criteria of a specific personality can also be applied.

Generalized anxiety disorder (GAD) Anxiety and worry that is chronic, persistent, and pervasive. The individual is jittery, distractible, and worried that something bad is about to happen. Muscle tension, difficulty sleeping, and restlessness often accompany the anxiety and worry.

Genotype An individual's unobservable, genetic constitution; the totality of genes possessed by an individual. Compare with *phenotype*.

Germ theory of disease The general view in medicine that disease is caused by infection of the body by minute organisms and viruses.

Goodness of fit hypothesis The notion that the effectiveness of a coping response depends on whether it is appropriate for a particular problem; that is, different situations call for different coping responses.

Grandiose delusions Found in paranoid schizophrenia, delusional disorder, and mania, an exaggerated sense of one's importance, power, knowledge, or identity.

Group-based trajectory models Conceptual models that predict different developmental trajectories based on the differential role of developmental factors that can influence treatment options and outcomes.

Guided self-change An approach to treating addiction and other types of disorders that emphasizes personal responsibility and problem-solving techniques that foster a sense of self-reliance.

Habit reversal training A behavioural approach to treating body-focused repetitive behaviour disorders. Key components include the identification of triggers (e.g., negative emotion may trigger the urge to pick skin or pull hair) and competing responses (e.g., sitting on one's hands may help in waiting for the urge to pass).

Hallucinations Perceptions in any sensory modality without relevant and adequate external stimuli.

Hallucinogen A drug or chemical whose effects include hallucinations. Hallucinogenic drugs such as LSD, psilocybin, and mescaline are often called "psychedelic."

Harm reduction therapy A form of treating addiction and other types of disorders that focuses on reducing the harmful consequences to some degree rather than striving initially for absolute abstinence.

Hashish The dried resin of the cannabis plant, stronger in its effects than the dried leaves and stems that constitute marijuana.

Health psychology A branch of psychology dealing with the role of psychological factors in health and illness. See also *behavioural medicine*.

Healthy immigrant effect The phenomenon that immigrants have comparatively lower rates of health problems than Canadian-born members of the population.

Heroin An extremely addictive narcotic drug derived from morphine.

Heroin antagonists Drugs, such as naloxone, that prevent a heroin user from experiencing any high.

Heroin substitutes Narcotics, such as methadone, that are cross-dependent with heroin and thus replace it and the body's craving for it.

High-risk method A research technique involving the intensive examination of people who have a high probability of later becoming abnormal.

Histrionic personality A disorder in which the person is overly dramatic and given to emotional excess, impatient with minor annoyances, immature, dependent on others, and often sexually seductive without taking responsibility for flirtations. Formerly called "hysterical personality."

Hoarding disorder A new diagnosis in the *DSM-5*, classified as part of the obsessive-compulsive and related disorders, in which the individual has great difficulty discarding possessions and as a result lives with extreme clutter, often compromising safety.

Humanistic therapies Insight psychotherapies that emphasize the individual's subjective experiences, free will, and ever-present ability to decide on a new life course.

Hypersexual disorder A disorder not included in the *DSM-5*. It can take the form of a sex addiction or compulsion and it is regarded as a nonparaphilia sexual desire disorder with an impulsivity component.

Hypoactive sexual desire disorder The absence of or deficiency in sexual fantasies and urges.

Hypochondriasis A somatoform disorder in which the person, misinterpreting rather ordinary physical sensations, is preoccupied with fears of having a serious disease and is not dissuaded by medical opinion. Difficult to distinguish from *somatization disorder*.

Hypomania An above-normal elevation of mood, but not as extreme as mania.

Hypothesis The specific prediction about the outcome of an experiment. It is based on the assumption that the theory in question is accurate.

Hysteria A disorder known to the ancient Greeks in which a physical incapacity—a paralysis, an anaesthesia, or an analgesia—is not due to a physiological dysfunction; for example, glove anaesthesia. It is an older term for "conversion disorder." In the late nineteenth century, dissociative disorders were identified as such and considered hysterical states.

Id In psychoanalytic theory, that part of the personality present at birth, composed of all the energy of the psyche, and expressed as biological urges that strive continually for gratification.

Ideas of reference Delusional thinking that reads personal significance into seemingly trivial remarks and activities of others and completely unrelated events.

Idiographic research Variable-centred research that aims to make generalizations about a population (e.g., anxiety and depression are correlated). Contrast with *nomothetic research*.

Illness anxiety disorder The term given in the *DSM-5* to refer to hypochondriasis and the tendency to worry obsessively about illness despite the apparent objective lack of a physical illness.

Implicit cognition Cognition that involves automatic appraisal of cues that is more uncontrolled and automatic and perhaps not subject to conscious awareness.

Inappropriate affect Emotional responses that are out of context, such as laughter when hearing sad news.

Incest Sexual relations between close relatives, most often between father and daughter or between brother and sister.

Incidence In epidemiological studies of a particular disorder, the rate at which new cases occur in a given place at a given time. Compare with *prevalence*.

Incoherence In schizophrenia, an aspect of thought disorder wherein verbal expression is marked by disconnectedness, fragmented thoughts, and jumbled phrases.

Independent variable In a psychological experiment, the factor, experience, or treatment that is under the experimenter's control and that is expected to have an effect on participants as assessed by changes in the dependent variable.

Index case (proband) The person who in a genetic investigation bears the diagnosis or trait in which the investigator is interested.

Informed consent The agreement of a person to serve as a research participant or to enter therapy after being told the possible outcomes, both benefits and risks.

Insanity defence The legal argument that a defendant should not be held ascriptively responsible for an illegal act if the conduct is attributable to mental illness.

Insight therapies Any psychotherapy that assumes that people become disordered because they do not adequately understand what motivates them, especially when their needs and drives conflict.

Instrumental support The provision of tangible assistance (e.g., meal preparation) to people in need.

Intelligence test A standardized means of assessing a person's current mental ability; for example, the Stanford–Binet test and the Wechsler Adult Intelligence Scale.

Interactionism The notion that behaviour is a joint function of personal characteristics and the properties of the situations that are experienced.

Internal consistency reliability The degree to which items on a test are related to one another.

Internal validity The extent to which the effect in a controlled experiment involving random assignment of participants and removal of extraneous factors can be confidently attributed to the manipulation of the independent variable.

Internalizing problems The emotional symptoms related to depression and anxiety that a person can be experiencing internally. Symptoms are directed toward the self but not overtly expressed.

Interoceptive exposure Exercises (e.g., breathing through a straw, spinning) used to expose people with panic disorder to the physical sensations of anxiety.

Interpersonal therapy (IPT) A psychodynamic psychotherapy that focuses on the client's interactions with others and that directly teaches how better to relate to others.

Interpretation In psychoanalysis, a key procedure in which the psychoanalyst points out to the client where resistance exists and what certain dreams and verbalizations reveal about impulses repressed in the unconscious; more generally, any statement by a therapist that construes the client's problem in a new way.

Inter-rater reliability The relationship between the judgements that at least two raters make independently about a phenomenon. See also *reliability*.

Intolerance of uncertainty   An inability to tolerate uncertain outcomes, often present among people with generalized anxiety disorder. As uncertainty rises, so does anxiety.

Introspection   A procedure whereby trained subjects are asked to report on their conscious experiences. This was the principal method of study in early twentieth-century psychology.

In vivo exposure   An exercise at home that requires the person to be exposed to feared stimuli or situations.

Irrational beliefs   Self-defeating assumptions that are assumed by rational-emotive therapists to underlie psychological distress.

Job burnout   A form of work-related stress. Burnout has three components: (1) emotional exhaustion; (2) depersonalization; and (3) a sense of a lack of personal accomplishment.

Job spillover   A form of family stress that reflects the impact and influence of job stress on the family.

Job stress   Perceived strain stemming from a demanding and perhaps uncontrollable occupational situation.

Kappa   A statistic that reflects the extent to which two or more raters select the same category when evaluating a person. In psychology, it is the extent to which two clinicians agree about diagnoses when evaluating the same people.

La belle indifférence   The blasé attitude people with conversion disorder have toward their symptoms.

Language disorder   A disorder in which the child has difficulty expressing himself or herself in speech despite an apparent eagerness or willingness to communicate.

Latent class growth analysis   A complicated multivariate statistical technique that examines groups in terms of developmental trajectories.

Latent content   In dreams, the presumed true meaning hidden behind the manifest content.

Lateral hypothalamus   A section of the brain that, if lesioned, is associated with a dramatic loss of appetite.

Law of effect   A principle of learning that holds that behaviour is acquired by virtue of its consequences.

Learned helplessness theory   The theory that individuals acquire passivity and a sense of being unable to act and to control their lives. This happens through unpleasant experiences and traumas against which their efforts were ineffective; according to Seligman, this brings on depression.

Learning disabilities   A group of disabilities that includes learning disorders, communication disorders, and motor disorder.

Learning disorders   A set of developmental disorders encompassing dyslexia, mathematics disorder, and disorder of written expression and characterized by failure to develop in a specific academic area to the degree expected by the child's intellectual level. Not diagnosed if the disorder is due to a sensory deficit.

Libido   In Freud's psychoanalytic theory, the instinctual drives of the id, primarily sexual in nature.

Lifetime prevalence   The proportion of a sample that has ever had a disorder.

Linkage analysis   A technique in genetic research whereby occurrence of a disorder in a family is evaluated alongside a known genetic marker.

Lithium carbonate   A drug useful in treating both mania and depression in bipolar disorder.

Longitudinal studies   Investigation that collects information on the same individuals repeatedly over time, perhaps over many years, in an effort to determine how phenomena change. Compare with *cross-sectional studies*.

Loose associations (derailment)   In schizophrenia, an aspect of thought disorder wherein the client has difficulty sticking to one topic and drifts off on a train of associations evoked by an idea from the past.

LSD   D-lysergic acid diethylamide, a drug synthesized in 1938 and discovered by accident to be a hallucinogen in 1943.

Magnetic resonance imaging (MRI)   A technique for measuring the structure (or, in the case of functional magnetic resonance imaging, the activity) of the living brain. The person is placed inside a large circular magnet that causes hydrogen atoms to move. The return of the atoms to their original positions when the current to the magnet is turned off is translated by a computer into pictures of brain tissue.

Major depressive disorder (MDD)   An extreme form of depression that satisfies the number of symptoms required for the category of depression to apply.

Male erectile disorder   A recurrent and persistent inability to attain or maintain an erection until completion of sexual activity.

Malingering   Faking a physical or psychological incapacity in order to avoid a responsibility or gain an end. The goal is readily recognized from the individual's circumstances. To be distinguished from *conversion disorder*, in which the incapacity is assumed to be beyond voluntary control.

Mania   An emotional state of intense but unfounded elation evidenced in talkativeness, flight of ideas, distractibility, grandiose plans, and spurts of purposeless activity.

Marijuana   A drug derived from the dried and ground leaves and stems of the female hemp plant, *Cannabis sativa*.

Mathematics disorder   Difficulties dealing with arithmetic symbols and operations; one of the learning disorders.

Medical forensic examination   The procedure used to collect medical evidence for legal purposes when it is alleged that a sexual assault has taken place.

Medical model   A conceptual model that maintains that dysfunction stems from internal biological processes and factors within the individual. The medical model is more likely to reflect psychiatry than psychology. Also called *disease model*.

Medicare   The system of health care in Canada.

Mental disorder   A behavioural or psychological syndrome associated with current distress and/or disability.

Mental health literacy   The knowledge that a person develops about mental illness, including its causes and treatment.

Mescaline   A hallucinogen and alkaloid that is the active ingredient of peyote.

Meta-analysis   A quantitative method of summarizing the results of many studies; often used for analyzing and comparing various therapies by standardizing their results.

Meta-meta-analysis   A procedure that involves combining the results of multiple meta-analyses performed on a particular topic.

Methadone   A synthetic addictive heroin substitute for treating heroin addicts that acts as a substitute for heroin by eliminating its effects and the craving for it.

Mild mental retardation   A limitation in mental development measured on IQ tests at between 50–55 and 70. Children with such a limitation are considered the educable mentally retarded and are usually placed in special classes.

Minnesota Multiphasic Personality Inventory (MMPI)   A lengthy personality inventory by which individuals are diagnosed through their true-false replies to groups of statements indicating states such as anxiety, depression, masculinity-femininity, and paranoia.

Mixed design   A research strategy in which both classificatory and experimental variables are used; assigning people from discrete populations to two experimental conditions is an example.

M'Naghten Rules   Criteria stemming from an 1843 British court decision stating that an insanity defence can be established by proving that the defendant did not know what he or she was doing or did not realize that it was wrong.

Modelling Learning by observing and imitating the behaviour of others.

Moderate mental retardation A limitation in mental development measured on IQ tests between 35–40 and 50–55. Children with this degree of retardation are often institutionalized, and their training is focused on self-care rather than on development of intellectual skills.

Moderator variables A variable that interacts with or influences how another variable is associated with a second variable. Moderator variables combine with other variables to jointly produce an outcome.

Monoamine oxidase (MAO) inhibitors A group of antidepressant drugs that prevent the enzyme monoamine oxidase from deactivating neurotransmitters of the central nervous system.

Monozygotic (MZ) twins Genetically identical siblings who have developed from a single fertilized egg. Also called "identical twins." Contrast with *dizygotic (DZ) twins*.

Mood disorders Disorders in which there are disabling disturbances in emotion.

Moral anxiety In psychoanalytic theory, the ego's fear of punishment for failure to adhere to the superego's standards of proper conduct.

Moral model The conceptual view that excessive drinking or other forms of addiction reflect personal failings and personal choices of the afflicted individual because they have a deficit or moral failing in their character.

Moral treatment A therapeutic regimen, introduced by Pinel during the French Revolution, whereby mental patients were released from their restraints and were treated with compassion and dignity rather than with contempt and denigration.

Morphine An addictive narcotic alkaloid extracted from opium, used primarily as an analgesic and as a sedative.

Motivational interviewing A client-centred treatment approach that was used originally to treat addictions. The goal is to enhance a client's desire for change by resolving conflicts and ambivalence. The implicit notion is that a more positive treatment response will result if the client is highly motivated to improve.

Multiaxial classification Classification having several dimensions, each of which is employed in categorizing. In the *DSM-IV*, five axes were used in the communication of a diagnosis. The multiaxial system was removed in the *DSM-5*.

Multicultural counselling and therapy Treatments with interventions that have been modified to address issues, beliefs, and dialogues that characterize people from various cultures.

Myocardial infarction Heart attack. See also *coronary heart disease*.

Narcissistic personality A disorder in which people are extremely selfish and self-centred; have a grandiose view of their uniqueness, achievements, and talents; and have an insatiable craving for admiration and approval from others. They are exploitative to achieve their own goals and expect much more from others than they themselves are willing to give.

Negative reinforcement The strengthening of a tendency to exhibit desired behaviour by rewarding responses in that situation with the removal of an aversive stimulus.

Negative schema A hypothesized negative cognitive category proposed by Beck as part of his cognitive theory of depression. The negative schema typically is composed of negative thoughts about the self. The schema is believed to influence what the person pays attention to and remembers (e.g., an excessive focus on negative information and feedback about the self).

Negative symptoms Behavioural deficits in schizophrenia, such as flat affect and apathy. Contrast with *positive symptoms*.

Negative triad In Beck's theory of depression, a person's baleful views of the self, the world, and the future. The triad is in a reciprocal causal relationship with pessimistic assumptions (schemata) and cognitive biases such as selective abstraction.

Nerve impulse A change in the electric potential of a neuron. A wave of depolarization spreads along the neuron and causes the release of a neurotransmitter.

Neurofibrillary tangles Abnormal protein filaments present in the cell bodies of brain cells in patients with Alzheimer's disease.

Neurolaw A new field of inquiry that stems from the use of neuroscientific data in legal contexts. It involves the use of neuroscience to influence legal decisions.

Neurologist A physician who studies the nervous system, especially its structure, functions, and abnormalities.

Neuron A single nerve cell.

Neuropsychological tests Psychological tests, such as the Luria-Nebraska, that can detect impairment in different parts of the brain.

Neuropsychologist A psychologist concerned with the relationships among cognition, affect, and behaviour on the one hand, and brain function on the other.

Neurotic anxiety In psychoanalytic theory, a fear of the consequences of expressing previously punished and repressed id impulses; more generally, unrealistic fear. Contrast with *objective (realistic) anxiety*.

Neurotransmitters A chemical substance important in transferring a nerve impulse from one neuron to another; for example, serotonin and norepinephrine.

Nicotine A colourless poisonous alkaloid present in tobacco.

Night eating syndrome A habitual tendency to wake up and eat in the middle of the night, leading to substantial personal distress.

Nomophobia A common and newly identified phobia focused on fear of losing access to cellphone contact and not being connected with other people (i.e., no mobile phone phobia).

Nomothetic research Case studies and qualitative research are examples of this approach; the focus is on the individual. Contrast with *idiographic research*.

Normal curve As applied in psychology, the bell-shaped distribution of a measurable trait depicting most people in the middle and few at the extremes.

Not criminally responsible A phrase used in the Criminal Code of Canada to refer to a situation in which an individual has taken actions that are defined as illegal but due to the effects of a mental disorder are not held legally responsible for their actions. Formerly referred to as "not guilty by reason of insanity."

Objective (realistic) anxiety In psychoanalytic theory, the ego's reaction to danger in the external world; realistic fear. Contrast with *neurotic anxiety*.

Obsessions An intrusive and recurring thought that seems irrational and uncontrollable to the person experiencing it.

Obsessive-compulsive and related disorders (OCRDs) A new category in the *DSM-5* that includes obsessive-compulsive disorder, hoarding disorder, body dysmorphic disorder, and the body-focused repetitive behaviour disorders.

Obsessive-compulsive disorder (OCD) Formerly classified as an anxiety disorder, currently part of the obsessive-compulsive and related disorders category. The individual with OCD is flooded with persistent and uncontrollable thoughts and/or the individual is compelled to repeat certain acts again and again, causing significant distress and interference with everyday functioning.

Obsessive-compulsive personality A disorder in which people have inordinate difficulty making decisions, are overly concerned with details and efficiency, and relate poorly to others because they demand that things be done their way. They are unduly conventional, serious, formal, perfectionistic, and have reduced emotional expression.

Operant conditioning The acquisition or elimination of a response as a function of the environmental contingencies of reward and punishment.

Opiates A group of addictive sedatives that in moderate doses relieve pain and induce sleep.

Opioids   A chemical from a drug class that is similar to morphine and is used to reduce pain, and in some instances, to lead to sedation.

Opium   One of the opiates, the dried, milky juice obtained from the immature fruit of the opium poppy. This addictive narcotic produces euphoria and drowsiness and reduces pain.

Oppositional defiant disorder (ODD)   An undercontrolled disorder of children marked by high levels of disobedience to authority but lacking the extremes of conduct disorder.

Orgasmic reorientation   A behaviour therapy technique for altering classes of stimuli to which people are sexually attracted. Individuals are confronted by a conventionally arousing stimulus while experiencing orgasm.

Outline for Cultural Formulation   A guide designed originally in the *DSM-IV* to facilitate treatment planning from a perspective sensitive to differences in ethnocultural backgrounds and context. The *DSM-5* version has five components including a consideration of the person's cultural identity and how distress is viewed in the individual's culture.

Overcontrolling type   One of three personality types found among children. It involves a sense of inhibition and anxiety that confers significant risk for subsequent life distress.

Overevaluation of appearance   A tendency to link thinness with positive self-esteem and positive self-evaluations.

Overgenerality effect   An effect stemming from the cognitive theory of depression that reflects the tendency for depression-prone people to recall broad negative memories with limited detail about the self.

OxyContin   A pain medication that can be highly addictive.

Pain disorder   A somatoform disorder in which the person complains of severe and prolonged pain that is not explainable by organic pathology. It tends to be stress-related or permits the client to avoid an aversive activity or to gain attention and sympathy.

Palliative coping   The tendency to respond to emotional problems through emotional expression and acts that are designed to soothe the self.

Panic disorder   An anxiety disorder in which the individual has sudden and inexplicable attacks of jarring symptoms, such as difficulty breathing, heart palpitations, dizziness, trembling, terror, and feelings of impending doom.

Paradigm   A set of basic assumptions that outlines the universe of scientific inquiry, specifying both the concepts regarded as legitimate and the methods to be used in collecting and interpreting data.

Paranoid personality   A disorder in which a person expects to be mistreated by others and becomes suspicious, secretive, jealous, and argumentative. He or she will not accept blame and appears cold and unemotional.

Paranoid schizophrenia   A type of schizophrenia in which the client has numerous systematized delusions as well as hallucinations and ideas of reference. He or she may also be agitated, angry, argumentative, and sometimes violent. Types of schizophrenia were dropped in the *DSM-5* in favour of the general term "schizophrenia."

Paraphilias   Sexual attraction to unusual objects and sexual activities unusual in nature.

Paraphrenia   Schizophrenia in an older adult.

Parasympathetic nervous system   The division of the autonomic nervous system that is involved with maintenance. It controls many of the internal organs and is active primarily when the organism is not aroused.

Parental mental disorder   The presence of a behavioural or psychological syndrome in one's mother or father.

Pedophilia   The sexual disorder of a pedophile, one who has a paraphilia involving sexual desires and urges toward children.

Permissive parenting   One of three parenting styles identified by Baumrind. It is a weak and passive form of parenting that involves a lack of direction and guidelines, which can result ultimately in distress and behavioural problems among adults raised according to this style.

Perseverative cognition   The experience of ruminative thoughts.

Perseverative cognitive hypothesis   The notion that rumination prolongs the stress response.

Persistent depressive disorder   A chronic form of depression lasting at least two years.

Personality disorders   A heterogeneous group of disorders regarded as long-standing, inflexible, and maladaptive personality traits that impair social and occupational functioning. Research suggests that personality disorders and dysfunction should be conceptualized as continuous dimensions rather than categories.

Personality inventory   A self-report questionnaire by which an examinee indicates whether statements assessing habitual tendencies apply to him or her.

Personalized therapy   An approach advocated by Millon and Grossman. Therapy is tailored to each person's unique personality and associated needs and personality styles.

Pervasive developmental disorders   Severe childhood problems marked by profound disturbances in social relations and oddities in behaviour. Autistic disorder is one.

PET scan   A computer-generated picture of the living brain, created by analysis of radioactive particles from isotopes injected into the bloodstream.

Phenotype   The totality of observable characteristics of a person. Compare with *genotype*.

Phenylketonuria   A genetic disorder that, through a deficiency in a liver enzyme, phenylalanine hydroxylase, causes severe mental retardation unless phenylalanine can be largely restricted from the diet.

Phonological disorder   A learning disability in which some words sound like baby talk because the person is not able to make certain speech sounds.

Phototherapy   A treatment designed for people with seasonal affective disorder. It involves exposure to intense white light.

Placebo effect   The action of a drug or psychological treatment that is not attributable to any specific operations of the agent. For example, a tranquilizer can reduce anxiety both because of its special biochemical action and because the recipient expects relief.

Plaques   Small, round areas composed of remnants of lost neurons and beta-amyloid, a waxy protein deposit; present in the brains of patients with Alzheimer's disease.

Pleasure principle   In psychoanalytic theory, the demanding manner by which the id operates, seeking immediate gratification of its needs.

Polydrug (polysubstance) abuse   The misuse of more than one drug at a time, such as drinking heavily and taking cocaine.

Positive reinforcement   The strengthening of a tendency to behave in a certain situation by presenting a desired reward following previous responses in that situation.

Positive symptoms   In schizophrenia, behavioural excesses, such as hallucinations and bizarre behaviour. Contrast with *negative symptoms*.

Post-event processing (PEP)   A type of cognitive processing engaged in by individuals with social anxiety disorder, after social situations. It is ruminative in nature. The focus is often on things they should have or could have done differently.

Postpartum depression (PD)   The depression experienced by some mothers after giving birth.

Post-traumatic stress disorder (PTSD)   An anxiety disorder in which a particularly stressful event, such as military combat, rape, or a natural disaster, brings in its aftermath intrusive re-experiencings of the trauma, a numbing of responsiveness to the outside world, estrangement from others, a tendency to be easily startled, and nightmares, recurrent dreams, and otherwise disturbed sleep.

Prefrontal lobotomy A surgical procedure that destroys the tracts connecting the frontal lobes to lower centres of the brain; once believed to be an effective treatment for schizophrenia.

Premature ejaculation Inability of the male to inhibit his orgasm long enough for mutually satisfying sexual relations.

Prescriptive authority The right to prescribe drugs. The current controversy is the extent to which psychologists should have the right to prescribe drugs even though this is usually restricted to medical doctors and, in some cases, nurse practitioners.

Prevalence In epidemiological studies of a disorder, the percentage of a population that has the disorder at a given time. Compare with *incidence*.

Prevention Efforts to reduce the incidence of new cases of psychological disorder. Primary prevention comprises efforts in community psychology to reduce the incidence of new cases of psychological disorder by such means as altering stressful living conditions and genetic counselling; secondary prevention includes efforts to detect disorders early, so that they will not develop into full-blown, perhaps chronic, disabilities; and tertiary prevention attempts to reduce the long-term consequences of having a disorder, equivalent in most respects to therapy. See also *community psychology*.

Primary process thinking The tendency to generate cognitive images of highly pleasurable things to presumably satisfy a current need for gratification and pleasure. Compare with *secondary process thinking*.

Prior capable wish The result of the process of getting a person to outline his or her treatment wishes at an earlier time when he or she is of sounder mind and is not incapacitated.

Privileged communication The communication between parties in a confidential relationship that is protected by statute. A spouse, doctor, lawyer, pastor, psychologist, or psychiatrist cannot be forced, except under unusual circumstances, to disclose such information. See also *confidentiality*.

Profound mental retardation A limitation in mental development measured on IQ tests at less than 20–25. Children with this degree of intellectual disability (the term now used instead of "mental retardation") require total supervision of all their activities.

Projection A defence mechanism whereby characteristics or desires unacceptable to the ego are attributed to someone else.

Projective hypothesis The notion that highly unstructured stimuli, as in the Rorschach inkblot test, are necessary to bypass defences in order to reveal unconscious motives and conflicts.

Projective test A psychological assessment device employing a set of standard but vague stimuli on the assumption that unstructured material will allow unconscious motivations and fears to be uncovered. The Rorschach series of inkblots is an example.

Prolonged exposure therapy A therapy developed specifically to treat post-traumatic stress disorder.

Pronoun reversal A speech problem in which the child refers to himself or herself as "he," "she," or "you" and uses "I" or "me" in referring to others; often found in the speech of children with autistic disorder.

Prospective memory The ability to look forward and to remember to perform a required or intended action at the right place or time.

Provincial psychiatric hospital A facility where chronic patients are treated. Such hospitals provide protection, but treatment is often custodial and may involve little psychosocial treatment.

Psilocybin A psychedelic drug extracted from the mushroom *Psilocybe mexicana*.

Psychache The intense and intolerable psychological suffering and pain of suicidal individuals.

Psychiatrist A physician (MD) who has taken specialized post-doctoral training, called a residency, in the diagnosis, treatment, and prevention of mental disorders.

Psychoactive drugs Chemical compounds having a psychological effect that alters mood or thought process. Valium is an example.

Psychoanalyst A therapist who has taken specialized post-doctoral training in psychoanalysis after earning an MD or a Ph.D. degree.

Psychoanalytic (psychodynamic) paradigm General view or conceptual framework based on psychoanalysis.

Psychodynamics In psychoanalytic theory, the mental and emotional forces and processes that develop in early childhood and their effects on behaviour and mental states.

Psychogenesis Development from psychological origins, as distinguished from somatic origins. Contrast with *somatogenesis*.

Psychological tests Standardized procedures designed to measure a person's performance on a particular task or to assess his or her personality.

Psychologizer An individual who emphasizes the psychological aspects and symptoms of depression.

Psychopathology The field concerned with the nature and development of mental disorders.

Psychopathy See *anti-social personality*.

Psychophysiological disorders Disorders with physical symptoms that may involve actual tissue damage, usually in one organ system, and that are produced in part by continued mobilization of the autonomic nervous system under stress. Hives and ulcers are examples.

Psychophysiology The discipline concerned with the bodily changes that accompany psychological events.

Psychosomatic disorders Disorders in which the psyche, or mind, is having an untoward effect on the soma, or body.

Psychotechnologies Emerging therapeutic techniques that incorporate technological advances such as smart phones and videoconferencing.

Psychotherapy A primarily verbal means of helping troubled individuals change their thoughts, feelings, and behaviour to reduce distress and to achieve greater life satisfaction. See also *insight therapies* and *behaviour therapy*.

Purging disorder A form of bulimia characterized primarily by self-induced vomiting or laxative use at least once a week for a minimum of six months.

Qualitative research A descriptive approach to research based on a relatively small number of people that involves describing phenomena in rich detail.

Quantitative research A numerical approach to research that typically involves numeral counts of a small number of variables assessed in a relatively large sample of participants.

Race norms Revised norms on a psychological measure that have been adjusted for various racial or cultural groups.

Random assignment A method of assigning people to groups in an experiment that gives each person an equal chance of being in each group. The procedure helps to ensure that groups are comparable before the experimental manipulation begins.

Rational-emotive behaviour therapy (REBT) A form of treatment that focuses on removing irrational dysfunctional thoughts that cause emotional distress and replacing these irrational thoughts with rational thoughts. Formerly called "rational-emotive therapy."

Rationalization A defence mechanism in which a plausible reason is unconsciously invented by the ego to protect itself from confronting the real reason for an action, thought, or emotion.

Reaction formation A defence mechanism whereby an unconscious and unacceptable impulse or feeling that would cause anxiety is converted into its opposite so that it can become conscious and can be expressed.

Reading disorder (dyslexia) A disorder in which children have significant difficulty with word recognition, reading comprehension, and typically written spelling as well.

Reality principle   In psychoanalytic theory, the manner in which the ego delays gratification and otherwise deals with the environment in a planned, rational fashion.

Reductionism   The view that whatever is being studied can, and should, be reduced to its most basic elements or constituents. Biological reductionism proposes that mental and emotional responses can best be understood by comprehending basic biological variables such as neurotransmitter levels and balances.

Regression   A defence mechanism in which anxiety is avoided by retreating to the behaviour patterns of an earlier psychosexual stage.

Reliability   The extent to which a test, measurement, or classification system produces the same scientific observation each time it is applied.

Repetitive transcranial magnetic stimulation   A newer biological form of treatment for depression that involves stimulating the brain using brief magnetic impulses.

Repression   A defence mechanism whereby impulses and thoughts unacceptable to the ego are pushed into the unconscious.

Residual schizophrenia   The diagnosis given to people who have had an episode of schizophrenia but who presently show no psychotic symptoms, though signs of the disorder do exist. This diagnosis is no longer possible given changes in the *DSM-5*.

Resilience   An individual's level of protection from risk factors or ability to recover from emotional difficulties or trauma.

Resilient type   The most adaptive of three personality types found among children. Resilient children tend to become resilient adults who are able to bounce back from adversity.

Resistances   During psychoanalysis, the defensive tendency of the unconscious part of the ego to ward off from consciousness particularly threatening repressed material.

Retrospective memory   The ability to remember recent events and experiences that have already occurred.

Reuptake   Process by which released neurotransmitters are pumped back into the pre-synaptic cell, making them available for enhancing transmission of nerve impulses.

Reversal (ABAB) design   An experimental design in which behaviour is measured during a baseline period (A), during a period when a treatment is introduced (B), during the reinstatement of the conditions that prevailed in the baseline period (A), and finally during a reintroduction of the treatment (B). It is commonly used in operant research to isolate cause–effect relationships.

Risk   A factor that increases the likelihood of a person developing a disorder or dysfunction. Risk factors are often triggered by environmental events or stressors. Risk factors can react to a characteristic of the person (e.g., their personality) or their life situation (e.g., poverty).

Risk factors   A condition or variable that, if present, increases the likelihood of developing a disorder.

Role-playing   A technique that teaches people to behave in a certain way by encouraging them to pretend that they are in a particular situation. It helps people acquire complex behaviours in an efficient way.

Rorschach Ink Blot Test   A projective test in which the examinee is instructed to interpret a series of 10 inkblots reproduced on cards.

Ruminative coping   A tendency to focus cognitively (perhaps to the point of obsession) on the causes of depression and associated feelings rather than engaging in forms of distraction.

Scarlett O'Hara effect   A tendency to eat lightly in an attempt to project an image of femininity.

Schema   A mental structure for organizing information about the world.

Schema therapy   A form of cognitive therapy developed primarily by Young. It focuses on identifying and modifying specific cognitive schemas believed to be at the root of personality dysfunction.

Schizoid personality   A disorder in which the person is emotionally aloof; indifferent to the praise, criticism, and feelings of others; and usually a loner with few, if any, close friends and with solitary interests.

Schizophrenia   A group of psychotic disorders characterized by major disturbances in thought, emotion, and behaviour; disordered thinking in which ideas are not logically related; faulty perception and attention; bizarre disturbances in motor activity; flat or inappropriate emotions; and reduced tolerance for stress in interpersonal relations. The patient withdraws from people and reality, often into a fantasy life of delusions and hallucinations.

Schizophrenogenic mother   A cold, dominant, conflict-inducing mother formerly believed to cause schizophrenia in her child.

Schizotypal personality   A disorder in which a person is eccentric, has oddities of thought and perception (magical thinking, illusions, depersonalization, derealization), speaks digressively and with overelaborations, and is usually socially isolated. Under stress he or she may appear psychotic.

Science   The pursuit of systematized knowledge through reliable observation.

Seasonal affective disorder   The "winter depressions" that stem from reduced exposure to daylight.

Secondary process thinking   The reality-based decision-making and problem-solving activities of the ego. Compare with *primary process thinking*.

Second-hand smoke   The smoke from the burning end of a cigarette, which contains higher concentrations of ammonia, carbon monoxide, nicotine, and tar than does the smoke inhaled by the smoker. Also called "environmental tobacco smoke."

Securely attached   An attachment orientation in which the infant can tolerate separations from the caregiver and will interact comfortably with a stranger.

Sedative   A drug that slows bodily activities, especially those of the central nervous system. It is used to reduce pain and tension and to induce relaxation and sleep.

Selective mortality   A possible confound in longitudinal studies, whereby the less healthy people in a sample are more likely to drop out of the study over time.

Selective mutism   A pattern of refusing to speak in a situation (usually school), even though the child understands spoken language and is able to speak in another situation (usually at home).

Selective serotonin reuptake inhibitors (SSRIs)   A major category of antidepressant drugs, such as fluoxetine (Prozac) and sertraline (Zoloft).

Self-actualization   The fulfillment of one's potential as an always-growing human being; believed by client-centred therapists to be the master motive.

Self-criticism   A personality style associated with vulnerability to depression. It involves excessive levels of self-criticism.

Self-efficacy   In Bandura's theory, the person's belief that he or she can achieve certain goals.

Self-instructional training   A cognitive-behavioural approach that tries to help people improve their overt behaviour by changing how they silently talk to themselves.

Self-medication theory of addiction   A theory that drinking is motivated highly by a desire to cope in order to reduce an aversive state.

Self-stigma   The tendency for distressed people to internalize negative views of the self for not being well-adjusted. In essence, people high in self-stigma are seeing themselves according to negative stereotypes.

Sensate focus   Exercises prescribed at the beginning of the Masters and Johnson sex therapy program. Partners are instructed to fondle each other to give pleasure but to refrain from intercourse, thus reducing anxiety about sexual performance.

Sensitivity An element of diagnostic reliability that reflects the agreement between assessors regarding the presence of a specific diagnosis.

Sensory-awareness procedures Techniques that help clients tune in to their feelings and sensations, as in sensate-focus exercises, and to be open to new ways of experiencing and feeling.

Separation anxiety A disorder in which the individual (often a child) feels intense fear and distress when away from someone on whom he or she is very dependent; said to be a significant cause of school phobia.

Severe abuse The traumatic experience of extreme mistreatment by someone else (e.g., childhood sexual abuse).

Severe mental retardation A limitation in mental development measured in IQ tests at between 20–25 and 35–40. Individuals often cannot care for themselves, communicate only briefly, and are listless and inactive.

Sex-reassignment surgery An operation in which the existing genitalia are altered to make them more like those of the opposite sex.

Sexual aversion disorder Avoidance of nearly all genital contact with other people.

Sexual dysfunctions Dysfunctions in which the appetitive or psychophysiological changes of the normal sexual response cycle are inhibited.

Sexual masochism A marked preference for obtaining or increasing sexual gratification through subjection to pain or humiliation.

Sexual sadism A marked preference for obtaining or increasing sexual gratification by inflicting pain or humiliation on another person.

Sexual value system As applied by Masters and Johnson, the activities that an individual holds to be acceptable and necessary in a sexual relationship.

Single-subject experimental design A design for an experiment conducted with a single subject; for example, the reversal and multiple-baseline designs in operant conditioning research.

Sleep apnea A respiratory disorder in which breathing ceases repeatedly for a period of 10 seconds or more hundreds of times throughout the night.

Social anxiety disorder A disorder in which a fear of being judged negatively is the core concern. Common anxiety-provoking situations include being observed by others (e.g., walking down the street, eating in front of others), social interactions (e.g., parties), and presentations.

Social (pragmatic) communication disorder A new disorder added to the *DSM-5* where the client has persistent difficulties in the social use of either verbal or non-verbal forms of communication with other people.

Social comparison orientation A personality variable that reflects the extent to which a person evaluates themselves by comparing how they are doing vs. how other people are doing.

Social distance A measure that is used to assess the extent to which stigma exists by determining how much contact exists with and how close a person is willing to get to someone with a disorder such as schizophrenia.

Social gradient of health The link between low socio-economic status and poor health.

Social-selection theory An attempt to explain the correlation between social class and schizophrenia by proposing that people with schizophrenia move downward in social status.

Social worker A mental health professional who holds a master of social work (M.S.W.) degree.

Sociogenic hypothesis Generally, an idea that seeks causes in social conditions; for example, that being in a low social class can cause one to become schizophrenic.

Sociotropy A personality style associated with vulnerability to depression. It involves high levels of dependency and an excessive need to please others.

Somatic nervous system That part of the nervous system that controls muscles under voluntary control.

Somatic symptom disorders A newly described diagnosis in the *DSM-5* devised to apply to disorders that have been removed from the latest version (i.e., somatization disorder, hypochondriasis, pain disorder). A central theme is experiencing somatic symptoms that cause significant distress or impairment and that involve excessive thoughts, feelings, and behaviours in response to these symptoms.

Somatic-weakness theory The hypothesis that a weakness in a particular organ or organ system can make it vulnerable to psychological stress and thereby to a particular psychophysiological disorder.

Somatization disorder A somatoform disorder in which the person continually seeks medical help for recurrent and multiple physical symptoms that have no discoverable physical cause. The medical history is complicated and dramatically presented. Difficult to distinguish from *hypochondriasis*.

Somatogenesis Development from bodily origins, as distinguished from psychological origins. Contrast with *psychogenesis*.

Specific learning disorder A particular type of learning disorder such as dyslexia or reading disorder.

Specific phobia An unwarranted fear and avoidance of a specific object or circumstance; for example, fear of nonpoisonous snakes or fear of heights.

Specific-reaction theory The hypothesis that an individual develops a given psychophysiological disorder because of the innate tendency of the autonomic nervous system to respond in a particular way to stress; for example, by increasing heart rate or developing tension in the forehead.

Specificity An element of diagnostic reliability that reflects the agreement between assessors concerning the absence of a specific diagnosis.

Spectator role As applied by Masters and Johnson, a pattern of behaviour in which the individual's focus on and concern with sexual performance impedes his or her natural sexual responses.

Split alliance An imbalanced therapeutic alliance between the client and therapist that tends to predict negative therapy outcomes because the therapist has a strong bond with one member of a couple.

Standardization The process of constructing an assessment procedure that has norms and meets the various psychometric criteria for reliability and validity.

Statistical significance A result that has a low probability of having occurred by chance alone and is by convention regarded as important.

Statutory rape See *forced rape*.

Stepped care A treatment strategy that begins with less complex and costly interventions followed by more complex attempts if initial attempts are not successful.

Stereotype threat The tendency for achieved test scores to fluctuate out of concern that they will be used to further a bias or will be interpreted according to a prejudiced viewpoint.

Stereotyping A fixed belief that typically involves a negative generalization about a group or class of people. Members of the general public often endorse a number of negative beliefs about mentally ill people, and thus engage in stereotyping.

Stigmatization A reduction in the status of a group of people, such as mentally ill people, due to perceived deficiencies.

Stimulant A drug that increases alertness and motor activity and at the same time reduces fatigue, allowing an individual to remain awake for an extended period of time. Examples are cocaine and amphetamines.

the Strange Situation An experimental setting devised by Mary Ainsworth to evaluate secure vs. anxious attachment among infants. The focus is on the child's reaction when the caregiver leaves and the child is left in the presence of a stranger.

Stress State of an organism subjected to a stressor. It can take the form of increased autonomic activity and in the long term can cause the breakdown of an organ or development of a mental disorder.

Stressor An event that occasions stress in an organism; for example, loss of a loved one.

Stroop task A measure of cognitive processing that requires respondents to identify the colour of a word while ignoring the word's content or meaning. It takes longer to colour-name a word if the word reflects a theme that is cognitively accessible for a particular individual.

Structural social support A person's network of social relationships; for example, number of friends. Contrast with *functional social support*.

Structured interview An interview in which the questions are set out in a prescribed fashion for the interviewer. Assists professionals in making diagnostic decisions based upon standardized criteria.

Stuttering One of the communication disorders of childhood, marked by frequent and pronounced verbal dysfluencies, such as repetitions of certain sounds.

Subjective age bias A tendency to feel younger than one's chronological age in a way that may reflect an age bias.

Sublimation Defence mechanism entailing the conversion of sexual or aggressive impulses into socially valued behaviours, especially creative activity.

Substance abuse The use of a drug to such an extent that the person is often intoxicated throughout the day and fails in important obligations and in attempts to abstain, but there is no physiological dependence.

Substance dependence The abuse of a drug sometimes accompanied by a physiological dependence on it, made evident by tolerance and withdrawal symptoms. Also called "addiction."

Substance-related and addictive disorders The new *DSM-5* category that encompasses the previously identified disorders of substance abuse and substance dependence.

Successive approximations Responses that closer and closer resemble the desired response in operant conditioning.

Suicide prevention centres Centres that are staffed primarily by paraprofessionals who are trained to be empathic and to encourage suicidal callers to consider nondestructive ways of dealing with what is bothering them. They are based on the assumption that people are often ambivalent about taking their own lives.

Superego In psychoanalytic theory, the part of the personality that acts as the conscience and reflects society's moral standards as learned from parents and teachers.

Sympathetic nervous system The division of the autonomic nervous system that acts on bodily systems—for example, contracting the blood vessels, reducing activity of the intestines, and increasing the heartbeat—to prepare the organism for exertion, emotional stress, or extreme cold.

Synapse A small gap between two neurons where the nerve impulse passes from the axon of the first to the dendrites, cell body, or axon of the second.

Syndrome A group or pattern of symptoms that tend to occur together in a particular disease.

Systematic desensitization A major behaviour therapy procedure that has a fearful person, while deeply relaxed, imagine a series of progressively more fearsome situations. The two responses of relaxation and fear are incompatible and fear is dispelled. This technique is useful for treating psychological problems in which anxiety is the principal difficulty.

Technical eclecticism A method of psychotherapy integration in which a particular style or school of psychotherapy is employed but one in which the therapist is free to borrow from other schools or methods deemed effective.

Temperament An individual difference variable that reflects variability in tendencies such as emotionality and activity level that are believed to reflect, in part, biologically inherited differences.

Test anxiety Feeling of tension, apprehension, and worry in actual or anticipated testing situations. It usually involves physiological symptoms and cognitive symptoms (e.g., worry).

Test-irrelevant thinking A component of test anxiety involving an inability to concentrate due to mind-wandering.

Test norms The means (i.e., typical scores) that are normative or usual for a particular population. The assessment of an individual is based, in part, on how his or her scores compare with the typical score for the population.

Test–retest reliability The extent to which people being observed twice or taking the same test twice score in generally the same way.

Thematic Apperception Test (TAT) A projective test consisting of a set of black-and-white pictures reproduced on cards, each depicting a potentially emotion-laden situation. The examinee, presented with the cards one at a time, is instructed to make up a story about each situation.

Theoretical integration An approach to psychotherapy integration that attempts to synthesize and combine not only various techniques but also various conceptual orientations.

Theory A formally stated and coherent set of propositions that purport to explain a range of phenomena, order them in a logical way, and suggest what additional information might be gleaned under certain conditions.

Theory-building case studies Case studies that are useful in developing theoretical formulations according to the principle that an acceptable theory must be able to account for the common and unique themes found across a series of relevant case studies.

Theory of mind Our understanding that other people have desires, beliefs, intentions, and emotions that may be different from our own.

Therapeutic (working) alliance The relationship or bond between the therapist and client.

Thinspiration effect A sense of being encouraged to lose weight by being influenced by depictions of idealized body types.

Third-variable problem The difficulty in the correlational method of research whereby the relationship between two variables may be attributable to a third factor.

Time-of-measurement effects A possible confound in longitudinal studies whereby conditions at a particular point in time can have a specific effect on a variable that is being studied over time.

Tolerance A physiological process in which greater and greater amounts of an addictive drug are required to produce the same effect. See *substance dependence*.

Transference The venting of the client's emotions, either positive or negative, by treating the psychoanalyst as the symbolic representative of someone important in the past. An example is the client's becoming angry with the psychoanalyst to release emotions actually felt toward his or her father.

Transinsitutionalization The tendency to reduce the number of people in psychiatric hospitals by transferring them to other institutions. Most typically, this results in increasing the number of people with mental health problems in general hospitals.

Transsexualism A feeling deep within oneself, usually from early childhood, that one is of the opposite sex. The person transitions from male to female or female to male, or desires to in future.

Transvestic disorder A disorder of becoming sexually aroused by dressing as the opposite sex but experiencing significant distress and impairment as a result of this behaviour.

Trepanning The act of making a surgical opening in a living skull. This act was sometimes performed because of the belief that it would allow evil spirits to leave the body.

Trichotillomania (hair-pulling disorder) A disorder in which people cannot resist the urge to pull out their hair, resulting in significant hair loss, usually on their scalp or face (e.g., eyebrows, eyelids). Trichotillomania is part of the new *DSM-5* obsessive-compulsive and related disorders category.

Tricyclic drugs A group of antidepressants with molecular structures characterized by three fused rings. Tricyclics are known to interfere with the reuptake of norepinephrine and serotonin by a neuron after it has fired.

Twin method Research strategy in behaviour genetics in which concordance rates of monozygotic and dizygotic twins are compared.

Type A behaviour pattern One of two contrasting psychological patterns revealed through studies seeking the cause of coronary heart disease. Type A people are competitive, rushed, hostile, and over-committed to their work, and are believed to be at heightened risk for heart disease. Those who meet the other pattern, Type B people, are more relaxed and relatively free of pressure.

Unconditional positive regard According to Rogers, a crucial attitude for the client-centred therapist to adopt toward the client, who needs to feel complete acceptance as a person in order to evaluate the extent to which current behaviour contributes to self-actualization.

Unconditioned response See *classical conditioning*.

Unconditioned stimulus See *classical conditioning*.

Unconscious A state of unawareness without sensation or thought. In psychoanalytic theory, it is the part of the personality, in particular the id impulses, or id energy, of which the ego is unaware.

Undercontrolling type One of three personality types found among children. Undercontrolled children are often impulsive and lack self-control and are prone to engaging in risky behaviours throughout their adolescence and adult periods.

Undifferentiated schizophrenia The diagnosis given for clients whose symptoms do not fit any listed category or who meet the criteria for more than one subtype.

Unilateral ECT Electroconvulsive therapy in which electrodes are placed on one side of the forehead so that the current passes through only one brain hemisphere.

Vaginismus Painful, spasmodic contractions of the outer third of the vagina, which make insertion of the penis impossible or extremely difficult.

Vicarious learning Learning by observing the reactions of others to stimuli or by listening to what they say.

Virtual reality (VR) exposure A treatment for phobias using computer-generated graphics and sound to construct an experience similar to one that a client fears.

Vital exhaustion An extreme form of physical depletion linked with cardiovascular disease. It can stem from extreme overwork and striving.

Voyeurism Marked preference for obtaining sexual gratification by watching others in a state of undress or having sexual relations.

Waxy flexibility An aspect of catatonic immobility in which the person's limbs can be moved into a variety of positions and maintained that way for unusually long periods of time.

Withdrawal Negative physiological and psychological reactions evidenced when a person suddenly stops taking an addictive drug; cramps, restlessness, and even death are examples. See also *substance dependence*.

Aase, D. M., Jason, L. A., & Robinson, W. L. (2008). 12-step participation among dually-diagnosed individuals: A review of individual and contextual factors. *Clinical Psychology Review, 28*, 1235–1248.

Abbass, A., Kisely, S., & Kroenke, R. (2009). Short-term psychodynamic therapy for somatic disorder: Systematic review and meta-analysis of clinical trials. *Psychotherapy and Psychosomatics, 78*, 265–274.

Abbass, A., Town, J., & Driessen, E. (2012). Intensive short-term dynamic psychotherapy: A systematic review and meta-analysis of outcome research. *Harvard Review of Psychiatry, 20*, 97–108.

Abbate-Daga, G., Marzola, E., Amianto, F., & Fassino, S. (in press). A comprehensive review of psychodynamic treatments for eating disorders. *Eating and Weight Disorders*.

Abel, A., Hayes, A. M., Henley, W., & Kuyken, W. (in press). Sudden gains in cognitive–behavior therapy for treatment-resistant depression: Processes of change. *Journal of Consulting and Clinical Psychology*.

Abma, D. (2011, September 8). Don't use Ritalin to stay awake: CMAJ. *The Vancouver Sun*.

Aboujaoude, E., Salame, W., & Naim, L. (2015). Telemental health: A status update. *World Psychiatry, 14*, 223–230.

Abracen, J., et al. (2006). Patterns of attachment and alcohol abuse in sexual and violent non-sexual offenders. *Journal of Sexual Aggression, 12*, 19–30.

Abraham, C. (2012, August 23). Part 3: Are we medicating a disorder or treating boyhood as a disease? *The Globe and Mail*.

Abramowitz, J. S. (2013). The practice of exposure therapy: Relevance of cognitive-behavioral theory and extinction theory. *Behavior Therapy, 44*, 548–558.

Abramowitz, J. S., & Jacoby, R. J. (2015). Obsessive-compulsive and related disorders: A critical review of the new diagnostic class. *Annual Review of Clinical Psychology, 11*, 165–186.

Abrams, R., Swartz, C. M., & Vedak, C. (1991). Antidepressant effects of high-dose unilateral electroconvulsive therapy. *Archives of General Psychiatry, 48*, 746–748.

Abramson, L. Y., Metalsky, G. I., & Alloy, L. B. (1989). Hopelessness depression: A theory-based subtype of depression. *Psychological Review, 96*, 358–372.

Abramson, L. Y., Seligman, M. E. P., & Teasdale, J. D. (1978). Learned helplessness in humans: Critique and reformulation. *Journal of Abnormal Psychology, 87*, 49–74.

Achenbach, T. M., & Rescorla, L. A. (2001). *Manual for the ASEBA School-Age Forms and Profiles*. Burlington, VT: University of Vermont.

Achim, A. M., Maziade, M., Raymond, É., Olivier, D., Mérette, C., & Roy, M. A. (2011). How prevalent are anxiety disorders in schizophrenia? A meta-analysis and critical review on a significant association. *Schizophrenia Bulletin, 37*, 811–821.

Ad Hoc Advisory Group of Experts, National Institutes of Health. (1997). Report to the Director: Workshop on the medical utility of marijuana. February 19-20. Retrieved from http://www.nih.gov/news/medmarijuana/MedicalMarijuana.

Adams, P., & Laghi, B. (2000, November). Medicare debate boils over. *The Globe and Mail*, A1, A7.

Addington, D. E., Labelle, A., Kulkarni, J., et al. (2009). A comparison of ziprasidone and risperidone in the long-term treatment of schizophrenia: A 44-week, double-blind, continuation study. *Canadian Journal of Psychiatry, 54*, 46–54.

Addington, D. E., McKenzie, E., Norman, R., Wang, J., & Bond, G. R. (2013). Essential evidence-based components of first-episode psychosis services. *Psychiatric Services, 64*, 452–457.

Addington, J., & Addington, D. (1998). Facial affect recognition and information processing in schizophrenia and bipolar disorder. *Schizophrenia Research, 32*, 171–181.

Addington, J., Collins, A., McCleery, A., & Baker, B. (2009). First episode psychosis: Managing self-harm. In F. Lobban & C. Barrowclough (Eds.), *A casebook of family interventions for psychosis* (pp. 47–66). Hoboken, NJ: John Wiley & Sons.

Addington, J., Collins, A., McCleery, A., & Addington, D. (2005). The role of family work in early psychosis. *Schizophrenia Research, 79*, 77–83.

Addington, J., McCleery, A., & Addington, D. (2005). Three-year outcome of family work in an early psychosis program. *Schizophrenia Research, 79*, 107–116.

Adlaf, E. M., & Paglia, A. (2003). Drug use among Ontario students: Detailed OSDUS finding, 1997–2001. Toronto: Centre for Addiction and Mental Health.

Adlaf, E. M., Demers, A., & Gliksman, L. (2005). *Canadian Campus Survey 2004*. Toronto: Centre for Addiction and Mental Health.

Adler, A. (1930). *Guiding the child on the principles of individual psychology*. New York: Greenberg.

Advisory Group on Suicide Prevention. (2003). *Acting on what we know: Preventing youth suicide in First Nations*. Ottawa: Government of Canada, First Nations and Inuit Health Branch.

Affrunti, N. W., & Woodruff-Borden, J. (2014). Perfectionism in pediatric anxiety and depressive disorders. *Clinical Child and Family Psychology Review, 17*, 299–317.

Afifi, T. O., & MacMillan, H. L. (2011). Resilience following child maltreatment: A review of protective factors. *Canadian Journal of Psychiatry, 56*, 266–272.

Afifi, T. O., MacMillan, H. L., Boyle, M., Taillieu, T., Cheung, K., & Sareen, J. (2014). Child abuse and mental disorders in Canada. *Canadian Medical Association Journal, 186*, E324–E332.

Afifi, T. O., MacMillan, H. L., Taillieu, T., Cheung, K., Turner, S., Tonmyr, L., & Hovdestad, W. (2015). Relationship between child abuse exposure and reported contact with child protection organizations: Results from the Canadian Community Health Survey. *Child Abuse and Neglect, 46*, 198–206.

Aggarwal, N. K., Nicasio, A. V., DeSilva, R., et al. (2013). Barriers to implementing the *DSM-5* Cultural Formulation Interview: A qualitative study. *Culture, Medicine, and Psychiatry, 37*, 505–533.

Aharoni, E., Funk, C., Sinnott-Armstrong, W., & Gazzaniga, M. (2008). Can neurological evidence help courts assess criminal responsibility? Lessons from neuroscience and the law. *Annals of the New York Academy of Sciences, 1124*, 145–160.

Ahmed v. Stefaniu, 2006 CanLII 34973 (ON CA).

Ahonen, T., Kooistra, L., Viholainen, H., & Cantwell, M. (2004). Developmental motor learning disability: A neuropsychological approach. In D. Dewey & D. E. Tupper (Eds.), *Developmental motor disorders: A neuropsychological perspective* (pp. 265–290). New York: Guilford.

Ainsworth, M. D. (1984). Attachment. In N. S. Endler & J. McV. Hunt (Eds.), *Personality and the behavioral disorders* (Vol. 1, 2nd ed., pp. 559–602). New York: John Wiley & Sons.

Ainsworth, M. D., Blehar, M. C., Waters, E., & Wall, S. (1978). *Patterns of attachment: A psychological study of the strange situation.* Hillsdale, NJ: Erlbaum.

Akbarian, S., et al. (1995). Gene expression for glutamic acid decarboxylase is reduced without loss of neurons in prefrontal cortex of schizophrenics. *Archives of General Psychiatry, 52,* 258–266.

Akyuz, G., Dogan, O., Sar, V., Yargic, L. I., & Tutkun, H. (1999). Frequency of dissociative identity disorder in the general population in Turkey. *Comprehensive Psychiatry, 40,* 151–159.

Alamian, A., & Paradis, G. (2009). Correlates of multiple chronic disease behavioral risk factors in Canadian children and adolescents. *American Journal of Epidemiology, 170,* 1279–1289.

AlAqeel, B., & Margolese, H. C. (2012). Remission in schizophrenia: Critical and systematic review. *Harvard Review of Psychiatry, 20,* 281–297.

Alden, L. E. (1989). Short-term structured treatment for avoidant personality disorder. *Journal of Consulting and Clinical Psychology, 57,* 756–764.

Alden, L. E., Laposa, J. M., Taylor, C. T., & Ryder, A. (2002). Avoidant personality disorder: current status and future directions. *Journal of Personality Disorders, 16,* 1–29.

Alegria, A. A., Blanco, C., Petry, N. M., Skodol, A. E., et al. (2013). Sex differences in antisocial personality disorder: Results from the National Epidemiological Survey on Alcohol and Related Conditions. *Personality Disorders: Theory, Research, and Treatment, 4,* 214–222.

Alexander, A. W., & Slinger-Constant, A. M. (2004). Current status of treatments for dyslexia: Critical review. *Journal of Child Neurology, 19,* 744–758.

Alexander, F. (1950). *Psychosomatic medicine.* New York: Norton.

Alexander, F., & French, T. M. (1946). *Psychoanalytic therapy.* New York: Ronald Press.

Alexander, P. C., & Lupfer, S. L. (1987). Family characteristics and long-term consequences associated with sexual abuse. *Archives of Sexual Behavior, 16,* 235–245.

Alexopoulos, G. S., et al. (2009). Reducing suicide ideation and depression in older primary care patients: 24-month outcomes of the PROSPECT study. *American Journal of Psychiatry, 166,* 882–890.

Alfonso, J., Hall, T. V., & Dunn, M. E. (2013). Feedback-based alcohol interventions for mandated students: An effectiveness study of three modalities. *Clinical Psychology and Psychotherapy, 20,* 411–423.

Ali, J. (2002). Mental health of Canada's immigrants. *Supplement to Health Reports, 13,* 1–12.

Alladi, S., Bak, T. H., Mekala, S., Rajan, A., et al. (2016). Impact of bilingualism on cognitive outcome after stroke. *Stroke, 47,* 258–261.

Allderidge, P. (1979). Hospitals, mad houses, and asylums: Cycles in the care of the insane. *British Journal of Psychiatry, 134,* 321–324.

Alloul, K., Sauriol, L., Kennedy, W., Laurier, C., Tessier, G., Novosel, S., et al. (1998). Alzheimer's disease: A review of the disease, its epidemiology, and economic impact. *Archives of Gerontology and Geriatrics, 27,* 189–221.

Alloy, L. B., & Abramson, L. Y. (2010). The role of the behavioral approach system (BAS) in bipolar spectrum disorders. *Current Directions in Psychological Science, 19,* 189–194.

Alloy, L. B., Abramson, L. Y., Whitehorse, W. G., et al. (2006). Prospective incidence of first onsets and recurrences of depression in individuals at high and low cognitive risk for depression. *Journal of Abnormal Psychology, 115,* 145–156.

Alpert, J. E., et al. (1997). Social phobia, avoidant personality disorder and atypical depression: Co-occurrence and clinical implications. *Psychological Medicine, 27,* 627–633.

Altamura, C., Paluello, M. M., Mundo, E., Medda, S., & Mannu, P. (2001). Clinical and subclinical body dysmorphic disorder. *European Archives of Psychiatry and Clinical Neuroscience, 251,* 105–108.

Altenburger, E. M., Tung, E. S., & Keuthen, N. J. (2014). Body esteem in adolescent hair pullers. *Journal of Behavioral Addictions, 3,* 124–127.

Althof, S. E., et al. (2005). Psychological and interpersonal dimensions of sexual function and dysfunction. *Journal of Sexual Medicine, 2,* 793–800.

Alzheimer Society of Canada. (2010). *Rising tide: The impact of dementia on Canadian society: Executive summary.* Toronto: Author.

Alzheimer Society of Canada. (2016). *Prevalence and monetary costs of dementia in Canada: A report by the Alzheimer Society of Canada.* Toronto: Author.

Amador, X. F., Flaum, M., Andreasen, N. C., Strauss, D. H., et al. (1994). Awareness of illness in schizophrenia and schizoaffective and mood disorders. *Archives of General Psychiatry, 51,* 826–836.

Amagoalik, J. (2009, April 1). There's little to celebrate on Nunavut's 10th birthday: Inuit territory suffers from unemployment, chronic social problems and high dropout rate. *Toronto Star,* A23.

American Association of Mental Retardation (AAMR). (1992). *Mental retardation: Definition, classification, and systems of support.* Washington, DC: Author.

American Association of Retired Persons (AARP). (1999). *Assisted living: Summary of state statutes (Vol. 1, Guide and table to state summaries).* Washington, DC: Author.

American Association of Retired Persons (AARP) & National Alliance for Caregiving. (2015). *Caregiving in the U.S. 2015.* Bethesda, MD: Authors.

American College Health Association. (2009). *American College Health Association-National College Health Assessment II: Ontario Reference Group Executive Summary Spring 2009.* Baltimore: Author.

American College Health Association. (2016). *American College Health Association – National College Health Assessment II: Canadian Reference Group Data Report Spring 2016.* Hanover, MD: Author.

American Psychiatric Association. (1952). *Diagnostic and statistical manual of mental disorders* (1st ed.). Washington, DC: Author.

American Psychiatric Association. (1968). *Diagnostic and statistical manual of mental disorders* (2nd ed.). Washington, DC: Author.

American Psychiatric Association. (1980). *Diagnostic and statistical manual of mental disorders* (3rd ed.). Washington, DC: Author.

American Psychiatric Association. (1987). *Diagnostic and statistical manual of mental disorders* (3rd ed., rev.). Washington, DC: Author.

American Psychiatric Association. (1993). Practice guidelines for major depressive disorder in adults. *American Journal of Psychiatry, 150,* All.

American Psychiatric Association. (1994). *Diagnostic and statistical manual of mental disorders (4th ed.).* Washington, DC: Author.

American Psychiatric Association. (2000). *Diagnostic and statistical manual of mental disorders* (4th ed., text rev.). Washington, DC: Author.

American Psychiatric Association. (2004). Practice guidelines for the treatment of patients with schizophrenia (2nd ed). *American Journal of Psychiatry, 161* (Suppl. 2), 1–114.

American Psychiatric Association. (2010, February 10). APA announces draft diagnostic criteria for DSM-5: New proposed changes posted for leading manual of mental disorders. Release No. 10-07. Washington, DC: Author.

American Psychiatric Association. (2013). *Diagnostic and statistical manual of mental disorders* (5th ed.). Washington, DC: Author.

American Psychological Association. (1996). Awards for distinguished contribution to research in public policy: Marnie E. Rice. *American Psychologist, 51,* 342–344.

American Psychological Association. (2003). *Guidelines for psychological practice with older adults.* Retrieved from http://www.apa.org/practice/guidelines/older-adults.aspx.

American Psychological Association. (2015). Guidelines on psychological practice with transgender and gender nonconforming people. *American Psychologist, 70,* 832–864.

American Psychological Association. (2015, August 13). APA review confirms link between playing violent video games and aggression. Washington, DC: Author.

Amoo, G., Abayomio, O., & Olashore, A. A. (2012). Zoophilic recidivism in schizophrenia: A case report. *African Journal of Psychiatry, 15,* 223–225.

Anand, A., et al. (2000). Brain SPECT imaging of amphetamine-induced dopamine release in euthymic bipolar disorder patients. *American Journal of Psychiatry, 157,* 1109–1114.

Andersen, B. L. (1983). Primary orgasmic dysfunction: Diagnostic considerations and review of treatment. *Psychological Bulletin, 93,* 105–136.

Andersen, E., Raffin-Bouchal, S., & Marcy-Edwards, D. (2008). Reasons to accumulate excess: Older adults who hoard possessions. *Home Health Care Services Quarterly, 27,* 187–216.

Andersen, E., Raffin-Bouchal, S., & Marcy-Edwards, D. (2013). "Do they think I am a pack rat?" *Journal of Elder Abuse & Neglect, 25,* 438–452.

Anderson, K. K., Cheng, J., Susser, E., McKenzie, K. J., & Kurdyak, P. (2015). Incidence of psychotic disorders among first-generation immigrants and refugees in Ontario. *Canadian Medical Association Journal, 10,* 1503.

Anderson, P., Chisholm, D., & Fuhr, D. C. (2009). Effectiveness and cost-effectiveness of policies and programmes to reduce the harm caused by alcohol. *Lancet, 373,* 2234–2246.

Anderson, P. L., Price, M., Edwards, S. M., Obasaju, M. A., Schmertz, S. K., Zimand, E., & Calamaras, M. R. (2013). Virtual reality exposure therapy for social anxiety disorder: A randomized controlled trial. *Journal of Consulting and Clinical Psychology, 81,* 751–760.

Anderssen, E. (2012, June 4). Glenn Close: Battling the stigma of mental illness. *The Globe and Mail.*

Anderssen, E. (2016, February 14). Gender identity debate swirls over CAMH psychologist, transgender program. *The Globe and Mail.*

Andersson, B., Hibell, B., Beck, F., et al. (2007). Alcohol and drug use among European 17-18 year old students: Data from the ESPAD project. Stockholm: Swedish Council for Information on Alcohol and Other Drugs.

Andersson, G., et al. (2006). Internet-based self-help with therapist feedback and in vivo group exposure for social phobia: A randomized controlled trial. *Journal of Consulting and Clinical Psychology, 74,* 677–686.

Andreasen, N. C. (1979). Thought, language, and communication disorders: 1. Clinical assessment, definition of terms, and evaluation of their reliability. 2. Diagnostic significance. *Archives of General Psychiatry, 36,* 1315–1330.

Andreasen, N. C., Flaum, M., Swayze, V. W., Tyrrell, G., & Arndt, S. (1990). Positive and negative symptoms in schizophrenia: A critical reappraisal. *Archives of General Psychiatry, 47,* 615–621.

Andreasen, N. C., & Olsen, S. A. (1982). Negative versus positive schizophrenia. Definition and validation. *Archives of General Psychiatry, 39,* 789–794.

Andreasen, N. C., Rice, J., Endicott, J., Coryell, W., Grove, W. W., & Reich, T. (1987). Familial rates of affective disorder. *Archives of General Psychiatry, 44,* 461–472.

Andreasen, N. C., Smith, M. R., Jaccoby, C. G., Dennert, J. W., & Olsen, S. A. (1982). Ventricular enlargement in schizophrenia: Definition and prevalence. *American Journal of Psychiatry, 139,* 292–296.

Andreescu, C., & Varon, D. (2015). New research on anxiety disorders in the elderly and an update on evidence-based treatments. *Current Psychiatry Reports, 17,* 53.

Andresen, M. (2006). Mental health moves up the agenda. *Canadian Medical Association Journal, 175*(2), 39.

Andress, V. R., & Corey, D. M. (1978). Survivor-victims: Who discovers or witnesses suicide? *Psychological Reports, 42,* 759–764.

Andrew, M. K., & Rockwood, K. (2007). Psychiatric illness in relation to frailty in community-dwelling elderly people with dementia: A report from the Canadian Study of Health and Aging. *Canadian Journal of Aging, 26,* 33–38.

Andrews, G. (2008). Reducing the burden of depression. *Canadian Journal of Psychiatry, 53,* 420–427.

Andrews, G., Hobbs, M. J., Borkovec, T. D., et al. (2010). Generalized worry disorder: A review of DSM-IV generalized anxiety disorder and options for DSM-V. *Depression and Anxiety, 27,* 134–147.

Angelakis, I., Gooding, P., Tarrier, N., & Panagioti, M. (2015). Suicidality in obsessive compulsive disorder (OCD): A systematic review and meta-analysis. *Clinical Psychology Review, 39,* 1–15.

Angrist, B., Lee, H. K., & Gershon, S. (1974). The antagonism of amphetamine-induced symptomatology by a neuroleptic. *American Journal of Psychiatry, 131,* 817–819.

Angus, L. E., & Kagan, F. (2009). Therapist empathy and client anxiety reduction in motivational interviewing: "She carries with me, the experience." *Journal of Clinical Psychiatry, 65,* 1156–1167.

Angus, L., Watson, J. C., Elliott, R., Schneider, K., & Timulak, L. (2015). Humanistic psychotherapy research 1990–2015: From methodological innovation to evidence-supported treatment outcomes and beyond. *Psychotherapy Research, 25,* 330–347.

Anisman, H., & Merali, Z. (1999). Understanding stress: Characteristics and caveats. *Alcohol Research and Health, 23,* 241–249.

Antoni, M. H. (2006). How stress management improves quality of life after treatment for breast cancer. *Journal of Consulting and Clinical Psychology, 74,* 1143–1152.

Antony, M. M., & McCabe, R. E. (2003). Anxiety disorders: Social and specific phobias. In A. Tasman, J. Kay, & J. A. Lieberman (Eds.), *Psychiatry* (2nd ed., pp. 1298–1330). New York: John Wiley & Sons.

Antshel, K. M., Faraone, S. V., Maglione, K., et al. (2009). Is adult attention deficit hyperactivity disorder a valid diagnosis in the presence of high IQ? *Psychological Medicine, 39,* 1325–1335.

APA Presidential Task Force on Evidence-Based Practice. (2006). Evidence-based practice in psychology. *American Psychologist, 61,* 271–285.

Apfelbaum, B. (1989). Retarded ejaculation: A much-misunderstood syndrome. In S. R. Leiblum & R. C. Rosen (Eds.), *Principles and practice of sex therapy: Update for the 1990s* (pp. 168–206). New York: Guilford.

Appel, L. J., et al., for the DASH Collaborative Research Group. (1997). A clinical trial of the effects of dietary patterns on blood pressure. *New England Journal of Medicine, 336,* 1117–1124.

Apt, C., & Hurlbert, D. H. (1994). The sexual attitudes, behavior, and relationships of women with histrionic personality disorder. *Journal of Sex and Marital Therapy, 20,* 125–133.

Araujo, A. B., Durante, R., Feldman, H. A., et al. (1998). The relationship between depressive symptoms and male erectile dysfunction: cross-sectional results from the Massachusetts Male Aging Study. *Psychosomatic Medicine, 60*, 458–465.

Arbuthnot, J., & Gordon, D. A. (1986). Behavioral and cognitive effects of a moral reasoning development intervention for high-risk behavior disordered adolescents. *Journal of Consulting and Clinical Psychology, 54*, 208–216.

Arcelus, J., et al. (2009). A case series evaluation of a modified version of interpersonal psychotherapy (IPT) for the treatment of bulimia eating disorders. *European Eating Disorders Review, 17*, 260–268.

Arcelus, J., Mitchell, A. J., Wales, J., & Nielsen, S. (2011). Mortality rates in patients with anorexia nervosa and other eating disorders: A meta-analysis of 36 studies. *Archives of General Psychiatry, 68*, 724–731.

Ard, B. N., Jr. (1977). Sex in lasting marriages: A longitudinal study. *Journal of Sex Research, 13*, 274–285.

Arieti, S. (1979). New views on the psychodynamics of phobias. *American Journal of Psychotherapy, 33*, 82–95.

Arkowitz, H., Westra, H. A., Miller, W. R., & Rollnick, S. (2007). *Motivational interviewing in the treatment of psychological problems.* New York: Guilford.

Armstrong, T., & Olatunji, B. (2009). What they see is what you get: Tracking of attention in the anxiety disorders. *Psychological Science Agenda, 23*(3).

Arnberg, A., & Öst, L. (2014). CBT for children with depressive symptoms: A meta-analysis. *Cognitive Behaviour Therapy, 43*, 275–288.

Aronson, K. (2003). Alcohol: A recently identified risk factor for breast cancer. *Canadian Medical Association Journal, 168*, 1147–1148.

Arpin-Cribbie, C., Irvine, J., & Ritvo, P. (2012). Web-based cognitive-behavioral therapy for perfectionism: A randomized controlled trial. *Psychotherapy Research, 22*, 194–207.

Arpin-Cribbie, C. A., Irvine, J., Ritvo, P., Cribbie, R. A., Flett, G. L., & Hewitt, P. L. (2008). Perfectionism and psychological distress: A modeling approach to understanding their therapeutic relationship. *Journal of Rational-Emotive and Cognitive-Behavior Therapy, 26*, 151–167.

Arria, A. M., Caldeira, K. M., Vincent, K. B., O'Grady, K. E., et al. (in press). Do college students improve their grades by using prescription stimulants nonmedically? *Addictive Behaviors.*

Arseneault, L., Tremblay, R. E., Boulerice, B., & Saucier, J. F. (2002). Obstetrical complications and violent delinquency: Testing two developmental pathways. *Child Development, 73*, 496–508.

Ashbaugh, A. (2015). Triskaidekaphobia (fear of the number 13). In I. Milosevic & R. E. McCabe (Eds.), *Phobias – the psychology of irrational fear: An encyclopedia.* Santa Barbara, CA: ABC-Clio.

Ashton, M. C., Lee, K., & Son, C. (2000). Honesty as the sixth factor of personality: Correlations with Machiavellianism, primary psychopathy, and social adroitness. *European Journal of Personality, 14*, 359–368.

Ashworth, F., Gracey, F., & Gilbert, P. (2011). Compassion focused therapy after traumatic brain injury: Theoretical foundations and a case illustration. *Brain Impairment, 12*, 128–139.

Askew, C., & Field, A. P. (2008). The vicarious learning pathway to fear 40 years on. *Clinical Psychology Review, 28*, 1249–1265.

Asmundson, G. J. G., Larsen, D. K., & Stein, M. B. (1998). Panic disorder and vestibular disturbance: An overview of empirical findings and clinical implications. *Journal of Psychosomatic Research, 44*, 107–120.

Asmundson, G. J. G., & Taylor, S. (2003). Anxiety disorders: Panic disorder with and without agoraphobia. In A. Tasman, J. Kay, & J. A. Lieberman (Eds.), *Psychiatry* (2nd ed., pp. 1281–1297). New York: John Wiley & Sons.

Asmundson, G. J. G., Taylor, S., Sevgur, S., & Cox, B. J. (2001). Health anxiety: Classification and clinical features. In G. J. G. Asmundson, S. Taylor, & B. J. Cox (Eds.), *Health anxiety: Clinical and research perspectives on hypochondriasis and related conditions* (pp. 3–21). Toronto: John Wiley & Sons.

Asmundson, G. J. G., Taylor, S., & Smits, J. A. J. (2014). Panic disorder and agoraphobia: An overview and commentary on DSM-5 changes. *Depression and Anxiety, 31*, 480–486.

Asmundson, G. J. G., Taylor, S., Wright, K. D., & Cox, B. J. (2001). Future directions and challenges in assessment, treatment, and investigation. In G. J. G. Asmundson, S. Taylor, & B. J. Cox (Eds.), *Health anxiety: Clinical and research perspectives on hypochondriasis and related conditions* (pp. 365–381). Toronto: John Wiley & Sons.

Asscher, J. J., Deković, M., Manders, W. A., van der Laan, P. H., et al. (2013). A randomized controlled trial of the effectiveness of multisystemic therapy in the Netherlands: Post-treatment changes and moderator effects. *Journal of Experimental Criminology, 9*, 169–187.

Atkinson, L., Paglia, A., Coolbear, J., Niccols, A., Parker, K. C. H., & Guger, S. (2000). Attachment security: A meta-analysis of maternal mental health correlates. *Clinical Psychology Review, 20*, 1019–1040.

Atmaca, M., Mermi, O., Yildirim, H., & Gurok, M. G. (2015). Orbitofrontal cortex and thalamus volumes in obsessive-compulsive disorder before and after pharmacotherapy. *Brain Imaging and Behavior* (epub ahead of print).

Atmaca, M., Yildirim, H., Yilmaz, S., Mermi, O., Korkmaz, S., Akaslan, U., Gurok, M. G., Kekilli, Y., & Turkcapar, H. (2016). Orbito-frontal cortex and thalamus volumes in the patients with obsessive-compulsive disorder before and after cognitive behavioral therapy. *International Journal of Psychiatry in Medicine* (epub ahead of print).

Attia, E. (2010). Anorexia nervosa: Current status and future directions. *Annual Review of Medicine, 61*, 425–435.

Auditor General of Canada. (2014). *2014 fall report of the Auditor General of Canada.* Ottawa: Government of Canada.

Auld, A. (2001, August 2). Convicted pedophile will be released from prison, but will go to psych centre. The Canadian Press.

Austin, S. B., Haines, J., & Veugelers, P. J. (2009). Body satisfaction and body weight: Gender differences and sociodemographic determinants. *BMC Public Health, 9*, 1–7.

Autism Genome Project Consortium. (2007). Mapping autism risk loci using genetic linkage and chromosomal rearrangements. *Nature Genetics, 39*, 319–328.

Awad, G. A., & Saunders, E. (1989). Adolescent child molesters: Clinical observations. *Child Psychiatry and Human Development, 19*, 195–206.

Aybek, S., Nicholson, T. R., Zelaya, F., O'Daly, O. G., Craig, J. T., David, A. S., & Kanaan, R. A. (2014). Neural correlates of recall of life events in conversion disorder. *JAMA Psychiatry, 71*, 52–60.

Ayearst, L., Flett, G. L., & Hewitt, P. L. (2012). Where is multidimensional perfectionism in DSM-5? A question posed to the DSM-5 Personality and Personality Disorders Work Group. *Personality Disorders: Theory, Research, and Treatment, 3*, 458–469.

Ayers, C. R., Saxena, S., Espejo, E., et al. (2014). Novel treatment for geriatric hoarding disorder: An open trial of cognitive rehabilitation paired with behaviour therapy. *American Journal of Geriatric Psychiatry, 22*, 248–252.

Ayers, C. R., Sorrell, J. T., Thorp, S. R., & Wetherell, J. L. (2007). Evidence-based psychological treatments for late-life anxiety. *Psychology and Aging, 22*, 8–17.

Ayllon, T. (1963). Intensive treatment of psychotic behavior by stimulus satiation and food reinforcement. *Behavior Research & Therapy, 1*, 53–61.

Azagba, S., Langille, D., & Ashbridge, M. (2013). The consumption of alcohol mixed with energy drinks: Prevalence and key correlates among Canadian high school students. *Canadian Medical Association Journal Open, 1*, E19–E26.

Azrin, N. H., & Nunn, R. G. (1973). Habit-reversal: A method of eliminating nervous habits and tics. *Behaviour Research and Therapy, 11*, 619–628.

Baardseth, T. P., Goldberg, S. B., Pace, B. T., Wislocki, A. P., et al. (2013). Cognitive therapy versus other therapies: Redux. *Clinical Psychology Review, 33*, 395–403.

Babchishin, K. M., Hanson, K. R., & Hermann, C. A. (2011). The characteristics of online sex offenders: A meta-analysis. *Sexual Abuse: A Journal of Treatment and Research, 23*, 92–123.

Bachelor, A. (2013). Clients' and therapists' views of the therapeutic alliance: Similarities, differences and relationship to therapy outcome. *Clinical Psychology and Psychotherapy, 20*, 118–135.

Baer, J. S., & Lichtenstein, E. (1988). Cognitive assessment. In D. M. Donovan & G. A. Marlatt (Eds.), *Assessment of addictive behaviors* (pp. 189–213). New York: Guilford.

Baer, R. A., & Sekirnjak, G. (1997). Detection of underreporting on the MMPI-II in a clinical population. Effects of information about validity scales. *Journal of Personality Assessment, 69*, 555–567.

Bagby, R. M., Sellbom, M., Costa, P. T., Jr., & Widiger, T. A. (2008). Predicting Diagnostic and Statistical Manual of Mental Disorders–IV personality disorders with the five-factor model of personality and the Personality Psychopathology Five. *Personality and Mental Health, 2*, 55–69.

Bagby, R. M., Ryder, A. G., Ben-Dat, D., Bacchiochi, J., & Parker, J. D. A. (2002). Validation of the dimensional factor structure of the Personality Psychopathology Five in clinical and nonclinical samples. *Journal of Personality Disorders, 16*, 304–316.

Bagby, R. M., Quilty, L. C., Segal, Z. V., et al. (2008). Personality and differential treatment response in major depression: A randomized controlled trial comparing cognitive-behavioural therapy and pharmacotherapy. *Canadian Journal of Psychiatry, 53*, 361–370.

Bagley, C., & Mallick, K. (2000). Prediction of sexual, emotional, and physical maltreatment and mental health outcomes in a longitudinal cohort of 290 adolescent women. *Child Maltreatment, 5*, 218–226.

Bahm, A., & Forchuk, C. (2009). Interlocking oppressions: The effect of a comorbid physical disability on perceived stigma and discrimination among mental health consumers in Canada. *Health & Social Care in the Community, 17*, 63–70.

Bailey, A., Le Couteur, A., Gottesman, I., Bolton, P., Simonoff, E., Yuzda, E., & Rutter, M. (1995). Autism as a strongly genetic disorder: evidence from a British twin study. *Psychological Medicine, 25*, 63–77.

Bailey, A. P., Parker, A. G., Colautti, L. A., Hart, L. M., Liu, P., & Hetrick, S. E. (2014). Mapping the evidence for the prevention and treatment of eating disorders in young people. *Journal of Eating Disorders, 2*(5).

Bailey, S. (2002, April 18). Forced drugging case goes to top court: Genius physicist's fight to decline anti-psychotic drugs goes to top court. Canadian Press.

Bailey, S. (2003, June 6). Man hailed by some as genius cannot be forcibly drugged for mental illness. Canadian Press.

Bailey, S., & Bronskill, J. (2006, November 23). Crisis looming as mentally ill jailed in disturbing numbers: Chief justice. *The Western Star*, 15.

Baillie, P. (2015). A valuable (and ongoing) study, the National Trajectory Project addresses many myths about the verdict of not criminally responsible on account of mental disorder. *Canadian Journal of Psychiatry, 60*, 93–95.

Baker, D., Earle, M., Medford, N., et al. (2007). Illness perceptions in depersonalization disorder: Testing an illness attribution model. *Clinical Psychology & Psychotherapy, 14*, 105–116.

Baker, T. B., Japuntich, S. J., Hogle, J. M., McCarthy, D. E., & Curti, J. J. (2006). Pharmacologic and behavioral withdrawal from addictive drugs. *Current Directions in Psychological Science, 15*, 232–236.

Bakken, I. J., Wenzel, H. G., Gotestam, K. G., et al. (2009). Internet addiction among Norwegian adults: A stratified probability sample study. *Scandinavian Journal of Psychology, 50*, 121–127.

Baldessarini, R. J., & Hennen, J. (2004). Genetics of suicide: An overview. *Harvard Review of Psychiatry, 12*, 1–13.

Ball, J. C., & Ross, A. (1991). *The effectiveness of methadone maintenance treatment: Patients, programs, services, and outcome.* New York: Springer-Verlag.

Baltes, M. M. (1988). The etiology and maintenance of dependency in the elderly: Three phases of operant research. *Behavior Therapy, 19*, 301–319.

Bamelis, L. L., Evers, S. M., Spinhoven, P., & Arntz, A. (2014). Results of a multicenter randomized controlled trial of the clinical effectiveness of schema therapy for personality disorders. *American Journal of Psychiatry, 17*, 305–322.

Bamidis, P. D., Vivas, A. B., Styliadis, C., Frantzidis, C., et al. (2014). A review of physical and cognitive interventions in aging. *Neuroscience and Biobehavioral Reviews, 44*, 206–220.

Bancroft, J. (1988). Sexual desire and the brain. *Sexual and Marital Therapy, 3*, 11–29.

Bandura, A. (1977). Self-efficacy: Toward a unifying theory of behavioral change. *Psychological Review, 84*, 191–215.

Bandura, A. (1986). *Social foundations of thought and action: A social cognitive theory.* Englewood Cliffs, NJ: Prentice-Hall.

Bandura, A. (1997). *Self-efficacy: The exercise of control.* New York: Freeman.

Bandura, A. (2001). Social cognitive theory: An agentic perspective. *Annual Review of Psychology, 52*, 1–26.

Bandura, A. (2006). Toward a psychology of human agency. *Perspectives in Psychological Science, 1*, 164–180.

Bandura, A. (2007). Autobiography. In M. G. Lindzey & W. M. Runyan (Eds.), *A history of psychology in autobiography* (Vol. IX, pp. 42–75). Washington, DC: American Psychological Association.

Bandura, A. (2015). *Moral disengagement.* London: Worth Publishing.

Bandura, A., & Menlove, F. L. (1968). Factors determining vicarious extinction of avoidance behavior through symbolic modeling. *Journal of Personality and Social Psychology, 8*, 99–108.

Bandura, A., & Rosenthal, T. L. (1966). Vicarious classical conditioning as a function of arousal level. *Journal of Personality and Social Psychology, 3*, 54–62.

Bandura, A., Ross, D., & Ross, S. A. (1961). Transmission of aggression through imitation of aggressive models. *Journal of Abnormal and Social Psychology, 63*, 575–582.

Bandura, A., & Walters, R. H. (1959). *Adolescent aggression.* New York: Ronald Press.

Bandura, A., & Walters, R. H. (1963). *Social learning and personality development.* New York: Holt, Rinehart & Winston.

Bank, L., Marlowe, J. H., Reid, J. B., Patterson, G. R., & Weinrott, M. R. (1991). A comparative evaluation of parent-training interventions for families of chronic delinquents. *Journal of Abnormal Child Psychology, 19*, 15–33.

Barbaree, H. E. (2005). Psychopathy, treatment behavior, and recidivism: An extended follow-up of Seto and Barbaree. *Journal of Interpersonal Violence, 20*, 1115–1131.

Barbaree, H. E., Seto, M. C., Langton, C. M., & Peacock, E. J. (2001). Evaluating the predictive accuracy of six risk assessment instruments for adult sex offenders. *Criminal Justice and Behavior, 28*, 490–521.

Barbaresi, W. J., Colligan, R. C., Weaver, A. L., Voigt, R. G., Killian, J. M., & Katusic, S. K. (2013). Mortality, ADHD, and psychosocial adversity in adults with childhood ADHD: A prospective study. *Pediatrics, 131*, 637–644.

Bardone-Cone, A. M., Wonderlich, S. A., Frost, R. O., et al. (2007). Perfectionism and eating disorders: Current status and future directions. *Clinical Psychology Review, 27*, 384–405.

Barker, E. D., & Maughan, B. (2009). Differentiating early-onset persistent versus childhood-limited conduct problem youth. *American Journal of Psychiatry, 166*, 900–908.

Barker, E. D., Boivin, M., Brendgen, M., et al. (2008). Predictive validity and early predictors of peer-victimization trajectories in preschool. *Archives of General Psychiatry, 65*, 1185–1192.

Barkley, R. A. (1990). *Attention-deficit hyperactivity disorder: A handbook for diagnosis and treatment*. New York: Guilford Press.

Barkley, R. A. (2002). International Consensus Statement on ADHD. *European Child and Adolescent Psychiatry, 11*, 96–98.

Barkley, R. A., DuPaul, G. J., & McMurray, M. B. (1990). Comprehensive evaluation of attention deficit disorder with and without hyperactivity as defined by research criteria. *Journal of Consulting and Clinical Psychology, 58*, 775–789.

Barkley, R. A., Karlsson, J., & Pollard, S. (1985). Effects of age on the mother-child interactions of hyperactive children. *Journal of Abnormal Child Psychology, 13*, 631–638.

Barlow, D. (1988). *Psychological treatment of panic*. New York: Guilford.

Barlow, D. H. (1999). NIMH Collaborative Trial on the Treatment of Panic Disorder. Paper presented at the annual convention of the Association for Advancement of Behavior Therapy, Toronto.

Barlow, D. H., Becker, R., Leitenberg, H., & Agras, W. S. (1970). A mechanical strain gauge for recording penile circumference. *Journal of Applied Behavior Analysis, 3*, 73–76.

Barlow, D. H., Blanchard, E. B., Vermilyea, J. A., Vermilyea, B. B., & Di Nardo, P. A. (1986). Generalized anxiety and generalized anxiety disorder: Description and reconceptualization. *American Journal of Psychiatry, 143*, 40–44.

Barlow, D. H., & Craske, M. G. (1994). *Mastery of your anxiety and panic II*. Albany, NY: Graywind Publications Incorporated.

Barlow, D. H., Vermilyea, J., Blanchard, E., Vermilyea, B., DiNardo, P., & Cerny, J. (1985). The phenomenon of panic. *Journal of Abnormal Psychology, 94*, 320–328.

Barnes, G. E. (1989). Gasoline sniffing in northern Canada. In S. Einstein (Ed.), *Drug and alcohol use: Issues and factors* (pp. 363–385). New York: Plenum Press.

Barnes, G. E., Barnes, M. D., & Patton, D. (2005). Prevalence and predictors of "heavy" marijuana use in a Canadian youth sample. *Substance Use and Misuse, 40*, 1849–1863.

Barnett, Z. L., Robleda-Gomez, S., & Pachana, N. A. (2012). Viagra: The little blue pill with big repercussions. *Aging and Mental Health, 16*, 84–88.

Barnhofer, T., Crane, C., Hargus, E., et al. (2009). Mindfulness-based cognitive therapy as a treatment for chronic depression: A preliminary study. *Behaviour Research and Therapy, 47*, 366–373.

Barnicot, K., Katsakou, C., Bhatti, N., Savill, M., et al. (2012). Factors predicting the outcome of psychotherapy for borderline personality disorder: A systematic review. *Clinical Psychology Review, 32*, 400–412.

Barrett, M., Wilson, R. J., & Long, C. (2003). Measuring motivation to change in sexual offenders from institutional intake to community treatment. *Sexual Abuse, 15*, 269–283.

Barrett, P. M., & Turner, C. (2001). Prevention of anxiety symptoms in primary school children: Preliminary results from a universal school-based trial. *British Journal of Clinical Psychology, 40*, 399–410.

Barrett, S. P., Gross, S. R., Garand, I., & Pihl, R. O. (2005). Patterns of simultaneous polysubstance use in Canadian rave attendees. *Substance Use & Misuse, 40*, 1525–1537.

Barrowclough, C., Haddock, G., Lobban, F., Jones, S., Siddle, R., Roberts, C., & Gregg, L. (2006). Group cognitive-behavioural therapy for schizophrenia. Randomised controlled trial. *British Journal of Psychiatry, 189*, 527–532.

Barsky, A. J., Fama, J. M., Bailey, E. D., & Ahern, D. K. (1998). A prospective 4- to 5-year study of DSM-III-R hyponchondriasis. *Archives of General Psychiatry, 55*, 737–744.

Bartholomew, K., & Horowitz, L. M. (1991). Attachment styles among young adults: A test of a four-category model. *Journal of Personality and Social Psychology, 61*, 226–244.

Bartlett, C. W., et al. (2002). A major susceptibility locus for specific language impairment is located on 13q21. *American Journal of Human Genetics, 71*, 45–55.

Bartlett, N. H., Vasey, P. L., & Bukowski, W. M. (2000). Is gender identity disorder in children a mental disorder? *Sex Roles, 43*, 753–785.

Bartlett, P. (2000). Structures of confinement in 19th-century asylums: A comparative study using England and Ontario. *International Journal of Law and Psychiatry, 23*, 1–13.

Barwick, A., Bazzini, D., Martz, D., Rocheleau, C., & Curtin, L. (2012). Testing the norm to fat talk for women of varying size: What's weight got to do with it? *Body Image, 9*, 176–179.

Basco, M. R., & Rush, A. J. (1996). *Cognitive-behavioral therapy for bipolar disorder*. New York: Guilford.

Bassani, D. G., Padoin, C. V., Philipp, D., & Veldhuizen, S. (2009). Estimating the number of children exposed to parental psychiatric disorders through a national health survey. *Child and Adolescent Psychiatry and Mental Health, 3*, 6.

Bassani, D. G., Padoin, C. V., & Veldhuizen, S. (2008). Counting children at risk. *Social Psychiatry and Psychiatric Epidemiology, 43*, 927–935.

Bastiani, A. M., Rao, R., Weltzin, T., & Kaye, W. H. (1995). Perfectionism in anorexia nervosa. *International Journal of Eating Disorders, 17*, 147–152.

Bates, G. W. (1990). *Social anxiety and self-presentation: Conversational behaviours and articulated thoughts of heterosexually anxious males*. Unpublished doctoral dissertation, University of Melbourne, Australia.

Batmaz, S., Kaymak, S. U., Kocbiyik, S., & Turkcapar, M. H. (2015). From the first episode to recurrences: The role of automatic thoughts and dysfunctional attitudes in major depressive disorder. *International Journal of Cognitive Therapy, 8*, 61–77.

Battaglia, M., Touchette, E., Caron-Carrier, G., Dionne, G., et al. (2016). Distinct trajectories of separation anxiety in the preschool years: Persistence at school entry and early-life associated factors. *Journal of Child Psychology and Psychiatry, 57*, 39–46.

Baucom, B. R., Atkins, D. C., Rowe, L. S., Doss, B. D., & Christensen, A. (2015). Prediction of treatment response at 5-year follow-up in a randomized clinical trial of behaviorally based couple therapies. *Journal of Consulting and Clinical Psychology, 83*, 103–114.

Baucom, B. R., Dickenson, J. A., Atkins, D. C., Baucom, D. H., Fischer, M. S., Weusthoff, S., . . . Zimmermann, T. (2015). The interpersonal process model of demand/withdraw behavior. *Journal of Family Psychology, 29*, 80–90.

Baucom, B. R., McFarland, P. T., & Christensen, A. (2010). Gender, topic, and time in observed demand–withdraw interaction in cross- and same-sex couples. *Journal of Family Psychology, 24*, 233–242.

Baucom, D. H., Belus, J. M., Adelman, C. B., Fischer, M. S., & Paprocki, C. (2014). Couple-based interventions for psychopathology: A renewed direction for the field. *Family Process, 53*, 445–461.

Baucom, D. H., Epstein, N., & Rankin, L. (1995). Integrative couple therapy. In N. S. Jacobson & A. S. Gurman (Eds.), *Clinical handbook of couple therapy* (pp. 65–90). New York: Guilford.

Baucom, D. H., Shoham, V., Mueser, K. T., Daiuto, A. D., & Stickle, T. R. (1998). Empirically supported couple and family interventions for marital distress and adult mental health problems. *Journal of Consulting and Clinical Psychology, 66*(1), 53.

Baucom, K. J. W., Baucom, B. R., & Christensen, A. (2015). Changes in dyadic communication during and after integrative and traditional behavioral couple therapy. *Behaviour Research and Therapy, 65*, 18–28.

Bauer, S., Schanda, H., Karakula, H., et al. (2011). Culture and the prevalence of hallucinations in schizophrenia. *Comprehensive Psychiatry, 52*, 319–325.

Bauermeister, J. J., Canino, C., Planczyk, G., & Rohde, L. A. (2010). ADHD across cultures: Is there evidence for a bidimensional organization of symptoms? *Journal of Clinical Child and Adolescent Psychology, 39*, 362–372.

Baumeister, R. F. (1990). Suicide as escape from self. *Psychological Review, 97*, 90–113.

Baumeister, R. F., & Butler, J. L. (1997). Sexual masochism: Deviance without pathology. *Sexual Deviance: Theory, Assessment, and Treatment, 225*–239.

Baumrind, D. H. (1971). Current patterns of parental authority. *Developmental Psychology Monographs, 4* (1, Part 2).

Baus, O., & Bouchard, S. (2014). Moving from virtual reality exposure-based therapy to augmented reality exposure-based therapy: A review. *Frontiers in Human Neuroscience, 8*, 1–15.

Baxter, D. (2015). Hoarding "epidemic" piling up in Winnipeg: Support group. *Winnipeg Metro.*

Be, D., Whisman, M. A., & Uebelacker, L. A. (2013). Prospective associations between marital adjustment and life satisfaction. *Personal Relationships, 20*, 728–739.

Beacher, F., Daly, E., Simmons, A., et al. (2009). Alzheimer's disease and Down's syndrome: An *in vivo* MRI study. *Psychological Medicine, 39*, 675–684.

Beal, A. L. (1995). Post-traumatic stress disorder in prisoners of war and combat veterans of the Dieppe raid: A 50-year follow-up. *Canadian Journal of Psychiatry, 40*, 177–184.

Beauchaine, T. P., Hinshaw, S. P., & Pang, K. L. (2010). Comorbidity of attention-deficit/hyperactivity disorder and early-onset conduct disorder: Biological, environmental, and developmental mechanisms. *Clinical Psychology: Science and Practice, 17*, 327–336.

Beaudet, A. (2009). As cited in R. Collier, Canadian Institutes of Health Research proposes major initiative on Alzheimer disease in step forward toward national dementia strategy. *Canadian Medical Association Journal, 181*, E36–E37.

Beaumont, E., & Hollins-Martin, C. (2015). A narrative review exploring the effectiveness of compassion-focused therapy. *Counselling Psychology Review, 30*, 21–32.

Bebbington, P. E., Cooper, C., Minot, S., et al. (2009). Suicide attempts, gender, and sexual abuse: Data from the 2000 British Psychiatric Morbidity Survey. *American Journal of Psychiatry, 166*, 1135–1140.

Beck, A. T. (1967). *Depression: Clinical, experimental and theoretical aspects.* New York: Harper & Row.

Beck, A. T. (1976). *Cognitive therapy and the emotional disorders.* New York: International Universities Press.

Beck, A. T. (1983). Cognitive therapy of depression: New perspectives. In P. J. Clayton & J. E. Barnett (Eds.), *Treatment of depression: Old controversies and new approaches* (pp. 265–290). New York: Raven Press.

Beck, A. T. (1987). Cognitive models of depression. *Journal of Cognitive Psychotherapy: An International Quarterly, 1*, 5–37.

Beck, A. T. (1988). *Love is never enough: How couples can overcome misunderstandings, resolve conflicts, and solve relationship problems through cognitive therapy.* New York: Harper Perennial.

Beck, A. T. (2008). The evolution of the cognitive model of depression and its neurobiological correlates. *American Journal of Psychiatry, 165*, 969–977.

Beck, A. T., Freeman, A., et al. (1990). *Cognitive therapy of personality disorders.* New York: Guilford.

Beck, A. T., Grant, P. M., Huh, G. A., Perivoliotis, D., & Chang, N. A. (2013). Dysfunctional attitudes and expectancies in deficit syndrome schizophrenia. *Schizophrenia Bulletin, 39*, 43–51.

Beck, A. T., & Haigh, E. A. P. (2014). Advances in cognitive theory and therapy: The generic cognitive model. *Annual Review of Clinical Psychology, 10*, 1–24.

Beck, A. T., Kovacs, M., & Weissman, A. (1979). Assessment of suicidal ideation: The Scale for Suicide Ideation. *Journal of Consulting and Clinical Psychology, 47*, 343–352.

Beck, A. T., & Rector, N. A. (2005). Cognitive approaches to schizophrenia: Theory and therapy. *Annual Review of Clinical Psychology, 1*, 577–606.

Beck, A. T., Steer, R. A., & Brown, G. K. (1996). *Manual for the Beck Depression Inventory—II.* San Antonio, TX: Psychological Corporation.

Beck, C. A., et al. (2005). Psychotropic medication use in Canada. *Canadian Journal of Psychiatry, 50*, 605–613.

Beck, J. G., & Bozman, A. (1995). Gender differences in sexual desire: The effects of anger and anxiety. *Archives of Sexual Behavior, 24*, 595–612.

Becker, E. S., Rinck, M., Roth, W. T., & Margraf, J. (1998). Don't worry and beware of white bears: Thought suppression in anxiety patients. *Journal of Anxiety Disorders, 12*, 39–55.

Becker, J. V. (1990). Treating adolescent sexual offenders. *Professional Psychology: Research and Practice, 21*, 362–365.

Becker, J. V., & Hunter, J. A. (1997). Understanding and treating child and adolescent sexual offenders. *Advances in clinical child psychology, 19*, 177–198.

Bedford, J. L., Linden, W., & Barr, S. I. (2011). Negative eating and body attitudes are associated with daytime ambulatory blood pressure in healthy young women. *International Journal of Psychophysiology, 79*, 147–154.

Bedi, R. P., Klubben, L. M., & Barker, G. T. (2012). Counselling vs. Clinical: A comparison of psychology doctoral programs in Canada. *Canadian Psychology, 53*, 238–253.

Beech, A. R., Ward, T., & Fisher, D. (2006). The identification of sexual and violent motivations in men who assault women: Implication for treatment. *Journal of Interpersonal Violence, 21*, 1635–1653.

Beecher, H. K. (1966). Ethics and clinical research. *New England Journal of Medicine, 274*, 1354–1360.

Beesdo, K., Knappe, S., & Pine, D. S. (2009). Anxiety and anxiety disorders in children and adolescents: Developmental issues and implications for *DSM-V. Psychiatric Clinics of North America, 32*, 483–524.

Beesdo-Baum, K., Knappe, S., Fehm, L., Hofler, M., Lieb, M., Hofmann, S. G., & Wittchen, H.-U. (2012). The natural course of social anxiety disorder among adolescents and young adults. *Acta Psychiatrica Scandinaniva, 126*, 411–425.

Beidel, D. C., Alfano, C. A., Kofler, M. J., Rao, P. A., Scharfstein, L., & Sarver, N. W. (2014). The impact of social skills training for social anxiety disorder: A randomized controlled trial. *Journal of Anxiety Disorders, 28*, 908–918.

Beirness, D. J., Beasley, E. E., & Boase, P. (2013). *Drug use among fatally injured drivers in Canada.* Paper presented at the 20th International Conference on Alcohol, Drugs, and Traffic Safety Conference, Brisbane, Australia.

Beiser, M., Hou, F., Hyman, I., & Tousignant, M. (1998). *Growing up Canadian: A study of new immigrant children* (No. W-98-24E). Ottawa: Human Resources Development Canada.

Beitchman, J. H., Wilson, B., Johnson, C. J., Atkinson, L., Young, A., Adlaf, E., et al. (2001). Fourteen-year follow-up of speech/language-impaired and control children: Psychiatric outcome. *Journal of the American Academy of Child and Adolescent Psychiatry, 40*, 75–82.

Belanger, L., LeBlanc, M., & Morin, C. M. (2012). Cognitive behavioral therapy for insomnia in older adults. *Cognitive and Behavioral Practice, 19*, 101–115.

Bell, A. C., & D'Zurilla, T. J. (2009). Problem-solving therapy for depression: A meta-analysis. *Clinical Psychology Review, 29*, 348–353.

Bellón, J. Á., Moreno-Peral, P., Motrico, E., Rodríguez-Morejón, A., Fernández, A., Serrano-Blanco, A., . . . Conejo-Cerón, S. (2015). Effectiveness of psychological and/or educational interventions to prevent the onset of episodes of depression: A systematic review of systematic reviews and meta-analyses. *Preventive Medicine, 76 Suppl*, S22–S32.

Belsky, J., & Pluess, M. (2009). Beyond diathesis-stress: Differential suspectibility to environmental influences. *Psychological Bulletin, 135*, 885–905.

Ben-Itzchak, E., & Zachor, D. A. (2007). The effects of intellectual functioning and autism severity on outcome of early behavioral intervention for children with autism. *Research in Developmental Disabilities, 28*, 287–303.

Ben-Porath, Y. S., & Tellegen, A. (2008). *MMPI-2-RF (Minnesota Multiphasic Personality Inventory-2 Restructured Form) manual for administration, scoring, and interpretation.* Minneapolis: University of Minnesota Press.

Bencherif, B., et al. (2005). Regional mu-opiod receptor binding in insular cortex is decreased in bulimia nervosa and correlates inversely with fasting behavior. *Journal of Nuclear Medicine, 46*, 1349–1351.

Bender, T. W., Anestis, M. D., Anestis, J. C., Gordon, K. H., & Joiner, T. E., Jr. (2012). Acquired capacity for suicide: Affective and behavioral paths toward the acquired capacity for suicide. *Journal of Social and Clinical Psychology, 31*, 81–100.

Bendetti, F., Sforzini, L., Colombo, C., Marrei, C., & Smeraldi, E. (1998). Low-dose clozapine in acute and continuation treatment of severe borderline personality disorder. *Journal of Clinical Psychiatry, 59*, 103–107.

Benkelfat, C., Ellenbogen, M. A., Dean, P., Palmour, R. M., & Young, S. N. (1994). Mood-lowering effect of tryptophan depletion: Enhanced susceptibility in young men at genetic risk for major affective disorders. *Archives of General Psychiatry, 51*, 687–700.

Bennett, K., Manassis, K., Walter, S. D., Cheung, A., et al. (2013). Cognitive behavioral therapy age effects in child and adolescent anxiety: An individual patient data meta-analysis. *Depression and Anxiety, 30*, 829–841.

Bennett, M. (2008, October). Criminal law as it pertains to mentally incompetent defendants: A M'Naghten Rule in light of cognitive neuroscience. Natural Judicial College of Australia conference, Sydney, Australia, October 25, 2008.

Bennett, V. (1997, February 22). Russia's forgotten children. *Los Angeles Times*, A1, A10.

Benowitz, N. L. (2008). Clinical pharmacology of nicotine: Implications for understanding, preventing, and treating tobacco addiction. *Clinical Pharmacology and Therapeutics, 83*, 531–543.

Bentaleb, L. A., Beauregard, M., Liddle, P., & Stip, E. (2002). Involvement of the left primary auditory cortex and left middle temporal regions in auditory verbal hallucinations: A functional magnetic resonance imaging single case study. *Journal of Neuroscience and Clinical Psychiatry, 27*, 110–115.

Benzies, K., Keown, L.-A., & Magill-Evans, J. (2009). Immediate and sustained effects of parenting on physical aggression in Canadian children aged 6 years and younger. *Canadian Journal of Psychiatry, 54*, 55–64.

Berenbaum, H., et al. (2008). Psychological trauma and schizotypal personality disorder. *Journal of Abnormal Psychology, 117*, 502–519.

Bergem, A. L., Engedal, K., & Kringlen, E. (1997). The role of heredity in late-onset Alzheimer's disease and vascular dementia: A twin study. *Archives of General Psychiatry, 54*, 264–270.

Bergeron, E., Poirier, L.-R., Fournier, L., Roberge, P., & Barrette, G. (2005). Determinants of service use among young Canadians with mental disorders. *Canadian Journal of Psychiatry, 50*, 629–636.

Bernecker, S. L., Constantino, M. J., Atkinson, L. R., Bagby, R. M., Ravitz, P., & McBride, C. (2016). Attachment style as a moderating influence on the efficacy of cognitive-behavioral and interpersonal psychotherapy for depression: A failure to replicate. *Psychotherapy, 53*, 22–33.

Bernecker, S., Levy, K. N., & Ellison, W. D. (2014). A meta-analysis of the relation between patient adult attachment style and the working alliance. *Psychotherapy Research, 24*, 12–24.

Bernstein, D. P., Useda, D., & Siever, L. J. (1993). Paranoid personality disorder: Review of the literature and recommendations for DSM-IV. *Journal of Personality Disorders, 7*, 53–62.

Bernstein, E. M., & Putnam, F. W. (1986). Development, rehability and validity of a dissociation scale. *Journal of Nervous and Mental Disease, 174*, 727–735.

Berry, J. C. (1967, September). Antecedents of schizophrenia, impulsive character and alcoholism in males. Paper presented at the annual meeting of the American Psychological Association, Washington, DC.

Berthiaume, L. (2006, May 6). Margaret Trudeau reveals fight with bipolar disorder. *The Vancouver Sun*, A6.

Besdine, R. W. (1980). Geriatric medicine: An overview. In C. Eisodorfer (Ed.), *Annual review of gerontology and geriatrics.* New York: Springer.

Bettelheim, B. (1967). *The empty fortress: Infantile autism and the birth of the self.* New York: The Free Press.

Bettelheim, B. (1973). Bringing up children. *Ladies Home Journal, 90*, 28.

Beutler, L. E. (1999). Manualizing flexibility: The training of eclectic therapists. *Journal of Clinical Psychology, 55*, 399–404.

Beutler, L. E. (2009). Making science matter in clinical practice: Redefining psychotherapy. *Clinical Psychology: Science and Practice, 16*, 301–317.

Beutler, L. E., & Harwood, T. M. (1995). Prescriptive psychotherapies. *Applied and Preventive Psychology, 4*, 89–100.

Beversdorf, D. Q., Manning, S. E., Hillier, A., et al. (2005). Timing of prenatal stressors and autism. *Journal of Autism and Developmental Disorders, 35,* 471–478.

Beynon, S., Soares-Weisser, K., Woolacott, N., et al. (2008). Psychosocial interventions for the prevention of relapse in bipolar disorder: Systematic review of controlled trials. *The British Journal of Psychiatry, 192,* 5–11.

Bhugra, D., Hilwig, M., Hosein, B., et al. (1996). First-contact incidence rates of schizophrenia in Trinidad and one-year follow-up. *British Journal of Psychiatry, 169,* 587–592.

Bialas, I., & Craig, T. K. (2007). Needs expressed and offers of care: An observational study of mothers with somatisation disorder and their children. *Journal of Child Psychology and Psychiatry, 48,* 97–104.

Bialystok, E., Craik, F. I. M., Klein, R., & Viswanathan, M. (2004). Bilingualism, aging, and cognitive control: Evidence from the Simon task. *Psychology and Aging, 19,* 290–303.

Bialystok, E., Poarch, G., Luo, L., & Craik, F. I. M. (2014). Effects of bilingualism and aging on executive function and working memory. *Psychology and Aging, 29,* 696–705.

Biedel, D. C., Turner, S. M., Sallee, F. R., et al. (2007). SET-C versus fluoxetine in the treatment of childhood social phobia. *Journal of the American Academy of Child and Adolescent Psychiatry, 46,* 1622–1632.

Biederman, J., et al. (1996). Predictors of persistence and remission of ADHD into adolescence: Results from a four-year prospective follow-up study. *Journal of the American Academy of Child and Adolescent Psychiatry, 35,* 343–351.

Biederman, J., & Farone, S. V. (2005). Attention-deficit hyperactivity disorder. *Lancet, 366,* 237–248.

Biederman, J., Petty, C. R., Wilens, T. E., et al. (2008). Familial risk analyses of attention deficit hyperactivity disorder and substance use disorders. *American Journal of Psychiatry, 165,* 107–115.

Bieling, P. J., & Alden, L. E. (2001). Sociotropy, autonomy, and the interpersonal model of depression: An integration. *Cognitive Therapy and Research, 25,* 167–184.

Bieling, P. J., Green, S. M., & Macqueen, G. (2007). The impact of personality disorders on treatment outcome in bipolar disorder: A review. *Personality and Mental Health, 1,* 2–13.

Bieling, P. J., & Kuyken, W. (2003). Is cognitive case formulation science or science fiction? *Clinical Psychology: Science and Practice, 10,* 52–69.

Billings, A. G., Cronkite, R. C., & Moos, R. H. (1983). Social-environmental factors in unipolar depression: Comparisons of depressed patients and nondepressed controls. *Journal of Abnormal Psychology, 92,* 119–133.

Bilsker, D., Goldner, E. M., & Jones, W. (2007). Health service patterns indicate potential benefit of supported self-management for depression in primary care. *Canadian Journal of Psychiatry, 52,* 86–95.

Binder, P.-E., Holgersen, H., & Nielsen, G. H. (2009). Why did I change when I went to therapy? A qualitative analysis of former patients' conceptions of successful psychotherapy. *Counselling and Psychotherapy Research, 9,* 250–256.

Birchwood, M., & Meaden, A. (2013). Cognitive therapy for reducing distress and harmful compliance with command hallucinations. In C. Steel (Ed.), *CBT for schizophrenia: Evidence-based interventions and future directions* (pp. 13–34). Chichester, England: Wiley-Blackwell.

Birmingham, C. L., et al. (2005). The mortality rate for anorexia nervosa. *International Journal of Eating Disorders, 38,* 143–146.

Birnbaum, M. (1960). The right to treatment. *American Bar Association Journal, 46,* 499–505.

Bittles, A. H., & Glasson, E. J. (2004). Clinical, social, and ethical implications of changing life expectancy in Down syndrome. *Developmental Medicine & Child Neurology, 46,* 282–286.

Blacher, J., Neece, C. L., & Paczkowski, E. (2005). Families and intellectual disability. *Current Opinions in Psychiatry, 18,* 507–513.

Black, S. E., Gauthier, S., Dalziel, W., Keren, R., et al. (2010). Canadian Alzheimer's Disease Caregiver Survey: Baby-boomer caregivers and burden of care. *International Journal of Geriatric Psychiatry, 25*(8), 807–813.

Blackwell, T. (2012, December 10). Decades after Sybil, multiple opinions remain. *National Post,* A1–A2.

Blagys, M., & Hilsenroth, M. J. (2000). Distinctive activities of short-term psychodynamic interpersonal psychotherapy: A review of the comparative psychiatric process literature. *Clinical Psychology: Science and Practice, 7,* 167–188.

Blair, R. J. D., Jones, L., Clark, F., & Smith, M. (1997). The psychopathic individual: A lack of responsiveness to distress cues? *Psychophysiology, 34,* 192–198.

Blais, M. A., Hilsenroth, M. J., & Castlebury, F. D. (1997). Content validity of the newly revised Diagnostic and Statistical Manual of Mental Disorders-IV (DSM-IV) narcissitic personality disorder (NPD) and borderline personality disorder (BPD) criteria sets. *Comprehensive Psychiatry, 38,* 31–37.

Blanchard, E. B. (1994). Behavioral medicine and health psychology. In A. E. Bergin & S. L. Garfield (Eds.), *Handbook of psychotherapy and behavior change* (4th ed., pp. 701–733). New York: John Wiley & Sons.

Blanchard, J. J., Squires, D., Henry, T., Horan, W. P., Bogenschutz, M., et al. (1999). Examining an affect regulation model of substance abuse in schizophrenia: The role of traits and coping. *Journal of Nervous and Mental Disease, 187,* 72–79.

Blanchard, R. (1989). The classification and labeling of nonhomosexual gender dysphorias. *Archives of Sexual Behavior, 18,* 315–334.

Blanchard, R. (1992). Nonmonotonic relation of autogynephilia and heterosexual attraction. *Journal of Abnormal Psychology, 101,* 271–276.

Blanco, C., Bragdon, L. B., Schneier, F. R., & Liebowitz, M. R. (2013). The evidence-based pharmacotherapy of social anxiety disorder. *International Journal of Neuropsychopharmacology, 16,* 235–249.

Blanco, C., et al. (2008). Mental health of college students and their non-college-attending peers: Results from the National Epidemiologic Study on Alcohol and related conditions. *Archives of General Psychiatry, 65,* 1429–1437.

Blanco, C., Heimberg, R. G., Schneier, F. R., Fresco, D. M., Chen, H., Turk, C. L., . . . Liebowitz, M. R. (2010). A placebo-controlled trial of phenelzine, cognitive behavioral group therapy, and their combination for social anxiety disorder. *Archives of General Psychiatry, 67,* 286–295.

Blankstein, K. R., Flett, G. L., & Koledin, S. (1991). The Brief College Students Hassles Scale: Development, validation, and relation with pessimism. *Journal of College Student Development, 32,* 258–264.

Blankstein, K. R., Lumley, C., & Crawford, A. (2007). Perfectionism, hopelessness, and suicide ideation: Revisions to diathesis-stress and specific vulnerability models. *Journal of Rational-Emotive and Cognitive-Behavior Therapy, 25,* 279–319.

Blashfeld, R. K., Keeley, J. W., Flanagan, E. H., & Miles, S. R. (2014). The cycle of classification: *DSM-I* through *DSM-5. Annual Review of Clinical Psychology, 10,* 25– 51.

Blaske, D. M., Borduin, C. M., Hengeler, S. W., & Mann, B. J. (1989). Individual, family, and peer characteristics of adolescent sex offenders and assaultive offenders. *Developmental Psychology, 25,* 846–855.

Blatt, S. J. (1974). Levels of object representation in anaclitic and introjective depression. *Psychoanalytic Study of the Child, 29,* 107–157.

Blatt, S. J. (1995). The destructiveness of perfectionism: Implications for the treatment of depression. *American Psychologist, 50,* 1003–1020.

Blatt, S. J., Zohar, A. H., Quinlan, D. M., Zuroff, D. C., & Mongrain, M. (1995). Subscales within the dependency factor of the Depressive Experiences Questionnaire. *Journal of Personality Assessment, 64,* 319–339.

Blatt, S. J., & Zuroff, D. C. (1992). Interpersonal relatedness and self-definition: Two prototypes for depression. *Clinical Psychology Review, 12,* 527–562.

Blatt, S. J., & Zuroff, D. C. (2002). Perfectionism and the therapeutic context. In G. L. Flett, & P. L. Hewitt (Eds.), *Perfectionism: Theory, research, and treatment* (pp. 393–406). Washington, DC: American Psychological Association.

Blaustein, M., & Fleming, A. (2009). Suicide from the Golden Gate Bridge. *American Journal of Psychiatry, 166,* 1111–1116.

Blazer, D. G., Hughes, D., & George, L. K. (1987). Stressful life events and the onset of a generalized anxiety syndrome. *American Journal of Psychiatry, 144,* 1178–1183.

Blazer, D. G., & Williams, C. D. (1980). Epidemiology of dysphoria and depression in the elderly population. *American Journal of Psychiatry, 137,* 439–444.

Blazer, D. G., & Wu, L. T. (2009). The epidemiology of at-risk and binge drinking among middle-aged and elderly community adults: National survey on drug use and health. *American Journal of Psychiatry, 166,* 1162–1169.

Bleuler, E. (1911). *Dementia praecox, oder die Gruppe der Schizophrenien (Dementia Praecox, or the Group of the Schizophrenias).* Leipzig, Germany: Franz Deuticke.

Bliwise, D., Carskadon, M., Carey, E., & Dement, W. (1984). Longitudinal development of sleep-related respiratory disturbance in adult humans. *Journal of Gerontology, 39,* 290–293.

Bloch, M. H., Bartley, C. A., Zipperer, L., Jakubovski, E., Landeros-Weisenberger, A., Pittenger, C., & Leckman, J. F. (2014). Meta-analysis: Hoarding symptoms associated with poor treatment outcome in obsessive-compulsive disorder. *Molecular Psychiatry, 19,* 1025–1030.

Block, J. S. (2008). Issues for DSM-V: Internet addiction. *American Journal of Psychiatry, 165,* 306–307.

Blote, A. W., Kint, M. J. W., Miers, A. C., & Westenberg, P. M. (2009). The relation between public speaking anxiety and social anxiety: A review. *Journal of Anxiety Disorders, 23,* 305–313.

Blume, A. W., Rudisill, D. M., Hendricks, S., & Santoya, N. (2013). Disease model. In P. Miller (Ed.), *Principles of addiction, Vol. 1* (pp. 71–76). New York: Academic Press.

Boak, A., Hamilton, H. A., Adlaf, E. M., & Mann, R. E. (2015). *Drug use among Ontario students, 1977-2015: Detailed OSDUHS findings* (CAMH Research Document Series No. 41). Toronto: Centre for Addiction and Mental Health.

Bockhoven, J. (1963). *Moral treatment in American psychiatry.* New York: Springer.

Bockting, C. L. H., Smid, N. H., Koeter, M. W. J., Spinhoven, P., Beck, A. T., & Schene, A. H. (2015). Enduring effects of preventive cognitive therapy in adults remitted from recurrent depression: A 10-year follow-up of a randomized controlled trial. *Journal of Affective Disorders, 185,* 188–194.

Bogels, S. M., Alden, L., Beidel, D., et al. (2010). Social anxiety disorder: Questions and answers for the DSM-V. *Depression and Anxiety, 27,* 168–189.

Bogulski, C. A., Rakoczy, M., Goodman, M., & Bialystok, E. (2015). Executive control in fluent and lapsed bilinguals. *Bilingualism: Language and Cognition, 18,* 561–567.

Bohlmeijer, E., Smit, F., & Cuijpers, P. (2003). Effects of reminiscence and life review on late-life depression: A meta-analysis. *International Journal of Geriatric Psychiatry, 18,* 1088–1094.

Boisvert, C. M., & Faust, D. (2003). Leading researchers' consensus on psychotherapy research findings: Implications for the teaching and conduct of psychotherapy. *Professional Psychology: Research and Practice, 34,* 508–513.

Boivin, M., Hymel, S., & Bukowski, W. M. (1995). The roles of social withdrawal, peer rejection, and victimization by peers in predicting loneliness and depressed mood in childhood. *Development and Psychopathology, 7,* 765–785.

Bolton, J., Cox, B. J., Clara, I., & Sareen, J. (2006). Use of alcohol and drugs to self-medicate anxiety disorders in a nationally representative sample. *Journal of Nervous and Mental Disease, 194,* 818–825.

Bonanno, G. A., & Kaltman, S. (2001). The varieties of grief experience. *Clinical Psychology Review, 21,* 705–734.

Bonin, M. P., McCreary, D. R., & Sadava, S. W. (2000). Problem drinking behavior in two community-based samples of adults: Influence of gender, coping, loneliness, and depression. *Psychology of Addictive Behaviors, 14,* 151–161.

Bonta, J., Law, M., & Hanson, K. (1998). The prediction of criminal and violent recidivism among mentally disordered offenders. *Psychological Bulletin, 123,* 123–142.

Bonvicini, C., Faraone, S. V., & Scassellati, C. (2016). Attention-deficit hyperactivity disorder in adults: A systematic review and meta-analysis of genetic, pharmacogenetic, and biochemical studies. *Molecular Psychiatry, 21,* 872–884.

Booij, L., Tremblay, R. E., Szyf, M., & Benkelfat, C. (2015). Genetic and environmental influences on the serotonin system: Consequences for brain development and risk for psychopathology. *Journal of Psychiatry and Neuroscience, 40,* 5–18.

Boon, S., & Draijer, N. (1993). Multiple personality disorder in the Netherlands: A clinical investigation of 71 patients. *American Journal of Psychiatry, 150,* 489–494.

Boonstra, N., Klaassen, R., Sytema, S., et al. (2012). Duration of untreated psychosis and negative symptoms: A systematic review and meta-analysis of individual patient data. *Schizophrenia Research, 142,* 12–19.

Bootzin, R., Manber, R., Loewy, D. H., Kuo, T. F. & Franzen, P L. (2002). Sleep disorders. In H. E. Adams & P. Sutker (Eds.), *Comprehensive handbook of psychopathology* (3rd ed., pp. 671–712). New York: Kluwer Academic Publishers.

Boraska, V., Franklin, C., Floyd, J., Thornton, L., Huckins, L., Southam, L., et al. (2014). A genome-wide association study of anorexia nervosa. *Molecular Psychiatry, 19,* 1085–1094.

Borges, G., et al. (2006). A risk index for 12-month suicide attempts in the National Comorbidity Survey Replication (NCS-R). *Psychological Medicine, 36,* 1747–1757.

Borkovec, T. D., & Inz, J. (1990). The nature of worry in generalized anxiety disorder: A predominance of thought activity. *Behaviour Research and Therapy, 28*(2), 153–158.

Borkovec, T. D., & Mathews, A. (1988). Treatment of nonphobic anxiety disorders: A comparison of nondirective, cognitive and coping desensitization therapy. *Journal of Consulting and Clinical Psychology, 56,* 877–884.

Borkovec, T. D., & Newman, M. G. (1998). Worry and generalized anxiety disorder. In P. M. Salkovskis (Ed.), *Adults: Clinical formulation and treatment* (pp. 439–459). Oxford, England: Pergamon Press.

Borkovec, T. D., & Whisman, M. A. (1996). Psychosocial treatment for generalized anxiety disorder. In M. Mavissakalian & R. E. Prien (Eds.), *Long-term treatment of anxiety disorders* (pp. 171–199). Washington, DC: American Psychiatric Association.

Bornstein, R. F. (1997). Dependent personality disorder in the DSM-IV and beyond. *Clinical Psychology: Science and Practice, 4,* 175–187.

Bosco, G. L., Renk, K., Dinger, T. M., Epstein, M. K., & Phares, V. (2003). The connections between adolescents' perceptions of parents, parental psychological symptoms, and adolescent functioning. *Journal of Applied Developmental Psychology, 24*, 179–200.

Boswell, J. F. (in press). Psychotherapy integration: Research, practice, and training at the leading edge. *Journal of Psychotherapy Integration.*

Bottos, S., & Dewey, D. (2004). Perfectionists' appraisal of daily hassles and chronic headache. *Headache, 44*(8), 772–779.

Bouchard, S., Côté, S., St-Jacques, J., Robillard, G., & Renaud, P. (2006). Effectiveness of virtual reality exposure in the treatment of arachnophobia using 3D games. *Technology and Health Care, 14,* 19–27.

Bourrie, M. (2010, March 9). The serial killer they couldn't cure dies behind bars: Peter Woodcock killed three Toronto children in the 50's. One day on a pass in 1991, he killed again. *Toronto Star.*

Boutin, C., Tremblay, N., & Ladouceur, R. (2009). Impact of visiting an onsite casino information centre on perceptions about randomness and gambling behaviours. *Journal of Gambling Studies, 25,* 317–330.

Bouton, M. E. (2014). Why behavior change is difficult to sustain. *Preventive Medicine: An International Journal Devoted to Practice and Theory, 68,* 29–36.

Bowden, S. C., Lange, R. T., Weiss, L. G., & Saklofske, D. H. (2008). Invariance of the measurement model underlying the Wechsler Adult Intelligence Scale—III in the United States and Canada. *Educational and Psychological Measurement, 68,* 1024–1040.

Bowers, J., Jorm, A. F., Henderson, S., & Harris, P. (1990). General practitioners' detection of depression and dementia in elderly patients. *The Medical Journal of Australia, 153,* 192–196.

Bowers, M. B., Jr. (1974). Central dopamine turnover in schizophrenic syndromes. *Archives of General Psychiatry, 31,* 50–54.

Bowlby, B. J., Peters, C., & MacKinnon, M. (2001). *An educator's guide to special education law.* Aurora, ON: Aurora Professional Press.

Bowlby, B. J., & Wootton Regan, J. (1998). *An educator's guide to human rights.* Aurora, ON: Aurora Professional Press.

Bowman, M. L. (2000). The diversity of diversity: Canadian-American differences and their implications for clinical training and APA accreditation. *Canadian Psychology, 41,* 244–256.

Boyle, M. (1991). *Schizophrenia: A scientific delusion?* New York: Routledge.

Boyle, M. H., Sanford, M., Szatmari, P., Merikangas, K., & Offord, D. R. (2001). Familial influences on substance use by adolescents and young adults. *Canadian Journal of Public Health, 92,* 206–208.

Boyle, T. (1998, February 10). Courts stymied on mentally ill. *Toronto Star,* E1, E5.

Boyle, T., & Vincent, D. (1998, January 10 to 16). Madness: Seven parts of how we're failing the mentally ill. *Toronto Star.*

Bozman, A., & Beck, J. G. (1991). Covariation of sexual desire and sexual arousal: The effects of anger and anxiety. *Archives of Sexual Behavior, 20,* 47–60.

Brache, K., & Stockwell, T. (2011). Drinking patterns and risk behaviours associated with combined alcohol and energy drink consumption in college students. *Addictive Behaviors, 36,* 1133–1140.

Bradford, J. M., & Fedoroff, J. P. (2009). The neuro-biology of sexual behavior and the paraphilias. In F. M. Saleh, A. J. Grudzinskas, J. M. Bradford, & D. J. Brodsky (Eds.), *Sex offenders: Identification, risk assessment, treatment, and legal issues* (pp. 36–47). New York: Oxford University Press.

Bradley, B., & Johnson, S. M. (2005). Emotionally focused couples therapy: An integrative contemporary approach. In M. Haraway (Ed.), *Couples therapy* (pp. 179–193). New York: John Wiley & Sons.

Bradley, B. P., Mogg, K., & Williams, R. (1995). Implicit and explicit memory for emotion-congruent information in clinical depression and anxiety. *Behaviour Research and Therapy, 33,* 755–770.

Bradley, E. A., Thompson, A., & Bryson, S. E. (2002). Mental retardation in teenagers: Prevalence data from the Niagara region, Ontario. *Canadian Journal of Psychiatry, 47,* 652–659.

Bradley, S. J., Blanchard, R., Coates, S., Green, R., Levine, S. B., Meyer-Bahlburg, H. F., et al. (1991). Interim report of the DSM-IV subcommittee on gender identity disorders. *Archives of Sexual Behavior, 20,* 333–343.

Bradley, S. J., Oliver, G. D., Chernick, A. B., & Zucker, K. J. (1998). Experiment of nurture: Albatio penis at 2 months, sex reassignment at 7 months, and a psychosexual follow-up in young adulthood. *Pediatrics, 102,* e1–e9.

Bradley, S. J., & Zucker, K. J. (1997). Gender identity disorder: A review of the past 10 years. *Journal of the American Academy of Child & Adolescent Psychiatry, 36,* 872–880.

Bradwejn, J., Koszycki, D., & Meterissian, G. (1990). Cholecystokinin-tetrapeptide induced panic attacks in patients with panic disorder. *Canadian Journal of Psychiatry, 35,* 83–85.

Braga, R. J., Mendlowicz, M. V., Marrocos, R. P., & Figueira, I. L. (2005). Anxiety disorders in outpatients with schizophrenia: Prevalence and impact on the subjective quality of life. *Journal of Psychiatric Research, 39,* 409–414.

Brakoulias, V., Eslick, G. D., & Starcevic, V. (2015). A meta-analysis of the response of pathological hoarding to pharmacotherapy. *Psychiatry Research, 229,* 272–276.

Brambilla, P., et al. (2007). Assessment of cerebral blood volume in schizophrenia: A magnetic resonance imaging study. *Journal of Psychiatric Research, 41,* 502–510.

Brand, B. L., Classen, C. C., Lanius, R., Lowenstein, R., McNary, S., Pain, C., & Putnam, F. (2009). A naturalistic study of dissociative identity disorder and dissociative disorder not otherwise specified patients treated by community clinicians. *Psychological Trauma: Theory, Research, Practice, and Policy, 1,* 153–171.

Brand, B. L., McNary, S. W., Myrick, A. C., Classen, C. C., Lanius, R., Loewenstein, R. J., et al. (2013). A longitudinal naturalistic study of patients with dissociative disorders treated by community clinicians. *Psychological Trauma: Theory, Research, Practice, and Policy, 5,* 301–308.

Brandon, Y. H., Zelman, D. C., & Baker, T. B. (1987). Effects of maintenance sessions on smoking relapse: Delaying the inevitable? *Journal of Consulting and Clinical Psychology, 55,* 780–782.

Brandt, J., Buffers, N., Ryan, C., & Bayoz, R. (1983). Cognitive loss and recovery in alcohol abusers. *Archives of General Psychiatry, 40,* 435–442.

Brandys, M. K., de Kovel, C. G. F., Kas, M. J., Van Elburg, A. A., & Aden, R. A. H. (2015). Overview of genetic research in anorexia nervosa: The past, the present, and the future. *International Journal of Eating Disorders, 48,* 814–825.

Branson, A., Shafran, R., & Myles, P. (2015). Investigating the relationship between competence and patient outcome with CBT. *Behaviour Research and Therapy, 68,* 19–26.

Brean, J. (2013, February 4). A beautiful mind of his own. *The National Post,* A3.

Brean, J. (2013, August 6). Troubling diagnosis: The latest edition of psychiatry's manual draws fierce criticism. *National Post,* A3.

Brecher, E. M., & the Editors of Consumer Reports. (1972). *Licit and illicit drugs.* Mount Vernon, NY: Consumers Union.

Brendgen, M., Girard, A., Vitaro, F., Dionne, G., & Boivin, M. (2015). The dark side of friends: A genetically informed study of victimization within early adolescents' friendships. *Journal of Clinical Child and Adolescent Psychology, 44,* 417–431.

Brennand, K., Simone, A., Jou, J., Gelboin-Burkhart, C., et al. (2011). Modeling schizophrenia using hiPSC neurons. *Nature, 473,* 221–225.

Bresin, K., & Gordon, K. H. (2013). Endogenous opioids and nonsuicidal self-injury: A mechanism of affect regulation. *Neuroscience and Biobehavioral Reviews, 37,* 374–383.

Breslau, N., Breslau, J., Peterson, E., et al. (2010). Change in teachers' ratings of attention problems and subsequent change in academic achievement: A prospective analysis. *Psychological Medicine, 40,* 159–166.

Bretteville-Jensen, A. L., Melberg, H. O., & Jones, A. M. (2008). Sequential patterns of drug use initiation—Can we believe the gateway theory? *The B.E. Journal of Economic Analysis and Policy, 2,* Article 1.

Breuer, J., & Freud, S. (1982). *Studies in hysteria.* (J. Strachey, Trans. and Ed., with the collaboration of A. Freud). New York: Basic Books. (Original work published 1895.)

Brewin, C. R. (2012). A theoretical framework for understanding recovered memory experiences. *Nebraska Symposium on Motivation, 58,* 149–173.

Brezo, J., Paris, J., & Turecki, G. (2006). Personality traits as correlates of suicidal ideation, suicide attempts, and suicide completions: A systematic review. *Acta Psychiatrica Scandinavica, 113,* 180–206.

Brian's Law *[Mental Health Legislative Reform],* 2000: S. O. 2000 C.9.

Brickman, A. S., McManus, M., Grapentine, W. L., & Alessi, N. (1984). Neuropsychological assessment of seriously delinquent adolescents. *Journal of the American Academy of Child Psychiatry, 23,* 453–457.

Bridge, J. A., Birmaher, B., Iyengar, S., et al. (2009). Placebo response in randomized controlled trials of antidepressants for pediatric major depressive disorder. *American Journal of Psychiatry, 166,* 42–49.

Bridger, W. H., & Mandel, I. J. (1965). Abolition of the PRE by instructions in GSR conditioning. *Journal of Experimental Psychology, 69,* 476–482.

Briere, J., & Runtz, M. (2015). Dissociation in individuals denying trauma exposure: Findings from two samples. *Journal of Nervous and Mental Disease, 203,* 439–442.

Broadus, A. D., Hartje, J. A., Roget, N. A., Cahoon, K. L., & Clinkinbeard, S. S. (2010). Attitudes about addiction: A national study of addiction educators. *Journal of Drug Education, 40,* 281–298.

Brock, G. B., et al. (2009). Canadian male sexual health council survey to assess prevalence and treatment of premature ejaculation in Canada. *Journal of Sex Medicine, 6,* 2115–2123.

Brockmeyer, T., Holtforth, M. G., Bents, H., et al. (in press). Self-esteem and low body weight in anorexia nervosa. *Clinical Psychology and Psychotherapy.*

Broidy, L. M., et al. (2003). Developmental trajectories of childhood disruptive behaviors and adolescent delinquency: A six-site, cross-national study. *Developmental Psychology, 39,* 222–245.

Brookoff, D., Cook, C. S., Williams, C., & Mann, C. S. (1994). Testing reckless drivers for cocaine and marijuana. *New England Journal of Medicine, 331,* 518–522.

Brooks, P. J., & Zakhari, S. (2013). Moderate alcohol consumption and breast cancer in women: From epidemiology to mechanisms and interventions. *Alcoholism: Clinical and Experimental Research, 37,* 23–30.

Brooks, S. A., O'Reilly, R. L., & Gray, J. E. (2003, August). Implications for psychiatrists of the Supreme Court of Canada Starson v. Swayze decision. CPA *Bulletin* de l'APC, p. 29.

Brosschot, J. F., Gerin, W., & Thayer, J. F. (2006). The perseverative cognition hypothesis: A review of worry, prolonged stress-related physiological activation, and health. *Journal of Psychosomatic Research, 60,* 113–124.

Brown, A. S., Begg, M. D., Gravenstein, S., et al. (2004). Serologic evidence of prenatal influenza in the etiology of schizophrenia. *Archives of General Psychiatry, 61,* 774–780.

Brown, A. S., & Derkits, E. J. (2010). Parental infection and schizophrenia: A review of epidemiologic and translational studies. *American Journal of Psychiatry, 167,* 261–280.

Brown, A. S., & Patterson, P. H. (2011). Maternal infection and schizophrenia: Implications for prevention. *Schizophrenia Bulletin, 37,* 284–290.

Brown, G. K., Beck, A. T., Steer, R. A., & Grisham, J. R. (2000). Risk factors for suicide in psychiatric outpatients: A 20-year prospective study. *Journal of Consulting and Clinical Psychology, 68,* 371–377.

Brown, G. P., & Beck, A. T. (2002). Dysfunctional attitudes, perfectionism, and models of vulnerability to depression. In G. L. Flett & P. L. Hewitt (Eds.), *Perfectionism: Theory, research, and treatment* (pp. 231–251). Washington, DC: American Psychological Association.

Brown, G. W., Bone, M., Dalison, B., & Wing, J. K. (1966). *Schizophrenia and social care.* London: Oxford University Press.

Brown, L. M., Bongar, B., & Cleary, K. M. (2004). A profile of psychologists' views of critical risk factors for completed suicide in older adults. *Professional Psychology: Research and Practice, 35,* 90–96.

Brown, L. S. (2011). Guidelines for treating dissociative identity disorder in adults, third revision: A tour de force for the dissociation field. *Journal of Trauma and Dissociation, 12,* 188–212.

Brown, R. T., Carpenter, L. A., & Simerly, E. (2005). *Mental health medications for children: A primer.* New York: Guilford.

Brown, S. L., & Forth, A. E. (1997). Psychopathy and sexual assault: Static risk factors, emotional precursors, and rapist subtypes. *Journal of Consulting and Clinical Psychology, 65,* 848–857.

Brown, T. A., Barlow, D. H., & Liebowitz, M. R. (1994). The empirical basis of generalized anxiety disorder. *American Journal of Psychiatry, 151,* 1272–1280.

Brownell, K. D., & Rodin, J. (1994). The dieting maelstrom: Is it possible or advisable to lose weight? *American Psychologist, 49,* 781–791.

Brownlie, E. B., Beitchman, J. H., Escobar, M., Young, A., et al. (2004). Early language impairment and young adult delinquent and aggressive behavior. *Journal of Abnormal Child Psychology, 32,* 453–467.

Brownmiller, S. (1975). *Against our will: Men, women and rape.* New York: Simon & Schuster.

Bruck, M. (1986). Social and emotional adjustments of learning disabled children: A review of the issues. In S. J. Ceci (Ed.), *Handbook of cognitive, social, and neuropsychological aspects of learning disabilities* (pp. 361–380). Hillsdale, NJ: Erlbaum.

Bruder, C. E., Piotrowski, A., Gijsbers, A. A., Andersson, R., et al. (2008). Phenotypically concordant and discordant monozygotic twins display different DNA copy-number-variation profiles. *American Journal of Human Genetics, 82,* 763–771.

Bryant, R. A., & Das, P. (2012). The neural circuitry of conversion disorder and its recovery. *Journal of Abnormal Psychology, 121,* 289–296.

Bryson, S. E., Rogers, S. J., & Fombonne, E. (2003). Autism spectrum disorders: Early detection, intervention, education, and psychopharmacological management. *Canadian Journal of Psychiatry, 48,* 506–516.

Buchanan, B., Rossell, S., Maller, J. J., Toh, W. L., Brennan, S., & Castle, D. (2014). Regional brain volumes in body dysmorphic disorder compared to controls. *Australian and New Zealand Journal of Psychiatry, 48,* 654–662.

Buchanan, R. W., Breier, A., Kirkpatrick, B., Ball, P., & Carpenter, W. T. (1998). Positive and negative symptom response to clozapine in schizophrenic patients with and without the deficit syndrome. *American Journal of Psychiatry, 155*, 751–760.

Buchsbaum, M. S., Kessler, R., King, A., Johnson, J., & Cappelletti, J. (1984). Simultaneous cerebral glucography with positron emission tomography and topographic electroencephalography. In G. Pfurtscheller, E. J. Jonkman, & F. H. Lopes da Silva (Eds.), *Brain ischemia: Quantitative EEG and imaging techniques.* Amsterdam: Elsevier.

Buckels, E., Jones, D., & Paulhus, D. (2013). Behavioural confirmation of everyday sadism. *Psychological Science, 24*, 2201–2209.

Buckner, J. D., & Schmidt, N. B. (2009). Social anxiety disorder and marijuana use problems: The mediating role of marijuana effect expectancies. *Depression and Anxiety, 26*, 864–870.

Budd, R., & Hughes, I. (2009). The Dodo bird verdict—controversial, inevitable, and important: A commentary on 30 years of meta-analyses. *Clinical Psychology and Psychotherapy, 16*, 510–522.

Bufkin, J. L., & Luttrell, U. R. (2005). Neuroimaging studies of aggressive and violent behavior: Current findings and implications for criminology and criminal justice. *Trauma, Violence, and Abuse, 6*, 176–191.

Buhlmann, U., Reese, H. E., Renaud, S., & Wilhelm, S. (2008). Clinical considerations for the treatment of body dysmorphic disorder with cognitive-behavioral therapy. *Body Image, 5*, 39–49.

Buhr, K., & Dugas, M. J. (2009). The role of fear of anxiety and intolerance of uncertainty in worry: An experimental manipulation. *Behaviour Research and Therapy, 47*, 215–223.

Bujold, A., Ladouceur, R., Sylvain, C., & Boisvert, J.-M. (1994). Treatment of pathological gamblers: An experimental study. *Journal of Behavioural Therapy and Experimental Psychiatry, 25*, 275–282.

Bulik, C. M., Sullivan, P. F., & Kendler, K. S. (2000). An empirical study of the classification of eating disorders. *American Journal of Psychiatry, 157*, 886–895.

Bulik, C. M., Sullivan P. F., Tozzi, F., et al. (2006). Prevalence, heritability, and prospective risk factors for anorexia nervosa. *Archives of General Psychiatry, 63*, 305–312.

Burgess, A. W., & Holmstrom, L. L. (1974). *Rape: Victim of crisis.* Bowie, MD: Robert J. Brady Company.

Burke, B. L., Arkowitz, H., & Menchola, M. (2003). The efficacy of motivational interviewing: A meta-analysis of controlled clinical trials. *Journal of Consulting and Clinical Psychology, 71*, 843–861.

Burke, M. J., Ghaffar, O., Staines, W. R., Downar, J., & Feinstein, A. (2014). Functional neuroimaging of conversion disorder: The role of ancillary activation. *NeuroImage: Clinical, 6*, 333–399.

Burke, R. J. (2006). Workaholism types, satisfaction and well-being: It's not how hard you work but why and how hard you work. In R. J. Burke & C. L. Cooper (Eds.), *Inspiring leaders* (pp. 273–289). New York: Routledge.

Burnham, J. J., Lomax, R. G., & Hooper, L. M. (2013). Gender, age, and racial differences in self-reported fears among school-aged youth. *Journal of Child and Family Studies, 22*, 268–278.

Burns, A. M. N., Erickson, D. H., & Brenner, C. A. (2014). Cognitive-behavioral therapy for medication-resistant psychosis: A meta-analytic review. *Psychiatric Services, 65*, 874–880.

Burstein, M., Georgiades, K., He, J.-P., Schmitz, A., et al. (2012). Specific phobia among U.S. adolescents: Phenomenology and typology. *Depression and Anxiety, 29*(12), 1072–1082.

Burton, C. L., Arnold, P. D., & Soreni, N. (2015). Three reasons why studying hoarding in children and adolescents is important. *Journal of the Canadian Academy of Child and Adolescent Psychiatry/Journal de l'Académie canadienne de psychiatrie de l'enfant et de l'adolescent, 24*, 128–130.

Butcher, J. N. (2010). Personality assessment from the nineteenth to the early twenty-first century: Past achievements and contemporary challenges. *Annual Review of Clinical Psychology, 6*, 1–20.

Butcher, J. N., Arbisi, P. A., Atlis, M. M., & McNulty, J. L. (2008). The construct validity of the Lees-Haley Fake Bad Scale: Does this scale measure somatic malingering and feigned emotional distress? *Archives of Clinical Neuropsychology, 23*, 855–864.

Butcher, J. N., Hass, G. A., Greene, R. L., & Nelson, L. D. (2015). Using the MMPI-2 in forensic assessment. Washington, DC: American Psychological Association.

Butcher, J. N., Nezami, E., & Exner, J. (1998). Psychological assessment of people in diverse cultures. In S. S. Kazarian and D. R. Evans (Eds.), *Cultural clinical psychology* (pp. 61–105). London: Oxford University Press.

Butler, A. C., Chapman, J. E., Forman, E. M., & Beck, A. T. (2006). The empirical status of cognitive behavior therapy: A review of meta-analyses. *Clinical Psychology Review, 26*, 17–31.

Butler, G., & Matthews, A. (1983). Cognitive processes in anxiety. *Advances in Behaviour Research and Therapy, 1*, 51–62.

Butler, L. D., Duran, R. E. F., Jasiukaitis, P., Koopman, C., & Spiegel, D. (1996). Hypnotizability and traumatic experience: A diathesis-stress model of dissociative symptomatology. *American Journal of Psychiatry, 153*, 42–63.

Butler, R. N. (1963). The life review: An interpretation of reminiscence in the aged. *Psychiatry, 119*, 721–728.

Byrd, A. L., & Manuck, S. B. (2014). *MAOA*, childhood maltreatment, and antisocial behavior: Meta-analysis of a gene-environment interaction. *Biological Psychiatry, 75*, 9–17.

Byrne, L. N., Avila, D., Seftel, A. D., Khera, M., & Parikh, P. T. (2011). Etiology and risk factors of erectile dysfunction. In K. T. McVary (Ed.), *Contemporary treatment of erectile dysfunction: A clinical guide* (pp. 51–67). New York: Springer.

Cacioppo, J. T., Cacioppo, S., Capitano, J. P., & Cole, S. W. (2015). The neuroendocrinology of social isolation. *Annual Review of Psychology, 66*, 733–767.

Cacioppo, J. T., Klein, D. J., Berntson, G. G., & Hatfield, E. (1993). The psychophysiology of emotion. In R. Lewis & J. M. Haviland (Eds.), *The handbook of emotion* (pp. 119–142). New York: Guilford.

Cadenhead, K. S., Perry, W., Shafer, K., & Braff, D. L. (1999). Cognitive functions in schizotypal personality disorder. *Schizophrenia Research, 37*, 123–132.

Cadoret, R. J., Yates, W. R., Troughton, E., Woodworth, G., & Stewart, M. A. (1995a). Adoption study demonstrating two genetic pathways to drug abuse. *Archives of General Psychiatry, 52*, 42–52.

Cadoret, R. J., Yates, W. R., Troughton, E., Woodworth, G., & Stewart, M. A. (1995b). Genetic-environment interaction in the genesis of aggressivity and conduct disorders. *Archives of General Psychiatry, 52*, 916–924.

Calero-Elvira, A., Krug, I., Lopez, C., et al. (2009). Meta-analysis on drugs in people with eating disorders. *European Eating Disorders Review, 17*, 243–259.

Calhoon, M. B. (2005). Effects of a peer-mediated phonological skill and reading comprehension program on reading skill acquisition for middle school students with reading disabilities. *Journal of Learning Disabilities, 38*, 424–435.

Calhoun, K. S., & Atkeson, B. M. (1991). *Treatment of rape victims: Facilitating psychosocial adjustment.* New York: Pergamon Press.

Cameron, D. J., Thomas, R. I., Mulvhill, M., & Bronheim, H. (1987). Delirium: A test of the Diagnostic and Statistical Manual III criteria on medical inpatients. *Journal of the American Geriatrics Society, 35*, 1007–1010.

Campbell, J., Stefan, S., & Loder, A. (1994). Putting violence in context. *Hospital and Community Psychiatry, 45*, 633.

Campbell, M. (2009, December 2). Attention, MLB: This is a testing program? 108 players permitted to use banned drugs because of ADHD. *Toronto Star.*

Campbell, M. A., French, S., & Gendreau, P. (2009). The prediction of violence in adult offenders: A meta-analytic comparison of instruments and methods of assessment. *Criminal Justice and Behavior, 36*, 567–590.

Campbell, M. A., Waller, G., & Pistrang, N. (2009). The impact of narcissism on drop-out from cognitive-behavioral therapy for the eating disorders: A pilot study. *The Journal of Nervous and Mental Disease, 197*, 278–281.

Campellone, T. R., Sanchez, A. H., & Kring, A. M. (in press). Defeatist performance beliefs, negative symptoms, and functional outcome in schizophrenia: A meta-analytic review. *Schizophrenia Bulletin.*

Camper, P. M., Jacobson, N. S., Holtzworth-Munroe, A., & Schmaling, K. B. (1988). Causal attributions for interactional behaviors in married couples. *Cognitive Therapy and Research, 12*, 195–209.

Canadian Association for Suicide Prevention. (2009). *The CASP blueprint for a Canadian National Suicide Prevention Strategy* (2nd ed.). Winnipeg, MB: Author.

Canadian Association on Gerontology (CAG). (1999). *Policy statement: Home care in Canada.* Ottawa: Author.

Canadian Association on Gerontology (CAG). (2000). *Position paper: Issues in the Canadian Association on Gerontology delivery of mental health services to older adults.* Toronto: Author.

Canadian Charter of Rights and Freedoms. (1982). Part I of the *Constitution Act, 1982*, being Schedule B to the *Canada Act 1982* (UK), 1982, c 11. Ottawa: Government of Canada.

Canadian Institute for Health Information. (2007). *Improving the health of Canadians: Mental health and homelessness.* Ottawa: Canadian Institute for Health Information.

Canadian Institute for Health Information. (2015, May). *Care for children and youth with mental disorders: Report.* Ottawa: Canadian Institute for Health Information.

Canadian Medical Association Journal (CMAJ). (2000). Alberta child abuse program swamped. *Canadian Medical Association Journal, 163*, 1492.

Canadian Medical Association Journal (CMAJ). (2001). Editorial: Look no strings: Publishing industry-funded research. *Canadian Medical Association Journal, 165*, 733.

Canadian Mental Health Association (CMHA). (2001, May 7). An astounding 91% of Canadians say maintaining mental health is very important, yet fewer Canadians willing to disclose receiving treatment (news release). Ottawa: Author.

Canadian Paediatric Society. (1998). Inhalant abuse: Position statement. *Paediatrics and Child Health, 3*, 123–126.

Canadian Panel on Violence Against Women. (1993). *Changing the landscape. Ending violence and achieving equality* (Catalogue No. SW45-1/1993E). Ottawa: Ministry of Supply and Services.

Canadian Pharmacists Association. (2004). *Final Report–Phase 1: Screening and managing medication problems in isolated, independent-living seniors.* Ottawa: Author.

Canadian Press. (2000). Ontario native suicide rate one of highest in world, expert says.

Canadian Press. (2006, August 16). Toronto physicist battling schizophrenia should be released, says doctor.

Canadian Psychological Association. (2000). *Canadian Code of Ethics* (3rd ed.). Ottawa: Author.

Canadian Psychological Association. (2002, December). *Psychology specific analysis of the Royal Commission on the Future of Health Care in Canada.* Ottawa: Canadian Psychological Association.

Canadian Psychological Association Psy.D. Task Force. (1998). Final Report to the Canadian Psychological Association Board of Directors November, 1998. Ottawa: Canadian Psychological Association.

Canadian Psychological Association Task Force. (2012). *Evidence-based practice of psychological treatments: A Canadian perspective.* Report of the CPA Task Force on Evidence-Based Practice of Psychological Treatments. Ottawa: Canadian Psychological Association.

Canadian Study of Health and Aging (CHSA) Working Group. (1994a). Canadian Study of Health and Aging: Study methods and prevalence of dementia. *Canadian Medical Association Journal, 150*, 899–913.

Canadian Study of Health and Aging (CSHA) Working Group. (1994b). Patterns of caring for people with dementia. *Canadian Journal on Aging, 13*, 470–487.

Canadian Study of Health and Aging (CSHA) Working Group. (2000). The incidence of dementia in Canada. *Neurology, 55*, 66–73.

Cane, D. B., Olinger, L., Gotlib, I. H., & Kuiper, N. A. (1986). Factor structure of the Dysfunctional Attitude Scale in a student population. *Journal of Clinical Psychology, 42*, 307–309.

Canetto, S. S. (2008). Women and suicidal behaviour: A cultural analysis. *American Journal of Orthopsychiatry, 78*, 259–266.

Canino, G., Polanczyk, G., Bauermeister, J. J., Rohde, L. A., & Frick, P. J. (2010). Does the prevalence of CD and ODD vary across cultures? *Social Psychiatry and Psychiatric Epidemiology, 45*, 695–704.

Cannon, T. D., & Mednick, S. A. (1993). The schizophrenia high-risk project in Copenhagen: Three decades of progress. *Acta Psychiatrica Scandanavica*, 33–47.

Cannon, T. D., Mednick, S. A., & Parnas, J. (1990). Antecedents of predominantly negative and predominantly positive-symptom schizophrenia in a high-risk population. *Archives of General Psychiatry, 47*, 622–632.

Canton-Cortes, D., & Canton, J. (2010). Coping with child sexual abuse among college students and post-traumatic stress disorder: The role of continuity of abuse and relationship with the perpetrator. *Child Abuse and Neglect, 34*, 496–506.

Cantor-Graae, E. (2007). The contribution of social factors to the development of schizophrenia: A review of recent findings. *Canadian Journal of Psychiatry, 52*, 277–286.

Cantwell, D. P., Baker, L., & Rutter, M. (1978). Family factors. In M. Rutter & E. Schopler (Eds.), *Autism: A reappraisal of concepts and treatment.* New York: Plenum.

Cao, X., Laplante, D. P., Brunet, A., Ciampi, A., & King, S. (2014). Prenatal maternal stress affects motor function in 5 1/2-year-old children: Project ice storm. *Developmental Psychobiology, 56*, 117–125.

Capano, L., Minden, D., Chen, S. X., et al. (2008). Mathematical learning disorder in school-age children with attention-deficit hyperactivity disorder. *Canadian Journal of Psychiatry, 53*, 392–399.

Capewell, S., & O'Flaherty, M. (2009). Trends in cardiovascular disease: Are we winning the war? *Canadian Medical Association Journal, 180*, 1285–1286.

Caplan, P. (1995). *They say you're crazy: How the world's most powerful psychiatrists decide who's normal.* Reading, MA: Addison-Wesley.

Cappadocia, M. C., Desrocher, M., Pepler, D., & Schroeder, J. H. (2009). Contextualizing the neurobiology of conduct disorder in an emotion dysregulation framework. *Clinical Psychology Review, 29,* 506–518.

Cappeliez, P. (1993). Depression in elderly persons: Prevalence, predictors, and psychological intervention. In P. Cappeliez & R. J. Flynn (Eds.), *Depression and the social environment: Research and intervention with neglected populations* (pp. 332–368). Montreal: McGill-Queen's University Press.

Cappeliez, P. (2000). Presentation of depression and response to group cognitive therapy with older patients. *Journal of Clinical Geropsychology, 6,* 165–174.

Cappeliez, P., & O'Rourke, N. (2006). Empirical validation of a model of reminiscence and health in later life. *The Journals of Gerontology Series B: Psychological Sciences and Social Sciences, 61,* P237–P244.

Capriotti, M. R., Ely, L. J., Snorrason, I., & Woods, D. W. (2015). Acceptance-enhanced behavior therapy for excoriation (skin-picking) disorder in adults: A clinical case series. *Cognitive and Behavioral Practice, 22,* 230–239.

Capron, A. M. (1999). Ethical and human rights issues in research on mental disorders that may affect decision-making capacity. *New England Journal of Medicine, 340,* 1430–1434.

Caravajal, S. C., Evans, R. I., Nash, S. G., & Getz, J. G. (2002). Global positive expectancies of the self and adolescents' substance use avoidance: Testing a social influence mediational model. *Journal of Personality, 70,* 421–442.

Cardena, E., & Gleaves, D. (2007). Dissociative disorders. In M. Hersen, S. M. Turner, & D. C. Beidel (Eds.), *Adult psychopathology and diagnosis* (pp. 473–503). New York: John Wiley & Sons.

Cardno, A. G., & Gottesman, I. I. (2000). Twin studies of schizophrenia: From bow-and-arrow concordances to Star Wars Mx and functional genomics. *American Journal of Medical Genetics, 97,* 12–17.

Carey, B. (2008, December 18). Psychiatrists revise the book of human troubles. *New York Times.*

Carey, B. (2011, June 23). Expert of mental illness reveals her own fight. *New York Times,* A1.

Carey, K. B., Scott-Sheldon, L. A. J., Elliott, J. C., Garey, L., & Carey, M. P. (2012). Face-to-face versus computer-delivered alcohol interventions for college drinkers: A meta-analytic review, 1998 to 2010. *Clinical Psychology Review, 32,* 690–703.

Carleton, R. N., Collimore, K. C., & Asmundson, G. J. G. (2007). Social anxiety and fear of negative evaluation: Construct validity of the BFNEII. *Journal of Anxiety Disorders, 21,* 131–141.

Carleton, R. N., Norton, M. A. P. J., & Asmundson, G. J. G. (2007). Fearing the unknown: A short version of the Intolerance of Uncertainty Scale. *Journal of Anxiety Disorders, 21,* 105–117.

Carlsson, A., Hanson, L. O., Waters, N., & Carlsson, M. L. (1999). A glutamatergic deficiency model of schizophrenia. *British Journal of Psychiatry, 174,* 2–6.

Carmel, A., Rose, M. L., & Fruzzetti, A. E. (2014). Barriers and solutions to implementing dialectical behavior therapy in a public behavioral health system. *Administration and Policy in Mental Health and Mental Health Systems Research, 41,* 608–614.

Carnelley, K. B., Pietromonaco, P. R., & Jaffe, K. (1994). Depression, working models of others and relationship functioning. *Journal of Personality and Social Psychology, 66,* 127–141.

Carnelley, K. B., Wortman, C. B., & Kessler, R. C. (1999). The impact of widowhood on depression: Findings from a prospective survey. *Psychological Medicine, 29,* 1111–1123.

Carnivez, G. L., & Watkins, M. W. (1998). Long-term stability of the Wechsler Intelligence Scale for Children—Third edition. *Psychological Assessment, 10,* 285–301.

Caron, J., Fleury, M.-J., Perrault, M., Crocker, A., et al. (2012). Prevalence of psychological distress and mental disorders, and use of mental health services in the epidemiological catchment area of Montreal South-West. *BMJ Psychiatry, 12,* 183.

Carpeggiani, C., & Skinner, J. E. (1991). Coronary flow and mental stress: Experimental findings. *Circulation, 83,* 90–93.

Carpenter, W. T., & Davis, J. M. (2012). Another view of the history of antipsychotic drug discovery and development. *Molecular Psychiatry, 17,* 1168–1173.

Carpenter, W. T., Heinrichs, D. W., & Wagman, A. M. I. (1988). Deficit and nondeficit forms of schizophrenia: The concept. *American Journal of Psychiatry, 145,* 578–583.

Carpentieri, S. C., & Morgan, S. B. (1994). Brief report: A comparison of patterns of cognitive functioning of autistic and nonautistic retarded children on the Stanford-Binet, 4th ed. *Journal of Autism and Developmental Disorders, 24,* 215–223.

Carrière, G. (2003). Seniors use of home care. *Health Reports, 17,* 43–47.

Carroll, K. M., Rounsaville, B. J., Gordon, L. T., et al. (1994). Psychotherapy and pharmacotherapy for ambulatory cocaine abusers. *Archives of General Psychiatry, 51,* 177–187.

Carroll, K. M., Rounsaville, B. J., Nich, C., Gordon, L. T., & Gawin, F. (1995). Integrating psychotherapy and pharmacotherapy for cocaine dependence: Results from a randomized clinical trial. In L. S. Onken, J. D. Blaine, & J. J. Boren (Eds.), *Integrating behavioral therapies with medications in the treatment of drug dependence* (pp. 19–36). Rockville, MD: National Institute on Drug Abuse.

Carroll, K. M., Rounsaville, B. J., Nich, C., Gordon, L. T., Wirtz, P. W., & Gawin, F. (1994). One-year follow-up of psychotherapy and pharmacotherapy for cocaine dependence. *Archives of General Psychiatry, 51,* 989–997.

Carstensen, L. L. (1996). Evidence for a life-span theory of socioemotional selectivity. *Current Directions in Psychological Science, 4,* 151–156.

Carter v. Canada (Attorney General), 2015 SCC 5, [2015] 1 S.C.R. 331.

Carter, F. A., Jordan, J., McIntosh, V. V. W., & Luty, S. E. (2011). The long-term efficacy of three psychotherapies for anorexia nervosa: A randomized, controlled trial. *International Journal of Eating Disorders, 44,* 647–654.

Carter, J. C., et al. (2009). Maintenance treatment for anorexia nervosa: A comparison of cognitive behavior therapy and treatment as usual. *International Journal of Eating Disorders, 42,* 202–207.

Carter, J. C., Mercer-Lynn, K. B., Norwood, S. J., et al. (2012). A prospective study of predictors of relapse in anorexia nervosa: Implications for response prevention. *Psychiatry Research, 200,* 518–523.

Carter, M. M., Forys, K. K., & Oswald, J. C. (2008). The cognitive-behavioral model. In M. Hersen & A. G. Gross (Eds.), *Handbook of clinical psychology, Volume 1, adults* (pp. 171–201). New York: Wiley.

Cartwright-Hatton, S., McNicol, K., & Doubleday, E. (2006). Anxiety in a neglected population: Prevalence of anxiety disorders in preadolescent children. *Clinical Psychology Review, 26,* 817–833.

Casey, J. E., Rourke, B. P., & Del Dotto, J. E. (1996). Learning disabilities in children with attention deficit disorder with and without hyperactivity. *Child Neuropsychology, 2,* 83–98.

Cashman, J. A. (1966). *The LSD story.* Greenwich, CT: Fawcett.

Caspi, A., McClay, J., et al. (2002). Role of genotype in the cycle of violence of maltreated children. *Science, 297,* 851–854.

Caspi, A., Sugden, K., Moffitt, T. E., Taylor, A., Craig, I. W., Harrington, H., … Poulton, R. (2003). Influence of life stress on depression:

Moderation by a polymorphism in the 5-HTT gene. *Science, 301,* 386–389.

Cassady, J. D., et al. (2005). Case series: Outbreak of conversion disorder among Amish adolescent girls. *Journal of the American Academy of Child and Adolescent Psychiatry, 44,* 291–297.

Cassidy, E. L., Atherton, R. J., Robertson, N., Walsh, D. A., & Gillett, R. (2012). Mindfulness, functioning, and catastrophizing after multidisciplinary pain management for chronic low back pain. *Pain, 153,* 644–650.

Castellanos, F. X., & Tannock, R. (2002). Neuro-science of attention-deficit/hyperactivity disorder: the search for endophenotypes. *Nature Reviews Neuroscience, 3,* 617–628.

Castonguay, L. G., Eubanks, C. F., Goldfried, M. R., Muran, J. C., & Lutz, W. (2015). Research on psychotherapy integration: Building on the past, looking to the future. *Psychotherapy Research, 25,* 365–382.

Castro-Schilo, L., & Ferrer, E. (2013). Comparison of nomothetic versus idiographic-oriented methods for making predictions about distal outcomes from time series data. *Multivariate Behavioral Research, 48,* 175–207.

Cautela, J. R. (1966). Treatment of compulsive behavior by covert sensitization. *Psychological Record, 16,* 33–41.

CBC News. (2000, November 10). Woman suing diet pill maker over deadly accident. CBCnews.ca.

CBC News. (2013, April 18). ADHD meds appear on Winnipeg campuses as "study drugs." CBCNews.ca.

CBC News. (2014, November 27). The psychopath next door, *Doc Zone.* Toronto: Canadian Broadcasting Corporation.

CBC News. (2015, July 16). PTSD diagnoses nearly triple among veterans in 8 years. CBCNews.ca.

Cecil, S. (2007, February 19). McMaster doctor plays lead role in autism gene research. *McMaster University Daily News.*

Centre for Addiction and Mental Health (CAMH). (2000). CAMH Best advice paper: Community treatment orders: Overview and recommendations. Toronto: Author.

Centre for Equality of Rights in Accommodation (CERA). (2009). *Sorry, it's rented: Measuring discrimination in Toronto's rental housing market.* Toronto: Author.

Centre for Research and Education on Violence Among Women and Children. (2010). *Confronting the many faces of child sexual abuse: Developing a comprehensive national prevention strategy.* London, ON: University of Western Ontario.

Chai, C. T. (2006). Treading a thin line. *Visions: BC's Mental Health and Addiction Journal, 3,* 11–12.

Chaiken, S., & Pliner, P. (1987). Women, but not men, are what they eat: The effects of meal size and gender on perceived femininity and masculinity. *Personality and Social Psychology Bulletin, 13,* 166–176.

Chaimowitz, G. A. (2004). Community treatment orders: An uncertain step. *Canadian Journal of Psychiatry, 49,* 577–578.

Chaimowitz, G. A., & Glancy, G. (2002). The duty to protect. Ottawa: Canadian Psychiatric Association.

Chaimowitz, G. A., Glancy, G. D., & Blackburn, J., (2000). The duty to warn and protect—Impact on practice. *Canadian Journal of Psychiatry, 45,* 899–904.

Chalder, M., Elgar, F. J., & Bennett, P. (2006). Drinking and motivations to drink among adolescent children of parents with alcohol problems. *Alcohol and Alcoholism, 41,* 107–113.

Chamberlain, E. A. L., & Solomon, R. M. (2008). Minimizing impairment-related youth traffic deaths: The need for comprehensive provincial action. *Canadian Journal of Public Health, 99,* 267–270.

Chambless, D. L., & Ollendick, T. H. (2001). Empirically supported psychological interventions: Controversies and evidence. *Annual Review of Psychology, 52,* 685–716.

Chambless, D. L., Sanderson, W. C., Shoham, V., Johnson, S. B., Pope, K. S., et al. (1996). An update on empirically validated therapies. *The Clinical Psychologist, 49,* 5–18.

Chandler, M. J., & Lalonde, C. (1998). Cultural continuity as a hedge against suicide in Canada's First Nations. *Transcultural Psychiatry, 35,* 191–220.

Chang, S. (2011, June 23). Cory Monteith reveals harrowing past drug abuse. *Enquirer.*

Chapman, L. J., & Chapman, J. P. (1969). Illusory correlation as an obstacle to the use of valid psychodiagnostic signs. *Journal of Abnormal Psychology, 74,* 271–287.

Chappell, N. L., & Dujela, C. (2008). Caregiving: Predicting at-risk status. *Canadian Journal on Aging, 27,* 169–179.

Chappell, N. L., & Funk, L. M. (2011). Social support, caregiving, and aging. *Canadian Journal on Aging, 30,* 355–370.

Chappell, N. L., & Penning, M. (1996). Behavioural problems and distress among caregivers of people with dementia. *Ageing and Society, 16,* 57–73.

Chappell, N. L., & Reid, R. C. (2002). Burden and well-being among caregivers. *Gerontologist, 42,* 772–780.

Charbonneau, J., & O'Connor, K. (1999). Depersonalization in a non-clinical sample. *Behavioral and Cognitive Psychotherapy, 27,* 377–381.

Charette, Y., Crocker, A. G., Seto, M. C., Salem, L., Nicholls, T. L., & Caulet, M. (2015). The National Trajectory Project of individuals found not criminally responsible on account of mental disorder in Canada. Part 4: Criminal recidivism. *Canadian Journal of Psychiatry, 60,* 127–134.

Charland, L. C. (2007). Benevolent theory: Moral treatment at the York Retreat. *History of Psychiatry, 18,* 61–80.

Charland, L. C. (2010). Science and morals in the affective psychopathology of Philippe Pinel. *History of Psychiatry, 21,* 385–451.

Charlesworth, A., & Glantz, S. A. (2005). Smoking in the movies increases adolescent smoking: A review. *Pediatrics, 116,* 1516–1528.

CHARLS Research Team. (2013). *Challenges of population aging in China: Evidence from the national baseline survey of the China Health and Retirement Longitudinal Study (CHARLS).* Retrieved from online. wsj.com/public/resources/documents/charls0530.pdf.

Charney, D. S., Woods, S. W., Goodman, W. K., & Heninger, G. R. (1987). Neurobiological mechanisms of panic anxiety: Biochemical and behavioral correlates of yohimbine-induced panic attacks. *American Journal of Psychiatry, 144,* 1030–1036.

Chartier, M. J., Walker, J. R., & Stein, M. B. (2003). Considering comorbidity in social phobia. *Social Psychiatry and Psychiatric Epidemiology, 38,* 728–734.

Chassin, L., Curran, P. J., Hussong, A. M., & Colder, C. R. (1996). The relation of parent alcoholism to adolescent substance abuse: A longitudinal follow-up. *Journal of Abnormal Psychology, 105,* 70–80.

Chen, E. (2007). Impact of socioeconomic status on physiological health in adolescents: An experimental manipulation of psychosocial factors. *Psychosomatic Medicine, 69,* 348–355.

Chen, E., Chim, L. S., Strunk, R. C., & Miller, G. E. (2007). The role of the social environment in children and adolescents with asthma. *American Journal of Respiratory and Critical Care Medicine, 176,* 644–649.

Chen, E., & Miller, G. E. (2013). Socioeconomic status and health: Mediating and moderating factors. *Annual Review of Clinical Psychology, 9,* 8.1–8.28.

Chen, I. (2009, November 19). The court will now call its expert witness: The brain. *Stanford University News.*

Chen, W. J., Liu, S. K., Chang, C.-G., Lien, Y.-J., et al. (1998). Sustained attention deficit and schizotypal personality features in nonpsychotic relatives of schizophrenic patients. *American Journal of Psychiatry, 155*, 1214–1220.

Chen, Y., Nettles, M. E., & Chen, S.-W. (2009). Rethinking dependent personality disorder: Comparing different human relatedness in cultural contexts. *The Journal of Nervous and Mental Disease, 197*, 793–800.

Cherian, A. V., Pandian, D., Math, S. B., Kandavel, T., & Reddy, Y. C. J. (2014). Family accommodation of obsessional symptoms and naturalistic outcome of obsessional–compulsive disorder. *Psychiatry Research, 215*, 372–378.

Chesser, M. (2009, September 9). Vancouver's drug dilemma. *McGill Tribune.*

Cheung, A. H., & Dewa, C. S. (2007). Mental health service use among adolescents and young adults with major depressive disorder and suicidality. *Canadian Journal of Psychiatry, 52*, 228–232.

Chew, B. H., Pace, K. T., & Honey, J. D'A. (2002). Munchausen syndrome presenting as gross hematuria in two women. *Urology, 59*, 601i–601iii.

Chida, Y., & Steptoe, A. (2009). The association of anger and hostility with future coronary heart disease: A meta-analytic review of prospective evidence. *Journal of the American College of Cardiology, 53*, 936–946.

Chiose, S. (2016, September 12). UBC response to sexual assaults questioned. *The Globe and Mail*, A4.

Chisuwa, N., & O'Dea, J. A. (2010). Body image and eating disorders amongst Japanese adolescents: A review of the literature. *Appetite, 54*, 5–15.

Chiu, T., et al. (2009). Internet-based caregiver support for Chinese Canadians taking care of a family member with Alzheimer's Disease and related dementia. *Canadian Journal of Aging, 28*, 323–336.

Chivers, M. L. (2008, March). Sex and sexual orientation differences in the specificity of sexual arousal. Presented at the 33rd annual meeting of the Society for Sex Therapy and Research (SSTAR), Chicago, IL.

Chivers, M. L., Seto, M. C., Lalumière, M. L., Laan, E., & Grimbos, T. (2010). Agreement of self-reported and genital measures of sexual arousal in men and women: A meta-analysis. *Archives of Sexual Behavior, 39*, 5–56.

Chobanian, A. V., et al. (2003). The Seventh Report of the Joint National Committee on prevention, detection, evaluation, and treatment of high blood pressure. *Journal of the American Medical Association, 289*, 2560–2572.

Chouinard, G., Jones, B., Remington, G., Bloom, D., Addington, D., MacEwan, G. W., et al. (1993). A Canadian multicentre placebo-controlled study of fixed doses of risperidone and haloperidol in the treatment of chronic schizophrenia patients. *Journal of Clinical Psychopharmacology, 13*, 25–40.

Chow, B. W.-Y., Ho, C. S.-H., Wong, S. W.-L., Waye, M. Y. M., & Bishop, D. M. V. (2013). Generalist genes and cognitive abilities in Chinese twins. *Developmental Science, 16*, 260–268.

Chow, E. W., & Choy, A. L. (2002). Clinical characteristics and treatment response to SSRI in a female pedophile. *Archives of Sexual Behavior, 31*, 211–215.

Chow, W. (2013, January 15–16). Hoarder rescued after being trapped under clutter. *Burnaby Newsleader.*

Choy, Y., Fyer, A., & Lipsitz, J. D. (2007). Treatment of specific phobia in adults. *Clinical Psychology Review, 27*, 266–286.

Choy, Y., Schneier, F. R., Heimberg, R. G., Oh, K.-S., & Liebowitz, M. R. (2008). Features of the offensive subtype of Taijin-Kyofu-Sho in US and Korean patients with DSM-IV social anxiety disorder. *Depression and Anxiety, 25*, 230–240.

Christenfeld, N., Gerin, W., Linden, W., Sanders, M., Mathur, J., Deich, J. D., & Pickering, T. G. (1997). Social support effects on cardiovascular reactivity: Is a stranger as effective as a friend? *Psychosomatic Medicine, 59*, 388–398.

Christensen, A., et al. (2004). Traditional versus integrative behavioral couple therapy for significantly and chronically distressed married couples. *Journal of Consulting and Clinical Psychology, 72*, 176–191.

Christensen, A., Atkins, D. C., Baucom, B., & Yi, J. (2010). Marital status and satisfaction five years following a randomized clinical trial comparing traditional versus integrative behavioral couple therapy. *Journal of Consulting and Clinical Psychology, 78*, 225–235.

Christensen, A., & Heavey, C. L. (1990). Gender and social structure in the demand/withdraw pattern of marital conflict. *Journal of Personality and Social Psychology, 59*, 73–81.

Christensen, A., Jacobson, N. S., & Babcock, J. C. (1995). Integrative behavioral couples therapy. In N. S. Jacobson & A. S. Gurman (Eds.), *Clinical handbook of couples therapy* (pp. 31–64). New York: Guilford.

Christensen, A., & Pasch, L. (1993). The sequence of marital conflict: An analysis of seven phases of marital conflict in distressed and non-distressed couples. *Clinical Psychology Review, 13*, 3–14.

Christian, M. A. (2008, May 19). Former football star tells of life with mental illness; "I'm not crazy." *Jet, 113(19)*, 16–17.

Christiansen, P., & Field, M. (2013). Implicit cognition. In J. MacKillop & H. de Wit (Eds.), *The Wiley-Blackwell handbook of addiction pharmacology* (pp. 489–514). New York: Wiley-Blackwell.

Christie, A. B. (1982). Changing patterns in mental illness in the elderly. *British Journal of Psychiatry, 140*, 154–159.

Chu, J. A. (2006). Guidelines for treating dissociative identity disorder in adults. *Journal of Trauma and Dissociation, 6*, 69–149.

Chung, A. (2012, August 9). Children as young as 5 seek eating disorder treatment: Doctor. Postmedia News.

Churchill, R., Owen, G., Singh, S., & Hotopf, M. (2007). *International experiences of using community treatment orders.* London: Department of Health and Institute of Psychiatry.

Cicchetti, D. (1984). The emergence of developmental psychopathology. *Child Development, 55*, 1–7.

Cicchetti, D., & Toth, S. L. (2009). The past achievements and future promises of developmental psychopathology: The coming of age of a discipline. *Journal of Child Psychology and Psychiatry, 50*, 16–25.

Claassen, C. A., et al. (2007). Clinical differences among depressed patients with and without a history of suicide attempts: Findings from the STAR*D trial. *Journal of Affective Disorders, 97*, 77–84.

Clark, C. C. (1985). *Report of the Electro-Convulsive Therapy Review Committee.* Toronto: Ontario Ministry of Health.

Clark, D. A., Beck, A. T., & Alford, B. A. (1999). *Scientific foundations of cognitive theory and therapy of depression.* New York: John Wiley & Sons.

Clark, D. A., & Oates, T. (1995). Daily hassles, major and minor life events, and their interaction with sociotropy and autonomy. *Behaviour Research and Therapy, 33*, 819–823.

Clark, D. A., Purdon, C., & Wang, A. (2003). The Meta-Cognitive Beliefs Questionnaire: Development of a measure of obsessional beliefs. *Behaviour Research and Therapy, 41*, 655–659.

Clark, D. A., Steer, R. A., Beck, A. T., & Ross, L. (1995). Psychometric characteristics of revised sociotropy and autonomy scales in college students. *Behaviour Research and Therapy, 33*, 325–334.

Clark, D. M. (2001). A cognitive perspective on social phobia. In R. W. Crozier & L. E. Alden (Eds.), *International handbook of social anxiety:*

Concepts, research, and interventions relating to the self and shyness (pp. 405–430). New York: John Wiley & Sons.

Clark, D. M., Ehlers, A., Hackmann, A., McManus, F., Fennel, M., Grey, N., ... Wild, J. (2006). Cognitive therapy versus exposure and applied relaxation in social phobia: A randomized controlled trial. *Journal of Consulting and Clinical Psychology, 74*, 568–578.

Clark, D. M., & Wells, A. (1995). A cognitive model of social phobia. In R. G. Heimberg, M. R. Liebowitz, D. A. Hope, & F. R. Schneier (Eds.), *Social phobia: Diagnosis, assessment, and treatment* (pp. 69–93). New York: Guilford.

Clark, L. A. (2005). Stability and change in personality pathology: Revelations of three longitudinal studies. *Journal of Personality Disorders, 19*, 524–532.

Clark, S. K., Jeglic, E. L., Calkins, C., & Tartar, J. R. (2016). More than a nuisance: The prevalence and consequences of frotteurism and exhibitionism. *Sexual Abuse: A Journal of Research and Treatment, 28*, 3–19.

Clarke, P. M., Murnen, S. K., & Smolak, L. (2010). Development and psychometric evaluation of a quantitative measure of "fat talk." *Body Image, 7*, 1–7.

Clarke-Stewart, A., & Apfel, N. (1979). Evaluating parental effects on child development. In L. S. Shulman (Ed.), *Review of research in education* (Vol. 6, pp. 47–119). Ithasca, IL: Peacock.

Clarkin, J. F., Levy, K. N., Lenzenweger, M. F., & Kernberg, O. F. (2007). Evaluating three treatments for borderline personality disorder: A multiwave study. *American Journal of Psychiatry, 164*, 922–928.

Classen, C. C., Palesh, O. G., & Aggarwal, R. (2005). Sexual revictimization: A review of the empirical literature. *Trauma, Violence, and Abuse, 6*, 103–129.

Cleckley, H. (1976). *The mask of sanity* (5th ed.). St. Louis, MO: Mosby.

Cleverley, K., Bennett, K., & Duku, E. (2013). Effects of functional impairment on internalizing symptom trajectories in adolescence: A longitudinal, growth curve modelling study. *Journal of Adolescence, 36*, 45–53.

Clough, B. A., & Casey, L. M. (2011). Technological adjuncts to enhance current psychotherapy practices: A review. *Clinical Psychology Review, 31*, 279–292.

CME Institute. (2007). Academic highlights: New developments in the treatment of schizophrenia. *Journal of Clinical Psychiatry, 68*, 463–478.

CNN. (2008, February 6). Britney Spears released from psychiatric hospital; cause of Heath Ledger's death finally known.

Cockell, S. J., Hewitt, P. L., Seal, B., Sherry, S. B., Goldner, E. M., Flett, G. L., & Remick, R. A. (2002). Trait and self-presentational dimensions of perfectionism among women with anorexia nervosa. *Cognitive Therapy and Research, 26*, 745–758.

Cody, M. J., Dunn, D., Hoppin, S., & Wendt, P. (1999). Silver surfers: Training and evaluating Internet use among older adult learners. *Communication Education, 48*, 269–286.

Coghill, D. R., Nigg, J. T., Rothenberger, A., Sonuga-Barke, E. J. S., & Tannock, R. (2005). Whither causal models in the neuroscience of ADHD. *Developmental Science, 8*, 105–114.

Cohen, A., Patel, V., & Minas, H. (2014). A brief history of global mental health. In V. Patel, H. Minas, A. Cohen, & M. J. Prince (Eds.), *Global mental health principles and practice* (pp. 3–26). Oxford: Oxford University Press.

Cohen, N. J., Davine, M., Horodezky, N., Lipsett, L., & Isaacson, L. (1993). Unsuspected language impairment in psychiatrically disturbed children: Prevalence and language and behavioral characteristics. *Journal of the American Academy of Child and Adolescent Psychiatry, 32*, 595–603.

Cohen, N. J., Vallance, D. D., Barwick, M., Im, N., Menna, R., Horodezky, N. B., et al. (2000). The interface between ADHD and language impairment: An examination of language, achievement, and cognitive processing. *Journal of Child Psychology and Psychiatry, 41*, 353–362.

Cohen, S., Alper, C. M., Doyle, W. J., Treanor, T. J., & Turner, R. B. (2006). Positive emotional style predicts resistance to illness after experimental exposure to rhinovirus or influenza A virus. *Psychosomatic Medicine, 68*, 809–815.

Cohen, S., & Herbert, T. B. (1996). Health psychology: Psychological factors and physical disease from the perspective of human psychoneuroimmunology. In J. T. Spence, J. M. Darley, & D. J. Foss (Eds.), *Annual review of psychology* (pp. 123–142). Stanford, CA: Stanford University Press.

Cohen, S., O'Leary, K. D., & Foran, H. (2010). A randomized clinical trial of a brief, problem-focused couple therapy for depression. *Behavior Therapy, 41*(4), 433–446.

Cohen, S., Tyrell, D. A. J., & Smith, A. P. (1991). Psychological stress and susceptibility to the common cold. *New England Journal of Medicine, 325*, 606–612.

Cohen, S., & Wills, T. A. (1985). Stress, social support, and the buffering process. *Psychological Bulletin, 98*, 310–357.

Colapinto, J. (1997). The true story of Joan/John. *Rolling Stone*, 55–97.

Colapinto, J. (2000). *As nature made him: The boy who was raised as a girl.* Toronto: Harper Collins.

Colapinto, J. (2004, June 3). Gender gap: What were the real reasons behind David Reimer's suicide? *Slate.*

Coldwell, C. M., & Bender, W. S. (2007). The effectiveness of assertive community treatment for homeless populations with severe mental illness: A meta-analysis. *American Journal of Psychiatry, 164*, 393–399.

Cole, D. A., Martin, J. M., Powers, B., & Truglio, R. (1990). Modeling causal relations between academic and social competence and depression: A multitrait-multimethod longitudinal study of children. *Journal of Abnormal Psychology, 105*, 258–270.

Cole, J. C., Bernacki, C. G., Helmer, A., Pinnitti, N., & O'Reardon, J. P. (2015). Efficacy of transcranial magnetic stimulation (TMS) in the treatment of schizophrenia: A review of the literature to date. *Innovations in Clinical Neuroscience, 12*, 12–19.

Cole, M. G., & Bellavance, F. (1997). The prognosis of depression in old age. *American Journal of Geriatric Psychiatry, 5*, 4–14.

Cole, M. G., Bellavance, F., & Mansour, A. (1999). Prognosis of depression in elderly community and primary care populations: A systematic review and meta-analysis. *American Journal of Psychiatry, 156*, 1182–1189.

Cole, M. G., & Dendukuri, N. (2003). Risk factors for depression among elderly community subjects: A systematic review and meta-analysis. *American Journal of Psychiatry, 160*, 1147–1156.

Coles, M., Schubert, J. R., Heimberg, R. G., & Weiss, B. D. (2014). Disseminating treatment for anxiety disorders: Step 1: Recognizing the problem as a precursor to seeking help. *Journal of Anxiety Disorders, 28*, 737–740.

Collaborative Outcome Data Committee (CODC). (2007). *Sexual offender treatment outcome research: CODC guidelines for evaluation.* Ottawa: Government of Canada.

Collier, R. (2009). Canadian Institutes of Health Research proposes major initiative on Alzheimer disease in step forward toward national dementia strategy. *Canadian Medical Association Journal, 181*, E36–E37.

Collins, A. (1988). *In the sleep room: The story of the CIA brainwashing experiments in Canada.* Toronto: Lester and Orpen Dennys Limited.

Collins, K. A., & Dozois, D. J. A. (2008). What are the active ingredients in preventative interventions for depression? *Clinical Psychology: Science and Practice, 15*, 313–330.

Colman, I., Wadsworth, M. E. J., Coudace, T. J., & Jones, P. B. (2007). Forty-year psychiatric outcomes following assessment for internalizing disorder in adolescence. *American Journal of Psychiatry, 164*, 126–133.

Compas, B. E., Haaga, D. A. F., Keefe, F. J., Leitenberg, H., & Williams, D. A. (1998). Sampling of empirically supported psychological treatments from health psychology: Smoking, chronic pain, cancer, and bulimia nervosa. *Journal of Consulting and Clinical Psychology, 66*, 89–112.

Compton, D. R., Dewey, W. L., & Martin, B. R. (1990). Cannabis dependence and tolerance production. *Advances in Alcohol and Substance Abuse, 9*, 129–147.

Condefer, K. A., Haworth, J., & Wilcock, G. K. (2004). Clinical utility of computed tomography in the assessment of dementia: A memory clinic study. *International Journal of Geriatric Psychiatry, 19*, 414–421.

Conley, R. R., et al. (2007). The burden of depressive symptoms in the long-term treatment of patients with schizophrenia. *Schizophrenia Research, 90*, 186–197.

Conley, R. R., Tamminga, C. A., Kelly, D. L., & Richardson, C. M. (1999). Treatment-resistant schizophrenic patients respond to clozapine after olanzapine non-response. *Biological Psychiatry, 46*, 73–77.

Connan, F., & Stanley, S. (2003). Biology of appetite and weight regulation. In J. Treasure, U. Schmidt, & E. van Furth (Eds.), *Handbook of eating disorders* (2nd ed., pp. 63–87). Chichester, England: John Wiley & Sons.

Conrod, P. J., Pihl, R. O., Stewart, S. H., & Dongier, M. (2000). Validation of a system of classifying female substance abusers on the basis of personality and motivational risk factors for substance abuse. *Psychology of Addictive Behaviors, 14*, 243–256.

Constantino, M. J. (2012). Believing is seeing: An evolving research program on patients' psychotherapy expectations. *Psychotherapy Research, 22*, 127–138.

Constantino, M. J., Ametrano, R. M., & Greenberg, R. P. (2012). Clinician interventions and participant characteristics that foster adaptive patient expectations for psychotherapy and psychotherapeutic change. *Psychotherapy, 49*, 557–569.

Constantino, M. J., Morrison, N. R., MacEwan, G., & Boswell, J. F. (2013). Therapeutic alliance researchers' perspectives on alliance-centered training practices. *Journal of Psychotherapy Integration, 23*, 284–289.

Constantino, M. J., Penek, S., Berenecker, S. L., & Overtree, C. E. (2014). A preliminary examination of participant characteristics in relation to patients' treatment beliefs in psychotherapy in a training clinic. *Journal of Psychotherapy Integration, 24*, 238–250.

Conwell, Y. (2001). Suicide in later life: A review and recommendations for prevention. *Suicide and Life-Threatening Behavior, 31*, 32–47.

Cook, J. M., Biyanova, T., & Coyne, J. (2009) Influential psychotherapy figures, authors, and books: an internet survey of over 2,000 psychotherapists. *Psychotherapy Theory, Research, Practice, Training, 46*, 42–51.

Cook, M., & Mineka, S. (1989). Observational conditioning of fear to fear-relevant versus fear-irrelevant stimuli in rhesus monkeys. *Journal of Abnormal Psychology, 98*, 448–459.

Cook, N. E., Barese, T. H., & Dicataldo, F. (2010). The confluence of mental health and psychopathic traits in adolescent female offenders. *Criminal Justice and Behavior, 37*, 119–136.

Coolidge, F. L., & Segal, D. L. (1998). Evolution of personality disorder diagnosis in the Diagnostic and Statistical Manual of Mental Disorders. *Clinical Psychology Review, 18*, 585–589.

Coons, P. M., & Milstein, V. (1992). Psychogenic amnesia: A clinical investigation of 25 cases. *Dissociation: Progress in the Dissociative Disorders, 5*, 73–79.

Coons, W. H. (1967). The dynamics of change in psychotherapy. *Canadian Psychiatric Association Journal, 12*, 239–245.

Coons, W. H., & Peacock, T. P. (1970). Interpersonal interaction and personality change in group psychotherapy. *Canadian Psychiatric Association Journal, 15*, 347–355.

Cooper, J. E., et al. (1972). *Psychiatric diagnosis in New York and London*. London: Oxford University Press.

Cooper, L. D., Balsis, S., & Oltmanns, T. F. (2012). Self- and informant-reported perspectives on symptoms of narcissistic personality disorder. *Personality Disorders, 3*, 140–154.

Cooper, M., Corrado, R., Karlberg, A. M., & Adams, L. P. (1992). Aboriginal suicide in British Columbia: An overview. *Canada's Mental Health, 40*, 19–23.

Cooper, M. L. (1994). Motivations for alcohol use among adolescents: Development and validation of a four-factor model. *Psychological Assessment, 6*, 117–128.

Copeland, W. E., Angold, A., Costello, E. J., & Egger, H. (2013). Prevalence, comorbidity, and correlates of *DSM-5* proposed disruptive mood dysregulation disorder. *American Journal of Psychiatry, 170*, 173–179.

Corbitt, E. M., & Widiger, T. A. (1995). Sex differences among the personality disorders: An exploration of the data. *Clinical Psychology: Science and Practice, 2*, 225–238.

Cordova, J. V., & Jacobson, N. S. (1993). Couple distress. In D. H. Barlow (Ed.), *Clinical handbook of psychological disorders* (2nd ed., pp. 461–512). New York: Guilford.

Cornblatt, B., & Erlenmeyer-Kimling, L. E. (1985). Global attentional deviance in children at risk for schizophrenia: Specificity and predictive validity. *Journal of Abnormal Psychology, 94*, 470–486.

Corning, A. F., & Gondoli, D. M. (2012). Who is most likely to fat talk? A social comparison perspective. *Body Image, 9*, 528–531.

Corona, G., Rastrelli, G., Limoncin, E., Sforza, A., Jannini, E. A. & Maggi, M. (2015). Interplay between premature ejaculation and erectile dysfunction: A systematic review and meta-analysis. *The Journal of Sexual Medicine, 12*, 2291–2300.

Correa, D. D., Graves, R. E., & Costa, L. (1996). Awareness of memory deficit in Alzheimer's disease patients and memory-impaired older adults. *Aging, Neuropsychology, and Cognition, 3*, 215–228.

Correctional Investigator Canada. (2012). *Annual report of the Office of the Correctional Investigator 2011–2012*. Ottawa: The Correctional Services of Canada for Her Majesty the Queen in Right of Canada.

Corrieri, S., Heider, D., Conrad, I., Blume, A., et al. (2014). School-based prevention programs for depression and anxiety in adolescence: A systematic review. *Health Promotion International, 29*, 427–441.

Corrigan, P. W., Druss, B. G., & Perlick, D. A. (2014). The impact of mental illness stigma on seeking and participating in mental health care. *Psychological Science in the Public Interest, 15*, 37–70.

Corsi, D. J., Lear, S. A., Chow, C. K., et al. (2013). Socioeconomic and geographic patterning of smoking behaviour in Canada: A cross-sectional multilevel analysis. *PLoS One, 8*, e57646.

Cortoni, F. A., & Marshall, W. L. (2001). Sex as a coping strategy and its relationship to juvenile sexual history and intimacy in sexual offenders. *Sexual Abuse: A Journal of Research and Treatment, 13*(1), 27–43.

Coryell, W., Leon, A., Winokur, G., et al. (1996). Importance of psychotic features to long-term course in major depressive disorder. *American Journal of Psychiatry, 153,* 483–489.

Costa, L. (1996). Lifespan neuropsychology. *The Clinical Neuropsychologist, 10,* 365–374.

Costello, C. G. (1982). Fears and phobias in women: A community survey. *Journal of Abnormal Psychology, 91,* 280–286.

Costello, E. J., Egger, H. L., Copeland, W., Erkanli, A., & Angold, A. (2011). The developmental epidemiology of anxiety disorders: Phenomenology, prevalence, and comorbidity. In W. K. Silverman & A. P. Field (Eds.), *Anxiety disorders in children and adolescents* (2nd ed., pp. 56–75). Cambridge, UK: Cambridge University Press.

Costello, E. J., He, J.-P., Sampson, N. A., Kessler, R. C., & Merikangas, K. R. (2014). Services for adolescent psychiatric disorders: 12-month data from the National Comorbidity Survey-Adolescent. *Psychiatric Services, 65,* 359–366.

Costello, M. J., Sproule, B., Victor, J. C., Leatherdale, S. T., Zawertailo, L., & Selby, P. (2011). Effectiveness of pharmacist counselling combined with nicotine replacement therapy: A pragmatic randomized trial with 6,987 smokers. *Cancer Causes and Control, 22,* 167–180.

Côté, S., & Bouchard, S. (2008). Virtual reality exposure for phobias: A critical review. *Journal of Cybertherapy and Rehabilitation, 1,* 75–91.

Côté, S. M., Boivin, M., Liu, X., et al. (2009). Depression and anxiety symptoms: Onset, developmental course and risk factors during early childhood. *Journal of Child Psychology and Psychiatry, 50,* 1201–1208.

Côté, S. M., Vaillancourt, T., LeBlanc, J. C., Nagin, D. S., & Tremblay, R. E. (2006). The development of physical aggression from toddlerhood to pre-adolescence: A nationwide longitudinal study of Canadian children. *Journal of Abnormal Child Psychology, 34,* 71–85.

County of Los Angeles. (2012). Case report for Whitney Elisebeth Houston. Los Angeles: Department of Coroner.

Courbasson, C. M. A., Smith, P. D., & Cleland, P. A. (2005). Substance use disorders, anorexia, bulimia, and concurrent disorders. *Canadian Journal of Public Health, 96,* 102–106.

Courbasson, C. M. A., & Schelkanova, I. (in press). Women and addictions: Body weight and shape concerns as barriers to recovery from substance use disorders. Let's address these issues in treatment and recovery now! *Journal of Drug Addiction, Education, and Eradication.*

Courneya, K. S., Plotnikoff, R. C., Hotz, S. B., & Birkett, N. J. (2000). Social support and the theory of planned behavior in the exercise domain. *American Journal of Health Behavior, 24,* 300–308.

Couturier, J., Kimber, M., & Szatmari, P. (2013). Efficacy of family-based treatment for adolescents with eating disorders: A systematic review and meta-analysis. *International Journal of Eating Disorders, 46,* 3–11.

Cox, B. J., Clara, I. P., Sareen, J., & Stein, M. B. (2008). The structure of feared social situations among individuals with a lifetime diagnosis of social anxiety disorder in two independent nationally representative mental health surveys. *Behaviour Research and Therapy, 46,* 477–486.

Cox, B. J., Endler, N. S., & Swinson, R. P. (1991). Clinical and nonclinical panic attacks: An empirical test of a panic anxiety continuum. *Journal of Anxiety Disorders, 5,* 21–34.

Cox, B. J., Enns, M. W., & Clara, I. P. (2004). Psychological dimensions associated with suicide ideation and attempts in the National Comorbidity Survey. *Suicide and Life-Threatening Behaviour, 34,* 209–219.

Cox, B. J., Pagura, J., Stein, M. B., & Sareen, J. (2009). The relationship between generalized social phobia and avoidant personality disorder in a national mental health survey. *Depression and Anxiety, 26,* 354–362.

Cox, B. J., Turnbull, D. L., Robinson, J. A., Grant, B. F., & Stein, M. B. (2011). The effect of avoidant personality disorder on the persistence of generalized social anxiety disorder in the general population: Results from a longitudinal, nationally representative mental health survey. *Depression and Anxiety, 28,* 250–255.

Cox, B. J., Walker, J. R., Enns, M. W., & Karpinski, D. C. (2002). Self-criticism in generalized social phobia and response to cognitive-behavioral treatment. *Behavior Therapy, 33,* 479–491.

Cox, M., & Klinger, E. (1988). A motivational model of alcohol use. *Journal of Abnormal Psychology, 97,* 168–180.

Cox, W. M., Fadardi, J. S., & Pothos, E. M. (2006). The addiction Stroop test: Theoretical considerations and procedural recommendations. *Psychological Bulletin, 132,* 443–476.

Coyle, J. (1999, April 17). Ignore an inquest and we're doomed to repeat it. *The Toronto Star.*

Coyne, J. C. (1976). Toward an interactional description of depression. *Psychiatry, 39,* 28–40.

Coyne, S. M. (2016). Effects of viewing relational aggression on television on aggressive behavior in adolescents: A three-year longitudinal study. *Developmental Psychology, 52,* 284–295.

Craddock, N., O'Donovan, M. C., & Owen, M. J. (2006). Genes for schizophrenia and bipolar disorder? Implications for psychiatric nosology. *Schizophrenia Bulletin, 32,* 9–16.

Craig, T., & Jenkins, C. L. (2007, May 25). Va. House to review psychiatric care gaps: Hearings spurred by massacre, presage a tide of reform efforts, lawmakers say. *Washington Post,* B1–B2.

Craighead, W. E., Evans, D. D., & Robins, C. J. (1992). Unipolar depression. In S. M. Turner, K. S. Calhoun, & H. E. Adams (Eds.), *Handbook of clinical behavior therapy* (2nd ed., pp. 99–116). New York: John Wiley & Sons.

Craighead, W. E., Miklowitz, D. J., Vajk, F. C., & Frank, E. (1998). *Psychosocial treatments for bipolar disorder.* New York: Oxford University Press.

Craik, F. I. M., Bialystok, E., & Freedman, M. (2010). Delaying the onset of Alzheimer's disease: Bilingualism as a form of cognitive reserve. *Neurology, 75,* 1726–1729.

Crane, D. R., Morton, L. B., Fawcett, D., Moore, A., Larson, J., & Sandberg, J. (2012). Somatoform disorder: Treatment utilization and cost by mental health professionals. *Contemporary Family Therapy, 34,* 322–333.

Craske, M. G., & Barlow, D. H. (1993). Panic disorder and agoraphobia. In D. H. Barlow (Ed.), *Clinical handbook of psychological disorders* (2nd ed., pp. 1–47). New York: Guilford.

Craske, M. G., Maidenberg, E., & Bystritsky, A. (1995). Brief cognitive-behavioral versus nondirective therapy for panic disorder. *Journal of Behavior Therapy & Experimental Psychiatry, 26,* 113–120.

Craske, M. G., Rapee, R. M., & Barlow, D. H. (1992). Cognitive-behavioral treatment of panic disorder, agoraphobia, and generalized anxiety disorder. In S. M. Turner, K. S. Calhoun, & H. E. Adams (Eds.), *Handbook of clinical behavior therapy* (2nd ed., pp. 39–65). New York: John Wiley & Sons.

Craske, M. G., Wolitzky-Taylor, K. B., Mineka, S., Zinbarg, R., et al. (2012). Elevated responding to safe conditions as a specific risk factor for anxiety versus depressive disorders: Evidence from a longitudinal investigation. *Journal of Abnormal Psychology, 121,* 315–324.

Crawford, C. (2002). Learning disabilities in Canada: Economic costs to individuals, families and society. Prepared for the Learning Disabilities Association of Canada by the Roeher Institute.

Crawford, T. (2009, September 3). Stress takes troubling toll on students in university. *Toronto Star.*

Creamer, M., & Parslow, R. (2008). Trauma exposure and posttraumatic stress disorder in the elderly: A community prevalence study. *American Journal of Geriatric Psychiatry, 16*, 853–856.

Crego, C., Sleep, C. E., & Widiger, T. A. (2016). Clinicians' judgments of the clinical utility of personality disorder trait descriptions. *The Journal of Nervous and Mental Disease, 204*, 49–56.

Crits-Christoph, P. (1992). The efficacy of brief dynamic psychotherapy. *American Journal of Psychiatry, 149*, 151–158.

Crocker, A. G., Charette, Y., Seto, M. C., Nicholls, T. L., Côté, G., & Caulet, M. (2015). The National Trajectory Project of individuals found not criminally responsible on account of mental disorder in Canada. Part 3: Trajectories and outcomes through the forensic system. *Canadian Journal of Psychiatry, 60*, 117–126.

Crocker, A. G., Nicholls, T. L., Seto, M. C., Charette, Y., Côté, G., & Caulet, M. (2015). The National Trajectory Project of individuals found not criminally responsible on account of mental disorder in Canada. Part 2: The people behind the label. *Canadian Journal of Psychiatry, 60*, 106–116.

Crocker, A. G., Nicholls, T. L., Seto, M. C., Côté, G., Charette, Y., & Caulet, M. (2015). The National Trajectory Project of individuals found not criminally responsible on account of mental disorder in Canada. Part 1: Context and methods. *Canadian Journal of Psychiatry, 60*, 98–105.

Cronbach, L. J., & Meehl, P. E. (1955). Construct validity in psychological tests. *Psychological Bulletin, 52*, 281–302.

Cross-Disorder Group of the Psychiatric Genomics Consortium. (2013). Identification of risk loci with shared effects on five major psychiatric disorders: A genome-wide analysis. *The Lancet, 381*, 1371–1379.

Crozier, L., & Lane, P. (2001). *Addicted: Notes from the belly of the beast.* Vancouver: Greystone Books.

Crum, R. M., La Flair, L., Storr, C. L., Green, K. M., et al. (2012). Reports of drinking to self-medicate anxiety symptoms: Longitudinal assessment for subgroups of individuals with alcohol dependence. *Depression and Anxiety, 30*, 174–183.

CSA Group. (2013). *Psychological health and safety in the workplace: Prevention, promotion, and guidance to staged implementation.* Mississauga, ON: Author.

Cuijpers, P., Berking, M., Andersson, G., Quigley, L., Kleiboer, A., & Dobson, K. S. (2013). A meta-analysis of cognitive-behavioural therapy for adult depression, alone and in comparison with other treatments. *Canadian Journal of Psychiatry, 58*, 376–385.

Cuijpers, P., Geraedts, A. S., van Oppen, P., Andersson, G., et al. (2011). Interpersonal psychotherapy for depression: A meta-analysis. *The American Journal of Psychiatry, 168*, 581–592.

Cuijpers, P., van Straten, A., Smit, F., et al. (2008). Preventing the onset of depressive disorders: A meta-analytic review of psychological interventions. *American Journal of Psychiatry, 165*, 1272–1280.

Culbert, K. M., Racine, S. E., & Klump, K. L. (2015). Research review: What we have learned about the causes of eating disorders: A synthesis of sociocultural, psychological, and biological research. *Journal of Child Psychology and Psychiatry, 56*, 1141–1164.

Cullen, C. (2016, November 22). Ottawa bringing in stricter limits on medical marijuana for veterans. CBCNews.ca.

Cullerton-Sen, C., Cassidy, A. R., Murray-Close, D., et al. (2008). Childhood maltreatment and the development of relational and physical aggression: The importance of a gender-informed approach. *Child Development, 79*, 1736–1751.

Cumming, E., & Cumming, J. (1957). *Closed ranks: An experiment in mental health education.* Cambridge, MA: Harvard University Press.

Cunningham, A. (2002). *One step forward: Lessons learned from a randomized study of multisystemic therapy in Canada.* London, ON: Centre for Children and Families in the Justice System.

Cunningham, J. A., Blomqvist, J., & Cordingley, J. (2007). Beliefs about drinking problems: Results from a general population telephone survey. *Addictive Behaviors, 32*, 166–169.

Cunningham, J. A., & Breslin, F. C. (2004). Only one in three people with alcohol abuse or dependence ever seek treatment. *Addictive Behaviors, 29*, 221–223.

Cunningham, J. A., Sobell, L. C., Gavin, D. R., Sobell, M. B., & Breslin, F. C. (1997). Assessing motivation for change: Preliminary development and evaluation of a scale for measuring the costs and benefits of changing alcohol or drug use. *Psychology of Addictive Behaviors, 11(2)*, 107–114.

Curtin, J. J., Lang, A. R., Patrick, C. J., & Strizke, W. G. K. (1998). Alcohol and fear-potentiated startle: The role of competing cognitive demands in the stress-reducing effects of intoxication. *Journal of Abnormal Psychology, 107*, 547–557.

Curtin, S. C., Warner, M., & Hedegaard, H. (2016). Increase in suicide in the United States, 1999–2014. NCHS data brief, no 241. Hyattsville, MD: National Center for Health Statistics.

Curtis, J. (2012, April 2). New research chair seeks to reduce stigma surrounding mental illness. *University Affairs.*

Cusin, C., & Dougherty, D. D. (2012). Somatic therapies for treatment-resistant depression: ECT, TMS, VNS, DBS. *Biology of Mood and Anxiety Disorders, 2*, 14.

Cutrona, C. E., Wallace, G., & Wesner, K. A. (2006). Neighborhood characteristics and depression: An examination of stress processes. *Current Directions in Psychological Science, 15*, 188–192.

Cuttler, C., & Graf, P. (2009). Checking-in on the memory deficit and meta-memory deficit theories of compulsive checking. *Clinical Psychology Review, 29*, 393–409.

Cyr, M., Wright, J., McDuff, P., & Perron, A. (2002). Intrafamilial sexual abuse: Brother-sister incest does not differ from father-daughter and stepfather-stepdaughter incest. *Child Abuse and Neglect, 26*, 957–973.

Daignault, I. V., & Hébert, M. (2008). Short-term correlates of child sexual abuse: An exploratory study predicting girls' academic, cognitive, and social functioning 1 year later. *Journal of Child and Adolescent Trauma, 1*, 301–316.

Dalenberg, C. J., Brand, B. L., Gleaves, D. H., Dorahy, M. J., Loewenstein, R. J., Cardeña, E., et al. (2012). Evaluation of the evidence for the trauma and fantasy models of dissociation. *Psychological Bulletin, 138*, 550–588.

D'Alesio, R. (2016, February 23). The unremembered. *Globe and Mail.*

Daley, M., Morin, C. M., LeBlanc, M., Grégoire, J.-P., & Savard, J. (2009). The economic burden of insomnia: Direct and indirect costs for individuals with insomnia syndrome, insomnia symptoms, and good sleepers. *Sleep, 32*, 55–64.

Dalgleish, T. L., Johnson, S. M., Burgess Moser, M., Lafontaine, M., Wiebe, S. A., & Tasca, G. A. (2015). Predicting change in marital satisfaction throughout emotionally focused couple therapy. *Journal of Marital and Family Therapy, 41*, 276–291.

Damian, R. I., Su, R., Shanahan, M., Trautwein, U., & Roberts, B. W. (2015). Can personality traits and intelligence compensate for background disadvantage? Predicting status attainment in adulthood. *Journal of Personality and Social Psychology, 109*, 473–489.

Danner, D. D., Snowdon, D. A., & Friesen, W. V. (2001). Positive emotions in early life and longevity: Findings from the Nun Study. *Journal of Personality and Social Psychology, 80*, 804–813.

Dar, M. E., & Kanaan, R. A. A. (2016). Uncovering the etiology of conversion disorder: Insights from functional neuroimaging. *Neuropsychiatric Disease and Treatment, 12*, 143–153.

Dare, C., Grange, D. L., Eisler, I., & Rutherford, J. (1994). Redefining the psychosomatic family: Family process of 26 eating disorder families. *International Journal of Eating Disorders, 16*, 211–226.

Darou, W. G. (1992). Native Canadians and intelligence testing. *Canadian Journal of Counselling, 26*, 96–99.

David, D., Szentagotai, A., Kallay, E., & Macavei, B. (2005). A synopsis of rational-emotive behavior therapy (REBT): Fundamental and applied research. *Journal of Rational-Emotive and Cognitive-Behavior Therapy, 23*, 175–221.

Davidson, K., et al. (2006). The effectiveness of cognitive behavior therapy for borderline personality disorder: Results from the borderline personality disorder study of cognitive therapy (BOSCOT) trial. *Journal of Personality Disorders, 20*, 450–465.

Davidson, L. L., & Heinrichs, R. W. (2003). Quantification of frontal and temporal lobe brain-imaging findings in schizophrenia: A meta-analysis. *Psychiatry Research, 122*, 69–87.

Davidson, R. J., Pizzagalli, D., Nitschke, J. B., & Putnam, K. (2002). Depression: Perspectives from affective neuroscience. *Annual Review of Psychology, 53*, 545–574.

Davila, J., Hammen, C. L., Burge, D., Paley, B., & Daley, S. E. (1995). Poor interpersonal problem solving as a mechanism of stress generation in depression among adolescent women. *Journal of Abnormal Psychology, 104*, 592–600.

Davis, C. (1996). The interdependence of obsessive-compulsiveness, physical activity, and starvation: A model for anorexia nervosa. In W. F. Epling & W. D. Pierce (Eds.), *Activity anorexia: Theory, research, and treatment* (pp. 209–218). Mahwah, NJ: Erlbaum.

Davis, C., Kaptein, S., Kaplan, A. S., Olmsted, M. P., & Woodside, D. B. (1998). Obsessionality in anorexia nervosa: The moderating influence of exercise. *Psychosomatic Medicine, 60*, 192–197.

Davis, K. L., Kahn, R. S., Ko, G., & Davidson, M. (1991). Dopamine and schizophrenia: A review and reconceptualization. *American Journal of Psychiatry, 148*, 1474–1486.

Davis, S. D., Lebow, J. L., & Sprenkle, D. H. (2012). Common factors of change in couple therapy. *Behavior Therapy, 43*, 36–48.

Davison, G. C. (1968). Elimination of a sadistic fantasy by a client-controlled counterconditioning technique. *Journal of Abnormal Psychology, 73*, 84–90.

Davison, G. C., Robins, C., & Johnson, M. K. (1983). Articulated thoughts during simulated situations: A paradigm for studying cognition in emotion and behavior. *Cognitive Therapy and Research, 7*, 17–40.

Dawson, G., Rogers, S., Munson, J., et al. (2010). Randomized controlled trial of the Early Start Denver Model: A developmental behavioral intervention for toddlers with autism. Effects on IQ, adaptive behavior, and autism diagnosis. *Pediatrics, 125*, e17–e23.

Day, A. L., Therrien, D. L., & Carroll, S. A. (2005). Predicting psychological health: Assessing the incremental validity of emotional intelligence beyond personality, Type A behaviour, and daily hassles. *European Journal of Personality, 19*, 519–536.

de Boo, G. M., & Prins, P. J. M. (2007). Social incompetence in children with ADHD: Possible moderators and mediators in social-skills training. *Clinical Psychology Review, 27*, 78–97.

De Jong, M. A., & Mather, J. (2009). Undergraduate students' perceptions of schizophrenia. *International Journal of Mental Health, 7*, 458–467.

De Krom, M., et al. (2009). Genetic variations and effects on human eating behavior. *Annual Review of Nutrition, 29*, 283–304.

De Leo, J. A., & Wulfert, E. (2013). Problematic internet use and other risky behaviors in college students: An application of problem-behavior theory. *Psychology of Addictive Behaviors, 27*, 133–141.

de Maat, S., Dekker, J., Schoevers, R., van Alst, G., Gijsbers-van Wijk, C., Hendricksen, M., et al. (2008). Short psychodynamic supportive psychotherapy, antidepressants, and their combination in the treatment of major depression: A mega-analysis based on three randomized clinical trials. *Depression and Anxiety, 25*, 565–574.

de Maat, S., de Jonge, F., Schoevers, R., & Dekker, J. (2009). The effectiveness of long-term psychoanalytic therapy: A systematic review of empirical studies. *Harvard Review of Psychiatry, 17*, 1–23.

de Mello, M. F., et al. (2005). A systematic review of research findings on the efficacy of interpersonal therapy for depressive disorders. *European Archives of Psychiatry and Clinical Neuroscience, 255*, 75–82.

De Rubeis, S., & Buxbaum, J. D. (2015). Recent advances in the genetics of autism spectrum disorder. *Current Neurological and Neuroscience Reports, 15*, 36.

Deacon, B. J., & Abramowitz, J. S. (2004). Cognitive and behavioral treatments for anxiety disorders: A review of meta-analytic findings. *Journal of Clinical Psychology, 60*, 429–441.

Dean, J., et al. (2008). Integrating partners into erectile dysfunction treatment: Improving the sexual experience of the couple. *International Journal of Clinical Practice, 62*, 127–133.

DeClerq, K. (2012, September 25). *Battling the stigma of mental illness on Ontario campuses.* Canadian University Press.

Dedobbeleer, N., Béland, F., Contandriopoulos, A. P., & Adrian, M. (2004). Gender and the social context of smoking behaviour. *Social Science & Medicine, 58*, 1–12.

Dedovic, K., D'Aguiar, C., & Pruessner, J. C. (2009). What stress does to your brain: A review of neuroimaging studies. *Canadian Journal of Psychiatry, 54*, 6–15.

DeFazio, A., & Cunningham, K. A. (1987). A paraphilia in a spinal-cord-injured patient: A case report. *Sexuality and Disability, 8*, 247–257.

Degnan, A., Seymour-Hyde, A., Harris, A., & Berry, K. (2016). The role of therapist attachment in alliance and outcome: A systematic literature review. *Clinical Psychology and Psychotherapy, 23*, 47–65.

DeGroot, J. M., Kennedy, S., Rodin, G., & McVey, G. (1992). Correlates of sexual abuse in women with anorexia nervosa and bulimia nervosa. *Canadian Journal of Psychiatry, 37*, 516–518.

DeKeseredy, W. S., Schwartz, M. D., & Tait, K. (1993). Sexual assault and stranger aggression on a Canadian university campus. *Sex Roles, 28*, 263–277.

Delenardo, S., & Terrion, J. L. (2014). Suck it up: Opinions and attitudes about mental health stigma and help-seeking behavior of male varsity football players. *Canadian Journal of Community Mental Health, 33*, 43–56.

Delgado, P. L., Charney, D. S., Price, L. H., Aghajanian, G. K., Landis, H., et al. (1990). Serotonin function and the mechanism of antidepressant action: Reversal of antidepressant induced remission by rapid depletion of plasma tryptophan. *Archives of General Psychiatry, 47*, 411–418.

deLint, J. (1978). Alcohol consumption and alcohol problems from an epidemiological perspective. *British Journal of Alcohol and Alcoholism, 17*, 109–116.

DeLongis, A., Coyne, J. C., Dakof, G., Folkman, S., & Lazarus, R. S. (1982). Relationship of daily hassles, uplifts, and major life events to health status. *Health Psychology, 1*, 119–136.

DeLongis, A., Folkman, S., & Lazarus, R. S. (1988). The impact of daily stress on health and mood: Psychological and social resources as mediators. *Journal of Personality and Social Pscyhology, 54*, 486–495.

Dembo, J. S., & Clemens, N. A. (2013). The ethics of providing hope in psychotherapy. *Journal of Psychiatric Practice, 19,* 316–322.

Dement, W. C., Laughton, E., & Carskadon, M. A. (1981). "White paper" on sleep and aging. *Journal of the American Geriatrics Society, 30,* 25–50.

DeMont, J. (1999, November 22). The tragedy of Andrew Rich. *Maclean's, 112*(47).

Denihan, A., Kirby, M., Bruce, I., Cunningham, C., Coakley, D., & Lawlor, B. A. (2000). Three-year prognosis of depression in the community-dwelling elderly. *British Journal of Psychiatry, 176,* 453–457.

Dennis, C.-L. (2003). The effect of peer support on postpartum depression: A pilot randomized controlled trial. *Canadian Journal of Psychiatry, 48,* 115–124.

Dennis, C.-L., Heaman, M., & Vigod, S. (2012). Epidemiology of postpartum depression among Canadian women: Regional and national results from a cross-sectional survey. *Canadian Journal of Psychiatry, 57,* 537–546.

Dennis, C.-L., & Vigod, S. (2013). The relationship between postpartum depression, domestic violence, childhood violence, and substance use: Epidemiologic study of a large community sample. *Violence Against Women, 19,* 503–517.

Denollet, J. (2005). DS14: Standard assessment of negative affectivity, social inhibition, and Type D personality. *Psychosomatic Medicine, 67,* 87–97.

Denton, L. R. (2000). From humane care to prevention. *Canadian Journal of Community Mental Health, 19,* 127–134.

DePrince, A. P., & Freyd, J. J. (2004). Forgetting trauma stimuli. *Psychological Science, 15,* 488–492.

DeRubeis, R. J., Tang, T. Z., & Beck, A. T. (2001). Cognitive therapy. In K. S. Dobson (Ed.), *Handbook of cognitive-behavioral therapies* (2nd ed., pp. 349–392). New York: Guilford.

DeRubeis, R. J., Webb, C. A., Tang, T. Z., & Beck, A. T. (2010). Cognitive therapy. In K. S. Dobson (Ed.), *Handbook of cognitive-behavioral therapies* (3rd ed., pp. 277–315). New York: Guilford.

DeSalvo, K. B., Fan, V. S., McDonell, M. B., & Fihn, S. D. (2005). Predicting mortality and healthcare utilization with a single question. *Health Services Research,* 1234–1246.

DeSantis, A. D., Anthony, K. E., & Cohen, E. L. (2013). Illegal college ADHD stimulant distributors: Characteristics and potential areas of intervention. *Substance Use and Misuse, 48,* 446–456.

DeSantis, A. D., Webb, E. M., & Noar, S. M. (2008). Illicit use of prescription ADHD medications on a college campus: A multimethodological approach. *Journal of American College Health, 57,* 315–324.

Desmarais, S. L., Hucker, S., Brink, J., & De Freitas, K. (2008). A Canadian example of insanity defense reform: Accused found not criminally responsible before and after the Winko decision. *International Journal of Forensic Mental Health, 7,* 1–14.

Dessaulles, A., Johnson, S. M., & Denton, W. H. (2003). Emotion-focused therapy for couples in the treatment of depression: A pilot study. *The American Journal of Family Therapy, 31,* 345–353.

Dèttore, D., Pozza, A., & Andersson, G. (2015). Efficacy of technology-delivered cognitive behavioural therapy for OCD versus control conditions, and in comparison with therapist-administered CBT: Meta-analysis of randomized controlled trials. *Cognitive Behaviour Therapy, 44,* 190–211.

Deutsch, A. (1949). *The mentally ill in America.* New York: Columbia University Press.

Devanand, D. P., Dwork, A. J., Hutchinson, E. R., Bolwig, T. G., & Sackeim, H. A. (1994). Does ECT alter brain structure? *American Journal of Psychiatry, 151,* 957–970.

DeWit, D. J., Hance, J., Offord, D. R., & Ogborne, A. (2000). The influence of early and frequent use of marijuana on the risk of desistance and of progression to marijuana-related harm. *Preventive Medicine, 31,* 455–464.

Dhalla, I. A., Mandami, M. M., Sivilotti, M. L. A., Kopp, A., Quresh, O., & Juurlink, D. N. (2012). Prescribing of opioid analgesics and related mortality before and after the introduction of long-acting oxycodone. *Canadian Medical Association Journal, 181,* 891–896.

Dhingra, S. S., Kroenke, K., Zack, M. M., Strine, T. W., & Balluz, L. S. (2011). PHQ-8 days: A measurement option for DSM-5 Major Depressive Disorder (MDD) severity. *Population Health Metrics, 9,* 11.

Diamond, S., Baldwin, R., & Diamond, R. (1963). *Inhibition and choice.* New York: Harper & Row.

Dickey, C. C., McCarley, R. W., Volgmaier, M. M., Niznikiewicz, M. A., Seidman, L. J., et al. (1999). Schizotypal personality disorder and MRI abnormalities of temporal grey matter. *Biological Psychiatry, 45,* 1392–1402.

Dickey, R. A., & Coffey, W. (2012). *Whenever I wind up: My quest for truth, authenticity, and the perfect knuckleball.* New York: Plume.

Dickin, K. L., & Ryan, B. A. (1983, March). Sterilization and the mentally retarded. *Canada's Mental Health, 31,* 4–8.

Dickinson, H. O., et al. (2008). Relaxation therapies for the management of primary hypertension in adults: A Cochrane review. *Journal of Human Hypertension, 22,* 809–820.

DiClemente, C. C. (1993). Changing addictive behaviors: A process perspective. *Current Directions in Psychological Science, 2,* 101–106.

Diedrich, A., & Voderholzer, U. (2015). Obsessive-compulsive personality disorder: A current review. *Current Psychiatry Reports, 17,* 2.

Dierckx, B., Heijnen, W. T., van den Broek, W., & Birkenhager, T. K. (2012). Efficacy of electroconvulsive therapy in bipolar versus unipolar major depression: A meta-analysis. *Bipolar Disorders, 14,* 146–150.

Diesrud, G., et al. (2003). Predicting repetition of suicide attempts: A prospective study of 50 suicide attempters. *Archives of Suicide Research, 7,* 1–15.

Dietz, P. E., Hazelwood, R. R., & Warren, J. (1990). The sexually sadistic criminal and his offenses. *Bulletin of the American Academy of Psychiatry and the Law, 18,* 163–178.

DiGiuseppe, R., & David, O. A. (2015). Rational emotive behavior therapy. In H. T. Prout & A. L. Fedewa (Eds.), *Counseling and Psychotherapy with Children and Adolescents: Theory and Practice for School and Clinical Settings* (5th ed., pp. 155–215). Hoboken, NJ: John Wiley & Sons, Inc.

DiMauro, J., Tolin, D. F., Frost, R. O., & Steketee, G. (2013). Do people with hoarding disorder under-report their symptoms? *Journal of Obsessive Compulsive and Related Disorders, 2,* 130–136.

DiNardo, P. A., Guzy, L. T., Jenkins, J. A., Bak, R. M., Tomasi, S. F., & Copland, M. (1988). Etiology and maintenance of dog fears. *Behaviour Research and Therapy, 26,* 241–244.

DiNardo, P. A., O'Brien, G. T., Barlow, D. H., Waddell, M. T., & Blanchard, E. B. (1993). Reliability of the DSM-III-R anxiety disorders categories using the Anxiety Disorders Interview Schedule-Revised (ADIS-R). *Archives of General Psychiatry, 50,* 251–256.

Dittmar, H., Halliwell, E., & Ive, S. (2006). Does Barbie make girls want to be thin? The effect of experimental exposure to images of dolls on the body image of 5- to 8-year old girls. *Developmental Psychology, 42,* 283–292.

Dixon, R. (2012, September 9). In Ghana's witch camps, the accused are never safe. *Los Angeles Times.*

Dobkin, P. L. (2008). Mindfulness-based stress reduction: What processes are at work? *Complementary Therapies in Clinical Practice, 14,* 8–16.

Dobson, K. S. (1989). A meta-analysis of the efficacy of cognitive therapy for depression. *Journal of Consulting and Clinical Psychology, 57,* 414–419.

Dobson, K. S. (2013). The science of CBT: Toward a metacognitive model of change? *Behavior Therapy, 44,* 224–227.

Dobson, K. S., Dobson, D. J. G., & Ritchie, P. L.-J. (1993). Professional psychology in Canada: Present status and future promises. In K. S. Dobson and D. J. Gora (Eds.), *Professional psychology in Canada* (pp. 433–454). Ashland, OH: Hogrefe & Huber Publishers.

Dobson, K. S., & Hamilton, K. E. (2002). The stage model for psychotherapy manual development: A valuable tool for promoting evidence-based practice. *Clinical Psychology: Science and Practice, 9,* 407–409.

Dobson, K. S., Hollon, S. D., Dimidjian, S., Schmaling, K. B., et al. (2008). Randomized trial of behavioral activation, cognitive therapy, and antidepressant medication in the prevention of relapse and recurrence in major depression. *Journal of Consulting and Clinical Psychology, 76,* 468–477.

Dobson, K. S., Shaw, B. F., & Vallis, T. M. (1985). The reliability of competency ratings on cognitive-behavior therapists. *British Journal of Clinical Psychology, 24,* 295–300.

Dodge, K. A., & Frame, C. L. (1982). Social cognitive biases and deficits in aggressive boys. *Child Development, 53,* 620–635.

Dodge, K. A., & Pettit, G. S. (2003). A biopsychosocial model of the development of chronic conduct problems in adolescents. *Developmental Psychology, 39,* 349–371.

Doerr, P., Fichter, M., Pirke, K. M., & Lund, R. (1980). Relationship between weight gain and hypothalamic-pituitary-adrenal function in patients with anorexia nervosa. *Journal of Steroid Biochemistry, 13,* 529–537.

Dohrenwend, B. P., Levav, P. E., Schwartz, S., Naveh, G., Link, B. G., Skodol, A. E., et al. (1992). Socioeconomic status and psychiatric disorders: The causation-selection issue. *Science, 255,* 946–952.

Doidge, N. (1999). Who is in psychoanalysis now? Empirical data and reflection on some common misperceptions. In H. Kaley, M. N. Eagle, & D. L. Wolitzky (Eds.), *Psychoanalytic therapy as health care: Effectiveness and economics in the 21st century* (pp. 177–198). Hillsdale, NJ: The Analytic Press.

Doidge, N., et al. (2002). Classics revisited: Freud's The Ego and the Id and Inhibitions, Symptoms, and Anxiety. *Journal of the American Psychoanalytic Association, 50,* 281–294.

Doidge, N., Simon, B., Gillies, L. A., & Ruskin, R. (1994). Characteristics of psychoanalytic patients under a nationalized health plan: DSM-III-R diagnoses, previous treatment and childhood trauma. *American Journal of Psychiatry, 151,* 586–590.

Dominus, S. (2012, March 7). What happened to the girls in Le Roy? *The New York Times.*

Dongier, M. (1999). In memoriam – Heinz E. Lehmann, 1911–1999. *Journal of Psychiatry and Neuroscience, 24,* 362.

Donnellan, M. B., & Robins, R. W. (2010). Resilient, overcontrolled, and undercontrolled personality types: Issues and controversies. *Social and Personality Psychology Compass, 4,* 1070–1083.

Doren, D. M., & Yates, P. M. (2008). Effectiveness of sex offender treatment for psychopathic sexual offenders. *International Journal of Offender Therapy and Comparative Criminology, 52,* 234–245.

Doucet, C., Ladouceur, R., Freeston, M. H., & Dugas, M. J. (1998). Worry themes and the tendency to worry in older adults. *Canadian Journal on Aging, 17,* 361–371.

Doughterty, D., Rezai, A. R., Carpenter, L. L., Howland, R. H., et al. (2015). A randomized sham-controlled trial of deep brain stimulation of the ventral capsule/ventral striatum for chronic treatment-resistant depression. *Biological Psychiatry, 78,* 240–248.

Douglas, A. C., Mills, J. E., Niang, M., et al. (2008). Internet addiction: Meta synthesis of qualitative research for the decade 1996–2006. *Computers in Human Behavior, 24,* 3027–3044.

Douglas, K. S., & Koch, W. J. (2001). Civil commitment and civil competence: Psychological issues. In R. A. Schuller & J. R. Ogloff (Eds.), *Introduction to psychology and law: Canadian perspectives* (pp. 351–374). Toronto: University of Toronto Press.

Douglas, K. S., Ogloff, J. R. P., & Hart, S. D. (2003). Evaluation of a model of violence risk assessment among forensic psychiatric patients. *Psychiatric Services, 54,* 1372–1379.

Douglas, K. S., & Reeves, K. A. (2010). Historical-Clinical-Risk Management-20 (HCR-20) Violence Risk Assessment Scheme: Rationale, application, and empirical overview. In R. K. Otto & K. S. Douglas (Eds.), *Handbook of violence risk assessment* (pp. 147–185). New York: Routledge/Taylor & Francis Group.

Douglas, V. I. (1972). Stop, look and listen: The problem of sustained attention and impulse control in hyperactive and normal children. *Canadian Journal of Behavioural Science, 4,* 259–282.

Doyle, M., & Dolan, M. (2006). Predicting community violence from patients discharged from mental health services. *British Journal of Psychiatry, 189,* 520–526.

Dozois, D. J. A. (2002). Cognitive organization of self-schematic content in nondysphoric, mildly dysphoric, and moderately-severely dysphoric individuals. *Cognitive Therapy and Research, 26,* 417–429.

Dozois, D. J. A., & Dobson, K. S. (2001). Information processing and cognitive organization in unipolar depression: Specificity and comorbidity issues. *Journal of Abnormal Psychology, 110,* 236–246.

Dozois, D. J. A., & Dobson, K. S. (2003). The structure of the self-schema in clinical depression: Differences related to episode recurrence. *Cognition and Emotion, 17,* 933–941.

Drake, K. L., & Ginsburg, G. S. (2012). Family factors in the development, treatment, and prevention of childhood anxiety disorders. *Clinical Child and Family Psychology Review, 15,* 144–162.

Draper, M. R., & Faulkner, G. E. (2009). Counseling a student presenting borderline personality disorder in the small college context: Case study and implications. *Journal of College Counseling, 12,* 85–96.

Driessen, E., et al. (2010). The efficacy of short-term psychodynamic psychotherapy for depression: A meta-analysis. *Clinical Psychology Review, 30,* 25–36.

Drob, S. L., Meehan, K. B., & Waxman, S. E. (2009). Clinical and conceptual problems in the attribution of malingering in forensic evaluations. *Journal of the American Academy of Psychiatry and the Law, 37,* 98–106.

Drucker, E. (2006). Insite: Canada's landmark safe injecting program at risk. *Harm Reduction Journal, 3,* 24–26.

Drury, V., Birchwood, M., Cochrane, R., & MacMillan, F. (1996). Cognitive therapy and recovery from acute psychosis: a controlled trial. II. Impact on recovery time. *The British Journal of Psychiatry, 169*(5), 602–607.

Dryden, W., David, D., & Ellis, A. (2010). Rational emotive behavior therapy. In K. S. Dobson (Ed.), *Handbook of cognitive-behavioral therapies* (3rd ed., pp. 226–276). New York: Guilford.

Du, L., Qiu, H., Liu, H., Zhao, W., Tang, Y., Fu, Y., . . . Luo, Q. (2016). Changes in problem-solving capacity and association with spontaneous brain activity after a single electroconvulsive treatment in major depressive disorder. *The Journal of ECT, 32,* 49–54.

Du Mont, J., White, D., & McGregor, M. T. (2009). Investigating the medical forensic examination from the perspectives of sexually assaulted women. *Social Science and Medicine, 68,* 774–780.

Duberstein, P. R., et al. (2004). Suicide at 50 years of age and older: Perceived physical illness, family discord, and financial strain. *Psychological Medicine, 34,* 137–146.

Dudeney, J., Sharpe, L., & Hunt, C. (2015). Attentional bias towards threatening stimuli in children with anxiety: A meta-analysis. *Clinical Psychology Review, 40*, 66–75.

Dugas, M. J., & Koerner, N. (2005). Cognitive-behavioral treatment for generalized anxiety disorder: Current status and future directions. *Journal of Cognitive Psychotherapy, 19*, 61–81.

Duhig, A. M., & Phares, V. (2003). Adolescents', mothers', and fathers' perspectives of emotional and behavioral problems: Distress, control, and motivation to change. *Child and Family Behavior Therapy, 25*, 39–52.

Duman, R. S., Heninger, G. R., & Nestler, E. J. (1997). A molecular and cellular theory of depression. *Archives of General Psychiatry, 54*, 597–606.

Duncan, R. D. (2000). Childhood maltreatment and college drop-out rates: Implications for child abuse researchers. *Journal of Interpersonal Violence, 15*, 987–995.

Dunham, H. W. (1965). *Community and schizophrenia: An epidemiological analysis*. Detroit: Wayne State University Press.

Dunkley, D. M., Schwartzman, D., Looper, K. J., Sigal, J. J., Pierre, A., & Kotowycz, M. A. (2012). Perfectionism dimensions and dependency in relation to personality vulnerability and psychosocial adjustment in patients with coronary artery disease. *Journal of Clinical Psychology in Medical Settings, 19*, 211–223.

Dunn, A. L., Marcus, B. H., Kampert, J. B., Garcia, M. E., et al. (1999). Comparison of lifestyle and structured interventions to increase physical activity and cardiorespiratory fitness. *Journal of the American Medical Association, 281*, 327–334.

Dunn, B. D., Stefanovitch, I., Buchan, K., et al. (2009). A reduction in positive self-judgment bias is uniquely related to the anhedonic symptoms of depression. *Behaviour Research and Therapy, 47*, 374–381.

DuPaul, G. J., McGoey, K. E., & Mautone, J. A. (2003). Pediatric pharmacology and psychopharmacology. In M. C. Roberts (Ed.), *Handbook of pediatric psychology* (pp. 234–250). New York: Guilford.

Dupere, V., et al. (2007). Affiliation in youth gangs during adolescence: The interaction between childhood psychopathic tendencies and neighbourhood disadvantage. *Journal of Abnormal Child Psychology, 35*, 1035–1045.

Dupere, V., Leventhal, T., & Lacourse, E. (2009). Neighbourhood poverty and suicidal thoughts and attempts in late adolescence. *Psychological Medicine, 39*, 1295–1306.

Duquette, A. (2001, February 2). Living with agoraphobia. Atlantic Journalism Awards. Retrieved July 17, 2002, from http://www.aja.kings.ns.ca.

Durbin, C. E., & Klein, D. N. (2006). Ten-year stability of personality disorders among outpatients with mood disorders. *Journal of Abnormal Psychology, 115*, 75–84.

Durbin, J., Selick, A., Hierlihy, D., Moss, S., & Cheng, C. (in press). A first step in system improvement: A survey of early psychosis intervention programs in Ontario. *Early Intervention in Psychiatry*.

Durkheim, E. (1951). *Suicide*. (J. A. Spaulding & G. Simpson, Trans.). New York: Free Press. (Original work published 1897; 2nd ed., 1930).

Durkin, K. L. (1997). Misuse of the internet by pedophiles: Implications for law enforcement and probation practice. *Federal Probation, 61*, 14–18.

Dussault, C. L., & Weyandt, L. L. (2013). An examination of prescription stimulant misuse and psychological variables among sorority and fraternity college populations. *Journal of Attention Disorders, 17*, 87–97.

Dvorak-Bertscha, J. D., Curtin, J. J., Rubinstein, T. J., & Newman, J. P. (2009). Psychopathic traits moderate the interaction between cognitive and affective processing. *Psychophysiology, 46*, 913–921.

Dwork, A. J. (1997). Postmortem studies of the hippocampal formation in schizophrenia. *Schizophrenia Bulletin, 23*, 385–402.

Dworkin, R. H., Lenzenweger, M. F., & Moldin, S. O. (1987). Genetics and the phenomenology of schizophrenia. In P. D. Harvey and E. F. Walker (Eds.), *Positive and negative symptoms of psychosis*. Hillsdale, NJ: Erlbaum.

Dworkin, R. H., Lenzenweger, M. F., Moldin, S. O., Skillings, G. F., & Levick, S. E. (1988). A multidimensional approach to the genetics of schizophrenia. *American Journal of Psychiatry, 145*, 1077–1083.

D'Zurilla, T. J., & Nezu, A. M. (2010). Problem-solving therapy. In K. S. Dobson (Ed.), *Handbook of cognitive-behavioral therapies* (3rd ed., pp. 197–225). New York: Guilford.

Eack, S. M., Hogarty, G. E., Cho, R. C., Prasad, K. M. R., et al. (2010). Neuroprotective effects of cognitive enhancement therapy against gray matter loss in early schizophrenia: Results from a 2-year randomized controlled trial. *Archives of General Psychiatry, 67*, 674–682.

Earleywine, M., & Gann, M. K. (1995). Challenging recovered memories in the courtroom. In J. Ziskin (Ed.), *Coping with psychiatric and psychological testimony* (pp. 1100–1134). Los Angeles: Law and Psychology Press.

Earls, C. M., & Lalumière, M. L. (2002). A case study of preferential bestiality (zoophilia). *Sexual Abuse, 14*, 83–88.

Earls, C. M., & Lalumière, M. L. (2009). A case study of preferential bestiality. *Archives of Sexual Behavior, 38*, 605–609.

Eastwood, J. D., et al. (2005). Individuals with social phobia are biased to become aware of negative faces. *Visual Cognition, 12*, 159–179.

Eaton, J. W., & Weil, R. J. (1953). The mental health of the Hutterites. *Scientific American, 189*, 31–37.

Eaves, D., Lamb, D., & Tien, G. (2000). Forensic psychiatric services in British Columbia. *International Journal of Law and Psychiatry, 23*, 615–631.

Eccleston, C. (1995). Chronic pain and distraction: An experimental investigation into the role of sustained and shifting attention in the processing of chronic persistent pain. *Behaviour Research and Therapy, 33*, 391–406.

Edelbrock, C., Rende, R., Plomin, T., & Thompson, L. A. (1995). A twin study of competence and problem behavior in childhood and early adolescence. *Journal of Child Psychology and Psychiatry and Allied Disciplines, 36*, 775–789.

Eden, G. F., & Zeffiro, T. A. (1996). PET and fMRI in the detection of task-related brain activity: Implications for the study of brain development. In R. W. Thatcher & G. R. Lyon (Eds.), *Developmental neuroimaging: Mapping the development of brain and behavior* (pp. 77–90). San Diego, CA: Academic Press.

Edens, J. F., Marcus, D. K., Lilienfeld, S. O., & Poythress, N. G. (2006). Psychopathic, not psychopath: Taxometric evidence for the dimensional structure of psychopathy. *Journal of Abnormal Psychology, 115*, 131–144.

Edens, J. F., Marcus, D. K., & Morey, L. C. (2009). Paranoid personality has a dimensional latent structure: Taxometric analyses of community and clinical samples. *Journal of Abnormal Psychology, 118*, 545–553.

Edmonds, C. V., Lockwood, G. A., & Cunningham, A. J. (1999). Psychological response to long-term group therapy: A randomized trial with metastatic breast cancer patients. *Psycho-oncology, 8*, 74–91.

Edmunds, A. (1998). My story: Thoughts of a survivor. In A. A. Leenaars, S. Wenckstern, I. Sakinofsky, R. J. Dyck, M. J. Kral, & R. C. Bland (Eds.), *Suicide in Canada* (pp. 369–374). Toronto: University of Toronto Press.

Edwards, D., & Arntz, A. (2012). Schema therapy in historical perspective. In M. van Vreeswijk, J. Broersen, & M. Nadort (Eds.), *The*

Wiley-Blackwell handbook of schema therapy: Theory, research, and treatment (pp. 3–26). New York: Wiley-Blackwell.

Egan, G. (1975). *The skilled helper*. Monterey, CA: Brooks/Cole.

Egan, T. (1990). As memory and music faded, Alzheimer patient met death. *New York Times, 89*, A1, A16.

Egeland, J. A., Gerhard, D. S., Pauls, D. L., Sussex, J. N., Kidd, K. K., Allen, C. R., et al. (1987). Bipolar affective disorders linked to DNA markers on chromosome 11. *Nature, 325*, 783–787.

Ehnvall, A., Parker, G., Hadzi-Pavlovic, D., & Malhi, G. (2008). Perception of rejecting and neglectful parenting in childhood relates to lifetime suicide attempts for females—but not for males. *Acta Psychiatrica Scandinavica, 117*, 50–56.

Ehrhardt, A., & Money, J. (1967). Progestin-induced hermaphroditism: IQ and psychosexual identity in a study of ten girls. *Journal of Sex Research, 3*, 83–100.

Eich, E. (1995). Searching for mood-dependent memory. *Psychological Science, 6*, 67–75.

Eisenberg, D., Gollust, S. E., Golberstein, E., & Hefner, J. L. (2007). Prevalence and correlates of depression, anxiety, and suicidality among university students. *American Journal of Orthopsychiatry, 77*, 534–542.

Eisenberg, D., Hunt, J., Speer, N., & Zivin, K. (2011). Mental health service utilization among college students in the United States. *Journal of Nervous and Mental Disease, 199*, 301–308.

Eissenberg, T., Bigelow, G. E., Strain, E. C., & Walsh, S. L. (1997). Dose-related efficacy of levomethadyl acetate for treatment of opioid dependence. *Journal of the American Medical Association, 277*, 1945–1951.

El-Gabalawy, R., Mackenzie, C. S., & Sareen, J. (2016). Mental health service use among older Canadians with anxiety and comorbid physical conditions. *Aging and Mental Health, 20*, 627–636.

Elbaum, B., & Vaughn, S. (2003). For which students with learning disabilities are self-concept interventions effective? *Journal of Learning Disabilities, 36*, 101–108.

Elbogen, E. B., & Johnson, S. C. (2009). The intricate link between violence and mental disorder: Results from the national epidemiologic survey on alcohol and related conditions. *Archives of General Psychiatry, 66*, 152–161.

Elbogen, E. B., Van Dorn, R. A., Swanson, J. W., Swartz, M. S., & Monahan, J. (2006). Treatment engagement and violence risk in mental disorders. *British Journal of Psychiatry, 189*, 354–360.

Elbulok-Charcape, M. M., Rabin, L. A., Barr, W. B., & Spadaccini, A. T. (2014). Trends in the neuropsychological assessment of ethnic/racial minorities: A survey of clinical neuropsychologists in the United States and Canada. *Cultural Diversity and Ethnic Minority Psychology, 20*, 353–361.

Elgar, F. J., Curtis, L. J., McGrath, P. J., Waschbusch, D. A., & Stewart, S. H. (2003). Antecedent–consequence conditions in maternal mood and child adjustment: A four-year cross-lagged study. *Journal of Clinical Child and Adolescent Psychology, 32*, 362–374.

Elie, M., Cole, M. G., Primeau, F. J., & Bellavance, F. (1998). Delirium risk factors in elderly hospitalized patients. *Journal of General Internal Medicine, 13*, 204–212.

Elkin, I., Parloff, M. B., Hadley, S. W., & Autry, J. H. (1985). NIMH Treatment of Depression Collaborative Research Program. *Archives of General Psychiatry, 42*, 305–316.

Elkin, I., Shea, M. T., Watkins, J. T., Imber, S. D., Sotsky, S. M., et al. (1989). NIMH Treatment of Depression Collaborative Research Program: 1. General effectiveness of treatments. *Archives of General Psychiatry, 46*, 971–983.

Ellason, J. W., & Ross, C. A. (1997). Two-year follow-up of inpatients with dissociative identity disorder. *American Journal of Psychiatry, 154*, 832–839.

Elliott, R., Bohart, A. C., Watson, J. C., & Greenberg, L. S. (2011). Empathy. *Psychotherapy, 48*, 43–49.

Ellis, A. (1962). *Reason and emotion in psychotherapy*. New York: Lyle Stuart.

Ellis, A. (2002). The role of irrational beliefs in perfectionism. In G. L. Flett & P. L. Hewitt (Eds.), *Perfectionism: Theory, research, and treatment* (pp. 217–229). Washington, DC: American Psychological Association.

Ellis, H. (1910). *Studies in the psychology of sex*. Philadelphia: FA Davis.

Ellis, S. R. (1995). Origins and elements of virtual environments. In W. Barfield & T. A. Furness III (Eds.), *Virtual environments and advanced interface design* (pp. 14–57). New York: Oxford University Press.

Ellsworth, R. M., & Bailey, D. H. (2013). Human female orgasm as evolved signal: A test of two hypotheses. *Archives of Sexual Behavior, 42*, 1545–1554.

Elsabbagh, M., Divan, G., Koh, Y.-J., Kim, Y. S., et al. (2012). Global prevalence of autism and other pervasive developmental disorders. *Autism Research, 5*, 160–179.

Eme, R. F. (2007). Sex differences in child-onset, life-course-persistent conduct disorder: A review of biological influences. *Clinical Psychology Review, 27*, 607–627.

Emslie, G. J. (2009). Understanding placebo response in pediatric depression trials. *American Journal of Psychiatry, 166*, 1–3.

Endler, N. S. (1982). *Holiday of darkness*. New York: John Wiley & Sons.

Endler, N. S. (1983). Interactionism: A personality model, but not yet a theory. In M. M. Page (Ed.), *Nebraska Symposium on Motivation 1982: Personality—Current theory and research* (pp. 241–266). San Francisco: Jossey Bass.

Endler, N. S. (2002). Multidimensional interactionism: Stress, anxiety, and coping. In L. Backman & R. C. von Hofsen (Eds.), *Psychology at the turn of the millennium, Vol. 1: Cognitive, biological, and health perspectives* (pp. 281–304). New York: Psychology Press.

Endler, N. S., Courbasson, C. M. A., & Fillion, L. (1998). Coping with cancer: The evidence for the temporal stability of the French Canadian version of the Coping With Health, Injuries, and Problems (CHIP). *Personality and Individual Differences, 25*, 711–717.

Endler, N. S., Crooks, D. S., & Parker, J. D. A. (1992). The interaction model of anxiety: An empirical test in a parachute jumping situation. *Anxiety, Stress and Coping, 5*, 301–311.

Endler, N. S., Kocovski, N. L., & Macrodimitris, S. D. (2001). Coping, efficacy, and perceived control in acute vs chronic illnesses. *Personality and Individual Differences, 30*, 617–625.

Endler, N. S., & Magnusson, D. (1976). Toward an interactional psychology of personality. *Psychological Bulletin, 83*, 956–979.

Endler, N. S., & Parker, J. D. A. (1990). *The Coping Inventory for Stressful Situations (CISS): Manual*. Toronto: Multi-Health Systems, Inc.

Endler, N. S., & Parker, J. D. A. (1994). Assessment of multidimensional coping: Task, emotion, and avoidance strategies. *Psychological Assessment, 6*, 50–60.

Endler, N. S., & Parker, J. D. A. (1999). *The Coping Inventory for Stressful Situations (CISS): Manual* (2nd ed.). Toronto: Multi-Health Systems, Inc.

Endler, N. S., & Parker, J. D. A. (2000). *Coping with health injuries and problems (CHIP): Manual*. Toronto: Multi-Health Systems, Inc.

Endler, N. S., Parker, J. D. A., & Summerfeldt, L. J. (1993). Coping with health problems: Conceptual and methodological issues. *Canadian Journal of Behavioural Science, 25*, 384–399.

Endler, N. S., & Persad, E. (1988). *Electroconvulsive therapy: The myths and the realities*. Toronto: Hans Huber.

Endler, N. S., Speer, R. L., Johnson, J. M., & Flett, G. L. (2000). Controllability, coping, efficacy, and distress. *European Journal of Personality, 14,* 245–264.

Engel, G. L. (1980). The clinical application of the biopsychosocial model. *American Journal of Psychiatry, 137,* 535–544.

Engeln-Maddox, R., Salk, R. H., & Miller, S. A. (2012). Assessing women's negative commentary on their own bodies: A psychometric investigation of the Negative Body Talk Scale. *Psychology of Women Quarterly, 36,* 162–178.

English, H. B. (1929). Three cases of the "conditioned fear response." *Journal of Abnormal and Social Psychology, 34,* 221–222.

Enns, M. W., & Cox, B. J. (2005a). Psychosocial and clinical predictors of symptom persistence vs remission in major depressive disorder. *Canadian Journal of Psychiatry, 50,* 769–777.

Enns, M. W., & Cox, B. J. (2005b). Perfectionism, stressful life events, and the 1-year outcome of depression. *Cognitive Therapy and Research, 29,* 541–553.

Epling, W. F., & Pierce, W. D. (1992). *Solving the anorexia puzzle: A scientific approach.* Toronto: Hogrefe and Huber.

Epp, A. M., & Dobson, K. S. (2010). The evidence base for cognitive-behavioral therapy. In K. S. Dobson (Ed.), *Handbook of cognitive-behavioral therapies* (3rd ed., pp. 39–73). New York: Guilford.

Epp, J. (Ed.). (1988). *Mental health for Canadians: Striking a balance.* Ottawa: Ministry of National Health and Welfare.

Epping-Jordan, J. E., Compas, B. E., & Howell, D. C. (1994). Predictors of cancer progression in young adult men and women: Avoidance, intrusive thoughts, and psychological symptoms. *Health Psychology, 13,* 539–547.

Erdberg, P., & Exner, J. E., Jr. (1984). Rorschach assessment. In G. Goldstein & M. Hersen (Eds.), *Handbook of psychological assessment.* New York: Pergamon.

Erikson, E. H. (1950). *Childhood and society.* New York: Norton.

Erikson, E. H. (1968). *Identity: Youth and crisis.* New York: Norton.

Erlangsen, A., Vach, W., & Jeune, B. (2005). The effect of hospitalization with medical illnesses on the suicide risk in the oldest old: A population-based register study. *Journal of the American Geriatrics Society, 53,* 771–776.

Erlenmeyer-Kimling, L. E., & Cornblatt, B. (1987). The New York high-risk project: A follow-up report. *Schizophrenia Bulletin, 13,* 451–461.

Ermer, E., Cope, L. M., Nyalakanti, P. K., Calhoun, V. D., & Kiehl, K. A. (2013). Aberrant paralimbic gray matter in incarcerated male adolescents with psychopathic traits. *Journal of the American Academy of Child and Adolescent Psychiatry, 52,* 94–103.

Erskine, H. E., Norman, R. E., Ferrari, A. J., Chan, G. C. K., et al. (2016). Long-term outcomes of attention-deficit/hyperactivity disorder and conduct disorder: A systematic review and meta-analysis. *Journal of the American Academy of Child and Adolescent Psychiatry, 55,* 841–850.

Eser, D., et al. (2009). Functional neuroanatomy of CCK-4-induced panic attacks in healthy volunteers. *Human Brain Mapping, 30,* 511–522.

Essau, C. A., Leung, P. W. L., Conradt, J., Cheng, H., & Wong, T. (2008). Anxiety symptoms in Chinese and German adolescents: Their relationship with early learning experiences, perfectionism, and learning motivation. *Depression and Anxiety, 25,* 801–810.

Esses, V. M., & Gardner, R. C. (1996). Multiculturalism in Canada: Context and current status. *Canadian Journal of Behavioural Science, 28,* 145–152.

Essex, M. J., et al. (2006). Exploring risk factors for the emergence of children's mental health problems. *Archives of General Psychiatry, 63,* 1246–1256.

Essex, M. J., Klein, M. H., Slattery, M. J., et al. (2010). Early risk factors and developmental pathways to chronic high inhibition and

social anxiety disorder in adolescence. *American Journal of Psychiatry, 167,* 40–46.

Etchegary, H., Lemyre, L., Wilson, B., and Krewski, D. (2009). Is genetic makeup a perceived health risk: Analysis of a national survey of Canadians. *Journal of Risk Research 12,* 223–237.

Etkin, A., & Wager, T. D. (2007). Functional neuroimaging of anxiety: A meta-analysis of emotional processing in PTSD, social anxiety disorder, and specific phobia. *American Journal of Psychiatry, 164,* 1476–1488.

Evans, P. D., & Edgerton, N. (1990). Life events as predictors of the common cold. *British Journal of Medical Psychology, 64,* 35–44.

Evensen, J., Rossberg, J. I., Barder, H., Haahr, U., et al. (2012). Apathy in first episode: A ten-year longitudinal follow-up study. *Schizophrenia Research, 136,* 19–24.

EW (Re), 2012 SKQB 1 (CanLII). (2012). Queen's Bench for Saskatchewan.

Exner, J. E., Jr. (1986). *The Rorschach: A comprehensive system: Vol. 1. Basic foundations* (2nd ed.). New York: John Wiley & Sons.

Fabiano, G. A., Pelham, W. E., Jr., Coles, E. K., et al. (2009). A meta-analysis of behavioral treatments for attention-deficit/hyperactivity disorder. *Clinical Psychology Review, 29,* 129–140.

Fairburn, C. G., et. al. (1998). The classification of recurrent overeating: The "binge eating disorder" proposal. *International Journal of Eating Disorders, 13,* 155–159.

Fairburn, C. G., Bailey-Straebler, S., Basden, S., Doll, H. A., Jones, R., Murphy, R., … Cooper, Z. (2015). A transdiagnostic comparison of enhanced cognitive behaviour therapy (CBT-E) and interpersonal psychotherapy in the treatment of eating disorders. *Behaviour Research and Therapy, 70,* 64–71.

Fairburn, C. G., & Cooper, Z. (2011). Eating disorders, *DSM-5*, and clinical reality. *British Journal of Psychiatry, 198,* 8–10.

Fairburn, C. G., Marcus, M. D., & Wilson, G. T. (1993). Cognitive behaviour therapy for binge eating and bulimia nervosa: A comprehensive treatment manual. In C. G. Fairburn & G. T. Wilson (Eds.), *Binge eating: Nature, assessment, and treatment.* New York: Guilford.

Fairburn, C. G., Shafran, R., & Cooper, Z. (1999). A cognitive behavioural theory of anorexia nervosa. *Behaviour Research and Therapy, 37,* 1–13.

Fairweather-Schmidt, A. K., & Wade, T. D. (2016). Characterizing and predicting trajectories of disordered eating over adolescence. *Journal of Abnormal Psychology, 125,* 369–380.

Fakhoury, M. (2015). New insights into the neurobiological mechanisms of major depressive disorders. *General Hospital Psychiatry, 37,* 172–177.

Fallon, J. H., et al. (2005). Gender: A major determinant of brain response to nicotine. *International Journal of Neuropsychopharmacology, 8,* 511–528.

Fang, A., & Wilhelm, S. (2015). Clinical features, cognitive biases, and treatment of body dysmorphic disorder. *Annual Review of Clinical Psychology, 11,* 187–212.

Farach, F. J., Pruitt, L. D., Jun, J. J., et al. (2012). Pharmacological treatment of anxiety disorders: Current treatment and future directions. *Journal of Anxiety Disorders, 26,* 833–843.

Faraone, S. V., Biederman, J., Weber, W., & Russell, R. L. (1998). Psychiatric, neuropsychological, and psychosocial features of DSM-IV subtypes of attention-deficit/hyperactivity disorder: Results from a clinically referred sample. *Journal of the American Academy of Child and Adolescent Psychiatry, 37,* 185–193.

Farber, E. W., Mirsalimi, H., Williams, K. A., & McDaniel, J. S. (2003). Meaning of illness and psychological adjustment to HIV/AIDS. *Psychosomatics, 44,* 485–491.

Farina, A. (1976). *Abnormal psychology*. Englewood Cliffs, NJ: Prentice-Hall.

Farrell, C., Shafran, R., & Lee, M. (2006). Empirically evaluated treatments for body image disturbance: A review. *European Eating Disorders Review, 14*, 289–300.

Farstad, S. M., McGeown, L. M., & von Ransom, L. M. (2016). Eating disorders and personality, 2004–2016: A meta-analysis. *Clinical Psychology Review, 46*, 91–105.

Faulkner, G., Irving, H., Paglia-Boak, A., & Adlaf, E. (2010). Adolescent knowledge of schizophrenia and social distancing: A province-wide survey. *Journal of Community Psychology, 38*, 933–942.

Faustman, W. O., Bardgett, M., Faull, K. F., Pfefferman, A., & Cseransky, J. G. (1999). Cerebrospinal fluid glutamate inversely correlates with positive symptom severity in unmedicated male schizophrenic/schizoaffective patients. *Biological Psychiatry, 45*, 68–75.

Fazel, S., Singh, J. P., Doll, H., & Grant, M. (2012). Use of risk assessment instruments to predict violence and antisocial behaviour in 73 samples involving 24,827 people: Systematic review and meta-analysis. *British Medical Journal, 345*, e4962.

Fedora, O., Reddon, J. R., & Yeudall, L. T. (1986). Stimuli eliciting sexual arousal in genital exhibitionists: A possible clinical application. *Archives of Sexual Behavior, 15*, 417–427.

Feingold, B. F. (1973). *Introduction to clinical allergy*. Springfield, IL: Charles C. Thomas.

Feldman, H. A., Goldstein, I., Hatzichristou, D. G., Krane, R. J., & McKinlay, J. B. (1994). Impotence and its medical and psychosocial correlates: Results of the Massachusetts Male Aging Study. *Journal of Urology, 151*, 54–61.

Feldman, M. A., Ducharme, J. M., & Case, L. (1999). Using self-instructional pictorial manuals to teach child-care skills to mothers with intellectual disabilities. *Behavior Modification, 23*, 480–497.

Feldman, R. D., Campbell, N. R., & Wyard, K. (2008). Canadian Hypertension Education Program: The evolution of hypertension management guidelines in Canada. *Canadian Journal of Cardiology, 24*, 477–481.

Felthouse, A. R., O'Shaughnessy, R., Kuten, J., Francois-Purcell, I., & Medrano, J. (2012). The clinician's duty to warn or protect: In the United States, England, Canada, New Zealand, France, and Spain. In A. Felthouse & H. Sass (Eds.), *International handbook on psychopathic disorders and the law* (pp. 75–94). New York: Wiley.

Felton, B. J., & Revenson, T. A. (1984). Coping with chronic illness: A study of illness controllability and the influence of coping strategies on psychological adjustment. *Journal of Consulting and Clinical Psychology, 12*, 343–353.

Fenton, F. R., Cole, M. G., Engelsmann, F., & Mansouri, I. (1997). Depression in older medical inpatients: One-year course and outcome. *International Journal of Geriatric Psychiatry, 12*, 389–394.

Fenton, L. R., et al. (2001). Perspective is everything: The predictive validity of six working alliance instruments. *Journal of Psychotherapy Practice and Research, 10*, 262–268.

Ferenczi, S. (1952). *First contributions to psychoanalysis*. New York: Brunner/Mazel.

Ferguson, C. J., & Colwell, J. (in press). A meaner, more callous digital world for youth? The relationship between violent digital games, motivation, bullying, and civic behaviour amongst children. *Psychology of Popular Media Culture*.

Ferguson, C. J., San Miguel, C., & Hartley, R. D. (2009). A multivariate analysis of youth violence and aggression: The influence of family, peers, depression, and media violence. *The Journal of Pediatrics, 155*, 904–908.

Ferguson, E. (2009). A taxometric analysis of health anxiety. *Psychological Medicine, 39*, 277–285.

Fergusson, D. M., Boden, J. M., & Horwood, J. (2009). Tests of causal links between alcohol abuse or dependent and major depression. *Archives of General Psychiatry, 66*, 260–266.

Fernandez, Y. M., & Marshall, W. L. (2003). Victim empathy, social self-esteem, and psychopathy in rapists. *Sexual Abuse, 15*, 11–26.

Ferster, C. B. (1961). Positive reinforcement and behavioral deficits of autistic children. *Child Development, 32*, 437–456.

Fichten, C. S., Libman, E., Takefman, J., & Brender, W. (1988). Self-monitoring and self-focus in erectile dysfunction. *Journal of Sex and Marital Therapy, 14*, 120–128.

Fichter, M. M., & Quadflieg, N. (2016). Mortality in eating disorders: Results of a large prospective clinical longitudinal study. *International Journal of Eating Disorders, 49*, 391–401.

Fillion, L., Kohn, P., Gagnon, P., van Wijk, M., & Cunningham, A. (2001). The Inventory of Recent Life Experiences for Cancer Patients (IRLEC): A decontaminated measure of cancer-based hassles. *Psychology and Health, 16*, 443–459.

Findlay, L. C., & Sunderland, A. (2014). Professional and informal; mental health support reported by Canadians aged 15 to 24. *Health Reports, 25*, 3–11.

Fineberg, A. M., Ellman, L. M., Buka, S., Yolken, R., & Cannon, T. D. (2013). Decreased birth weight in psychosis: Influence of prenatal exposure to serologically determined influenza and hypoxia. *Schizophrenia Bulletin, 39*, 1037–1044.

Fineberg, N. A., Kaur, S., Kolli, S., Mpavaenda, D., & Reghunandanan, S. (2015). Obsessive-compulsive personality disorder. In K. A. Phillips & D. J. Stein (Eds.), *Handbook on obsessive-compulsive and related disorders* (pp. 247–272). Washington, DC: American Psychiatric Association.

Finger, E. C., et al. (2008). Abnormal ventromedial prefrontal cortex function in children with psychopathic traits during reversal learning. *Archives of General Psychiatry, 65*, 586–594.

Finkelhor, D. (1979). *Sexually victimized children*. New York: Free Press.

Finkelhor, D., Shattuck, A., Turner, H. A., & Hamby, S. L. (2014). The lifetime prevalence of child sexual abuse and sexual assault assessed in late adolescence. *Journal of Adolescent Health, 55*, 329–333.

Finney, J. W., & Moos, R. H. (1998). Psychosocial treatments for alcohol use disorders. In P. E. Nathan & J. M. Gorman (Eds.), *A guide to treatments that work* (pp. 156–166). New York: Oxford University Press.

Firestone, P., Bradford, J. M., Greenberg, D. M., & Larose, M. R. (1998). Homicidal sex offenders: Psychological, psychometric, and diagnostic features. *Journal of the American Academy of Psychiatry and the Law, 26*, 57–552.

Firestone, P., Bradford, J. M., Greenberg, D. M., & Nunes, K. L. (2000). Differentiation of homicidal child molesters, nonhomicidal child molesters, and nonoffenders by phallometry. *American Journal of Psychiatry, 157*, 1847–1850.

Firestone, P., Kingston, D. A., Wexler, A., & Bradford, J. M. (2006). Long-term follow-up of exhibitionists: Psychological, phallometric, and offense characteristics. *Journal of the American Academy of Psychiatry and Law, 34*, 349–359.

First, M. B., Bhat, V., Adler, D., Dixon, L., Goldman, B., Koh, S., … Siris, S. (2014). Do clinicians actually use the Diagnostic and Statistical Manual of Mental Disorders in clinical practice and why we need to know more. *Journal of Nervous and Mental Disease, 202*, 841–844.

First, M. B., Koh, S., & Adler, D. (2015, May 21). How clinicians actually use the *DSM*: Psychiatric Times survey results. *Psychiatric Times*.

First, M. B., Williams, J. B. W., Karg, R. S., & Spitzer, R. L. (2016). *Structured Clinical Interview for DSM-5 Disorders – Clinician Version.* Arlington, VA: American Psychiatric Association.

First, M. B., Williams, J. B. W., Smith Benjamin, L., & Spitzer, R. L. (2016). *Structured Clinical Interview for DSM-5 Personality Disorders.* Arlington, VA: American Psychiatric Association.

Fischer, B., & Argento, E. (2012). Prescription opioid related misuse, harms, diversion, and interventions in Canada: A review. *Pain Physician, 15,* ES191–ES203.

Fischer, B., Ialomiteanu, A., Boak, A., et al. (2013). Prevalence and key covariates of non-medical prescription opioid use among the general secondary student and adult populations in Ontario, Canada. *Drug and Alcohol Review, 32,* 276–287.

Fischer, D. G., & McDonald, W. L. (1998). Characteristics of intrafamilial and extrafamilial child sexual abuse. *Child Abuse and Neglect, 22,* 915–929.

Fischer, M. (1971). Psychoses in the offspring of schizophrenic monozygotic twins and their normal co-twins. *British Journal of Psychiatry, 118,* 43–52.

Fischer, S., Gaab, J., Ehlert, U., & Nater, U. M. (2013). Prevalence, overlap, and predictors of functional somatic syndromes in a student sample. *International Journal of Behavioral Medicine, 20,* 184–193.

Fisher, J. E., & Noll, J. P. (1996). Anxiety disorders. In L. L. Carstensen, B. A. Edelstein, & L. Dornbrand (Eds.), *The practical handbook of clinical gerontology* (pp. 304–323). Thousand Oaks, CA: Sage.

Fishman, D. B. (1999). *The case for pragmatic psychology.* New York: NYU Press.

Fiske, A., Wetherell, J. L., & Gatz, M. (2009). Depression in older adults. *Annual Review of Clinical Psychology, 5,* 363–389.

Fitzgerald, P. B., et al. (2006). An analysis of functional neuroimaging studies of dorsolateral pre-frontal cortical activity in depression. *Psychiatry Research: Neuroimaging, 148,* 33–45.

Fitzgerald, P. J., Seemann, J. R., & Maren, S. (2014). Can fear extinction be enhanced? A review of pharmacological and behavioral findings. *Brain Research Bulletin, 105,* 46–60.

Fitzpatrick, M. R., Iwakabe, S., & Stalikas, A. (2005). Prospective divergence in the working alliance. *Psychotherapy Research, 15,* 69–80.

Flamenbaum, R., & Holden, R. R. (2007). Psychache as a mediator in the relationship between perfectionism and suicidality. *Journal of Counseling Psychology, 54,* 51–61.

Flessner, C. A., Francazio, S., Murphy, Y. E., & Brennan, E. (2015). An examination of executive functioning in young adults exhibiting body-focused repetitive behaviors. *Journal of Nervous and Mental Disease, 203,* 555–558.

Flessner, C. A., Penzel, F., Trichotillomania Learning Center–Scientific Advisory Board. (2010). Current treatment practices for children and adults with trichotillomania: Consensus among experts. *Cognitive and Behavioral Practice, 17,* 290–300.

Fletcher, P. C., McKenna, P. J., Frith, C. D., Friston, K. J., & Dolan, R. J. (1998). Brain activations in schizophrenia during a graded memory task studied with functional imaging. *Archives of General Psychiatry, 55,* 1001–1009.

Flett, G. L., Baricza, C., Gupta, A., Hewitt, P. L., & Endler, N. S. (2011). Perfectionism, psychosocial impact, and coping with irritable bowel disease: A study of patients with Crohn's disease and ulcerative colitis. *Journal of Health Psychology, 16,* 561–571.

Flett, G. L., & Blankstein, K. R. (1994). Worry as a component of test anxiety: A multidimensional analysis. In G. C. L. Davey & F. Tallis (Eds.), *Worrying: Perspectives on theory, assessment, and treatment* (pp. 135–181). London: Wiley.

Flett, G. L., Coulter, L.-M., & Hewitt, P. L. (2012). The Perfectionistic Self-Presentation Scale—Junior Form: Psychometric properties and association with social anxiety. *Canadian Journal of School Psychology, 27,* 136–149.

Flett, G. L., Endler, N. S., & Fairlie, P. (1997). The interactional model of coping and anxiety: The threat of Quebec's separation from Canada. *Journal of Personality and Social Psychology, 76,* 143–150.

Flett, G. L., Goldstein, A. L., Hewitt, P. L., & Wekerle, C. (2012). Predictors of deliberate self-harm behavior among emerging adolescents: An initial test of a self-punitiveness model. *Current Psychology, 31,* 49–64.

Flett, G. L., & Hewitt, P. L. (2013). Disguised distress in children and adolescents "flying under the radar": Why psychological problems are underestimated and how schools must respond. *Canadian Journal of School Psychology, 28,* 12–27.

Flett, G. L., Hewitt, P. L., Blankstein, K. R., & Gray, L. (1998). Psychological distress and the frequency of perfectionistic thinking. *Journal of Personality and Social Psychology, 75,* 1363–1381.

Flett, G. L., Hewitt, P. L., & Nepon, T. (2016). Perfectionism, worry, and rumination in health and mental health: A review and a conceptual framework for a cognitive theory of perfectionism. In F. M. Sirois & D. S. Molnar (Eds.), *Perfectionism, health, and well-being* (pp. 121–156). New York: Springer.

Flett, G. L., Hewitt, P. L., & Sherry, S. B. (2016). Deep, dark, and dysfunctional: The destructiveness of interpersonal perfectionism. In V. Zeigler-Hill & D. K. Marcus (Eds.), *The dark side of personality* (pp. 211–229). Washington, DC: American Psychological Association.

Flett, G. L., Nepon, T., Hewitt, P. L., Molnar, D. G., & Zhao, W. (2016). Projecting perfection by hiding effort: Supplementing the Perfectionistic Self-Presentation Scale with a brief self-presentation measure. *Self and Identity, 15,* 245–261.

Flett, G. L., Vredenburg, K., & Krames, L. (1997). The continuity of depression in clinical and nonclinical samples. *Psychological Bulletin, 121,* 395–416.

Fleury, M.-J., Grenier, G., Barnvita, J.-M., Perreault, M., & Caron, J. (in press). Variables associated with perceived unmet need for mental health care in a Canadian epidemiological catchment area. *Psychiatric Services.*

Flick, U., Garms-Homolova, V., & Rohnsch, G. (2012). "And mostly they have a need for sleeping pills": Physicians' views on treatment of sleep disorders with drugs in nursing homes. *Journal of Aging Studies, 26,* 484–494.

Flinn, L., Braham, L., & das Nair, R. (2015). How reliable are case formulations? A systematic literature review. *British Journal of Clinical Psychology, 54,* 266–290.

Flint, A. J. (1994). Epidemiology and comorbidity of anxiety disorders in the elderly. *American Journal of Psychiatry, 151,* 640–649.

Flint, A. J., & Rifat, S. L. (1996). The effect of sequential antidepressant treatment on geriatric depression. *Journal of Affective Disorders, 36,* 95–105.

Flint, A. J., & Rifat, S. L. (1997). Two-year outcome of elderly patients with anxious depression. *Psychiatry Research, 66,* 23–31.

Flint, A. J., & Rifat, S. L. (2000). Maintenance treatment for recurrent depression in late life: A four-year outcome study. *American Journal of Geriatric Psychiatry, 8,* 112–116.

Floyd, M., Scogin, F., McKendree-Smith, N. L., Floyd, D. L., & Rokke, P. D. (2004). Cognitive therapy for depression: A comparison of individual psychotherapy and bibliotherapy for depressed older adults. *Behavior Modification, 28,* 297–318.

Fluke, J. D., Chabot, M., Fallon, B., MacLaurin, B., & Blackstock, C. (2010). Placement decisions and disparities among aboriginal groups: An application of the decision making ecology through multi-level analysis. *Child Abuse & Neglect, 34,* 57–69.

Fluoxetine Bulimia Nervosa Collaborative Study Group. (1992). Fluoxetine in the treatment of bulimia nervosa: A multicenter, placebo-controlled, double blind trial. *Archives of General Psychiatry, 49,* 139–147.

Foa, E. B. (2010). Cognitive behavioral therapy of obsessive-compulsive disorder. *Dialogues in Clinical Neuroscience, 12,* 199–207.

Foa, E. B., Gillihan, S. J., & Bryant, R. A. (2013). Challenges and successes in the dissemination of evidence-based treatments for post-traumatic stress: Lessons learned from prolonged exposure therapy for PTSD. *Psychological Science in the Public Interest, 14,* 65–111.

Foa, E. B., & McLean, C. P. (2016). The efficacy of exposure therapy for anxiety-related disorder and its underlying mechanisms: The case of OCD and PTSD. *Annual Review of Clinical Psychology, 12,* 1–28.

Foa, E. B., Riggs, D. S., Marsie, E. D., & Yarczower, M. (1995). The impact of fear activation and anger on the efficacy of exposure treatment for post-traumatic stress disorder. *Behavior Therapy, 26,* 487–499.

Foellmi, M., & Rosenfeld, B. (2015). Tarasoff and the duty to warn. *The Encyclopedia of Clinical Psychology,* 1–3.

Folkman, S., Bernstein, L., & Lazarus, R. S. (1987). Stress processes and the misuse of drugs in older adults. *Psychology and Aging, 2,* 366–374.

Folks, D. G., Ford, C. V., & Regan, W. M. (1984). Conversion symptoms in a general hospital. *Psychosomatics, 25,* 285–295.

Folstein, M. F., Folstein, S. E., & McHugh, P. R. (1975). "Mini-mental state": A practical method for grading the cognitive state of patients for the clinician. *Journal of Psychiatric Research, 12,* 189–198.

Fombonne, E. (1999). The epidemiology of autism: A review. *Psychological Medicine, 29,* 769–786.

Fombonne, E. (2003). Epidemiology of pervasive developmental disorders. *Trends in Evidence-Based Neuropsychiatry, 5,* 29–36.

Fombonne, E. (2005). Epidemiology of autistic disorder and other pervasive developmental disorders. *Journal of Clinical Psychiatry, 66 (Supplement 10),* 3–8.

Fong, G. T., Hammond, D., & Hitchman, S. C. (2009). The impact of pictures on the effectiveness of tobacco warnings. *Bulletin of the World Health Organization, 87,* 640–643.

Fong, P. (2007, June 7). Vancouver eyes moving homeless back to institution: Many now on streets of Downtown Eastside were residents of sprawling facility in Coquitlam. *Toronto Star,* A23.

Fontaine, N. M. G., Brendgen, M., Vitaro, F., & Tremblay, R. E. (2016). Compensatory and protective factors against violent delinquency in late adolescence: Results from the Montreal longitudinal and experimental study. *Journal of Criminal Justice, 45,* 54–62.

Foong, J., Ridding, M., Cope, H., Mardsen, C. D., & Ron, M. A. (1997). Corticospinal function in conversion disorder. *Journal of Neuropsychiatry and Clinical Neurosciences, 9,* 302–303.

Foot, R. (2007, May 26). Jury still out on whether community treatment orders help mentally ill. *Canwest News.*

Ford, T., Fowler, T., Langley, K., et al. (2008). Five years on: Public sector service use related to mental health in young people with ADHD or hyperkinetic disorder five years after diagnosis. *Child and Adolescent Mental Health, 13,* 122–129.

Fordyce, W. E., Brockway, J. A., Bergman, J. A., & Spengler, D. (1986). Acute back pain: A control-group comparison of behavioral vs. traditional methods. *Journal of Behavioral Medicine, 9,* 127–140.

Forsman, M., et al. (2010). A longitudinal twin study of the direction of effects between psychopathic personality and antisocial behavior. *The Journal of Child Psychology and Psychiatry, 51,* 39–47.

Forsythe, C. J., & Compas, B. E. (1987). Interaction of cognitive appraisals of stressful events and coping: Testing the goodness of fit hypothesis. *Cognitive Therapy and Research, 11,* 473–485.

Forth, A. E. (2005). Hare Psychopathy Checklist: Youth Version. In T. Grisso, G. Vincent, & D. Seagrave (Eds.), *Mental health screening and assessment in juvenile justice* (pp. 324–338). New York: Guilford.

Forth, A. E., Kosson, D. S., & Hare, R. (2003). *Hare Psychopathy Checklist: Youth Version manual.* Toronto: Multi-Health Systems, Inc.

Foucault, M. (1965). *Madness and civilization.* New York: Random House.

Fournier, J. C., DeRubreis, R. C., Shelton, R. C., et al. (2008). Antidepressant medication v. cognitive therapy in people with depression with or without personality disorder. *The British Journal of Psychiatry, 192,* 124–129.

Foussias, G., Mann, S., Zakzanis, K. K., van Reekum, R., Agid, O., & Remington, G. (2011). Prediction of longitudinal functional outcomes in schizophrenia: The impact of baseline motivational deficits. *Schizophrenia research, 132,* 24–27.

Foussias, G., Mann, S., Zakzanis, K. K., van Reekum, R., & Remington, G. (2009). Motivational deficits as the central link to functioning in schizophrenia: A pilot study. *Schizophrenia Research, 115,* 333–337.

Fouts, G., & Burggraf, K. (2000). Television situation comedies: Female weight, male negative comments, and audience reactions. *Sex Roles, 42,* 925–932.

Fox, K. R., Franklin, J. C., Ribeiro, J. D., Kleiman, E. M., Bentley, K. H., & Nock, M. K. (2015). Meta-analysis of risk factors for nonsuicidal self-injury. *Clinical Psychology Review, 42,* 156–167.

Fox, N. A., Henderson, H. A., Marshall, P. J., Nichols, K. E., & Ghera, M. M. (2005). Behavioral inhibition: Linking biology and behavior within a developmental framework. *Annual Review of Psychology, 56,* 235–262.

Fox, N. A., Nichols, K. E., Henderson, H. A., Rubin, K., et al. (2005). Evidence for a gene-environment interaction predicting behavior inhibition in middle childhood. *Psychological Science, 16,* 921–926.

Foxcroft, D. R., & Tsertsvadse, A. (2011). Universal school-based prevention program or alcohol misuse in young people. *Cochrane Database of Systematic Reviews, 5,* CD009113.

Frances, A. (2013). *Saving normal: An insider's revolt against out-of-control psychiatric diagnosis, DSM-5, Big Pharma, and the medicalization of ordinary life.* New York: HarperCollins Publishers.

Frank, E., Anderson, C., & Rubenstein, D. (1978). Frequency of sexual dysfunctions in "normal" couples. *New England Journal of Medicine, 299,* 111–115.

Frank, E., Kupfer, D. J., Perel, J. M., et al. (1990). Three-year outcomes for maintenance therapies in recurrent depression. *Archives of General Psychiatry, 47,* 1093–1099.

Frank, J. D. (1961). *Persuasion and healing.* Baltimore: Johns Hopkins University Press. Second edition, 1973; third edition, 1978.

Frank, J. D. (1974). Psychotherapy: the restoration of morale. *American Journal of Psychiatry, 131,* 271–274.

Frank, J. D., & Frank, J. (1985). Therapeutic components shared by all psychotherapies. In A. Freeman, M. J. Mahoney, & P. Devito (Eds.), *Cognition and psychotherapy* (pp. 45–78). New York: Springer.

Franklin, M. E., & Foa, E. B. (1998). Cognitive-behavioral treatments for obsessive-compulsive disorder. In P. E. Nathan & J. M. Gorman (Eds.), *A guide to treatments that work* (pp. 339–357). New York: Oxford University Press.

Fraser, G. A. (1994). Dissociative phenomena and disorders: Clinical presentations. In R. M. Klein & B. K. Doane (Eds.), *Psychological concepts and dissociative disorders* (pp. 131–151). Hillsdale, NJ: Erlbaum.

Fraser, S. E. (2015). Hospital knows best: Court and unfit accused at the mercy of hospital administrators: The case of R. v. Conception. *Supreme Court Law Review: Osgoode's Annual Constitutional Cases Conference, 71,* 301–327.

Fraser Institute. (2008, October). *Waiting your turn: Hospital waiting lists in Canada 2008 report, 18th edition.* Vancouver: Author.

Frasure-Smith, N., & Lesperance, F. (2008). Depression and anxiety as predictors of 2-year cardiac events in patients with stable coronary artery disease. *Archives of General Psychiatry, 65,* 62–71.

Frasure-Smith, N., & Prince, R. (1989). Long-term follow-up of the Ischemic Heart Disease Life Stress Monitoring Program. *Psychosomatic Medicine, 51,* 485–513.

Frazier, P., Anders, S., Perera, S., Tomich, P., Tennen, H., Park, C., & Tashiro, T. (2009). Traumatic events among undergraduate students: Prevalence and associated symptoms. *Journal of Counseling Psychology, 56,* 450–460.

Freeston, M. H., et al. (1997). Cognitive-behavioral treatment of obsessive thoughts: A controlled study. *Journal of Consulting and Clinical Psychology, 65,* 405–413.

Fremouw, W. J., de Perczel, M., & Ellis, T. (1990). *Suicide risk: Assessment and response guidelines.* Elmsford, NY: Pergamon.

Freud, A. (1966). *The ego and the mechanisms of defense.* New York: International Universities Press.

Freud, S. (1917). Mourning and melancholia. In *Collected papers* (Vol. 4). London: Hogarth and the Institute of Psychoanalysis, 1950.

Freud, S. (1937). Analysis terminable and interminable. *International Journal of Psychoanalysis, 18,* 373–391.

Freund, K. (1967). Diagnosing homo- or heterosexuality and erotic age-preference by means of a psychophysiological test. *Behaviour Research and Therapy, 5,* 209–228.

Freund, K. (1990). Courtship disorders. In W. L. Marshall, D. R. Laws, & H. E. Barbaree (Eds.), *Handbook of sexual assault: Issues, theories, and treatment* (pp. 195–207). New York: Plenum Press.

Freund, K., & Watson, R. (1991). Assessment of the sensitivity and specificity of a phallometric test: An update of phallometric diagnosis of pedophilia. *Psychological Assessment, 3,* 254–260.

Frick, A., Åhs, F., Engman, J., Jonasson, M., Alaie, I., Björkstrand, J., ... Furmark, T. (2015). Serotonin synthesis and reuptake in social anxiety disorder: A positron emission tomography study. *JAMA Psychiatry, 72,* 794–802.

Frick, P. J. (2009). Extending the construct of psychopathy to youth: Implications for understanding, diagnosing, and treating antisocial children and adolescents. *Canadian Journal of Psychiatry, 54,* 803–812.

Frick, P. J. (2012). Developmental pathways to conduct disorder: Implications for future directions in research, assessment, and treatment. *Journal of Clinical Child and Adolescent Psychology, 41,* 378–389.

Frick, P. J., & Moffitt, T. E. (2010). A proposal to the DSM-V Childhood Disorders and the ADHD and Disruptive Behavior Disorders Work Groups to include a specifier to the diagnosis of conduct disorder based on the presence of callous-unemotional traits. Retrieved from http://www.dsm5.org/Proposed%20Revision%20Attachments/Proposal%20for%20Callous%20and%20Unemotional%20Specifier%20of%20Conduct%20Disorder.pdf.

Frick, P. J., & Nigg, J. T. (2012). Current issues in the diagnosis of attention deficit hyperactivity disorder, oppositional defiant disorder, and conduct disorder. *Annual Review of Clinical Psychology, 8,* 77–107.

Fried, P., Watkinson, B., James, D., & Gray, R. (2002). Current and former marijuana use: Preliminary findings of a longitudinal study of effects of IQ in young adults. *Canadian Medical Association Journal, 166,* 887–891.

Friedman, M. (1969). *Pathogenesis of coronary artery disease.* New York: McGraw-Hill.

Friedman, M. J., Kilpatrick, D. G., Schnurr, P. P., & Weathers, F. W. (2015). Correcting misconceptions about the diagnosis for post-traumatic stress disorder in *DSM-5. JAMA Psychiatry, 73,* 753–754.

Frise, S., Steingart, A., Sloan, M., Cotterchio, M., & Kreiger, N. (2002). Psychiatric disorders and use of mental health services by Ontario women. *Canadian Journal of Psychiatry, 47,* 849–856.

Fromm-Reichmann, F. (1948). Notes on the development of treatment of schizophrenics by psychoanalytic psychotherapy. *Psychiatry, 11,* 263–273.

Frost, R. O., & Gross, R. (1993). The hoarding of possessions. *Behaviour Research and Therapy, 31,* 367–381.

Frost, R. O., & Hartl, T. (1996). A cognitive-behavioral model of compulsive hoarding. *Behaviour Research and Therapy, 34,* 341–350.

Frost, R. O., Steketee, G., & Tolin, D. F. (2012). Diagnosis and assessment of hoarding disorder. *Annual Review of Clinical Psychology, 8,* 219–242.

Fruzzetti, A. E., & Erikson, K. R. (2010). Mindfulness and acceptance interventions in cognitive-behavioral therapy. In K. S. Dobson (Ed.), *Handbook of cognitive-behavioral therapies* (3rd ed., pp. 347–372). New York: Guilford.

Fry, P. S. (1993). Mediators of depression in community-based elders. In P. Cappeliez & R. J. Flynn (Eds.), *Depression and the social environment: Research and intervention with neglected populations* (pp. 369–394). Montreal: McGill-Queen's University Press.

Fry, P. S. (2001). The unique contribution of key existential factors to the prediction of psychological well-being of older adults following spousal loss. *The Gerontologist, 41,* 69–81.

Fuentes, K., & Cox, B. J. (1997). Prevalence of anxiety disorders in elderly adults: A critical analysis. *Journal of Behavior Therapy and Experimental Psychiatry, 28,* 269–279.

Fuerst, K. B., & Rourke, B. P. (1995). Human neuropsychology in Canada: The 1980s. *Canadian Psychology, 36,* 12–45.

Fuller, R. K. (1988). Disulfiram treatment of alcoholism. In R. M. Rose & J. E. Barrett (Eds.), *Alcoholism: Treatment and outcome.* New York: Raven.

Fuller-Thomson, E., Noack, A. M., & George, U. (2011). Health decline among recent immigrants to Canada: Findings from a nationally representative longitudinal survey. *Canadian Journal of Public Health, 102,* 273–280.

Fuller-Thomson, E., & Sawyer, J.-L. (2012). Is the cluster risk model of parental adversities better than the cumulative risk model as an indicator of childhood physical abuse? Findings from two representative community surveys. *Child: Care, Health, and Development, 40*(1), 124–133.

Funk, W. (1998). *What difference does it make? The journey of a soul survivor.* Cranbrook, BC: Wild Flower Publishing.

Furnham, A., & Telford, K. (2011). Public attitudes, lay theories, and mental health literacy: The understanding of mental health. Intech Open. Retrieved from http://cdn.intechweb.org/pdfs/25508.pdf.

Fusar-Poli, P., Bonoldi, I., Yung, A. R., Borgwardt, S., et al. (2012). Predicting psychosis: Meta-analysis of transition outcomes in individuals at high clinical risk. *Archives of General Psychiatry, 69,* 220–229.

Futa, K. T., Nash, C. L., Hansen, D. J., & Garbin, C. P. (2003). Adult survivors of childhood abuse: An analysis of coping mechanisms used for stressful childhood memories and current stressors. *Journal of Family Violence, 18,* 227–239.

Gabbay, F. H. (1992). Behavior genetic strategies in the study of emotion. *Psychological Science, 3,* 50–55.

Gable, S. L., Reis, H. T., & Elliot, A. J. (2000). Behavioral activation and inhibition in everyday life. *Journal of Personality and Social Psychology, 78,* 1135–1149.

Gadalla, T. (2008). Association of comorbid mood disorders and chronic illness with disability and quality of life in Ontario, Canada. *Chronic Diseases in Canada, 28*, 148–154.

Gadalla, T., & Piran, N. (2007). Co-occurrence of eating disorders and alcohol use disorders in women: A meta-analysis. *Archive of Women's Mental Health, 10*, 133–140.

Gafoor, R., Nitsch, D., McCrone, P., et al. (2010). Effect of early intervention on 5-year outcome in non-affective psychosis. *British Journal of Psychiatry, 196*, 372–376.

Gagné, A., & Morin, C. M. (2001). Predicting treatment response in older adults with insomnia. *Journal of Clinical Geropsychology, 7*, 131–143.

Gagnon, J. H. (1977). *Human sexualities*. Glenview, IL: Scott, Foresman.

Galaburda, A. M. (2005). Neurology of learning disabilities: What will the future bring? The answer comes from the successes of the recent past. *Learning Disability Quarterly, 28*, 107–109.

Gale, C., Gilbert, P., Read, N., & Goss, K. (2014). An evaluation of the impact of introducing compassion focused therapy to a standard treatment programme for people with eating disorders. *Clinical Psychology and Psychotherapy, 21*, 1–12.

Galera, C., Melchior, M., Chastang, J.-F., et al. (2009). Childhood and adolescent hyperactivity-inattention symptoms and academic achievement 8 years later: The GAZEL Youth study. *Psychological Medicine, 39*, 1895–1906.

Gallagher, D., & Thompson, L. W. (1982). *Elders' maintenance of treatment benefits following individual psychotherapy for depression: Results of a pilot study and preliminary data from an ongoing replication study*. Paper presented at the annual meeting of the American Psychological Association, Washington, DC.

Gallagher, D., & Thompson, L. W. (1983). Cognitive therapy for depression in the elderly. A promising model for treatment and research. In L. D. Breslau & M. R. Haug (Eds.), *Depression and aging: Causes, care and consequences*. New York: Springer.

Gallagher, M. W., Payne, L. A., White, K. S., Shear, K. M., Woods, S. W., Gorman, J. M., & Barlow, D. H. (2013). Mechanisms of change in cognitive behavioral therapy for panic disorder: The unique effects of self-efficacy and anxiety sensitivity. *Behaviour Research and Therapy, 51*, 767–777.

Gallagher-Thompson, D., & Coon, D. W. (2007). Evidence-based psychological treatments for distress in family caregivers of older adults. *Psychology and Aging, 22*, 37–51.

Gallagher-Thompson, D., & Thompson, L. W. (1995a). Efficacy of psychotherapeutic interventions with older adults. *The Clinical Psychologist, 48*, 24–30.

Gallagher-Thompson, D., & Thompson, L. W. (1995b). Psychotherapy with older adults in theory and practice. In B. Bongar & L. E. Beutler (Eds.), *Comprehensive textbook of psychotherapy: Theory and practice* (pp. 359–379). New York: Oxford University Press.

Galli, V., McElroy, S. L., Soutullo, C. A., Kizer, D., Raute, N., et al. (1999). The psychiatric diagnoses of twenty-two adolescents who have sexually molested children. *Comprehensive Psychiatry, 40*, 85–88.

Galloway, G. (2016, July 13). Veterans with mental illness forced to wait months for treatment care. *The Globe and Mail*.

Gallucci, A. R., Martin, R. J., Hackman, C., & Hutcheson, A. (in press). Exploring the relationship between the misuse of stimulant medications and academic dishonesty among a sample of college students. *Journal of Community Health*.

Gao, Y., Raine, A., Venables, P. H., et al. (2010). Association of poor childhood fear conditioning and adult crime. *American Journal of Psychiatry, 167*, 56–60.

Garb, H. N., Wood, J. M., Lilienfeld, S. O., & Nezworski, M. T. (2005). Roots of the Rorschach controversy. *Clinical Psychology Review, 25*, 97–118.

Garbutt, J. C., et al. (1994). Dose-response studies with protirelin. *Archives of General Psychiatry, 51*, 875–883.

Garcia, J., McGowan, B. K., & Green, K. F. (1972). Biological constraints on conditioning. In A. H. Black & W. F. Prokasy (Eds.), *Classical conditioning: 2. Current research and theory*. New York: Appleton-Century-Crofts.

Garcia-Lopez, L. J., et al. (2006). Efficacy of three treatment protocols for adolescents with social anxiety disorder: A 5-year follow-up assessment. *Journal of Anxiety Disorders, 20*, 175–191.

Gardener, H., Spiegelman, D., & Buka, S. L. (2009). Prenatal risk factors for autism: Comprehensive meta-analysis. *British Journal of Psychiatry, 195*, 7–14.

Garety, P. A., Fowler, D. G., Freeman, D., et al. (2008). Cognitive-behavioural therapy and family intervention for relapse prevention and symptom reduction in psychosis: Randomised controlled trial. *The British Journal of Psychiatry, 192*, 412–423.

Garfield, C. F., Dorsey, E. R., Zhu, S., Huskamp, H. A., et al. (2012). Trends in attention deficit hyperactivity disorder ambulatory diagnosis and medical treatment in the United States, 2000-2010. *Academic Pediatrics, 12*, 110–116.

Garfinkel, P. E. (2002). Classification and diagnosis of eating disorders. In C. G. Fairburn & K. D. Brownell (Eds.), *Eating disorders and obesity: A comprehensive handbook* (2nd ed., pp. 155–161). New York: Guilford.

Garfinkel, P. E., Kennedy, S. H., & Kaplan, A. S. (1995). Views on classification and diagnosis of eating disorders. *Canadian Journal of Psychiatry, 40*, 445–456.

Gariepy, G., & Elgar, F. J. (in press). Trends in psychological symptoms among Canadian adolescents from 2002 to 2014: Gender and socio-economic differences. *Canadian Journal of Psychiatry*.

Garland, R. J., & Dougher, M. J. (1991). Motivational interviewing in the treatment of sex offenders. In W. R. Miller & S. Rollnick (Eds.), *Motivational interviewing: Preparing people to change addictive behavior* (pp. 303–313). New York: Guilford.

Garner, D. M. (1997). Psychoeducational principles. In D. M. Garner & P. E. Garfinkel (Eds.), *Handbook of treatment for eating disorders* (pp. 145–177). New York: Guilford.

Garner, D. M., Garfinkel, P. E., Schwartz, D., & Thompson, M. (1980). Cultural expectations of thinness in women. *Psychological Reports, 47*, 483–491.

Garner, D. M., Olmsted, M. P., & Polivy, J. (1983). Development and validation of a multi-dimensional eating disorder inventory for anorexia nervosa and bulimia. *International Journal of Eating Disorders, 2*, 15–34.

Garner, D. M., Vitousek, K. M., & Pike, K. M. (1997). Cognitive-behavioral therapy for anorexia nervosa. In D. M. Garner & P. E. Garfinkel (Eds.), *Handbook of treatment for eating disorders* (pp. 94–144). New York: Guilford.

Garnier-Dykstra, L. M., Caldeira, K. M., Vincent, K. B., O'Grady, K. E., & Arria, A. M. (2012). Nonmedical use of prescription stimulants during college: Four-year trends in exposure opportunity, use, motives, and sources. *Journal of American College Health, 60*, 226–234.

Gasquoine, P. G. (2009). Race norming of neuropsychological tests. *Neuropsychological Review, 19*, 250–262.

Gatz, M., et al. (2006). Role of genes and environments for explaining Alzheimer's Disease. *Archives of General Psychiatry, 63*, 168–174.

Gatz, M., Kasl-Godley, J. E., & Karel, M. J. (1996). Aging and mental disorders. In J. E. Birren & K. W. Schaie (Eds.), *Handbook of the psychology of aging*. San Diego: Academic Press.

Gatz, M., & Pearson, C. G. (1988). Ageism revised and the provision of psychological services. *American Psychologist, 43*, 184–188.

Gatz, M., Popkin, S. J., Pino, C. D., & VandenBos, G. R. (1985). Psychological interventions with older adults. In J. E. Birren & W. K. Schaie (Eds.), *Handbook of the psychology of aging* (pp. 755–785). New York: Van Nostrand Reinhold.

Gauthier, J. G. (2002). Facilitating mobility for psychologists through a competency-based approach for regulation and accreditation: The Canadian experiment. *European Psychologist, 7*, 203–212.

Gauthier, S., & Scheltens, P. (2009). Can we do better in developing new drugs for Alzheimer's disease? *Alzheimer's and Dementia, 5*, 489–491.

Gautreau, C., Sherry, S., Battista, S., Goldstein, A., & Stewart, S. (2015). Enhancement motives moderate the relationship between high-arousal positive moods and drinking quantity: Evidence from a 22-day experience sampling study. *Drug and Alcohol Review, 34*, 595–602.

Gautreau, C. M., Sherry, S. B., Sherry, D. L., Birnie, K. A., Mackinnon, S. P., & Stewart, S. H. (2015). Does catastrophizing of bodily sensations maintain health-related anxiety? A 14-day daily diary study with longitudinal follow-up. *Behavioral and Cognitive Psychotherapy, 43*, 502–512.

Gaydukevych, D., & Kocovski, N. L. (2012). Effect of self-focused attention on post-event processing in social anxiety. *Behaviour Research and Therapy, 50*, 47–55.

Ge, X., Conger, R. D., Cadoret, R. J., et al. (1996). The developmental interface between nature and nurture: A mutual influence model of child antisocial behavior and parent behaviors. *Developmental Psychology, 32*, 574–589.

Gebhard, P. H., Gagnon, J. H., Pomeroy, W. B., & Christenson, C. V. (1965). *Sex offenders*. New York: Harper & Row.

Geddes, J. (2001, April 23). Northern son. *Maclean's*, 16–20.

Geer, J. H., Davison, G. C., & Gatchel, R. I. (1970). Reduction of stress in humans through nonveridical perceived control of aversive stimulation. *Journal of Personality and Social Psychology, 16*, 731–738.

Gefen, T., Peterson, M., Papastefan, S. T., Martersteck, A., et al. (2015). Morphometric and histologic substrates of cingulate integrity in elders with exceptional memory capacity. *The Journal of Neuroscience, 35*, 1781–1791.

Gelernter, C. S., et al. (1991). Cognitive behavioral and pharmacological treatments of social phobia: A controlled study. *Archives of General Psychiatry, 48*, 938–945.

Gelernter, J., & Kranzler, H. R. (2009). Genetics of alcohol dependence. *Human Genetics, 126*, 91–99.

Gellatly, R., & Beck, A. T. (2016). Catastrophic thinking: A transdiagnostic process across psychiatric disorders. *Cognitive Therapy and Research, 40*, 441–452.

Geller, G., & Thomas, C. D. (1999). A review of eating disorders in immigrant women: Possible evidence of a cultural-change model. *Eating Disorders: The Journal of Treatment and Prevention, 7*, 279–297.

Geller, J., Cockell, S. J., Hewitt, P. L., Goldner, E. M., & Flett, G. L. (2000). Inhibited expression of negative emotions and interpersonal orientation in anorexia nervosa. *International Journal of Eating Disorders, 28*, 8–19.

Gendreau, P., Little, T., & Goggin, C. (1996). A meta-analysis of the predictors of adult offender recidivism: What works! *Criminology, 34*, 575–608.

General Register Office. (1968). *A glossary of mental disorders* (Studies on Medical and Population Subjects No. 22). London: Her Majesty's Stationery Office.

Gentes, E. L., & Ruscio, A. M. (2011). A meta-analysis of the relation of intolerance of uncertainty to symptoms of generalized anxiety disorder, major depressive disorder, and obsessive-compulsive disorder. *Clinical Psychology Review, 31*, 923–933.

George, L. K. (1980). *Role transitions in later life*. Monterey, CA: Brooks/Cole.

Gerdes, A. B., Pauli, P., & Alpers, G. W. (2009). Toward and away from spiders: Eye-movements in spider-fearful participants. *Journal of Neural Transmitters, 116*, 725–733.

Gerlach, M. (2009). Peer-reviewed reports on all topics relevant to attention-deficit/hyperactivity disorder. *ADHD Attention Deficit and Hyperactivity Disorders, 1*, 1–2.

Gervais, A., et al. (2006). Milestones in the natural course of onset of cigarette use among adolescents. *Canadian Medical Association Journal, 175*, 255–261.

Ghaffar, O., Staines W. R., & Feinstein, A. (2006). Unexplained neurologic symptoms: An fMRI study of sensory conversion disorder. *Neurology, 67*, 2036–2038.

Ghoneim, M. M., & Mewaldt, S. P. (1990). Benzodiazepines and human memory: A review. *Anesthesiology, 72*, 926–938.

Gianaros, P. J., et al. (2008). Individual differences in stress-evoked blood pressure reactivity vary with activation, volume, and functional connectivity of the amygdala. *The Journal of Neuroscience, 28*, 990–998.

Gianaros, P. J., Hariri, A. R., Sheu, L. K., et al. (2009). Preclinical atherosclerosis covaries with individual differences in reactivity and functional connectivity of the amygdala. *Biological Psychiatry, 65*, 943–950.

Gibbons, C. R., Stirman, S. W., DeRubeis, R. J., Newman, C. F., & Beck, A. T. (2013). Research setting versus clinic setting: Which produces better outcomes in cognitive therapy for depression? *Cognitive Therapy and Research, 37*, 605–612.

Gilbert, F. S. (1991). Development of a "steps questionnaire." *Journal of Studies on Alcohol, 52*, 353–360.

Gilbert, P. (2014). The origins and nature of compassion focused therapy. *British Journal of Clinical Psychology, 53*, 6–41.

Gilger, J. W., & Kaplan, B. J. (2001). Atypical brain development: A conceptual framework for understanding developmental learning disabilities. *Developmental Neuropsychology, 20*, 465–481.

Gilhooly, M., & McDonach, E. (2003). An average old age: Associations between ageing, health, and behaviour. In S. P. Llewelyn & P. Kennedy (Eds.), *Handbook of clinical health psychology* (pp. 437–453). Chichester, England: John Wiley & Sons.

Gillan, C. M., Morein-Zamir, S., Urcelay, G. P., Sule, A., Voon, V., Apergis-Schoute, A., . . . Robbins, T. W. (2014). Enhanced avoidance habits in obsessive-compulsive disorder. *Biological Psychiatry, 75*, 631–638.

Gillmor, D. (1987). *I swear by Apollo: Dr. Ewen Cameron and the CIA-brainwashing experiments*. Montreal: Eden Press.

Gingrich, H. D. (2009). Assessing dissociative symptoms and dissociative disorders in college students in the Philippines. *Journal of Aggression, Maltreatment, and Trauma, 18*, 403–418.

Ginting, H., van de Ven, M., Becker, E. S., & Naring, G. (2016). Type D personality is associated with health behaviors and perceived social support in individuals with coronary heart disease. *Journal of Health Psychology, 21*, 727–737.

Girard, D. (2007, March 26). Childhood ills linked to reading troubles, lifelong woes. *Toronto Star*, A1, A6.

Gizewski, E. R., et al. (2009). Specific cerebral activation due to visual erotic stimuli in male-to-female transsexuals compared with male and female controls: An fMRI study. *Journal of Sexual Medicine, 6*, 440–448.

Gladstone, B. M., Boydell, K. M., Seeman, M. N., & McKeever, P. D. (2011). Children's experience of parental mental illness: A literature review. *Early Intervention in Psychiatry, 5,* 271–289.

Glancy, D. R., & Glancy, G. D. (2009). The case that has psychiatrists running scared: *Ahmed v. Stefaniu. Journal of the American Academy of Psychiatry and the Law, 37,* 250–256.

Glazier, K., Swing, M., & McGinn, L. K. (2015). Half of obsessive-compulsive disorder cases misdiagnosed: Vignette-based survey of primary care physicians. *Journal of Clinical Psychiatry, 76,* e761–e767.

Gleason, M. E. J., Powers, A. D., & Oltmanns, T. F. (2012). The enduring impact of borderline personality pathology: Risk for threatening events in later middle-age. *Journal of Abnormal Psychology, 121,* 447–457.

Gleaves, D. H. (1996). The sociocognitive model of dissociative identity disorder: A reexamination of the evidence. *Psychological Bulletin, 120,* 42–59.

Glenn, D., Golinelli, D., Rose, R. D., Roy-Byrne, P., Stein, M. B., Sullivan, G., . . . Craske, M. G. (2013). Who gets the most out of cognitive behavioral therapy for anxiety disorders? The role of treatment dose and patient engagement. *Journal of Consulting and Clinical Psychology, 81,* 639–649.

Glessner, J. T., Wang, K., Cai, G., et al. (2009). Autism genome-wide copy number variation reveals ubiquitin and neuronal genes. *Nature, 459,* 569–573.

Glick, I. D., Clarkin, J. F., Haas, G. L., Spencer, J. H., Jr., & Chen, C. L. (1991). A randomized clinical trial of inpatient family intervention: VI. Mediating variables and outcome. *Family Process, 30,* 85–89.

Gliksman, L., Demers, A., Adlaf, E., Newton-Taylor, B., & Schmidt, K. (2000). *Canadian Campus Survey 1998.* Toronto: Centre for Addiction and Mental Health.

Gloster, A. T., Sonntag, R., Hoyer, J., Meyer, A. H., Heinze, S., Ströhle, A., . . . Wittchen, H. (2015). Treating treatment-resistant patients with panic disorder and agoraphobia using psychotherapy: A randomized controlled switching trial. *Psychotherapy and Psychosomatics, 84,* 100–109.

Glynn, T. R., Gamarel, K. E., Kahler, C. W., Iwamoto, M., Operario, D., & Nemoto, T. (2016). The role of gender affirmation in psychological well-being among transgender women. *Psychology of Sexual Orientation and Gender Diversity, 3,* 336–344.

Goeree, R., et al. (2005). The economic burden of schizophrenia in Canada in 2004. *Current Medical Research and Opinion, 21,* 2017–2028.

Goering, P., Veldhuizen, S., Watson, A., Adair, C., Kopp, B., Latimer, E., . . . Aubry, T. (2014). *National At Home/Chez Soi final report.* Calgary, AB: Mental Health Commission of Canada. Retrieved from http://www.mentalhealthcommission.ca.

Goering, P., Wasylenki, D., & Durbin, J. (2000). Canada's mental health system. *International Journal of Law and Psychiatry, 23,* 345–359.

Gold, I. (2009). Reduction in psychiatry. *Canadian Journal of Psychiatry, 54,* 506–512.

Gold, P. B., et al. (2006). Randomized trial of supported employment integrated with assertive community treatment for rural adults with severe mental illness. *Schizophrenia Bulletin, 32,* 378–395.

Goldberg, J. O., & Schmidt, L. A. (2001). Shyness, sociability, and social dysfunction in schizophrenia. *Schizophrenia Research, 48,* 343–349.

Golden, C. J., Hammeke, T., & Purisch, A. (1978). Diagnostic validity of a standardized neuropsychological battery derived from Luria's neuropsychological tests. *Journal of Consulting and Clinical Psychology, 46,* 1258–1265.

Goldfield, G. S., & Boachie, A. (2003). Delivery of family therapy in the treatment of anorexia nervosa using telehealth. *Telemedicine and e-Health, 9,* 111–114.

Goldfried, M. R. (1991). Research issues in psychotherapy integration. *Journal of Psychotherapy Integration, 1,* 5–25.

Goldfried, M. R., & Davison, G. C. (1994). *Clinical behavior therapy.* Expanded edition. New York: John Wiley & Sons.

Goldfried, M. R., & Eubanks-Carter, C. (2004). On the need for a new psychotherapy research paradigm: A comment on Westen, Morrison, and Thompson-Brenner (2004). *Psychological Bulletin, 130,* 669–673.

Goldfried, M. R., Padawer, W., & Robins, C. (1984). Social anxiety and the semantic structure of heterosocial interactions. *Journal of Abnormal Psychology, 93,* 87–97.

Goldman, M. S., Del Boca, F. K., & Darkes, J. (1999). Alcohol expectancy theory: The application of cognitive neuroscience. In K. E. Leonard & H. T. Blane (Eds.), *Psychological theories of drinking and alcoholism* (2nd ed., pp. 203–246). New York: Guilford.

Goldner, E. M. (2008). Is it time to revise our understanding and management of depression? *Canadian Journal of Psychiatry, 53,* 409–410.

Goldner, E. M., Hsu, L., Waraich, P., & Somers, J. M. (2002). Prevalence and incidence studies of schizophrenic disorders: A systematic review of the literature. *Canadian Journal of Psychiatry, 47,* 833–843.

Goldsmith, S. K., Shapiro, R. M., & Joyce, J. N. (1997). Disrupted pattern of D2 dopamine receptors in the temporal lobe in schizophrenia: A postmortem study. *Archives of General Psychiatry, 54,* 649–658.

Goldstein, A. J., & Chambless, D. L. (1978). A reanalysis of agoraphobic behavior. *Behavior Therapy, 9,* 47–59.

Goldstein, A., Dery, N., Pilgrim, M., Ioan, M., & Becker, S. (in press). Stress and binge drinking: A toxic combination for the teenage brain. *Neuropsychologia.*

Goldstein, A. L., & Flett, G. L. (2009). Personality, alcohol use, and drinking motives: A comparison of independent and combined internal drinking motives groups. *Behavior Modification, 33,* 182–198.

Goldstein, A. L., Flett, G. L., Wekerle, C., & Wall, A.-M. (2009). Personality, child maltreatment, and substance use: Examining correlates of deliberate self-harm among university students. *Canadian Journal of Behavioural Sciences, 41,* 241–251.

Goldstein, J. M., et al. (1999). Cortical abnormalities in schizophrenia identified by structural magnetic resonance imaging. *Archives of General Psychiatry, 56,* 537–547.

Goleman, D. (1995). *Emotional intelligence.* New York: Bantam.

Gomberg, E. S. L., & Zucker, R. A. (1998). Substance use and abuse in old age. In I. H. Nordhus, G. R. VandenBos, S. Berg, & P. Fromholt (Eds.), *Clinical geropsychology* (pp. 189–204). Washington, DC: American Psychological Association.

Goode, E. (2016, July 11). Irving Gottesman; 85; led pioneering research, schizophrenia, genetics. *New York Times.*

Goodenough, O. R., & Tucker, M. (2010). Law and cognitive neuroscience. *Annual Review of Law and Science, 6,* 61–92.

Goodenow, C., Reisine, S. T., & Grady, K. E. (1990). Quality of social support and associated social and psychological function in women with rheumatoid arthritis. *Health Psychology, 9,* 266–284.

Goodman, G. S., Ghetti, S., Quas, J. A., Edelstein, R. S., Alexander, K. W., Cordon, I. M., & Jones, D. P. (2003). A prospective study of memory for child sexual abuse: New findings relevant to the repressed-memory controversy. *Psychological Sciences, 14,* 113–118.

Goodman, S. H., Rouse, M. H., Connell, A. M., Broth, M. R., et al. (2010). Maternal depression and child psychopathology: A meta-analytic review. *Clinical Child and Family Psychology Review, 14,* 1–27.

Goodsitt, A. (1997). Eating disorders: A self-psychological perspective. In D. M. Garner & P. E. Garfinkel (Eds.), *Handbook of psychotherapy for eating disorders* (pp. 205–228). New York: Guilford.

Goodwin, C. (2007, March). The calm at the eye of the storm. *Inside Entertainment, 6,* 43–46.

Goodwin, D., & Guze, S. (1984). *Psychiatric diagnosis.* New York: Oxford University Press.

Goodwin, F. K., & Jamison, K. R. (1990). *Manic depressive illness.* Washington, DC: Oxford Press.

Goorden, M., Muntingh, A., van Marwijk, H., Spinhoven, P., Adèr, H., van Balkom, A., . . . Hakkaart-van Roijen, L. (2014). Cost utility analysis of a collaborative stepped care intervention for panic and generalized anxiety disorders in primary care. *Journal of Psychosomatic Research, 77,* 57–63.

Goos, L. M., Crosbie, J., Payne, S., & Schachar, R. (2009). Validation and extension of the endophenotype model in ADHD patterns of inheritance in a family study of inhibitory control. *American Journal of Psychiatry, 166,* 711–717.

Gortner, E., Gollan, J., Dobson, K. S., & Jacobson, N. S. (1998). Cognitive-behavioral treatment for depression: Relapse prevention. *Journal of Consulting and Clinical Psychology, 66,* 377–384.

Gotlib, I. H., Joormann, J., Minor, K., & Hallmayer, J. (2008). HPA axis reactivity: A mechanism underlying the association among 5-HTTLPR, stress, and depression. *Biological Psychiatry, 63,* 847–851.

Gotlib, I. H., & McCann, C. D. (1984). Construct accessibility and depression: An examination of cognitive and affective factors. *Journal of Personality and Social Psychology, 47,* 427–439.

Gotlib, I. H., & Robinson, L. A. (1982). Responses to depressed individuals: Discrepancies between self-report and observer-rated behavior. *Journal of Abnormal Psychology, 91,* 231–240.

Gottesman, I. I. (1963). Heritability of personality: A demonstration. *Psychological Monographs: General and Applied, 77,* 1–21.

Gottesman, I. I., & Goldsmith, H. H. (1994). Developmental psychopathology of antisocial behavior: Inserting genes into its ontogenesis and epigenesis. In C. A. Nelson (Ed.), *Threats to optimal development.* Hillside, NJ: Erlbaum.

Gottesman, I. I., McGuffin, P., & Farmer, A. (1987). Is there really a split in schizophrenia? The genetic evidence. *Schizophrenia Bulletin, 13,* 23–47.

Gottesman, I. I., & Shields, J. (1966). Schizophrenia in twins: 16 years' consecutive admissions to a psychiatric clinic. *The British Journal of Psychiatry, 112,* 809–818.

Gottesman, I. I., & Shields, J. (1972). *Schizophrenia and genetics: A twin study vantage point.* Boston: Academic Press.

Gottlieb, B. H., & Johnson, J. (2000). Respite programs for caregivers of persons with dementia: A review with practice implications. *Aging and Mental Health, 4,* 119–129.

Gottlieb, B. H., & Rooney, J. A. (2004). Coping effectiveness: Determinants and relevance to the mental health and affect of family caregivers of persons with dementia. *Aging and Mental Health, 8,* 364–373.

Gould, M. S., Walsh, B. T., Munfakh, J. L., et al. (2009). Sudden death and use of stimulant medications in youths. *American Journal of Psychiatry, 166,* 992–1001.

Gould, R. L., Coulson, M. C., & Howard, R. J. (2012). Cognitive behavioral therapy for depression in older people: A meta-analysis and meta-regression of randomized controlled trials. *Journal of the American Geriatric Society, 60,* 1817–1830.

Goulet, K., Deschamps, B., Evoy, F., & Trudel, J. F. (2009). Use of brain imaging (computed tomography and magnetic resonance imaging) in first-episode psychosis: Review and retrospective study. *Canadian Journal of Psychiatry, 54,* 493–501.

Government of Canada. (2006). *The human face of mental health and mental illness in Canada 2006.* Ottawa: Minister of Public Works and Government Services Canada.

Government of Canada. (2014). *Eating disorders among girls and women in Canada.* Ottawa: Standing Committee on the Status of Women.

Goyer, P. F., Andreason, P. J., Semple, W. E., & Clayton, A. H. (1994). Positron-emission tomography and personality disorders. *Neuropsychopharmacology, 10,* 21–28.

Goyette, C. H., & Conners, C. K. (1977). *Food additives and hyperkinesis.* Paper presented at the 85th Annual Convention of the American Psychological Association.

Grabe, S., Hyde, J. S., & Lindberg, S. M. (2007). Body objectification and depression in adolescents: The role of gender, shame, and rumination. *Psychology of Women Quarterly, 31,* 164–175.

Grace, S. L., Bennett, S., Ardern, C. I., & Clark, A. M. (2014). Cardiac rehabiliation services: Canada. *Progress in Cardiovascular Diseases, 56,* 530–535.

Graham, J. (2009, February 19). Deep brain stimulation approved for obsessive-compulsive disorder. *Chicago Tribune.*

Graham, J. E., Rockwood, K., Beattie, B. L., Eastwood, R., Gauthier, S., Tuokko, H., & McDowell, I. (1997). Prevalence and severity of cognitive impairment with and without dementia in an elderly population. *The Lancet, 349,* 1793–1796.

Graham, J. R. (1990). *MMPI-2: Assessing personality and psychopathology.* New York: Oxford University Press.

Graham, K. (1988). Reasons for consumption and heavy caffeine use: Generalization of a model based on alcohol research. *Addictive Behaviors, 13,* 209–214.

Granato, H. F., Wilks, C. R., Miga, E. M., Korslund, K. E., & Linehan, M. M. (2015). The use of dialectical behavior therapy and prolonged exposure to treat comorbid dissociation and self-harm: The case of a client with borderline personality disorder and post-traumatic stress disorder. *Journal of Clinical Psychology, 71,* 805–815.

Grant, J. E., Redden, S. A., Leppink, E. W., & Odlaug, B. L. (2015). Skin picking disorder with co-occurring body dysmorphic disorder. *Body Image, 15,* 44–48.

Grant, P. M., & Beck, A. T. (2009). Defeatist beliefs as a mediator of cognitive impairment, negative symptoms, and functioning in schizophrenia. *Schizophrenia Bulletin, 35,* 798–806.

Grant, V. V., et al. (2007). Psychometric evaluation of the five-factor Modified Drinking Motives Questionnaire—Revised in undergraduates. *Addictive Behaviors, 32,* 2611–2632.

Grant, V. V., Stewart, S. H., & Mohr, C. D. (2009). Coping-anxiety and coping-depression motives predict different daily mood-drinking relationships. *Psychology of Addictive Behaviors, 23,* 226–237.

Gratzer, D., & Khalid-Khan, F. (2016). Internet-delivered cognitive behavioural therapy in the treatment of psychiatric illness. *Canadian Medical Association Journal, 188,* 263–272.

Gratzer, T., & Bradford, J. M. W. (1995). Offender and offense characteristics of sexual sadists: A comparative study. *Journal of Forensic Sciences, 40,* 450–455.

Gravel, R., & Beland, Y. (2005). The Canadian Community Health Survey: Mental health and well-being. *Canadian Journal of Psychiatry, 50,* 573–579.

Gray, J. A. (1990). Brain systems that mediate both emotion and cognition. *Cognition & Emotion, 4,* 269–288.

Gray, J. A. (1991). *The neuropsychology of temperament.* New York: Plenum Press.

Gray, J. A., & McNaughton, N. (2000). *Neuropsychology of anxiety: An inquiry into the functions of the septo-hippocampal system* (2nd ed.). New York: Oxford University Press.

Gray, J. E., & O'Reilly, R. L. (2001). Clinically significant differences among Canadian mental health acts. *Canadian Journal of Psychiatry, 46*, 315–321.

Gray, J. E., & O'Reilly, R. L. (2005). Canadian compulsory community treatment laws: Recent reforms. *International Journal of Law and Psychiatry, 28*, 13–22.

Gray, J. E., & O'Reilly, R. L. (2009). Supreme Court of Canada's "Beautiful Mind" case. *International Journal of Law and Psychiatry, 32*, 315–322.

Gray, N. S., et al. (2003). Prediction of violence and self-harm in mentally disordered offenders: A prospective study of the efficacy of HCR-20, PCL-R, and psychiatric symptomatology. *Journal of Consulting and Clinical Psychology, 71*, 443–451.

Green, R., & Blanchard, R. (1995). Gender identity disorders. In H. I. Kaplan & B. J. Sadock (Eds.), *Comprehensive textbook of psychiatry* (pp. 1347–1360). Baltimore: Williams & Wilkins.

Green, R., & Fleming, D. T. (1990). Transsexual surgery follow-up: Status in the 1990s. In J. Bancroft, C. Davis, & D. Weinstein (Eds.), *Annual review of sex research* (pp. 163–174). Lake Mills, IA: Society for the Scientific Study of Sex.

Greenberg, D. M. (1998). Sexual recidivism in sex offenders. *Canadian Journal of Psychiatry, 43*, 459–465.

Greenberg, L. S. (2004). Emotion-focused therapy. *Clinical Psychology and Psychotherapy, 11*, 3–16.

Greenberg, L. S. (2012). Emotions, the great captains of our lives: Their role in the process of change in psychotherapy. *American Psychologist, 67*, 697–707.

Greenberg, L. S., Elliot, R., & Lietaer, G. (1994). Research on experiential psychotherapies. In A. E. Bergin & S. L. Garfield (Eds.), *Handbook of psychotherapy and behavior change* (4th ed., pp. 509–539). New York: Wiley.

Greenberg, L. S., & Goldman, R. N. (2008). *Emotion-focused couples therapy: The dynamics of emotion, love, and power*. Washington, DC: American Psychological Association Books.

Greenberg, L. S., & Johnson, S. M. (1988). *Emotionally focussed couples therapy*. New York: Guilford.

Greenberg, L. S., Warwar, S. H., & Malcolm, W. M. (2008). Differential effects of emotion-focused therapy and psychoeducation in facilitating forgiveness and letting go of emotional injuries. *Journal of Counseling Psychology, 55*, 185–196.

Greenberg, R. P., Constantino, M. J., & Bruce, N. (2006). Are patient expectations still relevant for psychotherapy process and outcome? *Clinical Psychology Review, 26*, 657–678.

Greenhalgh, J., Dickson, R., & Dundar, Y. (2009). The effects of biofeedback for the treatment of essential hypertension: A systematic review. *Health Technology Assessment, 13*, 1–103.

Greven, C. U., Asherson, P., Rijsdijk, F. V., & Plomin, R. (2011). A longitudinal twin study on the association between inattentive and hyperactive-impulsive ADHD symptoms. *Journal of Abnormal Child Psychology, 39*, 623–632.

Grigorenko, E. L. (2009). Speaking genes or genes for speaking? Deciphering the genetics of speech and language. *Journal of Child Psychology and Psychiatry, 50*, 116–125.

Grilo, C. M., Shiffman, S., & Carter-Campbell, J. T. (1994). Binge eating antecedents in normal weight nonpurging females: Is there consistency? *International Journal of Eating Disorders, 16*, 239–249.

Grinker, R. B., & Spiegel, J. P. (1945). *Men under stress*. Philadelphia: Blakiston.

Grinspoon, L., & Bakalar, J. B. (1995). Marijuana as medicine: A plea for reconsideration. *Journal of the American Medical Association, 273*, 1875–1876.

Grisso, T., & Appelbaum, P. S. (1991). Mentally ill and non-mentally ill patients' abilities to understand informed consent disclosures for medication: Preliminary data. *Law and Human Behavior, 15*, 377–388.

Gross, S. R., Barrett, S. P., Shestowsky, J. S., & Pihl, R. O. (2002). Ecstasy and drug consumption patterns: a Canadian rave population study. *Canadian Journal of Psychiatry, 47*, 546–551.

Groth, N. A., Hobson, W. F., & Guy, T. S. (1982). The child molester: Clinical observations. In J. Conte & D. A. Shore (Eds.), *Social work and child sexual abuse*. New York: Haworth.

Grove, W. R., et al. (1990). Heritability of substance abuse and antisocial behavior in monozygotic twins reared apart. *Biological Psychiatry, 27*, 1293–1304.

Gruneir, A., Forrester, J., Camacho, X., Gill, S. S., & Bronskill, S. E. (2013). Gender differences in home care clients and admission to long-term care in Ontario, Canada: A population-based retrospective cohort study. *BMC Geriatrics, 13*, 48.

Guerra, N., & Slaby, R. (1990). Cognitive mediators of aggression in adolescent offenders: 2. Intervention. *Developmental Psychology, 26*, 269–277.

Guidi, J., Fava, G. A., Fava, M., & Papakostas, G. I. (2010). Efficacy of the sequential integration of psychotherapy and pharmacotherapy in major depressive disorder: A preliminary meta-analysis. *Psychological Medicine, 41*(2), 321–331.

Gum, A. M., King-Kallimanis, B., & Kohn, R. (2009). Prevalence of mood, anxiety, and substance-abuse disorders for older Americans in the National Comorbidity Survey replication. *American Journal of Geriatric Psychiatry, 117*, 769–781.

Gunderson, J. G., Kolb, J. E., & Austin, V. (1981). The diagnostic interview for borderline patients. *American Journal of Psychiatry, 138*, 896–903.

Gunderson, J. G., Stout, R. L., McGlashan, T. H., Shea, M. T., et al. (2011). Ten-year course of borderline personality disorder: Psychopathology and function from the Collaborative Personality Disorders Study. *Archives of General Psychiatry, 68*, 827–837.

Gunderson, J. G., Zanarini, M. C., Choi-Kai, L. W., Mitchell, K. S., Jang, K. L., & Hudson, J. I. (2011). Family study of borderline personality disorder and its sectors of psychopathology. *Archives of General Psychiatry, 68*, 753–762.

Gunn, J. F. III, Lester, D., Haines, J., & Williams, C. L. (2012). Thwarted belongingness and perceived burdensomeness in suicide notes. *Crisis: The Journal of Crisis Intervention and Suicide Prevention, 33*, 178–181.

Gunn, J., Elliott, P., Densley, K., Middleton, A., Ambresin, G., Dowrick, C., . . . Griffiths, F. (2013). A trajectory-based approach to understand the factors associated with persistent depressive symptoms in primary care. *Journal of Affective Disorders, 148*, 338–346.

Gupta, K. K., Gupta, V. K., & Shirasaka, T. (2016). An update of fetal alcohol syndrome: Pathogenesis, risks, and treatment. *Alcoholism: Clinical and Experimental Research, 40*, 1594–1602.

Gurland, B. (1991). Epidemiology of psychiatric disorders. In J. Sadavoy, L. W. Lazarus, & L. F. Jarvik (Eds.), *Comprehensive review of geriatric psychiatry* (pp. 25–40). Washington, DC: American Psychiatric Press.

Guyenet, P. G. (2006). The sympathetic control of blood pressure. *Nature Review of Neuroscience, 7*, 335–346.

Haaga, D. A. F. (1990). Issues in relating self-efficacy to smoking relapse: Importance of an "Achilles' Heel" situation and of prior quitting experience. *Journal of Substance Abuse, 2*, 191–200.

Haaga, D. A. F. (2000). Introduction to the special section on stepped care models in psychotherapy. *Journal of Consulting and Clinical Psychology, 68*, 547–548.

Haas, R. H., Townsend, J., Courchesne, E., Lincoln, A. J., & Schreibman, L. (1996). Neurologic abnormalities in infantile autism. *Journal of Child Neurology, 11*, 84–92.

Hadjipavlou, G., & Ogrodniczuk, J. S. (2007). A national survey of Canadian psychiatry residents' perceptions of psychotherapy training. *Canadian Journal of Psychiatry, 52*, 710–717.

Hadjistavropoulos, H. D., Asmundson, G. J. G., & Norton, G. R. (1999). Validation of the Coping with Health, Injuries, and Problems Scale in a chronic pain sample. *Clinical Journal of Pain, 15*, 41–49.

Haggarty, J. M., Cernovsky, Z., Husni, M., Minor, K., Kermeen, P., & Merskey, H. (2002). Seasonal affective disorder in an Arctic community. *Acta Psychiatrica Scandinavica, 105*, 378–384.

Hahn, T., Kircher, T., Straube, B., Wittchen, H., Konrad, C., Ströhle, A., . . . Lueken, U. (2015). Predicting treatment response to cognitive behavioral therapy in panic disorder with agoraphobia by integrating local neural information. *JAMA Psychiatry, 72*, 68–74.

Hajek, P., McRobbie, H. J., Myers, K. E., Stapleton, J., & Dhanji, A.-R. (2011). Use of varenicline for 4 weeks before quitting smoking: Decrease in ad lib smoking and increase in smoking cessation rates. *Archives of Internal Medicine, 171*, 770–777.

Hajek, P., Stead, L. F., West, R., Jarvis, M., & Lancaster, T. (2009). Relapse prevention interventions for smoking cessation (Review). *Cochrane Database of Systematic Reviews, 1*, CD003999.

Halchuk, R. E., Makinen, J. A., & Johnson, S. M. (2010). Resolving attachment injuries in couples using emotionally focused therapy: A three-year follow-up. *Journal of Couple and Relationship Therapy, 9*, 31–47.

Halford, W. K., & Doss, B. D. (2016). New frontiers in the treatment of couples. *International Journal of Cognitive Therapy, 9*, 124–139.

Halford, W. K., Hayes, S., Christensen, A., Lambert, M., Baucom, D. H., & Atkins, D. C. (2012). Toward making progress feedback an effective common factor in couple therapy. *Behavior Therapy, 43*, 49–60.

Halford, W. K., Pepping, C. A., & Petch, J. (2016). The gap between couple therapy research efficacy and practice effectiveness. *Journal of Marital and Family Therapy, 42*, 32–44.

Halford, W. K., & Snyder, D. K. (2012). Special series: Universal and common factors in couples therapy and relationship education. *Behavior Therapy, 43*, 1–12.

Hall, B. J., Tolin, D. F., Frost, R. O., & Steketee, G. (2013). An exploration of comorbid symptoms and clinical correlates of clinically significant hoarding symptoms. *Depression and Anxiety, 30*, 67–76.

Hall, E. (1900). The unofficial gynaecological treatment of the insane in British Columbia. *Medical Sentinel*. Retrieved from http://www.canadiana.ca.

Hall, G. C. N. (1995). Sexual offender recidivism revisited: A meta-analysis of treatment studies. *Journal of Consulting and Clinical Psychology, 63*, 802–809.

Hallis, L., Cameli, L., Dionne, F., & Knauper, B. (2016). Combining cognitive therapy with acceptance and commitment therapy for depression: A manualized group therapy. *Journal of Psychotherapy Integration, 26*, 186–201.

Halmi, K. A., et al. (2002). Relapse predictors of patients with bulimia nervosa who achieved abstinence through cognitive behavioral therapy. *Archives of General Psychiatry, 59*, 1105–1109.

Hamani, C., et al. (2014). Deep brain stimulation for obsessive-compulsive disorder: systematic review and evidence-based guideline sponsored by the American Society for Stereotactic and Functional Neurosurgery and the Congress of Neurological Surgeons (CNS) and endorsed by the CNS and American Association of Neurological Surgeons. *Neurosurgery, 75*, 327–333.

Hamilton, K. E., & Dobson, K. S. (2002). Cognitive therapy of depression: Pretreatment patient predictors of outcome. *Clinical Psychology Review, 22*, 875–893.

Hamilton, S. P. (2009). Linkage and association studies of anxiety disorders. *Depression and Anxiety, 26*, 976–983.

Hammen, C. L. (1991). Generation of stress in the course of unipolar depression. *Journal of Abnormal Psychology, 100*, 555–561.

Hammond, D. (2011). Health warning messages on tobacco products: A review. *Tobacco Control, 20*, 327–337.

Hammond, D., et al. (2005). Tobacco denormalization and industry beliefs among smokers from four countries. *American Journal of Preventive Medicine, 31*, 225–232.

Hammond, D., Fong, G. T., McDonald, P. W., Brown, S., & Cameron, R. (2004). Graphic Canadian cigarette warning labels and adverse outcomes: Evidence from Canadian smokers. *American Journal of Public Health, 94*, 1442–1445.

Hamza, C. A., & Willoughby, T. (2013). Nonsuicidal self-injury and suicidal behaviour: A latent class analysis among young adults. *PloS/ONE, 8*(3), e59955.

Hamza, C. A., & Willoughby, T. (2014). A longitudinal person-centered examination of non-suicidal self-injury among university students. *Journal of Youth and Adolescence, 43*, 671–685.

Handley, A. K., Egan, S. J., Kane, R. T., & Rees, C. S. (2015). A randomized controlled trial of group cognitive behavioural therapy. *Behaviour Research and Therapy, 68*, 37–47.

Hankin, B. L., Fraley, R. C., Lakey, B. B., & Waldman, J. D. (2005). Is depression best viewed as a continuum or discrete category? A taxometric analysis of childhood and adolescent depression in a population-based sample. *Journal of Abnormal Psychology, 114*, 96–110.

Hanson, R. K. (2009). The psychological assessment of risk for crime and violence. *Canadian Psychology, 50*, 172–182.

Hanson, R. K., & Bussière, M. T. (1998). Predicting relapse: A meta-analysis of sexual offender recidivism studies. *Journal of Consulting and Clinical Psychology, 66*, 348–362.

Hanson, R. K., & Harris, A. J. R. (1997). Voyeurism: Assessment and treatment. In D. R. Laws & W. O'Donohue (Eds.), *Sexual deviance* (pp. 311–331). New York: Guilford.

Hanson, R. K., & Morton-Bourgon, K. (2005). The characteristics of persistent sexual offenders: A meta-analysis of recidivism studies. *Journal of Consulting and Clinical Psychology, 73*, 1154–1163.

Hanson, R. K., & Yates, P. M. (2013). Psychological treatment of sex offenders. *Current Psychiatry Reports, 15*, 348.

Haque, F. N., Gottesmann, I. I., & Wong, A. H. (2009). Not really identical: Epigenetic differences in monozygotic twins and implications for twin studies in psychiatry. *American Journal of Medical Genetics, Part C, Seminars in Medical Genetics, 151C*, 136–141.

Hardaway, R., Schweitzer, J., & Suzuki, J. (2016). Hallucinogen use disorders. *Child and Adolescent Psychiatric Clinics, 25*, 489–496.

Hardy, B. W., & Waller, D. A. (1988). Bulimia as substance abuse. In W. G. Johnson (Ed.), *Advances in eating disorders*. New York: JAI.

Hare, E. (1969). *Triennial statistical report of the Royal Maudsley and Bethlem Hospitals*. London: Bethlem and Maudsley Hospitals.

Hare, R. D. (1970). *Psychopathy: Theory and research*. New York: John Wiley & Sons.

Hare, R. D. (1978). Electrodermal and cardiovascular correlates of sociopathy. In R. D. Hare & D. Schalling (Eds.), *Psychopathic behavior: Approaches to research*. New York: John Wiley & Sons.

Hare, R. D. (1991). *Manual for the Revised Psychopathy Checklist* (1st ed.). Toronto: Multi-Health Systems, Inc.

Hare, R. D. (1991). *The Hare Psychopathy Checklist-Revised*. Toronto: Multi-Health Systems, Inc.

Hare, R. D. (1996). Psychopathy and antisocial personality disorder: A case of diagnostic confusion. *Psychiatric Times, 13*, 39–40.

Hare, R. D., Clark, D., Grann, M., & Thornton, D. (2000). Psychopathy and the predictive utility of the PCL-R: An international perspective. *Behavioral Sciences and the Law, 18*, 623–645.

Hare, R. D., Hart, S. D., & Harpur, T. J. (1991). Psychopathy and the DSM-IV criteria for antisocial personality disorder. *Journal of Abnormal Psychology, 100*, 391–398.

Hare, R. D., & Neumann, C. S. (2009). Psychopathy: Assessment and forensic implication. *Canadian Journal of Psychiatry, 54*, 791–802.

Harenski, C. L., Harenski, K. A., Shane, M. S., & Kiehl, K. A. (2010). Aberrant neural processing of moral violations in criminal psychopaths. *Journal of Abnormal Psychology, 119*, 863–874.

Harkness, A. R., McNulty, J. L., & Ben-Porath, Y. S. (1995). The Personality Psychopathology Five (PSY-5): Constructs and MMPI-2 scales. *Psychological Assessment, 7*, 104–114.

Harkness, K. L., Bagby, R. M., & Kennedy, S. H. (2012). Childhood maltreatment and differential treatment response and recurrence in adult major depressive disorder. *Journal of Consulting and Clinical Psychology, 80*, 342–353.

Harkness, K. L., Bagby, R. M., Stewart, J. G., Larocque, C. L., Mazurka, R., Strauss, J. S., . . . Kennedy, J. L. (2015). Childhood emotional and sexual maltreatment moderate the relation of the serotonin transporter gene to stress generation. *Journal of Abnormal Psychology, 124*, 275–287.

Harkness, K. L., Frank, E., Anderson, B., Houck, P. R., Luther, J., & Kupfer, D. J. (2002). Does interpersonal psychotherapy protect women from depression in the face of stressful life events? *Journal of Consulting and Clinical Psychology, 70*, 908–915.

Harkness, K. L., Lumley, M. N., & Truss, A. E. (2008). Stress generation in adolescent depression: The moderating role of child abuse and neglect. *Journal of Abnormal Child Psychology, 36*, 421–432.

Harkness, K. L., Strauss, J., Bagby, R. M., Stewart, J. G., Larocque, C., Mazurka, R., . . . Kennedy, J. (2015). Interactions between childhood maltreatment and brain-derived neurotrophic factor and serotonin transporter polymorphisms on depression symptoms. *Psychiatry Research, 229*, 609–612.

Harpur, T. J., & Hare, R. D. (1990). Psychopathy and attention. In J. Enns (Ed.), *The development of attention: Research and theory*. Amsterdam: New Holland.

Harpur, T. J., & Hare, R. D. (1994). Assessment of psychopathy as a function of age. *Journal of Abnormal Psychology, 103*, 604–609.

Harpur, T. J., Hart, S. D., & Hare, R. D. (1994). Personality of the psychopath. In P. T. Costa, Jr. & T. A. Widiger (Eds.), *Personality disorders and the five-factor model of personality* (pp. 149–173). Washington, DC: American Psychological Association.

Harris, A. H. S. (2006). Does expressive writing reduce health care utilization? A meta-analysis of randomized trials. *Journal of Consulting and Clinical Psychology, 74*, 243–252.

Harris, G. T., Rice, M. E., & Cormier, C. A. (2002). Prospective replication of the Violence Risk Appraisal Guide in predicting violent recidivism among forensic patients. *Law and Human Behavior, 26*, 377–394.

Harris, G. T., Rice, M. E., Lalumière, M. L., Boer, D., & Lang, C. (2003). A multisite comparison of actuarial risk instruments for sex offenders. *Psychological Assessment, 15*, 413–425.

Harris, J., & Steele, A. M. (2014). Have we lost our minds? The siren song of reductionism in eating disorder research and theory. *Eating Disorders, 22*, 87–95.

Harrop, E. N., & Marlatt, G. A. (2010). The comorbidity of substance use disorders and eating disorders in women: Prevalence, etiology, and treatment. *Addictive Behaviors, 35*, 392–398.

Hart, S., & Hare, R. D. (1989). Discriminant validity of the Psychopathy Checklist in a forensic psychiatric population. *Psychological Assessment: A Journal of Consulting and Clinical Psychology, 1*, 211–218.

Hartman, L. I. (2012). *Reducing stigma of schizophrenia among high school youth*. Unpublished master's thesis, York University, Toronto.

Hartman, L. I., Michel, N. M., Winter, A., Young, R. E., Flett, G. L., & Goldberg, J. O. (2013). Self-stigma of mental illness in high school youth. *Canadian Journal of School Psychology, 28*, 28–42.

Harvard Mental Health Letter. (1996, August). *Treatment of alcoholism—Part I, 13*, 1–4.

Harvey, C. A., Pantelis, C., Taylor, J., McCabe, P. J., et al. (1996). The Camden schizophrenia surveys. II. High prevalence of schizophrenia in an inner London borough and its relationship to sociodemographic factors. *The British Journal of Psychiatry, 168*, 418–426.

Harvey, P.-O., Lepage, M., & Malla, A. (2007). Benefits of enriched intervention compared with standard care for patients with recent-onset psychosis: A metaanalytic approach. *Canadian Journal of Psychiatry, 52*, 464–472.

Harwood, M. T., Beutler, L. E., & Charvat, M. (2010). Cognitive-behavioral therapy and psychotherapy integration. In K. S. Dobson (Ed.), *Handbook of cognitive-behavioral therapies* (3rd ed., pp. 94–130). New York: Guilford.

Hasin, D. S., Stinson, F. S., Ogburn, E., & Grant, B. F. (2007). Prevalence, correlates, disability, and comorbidity of DSM-IV alcohol abuse and dependence in the United States: Results from the National Epidemiologic Survey of Alcohol and Related Conditions. *Archives of General Psychiatry, 64*, 830–842.

Hastings, M. E., Krishnan, S., Tangney, J. P., & Stuewig, J. (2011). Predictive and incremental validity of the Violence Risk Appraisal Guide scores with male and female jail inmates. *Psychological Assessment, 23*, 174–183.

Hathaway, S. R., & McKinley, J. C. (1943). *MMPI manual*. New York: Psychological Corporation.

Haug, T., Nordgreen, T., Öst, L., Kvale, G., Tangen, T., Andersson, G., . . . Havik, O. E. (2015). Stepped care versus face-to-face cognitive behavior therapy for panic disorder and social anxiety disorder: Predictors and moderators of outcome. *Behaviour Research and Therapy, 71*, 76–89.

Hawes, D. J., & Dadds, M. R. (2005). The treatment of conduct problems in children with callous-unemotional traits. *Journal of Consulting and Clinical Psychology, 73*(4), 737.

Hawes, S. W., Boccaccini, M. T., & Murrie, D. C. (2013). Psychopathy and the combination of psychopathy and sexual deviance as predictors of sexual recidivism: Meta-analytic findings using the Psychopathy Checklist-Revised. *Psychological Assessment, 25*, 233–243.

Haworth, C. M. A., Kovas, Y., Harlaar, N., et al. (2009). Generalist genes and learning disabilities: A multivariate genetic analysis of low performance in reading, mathematics, language and general cognitive ability in a sample of 8000 12-year-old twins. *Journal of Child Psychology and Psychiatry, 50*, 1318–1325.

Hawton, K., Catalan, J., & Fagg, J. (1992). Sex therapy for erectile dysfunction: Characteristics of couples, treatment outcome, and prognostic factors. *Archives of Sexual Behavior, 21*, 161–176.

Hawton, K., Catalan, J., Martin, P., & Fagg, J. (1986). Long-term outcome of sex therapy. *Behaviour Research and Therapy, 24*, 665–675.

Hay, D. P. (1991). Electroconvulsive therapy. In J. Sadavoy, L. W. Lazarus, & L. F. Jarvik (Eds.), *Comprehensive review of geriatric psychiatry* (pp. 469–485). Washington, DC: American Psychiatric Press.

Hayden, E. P., Dougherty, L. R., Maloney, B., et al. (2008). Early-emerging cognitive-vulnerability to depression and the serotonin transporter promoter region polymorphism. *Journal of Affective Disorders, 107*, 227–230.

Hayes, S. C. (2002). Acceptance, mindfulness, and science. *Clinical Psychology: Science and Practice, 9*, 101–106.

Hayes, S. C. (2004). Acceptance and commitment therapy, relational frame theory, and the third wave of behavioral and cognitive therapies. *Behavior Therapy, 35*, 639–665.

Hayes-Skelton, S. A., Calloway, A., Orsillo, S. M., & Roemer, L. (2015). Decentering as a potential common mechanism across two therapies for generalized anxiety disorder. *Journal of Consulting and Clinical Psychology, 83*, 395–404.

Hayes-Skelton, S. A., Roemer, L., & Orsillo, S. M. (2013). A randomized clinical trial comparing an acceptance-based behavior therapy to applied relaxation for generalized anxiety disorder. *Journal of Consulting and Clinical Psychology, 81*, 761–773.

Hayman-Abello, B. A., Hayman-Abello, S. E., & Rourke, B. (2003). The 1990s (a review of research by Canadian neuropsychologists conducted over the past decade). *Canadian Psychology, 44*, 100–138.

Hazelrigg, M. D., Cooper, H. M., & Borduin, C. M. (1987). Evaluating the effectiveness of family therapies: An integrative review and analysis. *Psychological Bulletin, 101*, 428–442.

Health Canada. (1991). *Schizophrenia: A handbook for families.* Ottawa: Ministry of Supply and Services Canada.

Health Canada. (1998). *The aboriginal headstart on reserve program.* Retrieved from http://www.hc-sc.gc.ca/fniah-spnia/famil/develop/ahsor-papa_intro-eng.php

Health Canada. (2011). Canadian Tobacco Use Monitoring Survey, 2011. Retrieved from http://www.hc-sc.gc.ca/hc-ps/tobac-tabac/research-recherche/stat/ctums-esutc_2011-eng.php.

Health Canada and the Canadian Coalition for High Blood Pressure Prevention and Control. (2000). *National high blood pressure prevention and control strategy: Report of the expert working group.* Ottawa: Health Canada.

Health Council of Canada. (2012). *Seniors in need, caregivers in distress: What are the home care priorities for seniors in Canada?* Toronto: Author.

Healy, M. (1994, January 8). Science of power and weakness. *Los Angeles Times*, A1, A12.

Heath, K. V., Wood, E., Bally, G., Cornelisse, P. G., & Hogg, R. S. (1999). Experience in treating persons with HIV/AIDS and the legalization of assisted suicide: The views of Canadian physicians. *AIDS Care, 11*, 501–510.

Heatherington, L., Messer, S. B., Angus, L., Strauman, T. J., Friedlander, M. L., & Kolden, G. G. (2012). The narrowing of theoretical orientations in clinical psychology doctoral training. *Clinical Psychology: Science and Practice, 19*, 364–374.

Heatherton, T. F., & Sargent, J. D. (2009). Does watching smoking in movies promote teenage smoking? *Current Directions in Psychological Science, 18*, 63–67.

Hebb, D. O. (1949). *The organization of behavior.* New York: John Wiley & Sons.

Hébert, M., Lavoie, F., Piché, C., & Poitras, M. (2001). Proximate effects of a child sexual abuse prevention program in elementary school children. *Child Abuse and Neglect, 25,* 505–522.

Hébert, M., Parent, N., Daignault, I. V., & Tourigny, M. (2006). A typological analysis of behavioral profiles of sexually abused children. *Child Maltreatment, 11*, 203–216.

Hébert, R. (2003). The big boom: What CIHR's Canadian longitudinal study on aging means to the baby boomer generation and Canada's healthcare system. *Hospital Quarterly* (Spring), 19–20.

Hébert, R., et al. (2003). Efficacy of a psychoeducative group program for caregivers of demented persons living at home: A randomized control trial. *Journals of Gerontology: B. Psychological Sciences and Social Sciences, 58*, S58–S67.

Hébert, R., et al. (2010). Impact of PRISMA, a coordination-type integrated service delivery system for frail older people in Quebec (Canada): A quasi-experimental study. *The Journals of Gerontology, Series B, 65B*, 107–118.

Hébert, R., Brayne, C., & Spiegelhalter, D. J. (1997). Incidence of functional decline and improvement in a community-dwelling very elderly population. *American Journal of Epidemiology, 145*, 935–944.

Hébert, R., Durand, P. J., Dubuc, N., Tourigny, A., & The PRISMA Group. (2003). PRISMA: A new model of integrated service delivery for the frail older people in Canada. *International Journal of Integrated Care, 3*, 1–8.

Heilbrun, K., Ogloff, J. R., & Picarello, K. (1999). Dangerous offender statutes in the United States and Canada: Implications for risk assessment. *International Journal of Law and Psychiatry, 22*, 393–415.

Heim, E., Valach, L., & Schaffner, L. (1997). Coping and psychosocial adaptation: Longitudinal effects over time and stages in breast cancer. *Psychosomatic Medicine, 59*, 408–418.

Heiman, J. R., Rowland, D. L., Hatch, J. P., & Gladue, B. A. (1991). Psychophysiological and endocrine responses to sexual arousal in women. *Archives of Sexual Behavior, 20*, 171–186.

Heimberg, R. G., et al. (1998). Cognitive behavioral group therapy vs phenelzine therapy for social phobia: 12-week outcome. *Archives of General Psychiatry, 55*, 1133–1142.

Heimberg, R. G., & Becker, R. E. (2002). *Cognitive-behavioral group therapy for social phobia.* New York: Guilford.

Heimberg, R. G., Hofmann, S. G., Liebowitz, M. R., Schneier, F. R., Smits, J. A. J., Stein, M. B., ... Craske, M. G. (2014). Social anxiety disorder in DSM-5. *Depression and anxiety, 31*, 472–479.

Heinrichs, R. W. (1993). Schizophrenia and the brain. *American Psychologist, 48*, 221–233.

Heinrichs, R. W. (2001). *In search of madness.* New York: Oxford University Press.

Heinrichs, R. W. (2005). The primacy of cognition in schizophrenia. *American Psychologist, 60*, 229–242.

Heinrichs, R. W., & Awad, A. G. (1993). Neuro-cognitive subtypes of chronic schizophrenia. *Schizophrenia Research, 9*, 49–58.

Heinrichs, R. W., Ruttan, L., Zakzanis, K. K., & Case, D. (1997). Parsing schizophrenia with neurocognitive tests: evidence of stability and validity. *Brain and Cognition, 35*, 207–224.

Heinrichs, R., & Zakzanis, K. K. (1998). Neurocognitive deficit in schizophrenia: A quantitative review of the evidence. *Neuropsychology, 12*, 426–445.

Heinz, A. J., Kassel, J. D., & Smith, E. V. (2009). Caffeine expectancy: Instrument development in the Rasch measurement framework. *Psychology of Addictive Behaviors, 23*, 500–511.

Heisel, M. J. (2006). Suicide and its prevention among older adults. *Canadian Journal of Psychiatry, 57*, 143–154.

Heisel, M. J., & Duberstein, P. R. (2005). Suicide prevention in older adults. *Clinical Psychology: Science and Practice, 12*, 242–259.

Heisel, M. J., Duberstein, P. R., Talbot, N. L., King, D. A., & Tu, X. M. (2009). Adapting interpersonal psychotherapy for older adults at risk for suicide. *Professional Psychology: Research and Practice, 40*, 156–164.

Heisel, M. J., & Flett, G. L. (2006). The development and initial validation of the Geriatric Suicide Ideation Scale. *American Journal of Geriatric Psychiatry, 14*, 742–757.

Heisel, M. J., & Flett, G. L. (2008). Psychological resilience to suicide ideation among older adults. *Clinical Gerontologist, 31*, 51–70.

Heisel, M. J., & Flett, G. L. (2014). Do meaning in life and purpose in life protect against suicide ideation among community-residing older adults? In A. Batthyany & P. Russo-Netzer (Eds.), *Meaning in existential and positive psychology* (pp. 303–324). New York: Springer.

Heisel, M. J., & Flett, G. L. (2016). Investigating the psychometric properties of the Geriatric Suicide Ideation Scale (GSIS) among community-residing older adults. *Aging and Mental Health, 20*, 208–221.

Heisel, M. J., Flett, G. L., & Besser, A. (2002). Cognitive functioning and geriatric suicide ideation: Testing a mediational model. *American Journal of Geriatric Psychiatry, 10*, 428–436.

Heisel, M. J., and the Meaning-Centered Men's Group Project Team (2016). Enhancing psychological resiliency in older men facing retirement with meaning-centered men's groups. In A. Batthyana (Ed.), *Logotherapy and existential analysis: Proceedings of the Viktor Frankl Institute* (Vol. 1, pp. 165–173). Switzerland: Springer International Publishing.

Heisel, M. J., Neufeld, E., & Flett, G. L. (2016). Reasons for living, meaning in life, and suicide ideation: Investigating the roles of key positive psychological factors in reducing suicide risk in community-residing older adults. *Aging and Mental Health, 20*, 195–207.

Hemels, M. E. H., Koren, G., & Einarson, T. R. (2002). Increased use of antidepressants in Canada: 1981–2000, *The Annals of Psychotherapy, 36*, 1375–1379.

Hemphill, J. R., Hare, R. D., & Wong, S. (1998). Psychopathy and recidivism: A review. *Legal and Criminological Psychology, 3*, 139–170.

Hendricks, P. S., & Thompson, J. K. (2005). An integration of cognitive-behavioral therapy and interpersonal psychotherapy for bulimia nervosa: A case study using the case formulation method. *International Journal of Eating Disorders, 37*, 171–174.

Henggeler, S. W. (2011). Efficacy studies to large-scale transport: The development and validation of multisystemic therapy programs. *Annual Review of Clinical Psychology, 7*, 351–381.

Henggeler, S. W., & Schaeffer, C. M. (2010). Treating serious emotional and behavioural problems using multisystemic therapy. *The Australian and New Zealand Journal of Family Therapy, 31*, 149–164.

Henggeler, S. W., & Schaeffer, C. M. (2016). Multisystemic therapy: Clinical overview, outcomes, and implementation research. *Family Process, 55*, 514–528.

Henggeler, S. W., Schoenwald, S. D., Borduin, C. M., Rowland, M. D., & Cunningham, P. B. (1998). *Multisystemic treatment of antisocial behavior in children and adolescents.* New York: Guilford.

Henriksson, M. M., et al. (1993). Mental disorders and comorbidity in suicide. *American Journal of Psychiatry, 150*, 935–940.

Henry, W. P., Strupp, H. H., Schacht, T. E., & Gaston, L. (1994). Psychodynamic approaches. In A. E. Bergin & S. L. Garfield (Eds.), *Handbook of psychotherapy and behavior change* (4th ed., pp. 467–508). New York: John Wiley & Sons.

Hentschel, F., Kreis, M., Damian, M., Krumm, B., & Frolich, L. (2005). The clinical utility of structural neuroimaging with MRI for diagnosis and differential diagnosis of dementia: A memory clinic study. *International Journal of Geriatric Psychiatry, 20*, 645–650.

Herman, J. L., Perry, J. C., & van der Kolk, B. A. (1989). Childhood trauma in borderline personality disorder. *American Journal of Psychiatry, 146*, 490–495.

Hermans, E. J., Nijenhuis, E. R., van Honk, J., Huntjens, R. J., & van der Hart, O. (2006). Identity state-dependent attentional bias for facial threat in dissociative identity disorder. *Psychiatry Research, 141*, 233–236.

Hertel, P. T., Brozovich, F., Joormann, J., & Gotlib, I. H. (2008). Biases in interpretation and memory in generalized social phobia. *Journal of Abnormal Psychology, 117*, 278–288.

Hester, R. K., & Miller, W. R. (1989). Self-control training. In R. K. Hester & W. R. Miller (Eds.), *Handbook of alcoholism treatment approaches: Effective alternatives* (pp. 141–149). New York: Pergamon.

Heston, L. L. (1966). Psychiatric disorders in foster home reared children of schizophrenic mothers. *British Journal of Psychiatry, 112*, 819–825.

Hetherington, E. M., & Martin, B. (1986). Family factors and psychopathology. In H. C. Quay & J. S. Werry (Eds.), *Psychopathological disorders of childhood* (3rd ed., pp. 332–390). New York: John Wiley & Sons.

Hettema, J. M., Prescott, C. A., Myers, J. M., Neale, M. C., & Kendler, K. S. (2005). The structure of genetic and environmental risk factors for anxiety disorders in men and women. *Archives of General Psychiatry, 62*, 182–189.

Hettema, J., Steele, J., & Miller, W. R. (2005). Motivational interviewing. *Annual Review of Clinical Psychology, 1*, 91–111.

Hewitt, P. L., & Flett, G. L. (1991a). Dimensions of perfectionism in unipolar depression. *Journal of Abnormal Psychology, 100*, 98–101.

Hewitt, P. L., & Flett, G. L. (1991b). Perfectionism in the self and social contexts: Conceptualization, assessment, and association with psychopathology. *Journal of Personality and Social Psychology, 60*, 456–470.

Hewitt, P. L., Flett, G. L., & Ediger, E. (1996). Perfectionism and depression: Longitudinal assessment of a specific vulnerability hypothesis. *Journal of Abnormal Psychology, 105*, 276–280.

Hewitt, P. L., Flett, G. L., Ediger, E., Norton, G. R., & Flynn, C. A. (1998). Perfectionism in chronic and state symptoms of depression. *Canadian Journal of Behavioural Science, 30*, 234–242.

Hewitt, P. L., Flett, G. L., & Mikail, S. F. (2017). *Perfectionism: A relational approach to conceptualization, assessment, and treatment.* New York: Guilford.

Hewitt, P. L., Flett, G. L., Sherry, S. B., & Caelian, C. F. (2006). Trait perfectionism dimensions and suicide behavior. In T. E. Ellis (Ed.), *Cognition and suicide: Theory, research, and therapy* (pp. 215–235). Washington, DC: American Psychological Association.

Hewitt, P. L., Mikail, S. F., Flett, G. L., Tasca, G. A., Flynn, C. A., Deng, X., … Chen, C. (2015). Psychodynamic/interpersonal group psychotherapy for perfectionism: Evaluating the effectiveness of a short-term treatment. *Psychotherapy, 52*, 205–217.

Hickman, E. E., Arnkoff, D. B., Glass, C. R., & Schottenbauer, M. A. (2009). Psychotherapy integration as practiced by experts. *Psychotherapy Theory, Research, Practice, and Training, 46*, 486–491.

Hicks, B. M., DiRago, A. C., Iacono, W. G., & McGue, M. (2009). Gene-environment interplay in internalizing disorders: Consistent findings across six environmental risk factors. *Journal of Child Psychology and Psychiatry, 50*, 1309–1317.

Hildebrandt, T., Alfano, L., Tricamo, M., & Pfaff, D. W. (2010). Conceptualizing the roles of estrogen and serotonin in the development and maintenance of bulimia nervosa. *Clinical Psychology Review, 30*, 655–668.

Hiller, R. M., Apetroaia, A., Clarke, K., Hughes, Z., et al. (2016). The effect of targeting tolerance of children's negative emotions among anxious parents of children with anxiety disorders: A pilot randomized controlled trial. *Journal of Anxiety Disorders, 42*, 52–59.

Hilton, N. Z., & Simmons, J. L. (2001). The influence of actuarial risk assessment in clinical judgments and tribunal decisions about mentally disordered offenders in maximum security. *Law and Human Behavior, 25*, 393–408.

Hilton, N. Z., Simpson, A. I., & Ham, E. (2016). The increasing influence of risk assessment on forensic patient review board decisions. *Psychological Services, 13,* 223–231.

Hingson, R., Heeren, T., Winter, M., & Wechsler, H. (2005). Magnitude of alcohol-related mortality and morbidity among U.S. college students ages 18–24: Changes from 1998 to 2001. *Annual Review of Public Health, 26,* 259–279.

Hirsch, S., Bowen, J., Enami, J., et al. (1996). A one-year prospective study of the effect of life events and medication in the aetiology of schizophrenic relapse. *British Journal of Psychiatry, 168,* 49–56.

Hirshfeld-Becker, D. R., Micco, J., Henin, A., et al. (2008). Behavioral inhibition. *Depression and Anxiety, 25,* 357–367.

Hoaken, P. N., & Stewart, S. H. (2003). Drugs of abuse and the elicitation of human aggressive behavior. *Addictive Behaviors, 28,* 1533–1554.

Hobson, R. P., & Lee, A. (1998). Hello and goodbye: A study of social engagement in autism. *Journal of Autism and Developmental Disorders, 28,* 117–127.

Hodapp, R. M., & Dykens, E. M. (2005). Measuring behavior in genetic disorders of mental retardation. *Mental Retardation and Developmental Disabilities Research Reviews, 11,* 340–346.

Hodges, E. L., Cochrane, C. E., & Brewerton, T. D. (1998). Family characteristics of binge-eating disorder patients. *International Journal of Eating Disorders, 23,* 145–151.

Hodgkinson, K. A., Murphy, J., O'Neill, S., Brzustowicz, L., & Bassett, A. S. (2001). Genetic counselling for schizophrenia in the era of molecular genetics. *Canadian Journal of Psychiatry, 46,* 123–130.

Hoebel, B. G., & Teitelbaum, P. (1966). Weight regulation in normal and hypothalamic hyperphagic rats. *Journal of Comparative and Physiological Psychology, 61,* 189–193.

Hofmann, S. G. (2008). Cognitive processes during fear acquisition and extinction in animals and humans: Implication for exposure therapy of anxiety disorders. *Clinical Psychology Review, 28,* 199–210.

Hofmann, S. G. (2014). D-cycloserine for treating anxiety disorders: Making good exposures better and bad exposures worse. *Depression and Anxiety, 31,* 175–177.

Hofmann, S. G., Asmundson, G. J. G., & Beck, A. T. (2013). The science of cognitive therapy. *Behavior Therapy, 44,* 199–212.

Hofmann, S. G., Newman, M. G., Ehlerr, A., & Roth, W. (1995). Psychophysiological differences between subgroups of social phobia. *Journal of Abnormal Psychology, 104,* 224–231.

Hofmann, S. G., Sawyer, A. T., Witt, A. A., & Oh, D. (2010). The effect of mindfulness-based therapy on anxiety and depression: A meta-analytic review. *Journal of Consulting and Clinical Psychology, 78,* 169–183.

Hogarty, G. E., et al. (2004). Cognitive enhancement therapy for schizophrenia: Effects of a 2-year randomized trial on cognition and behavior. *Archives of General Psychiatry, 61,* 866–876.

Hoge, C. W., Yehuda, R., Castro, C. A., McFarlane, A. C., et al. (2015). Unintended consequences of changing the definition of posttraumatic stress disorder in *DSM-5*: Critique and call to action. *JAMA Psychiatry, 73,* 750–752.

Holden, R. R. (1999). The Holden Psychological Screening Inventory and sexual efficacy in urological patients with erectile dysfunction. *Psychological Reports, 84,* 255–258.

Hollander, E., Phillips, A., Chaplin, W., et al. (2005). A placebo controlled crossover trial of liquid fluoxetine on repetitive behaviors in childhood and adolescent autism. *Neuropsychopharmacology, 30,* 582–589.

Hollander, M. J., et al. (2009). Increasing value for money in the Canadian healthcare system: New findings and the case for integrated health care for seniors. *Healthcare Quarterly, 12,* 38–47.

Hollander, M. J., & Chappell, N. L. (2007). A comparative analysis of costs to government for home care and long-term residential care service, standardized for client care needs. *Canadian Journal on Aging, 26,* 149–161.

Hollingshead, A. B., & Redlich, F. C. (1958). *Social class and mental illness: A community study.* New York: John Wiley & Sons.

Hollingworth, P., Harold, D., Jones, L., Owen, M. J., & Williams, L. (2011). Alzheimer's disease genetics: Current knowledge and future challenges. *International Journal of Geriatric Psychiatry, 26,* 793–802.

Hollon, S. D., DeRubeis, R. J., & Evans, M. D. (1996). Cognitive therapy in the treatment and prevention of depression. In P. M. Salkovskis (Ed.), *Frontiers of cognitive therapy* (pp. 293–317). New York: Guilford.

Hollon, S. D., DeRubeis, R. J., & Seligman, M. E. P. (1992). Cognitive therapy and the prevention of depression. *Applied and Preventive Psychology, 1,* 89–95.

Hollon, S. D., Stewart, M. O., & Strunk, D. (2006). Enduring effects for cognitive behavior therapy in the treatment of depression and anxiety. *Annual Review of Psychology, 57,* 285–315.

Holmes, T. S., & Holmes, T. H. (1970). Short-term intrusions into the life style routine. *Journal of Psychosomatic Research, 14,* 121–132.

Holmes, T. H., & Rahe, R. H. (1967). The social readjustment rating scale. *Journal of Psychosomatic Research, 11,* 213–218.

Holowaty, P., Feldman, L., Harvey, B., & Shortt, L. (2000). Cigarette smoking in multicultural, urban high school students. *Journal of Adolescent Health, 27,* 281–288.

Holtzheimer, P. E., Kelley, M. E., Gross, R. E., Filkowski, M. M., et al. (2012). Subcallosal cingulated deep brain stimulation for treatment-resistant unipolar and bipolar depression. *Archives of General Psychiatry, 69,* 150–158.

Hom, M. A., Stanley, I. H., & Joiner, T. E., Jr. (2015). Evaluating factors and interventions that influence help-seeking and mental health service utilization among suicidal individuals: A review of the literature. *Clinical Psychology Review, 40,* 28–39.

Honyashiki, M., Furukawa, T. A., Noma, H., Tanaka, S., Chen, P., Ichikawa, K., . . . Caldwell, D. M. (2014). Specificity of CBT for depression: A contribution from multiple treatments meta-analyses. *Cognitive Therapy and Research, 38,* 249–260.

Honywill, B. (1998, February 10). Tot's killer "not responsible": Stabbed Hamilton boy to death. *The Toronto Sun.*

Hooley, J. M., & Teasdale, J. D. (1989). Predictors of relapse in unipolar depressives: Expressed emotion, marital distress, and perceived criticism. *Journal of Abnormal Psychology, 98,* 229–235.

Hoon, E. F., & Hoon, P. W. (1978). Styles of sexual expression in women: Clinical implications of multivariate analyses. *Archives of Sexual Behavior, 7,* 105–116.

Hopwood, C. J., et al. (2009). The stability of personality traits in individuals with borderline personality disorder. *Journal of Abnormal Psychology, 118,* 806–815.

Horan, W. P., Rassovsky, Y., Kern, R. S., Lee, J., et al. (2010). Further support for the role of dysfunctional attitudes in models of real-world functioning in schizophrenia. *Journal of Psychiatric Research, 44,* 499–505.

Horn, A. S., & Snyder, S. H. (1971). Chlorpromazine and dopamine: Conformational similarities that correlate with the antischizophrenic activity of phenothiazine drugs. *Proceedings of the National Academy of Sciences, 68,* 2325–2328.

Horvath, A. O. (2000). The therapeutic relationship: From transference to alliance. *Journal of Clinical Psychology/In Session: Psychotherapy in Practice, 56,* 163–173.

Horvath, A. O. (2001). The alliance. *Psychotherapy, 38,* 365–372.

Horvath, A. O. (2006). The alliance in context: Accomplishments, challenges, and future directions. *Psychotherapy: Theory, Research, Practice, Training, 43*, 258–263.

Horvath, A. O., & Bedi, R. P. (2002). The alliance. In J. Norcross (Ed.), *Psychotherapy relationships that work: Therapist contributions and responsiveness to patients* (pp. 37–70). New York: Oxford University Press.

Horvath, A. O., & Greenberg, L. S. (1989). Development and validation of the Working Alliance Inventory. *Journal of Counseling Psychology, 36*, 223–233.

Horvath, A. O., & Greenberg, L. S. (1994). Introduction. In A. O. Horvath & L. S. Greenberg (Eds.), *The working alliance: Theory, research, and practice*. New York: Wiley.

Houenou, J., Perlini, C., & Brambilla, P. (2015). Epidemiological and clinical aspects will guide the neuroimaging research in bipolar disorder. *Epidemiology and Psychiatric Sciences, 24*, 117–120.

Howard, M. O., & Jenson, J. M. (1999). Inhalant abuse among antisocial youth. *Addictive Behaviors, 24*, 59–74.

Howes, O. D., McCutcheon, R., Owen, M. J., & Murray, R. (in press). The role of genes, stress, and dopamine in the development of schizophrenia. *Biological Psychiatry*.

Howitt, D. (1995). Pornography and the paedophile: Is it criminogenic? *British Journal of Medical Psychology, 68*, 15–27.

Howlett, K. (2016, August 23). Mounting cost of opioid abuse treatment taxes health system. *The Globe and Mail*, A1, A8.

Hoza, B., Waschbusch, D. A., Pelham, W. E., Molina, B. S. G., & Milich, R. (2000). Attention-deficit/hyperactivity disordered and control boys' responses to social success and failure. *Child Development, 71*, 432–446.

Hubbard, R. E., Searle, S. D., Mitnitski, A., & Rockwood, K. (2009). Effects of smoking on the accumulation of deficits, frailty, and survival in older adults: A secondary analysis from the Canadian Study of Health and Aging. *The Journal of Nutrition, Health, and Aging, 13*, 468–472.

Hubley, A. M., & Russell, L. B. (2009). Prediction of subjective age, desired age, and age satisfaction in older adults: Do some health dimensions contribute more than others? *International Journal of Behavioral Development, 33*, 12–21.

Hudson, J. I., Hiripi, E., Pope, H. G., Jr., & Kessler, R. C. (2007). The prevalence and correlates of eating disorders in the National Comorbidity Survey replication. *Biological Psychiatry, 61*, 348–358.

Hudson, S. M., & Ward, T. (1997). Rape: Psychopathology and theory. In D. R. Laws & W. O'Donohue (Eds.), *Sexual deviance* (pp. 332–355). New York: Guilford.

Huey, S. J., Jr., Henggeler, S. W., Brondino, M. J., & Pickrel, S. G. (2000). Mechanisms of change in multisystemic therapy: Reducing delinquent behavior through therapist adherence and improved family and peer functioning. *Journal of Consulting and Clinical Psychology, 68*, 451–467.

Hughes, C. & Agran, M. (1993). Teaching persons with severe disabilities to use self-instruction in community settings: An analysis of applications. *The Journal of the Association for Persons with Severe Handicaps, 18*, 261–274.

Hughes, C., Hugo, K., & Blatt, J. (1996). Self-instructional intervention for teaching generalized problem-solving within a functional task sequence. *American Journal on Mental Retardation, 100*, 565–579.

Hughes, J. R. (1995). Combining behavioural therapy and pharmacotherapy for smoking cessation: An update. *NIDA Research Monograph, 150*, 92–109.

Hughes, J. R., & Hatsukami, D. K. (1992). The nicotine withdrawal syndrome: A brief review and update. *International Journal of Smoking Cessation, 1*, 21–26.

Hughes, J. R., et al. (1991). Caffeine self-administration, withdrawal, and adverse effects among coffee drinkers. *Archives of General Psychiatry, 48*, 611–617.

Hultsch, D. F., Hertzog, C., Small, B. J., & Dixon, R. A. (1999). Use it or lose it: Engaged lifestyle as a buffer of cognitive decline in aging? *Psychology and Aging, 14*, 245–263.

Human Resources Development Canada and Statistics Canada. (1996). *Growing up in Canada: National Longitudinal Survey of Children and Youth*. Ottawa: Statistics Canada.

Humphrey, L. L. (1986). Family relations in bulimic-anorexic and nondistressed families. *International Journal of Eating Disorders, 5*, 223–232.

Hunsley, J., Aubry, T. D., Vestervelt, C. M., & Vito, D. (1999). Comparing therapist and client perspectives on reasons for psychotherapy termination. *Psychotherapy, 36*, 380–388.

Hunsley, J., & Bailey, J. M. (2001). Whither the Rorschach? An analysis of the evidence. *Psychological Assessment, 13*, 472–485.

Hunsley, J., Dobson, K. S., Johnston, C., & Mikail, S. F. (1999). Empirically supported treatments in psychology: Implications for Canadian professional psychology. *Canadian Psychology, 40*, 239–302.

Hunsley, J., Elliott, K., & Therrien, Z. (2013). The efficacy and effectiveness of psychological treatments. Report commissioned by the Canadian Psychological Association.

Hunsley, J., & Johnston, C. (2000). The role of empirically supported treatments in evidence-based psychological practice: A Canadian perspective. *Clinical Psychology: Science and Practice, 7*, 269–275.

Hunsley, J., & Lee, C. M. (2007). Research-informed benchmarks for psychological treatments: Efficacy studies, effectiveness studies, and beyond. *Professional Psychology: Research and Practice, 38*, 21–33.

Hunsley, J., Lee, C. M., & Aubry, T. (1999). Who uses psychological services in Canada? *Canadian Psychology, 40*, 232–240.

Hunsley, J., & Lefebvre, M. (1990). A survey of the practices and activities of Canadian clinical psychologists. *Canadian Psychology, 31*, 350–358.

Hunsley, J., & Mash, E. J. (2005). Introduction to the special section on developing guidelines for the evidence-based assessment (EBA) of adult disorders. *Psychological Assessment, 17*, 251–255.

Hunsley, J., & Mash, E. J. (2007). Evidence-based assessment. *Annual Review of Clinical Psychology, 3*, 29–51.

Hunsley, J., & Mash, E. J. (2008). *A guide to assessments that work*. New York: Oxford University Press.

Hunsley, J., & Mash, E. J. (2010). Evidence-based assessment. In D. H. Barlow (Ed.), *The Oxford handbook of clinical psychology* (pp. 76–97). Oxford: Oxford University Press.

Hunsley, J., & Rumstein-McKean, O. (1999). Improving psychotherapeutic services via randomized clinical trials, treatment manuals, and component analysis designs. *Journal of Clinical Psychology, 55*, 1507–1517.

Hunt, E., Bornovalova, M. A., & Patrick, C. J. (2015). Genetic and environmental overlap between borderline personality disorder traits and psychopathy: Evidence for promotive effects of factor 2 and protective effects of factor 1. *Psychological Medicine, 45*, 1471–1481.

Huntington's Disease Collaborative Research Group. (1993). A novel gene containing a trinucleotide repeat that is expanded and unstable on Huntington's disease chromosomes. *Cell, 72*, 971–983.

Huntjens, R. J. C., Peters, M. L., Woertman, L., van der Hart, O., & Postma, A. (2007). Memory transfer for emotionally valenced words between identities in dissociative identity disorder. *Behaviour Research and Therapy, 45*, 775–789.

Hurd, H. (1916–1917). *The institutional care of the insane in the United States and Canada, vols. I and IV*. Baltimore: The Johns Hopkins Press. (Reprint Edition, 1973. New York: Arno Press.)

Hurt, R. D., Sachs, D. P. L., & Glover, E. D. (1997). A comparison of sustained release buprioprion versus placebo for treatment of nicotine dependence. *New England Journal of Medicine, 337*, 1195–1202.

Hwang, W.-C., Myers, H., Abe-Kim, J., & Ting, J. Y. (2008). A conceptual paradigm for understanding culture's impact on mental health: The cultural influences on mental health (CIMH) model. *Clinical Psychology Review, 28*, 211–227.

Hydro-Québec v. Syndicat des employé-e-s de techniques professionnelles et de bureau d'Hydro-Québec, section locale 2000 (SCFP-FTQ) (2008), 63 C.H.R.R. D/301, 2008 SCC 43

Iacono, D., Zandi, P., Gross, M., Markesbery, W. R., et al. (2015). APOe2 and education in cognitively normal older subjects with high levels of AD pathology at autopsy: Findings from the Nun Study. *Oncotarget, 6*(16), 14082–14091.

Iacoviello, B. M., Alloy, L. B., Abramson, L. Y., Whitehouse, W. G., & Hogan, M. E. (2006). The course of depression in individuals at high and low cognitive risk for depression: A prospective study. *Journal of Affective Disorders, 93*, 61–69.

Ibraham, A. K., Kelly, S. J., Adams, C. E., & Glazebrook, C. (2013). A systematic review of depression prevalence in university students. *Journal of Psychiatric Research, 47*, 391–400.

Iervolino, A. C., Perroud, N., Fullana, M. A., Guipponi, M., et al. (2009). Prevalence and heritability of compulsive hoarding: a twin study. *American Journal of Psychiatry, 166*, 1156–1161.

Imperato-McGinley, J., Guerrero, L., Gautier, T., & Peterson, R. E. (1974). Steroid 5a-reductase deficiency in man: An inherited form of pseudo-hermaphroditism. *Science, 186*, 1213–1215.

Ingraham, C. (2016, August 17). The latest overdose outbreak shows just how dangerous the heroin epidemic has gotten. *The Washington Post.*

Ingram, K., & Roy, L. (1995). Complaints against psychiatrists: A five-year study. *Psychiatric Bulletin, 19*, 620–622.

Inouye, S. K., et al. (1999). A multicomponent intervention to prevent delirium in hospitalized older patients. *New England Journal of Medicine, 340*, 669–676.

Institute of Medicine. (1990). Matching. In *Broadening the base of treatment for alcohol problems* (pp. 279–302). Washington, DC: National Academy Press.

International Society for the Study of Dissociation (ISSD). (2004). Guidelines for the evaluation and treatment of dissociative symptoms in children and adolescents. *Journal of Trauma & Dissociation, 5*, 119–150.

International Society for the Study of Trauma and Dissociation (ISSD). (2011). Guidelines for treating dissociative identity disorder in adults, third revision: Summary version. *Journal of Trauma & Dissociation, 12*, 188–212.

Ipser, J. C., Singh, L., & Stein, D. J. (2013). Meta-analysis of functional brain imaging in specific phobia. *Psychiatry and Clinical Neurosciences, 67*, 311–322.

Irving, L., et al. (2004). The relationships between hope and outcomes at the pretreatment, beginning, and later phases of psychotherapy. *Journal of Psychotherapy Integration, 14*, 419–433.

Irwin, M., et al. (1985). Psychotic patients' understanding of informed consent. *American Journal of Psychiatry, 142*, 1351–1354.

Isaacs, C., Peshkin, B. N., Schwartz, M., et al. (2002). Breast and ovarian cancer screening practices in healthy women with a strong family history of breast or ovarian cancer. *Breast Cancer Research and Treatment, 71*, 103–112.

Islam, F. (2015). Immigrating to Canada during early childhood associated with increased risk for mood disorders. *Community Mental Health Journal, 51*, 723–732.

Ivanoff, A., Jang, S. J., Smyth, N. J., & Linehan, M. M. (1994). Fewer reasons for staying alive when you are thinking of killing yourself: The Brief Reasons for Living Inventory. *Journal of Psychopathology and Behavioral Assessment, 16*, 1–13.

Iversen, L. (2003). Cannabis and the brain. *Brain, 126*, 1252–1270.

Ivey, A. E., Ivey, M. B., & Simek-Morgan, L. (1997). *Counseling and psychotherapy: A multicultural perspective.* Needham Heights, MA: Allyn and Bacon.

Iyer, S., Jordan, G., MacDonald, K., Joober, R., & Malla, A. (2015). Early intervention for psychosis: A Canadian perspective. *Journal of Nervous and Mental Disease, 203*, 356–364.

Jack, D. C. (1999). Silencing the self: Inner dialogues and outer realities. In T. Joiner & J. C. Coyne (Eds.), *The interactional nature of depression.* Washington, DC: American Psychological Association.

Jacob, G. A., & Arntz, A. (2013). Schema therapy for personality disorders—A review. *International Journal of Cognitive Therapy, 6*, 171–185.

Jacob, R. G., et al. (1999). Ambulatory blood pressure responses and the circumplex model of mood: A 4-day study. *Psychosomatic Medicine, 61*, 319–333.

Jacobson, N. S., Dobson, K. S., Traux, P. A., et al. (1996). A component analysis of cognitive behavioural treatment for depression. *Journal of Consulting and Clinical Psychology, 64*, 295–304.

Jacobson, N. S., & Margolin, G. (1979). *Marital therapy: Strategies based on social learning.* New York: Brunner/Mazel.

Jadoulle, V., et al. (2006). Coping and adaptation to breast cancer: A six-month prospective study. *Cancer Bulletin, 93*, 10067–10072.

Jaffee, S. R., Caspi, A., Moffitt, T. E., et al. (2005). Nature X nurture: Genetic vulnerabilities interact with physical maltreatment to promote conduct problems. *Development and Psychopathology, 17*, 67–84.

Jaffer, M. S. B., & Brazeau, P. (2011, November 28). Senators Mobina S. B. Jaffer & Patrick Brazeau: Fighting back against sexual abuse. *National Post.*

Jager-Hyman, S., Cunningham, A., Wenzel, A., Mattei, S., Brown, G. K., & Beck, A. T. (2014). Cognitive distortions and suicide attempts. *Cognitive Therapy and Research, 38*, 369–374.

Jaimes, A., Larose-Hebert, K., & Moreau, N. (2015). Current trends in theoretical orientation of psychologists: The case of Quebec clinicians. *Journal of Clinical Psychology, 71*, 1042–1048.

Jandorf, L., Deblinger, E., Neale, J. M., & Stone, A. A. (1986). Daily vs. major life events as predictors of symptom frequency. *Journal of General Psychology, 113*, 205–218.

Janeck, A. S., Calamari, J. E., Riemann, B. C., & Heffelfinger, S. K. (2003). Too much thinking about thinking? Metacognitive differences in obsessive-compulsive disorder. *Anxiety Disorders, 17*, 181–195.

Jang, K. L., Vernon, P. A., & Livesley, W. J. (2000). Personality disorder traits, family environment, and alcohol misuse: A multivariate behavioural genetic analysis. *Addiction, 95*, 873–888.

Jang, K. L., Vernon, P. A., & Livesley, W. J. (2001). Perspectives on the genetics of personality function. *Canadian Journal of Psychiatry, 46*, 234–244.

Janicak, P. G., Davis, J. M., Preskorn, S. H., & Ayd, F. J. (1993). *Principles and practice of psychopharmacological therapy.* Baltimore: Williams & Wilkins.

Jarrett, M. A., & Ollendick, T. H. (2008). A conceptual review of the comorbidity of attention-deficit/hyperactivity disorder and anxiety: Implications for future research and practice. *Clinical Psychology Review, 28*, 1266–1280.

Jarrett, T. A. (2013). Warrior resilience and thriving (WRT): Rational emotive behavior therapy (REBT) as a resiliency and thriving foundation to prepare warriors and their families for combat deployment and posttraumatic growth in Operation Iraqi Freedom, 2005-2009. *Journal of Rational-Emotive and Cognitive-Behavior Therapy, 31*, 93–107.

Jarvis, G. E. (2007). The social causes of psychosis in North American psychiatry: A review of a disappearing literature. *Canadian Journal of Psychiatry, 52*, 287–294.

Jellinek, E. M. (1952). Phases of alcohol addiction. *Quarterly Journal of Studies on Alcohol, 13*, 673–684.

Jelovac, A., Kolshus, E., & McLoughlin, D. M. (2013). Relapse following successful electroconvulsive therapy for major depression: A meta analysis. *Neuropsychopharmacology, 38*, 2467–2474.

Jemmott, J. B. III, & Magloire, K. (1988). Academic stress, social support, and secretory immunoglobulin A. *Journal of Personality and Social Psychology, 55*, 803–810.

Jenike, M. A. (1986). Theories of etiology. In M. A. Jenike, L. Baer, & W. E. Minichiello (Eds.), *Obsessive-compulsive disorders*. Littleton, MA: PSG Publishing.

Jenike, M. A. (1990). Psychotherapy. In A. S. Bellack & M. Hersen (Eds.), *Handbook of comparative treatments for adult disorders* (pp. 245–255). New York: John Wiley & Sons.

Jenike, M. A., Baer, L., & Minichiello, W. E. (1986). *Obsessive-compulsive disorders: Theory and management*. Littleton, MA: PSG Publishing.

Jenkins, C. D. (1976). Recent evidence supporting psychologic and social risk factors for coronary disease. *New England Journal of Medicine, 294*, 1033–1038.

Jenn, H.-S., Dunkle, R., & Roberts, B. L. (2006). Worries of the oldest old. *Health and Social Work, 31*, 256–265.

Jensen, P. S., Arnold, L. E., Richters, J. E., et al. (1999). A 14-month randomized clinical trial of treatment strategies for attention-deficit/hyperactivity disorder. *Archives of General Psychiatry, 56*, 1073–1086.

Jensen-Doss, A. (2011). Practice involves more than treatment: How can evidence-based assessment catch up to evidence-based treatment. *Clinical Psychology: Science and Practice, 18*, 173–177.

Jespersen, A. F., Lalumière, M. L., & Seto, M. C. (2009). Sexual abuse history among adult sex offenders and non-sex offenders. *Child Abuse and Neglect, 33*, 179–192.

Jiang, Y.-H., Yuen, R. K. C., Jin, X., Wang, M., et al. (2013). Detection of clinically relevant genetic variants in autism spectrum disorder by whole-genome sequencing. *The American Journal of Human Genetics, 93*, 249–263.

Joanette, Y. (2013). Living longer, living better: Preview of CIHR Institute of Aging 2013-2018 Strategic Plan. *Canadian Journal on Aging, 32*, 209–213.

Johnsen, T. J., & Friborg, O. (2015). The effects of cognitive behavioral therapy as an anti-depressive treatment is falling: A meta-analysis. *Psychological Bulletin, 141*, 747–768.

Johnson, B. T., Low, R. E., & MacDonald, H. V. (2015). Panning for the gold in health research: Incorporating studies' methodological quality in meta-analysis. *Psychology & Health, 30*, 135–152.

Johnson, E. M., & Coles, M. E. (2013). Failure and delay in treatment-seeking across anxiety disorders. *Community Mental Health Journal, 49*(6), 668–674.

Johnson, J., Horvath, E., & Weissman, M. M. (1991). The validity of depression with psychotic features based on a community study. *Archives of General Psychiatry, 48*, 1075–1081.

Johnson, J., Wood, A. M., Gooding, P., Taylor, P. J., & Tarrier, N. (2011). Resilience to suicidality: The buffering hypothesis. *Clinical Psychology Review, 31*, 563–591.

Johnson, J. A., Key, B. L., Routledge, F. S., Gerin, W., & Campbell, T. S. (2014). High trait rumination is associated with blunted nighttime diastolic blood pressure dipping. *Annals of Behavioral Medicine, 48*, 384–391.

Johnson, J. A., Lavoie, K. L., Bacon, S. L., Carlson, L. E., & Campbell, T. S. (2012). The effect of trait rumination on adaptation to repeated stress. *Psychosomatic Medicine, 74*, 258–262.

Johnson, S. L. (2005). Mania and dysregulation in goal pursuit: A review. *Clinical Psychology Review, 25*, 241–262.

Johnson, S. M. (2000). Emotionally focused couples therapy. In F. M. Dattilio & L. J. Bevilacqua (Eds.), *Comparative treatments for relationship dysfunction: Springer series on comparative treatments for psychological disorders* (pp. 163–185). New York: Springer.

Johnson, S. M. (2002). *Emotionally focused couple therapy with trauma survivors: Strengthening attachment bonds*. New York: Guilford.

Johnson, S. M. (2007). The contribution of emotionally focused couples therapy. *Journal of Contemporary Psychotherapy, 37*, 47–52.

Johnson, S. M., Hunsley, J., Greenberg, L. S., & Schindler, D. (1999). Emotionally focused couples therapy: Status and challenges. *Clinical Psychology: Science and Practice, 6*, 67–79.

Johnson, S. M., & Greenberg, L. S. (1987). Emotionally focused marital therapy: An overview. *Psychotherapy, 24*, 552–560.

Johnson, S. M., & LeBow, J. (2000). The "coming of age" of couple therapy: A decade review. *Journal of Marital and Family Therapy, 26*, 23–38.

Johnson, S. M., & Whiffen, V. (2003). *Attachment processes in couples and families*. New York: Guilford.

Joiner, T. E., Jr. (2009). Suicide prevention in schools as viewed through the interpersonal-psychological theory of suicidal behaviour. *School Psychology Review, 38*, 244–248.

Joiner, T. E., Jr., Alfano, M. S., & Metalsky, G. I. (1992). When depression breeds contempt: Reassurance seeking, self-esteem, and rejection of depressed college students by their roommates. *Journal of Abnormal Psychology, 101*, 165–173.

Joiner, T. E., Jr., Ribeiro, J. D., & Silva, C. (2012). Nonsuicidal self-injury, suicidal behavior, and their co-occurrence as viewed through the lens of the interpersonal theory of suicide. *Current Directions in Psychological Science, 21*, 342–347.

Joiner, T. E., Jr., & Schmidt, N. B. (1998). Excessive reassurance-seeking predicts depressive but not anxious reactions to acute stress. *Journal of Abnormal Psychology, 107*, 533.

Jones, A. P., Laurens, K. R., Herba, C. M., Barker, G. J., & Viding, E. (2009). Amygdala hypoactivity to fearful faces in boys with conduct problems and callous unemotional traits. *American Journal of Psychiatry, 166*, 95–102.

Jones, C. M., Logan, J., Gladden, R. M., & Bohm, M. K. (2015). Vital signs: Demographic and substance use trends among heroin users – United States, 2002-2013. *CDC Morbidity and Mortality Weekly Report, 64*(26), 719–725.

Jones, J. M., Bennett, S., Olmsted, M. P., Lawson, M. L., & Rodin, G. (2001). Disordered eating attitudes and behaviours in teenaged girls: A school-based study. *Canadian Medical Association Journal, 165*, 547–552.

Jones, M. D., Crowther, J. H., & Ciesla, J. A. (2014). A naturalistic study of fat talk and its behavioral and affective consequences. *Body Image, 11*, 337–345.

Jones, O. D., & Shen, F. X. (2012). Law and neuroscience in the United States. In T. M. Spranger (Ed.), *International neurolaw* (pp. 349–380). Berlin Heidelberg: Springer-Verlag.

Jonsson, H., & Hougaard, E. (2009). Group cognitive behavioural therapy for obsessive-compulsive disorder: A systematic review and meta-analysis. *Acta Psychiatric Scandinavica, 119*, 98–106.

Jorenby, D. E., et al. (1999). A controlled trial of sustained-release buproprion, a nicotine patch, or both for smoking cessation. *New England Journal of Medicine, 340,* 685–691.

Joyal, C. C., et al. (2007). Violent persons with schizophrenia and co-morbid disorders: A functional magnetic resonance imaging study. *Schizophrenia Research, 91,* 97–102.

Joyce, A. S., Ogrodniczuk, J. S., Piper, W. E., & Sheptycki, A. R. (2010). Interpersonal predictors of outcome following short-term group therapy for complicated grief: A replication. *Clinical Psychology and Psychotherapy, 17,* 122–135.

Jung, H. H., et al. (2006). Bilateral anterior cingulotomy for refractory obsessive-compulsive disorder: Long-term follow-up results. *Stereotactic and Functional Neurosurgery, 84,* 184–189.

Jung, S., & Nunes, K. L. (2012). Denial and its relationship with treatment perceptions among sex offenders. *The Journal of Forensic Psychiatry and Psychology, 23,* 485–496.

Junginger, J., Barker, S., & Coe, D. (1992). Mood theme and bizarreness of delusions in schizophrenia and mood psychosis. *Journal of Abnormal Psychology, 101,* 287–292.

Kadis, L. B., & McClendon, R. A. (1998). *Concise guide to marital and family therapy.* Washington, DC: American Psychiatric Association.

Kafka, M. P. (2010). Hypersexual disorder: A proposed diagnosis for DSM-V. *Archives of Sexual Behavior, 39,* 377–400.

Kafka, M. P. (2013). The development and evolution of the criteria for a newly proposed diagnosis for DSM-5: Hypersexual disorder. *Sexual Addiction and Compulsivity: The Journal of Treatment and Prevention, 20,* 19–26.

Kafka, M. P. (2014). What happened to hypersexual disorder? *Archives of Sexual Behavior, 43,* 1259–1261.

Kagan, J. (1997). Temperament and the reactions to unfamiliarity. *Child Development, 68,* 139–143.

Kain, K. (1994). *Movement never lies: An autobiography.* Toronto: McClelland and Stewart.

Kairouz, S., & Adlaf, E. M. (2003). Schools, students and heavy drinking: A multilevel analysis. *Addiction Research and Theory, 11,* 427–439.

Kalant, H. (2015). Cannabis and youth: A summary of key findings and major questions, and a call to action. In T. George & F. Vaccarino (Eds.), *Substance abuse in Canada: The effects of cannabis use during adolescence* (pp. 76–93). Ottawa: Canadian Centre on Substance Abuse.

Kalichman, S. C. (1991). Psychopathology and personality characteristics of criminal sexual offenders as a function of victim age. *Archives of Sexual Behavior, 20,* 187–198.

Kalkhoran, S., & Glantz, S. A. (2016). E-cigarettes and smoking cessation in real-world and clinical settings; A systematic review and meta-analysis. *Lancet Respiratory Medicine, 4,* 116–128.

Kamarck, T. W., et al. (1998). Effects of task strain, social conflict, and emotional activation on ambulatory cardiovascular activity: Daily life consequences of recurring stress in a multiethnic adult sample. *Health Psychology, 17,* 17–29.

Kamarck, T. W., Annunziato, B., & Amateau, L. M. (1995). Affiliations moderate the effects of social threat on stress-related cardiovascular responses: Boundary conditions for a laboratory model of social support. *Psychosomatic Medicine, 57,* 183–194.

Kanner, A. D., Coyne, J. C., Schaefer, C., & Lazarus, R. S. (1981). Comparison of two modes of stress measurement: Daily hassles and uplifts versus major life events. *Journal of Behavioral Medicine, 4,* 1–39.

Kanner, L., & Eisenberg, L. (1955). Notes on the follow-up studies of autistic children. In P. Hoch & J. Zubin (Eds.), *Psychopathology of childhood.* New York: Grune & Stratton.

Kantorovich, N. V. (1930). An attempt at associative-reflex therapy in alcoholism. *Psychological Abstracts, 4,* 493.

Kaplan, G. A., Wilson, T. W., Cohen, R. D., Kauhanen, J., Wu, M., & Salonen, J. T. (1994). Social functioning and overall mortality: Prospective evidence from the Kuopio ischemic heart disease risk factor study. *Epidemiology, 5,* 495–500.

Kaplan, H. I., & Sadock, B. J. (1991). *Synopsis of psychiatry: Behavioral sciences, clinical psychiatry.* Baltimore: Williams & Wilkins.

Kaplan, H. S. (1974). *The new sex therapy: Active treatment of sexual dysfunctions.* New York: Brunner/Mazel, Publishers, Inc.

Kaplan, H. S. (1997). Sexual desire disorders (hypoactive sexual desire and sexual aversion). In G. O. Gabbard & S. D. Atkinson (Eds.), *Synopsis of treatments of psychiatric disorders* (2nd ed., pp. 771–780). Washington, DC: American Psychiatric Press.

Kaplan, M. S., & Kreuger, R. B. (1997). Voyeurism: Psychopathology and theory. In D. R. Laws & W. O'Donohue (Eds.), *Sexual deviance* (pp. 297–310). New York: Guilford.

Kaplow, J. B., & Widom, C. S. (2007). Age of onset of child maltreatment predicts long-term mental health outcomes. *Journal of Abnormal Psychology, 116,* 176–187.

Kapur, S. (2003). Psychosis as a state of aberrant salience: A framework linking biology, phenomenology, and pharmacology in schizophrenia. *American Journal of Psychiatry, 160,* 13–23.

Karakurt, G., Whiting, K., van Esch, C., Bolen, S. D., & Calabrese, J. R. (2016). Couples therapy for intimate partner violence: A systematic review and meta-analysis. *Journal of Marital and Family Therapy, 42*(4), 567–583.

Karel, M. J., Gatz, M., & Smyer, M. A. (2012). Aging and mental health in the decade ahead: What psychologists need to know. *American Psychologist, 67,* 184–198.

Karlin, B. E., & Agarwal, M. (2013). Achieving the promise of evidence-based psychotherapies for posttraumatic stress disorder and other mental health conditions for veterans. *Psychological Science in the Public Interest, 14,* 62–64.

Karlin, B. E., Ruzek, J. I., Chard, K. M., Eftekhari, A., et al. (2010). Dissemination of evidence-based psychological treatments for posttraumatic stress disorder in the Veterans Health Administration. *Journal of Traumatic Stress, 23,* 663–673.

Kashden, J., & Franzen, M. D. (1996). An inter-rater reliability study of the Luria-Nebraska Neuropsychological Battery Form-II quantitative scoring system. *Archives of Clinical Neuropsychology, 11,* 155–163.

Kasl-Godley, J., & Gatz, M. (2000). Psychosocial interventions for individuals with dementia: An integration of theory, therapy, and a clinical understanding of dementia. *Clinical Psychology Review, 20,* 755–782.

Katzman, M. A., et al. (2014). Canadian clinical practice guidelines for the management of anxiety, posttraumatic stress and obsessive-compulsive disorders. *BMC Psychiatry, 14 (Suppl 1),* 51.

Kauer-Sant'Anna, M., Frey, B. N., Andreazza, A. C., et al. (2007). Anxiety comorbidity and quality of life in bipolar disorder patients. *Canadian Journal of Psychiatry, 52,* 175–181.

Kaufman, J., Yang, B., Douglas-Palumberi, H., et al. (2006). Brain-derived neurotrophic factor 5-HTTLPR gene interactions and environmental modifiers of depression in children. *Biological Psychiatry, 59,* 673–680.

Kavale, K. A. (2002). Mainstreaming to full inclusion: From orthogenesis to pathogenesis of an idea. *International Journal of Disability, Development, and Education, 49,* 201–214.

Kavale, K. A., & Forness, S. R. (1999). Effectiveness of special education. In C. R. Reynolds & T. B. Gutkin (Eds.), *The handbook of school psychology* (3rd ed., pp. 984–1024). New York: John Wiley & Sons.

Kawachi, I., Colditz, G. A., Ascherio, A., Rimm, E. B., Giovannucci, E., et al. (1994). Prospective study of phobic anxiety and risk of coronary heart disease in men. *Circulation, 89*, 1992–1997.

Kazdin, A. E. (1985). *Treatment of antisocial behavior in children and adolescents*. Homewood, IL: Dorsey Press.

Kazdin, A. E. (2003). Psychotherapy for children and adolescents. *Annual Review of Psychology, 54*, 253–276.

Kazdin, A. E. (2005). *Parent management training: Treatment for oppositional, aggressive, and antisocial behavior in children and adolescents*. New York: Oxford University Press.

Kazdin, A. E. (2008). Evidence-based treatment and practice: New opportunities to bridge clinical research and practice, enhance the knowledge base, and improve patient care. *American Psychologist, 63*, 146–159.

Kazdin, A. E., & Blase, S. L. (2011). Rebooting psychotherapy research and practice to reduce the burden of mental illness. *Perspectives on Psychological Science, 6*, 21–37.

Kazdin, A. E., & Rabbitt, S. M. (2013). Novel models for delivering mental health services and reducing the burdens of mental illness. *Clinical Psychology Science, 1*, 170–191.

Kazdin, A. E., & Weisz, J. R. (1998). Identifying and developing empirically supported child and adolescent treatments. *Journal of Consulting and Clinical Psychology, 66*, 19–36.

Keck, P. E., McElroy, S. L., Strakowski, S. M., West, S. A., Sax, K. W., et al. (1998). 12-month outcome of patients with bipolar disorder following hospitalization for a manic or mixed episode. *American Journal of Psychiatry, 155*, 646–652.

Keel, P. K. (2007). Purging disorder: Subthreshold variant or full-threshold eating disorder. *International Journal of Eating Disorders, 40, Suppl*: S89–S94.

Keel, P. K., Brown, T. A., Holland, L. A., & Bodell, L. P. (2012). Empirical classification of eating disorders. *Annual Review of Clinical Psychology, 8*, 381–404.

Keel, P. K., Haedt, A., & Edler, C. (2005). Purging disorder: an ominous variant of bulimia nervosa? *International Journal of Eating Disorders, 38*, 191–199.

Keel, P. K., & Klump, K. L. (2003). Are eating disorders culture-bound syndromes? Implications for conceptualizing their etiology. *Psychological Bulletin, 129*, 747–769.

Keel, P. K., & Mitchell, J. E. (1997). Outcome in bulimia nervosa. *American Journal of Psychiatry, 154*, 313–321.

Keel, P. K., Mitchell, J. E., Miller, K. B., Davis, T. L., & Crowe, S. J. (1999). Long-term outcome of bulimia nervosa. *Archives of General Psychiatry, 56*, 63–69.

Keith, J. (1982). *Old people as people*. Boston: Little, Brown.

Keller, M. C., Neale, M. C., & Kendler, K. S. (2007). Association of different adverse life events with distinct patterns of depressive symptoms. *American Journal of Psychiatry, 164*, 1521–1529.

Kellner, C. H., et al. (2014). Letter to the editor. *Journal of Clinical Psychiatry, 75*, 777.

Kellogg, S. H., & Young, J. E. (2006). Schema therapy for borderline personality disorder. *Journal of Clinical Psychology, 62*, 445–458.

Kelly, A. C., Zuroff, D. C., Foa, C. L., & Gilbert, P. (2010). Who benefits from training in self-compassionate self-regulation? A study of smoking reduction. *Journal of Social and Clinical Psychology, 29*, 727–755.

Kemner, C., Willemsen-Swinkels, S. H., de Jonge, M., Tuynman-Qua, H., & van Engeland, H. (2002). Open-label study of olanzapine in children with pervasive developmental disorder. *Journal of Clinical Psychopharmacology, 22*, 455–460.

Kemper, S., Greiner, L. H., Marquis, J. G., Prenovost, K., & Mitzner, T. L. (2001). Language decline across the life span: Findings from the Nun Study. *Psychology and Aging, 16*, 227–239.

Kenardy, J., Robinson, S., & Dob, R. (2005). Cognitive behaviour therapy for panic disorder: Long-term follow-up. *Cognitive Behaviour Therapy, 34*, 75–78.

Kendall, P. C., & Clarkin, J. F. (1992). Introduction to special section: Comorbidity and treatment implications. *Journal of Consulting and Clinical Psychology, 60*, 833.

Kendall, P. C., & Hedtke, K. (2006a). *Cognitive-behavioral therapy for anxious children: Therapist's manual* (3rd ed.). Ardmore, PA: Workbook Publishing.

Kendall, P. C., & Hedtke, K. (2006b). *The coping cat workbook* (2nd ed.). Ardmore, PA: Workbook Publishing.

Kendall, P. C., Settipani, C. A., & Cummings, C. M. (2012). No need to worry: The promising future of child anxiety research. *Journal of Clinical Child and Adolescent Psychology, 41*, 103–115.

Kendler, K. S. (2008). Explanatory models for psychiatric illness. *American Journal of Psychiatry, 165*, 695–702.

Kendler, K. S., & Diehl, S. R. (1993). The genetics of schizophrenia: A current, genetic-epidemiologic perspective. *Schizophrenia Bulletin, 19*, 87–113.

Kendler, K. S., & Gardner, C. O. (1998). Boundaries of major depression: An evaluation of DSM-IV criteria. *American Journal of Psychiatry, 155*, 172–177.

Kendler, K. S., & Gruenberg, A. M. (1984). An independent analysis of the Danish adoption study of schizophrenia: VI. The relationship between psychiatric disorders as defined by *DSM-III* in the relatives and adoptees. *Archives of General Psychiatry, 41*, 555–564.

Kendler, K. S., Karkowski, L. M., & Prescott, C. A. (1999). Fears and phobias: Reliability and heritability. *Psychological Medicine, 29*, 539–553.

Kendler, K. S., Neale, M. C., & Walsh, D. (1995). Evaluating the spectrum concept of schizophrenia in the Roscommon Family Study. *American Journal of Psychiatry, 152*, 749–754.

Kendler, K. S., & Prescott, C. A. (1998). Cannabis use, abuse, and dependence in a population-based sample of female twins. *American Journal of Psychiatry, 155*, 1016–1022.

Kendler, K. S., & Prescott, C. A. (1999). Caffeine intake, tolerance, and withdrawal in women: A population-based twin study. *American Journal of Psychiatry, 156*, 223–228.

Kendler, K. S., et al. (2008). The structure of genetic and environmental risk factors for DSM-IV personality disorders. *Archives of General Psychiatry, 65*, 1438–1446.

Kennard, B. D., et al. (2009). Effective components of TORDIA cognitive-behavioral therapy for adolescent depression: Preliminary findings. *Journal of Consulting and Clinical Psychology, 77*, 1033–1041.

Kennedy, S. H., Giacobbe, P., Rizvi, S. J., Placenza, F. M., et al. (2011). Deep brain stimulation for treatment-resistant depression: Follow-up after 3 to 6 years. *American Journal of Psychiatry, 168*, 502–510.

Keough, M. T., Battista, S. R., O'Connor, R. M., Sherry, S. B., & Stewart, S. H. (2016). Getting the party started—alone: Solitary predrinking mediates the effect of social anxiety on alcohol-related problems. *Addictive Behaviors, 55*, 19–24.

Keough, M. T., O'Connor, R. M., & Colder, C. R. (2016). Testing the implicit and explicit cognitions underlying behavioral inhibition system-related drinking in young adults. *Alcoholism: Clinical and Experimental Research, 40*, 1065–1074.

Keri, S., Kiss, I., Seres, I., & Kelemen, O. (2009). A polymorphism of the neuregulin 1 gene (SNP8NRG243177/rs6994992) affects reactivity to the expressed emotion in schizophrenia. *American Journal of Medical Genetics Part B: Neuropsychiatric Genetics, 150B*, 418–420.

Kernberg, O. F. (1985). *Borderline conditions and pathological narcissism.* Northvale, NJ: Jason Aronson.

Keshavan, M. S., Tandon, R., & Nasrallah, H. A. (2013). Renaming schizophrenia: Keeping up with the facts. *Schizophrenia Research, 148,* 1–2.

Kessler, R. C., et al. (2010). Age differences in the prevalence and co-morbidity of DSM-IV major depressive episodes: Results from the WHO World Mental Health Survey initiative. *Depression and Anxiety, 25*(8), 670–679.

Kessler, R. C., Adler, L., Barkley, R., et al. (2006). The prevalence and correlates of adult ADHD in the United States: Results from the National Comorbidity Survey Replication. *American Journal of Psychiatry, 163,* 716–723.

Kessler, R. C., Berglund, P. A., Chiu, W. T., & Deitz, A. C. (in press). The prevalence and correlates of binge eating disorder in the World Health Organization World Mental Health Surveys. *Biological Psychiatry.*

Kessler, R. C., Chiu, W. T., Demler, O., Merikangas, K. R., & Walters, E. E. (2005). Prevalence, severity, and comorbidity of 12-month DSM-IV disorders in the National Comorbidity Survey Replication. *Archives of General Psychiatry, 62,* 617–627.

Kessler, R. C., Davis, C. G., & Kendler, K. S. (1997). Childhood adversity and adult psychiatric disorder in the US National Comorbidity Survey. *Psychological Medicine, 27,* 1101–1119.

Kessler, R. C., Lane, M., Stang, P. E., & Van Brunt, D. L. (2009). The prevalence and workplace costs of adult attention deficit hyperactivity disorder in a large manufacturing firm. *Psychological Medicine, 39,* 137–147.

Kessler, R. C., McGonagle, K. A., Zhao, S., Hughes, M., et al. (1994). Lifetime and 12-month prevalence of *DSM-III-R* psychiatric disorders in the United States: Results from the National Comorbidity Survey. *Archives of General Psychiatry, 51,* 8–19.

Kessler, R. C., Petukhova, M., Sampson, N. A., Zaslavsky, A. M., & Wittchen, H.-Y. (2012). Twelve-month and lifetime prevalence and lifetime morbid risk of anxiety and mood disorders in the United States. *International Journal of Methods in Psychiatric Research, 21,* 169–184.

Kessler, R. C., Shahly, V., Hudson, J. I., Supina, D., Berglund, P. A., Chiu, W. T., et al. (2014). A comparative analysis of role attainment and impairment in binge-eating disorder and bulimia nervosa: Results from the WHO World Mental Health Surveys. *Epidemiology Psychiatrica Scandinavica, 23,* 27–41.

Kety, S. S., Rosenthal, D., Wender, P. H., & Schulsinger, F. (1968). The types and prevalence of mental illness in the biological and adoptive families of adopted schizophrenics. In D. Rosenthal & S. S. Kety (Eds.), *The transmission of schizophrenia.* Elmsford, NY: Pergamon.

Kety, S. S., Rosenthal, D., Wender, P. H., & Schulsinger, F. (1975). Mental illness in the adoptive and biological families of adopted individuals who have become schizophrenic. In R. R. Fieve, D. Rosenthal, & H. Brill (Eds.), *Genetic research in psychiatry.* Baltimore: Johns Hopkins University Press.

Kety, S. S., Wender, P. H., Jacobsen, B., Ingraham, L. T., Jansson, L., et al. (1994). Mental illness in the biological and adoptive relatives of schizophrenic adoptees: Replication of the Copenhagen study in the rest of Denmark. *Archives of General Psychiatry, 51,* 442–468.

Keuthen, N. J., Tung, E. S., Reese, H. E., Raikes, J., Lee, L., & Mansueto, C. S. (2015). Getting the word out: Cognitive-behavioral therapy for trichotillomania (hair-pulling disorder) and excoriation (skin-picking) disorder. *Annals of Clinical Psychiatry, 27,* 10–15.

Key, B. L., Campbell, T. S., Bacon, S. L., & Gerin, W. (2008). The influence of trait and state rumination on cardiovascular recovery from a negative emotional stressor. *Journal of Behavioral Medicine, 31,* 237–248.

Keys, A., Brozek, J., Hsu, L. K. G., McConoha, C. E., & Bolton, B. (1950). *The biology of human starvation.* Minneapolis: University of Minnesota Press.

Khandaker, G. M., Zimbron, J., Dalman, C., Lewis, G., & Jones, P. B. (2012). Childhood infection and adult schizophrenia: A meta-analysis of population-based studies. *Schizophrenia Research, 139,* 161–168.

Khemlani-Patel, S., Neziroglu, F., & Mancusi, L. M. (2011). Cognitive-behavioral therapy for body dysmorphic disorder: A comparative investigation. *Journal of Cognitive Therapy, 4,* 363–380.

Kidd, G. E. (1946). Trepanation among the early Indians of British Columbia. *Canadian Medical Association Journal, 55,* 513–516.

Kidd, S. A. (2013). From social experience to illness experience: Reviewing the psychological mechanisms linking psychosis with social context. *Canadian Journal of Psychiatry, 58,* 52–58.

Kidd, S. A., George, L., O'Connell, M., Sylvestre, J., et al. (2011). Recovery-oriented service provision and clinical outcomes in assertive community treatment. *Psychiatric Rehabilitation Journal, 34,* 194–201.

Kiecolt-Glaser, J. K. (2009). Psychoneuroimmunology: Psychology's gateway to the biomedical future. *Perspectives on Psychological Science, 4,* 367–369.

Kiecolt-Glaser, J. K., McGuire, L., Robles, T. F., & Glaser, R. (2002). Psychoneuroimmunology: Psychological influences on immune function and health. *Journal of Consulting and Clinical Psychology, 70,* 537–547.

Kiehl, K. A., et al. (2001). Limbic abnormalities in affective processing by criminal psychopaths as revealed by functional magnetic resonance imaging. *Biological Psychiatry, 50,* 677–684.

Kihlstrom, J. F., Tataryn, D. J., & Hoyt, I. P. (1993). Dissociative disorders. In P. B. Sutker & H. E. Adams (Eds.), *Comprehensive handbook of psychopathology* (pp. 203–234). New York: Plenum.

Killen, J. D., et al. (1997). Prospective study of risk factors for the initiation of cigarette smoking. *Journal of Consulting and Clinical Psychology, 65,* 1011–1016.

Kilpatrick, D. G., & Best, C. L. (1990, April). *Sexual assault victims: Data from a random national probability sample.* Paper presented at the annual convention of the Southeastern Psychological Association, Atlanta.

Kim, J. E., & Zane, N. (in press). Help-seeking intentions among Asian American and White American students in psychological distress: Application of the health belief model. *Cultural Diversity and Ethnic Minority Psychology.*

King, A. L. S., Valenca, A. M., & Nardi, A. E. (2010). Nomophobia: The mobile phone in panic disorder with agoraphobia: Reducing phobias or worsening of dependence? *Cognitive and Behavioral Neurology, 23,* 52–54.

King, P., Devichand, P., & Rockwood, K. (2005). Dementia of acute onset in the Canadian Study of Health and Aging. *International Psychogeriatrics, 17,* 451–459.

King, S. (2000). Is expressed emotion cause or effect in the mothers of schizophrenic young adults? *Schizophrenia Research, 45,* 65–78.

King, S. M., Burt, S. A., Malone, S. M., McGue, M., & Iacono, W. G. (2005). Etiological contributions to heavy drinking from late adolescence to young adulthood. *Journal of Abnormal Psychology, 114,* 587–598.

Kingston, D. A., et al. (2008). Pornography use and sexual aggression: The impact of frequency and type of pornography use on recidivism among sexual offenders. *Aggressive Behavior, 34,* 1–11.

Kinley, D. J., Cox, B. J., Clara, I., et al. (2009). Panic attacks and their relation to psychological and physical functioning in Canadians: Results from a nationally representative sample. *Canadian Journal of Psychiatry, 54*, 113–122.

Kinsey, A. C., Pomeroy, W. B., & Martin, C. E. (1948). *Sexual behavior in the human male*. Philadelphia: Saunders.

Kinsey, A. C., Pomeroy, W. B., Martin, C. E., & Gebhard, P. H. (1953). *Sexual behavior in the human female*. Philadelphia: Saunders.

Kirby, M. (2013). Framing school-based health within the national mental health strategy: A note from the Honorable Michael Kirby. *Canadian Journal of School Psychology, 28*, 3–4.

Kirby, M. J. L., & Keon, W. J. (2006). *Out of the shadows at last: Transforming mental health, mental illness and addiction services in Canada*. Ottawa: The Senate.

Kirchner, J. E., et al. (2007). Alcohol consumption among older adults in primary care. *Journal of General Internal Medicine, 22*, 92–97.

Kirkey, S. (2008, August 18). Nearly half of Canadians say mental illness used as an excuse: Poll shows extent of discrimination, CMA says. *The Ottawa Citizen*, A1.

Kirkland, S. A., et al. (1999). Knowledge and awareness of risk factors for cardiovascular disease among Canadians 55 to 74 years of age: Results from the Canadian Health Surveys, 1986–1992. *Canadian Medical Association Journal, 161* (Suppl. 8), S10–S16.

Kirkup, K. (2016, July 26). Health Minister not sure why Canada tops opioid-consuming countries. The Canadian Press.

Kirmayer, L. J. (2001). Cultural variations in the clinical presentation of depression and anxiety: Implications for diagnosis and treatment. *Journal of Clinical Psychiatry, 62* (Suppl. 13), 22–28.

Kirmayer, L. J., Boothroyd, L. J., & Hodgins, S. (1998). Attempted suicide among Inuit youth: Psychosocial correlates and implications for prevention. *Canadian Journal of Psychiatry, 43*, 816–822.

Kirmayer, L. J., Boothroyd, L. J., Tanner, A., Adelson, N., & Robinson, E. (2000). Psychological distress among the Cree of James Bay. *Transcultural Psychiatry, 37*, 35–56.

Kirmayer, L. J., Brass, G. M., & Tait, C. L. (2000). The mental health of Aboriginal peoples: Transformations of identity and community. *Canadian Journal of Psychiatry, 45*, 607–616.

Kirmayer, L. J., Malus, M., & Boothroyd, L. J. (1996). Suicide attempts among Inuit youth: A community survey of prevalence and risk factors. *Acta Psychiatrica Scandinavica, 94*, 8–17.

Kirmayer, L. J., Robbins, J. M., & Paris, J. (1994). Somatoform disorders: Personality and the social matrix of somatic distress. *Journal of Abnormal Psychology, 103*, 125–136.

Kirmayer, L. J., Rousseau, C., Jarvis, G. E., & Guzder, J. (2003). The cultural context of clinical assessment. In A. Tasman, J. Lieberman, & J. Kay (Eds.), *Psychiatry* (2nd ed.). New York: John Wiley & Sons.

Kirmayer, L. J., Rousseau, C., Rosenberg, E., et al. (2008). *Report on the evaluation of a cultural consultation service in mental health*. Montreal: McGill University, Division of Social and Transcultural Psychiatry.

Kirmayer, L. J., Rousseau, C., & Santhanam, R. (2003). Models of diagnosis and treatment planning in mental health. In A. Rummens, M. Beiser, & S. Noh (Eds.), *Immigration, health, and ethnicity*. Toronto: University of Toronto Press.

Kirschbaum, C., Prussner, J. C., & Stone, A. A. (1995). Persistent high cortisol responses to repeated psychological stress in a subpopulation of healthy men. *Psychosomatic Medicine, 57*, 468–474.

Kjølseth, I., Ekeberg, O., & Steihaug, S. (2010). Why suicide? Elderly people who committed suicide and their experience of life in the period before their death. *International Psychogeriatrics, 22*, 209–218.

Kleim, B., et al. (2013). Cognitive changes predict symptom reduction with cognitive therapy for posttraumatic stress disorder. *Journal of Consulting and Clinical Psychology, 81*, 383–393.

Klein, R. G. (2009). Anxiety disorders. *Journal of Child Psychology and Psychiatry, 50*, 153–162.

Kleinhaus, K., Harlap, S., Perrin, M. C., et al. (2012). Catatonic schizophrenia: A cohort prospective study. *Schizophrenia Bulletin, 38*, 331–337.

Kleinstauber, M., Witthoft, M., & Hiller, W. (2011). Efficacy of short-term psychotherapy for multiple medically unexplained physical symptoms: A meta-analysis. *Clinical Psychology Review, 31*, 146–160.

Klerman, G. L., et al. (1994). Medication and psychotherapy. In A. E. Bergin & S. L. Garfield (Eds.), *Handbook of psychotherapy and behavior change* (4th ed., pp. 734–782). New York: John Wiley & Sons.

Klerman, G. L., Weissman, M. M., Rounsaville, B. J., & Chevron, E. S. (1984). *Interpersonal psychotherapy of depression*. New York: Basic Books.

Klinger, E., Bouchard, S., et al. (2005). Virtual reality therapy for social phobia: A preliminary controlled strategy. *Cyberpsychology and Behavior, 8*, 70–88.

Klinger, L. G., Dawson, G., & Renner, P. (2003). Autistic disorder. In E. J. Marsh & B. A. Barkley (Eds.), *Child psychopathology* (2nd ed., pp. 409–454). New York: Guilford.

Klonsky, E. D., May, A. M., & Glenn, C. R. (2013). The relationship between non-suicidal self-injury and attempted suicide. *Journal of Abnormal Psychology, 122*, 231–237.

Kluft, R. P. (1988). The dissociative disorders. In R. E. Hales & S. C. Yudofsky (Eds.), *Textbook of psychiatry* (pp. 557–585). Washington, DC: American Psychiatric Press.

Kluft, R. P. (1994). Treatment trajectories in multiple personality disorder. *Dissociation, 7*, 63–75.

Kluft, R. P. (2001). Dissociative identity disorder. In G. O. Gabbard (Ed.), *Treatment of psychiatric disorders* (Vol. 2, pp. 1653–1693). Washington, DC: American Psychiatric Press.

Knapp, S., & Vandecreek, L. (1982). Tarasoff: Five years later. *Professional Psychology, 13*, 511–516.

Knekt, P., Virtala, E., Härkänen, T., Vaarama, M., Lehtonen, J., & Lindfors, O. (2016). The outcome of short- and long-term psychotherapy 10 years after start of treatment. *Psychological Medicine, 46*, 1175–1188.

Knight, B. G. (2004). *Psychotherapy with older adults* (3rd ed.). Thousand Oaks, CA: Sage.

Knight, B. G., Kelly, M., & Gatz, M. (1992). Psychotherapy and the older adult: An historical review. In D. K. Freedheim (Ed.), *History of psychotherapy: A century of change* (pp. 528–551). Washington, DC: American Psychological Association.

Knopik, V. S., Bidwell, L. C., Flessner, C., Nugent, N., et al. (2014). *DSM-IV* defined conduct disorder and oppositional defiant disorder: An investigation of shared liability in female twins. *Psychological Medicine, 44*, 1053–1064.

Kocovski, N. L., Abbott, K. A., & Fleming, J. E. (2015). Erythrophobia (fear of blushing). In I. Milosevic & R. E. McCabe (Eds.), *Phobias: The psychology of irrational fear. An encyclopedia*. Santa Barbara, CA: ABC-Clio.

Kocovski, N. L., Endler, N. S., Rector, N. A., & Flett, G. L. (2005). Rumination and post-event processing. *Behaviour Research and Therapy, 43*, 971–984.

Kocovski, N. L., Fleming, J. E., Hawley, L. L., Huta, V., & Antony, M. M. (2013). Mindfulness and acceptance-based group therapy versus traditional cognitive behavioral group therapy for social anxiety disorder: A randomized controlled trial. *Behaviour Research and Therapy, 51*, 889–898.

Koen, N., & Stein, D. J. (2011). Pharmacotherapy of anxiety disorders: A critical review. *Dialogues in Clinical Neuroscience, 13*, 423–437.

Koerner, N., & Dugas, M. J. (2006). A cognitive model of generalized anxiety disorder: The role of intolerance of uncertainty. In G. C. L. Davey & A. Wells (Eds.), *Worry and its psychological disorders: Theory, assessment & treatment.* Chichester, England: John Wiley and Sons, Ltd.

Koerner, N., & Dugas, M. J. (2008). An investigation of appraisals in individuals vulnerable to excessive worry: The role of intolerance of uncertainty. *Cognitive Therapy and Research, 32*, 619–638.

Kohen, D., Brooks-Gunn, J., Leventhal, T., & Hertzman, C. (2002). Neighborhood income and physical and social disorder in Canada: Associations with young children's competencies. *Child Development, 73*, 1844–1860.

Köhler, S., Wiethoff, K., Ricken, R., Stamm, T., Baghai, T. C., Fisher, R., . . . Adli, M. (2015). Characteristics and differences in treatment outcome of inpatients with chronic vs. episodic major depressive disorders. *Journal of Affective Disorders, 173*, 126–133.

Kohn, M. L. (1968). Social class and schizophrenia: A critical review. In D. Rosenthal & S. S. Kety (Eds.), *The transmission of schizophrenia.* Elmsford, NY: Pergamon.

Kohn, P. M., & Milrose, J. A. (1993). The Inventory of High-School Students Recent Life Experiences: A decontaminated measure of adolescents' hassles. *Journal of Youth and Adolescence, 22*, 43–55.

Kohut, H. (1971). *The analysis of the self.* New York: International Universities Press.

Kohut, H. (1977). *The restoration of the self.* New York: International Universities Press.

Kohut, H., & Wolf, E. S. (1978). The disorders of the self and their treatment: An outline. *International Journal of Psychoanalysis, 59*, 413–425.

Kolodny, A., Courtright, D. T., Hwang, C. S., Kreiner, P., et al. (2015). The prescription opioid and heroin crisis: A public health approach to an epidemic of addiction. *Annual Review of Public Health, 36*, 559–574.

Kong, L. L., Allen, J. J. B., & Glisky, E. L. (2008). Interidentity memory transfer in Dissociative Identity Disorder. *Journal of Abnormal Psychology, 117*, 686–692.

Konnert, C., Dobson, K. S., & Watt, A. (2009). Geropsychology training in Canada: A survey of doctoral and internship programs. *Canadian Psychology, 50*, 255–266.

Kopelowicz, A., & Liberman, R. P. (1998). Psychological and behavioral treatments for schizophrenia. In P. E. Nathan & J. M. Gorman (Eds.), *Treatments that work* (1st ed.) (pp. 190–211). New York: Oxford University Press.

Kopelowicz, A., Liberman, R. P., & Zarate, R. (2006). Recent advances in social skills training for schizophrenia. *Schizoprenia Bulletin, 32*, S1, 512–523.

Koponen, H. J., et al. (2007). Rates and previous disease history in old age suicide. *International Journal of Geriatric Psychiatry, 22*, 38–46.

Koren, G., Nulman, I., Chudley, A. E., & Loock, C. (2003). Fetal alcohol spectrum disorder. *Canadian Medical Association Journal, 169*, 1181–1185.

Koski-Jannes, A., & Cunningham, J. (2001). Interest in different forms of self-help in a general population sample of drinkers. *Addictive Behaviors, 26*, 91–99.

Koss, M. P., & Shiang, J. (1994). Research of brief psychotherapy. In A. E. Bergin & S. L. Garfield (Eds.), *Handbook of psychotherapy and behavior change* (4th ed., pp. 664–700). New York: John Wiley & Sons.

Kossowsky, J., Wilhelm, F. H., Roth, W. T., & Schneider, S. (2012). Separation anxiety disorder in children: Disorder-specific responses to experimental separation from the mother. *Journal of Child Psychology and Psychiatry, 53*, 178–187.

Kosteniuk, J. G., & Dickinson, H. D. (2003). Tracing the social gradient in the health of Canadians: Primary and secondary determinants. *Social Science and Medicine, 57*, 263–276.

Koszycki, D., Torres, S., Swain, J. E., & Bradwejn, J. (2005). Central cholecystokinin activity in irritable bowel syndrome, panic disorder, and healthy controls. *Psychosomatic Medicine, 67*, 590–595.

Kowalewski, K., McLennan, J. D., & McGrath, P. J. (2011). A preliminary investigation of wait times for child and adolescent mental health services in Canada. *Journal of the Canadian Academy of Child and Adolescent Psychiatry, 20*, 112–119.

Kowalik, D. L., & Gotlib, I. H. (1987). Depression and marital interaction: Concordance between intent and perception of communication. *Journal of Abnormal Psychology, 96*, 127–134.

Kozel, N. J., & Adams, E. H. (1986). Epidemiology of drug abuse: An overview. *Science, 234*, 970–974.

Kozlowska, K., Palmer, D. M., Brown, K. J., Scher, S., Chudleigh, C., Davies, F., & Williams, L. M. (2015). Conversion disorder in children and adolescents: A disorder of cognitive control. *Journal of Neuropsychology, 9*, 87–108.

Kozol, H. L., Boucher, R. J., & Garofalo, R. F. (1972). The diagnosis and treatment of dangerousness. *Crime & Delinquency, 18*, 371–392.

Kraus, S. W., Voon, V., & Potenza, M. N. (in press). Should compulsive sexual behavior be considered an addiction? *Addiction.*

Krausz, R. M., Clarkson, A. F., Strehlau, V., Torchalla, I., Li, K., & Schuetz, C. G. (2013). Mental disorder, service use, and barriers to care among 500 homeless people in 3 different urban settings. *Social Psychiatry and Psychiatric Epidemiology, 48*, 1235–1243.

Krausz, R. M., & Scheutz, C. (2011). *British Columbia Health of the Homeless survey report.* Vancouver: Centre for Health and Evaluation Services.

Kring, A. M., & Neale, J. M. (1996). Do schizophrenics show a disjunctive relationship among expressive, experiential and physiological components of emotion? *Journal of Abnormal Psychology, 105*, 249–257.

Kristiansen, C. M., Gareau, C., Mittleholt, J., DeCourville, N. H., & Hovdestad, W. E. (1999). The sociopolitical context of the delayed memory debate. In L. M. Williams & V. L. Banyard (Eds.), *Trauma and recovery* (pp. 331–347). Thousand Oaks, CA: Sage Publications.

Kristjannsson, A. L., Sigfusdottir, I. D., Frost, S. S., & James, J. E. (2013). Adolescent caffeine consumption and self-reported violence and conduct disorder. *Journal of Youth and Adolescence, 42*, 1053–1062.

Kroenke, K. (2007). Efficacy of treatment for somatoform disorders: A review of randomized controlled trials. *Psychosomatic Medicine, 69*, 881–888.

Kroenke, K., Sharpe, M., & Sykes, R. (2007). Revising the classification of somatoform disorders: Key questions and preliminary recommendations. *Psychosomatics, 48*, 277–285.

Kroneman, L. M., Hipwell, A. E., Loeber, R., Koot, H. M., & Pardini, D. A. (2011). Contextual risk factors as predictors of disruptive behavior disorder trajectories in girls: The moderating effect of callous-unemotional features. *Journal of Child Psychology and Psychiatry, 52*, 167–175.

Krueger, R. B. (in press). Diagnosis of hypersexual or compulsive sexual behavior can be made using ICD-10 and DSM-5 despite rejection of this diagnosis by the American Psychiatric Association. *Addiction.*

Kuehnle, K. (1998). Child sexual abuse allegations: The scientist-practitioner model. *Behavioral Science and the Law, 16*, 5–20.

Kuepper, R., Morrison, P. D., Van Os, J., et al. (2010). Does dopamine mediate the psychosis-inducing effects of cannabis? A review and integration of findings across disciplines. *Schizophrenia Research, 121,* 107–117.

Kuester, A., Niemeyer, H., & Knaevelsrud, C. (2016). Internet-based interventions for posttraumatic stress: A meta-analysis of randomized controlled trials. *Clinical Psychology Review, 43,* 1–16.

Kuhn, T. S. (1962). *The structure of scientific revolutions.* Chicago: University of Chicago Press.

Kuller, A. M., Ott, B. D., Goisman, R. M., et al. (2010). Cognitive behavioral therapy and schizophrenia: A survey of clinical practices and views on efficacy in the United States and the United Kingdom. *Community Mental Health Journal, 46,* 2–9.

Kuntsche, E., Knibbe, R., Gmel, G., & Engels, R. (2005). Why do young people drink? A review of drinking motives. *Clinical Psychology Review, 25,* 841–861.

Kupfer, D. J. (2013, August 10). *DSM-5's* new approach to suicide risk, behavior. *The Huffington Post.*

Kupfer, D. J., Kuhl, E. A., & Wulsin, L. (2013). Psychiatry's integration with medicine: The role of *DSM-5. Annual Review of Medicine, 64,* 385–392.

Kupper, N., Denollet, J., Widdenshoven, J., & Kop, W. J. (2013). Type D personality is associated with low cardiovascular reactivity to acute mental stress in heart failure patients. *International Journal of Psychophysiology, 90,* 44–49.

Kuriansky, J. B., Deming, W. E., & Gurland, B. J. (1974). On trends in the diagnosis of schizophrenia. *American Journal of Psychiatry, 131,* 402–407.

Kurtz, M. M., & Mueser, K. T. (2008). A meta-analysis of controlled research on social skills training for schizophrenia. *Journal of Consulting and Clinical Psychology, 76,* 491–504.

Kushner, M. G., Menary, K. R., Maurer, E. W., & Thuras, P. (2012). Greater elevation in risk for nicotine dependence per pack of cigarettes smoked among those with an anxiety disorder. *Journal of Studies on Alcohol and Drugs, 73,* 920–924.

Kuss, D. J., Griffiths, M. D., & Binder, J. F. (2013). Internet addiction in students: Prevalence and risk factors. *Computers in Human Behavior, 29,* 959–966.

Kutcher, S., Aman, M., Brooks, S. J., Buitelaar, J., et al. (2004). International consensus statement on attention-deficit/hyperactivity disorder (ADHD) and disruptive behaviour disorders (DBDs): clinical implications and treatment practice suggestions. *European Neuropsychopharmacology, 14,* 11–28.

Kutcher, S., Hampton, M. J., & Wilson, J. (2010). Child and adolescent mental health policy and plans in Canada: An analytical review. *Canadian Journal of Psychiatry, 55,* 100–107.

Kutchinsky, B. (1970). *Studies on pornography and sex crimes in Denmark.* Copenhagen: New Social Science Monographs.

Kuyken, W. (2004). Cognitive therapy outcome: The effects of hopelessness in a naturalistic outcome study. *Behaviour Research and Therapy, 42,* 631–646.

Kuyken, W., & Beck, A. T. (2007). Cognitive therapy. In C. Freeman and M. Power (Eds.), *Handbook of evidence-based psychotherapies: a guide for research and practice.* Chichester, England: John Wiley & Sons.

Kuyken, W., & Tsivrikos, D. (2009). Therapist competence, comorbidity and cognitive-behavioral therapy for depression. *Psychotherapy and Psychosomatics, 78,* 42–48.

Laan, E., Rellini, A. H., & Barnes, T. (2013). Standard operating procedures for female orgasmic disorder: Consensus of the International Society for Sexual Medicine. *The Journal of Sexual Medicine, 10,* 74–82.

Labelle, R., Lachance, L., & Morval, M. (1996). Validation of a French-Canadian version of the Reasons For Living Inventory. *Science et Comportement, 24,* 237–248.

Laberge, M., Dugas, M. J., & Ladouceur, R. (2000). Changes in dysfunctional beliefs before and after a cognitive-behavioural treatment for people with generalized anxiety disorder. *Canadian Journal of Behavioural Science, 32,* 91–96.

Lac, A., & Crano, W. D. (2009). Monitoring matters: Meta-analytic review reveals the reliable linkage of parental monitoring with adolescent marijuana use. *Perspectives on Psychological Science, 4,* 578–586.

Lacey, J. I. (1967). Somatic response patterning and stress: Some revisions of activation theory. In M. H. Appley & R. Trumball (Eds.), *Psychological stress.* New York: McGraw-Hill.

LaCourse, E., Cote, S., Nagin, S., et al. (2002). A longitudinal experimental approach to testing theories of antisocial behavior development. *Development and Psychopathology, 14,* 903–924.

Ladouceur, R., Freeston, M. H., Gagnon, F., Thibodeau, N., & Dumont, J. (1995). Cognitive-behavioral treatment of obsessions. *Behavior Modification, 19,* 247–257.

Ladouceur, R., Gosselin, P., & Dugas, M. J. (2000). Experimental manipulation of intolerance of uncertainty: A study of a theoretical model of worry. *Behaviour Research and Therapy, 38,* 933–941.

Ladouceur, R., & Walker, M. (1998). Cognitive approach to understanding and treating pathological gambling. In A. S. Bellack & M. Hersen (Eds.), *Comprehensive clinical psychology,* Vol. 6 (pp. 587–601). Oxford, England: Elsevier Science.

Ladowsky-Brooks, R. L., & Fischer, C. E. (2003). Ganser symptoms in a case of front temporal-lobe dementia: Is there a common neural substrate? *Journal of Clinical and Experimental Neuropsychiatry, 25,* 761–768.

Lafrance, M. N., & Stoppard, J. M. (2006). Constructing a non-depressed self: Women's accounts of recovery from depression. *Feminism and Psychology, 16,* 307–325.

Lafrance Robinson, A., Boachie, A., & Lafrance, G. A. (2013). "I want help!": Psychologists' and physicians' competence, barriers, and needs in the management of eating disorders in children and adolescents in Canada. *Canadian Psychology, 54,* 160–165.

Lahey, B. B., Loeber, R., Hart, E. L., Frick, P. J., Applegate, B., Zhang, Q., et al. (1995). Four-year longitudinal study of conduct disorder in boys: Patterns and predictors of persistence. *Journal of Abnormal Psychology, 104,* 83–93.

Laidlaw, K., & Pachana, N. A. (2009). Aging, mental health and demographic change: Challenges for psychotherapists. *Professional Psychology: Research and Practice, 40,* 601–608.

LaJeunesse, R. (2002). *Political asylums.* Edmonton: University of Alberta Press.

Lalinec-Michaud, M., Subak, M. E., Ghadirian, A. M., & Kovess, V. (1991). Substance misuse among native and rural high school students in Quebec. *International Journal of the Addictions, 26,* 1003–1012.

Lally, J., & MacCabe, J. H. (2015). Antipsychotic medication in schizophrenia: A review. *British Medical Bulletin, 114,* 169–179.

Lalonde, J. K., Hudson, J. I., Gigante, R. A., & Pope, H. G. (2001). Canadian and American psychiatrists' attitudes toward dissociative disorders diagnoses. *Canadian Journal of Psychiatry, 46,* 407–412.

Lalumière, M. L., & Quinsey, V. L. (1998). Pavlovian conditioning of sexual interests in human males. *Archives of Sexual Behavior, 27,* 241–252.

Lam, D. (2006). What can we conclude from studies on psychotherapy in bipolar disorder? Invited commentary on...Cognitive-behavioural therapy for severe and recurrent bipolar disorders. *British Journal of Psychiatry, 188*, 321–322.

Lam, R. W., Chan, P., Wilkins-Ho, M., & Yatham, L. N. (2008). Repetitive transcranial magnetic stimulation for treatment-resistant depression: A systematic review and meta-analysis. *Canadian Journal of Psychiatry, 53*, 621–631.

Lam, R. W., & Levitt, A. J. (1999). *Canadian consensus guidelines for the treatment of seasonal affective disorder.* Vancouver: Clinical and Academic Publishing.

Lam, R. W., Tam, E. M., Shiah, I. S., Yatham, L. N., & Zis, A. P. (2000). Effects of light therapy on suicidal ideation in patients with winter depression. *Journal of Clinical Psychiatry, 61*, 30–32.

Lambe, E. K., Katzman, D. K., Mikulis, D. J., Kennedy, S. H., & Zipursky, R. B. (1997). Cerebral gray matter volume deficits after weight recovery from anorexia nervosa. *Archives of General Psychiatry, 54*, 537–542.

Lamberg, L. (1998). New drug for erectile dysfunction boon for many, "Viagravation" for some. *Journal of the American Medical Association, 280*, 867–869.

Lambert, M. J. (1992). Implications of outcome research for psychotherapy integration. In J. C. Norcross & M. R. Goldstein (Eds.), *Handbook of psychotherapy integration* (pp. 94–129). New York: Basic Books.

Lambert, M. J., & Ogles, B. M. (2004). The efficacy and effectiveness of psychotherapy. In M. J. Lambert (Ed.), *Bergin and Garfield's handbook of psychotherapy and behavior change* (5th ed., pp. 139–193). Hoboken, NJ: John Wiley & Sons.

Lambert, M. J., Shapiro, D. A., & Bergin, A. E. (1986). The effectiveness of psychotherapy. In S. L. Garfield & A. E. Bergin (Eds.), *Handbook of psychotherapy and behavior change* (3rd ed.). New York: John Wiley & Sons.

Landerl, K., & Moll, K. (2010). Comorbidity of learning disorders: Prevalence and familial transmission. *Journal of Child Psychology and Psychiatry, 51*, 287–294.

Lando, H. A. (1977). Successful treatment of smokers with a broad-spectrum behavioral approach. *Journal of Consulting and Clinical Psychology, 45*, 361–366.

Landon, T. M., & Barlow, D. H. (2004). Cognitive-behavioral treatment for panic disorder: Current status. *Journal of Psychiatric Practice, 10*, 211–226.

Landy, C. K., Sword, W., & Valaitis, R. (2009). The experiences of socioeconomically disadvantaged postpartum women in the first 4 weeks at home. *Qualitative Health Research, 19*, 194–206.

Lane v. ADGA Group Consultants Inc., 2007 HRTO 34 (CanLII).

Lane, E. A., & Albee, G. W. (1965). Childhood intellectual differences between schizophrenic adults and their siblings. *American Journal of Orthopsychiatry, 35*, 747–753.

Laney, C., & Loftus, E. F. (2005). Traumatic memories are not necessarily accurate memories. *Canadian Journal of Psychiatry, 50*, 823–828.

Lang, I., Guralnik, J., Wallace, R. B., & Melzer, D. (2007). What level of alcohol consumption is hazardous for older people? Functioning and mortality in U.S. and English national cohorts. *Journal of the American Geriatric Society, 55*, 49–57.

Langenbucher, J. W., & Chung, T. (1995). Onset and staging of DSM-IV alcohol dependence using mean age and survival hazard methods. *Journal of Abnormal Psychology, 104*, 346–354.

Langille, D. B., et al. (1999). Prevalence of risk factors for cardiovascular disease in Canadians 55 to 74 years of age: Results from the Canadian Heart Health Surveys, 1986–1992. *Canadian Medical Association Journal, 161* (Suppl. 8), S3–S9.

Lanyon, R. I. (1986). Theory and treatment in child molestation. *Journal of Consulting and Clinical Psychology, 54*, 176–182.

Laplante, D. P., Barr, R. G., Brunet, A., et al. (2004). Stress during pregnancy affects general intellectual and language functioning in human toddlers. *Pediatric Research, 56*, 400–410.

Laplante, D. P., Brunet, A., Schmitz, N., Ciampi, A., & King, S. (2008). Project Ice Storm: Prenatal maternal stress affects cognitive and linguistic functioning in 5.5 year old children. *Journal of the American Academy of Child and Adolescent Psychiatry, 47*, 1063–1072.

Laposa, J. M., & Alden, L. E. (2003). Posttraumatic stress in the emergency room: Exploration of a cognitive model. *Behaviour Research and Therapy, 41*, 49–65.

LaRoche, M. J., Fuentes, M. A., & Hinton, D. (2015). A cultural examination of the *DSM-5*: Research and clinical implications for cultural minorities. *Professional Psychology: Research and Practice, 46*, 183–189.

Larsen, D. J., & Stege, R. (2012). Client accounts of hope in early counseling sessions: A qualitative study. *Journal of Counseling & Development, 90*, 45–54.

Larsen, D. J., Stege, R., Edey, W., & Ewasiw, J. (2014). Working with unrealistic or unshared hope in the counselling session. *British Journal of Guidance & Counselling, 42*, 271–283.

Larstone, R. M., Jang, K. L., Livesley, W. J., Vernon, P. A., & Wolf, K. (2002). The relationship between Eysenck's P-E-N model of personality, the five-factor model of personality, and traits delineating personality dysfunction. *Personality and Individual Differences, 33*, 25–37.

LaRue, A., Dessonville, C., & Jarvik, L. F. (1985). Aging and mental disorders. In J. E. Birren & K. W. Schaie (Eds.), *Handbook of psychology of aging* (2nd ed.). New York: Van Nostrand-Reinhold.

Latimer, E. (2005). Community-based care for people with severe mental illness in Canada. *International Journal of Law and Psychiatry, 28*, 561–573.

Latimer, J. (2006). *The Review Board Systems in Canada: Overview of results for the Mentally Disordered Accused Data Collection Study.* Ottawa: Department of Justice Canada.

Lau, M. A., & McMain, S. F. (2005). Integrating mindfulness meditation with cognitive and behavioural therapies: The challenge of combining acceptance- and change-based strategies. *Canadian Journal of Psychiatry, 50*, 863–869.

Laub, J. H., & Sampson, R. J. (1995). The long-term effects of punitive discipline. In J. McCord (Ed.), *Coercion and punishment in long-term perspectives* (pp. 247–258). Cambridge, MA: Cambridge University Press.

Laumann, E. O., Paik, A., & Rosen, R. C. (1999). Sexual dysfunction in the United States. *JAMA: The Journal of the American Medical Association, 281*, 537–544.

Laurens, K. R., & Cullen, A. E. (2016). Toward earlier intervention and preventative intervention in schizophrenia: Evidence from the London Child Health and Development Study. *Social Psychiatry and Psychiatric Epidemiology, 51*, 475–491.

Laursen, T. M., Nordentoft, M., & Mortensen, P. B. (2014). Excess early mortality in schizophrenia. *Annual Review of Clinical Psychology, 10*, 425–448.

Lautenschlager, N. T., Cupples, L. A., Rao, V. S., Auerbach, S. A., Becker, R., & Burke, J. (1996). Risk of dementia among relatives of Alzheimer's disease patients in the MIRAGE study: What is in store for the oldest old? *Neurology, 46*, 641–650.

Lavner, J. A., & Bradbury, T. N. (2010). Patterns of change in marital satisfaction over the newlywed years. *Journal of Marriage and the Family, 72*, 1171–1187.

Lavner, J. A., Karney, B. R., & Bradbury, T. N. (2014). Relationship problems over the early years of marriage: Stability or change? *Journal of Family Psychology, 28*, 979–985.

Law, M., & Tang, J. L. (1995). An analysis of the effectiveness of interventions intended to help people stop smoking. *Archives of Internal Medicine, 155*, 1933–1941.

Lawrence, A. A. (2003). Factors associated with satisfaction or regret following male-to-female sex reassignment surgery. *Archives of Sexual Behavior, 32*, 299–315.

Laws, D. R., Hanson, K. R., Osborn, C. A., & Greenbaum, P. E. (2000). Classification of child molesters by plethysmographic assessment of sexual arousal and a self-report measure of sexual preference. *Journal of Interpersonal Violence, 15*, 1297–1312.

Laws, D. R., & Marshall, W. L. (1991). Masturbatory reconditioning with sexual deviates: An evaluative review. *Advances in Behaviour Research and Therapy, 13*(1), 13–25.

Lawton, V. (2003, May 28). Backbench does not like Cauchon's pot bill. *The Toronto Star.*

Lazarus, R. S. (1966). *Psychological stress and the coping process.* New York: McGraw-Hill.

Lazarus, R. S., & Folkman, S. (1984). *Stress, appraisal, and coping.* New York: Springer.

Lazarus, S. A., and Cheavens, J. S. (in press). An examination of social network quality and composition in women with and without borderline personality disorder. *Personality Disorders: Theory, Research, and Treatment.*

Leadbeater, B., Sukhawathanakul, P., Smith, D., & Bowen, F. (2015). Reciprocal associations between interpersonal and values dimensions of school climate and peer victimization in elementary school children. *Journal of Clinical Child and Adolescent Psychology, 44*, 480–493.

Le Couteur, A., Bailey, A., Goode, S., Pickles, A., Robertson, S., Gottesman, I., et al. (1996). A broader phenotype of autism: The clinical spectrum in twins. *Journal of Child Psychology and Psychiatry and Allied Disciplines, 37*, 785–801.

Le Foll, B., Wertheim, C., & Goldberg, S. R. (2007). High reinforcing efficacy of nicotine in non-human primates. *PLoS ONE, 2*, e230.

Leaviss, J., & Uttley, L. (2015). Psychotherapeutic benefits of compassion-focused therapy: An early systematic review. *Psychological Medicine, 45*, 927–945.

Lebowitz, M. S., Ahn, W., & Oltman, K. (2015). Sometimes more competent, but always less warm: Perceptions of biologically oriented mental-health clinicians. *International Journal of Social Psychiatry, 61*, 668–676.

Lecomte, J., & Mercier, C. (2007). The Montreal Declaration on Intellectual Disabilities of 2004: An important first step. *Journal of Policy and Practice in Intellectual Disabilities, 4*, 66–69.

Lee, B. K., & Awosoga, O. (2015). Congruence couple therapy for pathological gambling: A pilot randomized controlled trial. *Journal of Gambling Studies, 31*, 1047–1068.

Lee, D. S., et al. (2009). Trends in risk factors for cardiovascular disease in Canada: Temporal, socio-demographic, and geographic factors. *Canadian Medical Association Journal, 181*, E55–E66.

Lee, K., & Ashton, M. C. (2004). Psychometric properties of the HEXACO Personality Inventory. *Multivariate Behavioral Research, 39*, 329–358.

Lee, X., Klaver, J. R., Hart, S. D., Moretti, M. M., & Douglas, K. S. (2009). Short-term stability of psychopathic traits in adolescent offenders. *Journal of Clinical Child and Adolescent Psychology, 38*, 595–605.

Lee, Y., & Lin, P.-Y. (2010). Association between serotonin transporter gene polymorphism and eating disorders: A meta-analytic study. *International Journal of Eating Disorders, 43*, 498–504.

Leenaars, A. (2000). Suicide prevention in Canada: A history of a community approach. *Canadian Journal of Community Mental Health, 19*, 57–73.

Lehmann, H. E. (1996). Psychopharmacotherapy. In D. Healy (Ed.), *The psychopharmacologists,* Vol. 1 (pp. 159–186). London: Arnold.

Lehmann, H. E., & Ban, T. A. (1997). The history of psychopharmacology of schizophrenia. *Canadian Journal of Psychiatry, 42*, 152–162.

Lehmann, H. E., & Hanrahan, G. E. (1954). Chlorpromazine, new inhibiting agent for psychomotor excitement and manic states. *Archives of Neurology and Psychiatry, 71*, 227–237.

Lehoux, P. M., Steiger, H., & Jabalpurlawa, S. (2000). State-trait distinctions in bulimic syndromes. *International Journal of Eating Disorders, 27*, 36–42.

Lehrer, P. M., Hochron, S. M., Mayne, T., et al. (1994). Relaxation and music therapies for asthma among patients prestabilised on asthma medication. *Journal of Behavioral Medicine, 17*, 1–24.

Lehrer, P. M., et al. (2008). Psychological treatment of comorbid asthma and panic disorder: A pilot study. *Journal of Anxiety Disorders, 22*, 671–683.

Leibenluft, E. (1996). Women with bipolar illness: Clinical and research issues. *American Journal of Psychiatry, 153*, 163–173.

Leiblum, S. R., & Rosen, R. C. (Eds.). (1988). *Sexual desire disorders.* New York: Guilford.

Leichsenring, F. (2001). Comparative effects of short-term psychodynamic psychotherapy and cognitive-behavioral therapy in depression: A meta-analytic approach. *Clinical Psychology Review, 21*, 401–419.

Leichsenring, F., & Klein, S. (2014). Evidence for psychodynamic psychotherapy in specific mental disorders: A systematic review. *Psychoanalytic Psychotherapy, 28*, 4–32.

Leichsenring, F., & Leibing, E. (2007). Psychodynamic psychotherapy: A systematic review of techniques, indications, and empirical evidence. *Psychology and Psychotherapy, 80*, 217–228.

Leichsenring, F., Luyten, P., Hilsenroth, M. J., Abbass, A., Barber, J. P., Keefe, J. R., . . . Steinert, C. (2015). Psychodynamic therapy meets evidence-based medicine: A systematic review using updated criteria. *The Lancet Psychiatry, 2*, 648–660.

Leland, J. (1995, October 30). A risky RX for fun. *Newsweek, 126*, 74.

Lemonick, M. D., & Park, A. (2001, May 14). The Nun Study: How one scientist and 678 sisters are helping unlock the secrets of Alzheimer's. *Time:* Canadian Edition, p. 54.

Lenzenweger, M. F., Dworkin, R. H., & Wethington, E. (1991). Examining the underlying structure of schizophrenic phenomenology: evidence for a three-process model. *Schizophrenia Bulletin, 17*, 515–524.

Leon, D. A., et al. (2007). Hazardous alcohol drinking and premature mortality in Russia: A population-based case-control study. *Lancet, 369*, 2001–2009.

Leonard, S., Steiger, H., & Kao, A. (2003). Childhood and adulthood abuse in bulimic and nonbulimic women: Prevalences and psychological correlates. *International Journal of Eating Disorders, 33*, 397–405.

Lerman, C. E., Schnoll, R. A. & Munafo, M. R. (2007). Genetics and smoking cessation: Improving outcomes in smokers at risk. *American Journal of Preventive Medicine, 33*, S398–S405.

Lerner, H. D. (2008). Psychodynamic perspectives. In A. M. Gross (Ed.), *Handbook of clinical psychology, adults* (pp. 127–160). Hoboken, NJ: John Wiley & Sons.

Lesage, A. D., Boyer, R., Grunberg, R., Vanier, C., Morrisette, R., Menard-Buteau, C., et al. (1994). Suicide and mental disorders: A case-control study of young men. *American Journal of Psychiatry, 151*, 1063–1068.

Leschied, A. W., & Cunningham, A. (2000). A review of the use of custody in Canada's young offender system and the development of a community-based program for high-risk offenders. In A. M. Kalmthoutet, et al. (Eds.), *Community sanctions: Measures and execution modalities in Europe, the USA, and Canada.* The Netherlands: Kluwer Publishing.

Leschied, A. W., Cunningham, A., & Hawkins, L. (April, 2000). *Clinical trials of multisystemic therapy in Ontario, 1997 to 2001: Evaluation Update Report.* London, ON: London Family Court Clinic.

Lespérance, F., Frasure-Smith, N., Kozycki, D., Laliberté, M.-A., et al. (2007). Effects of citalopram and interpersonal psychotherapy on depression in patients with coronary artery disease: The Canadian Cardiac Randomized Evaluation of Antidepressant and Psychotherapy Efficacy (CREATE) trial. *Journal of the American Medical Association, 297,* 367–379.

Lespérance, F., Frasure-Smith, N., Talajic, M., & Bourassa, M. G. (2002). Five-year risk of cardiac mortality in relation to initial severity and one-year changes in depression symptoms after myocardial infarction. *Circulation, 105,* 1049–1053.

Lessard, J. C., & Moretti, M. M. (1998). Suicidal ideation in an adolescent clinical sample: Attachment patterns and clinical implications. *Journal of Adolescence, 21,* 383–395.

Letourneau, N., Stewart, M., Dennis, C.-L., Hegadoren, K., & Watson, B. (2011). The effect of home-based peer support on maternal-infant interactions among women with postpartum depression: A randomized controlled trial. *International Journal of Mental Health Nursing, 20, 345–357.*

Lev-Wiesel, R. (2008). Child sexual abuse: A critical review of intervention and treatment modalities. *Children and Youth Services Review, 30,* 665–673.

Levenson, J. L. (2003). Psychological factors affect medical condition. In A. Tasman, J. Kay, & J. A. Lieberman (Eds.), *Psychiatry* (2nd ed., pp. 1638–1656). Hoboken, NJ: John Wiley & Sons.

Levine, S. B. (2003). Sexual disorders. In A. Tasman, J. Kay, & J. A. Lieberman (Eds.), *Psychiatry* (2nd ed., p. 1490). Hoboken, NJ: John Wiley & Sons.

Levitt, A. J., Boyle, M. H., Joffe, R. T., & Baumal, Z. (2000). Estimated prevalence of the seasonal subtype of major depression in a Canadian community sample. *Canadian Journal of Psychiatry, 45,* 650–654.

Levitt, A. J., Lam, R. W., & Levitan, R. (2002). A comparison of open treatment of seasonal major and minor depression with light therapy. *Journal of Affective Disorders, 71,* 243–248.

Levitt, H. M., Pomerville, A., & Surace, F. I. (2016). A qualitative meta-analysis examining clients' experiences of psychotherapy: A new agenda. *Psychological Bulletin, 142,* 801–830.

Levitt, J. J., McCarley, R. W., Nestor, P. G., et al. (1999). Quantitative volumetric MRI study of the cerebellum and vermis in schizophrenia: Clinical and cognitive correlates. *American Journal of Psychiatry, 156,* 1105–1107.

Levy, B. R., Ferrucci, L., Zonderman, A. B., Slade, M. D., et al. (2016). A culture-brain link: Negative age stereotypes predict Alzheimer's disease biomarkers. *Psychology and Aging, 31,* 82–88.

Levy, B. R., Zonderman, A., Slade, M., & Ferrucci, L. (2009). Age stereotypes held earlier in life predict cardiovascular events later in life. *Psychological Science, 20,* 296–298.

Levy, D., et al. (2009). Genome-wide association study of blood pressure and hypertension. *Nature Genetics, 41,* 677–687.

Levy, F., Hay, D. A., Bennett, K. S., & McStephen, M. (2005). Gender differences in ADHD subtype comorbidity. *Journal of the American Academy of Child and Adolescent Psychiatry, 44,* 368–376.

Levy, K. N. (2008). Psychotherapies and lasting change. *American Journal of Psychiatry, 165,* 556–559.

Levy, K. N., & Anderson, T. (2013). Is clinical psychology doctoral training becoming less intellectually diverse? What can be done? *Clinical Psychology: Science and Practice, 20,* 211–220.

Levy, K. N., Ellison, W. D., Scott, L. N., & Bernecker, S. L. (2011). Attachment style. *Journal of Clinical Psychology, 67,* 193–203.

Levy, K. N., Johnson, B. N., Clouthier, T. L., Scala, J. W., & Temes, C. M. (2015). An attachment theoretical framework for personality disorders. *Canadian Psychology, 56,* 197–207.

Levy, M. L., Miller, B. L., Cummings, J. L., Fairbanks, L. A., & Craig, A. (1996). Alzheimer disease and frontotemporal dementias. *Archives of Neurology, 53,* 687–690.

Levy, S., & Fletcher, E. (1998). Kamatsiaqtut, Baffin Crisis Line: Community ownership of support in a small town. In A. A. Leenaars, S. Wenckstern, I. Sakinofsky, R. J. Dyck, M. J. Kral, & R. C. Bland (Eds.), *Suicide in Canada* (pp. 351–366). Toronto: University of Toronto Press.

Lewinsohn, P. M., & Graf, M. (1973). Pleasant activities and depression. *Journal of Consulting and Clinical Psychology, 41,* 261–268.

Lewinsohn, P. M., Roberts, R. E., Seeley, J. R., Rohde, P., Gotlib, I. H., & Hops, H. (1994). Adolescent psychopathology: 2. Psychosocial risk factors for depression. *Journal of Abnormal Psychology, 103,* 302–315.

Lewis, C. C., et al. (2009). The role of readiness to change in response to treatment of adolescent depression. *Journal of Consulting and Clinical Psychology, 77,* 422–428.

Lewis, D. O., Yeager, C. A., Swica, Y., Pincus, J. H., & Lewis, M. (1997). Objective documentation of child abuse and dissociation on 12 murderers with dissociative identity disorder. *American Journal of Psychiatry, 154,* 1703–1710.

Li, M. D., & Burmeister, M. (2009). New insights into the genetics of addiction. *Nature Review, Genetics, 10,* 225–231.

Liashko, V., & Manassis, K. (2003). Medicated anxious children: Characteristics and cognitive-behavioural treatment response. *Canadian Journal of Psychiatry, 48,* 741–748.

Liberman, R. P., DeRisi, W. J., & Mueser, K. T. (1989). *Social skills training for psychiatric patients.* New York: Pergamon Press.

Liberman, R. P., Jacobs, H. E., Boone, S. E., Foy, D., et al. (1987). Skills training for the community adaptation of schizophrenics. In W. Boker & H. D. Brenner (Eds.), *Psychosocial treatment of schizophrenia* (pp. 94–109). Toronto: H. Huber Publishers.

Liberman, R. P., Wallace, C. J., Blackwell, G., Mintz, J., Kopelowicz, A., & Vaccaro, J. V. (1998). Skills training vs. psychosocial occupational therapy for persons with persistent schizophrenia. *American Journal of Psychiatry, 155,* 1087–1091.

Liberto, J. G., Oslin, D. W., & Ruskin, P. E. (1996). Alcoholism in the older population. In L. L. Carstensen, B. A. Edelstein, & L. Dornbrand (Eds.), *The practical handbook of clinical gerontology* (pp. 324–348). Thousand Oaks, CA: Sage.

Libman, E., Rothenberg, I., Fichten, C. S., & Amsel, R. (1985). The SSES-E—A measure of sexual self-efficacy in erectile functioning. *Journal of Sex and Marital Therapy, 11,* 233–247.

Lichstein, K. L., & Morin, C. M. (2000). *Treatment of late-life insomnia.* Thousand Oaks, CA: Sage.

Liddle, P. F. (2000). Cognitive impairment in schizophrenia: Its impact on social functioning. *Acta Psychiatrica Scandinavica, 400* (Suppl.), 11–16.

Lieberman, J. A., Stroup, T. S., McEvoy, J. P., et al. (2005). Effectiveness of antipsychotic drugs in patients with chronic schizophrenia. *New England Journal of Medicine, 353,* 1209–1223.

Lilienfeld, S. O. (2005). Scientifically unsupported and supported interventions for childhood psychopathology: A summary. *Pediatrics*, *115*, 761–764.

Lilienfeld, S. O., Lynn, S. J., Kirsch, I., Chaves, J. F., et al. (1999). Dissociative identity disorder and the sociogenic model: Recalling lessons from the past. *Psychological Bulletin, 125, 507–523.*

Lim, S. L., & Kim, J. H. (2005). Cognitive processing of emotional information in depression, panic, and somatoform disorder. *Journal of Abnormal Psychology*, *114*, 50–61.

Lin, E., Goering, P., Offord, D. R., Campbell, D., & Boyle, M. H. (1996). The use of mental health services in Ontario: Epidemiological findings. *Canadian Journal of Psychiatry*, *41*, 572–577.

Lindemann, E. (1944). Symptomatology and management of acute grief. *American Journal of Psychiatry*, *101*, 141–148.

Linden, W., & Moseley, J. V. (2006). The efficacy of behavioral treatments for hypertension. *Applied Psychophysiology and Biofeedback*, *31*, 51–63.

Lindesay, J., et al. (2006). Worry content across the lifespan: An analysis of 16- to 74-year old participants in the British National Survey of Psychiatric Mobility 2000. *Psychological Medicine*, *36*, 1625–1633.

Lindquist, C. H., Barrick, K., Krebs, C., Crosby, C. M., Lockard, A. J., & Sanders-Phillips, K. (2013). The context and consequences of sexual assault among undergraduate women at historically Black colleges and universities (HBCUs). *Journal of Interpersonal Violence*, *28*, 2437–2461.

Lindquist, C. H., Crosby, C. M., Barrick, K., Krebs, C. P., & Settles-Reaves, B. (2016). Disclosure of sexual assault experiences among undergraduate women at historically black colleges and universities (HBCUs). *Journal of American College Health*, *64*, 469–480.

Linehan, M. M. (1985). The Reasons For Living Inventory. In P. Keller & L. Ritt (Eds.), *Innovations in clinical practice: A sourcebook* (pp. 321–330). Sarasota, FL: Professional Resource Exchange.

Linehan, M. M. (1987). Dialectical behavior therapy for borderline personality disorder. *Bulletin of the Menninger Clinic*, *51*, 261–276.

Linehan, M. M. (1993a). *Behavioral skills training manual for treating borderline personality disorder*. New York: Guilford.

Linehan, M. M. (1993b). *Cognitive behavioral treatment of borderline personality disorder: The dialectics of effective treatment*. New York: Guilford.

Linehan, M. M. (1997). Behavioral treatments of suicidal behaviors: Definitional obfuscation and treatment outcomes. *Annals of the New York Academy of Sciences*, *836*, 302–328.

Linehan, M. M., Armstrong, H. E., Suarez, A., Allmon, D., & Heard, H. L. (1991). Cognitive-behavioral treatment of chronically parasuicidal borderline patients. *Archives of General Psychiatry*, *48*, 1060–1064.

Linehan, M. M., Camper, P., Chiles, J. A., Strosahl, K., & Shearin, E. (1987). Interpersonal problem solving and parasuicide. *Cognitive Therapy and Research*, *11*, 1–12.

Linehan, M. M., Heard, H. L., & Armstrong, H. E. (1993). Naturalistic follow-up of a behavioral treatment for chronically parasuicidal borderline patients. *Archives of General Psychiatry*, *50*, 971–974.

Linehan, M. M., Schmidt, H., Dimeff, L. A., Craft, J. C., Kanter, J., & Comtois, K. A. (1999). Dialectical behavior therapy for patients with borderline personality disorder and drug dependence. *American Journal on Addiction*, *8*, 279–292.

Linehan, M. M., & Shearin, E. N. (1988). Lethal stress: A social-behavioral model of suicidal behavior. In S. Fisher & J. Reason (Eds.), *Handbook of life stress, cognition, and health*. New York: John Wiley & Sons.

Links, P. S., Eynan, R., Heisel, M. J., & Nisenbaum, R. (2008). Elements of affective instability associated with suicidal behaviour in patients with borderline personality disorder. *Canadian Journal of Psychiatry*, *53*, 112–116.

Links, P. S., Gould, B., & Ratnayake, R. (2003). Assessing suicidal youth with antisocial, borderline, or narcissistic personality disorder. *Canadian Journal of Psychiatry*, *48*, 301–310.

Links, P. S., Heslegrave, R., & van Reekum, R. (1998). Prospective follow-up study of borderline personality disorder: Prognosis, prediction outcome, and Axis II comorbidity. *Canadian Journal of Psychiatry*, *43*, 265–270.

Links, P. S., & van Reekum, R. (1993). Childhood sexual abuse, parental impairment and the development of borderline personality disorder. *Canadian Journal of Psychiatry*, *38*, 472–474.

Linn, R. T., Wolf, P. A., Bachman, D. L., Knoefel, J. E., Cobb, J., et al. (1995). The "preclinical phase" of probable Alzheimer's disease: A 13-year prospective study of the Framingham cohort. *Archives of Neurology*, *52*, 485–490.

Linscott, R. J., Allardyce, J., & van Os, J. (2009). Seeking verisimilitude in a class: A systematic review of evidence that the clinical symptoms of schizophrenia are taxonic. *Schizophrenia Bulletin*, *35*, 811–829.

Liotti, G. (1992). Disorganized disoriented attachment in the etiology of dissociative disorders. *Dissociation*, *4*, 196–204.

Lipowski, Z. J. (1983). Transient cognitive disorders (delirium and acute confusional states) in the elderly. *American Journal of Psychiatry*, *140*, 1426–1436.

Lipsman, N., Woodside, D. B., Giacobbe, P., et al. (2013). Subcallosal cingulated deep brain stimulation for treatment-refractory anorexia nervosa: A phase 1 pilot trial. *Lancet*, *381*, 1361–1370.

Lisak, D., & Roth, S. (1990). Motives and psychodynamics of self-reported, unincarcerated rapists. *American Journal of Orthopsychiatry*, *60*, 268–280.

Litman, L. C. (2004). A case of erotic violence syndrome. *Canadian Journal of Psychiatry*, *49*, 217–218.

Liu, R. T., Alloy, L. B., Abramson, L. Y., Iacoviella, B. M., & Whitehouse, W. G. (2009). Emotional maltreatment and depression: Prospective prediction of depressive episodes. *Depression and Anxiety*, *26*, 174–181.

Liu, R. T., Kleiman, E. M., Nestor, B. A., & Cheek, S. M. (2015). The hopelessness theory of depression: A quarter-century in review. *Clinical Psychology: Science and Practice*, *22*(4), 345–365.

Livesley, W. J. (1998). Suggestions for a framework for an empirically based classification of personality disorders. *Canadian Journal of Psychiatry*, *43*, 137–147.

Livesley, W. J., & Jackson, D. N. (2002). *Manual for the Dimensional Assessment of Personality Pathology-Basic Questionnaire (DAPP)*. London, ON: Research Psychologists' Press.

Livesley, W. J., Jang, K. L., & Vernon, P. A. (1998). Phenotypic and genetic structure of traits in delineating personality disorder. *Archives of General Psychiatry*, *55*, 941–948.

Livesley, W. J., Schroeder, M. L., & Jackson, D. N. (1990). Dependent personality disorder and attachment problems. *Journal of Personality Disorders*, *4*, 131–140.

Livesley, W. J., Schroeder, M. L., Jackson, D. N., & Jang, K. L. (1994). Categorical distinctions in the study of personality disorder: Implications for classification. *Journal of Abnormal Psychology*, *103*, 6–17.

Livingston, J. D., Nijdan-Jones, A., & Brink, J. (2012). A tale of two cultures: Examining patient-centered case in a forensic mental hospital. *The Journal of Forensic Psychiatry and Psychology*, *23*, 345–360.

Livingston, J. D., Wilson, D., Tien, G., & Bond, L. (2003). A follow-up study of persons found not criminally responsible on account of mental disorder in British Columbia. *Canadian Journal of Psychiatry, 48*, 408–415.

Lloyd-Evans, B., Crosby, M., Stockton, S., Pilling, S., Hobbs, L., Hinton, M., & Johnson, S. (2011). Initiatives to shorten duration of untreated psychosis: systematic review. *The British Journal of Psychiatry, 198*(4), 256–263.

Lobel, T. E., Gilat, I., & Endler, N. S. (1993). The Gulf War: Distressful reactions to SCUD missile attacks. *Anxiety, Stress and Coping, 6*, 9–23.

Lochman, J. E., & Wells, K. C. (1996). A social-cognitive intervention with aggressive children: Prevention effects and contextual implementation issues. In R. Dev. Peters & R. J. McMahon (Eds.), *Prevention and early intervention: Childhood disorders, substance use, and delinquency* (pp. 111–143). Newbury Park, CA: Sage.

Lock, J., & Couturier, J. (2007). Evidence-based family psychotherapy interventions. In T. Jaffa & B. McDermott (Eds.), *Eating disorders in children and adolescents* (pp. 238–247). New York: Cambridge University Press.

Lock, S., LeGrange, D., Agras, W. S., & Dare, C. (2001). *Treatment manual for anorexia nervosa: A family-based approach*. New York: Guilford.

Lock, J., Le Grange, D., Agras, W. S., Moye, A., Bryson, S. W., & Booil, J. (2010). Randomized clinical trial comparing family-based treatment with adolescent-focused individual therapy for adolescents with anorexia nervosa. *Archives of General Psychiatry, 67*, 1025–1032.

Loeber, R., Keenan, K., Lahey, B. B., Green, S. M., & Thomas, C. (1993). Evidence for developmentally based diagnoses of oppositional defiant disorder and conduct disorder. *Journal of Abnormal Child Psychology, 21*, 377–410.

Loewenstein, R. J. (1991). Psychogenic amnesia and psychogenic fugue: A comprehensive review. In A. Tasman & S. M. Goldfinger (Eds.), *American Psychiatric Press review of psychiatry* (pp. 189–222). Washington, DC: American Psychiatric Press.

LoFrisco, B. M. (2011). Female sexual pain disorders and cognitive behavioral therapy. *Journal of Sex Research, 48*, 573–579.

Lofthouse, N., Arnold, L. E., Hersch, S., Hurt, E., & DeBeus, R. (2012). A review of neurofeedback treatment for pediatric ADHD. *Journal of Attention Disorders, 16*, 351–372.

Loftus, E. F. (1993). The reality of repressed memories. *American Psychologist, 48*, 518–537.

Loftus, E. F. (1997, September). Creating false memories. *Scientific American, 277*, 70–75.

London, P. (1964). *The modes and morals of psychotherapy.* New York: Holt, Rinehart & Winston.

London, P. (1986). *The modes and morals of psychotherapy* (2nd ed.). New York: Hemisphere.

Longley, S. L., Broman-Fulks, J. J., Calamari, J. E., Noyes, R., Wade, M., & Orlando, C. M. (2010). A taxometric study of hypochondriasis symptoms. *Behavior Therapy, 41*, 505–514.

Longmore, R. J., & Worrell, M. (2007). Do we need to challenge thoughts in cognitive behavior therapy? *Clinical Psychology Review, 27*, 173–187.

Loock, C., et al. (2005). Identifying fetal alcohol spectrum disorder in primary care. *Canadian Medical Association Journal, 172*, 628–630.

Looman, J. (1995). Sexual fantasies of child molesters. *Canadian Journal of Behavioural Science, 27*, 321–332.

Looper, K. J., & Paris, J. (2000). What dimensions underlie Cluster B personality disorders? *Comprehensive Psychiatry, 41*, 432–437.

Loos, C., & Bowd, A. (1997). Caregivers of persons with Alzheimer's disease: Some neglected implications of the experience of personal loss and grief. *Death Studies, 21*, 501–514.

LoPiccolo, J. (1977). Direct treatment of sexual dysfunction in the couple. *Handbook of sexology, 5*, 1227–1244.

LoPiccolo, J. (1992). Psychological evaluation of erectile failure. In R. Kirby, C. Carson, & G. Webster (Eds.), *Diagnosis and management of male erectile failure dysfunction*. Oxford: Butterworth-Heinemann.

LoPiccolo, J. (2002). Postmodern sex therapy. In F. W. Kaslow & J. L. Lebow (Eds.), *Comprehensive handbook of psychotherapy, Vol. 4, Integrative/eclectic* (pp. 411–435). London: John Wiley & Sons.

LoPiccolo, J., & Friedman, J. (1988). Broad-spectrum treatment of low sexual desire: Integration of cognitive, behavioral, and systemic therapy. In S. Leiblum & R. C. Rosen (Eds.), *Sexual desire disorders*. New York: Guilford.

LoPiccolo, J., & Hogan, D. R. (1979). Multidimensional treatment of sexual dysfunction. In O. F. Pomerleau & J. P. Brady (Eds.), *Behavioral medicine: Theory and practice*. Baltimore: Williams & Wilkins.

LoPiccolo, J., & Lobitz, W. C. (1972). The role of masturbaton in the treatment of orgasmic dysfunction. *Archives of Sexual Behavior, 2*, 163–171.

Loranger, A. W. (1988). *Personality disorder examination (PDE) manual.* Yonkers, NY: DV Communications.

Loranger, A. W., Oldham, J., Russakoff, L. M., & Susman, V. (1987). Structured interviews and borderline personality disorder. *Archives of General Psychiatry, 41*, 565–568.

Lorber, M. F. (2004). Psychophysiology of aggression, psychopathy, and conduct problems: A meta-analysis. *Psychological Bulletin, 130*, 531–552.

Lord, C., & Bishop, S. L. (2015). Recent advances in autism research as reflected in *DSM-5* criteria for autism spectrum disorder. *Annual Review of Clinical Psychology, 11*, 53–70.

Lotter, V. (1978). Follow-up studies. In M. Rutter & E. Schopler (Eds.), *Autism: A reappraisal of concepts and treatment*. New York: Plenum.

Lovaas, O. I. (1987). Behavioral treatment and normal educational and intellectual functioning in young autistic children. *Journal of Consulting and Clinical Psychology, 55*, 3–9.

Lovaas, O. I., Newsom, C., & Hickman, C. (1987). Self-stimulatory behavior and perceptual reinforcement. *Journal of Applied Behavior Analysis, 20*, 45–68.

Lozano, A. M., Mayberg, H. S., Giacobbe, P., et al. (2008). Subcallosal cingulated gyrus deep brain stimulation for treatment-resistant depression. *Biological Psychology, 64*, 461–467.

Luborsky, L., Chandler, M., Auerbach, A. H., Cohen, J., & Bachrach, H. M. (1971). Factors influencing the outcome of psychotherapy: A review of quantitative research. *Psychological Bulletin, 75*, 145–185.

Luborsky, L., Rosenthal, R., Diguer, L., et al. (2002). The Dodo bird verdict is alive and well—mostly. *Clinical Psychology: Science and Practice, 9*, 1–12.

Luby, E. D., & Koval, D. (2009). CNS opiate systems and eating disorders. In R. L. Dean III, E. J. Bilsky, & S. S. Negus (Eds.), *Opiate receptors and antagonists* (pp. 407–421). New York: Springer.

Lui, S., Deng, W., Huang, X., et al. (2009). Association of cerebral deficits with clinical symptoms in antipsychotic-naive first-episode schizophrenia: An optimized voxel-based morphometry and resting state functional connectivity study. *American Journal of Psychiatry, 166*, 196–205.

Luthar, S. S., & Becker, B. E. (2002). Privileged but pressured? A study of affluent youth. *Child Development, 73*, 1593–1610.

Lykken, D. T. (1957). A study of anxiety in the sociopathic personality. *Journal of Abnormal and Social Psychology, 55*, 6–10.

Lymburner, J. A., & Roesch, R. (1999). The insanity defense: Five years of research (1993–1997). *International Journal of Law and Psychiatry, 22*, 213–240.

Lynam, D. R. (1997). Pursuing the psychopath: Capturing the fledgling psychopath in a nomological net. *Journal of Abnormal Psychology, 106*, 425–438.

Lynch, J., Krause, N., Kaplan, G. A., et al. (1997a). Workplace conditions, socioeconomic status, and the risk of mortality and acute myocardial infarction: The Kuopio Ischemic Heart Disease Risk Factor Study. *American Journal of Public Health, 87*, 617–622.

Lynch, J., Krause, N., Kaplan, G. A., et al. (1997b). Workplace demands, economic reward, and progression of carotid atherosclerosis. *Circulation, 96*, 302–307.

Lynch, T. R., Compton, J. S., Mendelson, T., Robins, C. J., & Krishnan, K. R. R. (2000). Anxious depression among the elderly: Clinical and phenomenological correlates. *Aging and Mental Health, 4*, 268–274.

Lynn, S. J., & Rhue, J. W. (1988). Fantasy proneness: Hypnosis, developmental antecedents, and psychopathology. *American Psychologist, 43*, 35–44.

Lynn, S. L., Merckelbach, H., Giesbrecht, T., Lilienfeld, S. O., Lemons, P., & van der Kloet, D. (2015). Dissociative disorders. In R. L. Cautin & S. O. Lilienfeld (Eds.), *Encyclopedia of clinical psychology*. New York: Wiley.

Lyon, D. R., Hart, S. D., & Webster, C. D. (2001). Violence and risk assessment. In R. A. Schuller & J. R. Ogloff (Eds.), *Introduction to psychology and law: Canadian perspectives* (pp. 314–350). Toronto: University of Toronto Press.

Lyon, G. R., & Cutting, L. (1998). Treatment of learning disabilities. In E. Mash & R. Barkley (Eds.), *Treatment of childhood disorders* (pp. 468–500). New York: Guilford.

Lyon, H. M., Startup, M., & Bentall, R. P. (1999). Social cognition and the manic defense: Attribution, selective attention, and self-schema in bipolar affective disorder. *Journal of Abnormal Psychology, 108*, 273–282.

Lyons, M. J., True, W. R., Eisen, S. A., et al. (1995). Differential heritability of adult and juvenile antisocial traits. *Archives of General Psychiatry, 52*, 906–915.

MacAdam, M. (2015). PRISMA: Program of research to integrate the services for the maintenance of autonomy: A system-level integration model in Quebec. *International Journal of Integrated Care, 15*, e018.

MacCallum, E. (2012, March 15). Sufferers of chronic pain and the government's war on OxyContin. *Maclean's*.

Maccoby, N., & Altman, D. G. (1988). Disease prevention in communities: The Stanford Heart Disease Prevention Program. In R. H. Price, E. L. Cowen, R. P. Lorion, & J. Ramos-McKay (Eds.), *14 ounces of prevention: A casebook for practitioners* (pp. 165–174). Washington, DC: American Psychological Association.

MacDonald, A. W., & Carter, C. S. (2003). Event-related fMRI study of context processing in dorsolateral prefrontal cortex of patients with schizophrenia. *Journal of Abnormal Psychology, 112*, 689–697.

MacDonald, M. R., & Kuiper, N. A. (1984). Self-schema decision consistency in clinical depression. *Journal of Social and Clinical Psychology, 2*, 264–272.

MacGregor, M. W. (1996). Multiple personality disorder: Etiology, treatment, and techniques from a psychodynamic perspective. *Psychoanalytic Psychology, 13*, 389–402.

MacIntosh, H. B., & Butters, M. (2014). Measuring outcomes in couple therapy: A systematic review and critical discussion. *Journal of Couple & Relationship Therapy, 13*, 44–62.

Mackenzie, C. S., Gekoski, W. L., & Knox, J. V. (1999). Do family physicians treat older patients with mental disorders differently from younger patients? *Canadian Family Physician, 45*, 1219–1224.

MacKenzie, M. B., & Kocovski, N. L. (2016a). Mindfulness-based cognitive therapy for depression: Trends and developments. *Psychology Research and Behavior Management, 9*, 125–132.

MacKenzie, M. B., & Kocovski, N. L. (2016b). Self-help behaviour of Canadians with perceived needs for mental health care. *Canadian Psychology, 57*, 130–141.

Mackrael, K. (2013, March 15). High-risk offender label "misses target," says head of the Ontario Review Board. *The Globe and Mail*.

Mackrill, T., & Iwakabe, S. (2013). Making a case for case studies in psychotherapy training: A small step towards establishing an empirical basis for psychotherapy training. *Counselling Psychology Quarterly, 3–4*, 250–266.

MacLatchy-Gaudet, H. A., & Stewart, S. H. (2001). The context-specific positive alcohol outcome expectancies of university women. *Addictive Behaviors, 26*, 31–49.

MacLeod, A. K., Haynes, C., & Sensky, T. (1998). Attributions about common bodily sensations: Their associations with hyponchondriasis and anxiety. *Psychological Medicine, 28*, 225–228.

MacLeod, C., Mathews, A., & Tata, P. (1986). Attentional bias in emotional disorders. *Journal of Abnormal Psychology, 95*(1), 15–20.

MacMillan, H. L., Fleming, J. E., Streiner, D. L., Lin, E., Boyle, M. H., et al. (2001). Childhood abuse and lifetime psychopathology in a community sample. *American Journal of Psychiatry, 158*, 1878–1883.

MacMillan, H. L., Georgiades, K., Duku, E., Shea, A., Steiner, M., Niec, A., ... Schmidt, L. A. (2009). Cortisol response to stress in female youths exposed to childhood maltreatment: Results of the Youth Mood Project. *Biological Psychiatry, 66*, 62–68.

MacMillan, H. L., Tanaka, M., Duku, E., Vaillancourt, T., & Boyle, M. H. (2013). Child physical and sexual abuse in a community sample of young adults. Results from the Ontario Child Health Study. *Child Abuse & Neglect, 37*, 14–21.

Macrodimitris, S. D., & Endler, N. S. (2001). Coping, control, and adjustment in Type II diabetes. *Health Psychology, 20*, 208–216.

Madigan, S., Atkinson, L., Laurin, K., & Benoit, D. (2013). Attachment and internalizing behavior in early childhood: A meta-analysis. *Developmental Psychology, 49*, 672–689.

Madonna, P. G., Van Scoyk, S., & Jones, D. B. (1991). Family interactions within incest and nonincest families. *American Journal of Psychiatry, 148*, 46–49.

Magnusson, A., & Axelsson, J. (1993). The prevalence of seasonal affective disorder is low among descendants of Icelandic emigrants in Canada. *Archives of General Psychiatry, 50*, 947–951.

Maheu, M. M., Pulier, M. L., McMenamin, J. P., & Posen, L. (2012). Future of telepsychology, telehealth, and various technologies in psychological research and practice. *Professional Psychology: Research and Practice, 43*, 613–621.

Maisel, N. C., Blodgett, J. C., Wilbourne, P. L., Humphreys, K., & Finney, J. W. (2013). Meta-analysis of naltrexone and acamprosate for treating alcohol use disorders: When are these medications most helpful? *Addiction, 108*, 275–293.

Maj, M., Pirozzi, R., Magliono, L., & Bartoli, L. (1998). Long-term outcome of lithium prophylaxis in bipolar disorder: A 5-year prospective study of 402 patients at a lithium clinic. *American Journal of Psychiatry, 155*, 30–35.

Mäkelä, K., et al. (1981). *Alcohol, society, and the state 1. A comparative study of alcohol control*. Toronto: Addiction Research Foundation.

Makin, K. (2013, February 1). Courts uphold Canada's medical marijuana laws. *The Globe and Mail*.

Makin, K. (2013, June 15). Meet Canada's longest-serving chief justice. *The Globe and Mail*, A10–A11.

Malaiyandi, U., et al. (2006). Impact of CYP2A6 genotype on pretreatment smoking behavior and nicotine levels from and usage of nicotine replacement therapy. *Molecular Psychiatry, 11,* 400–409.

Malaspina, D., et al. (2000). Relation of familial schizophrenia to negative symptoms but not to the deficit syndrome. *American Journal of Psychiatry, 157,* 994–1003.

Malbos, E. (2015). Virtual reality in exposure therapy: The next frontier. In E. Aboujaoude & V. Starcevic (Eds.), *Mental health in the digital age: Grave dangers, great promise* (pp. 220–237). New York: Oxford University Press.

Malcolm. S. (2011, June 24). Cory Monteith's turning point. *Parade.*

Maldonado, J. R., Butler, L. D., & Spiegel, D. (1998). Treatments for dissociative disorders. In P. E. Nathan & J. M. Gorman (Eds.), *A guide to treatments that work* (pp. 423–446). New York: Oxford University Press.

Maletzky, B. M. (1997). Exhibitionism: Assessment and treatment. In D. R. Laws & W. O'Donohue (Eds.), *Sexual deviance* (pp. 40–74). New York: Guilford.

Malizia, A. L., Cunningham, V. J., Bell, C. J., Liddle, P. F., et al. (1998). Decreased brain GABAa-benzodiazepine receptor binding in panic disorder: Preliminary results from a quantitative study. *Archives of General Psychiatry, 55,* 715–720.

Malkoff-Schwartz, S., Frank, E., Anderson, B., Sherrill, J. T., Siegel, L., et al. (1998). Stressful life events and social rhythm disruption in the onset of manic and depressive bipolar episodes: A preliminary investigation. *Archives of General Psychiatry, 55,* 702–707.

Malla, A., Iver, S., McGorry, P., & Cannon, M. (2016). From early intervention in psychosis to youth mental health reform: A review of the evolution and transformation of mental health services for young people. *Social Psychiatry and Psychiatric Epidemiology, 51,* 319–326.

Malla, A. K., Mittal, C., Lee, M., Scholten, D. J., Assis, L., & Norman, R. M. G. (2002). Computed tomography of the brain morphology of patients with first-episode schizophrenic psychosis. *Journal of Psychiatry and Neuroscience, 27,* 350–358.

Malla, A. K., Norman, R. M. G., Manchanda, R., Ahmed, R. A., et al. (2002). One-year outcome in first-episode psychosis: Influence of DUP and other predictors. *Schizophrenia Research, 54,* 231–242.

Malla, A. K., Norman, R. M. G., Scholten, D. J., Zirul, S., & Kotteda, V. (2001). A comparison of long-term outcome in first-episode schizophrenia following treatment with risperidone or a typical antipsychotic. *Journal of Clinical Psychiatry, 62,* 179–184.

Malla, A., Schmitz, N., Norman, R. M. G., et al. (2007). A multisite Canadian study of outcome of first-episode psychosis treated in publicly funded early intervention services. *Canadian Journal of Psychiatry, 52,* 563–571.

Maloney, B., et al. (2008). Early-emerging cognitive-vulnerability to depression and the serotonin transporter promoter region polymorphism. *Journal of Affective Disorders, 107,* 227–230.

Malouff, J., Thorsteinsson, E. B., & Schutte, N. S. (2007). The efficacy of problem solving therapy in reducing mental and physical health problems: A meta-analysis. *Clinical Psychology Review, 27,* 46–57.

Manassis, K. (2013). Empirically supported psychosocial treatments. In C. A. Essau & T. H. Ollendick (Eds.), *The Wiley-Blackwell handbook of the treatment of childhood and adolescent anxiety* (pp. 207–228). Chichester, England: John Wiley & Sons.

Manassis, K., Avery, D., Butalia, S., & Mendlowitz, S. (2004). Cognitive-behavioral therapy with childhood anxiety disorders: Functioning in adolescence. *Depression and Anxiety, 19,* 209–216.

Manassis, K., & Monga, S. (2001). A therapeutic approach to children and adolescents with anxiety disorders and associated comorbid conditions. *Journal of the American Academy of Child and Adolescent Psychiatry, 40,* 115–117.

Mancebo, M. C., Eisen, J. L., Grant, J. E., & Rasmussen, S. A. (2005). Obsessive compulsive personality disorder and obsessive compulsive disorder: Clinical characteristics, diagnostic difficulties, and treatment. *Annals of Clinical Psychiatry, 17,* 197–204.

Mancini, C., van Ameringen, M., Szatmari, P., Fugere, C., & Boyle, M. (1996). A high-risk pilot study of the children of adults with social phobia. *Journal of the American Academy of Child and Adolescent Psychiatry, 35,* 1511–1517.

Mandler, G. (1966). Anxiety. In D. L. Sills (Ed.), *International encyclopedia of the social sciences.* New York: Macmillan.

Manicavasagar, V., Perich, T., & Parker, G. (2012). Cognitive predictors of change in cognitive behaviour therapy and mindfulness-based cognitive therapy for depression. *Behavioural and Cognitive Psychotherapy, 40,* 227–232.

Manion, I., Short, K. H., & Ferguson, B. (2013). A snapshot of school-based mental health and substance abuse in Canada: Where we are and where it leads us. *Canadian Journal of School Psychology, 28,* 119–135.

Manuck, S. B., Kaplan, J. R., & Clarkson, T. B. (1983). Behaviorally induced heart rate reactivity and atherosclerosis in cynomolgus monkeys. *Psychosomatic Medicine, 49,* 95–108.

Manuel, D. G., Leung, M., Nguyen, K., Tanuseputro, P., & Johansen, H. (2003). Burden of cardiovascular disease in Canada. *Canadian Journal of Cardiology, 19,* 997–1004.

Maravilla, K. R., & Yang, C. C. (2008). Magnetic resonance imaging and the female sexual response: Overview of techniques, results, and future directions. *The Journal of Sexual Medicine, 5,* 1559–1571.

Marazzi, M. A., & Luby, E. D. (1986). An auto-addiction opioid model of chronic anorexia nervosa. *International Journal of Eating Disorders, 5,* 191–208.

Marcus, J., et al. (1987). Review of the NIMH Israeli Kibbutz-City and the Jerusalem infant development study. *Schizophrenia Bulletin, 13,* 425–438.

Marcus, M. A., Westra, H. A., Eastwood, J. D., & the Mobilizing Minds Research Group. (2012). What are young people saying about mental health? An analysis of internet blogs. *Journal of Medical Internet Research, 14,* e17.

Margolin, G. (1982). Ethical and legal considerations in marital and family therapy. *American Psychologist, 37,* 788–801.

Marin, T. J., Chen, E., & Miller, G. E. (2008). What do trajectories of childhood socioeconomic status tell us about markers of cardiovascular health in adolescence? *Psychosomatic Medicine, 70,* 152–159.

Maris, R. W., Berman, A. L., Maltsberger, J. T., & Yufit, R. I. (1992). *Assessment and prediction of suicide.* New York: Guilford.

Marlatt, G. A. (1983). The controlled drinking controversy: A commentary. *American Psychologist, 38,* 1097–1110.

Marlatt, G. A. (1999). From hindsight to foresight: A commentary on Project MATCH. In J. A. Tucker, D. M. Donovan, & G. A. Marlatt (Eds.), *Changing addictive behavior: Bridging clinical and public health strategies* (pp. 45–66). New York: Guilford.

Marlatt, G. A., Baer, J. S., & Larimer, M. (1995). Preventing alcohol abuse in college students: A harm-reduction approach. In G. M. Boyd, J. Howard, & R. A. Zucker (Eds.), *Alcohol problems among adolescents: Current directions in prevention research* (pp. 147–172). Hillsdale, NJ: Erlbaum.

Marlatt, G. A., Blume, A. W., & Parks, G. A. (2001). Integrating harm reduction therapy and traditional substance abuse treatment. *Journal of Psychoactive Drugs, 33,* 13–21.

Marlatt, G. A., & Gordon, J. R. (Eds.). (1985). *Relapse prevention: Maintenance strategies in the treatment of addictive behaviors.* New York: Guilford.

Marlatt, G. A., & Witkiewitz, K. (2002). Harm reduction approaches to alcohol use: Health promotion, prevention, and treatment. *Addictive Behaviors, 27,* 867–886.

Marlatt, G. A., et al. (1998). Screening and brief intervention for high-risk college student drinkers: Results from a 2-year follow-up assessment. *Journal of Consulting and Clinical Psychology, 66,* 604–615.

Marmar, C. R., Schlenger, W., Henn-Haase, C., Qian, M., et al. (2015). Course of posttraumatic stress disorder 40 years after the Vietnam War: Findings from the National Vietnam Veterans Longitudinal Study. *JAMA Psychiatry, 72,* 875–881.

Marmot, M. G., Bosma, H., Hemingway, H., Brunner, E., & Stansfeld, S. (1997). Contribution of job control and other risk factors to social variations in coronary heart disease incidence. *The Lancet, 350,* 235–239.

Marsh, A. A., Finger, E. C., Mitchell, D. G. V., et al. (2008). Reduced amygdale response to fearful expressions in children and adolescents with callous-unemotional traits and disruptive behavior disorders. *American Journal of Psychiatry, 165,* 712–720.

Marshall, W. L. (1996). Assessment, treatment, and theorizing about sex offenders: Developments during the past twenty years and future directions. *Criminal Justice and Behavior, 23,* 162–199.

Marshall, W. L. (1997). Pedophilia: Psychopathology and theory. In D. R. Laws & W. O'Donohue (Eds.), *Sexual deviance* (pp. 152–174). New York: Guilford.

Marshall, W. L. (1999). Current status of North American assessment and treatment programs for sexual offenders. *Journal of Interpersonal Violence, 14,* 221–239.

Marshall, W. L., & Barbaree, H. E. (1990). Outcome of comprehensive cognitive-behavioral treatment programs. In W. L. Marshall & D. R. Laws (Eds.), *Handbook of sexual assault: Issues, theories, and treatment of the offender* (pp. 363–385). New York: Plenum Press.

Marshall, W. L., Barbaree, H., & Christophe, D. (1986). Sexual offenders against female children: Sexual preferences for age of victims and type of behaviour. *Canadian Journal of Behavioural Science, 18,* 424–439.

Marshall, W. L., Champagne, F., Sturgeon, C., & Bryce, P. (1997). Increasing the self-esteem of child molesters. *Sexual Abuse, 9,* 321–333.

Marshall, W. L., Cripps, E., Anderson, D., & Cortoni, F. A. (1999). Self-esteem and coping strategies in child molesters. *Journal of Interpersonal Violence, 14,* 955–962.

Marshall, W. L., & Fernandez, Y. M. (2000). Phallometric testing with sexual offenders: Limits to its value. *Clinical Psychology Review, 20,* 807–822.

Marshall, W. L., Jones, R., Ward, T., Johnston, P., & Barbaree, H. E. (1991). Treatment outcomes with sex offenders. *Clinical Psychology Review, 11,* 465–485.

Marshall, W. L., Hamilton, K., & Fernandez, Y. (2001). Empathy deficits and cognitive distortions in child molesters. *Sexual Abuse: A Journal of Research and Treatment, 13,* 123–130.

Marshall, W. L., & Marshall, L. E. (2013). Ethical issues in treating sex offenders. In K. Harrison & B. Rainey (Eds.), *The Wiley-Blackwell handbook of legal and ethical aspects* (pp. 236–250). Chichester, England: Wiley.

Marshall, W. L., & Moulden, H. (2001). Hostility toward women and victim empathy in rapists. *Sexual Abuse, 13,* 249–255.

Marshall, W. L., & Serin, R. (1997). Personality disorder. In S. M. Turner & M. Hersen (Eds.), *Adult psychopathology and diagnosis,* Vol. 3 (pp. 508–543). New York: John Wiley & Sons.

Martens, P. J., et al. (2007). Prevalence of mental illness and its impact on the use of home care and nursing homes: A population-based study of older adults in Manitoba. *Canadian Journal of Psychiatry, 52,* 581–590.

Martin, B. A. (2000). The Clarke Institute experience with completed suicide: 1966 to 1997. *Canadian Journal of Psychiatry, 45,* 630–638.

Martin, C. S., Chung, T., & Langenbucher, J. W. (2008). How should we revise diagnostic criteria for substance abuse disorders in DSM-V? *Journal of Abnormal Psychology, 117,* 561–575.

Martin, R., & Young, J. (2010). Schema therapy. In K. S. Dobson (Ed.), *Handbook of cognitive-behavioral therapies* (3rd ed., pp. 317–346). New York: The Guilford.

Martin, S. (2012). *50 lives that changed Canada.* Toronto: House of Anansi Press.

Martins, N., Williams, D. C., Harrison, K., & Ratan, R. A. (2009). A content analysis of female body imagery in video games. *Sex Roles, 61,* 824–836.

Martins, N., Williams, D. C., Ratan, R. A., & Harrison, K. (2011). Virtual muscularity: A content analysis of male video game characters. *Body Image, 8,* 43–51.

Masellis, M., Rector, N. A., & Richter, M. A. (2003). Quality of life in OCD: Differential impact of obsessions, compulsions, and depression comorbidity. *Canadian Journal of Psychiatry, 48,* 72–77.

Maslach, C., & Jackson, S. E. (1981). The measurement of experienced burnout. *Journal of Occupational Behaviour, 2,* 99–113.

Maslach, C., Schaufeli, W. B., & Leiter, M. (2001). Job burnout. *Annual Review of Psychology, 52,* 397–422.

Masland, S. R., & Hooley, J. M. (2015). Perceived criticism: A research update for clinical practitioners. *Clinical Psychology: Science and Practice, 22,* 211–222.

Masley, S. A., Gillanders, D. T., Simpson, S. G., & Taylor, M. A. (2012). A systematic review of the evidence base for schema therapy. *Cognitive Behavior Therapy, 41,* 185–202.

Mason, F. L. (1997). Fetishism: Psychopathology and theory. In D. R. Laws & W. O'Donohue (Eds.), *Sexual deviance* (pp. 75–91). New York: Guilford.

Mason, O., Startup, M., Halpin, S., Schall, U., Conrad, A., & Carr, V. (2004). Risk factors for transition to first-episode psychosis among individuals with 'at-risk mental states'. *Schizophrenia Research, 71,* 227–237.

Massachusetts Association for Mental Health, et al. (2016, July 1). Joint statement in response to initial story in Globe Spotlight series on mental health in Massachusetts. Boston: National Alliance on Mental Health of Massachusetts.

Masters, W. H., & Johnson, V. E. (1966). *Human sexual response.* Boston: Little, Brown.

Masters, W. H., & Johnson, V. E. (1970). *Human sexual inadequacy.* Boston: Little, Brown.

Mataix-Cols, D., Bilotti, D., Fernández de la Cruz, L., & Nordsletten, A. E. (2013). The London field trial for hoarding disorder. *Psychological Medicine, 43,* 843–847.

Matelski, L., & Van de Water, J. (2016). Risk factors in autism: Thinking outside the brain. *Journal of Autoimmunity, 67,* 1–7.

Mathews, A., & MacLeod, C. (1994). Cognitive approaches to emotion and emotional disorders. In L. W. Porter & M. R. Rosenzweig (Eds.), *Annual Review of Psychology* (pp. 25–50). Stanford, CA: Stanford University Press.

Matlow, J. N. (2011). Guidelines and strategies for screening fetal alcohol spectrum disorder in Canada. *University of Toronto Medical Journal, 89,* 16–21.

Mattheisen, M., Samuels, J. F., Wang, Y., Greenberg, B. D., Fyer, A. J., McCracken, J. T., . . . Nestadt, G. (2015). Genome-wide association study in obsessive-compulsive disorder: Results from the OCGAS. *Molecular Psychiatry, 20*, 337–344.

Matthews, K. A., Zhu, S., Tucker, D. C., & Whooley, M. A. (2006). Blood pressure to psychosocial stress and coronary classification in the coronary artery risk development in young adults study. *Hypertension, 47*, 391–395.

Mattson, M. E., Allen, J. P., Longabaugh, R., Nickless, C. J., Connors, G. J., & Kadden, R. M. (1994). A chronological review of empirical studies matching alcoholic clients to treatment. *Journal of Studies on Alcohol, 55*, 16–29.

Mayberg, H. S. (2006). Defining neurocircuits in depression: Insights from functional neuroimaging studies of diverse treatments. *Psychiatric Annals, 4*, 258–267.

Mayberg, H. S., et al. (2005). Deep brain stimulation for treatment-resistant depression. *Neuron, 45*, 651–660.

Mayhew, D. R., Beirness, D. J., & Simpson, H. M. (2000). Trends in drinking-driving fatalities in Canada—progress continues. In *Alcohol, Drugs, and Traffic Safety—T2000*. Stockholm: Swedish National Road Safety.

Mayhew, S. L., & Gilbert, P. (2008). Compassion mind training with people who hear malevolent voices: A case series report. *Clinical Psychology and Psychotherapy, 15*, 113–138.

Mayor's Homelessness Action Task Force. (1999). *Taking responsibility for homelessness: An action plan for Toronto: Report of the Mayor's Homelessness Action Task Force.* Toronto: City of Toronto.

Mayou, R., Kirmayer, L. J., Simon, G., Kroenke, K., & Sharpe, M. (2005). Somatoform disorders: time for a new approach in DSM-V. *American Journal of Psychiatry, 162*, 847–855.

McAlister, F. A., Wilkins, K., Joffres, M., et al. (2011). Changes in the rates of awareness, treatment, and control of hypertension in Canada over the past two decades. *Canadian Medical Association Journal, 183*, 1007–1013.

McAlonan, G. M., Cheung, V., Cheung, C., et al. (2005). Mapping the brain in autism. A voxel-based MRI study of volumetric differences and intercorrelations in autism. *Brain, 128*, 268–276.

McCabe, R. E. (1999). Implicit and explicit memory for threat words in high- and low-anxiety-sensitive participants. *Cognitive Therapy and Research, 23*, 21–38.

McCabe, R. E., Antony, M. M., Summerfeldt, L. J., Liss, A., & Swinson, R. P. (2003). Preliminary examination of the relationship between anxiety disorders in adults and self-reported history of teasing or bullying experiences. *Cognitive Behaviour Therapy, 32*, 187–193.

McCabe, S. B., Gotlib, I. H., & Martin, R. (2000). Cognitive vulnerability for depression: Deployment of attention as a function of history of depression and current mood state. *Cognitive Therapy and Research, 24*, 427–444.

McCabe, S. B., & Tonan, P. E. (2000). Stimulus exposure duration in a deployment-of-attention task: Effects on dysphoric, recently dysphoric, and nondysphoric individuals. *Cognition and Emotion, 14*, 125–142.

McCain, M. N., Mustard, F., & Shanker, S. (2007). *Early years study 2: Putting science into action.* Toronto: Council for Early Childhood Development.

McCarthy, B., & Thestrup, M. (2008a). Couple therapy and the treatment of sexual dysfunction. In A. Gurman (Ed.), *Clinical handbook of couple therapy* (4th ed., pp. 591–617). New York: Guilford.

McCarthy, B., & Thestrup, M. (2008b). Integrating sex therapy interventions with couple therapy. *Journal of Contemporary Psychotherapy, 38*, 139–149.

McClure, M. M., Barch, D. M., Flory, J. D., Harvey, P. D., & Siever, L. J. (2008). Context processing in schizotypal personality disorder: Evidence of specificity of impairment to the schizophrenia spectrum. *Journal of Abnormal Psychology, 117*, 342–354.

McConaghy, N. (1990). Sexual deviation. In A. S. Bellack, M. Hersen, & A. E. Kazdin (Eds.), *International handbook of behavior modification and therapy* (2nd ed., pp. 565–580). New York: Plenum.

McConaghy, N. (1994). Paraphilias and gender identity disorders. In M. Hersen & R. T. Ammerman (Eds.), *Handbook of prescriptive treatments for adults* (pp. 317–346). New York: Plenum.

McCool, M. E., Zuelke, A., Theurich, M. A., Knuettel, H., Ricci, C., & Apfelbacher, C. (in press). Prevalence of female sexual dysfunction among premenopausal women: A systematic review and meta-analysis of observational studies. *Sexual Medicine Reviews.*

McCord, W., & McCord, J. (1964). *The psychopath: An essay on the criminal mind.* New York: Van Nostrand-Reinhold.

McCrady, B. S. (1985). Alcoholism. In D. H. Barlow (Ed.), *Clinical handbook of psychological disorders.* New York: Guilford.

McCrady, B. S., Epstein, E. E., & Kahler, C. W. (2004). Alcoholics Anonymous and relapse prevention as maintenance strategies after conjoint behavioral alcohol treatment for men: 18-month outcomes. *Journal of Consulting and Clinical Psychology, 72*, 870–878.

McCrady, B. S., Wilson, A. D., Muñoz, R. E., Fink, B. C., Fokas, K., & Borders, A. (in press). Alcohol-focused behavioral couple therapy. *Family Process.*

McCrae, R. R., & Costa, P. T., Jr. (1990). *Personality in adulthood.* New York: Guilford.

McCullough, M. E., Orsulak, P., Brandon, A., & Akers, L. (2007). Rumination, fear, and cortisol: An *in vivo* study of interpersonal transgressions. *Health Psychology, 26*, 126–132.

McCusker, J., Cole, M., Abrahamowicz, M., Primeau, F., & Belzile, E. (2002). Delirium predicts 12-month mortality. *Archives of Internal Medicine, 162*, 457–463.

McCusker, J., Cole, M., Dendukuri, N., Belzile, E., & Primeau, F. (2001). Delirium in older medical inpatients and subsequent cognitive and functional status: A prospective study. *Canadian Medical Association Journal, 165*, 575–583.

McDaid, C., Trowman, R., Golder, S., et al. (2008). Interventions for people bereaved through suicide: Systematic review. *British Journal of Psychiatry, 193*, 438–443.

McEachin, J. J., Smith, T., & Lovaas, O. I. (1993). Long-term outcome for children with autism who received early intensive behavioral treatment. *American Journal of Mental Retardation, 97*, 359–372.

McElroy, S. L., Guerdijkova, A. I., Mori, N., & Keck, P. E., Jr. (2015). Psychopharmacologic treatment of eating disorders: Emerging findings. *Current Psychiatry Reports, 17*, 35.

McEwen, B. S. (1998). Protective and damaging effects of stress mediators. *New England Journal of Medicine, 338*, 171–179.

McGirr, A., et al. (2006). Risk factors for completed suicide in schizophrenia and other chronic psychotic disorders: A case-control study. *Schizophrenia Research, 84*, 132–143.

McGirr, A., et al. (2007). An examination of DSM-IV depressive symptoms and risk for suicide completion in major depressive disorder: A psychological autopsy study. *Journal of Affective Disorders, 97*, 203–209.

McGirr, A., Alda, M., Seguin, M., et al. (2009). Familial aggregation of suicide explained by cluster B traits: A three-group family study of suicide controlling for major depressive disorder. *American Journal of Psychiatry, 166*, 1124–1134.

McGirr, A., Paris, J., Lesage, A., Renaud, J., & Turecki, G. (2007). Risk factors for suicide completion in borderline personality disorder:

A case-control study of cluster B comorbidity and impulsive aggression. *Journal of Clinical Psychiatry, 68*, 721–729.

McGlynn, F. D., Karg, S., & Lawyer, S. R. (2003). Fear responses to mock magnetic resonance imaging among college students: Toward a prototype experiment. *Journal of Anxiety Disorders, 17*, 335–347.

McGrath, J. J. (2006). Variations in the incidence of schizophrenia: Data versus dogma. *Schizophrenia Bulletin, 32*, 195–197.

McGrath, R. E. (2010). Prescriptive authority for psychologists. *Annual Review of Clinical Psychology, 6*, 21–47.

McGregor, M. T., Du Mont, J., & Myhr, T. L. (2002). Sexual assault forensic medical examination: Is evidence related to successful prosecution? *Annals of Emergency Medicine, 39*, 639–647.

McGuffin, P., et al. (2003). The heritability of bipolar affective disorder and the genetic relationship to unipolar depression. *Archives of General Psychiatry, 60*, 497–502.

McGurk, S. R., Twamley, E. W., Sitzer, D. I., et al. (2007). A meta-analysis of cognitive remediation in schizophrenia. *American Journal of Psychiatry, 164*, 1791–1802.

McIlroy, A., & Baluja, T. (2012, April 16). Home care's shortcomings: Ailing seniors too soon pushed into nursing homes, leaving caregivers stressed, Health Council says. *The Globe and Mail*, A7.

McIntyre, L., Williams, J. V. A., Lavorato, D. H., & Patten, S. (2013). Depression and suicide ideation in late adolescence and early adulthood are an outcome of child hunger. *Journal of Affective Disorders, 150*, 123–129.

McIntyre-Kingsolver, K., Lichtenstein, E., & Mermelstein, R. J. (1986). Spouse training in a multicomponent smoking-cessation program. *Behavior Therapy, 17*, 67–74.

McKim, W. A. (1991). *Drugs and behavior: An introduction to behavioral pharmacology*. Englewood Cliffs, NJ: Prentice-Hall.

McKinley, N. M., & Hyde, J. S. (1996). The objectified body consciousness scale: Development and validation. *Psychology of Women Quarterly, 20*, 181–215.

McKinnon, M. C., Palombo, D. J., Nazarov, A., Kumar, N., Khuu, W., & Levine, B. (2015). Threats of death and autobiographical memory: A study of passengers from Flight AT236. *Clinical Psychological Science, 3*, 487–502.

McKinnon, M. C., Yucel, K., Nazarov, A., & MacQueen, G. M. (2009). A meta-analysis examining clinical predictors of hippocampal volume in patients with major depressive disorder. *Journal of Psychiatry & Neuroscience, 34*, 41–54.

McKnight, R. F., et al. (2012). Lithium toxicity profile: A systematic review and meta-analysis. *The Lancet, 379*, 721–728.

McLachlan, J., Zimmer-Gembeck, M. J., & McGregor, L. (2010). Rejection sensitivity in childhood and early adolescence: Peer rejection and protective effects of parents and friends. *Journal of Relationships Research, 1*, 31–40.

McLaren, A. (1986). The creation of a haven for "human thoroughbreeds": The sterilization of the feeble-minded and the mentally ill in British Columbia. *Canadian Historical Review, 67*, 127–150.

McLeod, B. D. (2011). Relation of the alliance with outcomes in youth psychotherapy: A meta-analysis. *Clinical Psychology Review, 31*, 603–616.

McLeod, J. (2015). Reading case studies to inform therapeutic practice. *Psychotherapie Forum, 20*, 3–9.

McLeod, J., & Elliott, R. (2011). Systematic case study research: A practice-oriented introduction to building an evidence base for counselling and psychotherapy. *Counselling and Psychotherapy Research, 11*, 1–10.

McLuckie, A., Allan, R., & Ungar, M. (2013). Couple and family therapy within the current pan-Canadian context. *Contemporary Family Therapy: An International Journal, 35*, 329–341.

McLuckie, A., Kutcher, S., Wei, Y., & Weaver, C. (2014). Sustained improvements in students' mental health literacy with use of a mental health curriculum in Canadian schools. *BMC Psychiatry, 14*, 379.

McMahon, J., & DiGiuseppe, R. (2013). A personal reprise of couples intervention. *Journal of Rational-Emotive and Cognitive-Behavior Therapy, 31*, 49–56.

McMain, S. F. (2015). Advances in the treatment of borderline personality disorder: An introduction to the special issue. *Journal of Clinical Psychology: In Session, 71*, 741–746.

McMain, S. F., et al. (2009). A randomized trial of dialectical behavior therapy versus general psychiatric management for borderline personality disorder. *American Journal of Psychiatry, 166*, 1365–1374.

McMain, S. F., Guimond, T., Streiner, D. L., Cordish, R. J., & Links, P. S. (2012). Dialectical behavior therapy compared with general psychiatric management for borderline personality disorder: Clinical outcomes and functioning over a 2-year follow-up. *American Journal of Psychiatry, 169*, 650–661.

McMain, S., Korman, L. M., & Dimeff, L. (2001). Dialectical behavior therapy and the treatment of emotion dysregulation. *Journal of Clinical Psychology, 57*, 183–196.

McMain, S., Newman, M. G., Segal, Z. V., & DeRubeis, R. J. (2015). Cognitive behavioral therapy: Current status and future research directions. *Psychotherapy Research, 25*, 321–329.

McMillan, K. A., Asmundson, G. J. G., Zvolensky, M. J., & Carleton, R. N. (2012). Startle response and anxiety sensitivity: Subcortical indices of physiological arousal and fear responding. *Emotion, 12*(6), 1264–1272.

McMillan, K. A., Enns, M. W., Cox, B. J., & Sareen, J. (2009). Comorbidity of Axis I and II mental disorders with schizophrenia and psychotic disorders: Findings from the National Epidemiologic Survey on Alcohol and Related Conditions. *Canadian Journal of Psychiatry, 54*, 477–486.

McMullen, S., & Rosen, R. C. (1979). Self-administered masturbation training in the treatment of primary orgasmic dysfunction. *Journal of Consulting and Clinical Psychology, 47*, 912–918.

McMurty, C. M., Noel, M., Taddio, A., Antony, M. M., Asmundson, G. J. G., Riddell, R. P., ... HELPinKids&Adults Team. (2015). Interventions for individuals with high levels of needle fear: Systematic review of randomized controlled trials and quasi-randomized controlled trials. *Clinical Journal of Pain, 31*, S109–S123.

McNally, R. J. (1994). *Panic disorder: A critical analysis*. New York: Guilford.

McNally, R. J. (1997). Atypical phobias. In G. C. L. Davey (Ed.), *Phobias: A handbook of theory, research and treatment* (pp. 183–199). Chichester, England: John Wiley & Sons.

McNally, R. J. (2005a). Troubles in traumatology. *Canadian Journal of Psychiatry, 50*, 815–816.

McNally, R. J. (2005b). Debunking myths about trauma and memory. *Canadian Journal of Psychiatry, 50*, 817–822.

McNally, R. J. (2007). Mechanisms of exposure therapy: How neuroscience can improve psychological treatments for anxiety disorders. *Clinical Psychology Review, 27*, 750–759.

McNulty, J. L., Graham, J. R., Ben-Porath, Y. S., & Stein, L. A. R. (1997). Comparative validity of MMPI-II scales of African-American and Caucasian mental health center clients. *Psychological Assessment, 9*, 464–470.

McRae, T. R., Dalgleish, T. L., Johnson, S. M., Burgess-Moser, M., & Killian, K. D. (2014). Emotion regulation and key change events in emotionally focused couple therapy. *Journal of Couple & Relationship Therapy, 13*, 1–24.

McVey, G. L., & Davis, R. (2002). A program to promote positive body image: A 1-year follow-up evaluation. *Journal of Early Adolescence, 22,* 96–108.

McVey, G. L., Gusella, J., Tweed, S., & Ferrari, M. (2009). A controlled evaluation of web-based training for teachers and public health practitioners for the prevention of eating disorders. *Eating Disorders, 17,* 1–26.

McVey, G. L., Kirsch, G., Maker, D., Walker, K. S., et al. (2010). Promoting positive body image among university students: A collaborative pilot study. *Body Image, 7,* 200–204.

McVey, G. L., Lieberman, M., Voorberg, N., Wardrope, D., & Blackmore, E. (2003). School-based peer support groups: A new approach to the prevention of disordered eating. *Eating Disorders, 11,* 169–186.

McVey, G. L., Lieberman, M., Voorberg, N., et al. (2003). Replication of a peer support program designed to prevent disordered eating: Is a life skills approach sufficient for all middle school students? *Eating Disorders, 11,* 87–95.

McVey, G. L., Tweed, S., & Blackmore, E. (2004). Dieting among preschoolers and young adolescent females. *Canadian Medical Association Journal, 170,* 1559–1561.

McWilliams, N. (in press). Integrative research for integrative practice: A plea for respectful collaboration across clinician and researcher roles. *Journal of Psychotherapy Integration.*

Meana, M., & Jones, S. (2011). Developments and trends in sex therapy. In R. Balon (Ed.), *Sexual dysfunction: Beyond the brain-body connection. Advances in Psychosomatic Medicine, Vol. 31* (pp. 57–71). Basel: Karger.

Mednick, S. A., Huttonen, M. O., & Machon, R. A. (1994). Prenatal influenza infections and adult schizophrenia. *Schizophrenia Bulletin, 20,* 263–267.

Mednick, S. A., & Schulsinger, F. (1968). Some premorbid characteristics related to breakdown in children with schizophrenic mothers. In D. Rosenthal & S. S. Kety (Eds.), *The transmission of schizophrenia.* Elmsford, NY: Pergamon.

Meehl, P. E. (1962). Schizotaxia, schizotypy, schizophrenia. *American Psychologist, 17,* 827–838.

Meichenbaum, D. (1995). Cognitive behavioral therapy in historical perspective. In B. Bongar & L. Beutler (Eds.), *Comprehensive textbook of psychotherapy* (pp. 141–158). New York: Oxford University Press.

Meier, M. H., Caspi, A., Ambler, A., et al. (2012). Persistent cannabis uses show neuropsychological decline from childhood to midlife. *Proceedings of the National Academy of Sciences of the United States of America, 109.*

Meier, S. M., Mattheisen, M., Mors, O., Schendel, D. E., Mortensen, P. B., & Plessen, K. J. (2016). Mortality among persons with obsessive-compulsive disorder in Denmark. *JAMA Psychiatry, 73,* 268–274.

Melamed, S., et al. (2006). Burnout and risk of cardiovascular disease: Evidence, possible causal paths, and promising research. *Psychological Bulletin, 132,* 327–353.

Mello, N. K., & Mendelson, J. H. (1970). Experimentally induced intoxication in alcoholics: A comparison between programmed and spontaneous drinking. *Journal of Pharmacology and Experimental Therapy, 173,* 101.

Mellor, C. S. (1970). First rank symptoms of schizophrenia. *British Journal of Psychiatry, 117,* 15–23.

Melman, A., & Rossman, B. (1989). *Penile vein ligation for corporal incompetence: An evaluation of short and long term results.* Paper presented at the 15th Annual Meeting of the International Academy of Sex Research, Princeton. As cited in Wincze & Carey (1991).

Meltzer, H. Y. (2013). Update on typical and atypical antipsychotic drugs. *Annual Review of Medicine, 64,* 393–406.

Meltzer, H. Y., et al. (2003). Clozapine treatment for suicidality in schizophrenia: International Suicide Prevention Trial (InterSept). *Archives of General Psychiatry, 60,* 82–91.

Menary, K. R., Kushner, M. G., Maurer, E., & Thuras, P. (2011). The prevalence and clinical implications of self-medication among anxiety disorders. *Journal of Anxiety Disorders, 25,* 335–339.

Meneses, C. W., & Greenberg, L. S. (2014). Interpersonal forgiveness in emotion-focused couples' therapy: Relating process to outcome. *Journal of Marital and Family Therapy, 40,* 49–67.

Menezes, N. M., Malla, A. M., Norman, R. M., et al. (2009). A multisite Canadian perspective: Examining the functional outcome from first-episode psychosis. *Acta Psychiatrica Scandinavica, 120,* 138–146.

Meng, X., D'Arcy, C., Morgan, D., & Mousseau, D. (2013). Predicting the risk of dementia among Canadian seniors: A useable practice-friendly diagnostic algorithm. *Alzheimer Disease and Associated Disorders, 27,* 23–29.

Mental Health Commission of Canada. (2012a). *Changing directions, changing lives: The mental health strategy for Canada.* Calgary, AB: Author.

Mental Health Commission of Canada. (2012b). *Beyond housing: At Home/Chez Soi early findings report: Volume 3.* Ottawa: Mental Health Commission of Canada.

Menzies, R., & Webster, C. D. (1995). Construction and validation of risk assessments in a six-year follow-up of forensic patients: A tridimensional analysis. *Journal of Consulting and Clinical Psychology, 63,* 766–778.

Merckelbach, H., de Ruiter, C., van den Hout, M. A., & Hoekstra, R. (1989). Conditioning experiences and phobias. *Behaviour Research and Therapy, 27,* 657–662.

Merikangas, K. R., He, J. P., Burstein, M., Swanson, S. A., et al. (2010). Lifetime prevalence of mental disorders in US adolescents: results from the National Comorbidity Survey Replication–Adolescent Supplement (NCS-A). *Journal of the American Academy of Child & Adolescent Psychiatry, 49*(10), 980–989.

Merikangas, K. R., He, J. P., Burstein, M., Swendsen, J., et al. (2011). Service utilization for lifetime mental disorders in US adolescents: Results of the National Comorbidity Survey–Adolescent Supplement (NCS-A). *Journal of the American Academy of Child & Adolescent Psychiatry, 50*(1), 32–45.

Merikangas, K. R., Mehta, R. L., Molnar, B. E., et al. (1998). Comorbidity of substance use disorders with mood and anxiety disorders: Results of the International Consortium in Psychiatric Epidemiology. *Addictive Behaviors, 23,* 893–907.

Merskey, H., & Mai, F. (2005). Somatization and conversion disorders: A review. In M. Maj, H. S. Akiskal, J. E. Mezzich, & A. Okasha (Eds.), *Somatoform disorders* (pp. 1–22). Chichester, England: John Wiley & Sons.

Messer, S. B., & Abbass, A. A. (2010). Evidence-based psychodynamic therapy with personality disorders. In J. Magnavita (Ed.), *Evidence-based treatment of personality dysfunction: Principles, methods, and processes.* Washington, DC: American Psychological Association Press.

Meston, C. M., & Gorzalka, B. B. (1996). Differential effects of sympathetic activation on sexual arousal in sexually dysfunctional and functional women. *Journal of Abnormal Psychology, 105,* 582–591.

Metalsky, G. I., Joiner, T. E., Hardin, T. S., & Abramson, L. Y. (1993). Depressive reactions to failure in a natural setting: A test of the hopelessness and self-esteem theories of depression. *Journal of Abnormal Psychology, 102,* 101–109.

Metz, M. E., Pryor, J. L., Nesvacil, L. J., Abuzzahab, F., et al. (1997). Premature ejaculation: A psychophysiological review. *Journal of Sex and Marital Therapy, 23,* 3–23.

Mewton, L., Smith, J., Rossouw, P., & Andrews, G. (2014). Current perspectives on internet-delivered cognitive behavioral therapy for adults with anxiety and related disorders. *Psychology Research and Behavior Management, 7.*

Meyer, J. H., et al. (2006). Elevated monoamine oxidase A levels in the brain: An explanation of the monoamine imbalance of major depression. *Archives of General Psychiatry, 63,* 1209–1216.

Meyer, J. J., & Reter, D. J. (1979). Sex reassignment follow-up. *Archives of General Psychiatry, 36,* 1010–1015.

Meyer, V. (1966). Modification of expectations in cases with obsessional rituals. *Behaviour Research and Therapy, 4,* 273–280.

Meyers, J. (1999). *Hemingway: A biography.* New York: Da Capo Press.

Mezzich, A. C., Moss, H., Tarter, R. E., Wolfenstein, M., et al. (1994). Gender differences in the pattern and progression of substance use in conduct disordered adolescents. *American Journal on Addiction, 3,* 289–295.

Mfoafo-M'Carthy, M., & Shera, W. (2012–2013). Beyond community treatment orders: Empowering clients to achieve community integration. *International Journal of Mental Health, 41,* 62–81.

Michelson, D., Davenport, C., Dretzke, J., Barlow, J., & Day, C. (2013). Do evidence-based interventions work when tested in the "real world"? A systematic review and meta-analysis of parent management training for the treatment of child disruptive behavior. *Clinical Child and Family Psychology Review, 16,* 18–34.

Middleton, D. (2008). The development of the Internet Sex Offender Treatment Programme (I-SOTP). *Irish Probation Journal, 5, 49–64.*

Midgley, N. (2006). "Re-reading" Little Hans: Freud's case study and the question of competing paradigms in psychoanalysis. *Journal of the American Psychoanalytic Association, 54,* 537–559.

Mihura, J. L., Meyer, G. J., Dumitrascu, N., & Bombel, G. (2013). The validity of individual Rorschach variables: Systematic reviews and meta-analyses of the comprehensive system. *Psychological Bulletin, 139,* 548–605.

Miklowitz, D. J. (1985). *Family interaction and illness outcome in bipolar and schizophrenic patients.* Unpublished Ph.D. thesis, University of California at Los Angeles.

Miklowitz, D. J., Simoneau, T. L., Sachs-Ericsson, N., Warner, R., & Suddath, R. (1996). Family risk indicators in the course of bipolar affective disorder. In E. Mundt, et al. (Eds.), *Interpersonal factors in the origin and course of affective disorders* (pp. 204–217). London: Gaskell Press.

Mikolajcdyk, R. T., Brzoska, P., Maier, C., et al. (2008). Factors associated with self-rated health status in university students: A cross-sectional study in three European countries. *BMC Public Health, 18,* 215.

Mikulincer, M., Shaver, P. R., & Berant, E. (2013). An attachment perspective on therapeutic processes and outcomes. *Journal of Personality, 81,* 606–616.

Miles, L. E., & Dement, W. C. (1980). Sleep and aging. *Sleep, 3,* 119–220.

Milgram, N. W., Siwak-Tapp, C. T., Araujo, J., & Head, E. (2006). Neuroprotective effects of cognitive enrichment. *Ageing Research Reviews, 5,* 354–369.

Miller, A., Lee, S. K., Raina, P., Klassen, A., Zupancic, J., & Olsen, L. (1998). *A review of therapies for attention-deficit hyperactivity disorder.* Ottawa: Canadian Coordinating Office for Health Technology Assessment.

Miller, G. E., & Blackwell, E. (2006). Turning up the heat: Inflammation as a mechanism linking chronic stress, depression, and heart disease. *Current Directions in Psychological Science, 15,* 269–272.

Miller, G. E., Chen, E., & Zhou, E. S. (2007). If it goes up, must it come down? Chronic stress and the hypothalamic-pituitary-adrenocortical axis in humans. *Psychological Bulletin, 133,* 25–45.

Miller, J. D., & Lynam, D. R. (2015). Using self- and informant reports in the assessment of personality pathology in clinical settings—An easy and effective 1-2 combination. *Clinical Psychology: Science and Practice, 22,* 1–19.

Miller, J. L., Weiss, L. G., Beal, A. L., Saklofske, D. H., Zhu, J., & Holdnack, J. A. (2015). Intelligent use of intelligence tests: Empirical and clinical support for Canadian WAIS-IV norms. *Journal of Psychoeducational Assessment, 33,* 312–328.

Miller, J. R. (1996). *Shingwauk's vision: A history of native residential schools.* Toronto: University of Toronto Press.

Miller, M. A., & Rahe, R. H. (1997). Life changes scaling for the 1990s. *Journal of Psychosomatic Research, 43,* 279–292.

Miller, M. D., et al. (2003). The value of maintenance interpersonal psychotherapy (IPT) in older adults with different IPT foci. *American Journal of Geriatric Psychiatry, 11,* 97–102.

Miller, T. Q., & Volk, R. J. (1996). Weekly marijuana use as a risk factor for initial cocaine use: Results from a six-wave national survey. *Journal of Child and Adolescent Substance Abuse, 5,* 55–78.

Miller, T. W., Nigg, J. T., & Miller, R. L. (2009). Attention deficit disorder in African American children: What can be concluded from the past 10 years? *Clinical Psychology Review, 29,* 77–86.

Miller, W. R. (1983). Motivational interviewing with problem drinkers. *Behavioural Psychotherapy, 11,* 147–172.

Miller, W. R., & Heather, N. (1998). *Treating addictive behaviours* (2nd ed.). New York: Plenum.

Miller, W. R., & Rollnick, S. (Eds). (1991). *Motivational interviewing: Preparing people to change addictive behavior.* New York: Guilford.

Miller, W. R., & Rollnick, S. (2002). *Motivational interviewing: Preparing people for change* (2nd ed.). New York: Guilford.

Millon, T. (1986). Personality prototypes and their diagnostic criteria. In T. Millon & G. L. Klerman (Eds.), *Contemporary directions in psychopathology.* New York: Guilford.

Millon, T. (1996). *Disorders of personality: DSM-IV and beyond* (2nd ed.). New York: John Wiley & Sons.

Millon, T., & Davis, R. (2000). *Personality disorders in modern life.* New York: Wiley.

Millon, T., Davis, R., Millon, C., & Grossman, S. (2009). The Millon Clinical Multiaxial Inventory—III, Third Edition (MCMI-III) (2009) with new norms and updated scoring. New York: Pearson.

Millon, T., & Grossman, S. (2007). *Moderating severe personality disorders: A personalized psychotherapy approach.* Hoboken, NJ: John Wiley & Sons.

Millon, T., Grossman, S., & Millon, C. (2015). *Millon Clinical Multiaxial Inventory-IV.* London: Pearson.

Mills, J. A. (1997). Lessons from the periphery: Psychiatry in Saskatchewan, Canada, 1944-68. *History of Psychiatry, 18,* 179–201.

Mills, J. F., Anderson, D., & Kroner, D. G. (2004). The antisocial attitudes and associates of sex offenders. *Criminal Behavior and Mental Health, 14,* 134–145.

Mills, J. S., Polivy, J., Herman, C. P., & Tiggemann, M. (2002). Effects of exposure to thin media images: Evidence of self-enhancement among restrained eaters. *Personality and Social Psychology Bulletin, 28,* 1687–1699.

Milosevic, I., & McCabe, R. E. (2015). *Phobias: The psychology of irrational fear. An encyclopedia.* Santa Barbara, CA: ABC-Clio.

Milrod, B., Leon, A. C., & Busch, F. (2007). A randomized controlled clinical trial of psychoanalytic psychotherapy for panic disorder. *American Journal of Psychiatry, 164,* 265–272.

Milroy, S. (2009, July 13). "They were looking for the ideal Manchurian candidate." *The Globe and Mail.*

Minde, K., Eakin, L., Hechtman, L., Ochs, E., Bouffard, R., Greenfield, B., et al. (2003). The psychosocial functioning of children and spouses of adults with ADHD. *Journal of Child Psychology and Psychiatry and Allied Disciplines, 44*, 637–646.

Mineka, S. (1992). Evolutionary memories, emotional processing, and the emotional disorders. *The Psychology of Learning and Motivation, 28*, 161–206.

Mineka, S., & Oehlberg, K. (2008). The relevance of recent developments in classical conditioning to understanding the etiology and maintenance of anxiety disorders. *Acta Psychologia, 127*, 567–580.

Mineka, S., & Zinbarg, R. (1996). Perspectives on anxiety, panic, and fear. In *Nebraska symposium on motivation* (pp. 135–210). Lincoln, NE: University of Nebraska Press.

Mintz, A. R., Dobson, K. S., & Romney, D. M. (2003). Insight in schizophrenia: A meta-analysis. *Schizophrenia Research, 61*, 75–88.

Minuchin, S., Baker, L., Rosman, B. L., Lieberman, R., Milman, L., & Todd, T. C. (1975). A conceptual model of psychosomatic illness in children. *Archives of General Psychiatry, 32*, 1031–1038.

Miranda, R., Ray, L., Justus, A., et al. (2010). Initial evidence of an association between OPRM1 and adolescent alcohol misuse. *Alcoholism Clinical and Experimental Research, 34*, 112–122.

Mireault, M., & De Man, A. F. (1996). Suicidal ideation among the elderly: Personality variables, stress and social support. *Social Behavior and Personality, 24*, 385–392.

Mirenda, P. L., Donnellan, A. M., & Yoder, D. E. (1983). Gaze behavior: A new look at an old problem. *Journal of Autism and Developmental Disorders, 13*, 397–409.

Mirsky, A. F., Bieliauskas, L. A., French, L. M., Van Kammen, D. P., Jonsson, E., & Sedvall, G. (2000). A 39-year followup of the Genain quadruplets. *Schizophrenia Bulletin, 26*, 699–708.

Misri, S. (2007). Suffering in silence: The burden of perinatal depression. *Canadian Journal of Psychiatry, 52*, 477–478.

Mitchell, J. E., Agras, S., & Wonderlich, S. (2007). Treatment of bulimia nervosa: Where are we and where are we going? *International Journal of Eating Disorders, 40*, 95–101.

Mitchell, J. H., Newall, C., Broeren, S., & Hudson, J. L. (2013). The role of perfectionism in cognitive behaviour therapy outcomes for clinically anxious children. *Behaviour Research and Therapy, 51*, 547–554.

Mitchell, S. R., Reiss, A. L., Tatusko, D. H., et al. (2009). Neuroanatomic alterations and social and communication deficits in monozygotic twins discordant for autism disorder. *American Journal of Psychiatry, 166*, 917–925.

Mittleman, M. A., Maclure, M., Sherwood, J. B., Murly, R. P., Tofler, G. A., et al. (1997). Triggering of acute myocardial infarction onset by episodes of anger. *Circulation, 92*, 1720–1725.

Miziou, S., Tsitsipa, E., Moysidou, S., Karavelas, V., Dimelis, D., Polyzoidou, V., & Fountoulakis, K. N. (2015). Psychosocial treatment and interventions for bipolar disorder: A systematic review. *Annals of General Psychiatry, 14*, 19.

Mobley, A. K. (2008). College student depression: Counseling Billy. *Journal of College Counseling, 11*, 87–96.

Modin, B., Ostberg, V., & Almquist, Y. (2011). Childhood peer status and adult susceptibility to anxiety and depression: A 30-year hospital follow-up. *Journal of Abnormal Child Psychology, 39*, 187–199.

Moeller, S. J., Tomassi, D., Woicik, P. A., Maloney, T., et al. (2012). Enhanced midbrain response at 6-month follow-up in cocaine addiction: Association with reduced drug-related choice. *Addiction Biology, 17*, 1013–1025.

Moffitt, T. E. (1993). Adolescence-limited and life-course-persistent antisocial behavior: A developmental taxonomy. *Psychological Review, 100*, 674–701.

Moffitt, T. E. (2003). Life-course persistent and adolescent-limited antisocial behavior: A 10-year research review and research agenda. In B. Lahey, T. E. Moffitt, & A. Caspi (Eds.), *The causes of conduct disorder and serious juvenile delinquency* (pp. 49–75). New York: Guilford.

Moffitt, T. E., Caspi, A., Harrington, H., & Milne, B. (2002). Males on the life-course persistent and adolescence-limited antisocial pathways: Follow-up at age 26. *Development and Psychopathology, 14*, 179–207.

Moffitt, T. E., Caspi, A., & Rutter, M. (2006). Measured gene–environment interactions in psychopathology: Concepts, research strategies, and implications for research, intervention, and public understanding of genetics. *Perspectives on Psychological Science, 1*, 5–27.

Moffitt, T. E., Lynam, D., & Silva, P. A. (1994). Neuropsychological tests predict persistent male delinquency. *Criminology, 32*, 101–124.

Mohler, H. (2012). The GABA system in anxiety and depression and its therapeutic potential. *Neuropharmacology, 62*, 42–53.

Monahan, J. (1992). Mental disorder and violent behavior: Perceptions and evidence. *American Psychologist, 47*, 511–521.

Monahan, J., et al. (2001). *Rethinking violence risk assessment: The MacArthur Study of Mental Disorder and Violence.* New York: Oxford University Press.

Moncrieff, J. (2007a). In debate: Are antidepressants as effective as claimed? No, they are not effective at all. *Canadian Journal of Psychiatry, 52*, 96–97.

Moncrieff, J. (2007b). In debate: Rebuttal: Depression is not a brain disease. *Canadian Journal of Psychiatry, 52*, 100–101.

Moncrieff, J., & Kirsch, I. (2005). Efficacy of antidepressants in adults. *British Medical Journal, 331*, 155–157.

Mongrain, M., & Blackburn, S. (2005). Cognitive vulnerability, lifetime risk, and the recurrence of major depression in graduate students. *Cognitive Therapy and Research, 29*, 747–768.

Mongrain, M., & Leather, F. (2006). Immature dependence and self-criticism predict the recurrence of major depression. *Journal of Clinical Psychology, 62*, 705–713.

Mongrain, M., & Zuroff, D. C. (1994). Ambivalence over emotional expression and negative life events: Mediators for depression in dependent and self-critical individuals. *Personality and Individual Differences, 16*, 447–458.

Moñiz, E. (1936). *Tentatives operatoires dans le traitement de certaines psychoses.* Paris: Mason.

Monnier, J., Lydiard, R. B., & Brawman-Mintzer, O. (2003). Anxiety disorders: Generalized anxiety disorder. In A. Tasman, J. Kay, & J. A. Lieberman (Eds.), *Psychiatry* (2nd ed., pp. 1380–1404). New York: John Wiley & Sons.

Monroe, S. M., & Simons, A. D. (1991). Diathesis-stress theories in the context of life stress research: Implications for the depressive disorders. *Psychological Bulletin, 110*, 406–425.

Monsebraaten, L., & Talaga, T. (2009, May 7). "Historic" law compels Ontario to fight poverty: Requires the province to create goals to cut numbers living in need. *Toronto Star*, A11.

Monzani, B., Rijsdijk, F., Harris, J., & Mataix-Cols, D. (2014). The structure of genetic and environmental risk factors for dimensional representations of DSM-5 obsessive-compulsive spectrum disorders. *JAMA Psychiatry, 71*, 182–189.

Monzani, B., Rijsdijk, F., Iervolino, I. C., Anson, M., Cherkas, L., & Mataix-Cois, D. (2012). Evidence for a genetic overlap between body dysmorphic disorder concerns and obsessive-compulsive symptoms in an adult female community twin study. *American Journal of Medical Genetics Part B: Neuropsychiatric Genetics, 159B*, 376–382.

Moore, B. A., et al. (2005). Respiratory effects of marijuana and tobacco use in a U.S. sample. *Journal of General Internal Medicine, 20*, 33–37.

Moore, D. (2007, January 8). Brainwashed "guinea pig" seeks more damages. *The Toronto Star*.

Morain, D. (1998). New state TV ads link smoking to impotence in men. *Los Angeles Times*, A3–A18.

Morenz, B., & Becker, J. V. (1995). The treatment of youthful sexual offenders. *Applied and Preventive Psychology, 4*, 247–256.

Moretti, M. M., Emmrys, C., Grizenko, N., et al. (1997). The treatment of conduct disorders: Perspectives from across Canada. *Canadian Journal of Psychiatry, 42*, 637–648.

Moretti, M. M., Segal, Z. V., McCann, C. D., Shaw, B. F., Miller, D. T., & Vella, D. (1996). Self-referent versus other-referent information processing in dysphoric, clinically depressed, and remitted depressed subjects. *Personality and Social Psychology Bulletin, 22*, 68–80.

Morey, L. C. (1988). Personality disorders in DSM-III and DSM-IIIR: Convergence, coverage, and internal consistency. *American Journal of Psychiatry, 145*, 573–577.

Morey, L. C., & Hopwood, C. J. (2013). Stability and change in personality disorders. *Annual Review of Clinical Psychology, 9*, 12.1–12.31.

Morey, L. C., & Skodol, A. (2013). Convergence between DSM-IV-TR and DSM-5 diagnostic models for personality disorder: Evaluation of strategies for establishing diagnostic thresholds. *Journal of Psychiatric Practice, 19*, 179–193.

Morey, L. C., Waugh, M. H., & Blashfield, R. K. (1985). MMPI scales for DSM-III personality disorders: Their derivation and correlates. *Journal of Personality Assessment, 49*, 245–251.

Morgan, P. L., Staff, J., Hillemeier, M. M., et al. (2013). Racial and ethnic disparities in ADHD diagnosis from kindergarten to eighth grade. *Pediatrics, 132*, 85–93.

Moriconi, P.-A., Nadeau, L., & Demers, A. (2012). Drinking habits of older Canadians: A comparison of the 1994 and 2004 national surveys. *Canadian Journal on Aging, 31*, 379–393.

Morin, C. M. (1993). *Insomnia: Psychological assessment and management*. New York: Guilford.

Morin, C. M., et al. (2006). Psychological and behavioral treatment of insomnia: Update of the recent evidence (1998–2004). *Sleep, 29*, 1398–1414.

Morin, C. M., Bastien, C. H., Brink, D., & Brown, T. R. (2003). Adverse effects of temazepam in older adults with chronic insomnia. *Human Psychopharmacology, 18*, 75–82.

Morin, C. M., Bélanger, L., LeBlanc, M., Ivers, H., Savard, J., Espie, C. A., ... Grégoire, J. P. (2009). The natural history of insomnia: A population-based three-year longitudinal study. *Archives of Internal Medicine, 169*, 447–453.

Morin, C. M., & Benca, R. (2012). Chronic insomnia. *The Lancet, 379*, 1129–1141.

Morin, C. M., Blais, F., & Savard, J. (2002). Are changes in beliefs and attitudes about sleep related to sleep improvements in the treatment of insomnia? *Behaviour Research and Therapy, 40*, 741–752.

Morin, C. M., Colecchi, C., Stone, J., Sood, R., & Brink, D. (1999). Behavioral and pharmacological therapies for late-life insomnia: A randomized controlled trial. *Journal of the American Medical Association, 281*, 991–999.

Morin, C. M., & Gramling, S. E. (1989). Sleep patterns and aging: Comparisons of older adults with and without insomnia complaints. *Psychology and Aging, 4*, 290–294.

Morin, C. M., LeBlanc, M., Bélanger, L., Ivers, H., Mérette, C., & Savard, J. (2011). Prevalence of insomnia and its treatment in Canada. *Canadian Journal of Psychiatry, 56*, 540–548.

Morin, C. M.,Vallières, A., Guay, B., et al. (2009). Cognitive behavioral therapy, singly and combined with medication, for persistent insomnia: A randomized controlled trial. *Journal of the American Medical Association, 301*, 2005–2015.

Moritz, S., Von Muhlenen, A., Randjbar, S., Fricke, S., & Jelinek, L. (2009). Evidence for an attentional bias for washing- and checking-relevant stimuli in obsessive-compulsive disorder. *Journal of the International Neuropsychologial Society, 15*, 365–371.

Moroney, J. T., et al. (1999). Low-density lipoprotein cholesterol and the risk of dementia with stroke. *Journal of the American Medical Association, 282*, 254–260.

Morris, A. A. (1968). *Criminal insanity. Washington Review, 43*, 583–622.

Morris, S. H., Jaffee, S. R., Goodwin, G. P., & Franklin, M. E. (in press). Hoarding in children and adolescents: A review. *Child Psychiatry and Human Development*.

Morse, R. M. (1988). Substance abuse among the elderly. *Bulletin of the Menninger Clinic, 52*, 259–268.

Morse, S. J. (1992). The "guilty mind": Mens rea. In D. K. Kagehiro & W. S. Lanfer (Eds.), *Handbook of psychology and law* (pp. 207–229). New York: Springer-Verlag.

Mortimer, J. A. (2012). The Nun Study: Risk factors for pathology and clinical-pathologic correlates. *Current Alzheimer Research, 9*, 621–627.

Moscovitch, D. A. (2009). What is the core fear in social phobia? A new model to facilitate individualized case conceptualization and treatment. *Cognitive and Behavioral Practice, 16*, 123–134.

Moscovitch, D. A., Orr, E., Rowa, K., Reimer, S. G., & Antony, M. (2009). In the absence of rose-colored glasses: Ratings of self-attributes and their differential certainty and importance across multiple dimensions in social phobia. *Behaviour Research and Therapy, 47*, 66–70.

Moscovitch, D. A., Waechter, S., Bielak, T., Rowa, K., & McCabe, R. E. (2015). Out of the shadows and into the spotlight: Social blunders fuel fear of self-exposure in social anxiety disorder. *Journal of Anxiety Disorders, 34*, 24–32.

Moser, C., & Levitt, E. E. (1987). An exploratory-descriptive study of a sadomasochistically oriented sample. *Journal of Sex Research, 23*, 322–337.

Moser, P. W. (1989, January). Double vision: Why do we never match up to our mind's ideal? *Self Magazine*, 51–52.

Moses, J. A., & Purisch, A. D. (1997). The evolution of the Luria-Nebraska Battery. In G. Goldstein & T. Incagnoli (Eds.), *Contemporary approaches to neuropsychological assessment* (pp. 131–170). New York: Plenum.

Mosier, K. E., et al. (2010). Prevalence of mental disorders and service utilization in seniors: Results from the Canadian Community Health Survey cycle 1.2. *International Journal of Geriatric Psychiatry* (early view online).

Moss, D., & Redelmeier, D. A. (2010). Outcomes following appeal and reversal of civil commitment. *General Hospital Psychiatry, 32*, 94–98.

Moulding, R., Coles, M. E., Abramowitz, J. S., Alcolado, G. M., Alonso, P., Belloch, A., . . . Wong, W. (2014). Part 2. They scare because we care: The relationship between obsessive intrusive thoughts and appraisals and control strategies across 15 cities. *Journal of Obsessive-Compulsive and Related Disorders, 3*, 280–291.

Moyers, T. B., & Houck, J. (2011). Combining motivational interviewing with cognitive-behavioral treatments for substance abuse: Lessons from the COMBINE research project. *Cognitive and Behavioral Practice, 18*, 38–45.

Moylan, C. A., Herrenkohl, T. I., Sousa, C., Tajima, E. A., Herrenkohl, R. C., & Russo, M. J. (2010). The effects of child abuse and exposure to domestic violence on adolescent internalizing and externalizing behavior problems. *Journal of Family Violence, 25*, 53–63.

MTA Cooperative Group. (1999). A 14-month randomized clinical trial of treatment strategies for attention-deficit/hyperactivity disorder. *Archives of General Psychiatry, 56*, 1073–1086.

Muehlenkamp, J. J., Claes, L., Havertape, L., & Plener, P. L. (2012). International prevalence of adolescent non-suicidal self-injury and deliberate self-harm. *Child and Adolescent Psychiatry and Mental Health, 6*, 10.

Mueller, A., Mitchell, J., Crosby, R., Glaesmer, H., & de Zwaan, M. (2009). The prevalence of compulsive hoarding and its association with compulsive buying in a German population-based sample. *Behaviour Research and Therapy, 47*, 705–709.

Mueser, K. T., Deavers, F., Penn, D. L., & Cassisi, J. (2013). Psychosocial treatments for schizophrenia. *Annual Review of Clinical Psychology, 19*, 25.1–25.33.

Mueser, K. T., Penn, D. L., Addington, J., Brunette, M. F., et al. (2015). The NAVIGATE Program for First-Episode Psychosis: Rationale, overview, and description of psychosocial components. *Psychiatric Services, 66*, 680–690.

Muller, D. J., et al. (2006). Brain-derived neurotrophic factor (BDNF) gene and rapid-cycling bipolar disorder: Family-based association study. *British Journal of Psychiatry, 189*, 317–323.

Muller, J., & Roberts, J. E. (2005). Memory and attention in obsessive-compulsive disorder: A review. *Journal of Anxiety Disorders, 19*, 1–28.

Muller, R. T., Goh, H. H., Lemieux, K. E., & Fish, S. (2000). The social supports of high-risk, formerly maltreated adults. *Canadian Journal of Behavioural Science, 32*, 1–5.

Mullins, N., Power, R. A., Fisher, H. L., Hanscombe, K. B., Euesden, J., Iniesta, R., . . . Lewis, C. M. (2016). Polygenic interactions with environmental adversity in the aetiology of major depressive disorder. *Psychological Medicine, 46*, 759–770.

Mulveen, R., & Hepworth, J. (2006). An interpretive phenomenological analysis of participation in a pro-anorexia internet site and its relationship with disordered eating. *Journal of Health Psychology, 11*, 283–296.

Mulvey, E. P. (1994). Assessing the evidence of a link between mental illness and violence. *Hospital and Community Psychiatry, 45*, 663–668.

Munafò, M., Brown, S., & Hariri, A. (2008). Serotonin transporter (5-HTTLPR) genotype and amygdale activation: A meta-analysis. *Biological Psychiatry, 63*, 852–857.

Murdoch, D., Pihl, R. O., & Ross, D. (1990). Alcohol and crimes of violence: Present issues. *International Journal of Addiction, 25*, 1059–1075.

Muris, P., & Ollendick, T. H. (2015). Children who are anxious in silence: A review of selective mutism, the new anxiety disorder in *DSM-5. Clinical Child and Family Psychology Review, 18*, 151–169.

Muroff, J., Steketee, G., Frost, R. O., & Tolin, D. F. (2014). Cognitive behavior therapy for hoarding disorder: Follow-up findings and predictors of outcome. *Depression and Anxiety, 31*, 964–971.

Murphy, J. A., & Byrne, G. J. (2012). Prevalence and correlates of the proposed DSM-5 diagnosis of chronic depressive disorder. *Journal of Affective Disorders, 139*, 172–180.

Murphy, R., Cooper, Z., Hollon, S. D., & Fairburn, C. G. (2009). How do psychological treatments work? Investigating mediators of change. *Behaviour Research and Therapy, 47*, 1–5.

Murphy, W. D. (1997). Exhibitionism: Psychopathology and theory. In D. R. Laws & W. O'Donohue (Eds.), *Sexual deviance* (pp. 22–39). New York: Guilford.

Murray, L., Creswell, C., & Cooper, P. J. (2009). The development of anxiety disorders in childhood: An integrative review. *Psychological Medicine, 39*, 1413–1423.

Murthi, M., Servaty-Seib, H. L., & Elliott, A. N. (2006). Childhood sexual abuse and multiple dimensions of self-concept. *Journal of Interpersonal Violence, 21*, 982–999.

Muse, K., & McManus, F. (2016). Expert insight into the assessment of competence in cognitive–behavioural therapy: A qualitative exploration of experts' experiences, opinions and recommendations. *Clinical Psychology and Psychotherapy, 23*, 246–259.

Mustelin, L., Silen, Y., Raevuori, A., Hoek, H. W., Kaprio, J., & Keski-Rahkonen, A. (2016). The *DSM-5* diagnostic criteria for anorexia nervosa may change its population prevalence and prognostic value. *Journal of Psychiatric Research, 77*, 85–91.

Myers, J. K., et al. (1984). Six-month prevalence of psychiatric disorders in three communities: 1980–1982. *Archives of General Psychiatry, 41*, 959–967.

Myers, M. G., Stewart, D. G., & Brown, S. A. (1998). Progression from conduct disorder to antisocial personality disorder following treatment for adolescent substance abuse. *American Journal of Psychiatry, 155*, 479–485.

Myers, N. A. L. (2012). Toward an applied neuroanthropology of psychosis: The interplay of cultures, brains, and experience. *Annals of Anthropological Practice, 36*, 113–130.

Myers, N. L. (2011). Update: Schizophrenia across cultures. *Current Psychiatry Reports, 13*, 305–311.

Myers, S. M., Johnson, C., & the Council on Children with Disabilities. (2007). Management of children with autism spectrum disorders. *Pediatrics, 120*, 1162–1182.

Nagin, D. S., & Odgers, C. L. (2010). Group-based trajectory modeling in clinical research. *Annual Review of Clinical Psychology, 6*, 109–138.

Nagin, D. S., & Tremblay, R. E. (2001). Parental and early childhood predictors of persistent physical aggression in boys from kindergarten to high school. *Archives of General Psychiatry, 58*, 389–394.

Nakao, T., Nakagawa, A., Yoshiura, T., et al. (2009). Duration effect of obsessive-compulsive disorder on cognitive function: A functional MRI study. *Depression and Anxiety, 26*, 814–823.

Nakoneczny, R. (2010). *Put your mind to it.* Toronto: Alzheimer Society of Canada.

Nam, S. K., et al. (2013). Psychological factors in college students; attitudes toward seeking professional help: A meta-analysis. *Professional Psychology: Research and Practice, 44*, 37–45.

Naragon-Gainey, K. (2010). Meta-analysis of the relations of anxiety sensitivity to the depressive and anxiety disorders. *Psychological Bulletin, 136*, 128–150.

Nasrallah, H. A. (2012). Psychiatry and the politics of incarceration. *Current Psychiatry, 11*, 4–5.

Nathan, P. E., & Gorman, J. M. (1998). *Treatments that work.* New York: Oxford University Press.

Nathan, P. E., & Langenbucher, J. W. (1999). Psychopathology: Description and classification. *Annual Review of Psychology, 50*, 79–107.

Nathan, P. E., Stuart, S. P., & Dolan, S. L. (2000). Research on psychotherapy efficacy and effectiveness: Between Scylla and Charybdis? *Psychological Bulletin, 126*, 964–981.

National Advisory Council on Aging. (1999). 1999 and beyond: Challenges of an aging Canadian population. Ottawa: National Advisory Council on Aging.

National Center for PTSD. (2016.) PTSD: National Center for PTSD. Retrieved from http://www.ptsd.va.gov/about/mission/education/dissemination_education_within_the_va.asp.

National Council of Welfare. (Fall 2007). *First Nations, Métis and Inuit children and youth: Time to act*, Volume 127. Ottawa: Author.

National Film Board of Canada. (1996). *The sterilization of Leilani Muir.* Retrieved from onf-nfb.gc.ca/en/our-collection/?idfilm-33077.

Neale, J. M., & Liebert, R. M. (1980). *Science and behavior: An introduction to methods of research.* Englewood Cliffs, NJ: Prentice-Hall.

Neale, J. M., & Oltmanns, T. (1980). *Schizophrenia.* New York: John Wiley & Sons.

Neckelmann, D. (1996). Treatment of chronic insomnia and recommendations with special emphasis on problems of the elderly. *Tidsskr Nor Laegeforen, 10,* 854–859.

Neighbors, C., Larimer, M. E., Lostutter, T. W., & Woods, B. A. (2006). Harm reduction and individually focused alcohol prevention. *International Journal of Drug Policy, 17,* 304–309.

Neil, A. L., & Christensen, H. (2009). Efficacy and effectiveness of school-based prevention and early intervention programs for anxiety. *Clinical Psychology Review, 29,* 208–215.

Neimeyer, R. A., & Raskin, J. D. (2001). Varieties of constructivism in psychotherapy. In K. S. Dobson (Ed.), *Handbook of cognitive-behavioral therapies* (2nd ed., pp. 393–430). New York: Guilford.

Nelson, A. L., Vorstenbosch, V., & Antony, M. M. (2014). Assessing fear of storms and severe weather: Validation of the storm fear questionnaire (SFQ). *Journal of Psychopathology and Behavioral Assessment, 36,* 105–114.

Nelson, G., Lavoie, L., & Mitchell, T. (2007). The history and theories of community psychology in Canada. In S. M. Reich, M. Reimer, I. Prilletensky, & M. Montero (Eds.), *International community psychology: History and theories* (pp. 13–36). New York: Springer-Verlag.

Nelson, J. C., & Davis, J. M. (1997). DST studies in psychotic depression: A meta-analysis. *American Journal of Psychiatry, 154,* 1497–1503.

Nelson, J. C., Delucchi, K., & Schneider, L. (2008). Efficacy of second-generation antidepressants in late-life depression: A meta-analysis of the evidence. *American Journal of Geriatric Psychiatry, 16,* 558–567.

Nelson, M. D., et al. (1998). Hippocampal volume reduction in schizophrenia as assessed by magnetic resonance imaging: A meta-analytic study. *Archives of General Psychiatry, 55,* 443–440.

Nelson, N. W., Sweet, J. J., & Demakis, G. J. (2006). Meta-analysis of the MMPI-2 Fake Bad Scale: Utility in forensic practice. *Clinical Neuropsychologist, 20,* 39–58.

Nemeroff, C. B., & Goldschmidt-Clermont, P. J. (2012). Heartache and heartbreak: The link between depression and cardiovascular disease. *Nature Reviews Cardiology, 9,* 526–539.

Nemeroff, C. J., & Karoly, P. (1991). Operant methods. In F. H. Kanfer & A. P. Goldstein (Eds.), *Helping people change: A textbook of methods* (4th ed.). Elmsford, NY: Pergamon.

Nemeth, M. (1995, June 26). "Nobody has the right to play God." Sterilized Alberta, Canada woman sues the government. *Maclean's.*

Nepon, T., Flett, G. L., & Hewitt, P. L. (in press). Self-image goals in trait perfectionism and perfectionistic self-presentation: Toward a broader understanding of the drives and motives of perfectionists. *Self and Identity.*

Nepon, T., Flett, G. L., Hewitt, P. L., & Molnar, D. (2011). Perfectionism, negative social feedback, and interpersonal rumination in depression and social anxiety. *Canadian Journal of Behavioural Science, 43,* 297–308.

Nestadt, G., Costa, P. T., Jr., Hsu, F. C., Samuels, J., Bienvenu, O. J., & Eaton, W. W. (2008). The relationship between the five-factor model and latent *Diagnostic and Statistical Manual of Mental Disorders, Fourth Edition* personality disorder dimensions. *Comprehensive Psychiatry, 49,* 98–105.

Nestadt, G., Romanoski, A., Chahal, R., Merchant, A., et al. (1990). An epidemiological study of histrionic personality disorder. *Psychological Medicine, 20,* 413–422.

Neufeld, R. W. J. (1999). Dynamic differentials of stress and coping. *Psychological Review, 106,* 385–397.

Neugebauer, R. (1979). Mediaeval and early modern theories of mental illness. *Archives of General Psychiatry, 36,* 477–484.

Neumeister, A., et al. (2005). Reduced hippocampal volume in unmedicated, remitted patients with major depression versus control subjects. *Biological Psychiatry, 57*(8), 935–937.

Newman, D. L., Moffitt, T. E., Caspi, A., & Silva, P. A. (1998). Comorbid mental disorders: Implications for treatment and sample selection. *Journal of Abnormal Psychology, 107,* 305–311.

Newman, J. P., Patterson, C. M., & Kosson, D. S. (1987). Response perseveration in psychopaths. *Journal of Abnormal Psychology, 96,* 145–148.

Newman, J. P., Schmitt, W. A., & Voss, W. D. (1997). The impact of motivationally neutral cues on psychopathic individuals: Assessing the generality of the response modulation hypothesis. *Journal of Abnormal Psychology, 196,* 563–575.

Newman, N., Ryan, P., LeMasters, G., Levin, L., et al. (2013). Traffic-related air pollution exposure in the first year of life and behavioral scores at seven years of age. *Environmental Health Perspectives, 121,* 731–738.

Newman, S. C., Bland, R. C., & Orn, H. T. (1998). The prevalence of mental disorders in the elderly in Edmonton: A community survey using GMS-AGECAT. *Canadian Journal of Psychiatry, 43,* 910–914.

Newth, S., & Rachman, S. (2001). The concealment of obsessions. *Behaviour Research and Therapy, 39,* 457–464.

Newton-Cheh, C., et al. (2009). Genome-wide association study identifies eight loci associated with blood pressure. *Nature Genetics, 41,* 666–676.

Newton-Howes, G., & Wood, R. (2013). Cognitive behavioural therapy and the psychopathology of schizophrenia: Systematic review and meta-analysis. *Psychology and Psychotherapy, 86,* 127–138.

Newton-Taylor, B., DeWit, D., & Gliksman, L. (1998). Prevalence and factors associated with physical and sexual assault of female university students in Ontario. *Health Care for Women International, 19,* 155–164.

Nezu, A. M., Nezu, C. M., Friedman, S. H., Faddis, S., & Houts, P. S. (1998). *Helping cancer patients cope: A problem-solving approach.* Washington, DC: American Psychological Association.

Ng, E., Pottie, K., & Spitzer, D. (2011). Official language proficiency and self-reported health among immigrants to Canada. *Health Reports, 22,* 15–23.

Nicholls, T. L., Ogloff, J. R. P., Brink, J., & Spidel, A. (2005). Psychopathy in women: A review of its clinical usefulness for assessing risk for aggression and criminality. *Behavioral Sciences and the Law, 23,* 779–802.

Nichols, M. (with S. Doyle Driedger & D. Ballon). (1995, January 30). Schizophrenia: Hidden torment. *Maclean's,* 70–74.

Nichter, M. (2000). *Fat talk: What girls and their parents say about dieting.* Cambridge, MA: Harvard University Press.

Nicolosi, A., et al. (2006). Sexual activity, sexual disorders, and associated help-seeking behaviour among mature adults in five Anglophone countries from the Global Survey of Sexual Attitudes and Behaviors (GSSAB). *Journal of Sex and Marital Therapy, 32,* 331–342.

Nicolson, R., & Szatmari, P. (2003). Genetic and neurodevelopmental influences in autistic disorder. *Canadian Journal of Psychiatry, 48,* 526–537.

Niedhammer, I., Goldberg, M., Leclerc, A., David, S., et al. (1998). Psychosocial work environment and cardiovascular risk factors in an occupational cohort in France. *Journal of Epidemiology and Community Health, 52,* 93–100.

Nigg, J. T. (2012). Future directions in ADHD etiology research. *Journal of Clinical Child and Adolescent Psychology, 41,* 524–533.

Nigg, J. T., & Goldsmith, H. H. (1994). Genetics of personality disorders: Perspectives from personality and psychopathology research. *Psychological Bulletin, 115*, 346–380.

Nimgaonkar, V. L., Fujiwara, T. M., Dutta, M., Wood, J., Gentry, K., Maendel, S., et al. (2000). Low prevalence of psychoses among the Hutterites, an isolated religious community. *American Journal of Psychiatry, 157*, 1065–1070.

Nisbett, R. E., Aronson, J., Blair, C., Dickens, W., Flynn, J., Halpern, D. F., & Turkheimer, E. (2012). Intelligence: New findings and theoretical developments. *American Psychologist, 67*, 130–159.

Nitschke, J., Blendl, V., Ottermann, B., Osterhelder, M., & Mokros, A. (2009). Severe sexual sadism—an underdiagnosed disorder? Evidence from a sample of forensic inpatients. *Journal of Forensic Sciences, 54*, 685–691.

Nitschke, J. B., Sarinopoulos, I., Oathes, D. J., Johnstone, T., et al. (2009). Anticipatory activation in the anterior cingulate in generalized anxiety disorder and prediction of treatment responses. *American Journal of Psychiatry, 166*, 302–310.

Nixon, M. J., Cloutier, P., & Jansson, S. M. (2008). Nonsuicidal self-harm in youth: A population-based survey. *Canadian Medical Association Journal, 178*, 306–312.

Nobel, R., Manassis, K., & Wilansky-Trainor, P. (2012). The role of perfectionism in relation to an intervention to reduce anxious and depressive symptoms in children. *Journal of Rational-Emotive and Cognitive-Behavior Therapy, 30*, 77–90.

Nock, M. K., & Kessler, R. C. (2006). Prevalence of and risk factors for suicide attempts versus suicide gestures: Analysis of the National Comorbidity Survey. *Journal of Abnormal Psychology, 115*, 616–623.

Nock, M. K., & Prinstein, M. J. (2004). A functional approach to the assessment of self-mutilative behavior. *Journal of Consulting and Clinical Psychology, 72*, 885–890.

Nock, M. K., Teper, R., & Hollander, M. (2007). Psychological treatment of self-injury among adolescents. *Journal of Clinical Psychology, 63*, 1081–1089.

Nolen-Hoeksema, S. (2002). Gender differences in depression. In I. H. Gotlib & C. Hammen (Eds.), *Handbook of depression* (pp. 492–509). New York: Guilford.

Nolen-Hoeksema, S., & Girgus, J. S. (1994). The emergence of gender differences in depression during adolescence. *Psychological Bulletin, 115*, 424–443.

Nolen-Hoeksema, S., Larson, J., & Grayson, C. (1999). Explaining the gender difference in depressive symptoms. *Journal of Personality and Social Psychology, 77*, 1061–1072.

Nopoulos, P., Flaum, M., & Andreasen, N. C. (1997). Sex differences in brain morphology in schizophrenia. *American Journal of Psychiatry, 154*, 1648–1654.

Norcross, J. C., & Karpiak, C. P. (2012). Clinical psychologists in the 2010s: 50 years of the APA division of clinical psychology. *Clinical Psychology: Science and Practice, 19*, 1–12.

Norcross, J. C., Karpiak, C. P., & Lister, K. M. (2005). What's an integrationist? A study of self-identified integrative and (occasionally) eclectic psychologists. *Journal of Clinical Psychology, 61*, 1587–1594.

Norcross, J. C., Nolan, B. M., Kosman, D. C., & Fernandez-Alvarez, H. (in press). Redefining the future of SEPI: Member characteristics, integrative practices, and organizational satisfactions. *Journal of Psychotherapy Integration.*

Nordgreen, T., Haug, T., Öst, L., Andersson, G., Carlbring, P., Kvale, G., . . . Havik, O. E. (2016). Stepped care versus direct face-to-face cognitive behavior therapy for social anxiety disorder and panic disorder: A randomized effectiveness trial. *Behavior Therapy, 47*, 166–183.

Nordsletten, A. E., Fernández de la Cruz, L., Billotti, D., & Mataix-Cols, D. (2013). Finders keepers: The features differentiating hoarding disorder from normative collecting. *Comprehensive Psychiatry, 54*, 229–237.

Nordsletten, A. E., Monzani, B., Fernández de la Cruz, L., Iervolino, A. C., Fullana, M. A., Harris, J., . . . Mataix-Cols, D. (2013). Overlap and specificity of genetic and environmental influences on excessive acquisition and difficulties discarding possessions: Implications for hoarding disorder. *American Journal of Medical Genetics Part B: Neuropsychiatric Genetics, 162*, 380–387.

Nordt, C., Rossler, W., & Lauber, C. (2006). Attitudes of mental health professionals toward people with schizophrenia and major depression. *Schizophrenia Bulletin, 32*, 709–714.

Norko, M., & Baranoski, M. V. (2005). The state of contemporary risk assessment research. *Canadian Journal of Psychiatry, 50*, 18–26.

Norman, R. M. G., et al. (2002). An evaluation of a stress management program for individuals with schizophrenia. *Schizophrenia Research, 58*, 293–303.

Norman, R. M. G., Manchanda, R., Malla, A. K., Windell, D., Harricharan, R., & Northcott, S. (2011). Symptom and functional outcomes for a 5-year early intervention program for psychoses. *Schizophrenia Research, 139*, 111–115.

Norman, R. M. G., Sorrentino, R. M., Gawronski, B., Szeto, A. C. H., et al. (2010). Attitudes and physical distance to an individual with schizophrenia: The moderating effect of self-transcendent values. *Social Psychiatry and Psychiatric Epidemiology, 45*, 751–758.

Norman, R. M. G., Sorrentino, R. M., Windell, D., & Manchanda, R. (2008). The roles of perceived norms in the stigmatization of mental illness. *Social Psychiatry and Psychiatric Epidemiology, 43*, 851–859.

Norman, R. M. G., Windell, D., Manchanda, R., Harricharan, R., & Northcott, S. (2012). Social support and functional outcomes in an early intervention program. *Schizophrenia Research, 140*, 37–40.

Norton, G. R., Harrison, B., Hauch, J., & Rhodes, L. (1985). Characteristics of people with infrequent panic attacks. *Journal of Abnormal Psychology, 94*, 216–221.

Norton, J. P. (1982). Expressed emotion, affective style, voice tone and communication deviance as predictors of offspring schizophrenia spectrum disorders. Unpublished doctoral dissertation, University of California at Los Angeles.

Norton, P. J., Zvolensky, M. J., Bonn-Miller, M. O., Cox, B. J., & Norton, G. R. (2008). Use of the Panic Attack Questionnaire-IV to assess non-clinical panic attacks and limited symptom panic attacks in student and community samples. *Journal of Anxiety Disorders, 22*, 1159–1171.

Noyes, R., Stuart, S., Watson, D. B., & Langbehn, D. R. (2006). Distinguishing between hypochondriasis and somatization disorder: A review of the existing literature. *Psychotherapy and Psychosomatics, 75*, 270–281.

Nunes, J., & Simmie, S. (2002). *Beyond crazy: Journeys through mental illness.* Toronto: McClelland and Stewart.

Nunes, K. L., & Jung, S. (2013). Are cognitive distortions associated with denial and minimization among sex offenders? *Sexual Abuse, 25*, 166–188.

Nunes, K. L., Hermann, C. A., Malcolm, J. R., & Lavoie, K. (2013). Childhood sexual victimization, pedophilic interest, and sexual recidivism. *Child Abuse and Neglect, 37*, 703–711.

Nunes, M., Walker, J. R., Syed, T., De Jong, M., Stewart, D. W., Provencher, M. D., et al. (2014). A national survey of student extended health insurance programs in postsecondary institutions in Canada: Limited support for students with mental health problems. *Canadian Psychology, 55*, 101–109.

O'Brien, A.-M., Farrell, S. J., & Faulkner, S. (2009). Community treatment orders: Beyond hospital utilization rates examining the association of community treatment orders with community engagement and supportive housing. *Community Mental Health Journal, 45*, 415–419.

O'Brien, P. R. (1989). Out of mind, out of sight: A history of the Waterford Hospital. St. John's, NL: Breakwater.

O'Connor, B. P. (2002). The search for dimensional structure differences between normality and abnormality: A statistical review of published data on personality and psychopathology. *Journal of Personality and Social Psychology, 83*, 962–982.

O'Connor, B. P., & Dyce, J. A. (2001). Rigid and extreme: A geometric representation of personality disorders in five-factor model space. *Journal of Personality and Social Psychology, 81*, 1119–1130.

O'Connor, K. (2009). Cognitive and meta-cognitive dimensions of psychosis. *Canadian Journal of Psychiatry, 54*, 152–159.

O'Connor, K., Aardema, F., & Pélissier, M.-C. (2005). *Beyond reasonable doubt: Reasoning processes in obsessive-compulsive disorder and related disorders.* New York: John Wiley & Sons.

O'Connor, K., & Robillard, S. (2000). A cognitive approach to the treatment of primary inferences in obsessive-compulsive disorder. *Journal of Cognitive Psychotherapy: An International Quarterly, 13*, 359–375.

O'Connor, R. C. (2007). The relations between perfectionism and suicidality: A systematic review. *Suicide and Life-Threatening Behavior, 37*, 698–714.

O'Donnell, P., & Grace, A. A. (1998). Dysfunctions in multiple interrelated systems as the neurobiological bases of schizophrenic symptom clusters. *Schizophrenia Bulletin, 24*, 267–283.

O'Donohue, W., & Plaud, J. J. (1994). The conditioning of human sexual arousal. *Archives of Sexual Behavior, 23*, 321–344.

O'Donohue, W., Dopke, C. A., & Swingen, D. N. (1997). Psychotherapy for female sexual dysfunction: A review. *Clinical Psychology Review, 17*, 537–566.

O'Malley, S. S., Jaffe, A. J., Chang, G., Rode, S., Schottenfeld, R., et al. (1996). Six-month follow-up of naltrexone and psychotherapy for alcohol dependence. *Archives of General Psychiatry, 53*, 217–224.

O'Reilly, R. (2004). Why are community treatment orders controversial? *Canadian Journal of Psychiatry, 49*, 579–584.

O'Reilly, R. L., et al. (2009). Mandatory outpatient treatment: Canadian Psychiatric Association position paper. Ottawa: Canadian Psychiatric Association.

O'Reilly, R. L., Keegan, D. L., Corring, D., Shrikhande, S., & Natarajan, D. (2006). A qualitative analysis of the use of community treatment orders in Saskatchewan. *International Journal of Law and Psychiatry, 29*, 516–524.

O'Reilly, R. L., Keegan, D. L., & Elias, J. W. (2000). A survey of the use of community treatment orders by psychiatrists in Saskatchewan. *Canadian Journal of Psychiatry, 45*, 79–81.

O'Rourke, N., & Tuokko, H. A. (2004). Caregiver burden and depressive symptomatology: The dissociation between constructs over time. *Clinical Gerontologist, 27*, 41–52.

Odlaug, B. L., Chamberlain, S. R., Derbyshire, K. L., Leppink, E. W., & Grant, J. E. (2014). Impaired response inhibition and excess cortical thickness as candidate endophenotypes for trichotillomania. *Journal of Psychiatric Research, 59*, 167–173.

Odlaug, B. L., & Grant, J. E. (2012). Pathological skin picking. In J. E. Grant, D. J. Stein, D. W. Woods, & N. J. Keuthen (Eds.), *Trichotillomania, skin picking, and other body-focused repetitive behaviors* (pp. 21–41). Arlington, VA: American Psychiatric Association Publishing.

Odlaug, B. L., Lust, K., Schreiber, L. R. N., Christenson, G., Derbyshire, K., & Grant, J. E. (2013). Skin picking disorder in university students: Health correlates and gender differences. *General Hospital Psychiatry, 35*, 168–173.

Oeztuerk, E., & Sar, V. (2008). Somatization as a predictor of suicidal ideation in dissociative disorders. *Psychiatry and Clinical Neuroscience, 62*, 662–668.

Offord, D. R., Boyle, M. H., Racine, Y., et al. (1996). Integrating assessment data from multiple informants. *Journal of the American Academy of Child and Adolescent Psychiatry, 35*, 1078–1085.

Ogborne, A. C., & DeWit, D. J. (1999). Lifetime use of professional and community services for help with drinking: Results from a Canadian population survey. *Journal of Studies in Alcohol, 60*, 867–872.

Ogloff, J. R. P. (1999). Ethical and legal contours of forensic psychology. In R. Roesch & S. D. Hart (Eds.), *Psychology and law: The state of the discipline* (pp. 401–435). New York: Plenum.

Ogloff, J. R. P., & Whittemore, K. E. (2001). Fitness to stand trial and criminal responsibility in Canada. In R. A. Schuller & J. R. P. Ogloff (Eds.), *Introduction to psychology and law: Canadian perspectives* (pp. 283–313). Toronto: University of Toronto Press.

Ogloff, J. R. P., Wong, S., & Greenwood, A. (1990). Treating criminal psychopaths in a therapeutic community program. *Behavioral Sciences and the Law, 8*, 181–190.

Ogrodniczuk, J. S., Piper, W. E., Joyce, A. S., Lau, M. A., & Sochting, I. (2010). A survey of Canadian group psychotherapy association members' perceptions of psychotherapy research. *International Journal of Group Psychotherapy, 60*, 159–172.

Ohayan, M. M. (2002). Epidemiology of insomnia: What we know and what we still need to know. *Sleep Medicine Reviews, 6*, 97–111.

Ohman, O., & Mineka, S. (2001). Fears, phobias, and preparedness: Toward an evolved module of fear and fear learning. *Psychological Review, 108*, 483–522.

Olatunji, B. B., Kauffman, B. Y., Meltzer, S., Davis, M. L., Smits, J. A. J., & Powers, M. B. (2014). Cognitive-behavioral therapy for hypochondriasis/health anxiety: A meta-analysis of treatment outcome and moderators. *Behaviour Research and Therapy, 58*, 65–74.

Oleksyn, V., & Kole, W. J. (2009, March 19). "I plead guilty—and I realize how cruel I was"—Fritzl brings trial to shocking end. *New York Post.*

Oliveira, E. C. B., Leppink, E. W., Derbyshire, K. L., & Grant, J. E. (2015). Excoriation disorder: Impulsivity and its clinical associations. *Journal of Anxiety Disorders, 30*, 19–22.

Oliver, L. N., Peters, P. A., & Kohen, D. E. (2012). Mortality rates among children and teenagers living in Inuit Nunangat, 1994 to 2008, *Health Reports, 23*(3), 17–22.

Olley, M. C., Nicholls, T. L., & Brink, J. (2009). Mentally ill individuals in limbo: Obstacles and opportunities for providing psychiatric services to corrections inmates with mental illness. *Behavioral Sciences and the Law, 27*, 811–831.

Olsen, R. K., Pangelinan, M. M., Bogulski, C., Chakravarty, M. M., et al. (2015). The effect of lifelong bilingualism on regional grey and white matter volume. *Brain Research, 1612*, 128–139.

Olsson, A., & Phelps, E. A. (2004). Learned fear of "unseen faces" after Pavlovian, observational, and instructed fear. *Psychological Science, 15*, 823–828.

Olver, M. E., & Wong, S. C. (2006). Psychopathy, sexual deviance, and recidivism among sex offenders. *Sexual Abuse, 18*, 65–82.

Omalu, B., Hamilton, R. L., Kamboh, M. I., DeKosky, S. T., & Bailes, J. (2010). Chronic traumatic encephalopathy (CTE) in a National Football League player: Case report and emerging medicolegal practice questions. *Journal of Forensic Nursing, 6*, 40–46.

Omalu, B., Hammers, J. L., Bailes, J., Hamilton, R. L., Kamboh, M. I., Webster, G., & Fitzsimmons, R. P. (2011). Chronic traumatic encephalopathy in an Iraqi war veteran with posttraumatic stress disorder who committed suicide. *Neurosurgery Focus, 31*, E3.

Ono, Y., et al. (1996). Avoidant personality disorder and taijin kyoufu: Sociocultural implications of the WHO/ADAMHA International Study of Personality Disorders in Japan. *Acta Psychiatrica Scandanavica, 93*, 172–176.

Ontario Human Rights Commission. (2012). *Minds that matter: Report on the consultation on human rights, mental health and addictions.* Toronto: Author.

Ontario Ministry of Health. (1994). *Ontario Health Survey: Mental health supplement* (Catalogue No. 2224153). Toronto: Queen's Printer for Ontario.

Opris, D., Pintea, S., Garcia-Palacios, A., et al. (2012). Virtual reality exposure therapy in anxiety disorders: A quantitative meta-analysis. *Depression and Anxiety, 29*, 85–93.

Oquendo, M. A., Baca-Garcia, E., Mann, J. J., & Giner, J. (2008). Issues for DSM-V: Suicidal behavior as a separate diagnosis on a separate axis. *American Journal of Psychiatry, 165*, 1383–1384.

Ormel, J., Petukhova, M., Chatterji, S., Aguilar-Gaxiola, S., et al. (2008). Disability and treatment of specific mental and physical disorders around the world. *The British Journal of Psychiatry, 192*, 368–375.

Orne, M. T., Dinges, D. F., & Orne, E. C. (1984). The differential diagnosis of multiple personality in the forensic court. *International Journal of Clinical and Experimental Hypnosis, 32*, 118–169.

Ornitz, E. M. (1989). Autism at the interface between sensory and information processing. In G. Dawson (Ed.), *Autism: Nature, diagnosis, and treatment* (pp. 174–207). New York: Guilford.

Oshri, A., Rogosch, F. A., & Cicchetti, D. (in press). Child maltreatment and mediating influences of childhood personality types on the development of adult psychopathology. *Development and Psychopathology.*

Öst, L.-G. (1992). Blood and injection phobia: Background and cognitive, physiological, and behavioral correlates. *Journal of Abnormal Psychology, 101*, 68–74.

Öst, L.-G. (2012). One-session treatment: Principles and procedures with adults. In T. E. Davis III, T. H. Ollendick, & L.-G. Öst (Eds.), *Intensive one-session treatment of specific phobias* (pp. 59–95). New York: Springer-Verlag.

Öst, L.-G., Havnen, A., Hansen, B., & Kvale, G. (2015). Cognitive behavioral treatments of obsessive-compulsive disorder. A systematic review and meta-analysis of studies published 1993–2014. *Clinical Psychology Review, 40*, 156–169.

Öst, L.-G., Riise, E. N., Wergeland, G. J., Hansen, B., & Kvale, G. (2016). Cognitive behavioral and pharmacological treatments of OCD in children: A systematic review and meta-analysis. *Journal of Anxiety Disorders, 43*, 58–69.

Öst, L.-G., Svensson, L., Hellström, K., & Lindwall, R. (2001). One-session treatment of specific phobias in youth: A randomized clinical trial. *Journal of Consulting and Clinical Psychology, 69*, 814–824.

Ostbye, T., et al. (2005). Prevalence and predictors of depression in elderly Canadians: The Canadian Study of Health and Aging. *Chronic Diseases in Canada, 26*, 93–99.

Ostbye, T., Steenhuis, R., Walton, R., & Cairney, J. (2000). Correlates of dysphoria in Canadian seniors: The Canadian Study of Health and Aging. *Canadian Journal of Public Health, 91*, 313–317.

Osterling, J. A., Dawson, G., & Munson, J. A. (2002). Early recognition of 1-year-old infants with autism spectrum disorder versus mental retardation. *Development and Psychopathology, 14*, 239–251.

Ostojic, M. S., and Hansen, A. M. J. (in press). Sociocultural factors in the development of bulimia nervosa in a blind woman: A case report. *International Journal of Eating Disorders.*

Ottaviani, C., Shapiro, D., Davydov, D. M., Goldstein, I. B., & Mills, P. J. (2009). The autonomic phenotype of rumination. *International Journal of Psychophysiology, 72*, 267–275.

Ottaviani, C., Shapiro, D., & Fitzgerald, L. (2011). Rumination in the laboratory: What happens when you go back to everyday life? *Psychophysiology, 48*, 453–461.

Otto, M. W., Pollack, M. H., & Maki, K. M. (2000). Empirically supported treatments for panic disorder: Costs, benefits, and stepped care. *Journal of Consulting and Clinical Psychology, 68*, 556–563.

Ouelette-Kuntz, H., Coo, H., Lam, M., Breitenbach, M. M., Hennessey, P. E., Jackman, P. D., ... Chung, A. M. (2014). The changing prevalence of autism in three regions of Canada. *Journal of Autism and Developmental Disorders, 44*, 120–136.

Ouimette, P. C., Finney, J. W., & Moos, R. H. (1997). Twelve-step and cognitive-behavioral treatment for substance abuse: A comparison of treatment effectiveness. *Journal of Consulting and Clinical Psychology, 65*, 230–240.

Ovalle, D. (2010, December 2). Miami-Dade killer gets life sentence for murder, stabbings, rape. *Miami Herald.*

Oveisgharan, S., & Hachinski, V. (2010). Hyper-tension, executive dysfunction, and progression to dementia: The Canadian Study of Health and Aging. *Archives of Neurology, 67*, 187–192.

Owen, J., Duncan, B., Reese, R. J., Anker, M., & Sparks, J. (2014). Accounting for therapist variability in couple therapy outcomes: What really matters? *Journal of Sex and Marital Therapy, 40*, 488–502.

Owens, E. B., et al. (2003). Which treatment for whom for ADHD? Moderators of treatment response in the MTA. *Journal of Consulting and Clinical Psychology, 71*, 540–552.

Pabian, Y. L., Welfel, E., & Beebe, R. S. (2009). Psychologists' knowledge of their states' laws pertaining to Tarasoff-type situations. *Professional Psychology: Research and Practice, 40*, 8–14.

Padilla-Walker, L. M., Coyne, S. M., Collier, K. M., & Nielson, M. G. (2015). Longitudinal relations between prosocial television content and adolescents' prosocial and aggressive behavior: The mediating role of empathic concern and self-regulation. *Developmental Psychology, 51*, 1317–1328.

Pagani, L. S., & Fitzpatrick, C. (2013). Prospective associations between early long-term household tobacco smoke exposure and antisocial behaviour in later childhood. *Journal of Epidemiology and Community Health, 67*, 552–557.

Page, A. C. (1994). Blood-injection phobia. *Clinical Psychology Review, 14*, 443–461.

Paglia, A., & Room, R. (1999). Expectancies about the effects of alcohol on the self and others as determinants of alcohol policy attitudes. *Journal of Applied Social Psychology, 29*, 2632–2651.

Paglia-Boak, A., Mann, R. E., Adlaf, E. M., & Rehm, J. (2009). Ontario Student Drug Use and Health Survey. Toronto: Centre for Addiction and Mental Health.

Pahkala, K. (1990). Social and environmental factors and atypical depression in old age. *International Journal of Geriatric Psychiatry, 5*, 99–113.

Palamar, J. J., Davies, S., Ompad, D. C., Cleland, C. M., & Weitzman, M. (2015). Powder cocaine and crack use in the United States: An examination of risk for arrest and socioeconomic disparities in use. *Drug and Alcohol Dependence, 145*, 108–116.

Palaniyappan, L., Balain, V., Radua, J., & Liddle, P. F. (2012). Structural correlates of auditory hallucinations in schizophrenia: A meta-analysis. *Schizophrenia Research, 137*, 169–173.

Palombo, D. J., McKinnon, M. C., McIntosh, A. R., Anderson, A. R., Todd, R. M., & Levine, B. (2016). The neural correlates of memory for a life-threatening event: An fMRI study of passengers from Flight AT236. *Clinical Psychological Science, 4,* 312–319.

Pantin, H., Coatsworth, J. D., Feaster, D. J., et al. (2003). Familias Unidas: The efficacy of an intervention to promote parental investment in Hispanic immigrant families. *Prevention Science, 4,* 189–201.

Paperny, A. M. (2012, February 17). Provinces clamp down on OxyContin abuse. *The Globe and Mail.*

Pardini, D., Stepp, S., Hipwell, A., Stouthamer-Loeber, M., & Loeber, R. (2012). The clinical utility of the proposed *DSM-5* callous-unemotional subtype of conduct disorder in young girls. *Journal of the American Academy of Child and Adolescent Psychiatry, 51,* 62–73.

Parent, K., & Anderson, M. (2001). *Home care by default, not by design*: CARP's report card on home care in Canada 2001. Retrieved from http://www.50plus.com.

Parikh, S. (2015). Improving access to psychosocial treatments—Integrating patient, provider, and systems approaches. *Canadian Journal of Psychiatry, 60,* 242–244.

Paris, J. (2002). Chronic suicidality among patients with borderline personality disorder. *Psychiatric Services, 53,* 738–742.

Paris, J. (2009a). Psychiatry and neuroscience. *Canadian Journal of Psychiatry, 54,* 513–517.

Paris, J. (2009b). The treatment of borderline personality disorder: Implications of research on diagnosis, etiology, and outcome. *Annual Review of Clinical Psychology, 5,* 277–290.

Paris, J. (2012). The rise and fall of dissociative identity disorder. *The Journal of Nervous and Mental Disease, 200,* 1076–1079.

Paris, J. (2013). *The intelligent clinician's guide to the DSM-5.* Oxford, England: Oxford University Press.

Paris, J., & Zweig-Frank, H. (2001). A 27-year follow-up of patients with borderline personality disorder. *Comprehensive Psychiatry, 42,* 482–487.

Paris, J., Zweig-Frank, H., & Guzder, J. (1994). Psychological risk factors for borderline personality disorder in female patients. *Comprehensive Psychiatry, 35,* 301–305.

Park, D. C., & Radford, J. P. (1998). Reconstructing a history of involuntary sterilisation. *Disability and Society, 13,* 317–342.

Park, S. G., Bennett, M. E., Couture, S. M., & Blanchard, J. J. (2013). Internalized stigma in schizophrenia: Relations with dysfunctional attitudes, symptoms, and quality of life. *Psychiatry Research, 205,* 43–47.

Parker, G., Gladstone, G., & Chee, K. T. (2001). Depression in the planet's largest ethnic group: The Chinese. *American Journal of Psychiatry, 158,* 857–864.

Parrish, B. P., Cohen, L. H., Gunthert, K. C., et al. (2009). Effects of cognitive therapy for depression on daily stress-related variables. *Behaviour Research and Therapy, 47,* 444–448.

Parry, G., Castonguay, L. G., Borkovec, T. D., & Wolf, A. M. (2010). Practice research networks and psychological services research in the UK and USA. In M. Barkham, G. Hardy, & J. Mellon-Clark (Eds.), *Developing and delivering practice-based evidence* (pp. 311–326). Chichester, England: John Wiley & Sons.

Pasalich, D. S., Dadds, M. R., Hawes, D. J., & Brennan, J. (2011). Callous-unemotional traits moderate the relative importance of parental coercion versus warmth in child conduct problems: An observational study. *Journal of Child Psychology and Psychiatry, 52*(12), 1308–1315.

Patch, N. (2009, March 10). Good shares his story; Healthy Canadian rocker talks about his struggles with depression. *Telegraph-Journal* (Saint John), D4.

Patel, S., & Adams, M. R. (2008). Prevention of cardiac disease: Lifestyle modification or pharmacotherapy? *Internal Medicine Journal, 38,* 199–203.

Patrick, C. J., Hicks, B. M., Krueger, R. F., & Lang, A. R. (2005). Relations between psychopathy facets and externalizing in a criminal offender sample. *Journal of Personality Disorders, 19,* 339–356.

Patrick, M., Hobson, R. P., Castle, P., et al. (1994). Personality disorder and the mental representation of early social experience. *Developmental Psychopathology, 94,* 375–388.

Patten, S. B. (2008). Major depression prevalence is very high, but the syndrome is a poor proxy for community populations' clinical treatment needs. *Canadian Journal of Psychiatry, 53,* 411–419.

Patten, S. B., Bilsker, D., & Goldner, E. (2008). The evolving understanding of major depression epidemiology: Implications for practice and policy. *Canadian Journal of Psychiatry, 53,* 689–695.

Patten, S. B., Williams, J. V. A., Lavorato, D. H., Wang, J. L., McDonald, K., & Bulloch, A. G. M. (2015). Descriptive epidemiology of major depressive disorder in Canada in 2012. *Canadian Journal of Psychiatry, 60,* 23–30.

Patterson, A. A., & Holden, R. R. (2012). Psychache and suicide ideation among men who are homeless: A test of Shneidman's model. *Suicide and Life-Threatening Behavior, 42,* 147–156.

Patterson, C. M., & Newman, J. P. (1993). Reflectivity and learning from aversive events: Toward a psychological mechanism for the syndromes of disinhibition. *Psychological Review, 100,* 716–736.

Patterson, G. R. (1982). *Coercive family process.* Eugene, OR: Castilia.

Patterson, G. R., & Stouthamer-Loeber, M. (1984). The correlation of family management practices and delinquency. *Child Development, 55,* 1299–1307.

Patterson, M. L., Somers, J. M., & Moniruzzaman, A. (2012). Prolonged and persistent homelessness: Multivariate analyses in a cohort experiencing current homelessness and mental illness in Vancouver, British Columbia. *Mental Health and Substance Use, 5,* 85–101.

Pattyn, T., van den Eede, F., Lamers, F., Veltman, D., Sabbe, B. G., & Penninx, B. W. (2015). Identifying panic disorder subtypes using factor mixture modeling. *Depression and Anxiety, 32,* 509–517.

Paul, G. L., & Lentz, R. J. (1977). *Psychosocial treatment of chronic mental patients: Milieu versus social-learning programs.* Cambridge, MA: Harvard University Press.

Paul, G. L., & Shannon, D. T. (1966). Treatment of anxiety through systematic desensitization in therapy groups. *Journal of Abnormal Psychology, 71,* 124–135.

Paul, T., et al. (2002). Self-injurious behavior in women with eating disorders. *American Journal of Psychiatry, 159,* 408–411.

Paulhus, D. J., & Martin, C. L. (1987). The structure of personality capabilities. *Journal of Personality and Social Psychology, 52,* 354–365.

Paulhus, D. J., & Martin, C. L. (1988). Functional flexibility: A new conception of interpersonal flexibility. *Journal of Personality and Social Psychology, 55,* 88–101.

Paulhus, D. L., & Williams, K. M. (2002). The dark triad of personality: Narcissism, Machiavellianism, and psychopathy. *Journal of Research in Personality, 36,* 556–563.

Pauls, D. L., Alsobrook, J. P., Goodman, W., Rasmussen, S., & Leckman, J. F. (1995). A family study of obsessive-compulsive disorder. *American Journal of Psychiatry, 152,* 76–84.

Paulus, M. P. (2008). The role of neuroimaging for the diagnosis and treatment of anxiety disorders. *Depression and Anxiety, 25,* 348–356.

Paulus, M. P. (2015). Pragmatism instead of mechanism: A call for impactful biological psychiatry. *JAMA Psychiatry, 72*(7), 631–632.

Paxton, S. J., Wertheim, E. H., Gibbons, K., et al. (1991). Body image satisfaction, dieting beliefs, and weight loss behaviors in adolescent girls and boys. *Journal of Youth and Adolescence, 20*, 361–379.

Pearce, T. (2008, May 25). Schizophrenia: A disorder in disguise. *The Globe and Mail.*

Pearson, C., Janz, T., & Ali, J. (2013). Mental and substance use disorders in Canada. *Health at a Glance*, September, 1–8.

Pearson, C., Zamorski, M., & Janz, T. (2014, November 25). *Mental health of the Canadian Armed Forces* (Catalogue No. 82-624-X). Ottawa: Statistics Canada.

Pearson, C. M., & Smith, G. T. (2015). Bulimic symptom onset in young girls: A longitudinal trajectory analysis. *Journal of Abnormal Psychology, 124*, 1003–1013.

Pearson, J. L., & Brown, G. K. (2000). Suicide prevention in late life: Directions for science and practice. *Clinical Psychology Review, 20*, 685–705.

Pedersen, S. S., & Denollet, J. (2003). Type D personality, cardiac events, and impaired quality of life: A review. *Journal of Cardiovascular Risk, 10*, 241–248.

Pelissier, M.-C., & O'Connor, K. (2004). Cognitive-behavioral treatment of trichotillomania, targeting perfectionism. *Clinical Case Studies, 1*, 57–68.

Pelle, A. J., et al. (2008). Type D patients report poorer health status prior to and after cardiac rehabilitation compared to non Type-D patients. *Annals of Behavioral Medicine, 36*, 167–175.

Peluso, D. L., Carleton, R. N., & Asmundson, G. J. G. (2010). Clinical psychology graduate students' perceptions of their scientific and practical training: A Canadian perspective. *Canadian Psychology, 51*, 133–139.

Penn, D. L., & Mueser, K. T. (1996). Research update on the psychosocial treatment of schizophrenia. *American Journal of Psychiatry, 153*, 607–617.

Pennebaker, J., Kiecolt-Glaser, J. K., & Glaser, R. (1988). Disclosure of traumas and immune function: Health implications for psychotherapy. *Journal of Consulting and Clinical Psychology, 56*, 239–245.

Pennessi, J. L., & Wade, T. D. (2016). A systematic review of the existing models of disordered eating: Do they inform the development of effective interventions? *Clinical Psychology Review, 43*, 175–192.

Pepler, D. J., & Sedighdeilami, F. (1998). *Aggressive girls in Canada* (No. W-98-30E). Ottawa: Human Resources Development Canada.

Pepping, C. A., Halford, W. K., & Doss, B. D. (2015). Can we predict failure in couple therapy early enough to enhance outcome? *Behaviour Research and Therapy, 65*, 60–66.

Pereda, N., Guilera, G., Forns, M., & Gomez-Benito, J. (2009). The prevalence of child sexual abuse in community and student samples: A meta-analysis. *Clinical Psychology Review, 29*, 328–338.

Pergadia, M. L., Heath, A. C., Agrawal, A., et al. (2006). The implications of simultaneous smoking initiation for inferences about the genetics of smoking behavior from twin data. *Behavior Genetics, 36*, 567–576.

Perkel, C. (2013, April 9). Textbook case of antisocial personality disorder, but Ashley Smith not unique. *Maclean's.*

Perlin, M. L. (1994). *Law and mental disability.* Charlottesville, VA: The Michie Company.

Perr, I. N. (1992). The trial of Louis Riel: A study in Canadian psychiatry. *Journal of Forensic Sciences, 37*, 845–852.

Perr, I. N., & Federoff, J. P. (1992). Misunderstanding of self and the Riel phenomenon. *Journal of Forensic Sciences, 37*, 839–844.

Perreault, V., & O'Connor, K. (2014). Inference-based therapy: Processes of change in compulsions and obsessional beliefs. *International Journal of Cognitive Therapy, 7*, 6–28.

Persons, J. B. (2005). Empiricism, mechanism, and the practice of cognitive-behavior therapy. *Behavior Therapy, 36*, 107–118.

Persons, J. B., Beckner, V. L., & Tompkins, M. A. (2013). Testing case formulation hypotheses in psychotherapy: Two case examples. *Cognitive and Behavioral Practice, 20*, 399–409.

Persons, J. B., & Davidson, J. (2010). Cognitive-behavioural case formulation. In K. S. Dobson (Ed.), *Handbook of cognitive-behavioral therapies* (3rd ed., pp. 172–193). New York: Guilford.

Pescatello, L. S., Guidry, M. A., Blanchard, B. E., et al. (2004). Exercise intensity alters postexercise hypotension. *Journal of Hypertension, 22*, 1881–1888.

Peterman, J. S., Read, K. L., Wei, C., & Kendall, P. C. (2015). The art of exposure: Putting science into practice. *Cognitive and Behavioral Practice, 22*, 379–392.

Peterson, C., & Seligman, M. E. P. (1984). Causal explanations as a risk factor for depression: Theory and evidence. *Psychological Review, 91*, 347–374.

Peterson, R. A., & Reiss, R. L. (1987). The Anxiety Sensitivity Index: Construct validity and factor analytic structure. *Journal of Anxiety Disorders, 1*, 265–277.

Peterson-Post, K., Rhoades, G. K., Stanley, S. M., & Markman, H. J. (2014). Perceived criticism and marital adjustment predict depressive symptoms in a community sample. *Behavior Therapy, 45*, 564–575.

Petitclerc, A., Boivin, M., Dionne, G., et al. (2009). Disregard for rules: The early development and predictors of a specific dimension of disruptive behavior disorders. *Journal of Child Psychology and Psychiatry, 50*, 1477–1484.

Petitclerc, A., & Tremblay, R. E. (2009). Childhood disruptive behaviour disorders: Review of their origin, development, and prevention. *Canadian Journal of Psychiatry, 54*, 222–231.

Pfefferbaum, A., Adalsteinsson, E., & Sullivan, E. V. (2006). Dysmorphology and microstructural degradation of the corpus callosum: Interaction of age and alcoholism. *Neurobiology of Aging, 27*, 994–1009.

Pfefferman, A., Sullivan, E. V., Rosenbloom, M. J., Mathalon, D. H., & Lim, K. O. (1998). A controlled study of cortical grey matter and ventricular changes in alcoholic men over a 5-year interval. *Archives of General Psychiatry, 55*, 905–912.

Pfeiffer, P. N., Ganoczy, D., Ilgen, M., Zivin, K., & Valenstein, M. (2009). Comorbid anxiety as a suicide risk factor among depressed veterans. *Depression and Anxiety, 26*, 752–757.

Pfiffner, L. J., & Barkley, R. A. (1998). Treatment of ADHD in school settings. In R. A. Barkley (Ed.), *Attention deficit hyperactivity disorder: A handbook for diagnosis and treatment* (2nd ed., pp. 458–490). New York: Guilford.

Phares, V. (2003). Mothers, fathers, gender role, and time parents spent with their children. *Sex Roles, 48*, 305–315.

Phares, V. (2008). *Understanding abnormal child psychology* (2nd ed.). Hoboken, NJ: John Wiley & Sons.

Phillips, J. A. (2014). A changing epidemiology of suicide? The influence of birth cohorts on suicide rates in the United States. *Society of Science Medicine, 114C*, 151–160.

Phillips, K. A. (2009). *Understanding body dysmorphic disorder: An essential guide.* London: Oxford University Press.

Phillips, K. A., Menard, W., Quinn, E., Didie, E. R., & Stout, R. L. (2013). A 4-year prospective observational follow-up study of course and predictors of course in body dysmorphic disorder. *Psychological Medicine, 43*, 1109–1117.

Phillips, L. J., Francey, S. M., Edwards, J., McMurray, N. (2007). Stress and psychosis: Towards the development of new models of investigation. *Clinical Psychology Review, 27*, 307–317.

Phipps, S. (1999). *An international comparison of policies and outcomes for young children*. CPRN Study No. F-05. Ottawa: Canadian Policy Research Networks, Inc.

Picard, A. (2008, June 27). A 12-step program for Canada: Setting priorities and solutions to address the mental health crisis. *The Globe and Mail.*

Picard, A. (2009, September 18). Burying the story won't stop suicide. *The Globe and Mail.*

Picard, A. (2009, October 28). Hypertension doubles for Quebec Inuit. *The Globe and Mail.*

Picard, A. (2013, September 23). Balancing act: The freedom to be sick, and the right to be well. *The Globe and Mail.*

Pincus, A. L., Ansell, E. B., Pimentel, C. A., Cain, N. M., Wright, A. C., & Levy, K. N. (2009). Initial construction and validation of the Pathological Narcissism Inventory. *Psychological Assessment, 21,* 365–379.

Pincus, A. L., Dowgwillo, E. A., & Greenberg, L. S. (2016). Three cases of narcissistic personality disorder through the lens of the *DSM-5* alternative model for personality disorders. *Practice Innovations, 1,* 164–177.

Pincus, H. A., Tanielian, T. L., Marcus, S. C., Olfson, M., et al. (1998). Prescribing trends in psychotropic medications: Primary care, psychiatry, and other medical specialities. *Journal of the American Medical Association, 279,* 526–531.

Pine, D. S. (2007). Developmental perspectives on psychopathology. *American Journal of Psychiatry, 164,* 1781.

Pine, D. S., & Kline, R. G. (2008). Anxiety disorders. In M. Rutter, D. V. M. Bishop, et al. (Eds.), *Rutter's child and adolescent psychiatry*, Vol. 5 (pp. 628–647). New York: Wiley-Blackwell.

Pinhas, L., Toner, B. B., Ali, A., Garfinkel, P. E., & Stuckless, N. (1999). The effects of the ideal of female beauty on mood and satisfaction. *International Journal of Eating Disorders, 25,* 223–226.

Pinquart, M., & Forstmeier, S. (2012). Effects of reminiscence interventions on psychosocial outcomes: A meta-analysis. *Aging and Mental Health, 16,* 541–558.

Pinto, A. M., et al. (2008). The Eating Disorder Recovery Self-Efficacy Questionnaire: Change with treatment and prediction of outcome. *Eating Behaviors, 9,* 143–153.

Piper, A., & Merskey, H. (2004a). The persistence of folly: A critical examination of Dissociative Identity Disorder. Part I. The excesses of an improbable concept. *Canadian Journal of Psychiatry, 49,* 592–600.

Piper, A., & Merskey, H. (2004b). The persistence of folly: A critical examination of Dissociative Identity Disorder. Part II. The defence and decline of multiple personality or dissociative identity disorder. *Canadian Journal of Psychiatry, 49,* 678–683.

Piran, N., & Gadella, T. (2006). Eating disorders and substance abuse in Canadian women: A national study. *Addiction, 102,* 105–113.

Pires, P., & Jenkins, J. M. (2007). A growth curve analysis of the joint influences of parenting affect, child characteristics and deviant peers on adolescent illicit drug use. *Journal of Youth and Adolescence, 36,* 169–183.

Pistorello, J., Fruzetti, A. E., MacLane, C., Gallop, R., & Iverson, K. M. (2012). Dialectical behavior therapy (DBT) applied to college students: A randomized clinical trial. *Journal of Consulting and Clinical Psychology, 80,* 982–994.

Placidi, G. P., et al. (2001). Aggressivity, suicide attempts, and depression: Relationship to cerebral spinal fluid monoamine metabolite levels. *Biological Psychiatry, 50,* 783–791.

Plassman, B. L., et al. (2007). Prevalence of dementia in the United States: The Aging, Demographics, and Memory Study. *Neuroepidemiology, 29,* 125–132.

Plassman, B. L., et al. (2008). Prevalence of cognitive impairment without dementia in the United States. *Annals of Internal Medicine, 148,* 427–434.

Plener, P. L., & Fegert, J. M. (2012). Non-suicidal self-injury: State of the art perspective of a proposed new syndrome for *DSM V*. *Child and Adolescent Psychiatry and Mental Health, 6,* 9.

Pliner, P., & Chaiken, S. (1990). Eating, social motives, and self-presentation in women and men. *Journal of Experimental Social Psychology, 26,* 240–254.

Plomin, R., & Kovas, Y. (2005). Generalist genes and learning disabilities. *Psychological Bulletin, 131,* 592–617.

Podymow, T., Turnbull, J., Coyle, D., Yetisir, E., & Wells, G. (2006). Shelter-based managed alcohol administration to chronically homeless people addicted to alcohol. *Canadian Medical Association Journal, 174,* 45–49.

Poissant, H., Emond, V., & Joyal, C. (2008). Structural and functional neuroanatomy in attention deficit and hyperactivity disorder (ADHD). *International Journal of Developmental Neuroscience, 26,* 842.

Poissant, H., Neault, I., Dallaire, S., et al. (2008). Development of self-regulation and inhibition in children exhibiting attention deficit disorder with or without hyperactivity (ADHD). *Encephale, 34,* 161–169.

Polanczyk, G. V., de Lima, M. S., Horta, B. L., et al. (2007). The worldwide prevalence of ADHD: A systematic review and metaregression analysis. *American Journal of Psychiatry, 164,* 942–948.

Polanczyk, G. V., Salum, G. A., Sugaya, L. S., Caye, A., & Rohde, L. A. (2015). Annual research review: A meta-analysis of the worldwide prevalence of mental disorders in children and adolescents. *Journal of Child Psychology and Psychiatry, 56,* 345–365.

Poletti, S., Radaelli, D., Cucchi, M., Ricci, L., Vai, B., Smeraldi, E., & Benedetti, F. (2015). Neural correlates of anxiety sensitivity in panic disorder: A functional magnetic resonance imaging study. *Psychiatry Research: Neuroimaging, 233,* 95–101.

Polich, J. M., Armor, D. J., & Braiker, H. B. (1980). Patterns of alcoholism over four years. *Journal of Studies on Alcohol, 41,* 397–415.

Polivy, J., & Herman, C. P. (1985). Dieting and binging: A causal analysis. *American Psychologist, 40,* 193–201.

Ponseti, J., Granert, O., Jansen, O., Wolff, S., et al. (2012). Assessment of pedophilia using hemodynamic brain response to sexual stimuli. *Archives of General Psychiatry, 69,* 187–194.

Poole, N., Schmidt, R. A., Green, C., & Hemsing, N. (2016). Prevention of fetal alcohol spectrum disorder: Current Canadian efforts and analysis of gaps. *Substance Abuse: Research and Treatment, 10*(S1), 1–11.

Pope, H. G., Jr., Barry, S., Bodkin, A., & Hudson, J. I. (2006). Tracking scientific interest in the dissociative disorders: A study of scientific publication output: 1984–2003. *Psychotherapy and Psychosomatics, 75,* 19–24.

Pope, H. G., Jr., Oliva, P. S., Hudson, J. I., Bodkin, J. A., & Gruber, A. J. (1999). Attitudes toward DSM-IV dissociative disorders among board-certified American psychiatrists. *American Journal of Psychiatry, 156,* 321–323.

Pope, K. S. (1995). What psychologists better know about recovered memories, research, lawsuits, and the pivotal experiment: A review of "The Myth of Repressed Memory: False Memories and Allegations of Sexual Abuse," by Elizabeth Loftus and Katherine Ketcham. *Clinical Psychology: Science and Practice, 2,* 304–315.

Popova, S., Lange, S., Burd, L., & Rehm, J. (2015). *The burden and economic impact of fetal alcohol syndrome disorder in Canada.* Toronto: Centre for Addiction and Mental Health.

Popova, S., Lange, S., Shield, K., Mihic, A., et al. (2016). Comorbidity of fetal alcohol spectrum disorder: A systematic review and meta-analysis. *The Lancet, 387,* 978–987.

Porath-Waller, A. J. (2009). *Clearing the smoke on cannabis: Chronic use and cognitive functioning and mental health.* Ottawa: Canadian Centre on Substance Abuse.

Porter, S., ten Brinke, L., & Wilson, K. (2009). Crime profiles and conditional release performance of psychopathic and non-psychopathic sexual offenders. *Legal and Criminological Psychology, 14,* 109–118.

Porter, S., & Woodworth, M. (2006). Psychopathy and aggression. In C. J. Patrick (Ed.), *Handbook of psychopathy* (pp. 481–494). New York: Guilford.

Porter, S., & Woodworth, M. (2007). "I'm sorry I did it but he started it": A comparison of the official and self-reported homicide descriptions of psychopaths and non-psychopaths. *Law and Human Behavior, 31,* 91–107.

Porter, S., Woodworth, M., Earle, J., Drugge, J., & Boer, D. (2003). Characteristics of sexual homicides committed by psychopathic and nonpsychopathic offenders. *Law and Human Behavior, 27,* 459–470.

Portero, A. K., Durmaz, D. A., Raines, A. M., Short, N. A., & Schmidt, N. B. (2015). Cognitive processes in hoarding: The role of rumination. *Personality and Individual Differences, 86,* 277–281.

Pos, A. E., Greenberg, L. S., Goldman, R. N., & Korman, L. M. (2003). Emotional processing during experiential treatment of depression. *Journal of Consulting and Clinical Psychology, 71,* 1007–1016.

Pot, A. M., et al. (2010). The impact of life review on depression in older adults: A randomized controlled trial. *International Psychogeriatrics, 22,* 572–581.

Potkin, S. C., & Ford, J. M. (2009). Widespread cortical dysfunction in schizophrenia: The FBIRN Imaging Consortium. *Schizophrenia Bulletin, 35,* 15–18.

Potter, M. (2009, September 2). Pills and America's pursuit of happiness. *Toronto Star,* A12.

Powers, A., Ressler, K. J., & Bradley, R. G. (2009). The protective role of friendship on the effects of childhood abuse and depression. *Depression and Anxiety, 26,* 46–53.

Powers, M. B., Asmundson, G. J. G., & Smits, J. A. J. (2015). Exercise for mood and anxiety disorders: The state-of-the science. *Cognitive Behaviour Therapy, 44,* 237–239.

Powers, M. B., Halpern, J. M., Ferenschak, M. P., Gillihan, S. J., & Foa, E. B. (2010). A meta-analytic review of prolonged exposure for posttraumatic stress disorder. *Clinical Psychology Review, 30,* 635–641.

Powers, M. B., Vedel, E., & Emmelkamp, P. M. G. (2008). Behavioral couples therapy (BCT) for alcohol and drug use disorders: A meta-analysis. *Clinical Psychology Review, 28,* 952–962.

Prentky, R., & Burgess, A. W. (1990). Rehabilitation of child molesters: A cost-benefit analysis. *American Journal of Orthopsychiatry, 60,* 108–117.

Pressly, L. (2012, March 28). OxyContin abuse hits Canada First Nations communities. *BBC News Magazine.*

Preville, M., et al. (2005). Correlates of suicide in the older adult population in Quebec. *Suicide and Life Threatening Behavior, 35,* 91–105.

Prien, R. F., & Potter, W. Z. (1993). Maintenance treatment for mood disorders. In D. L. Dunner (Ed.), *Current psychiatric therapy.* Philadelphia: Saunders.

Prilleltensky, I., & Nelson, G. (2000). Promoting child and family wellness: Priorities for psychological and social interventions. *Journal of Community and Applied Social Psychology, 10,* 85–105.

Prince, M., Wimo, A., Guerchet, M., Ali, G.-C., Wu, Y.-T., Prina, M., & Alzheimer's Disease International. (2015). *World Alzheimer Report 2015: The global impact of dementia: An analysis of prevalence, incidence, cost, and trends.* London: Alzheimer's Disease International.

Prochaska, J. O., DiClemente, C. C., & Norcross, J. C. (1992). In search of how people change. Applications to addictive behaviors. *American Psychologist, 47,* 1102–1114.

Project Match Research Group. (1997). Matching alcoholism treatments to client heterogeneity: Project MATCH posttreatment drinking outcomes. *Journal of Studies on Alcohol, 58,* 7–29.

Proudfoot, J. (2013). The future is in our hands: The role of mobile phones in the prevention and management of mental disorders. *Australian and New Zealand Journal of Psychiatry, 47,* 111–113.

Prout, P. I., & Dobson, K. S. (1998). Recovered memories of childhood sexual abuse: Searching for the middle ground in clinical practice. *Canadian Psychology, 39,* 257–265.

Provencher, H. L., & Fincham, F. D. (2000). Attributions of causality, responsibility and blame for positive and negative symptom behaviours in caregivers of persons with schizophrenia. *Psychological Medicine, 30,* 899–910.

Provencher, H. L., Perreault, M., St-Onge, M., & Rousseau, M. (2003). Predictors of psychological distress in family caregivers of persons with psychiatric disabilities. *Journal of Psychiatric and Mental Health Nursing, 10,* 592–607.

Pu, T., Mohamed, E., Imam, K., & El-Roey, A. M. (1986). One hundred cases of hysteria in eastern Libya. *British Journal of Psychiatry, 148,* 606–609.

Public Health Agency of Canada. (2009). *Tracking heart disease and stroke in Canada.* Ottawa: Author.

Pulay, A. J., et al. (2009). Prevalence, correlates, disability, and comorbidity of DSM-IV schizotypal personality disorder: Results for the Wave 2 National Epidemiologic Survey on Alcohol and Related Conditions. *Journal of Clinical Psychiatry, 11,* 53–67.

Purdie, F. R., Honigman, T. B., & Rosen, P. (1981). Acute organic brain syndrome: A view of 100 cases. *Annals of Emergency Medicine, 10,* 455–461.

Putnam, F. W. (1997). *Dissociation in children and adolescents: A developmental approach.* New York: Guilford.

Puxley, C. (2009, March 6). Greyhound attacker 'getting away with murder,' family says: Judge rules killer not criminally responsible due to mental illness for 'barbaric' bus attack. *Toronto Star,* A2.

Qizilbash, N., Whitehead, A., Higgins, J., Wilcock, G., Schneider, L., et al. (1998). Cholinesterase inhibition for Alzheimer disease: A meta-analysis of Tacrine trials. *Journal of the American Medical Association, 280,* 1777–1782.

Qualls, S. H. (2016). Caregiving families within the long-term services and support system for older adults. *American Psychologist, 71,* 283–293.

Quinsey, V. L., Harris, G. T., Rice, M. E., & Cormier, C. A. (1998). *Violent offenders: Appraising and managing risk.* Washington, DC: American Psychological Association.

R. v. Campagna, 1999 6659 (BC SC).

R. v. Conception, 2014 SCC 60.

Rabin, L. A., Spadaccini, A. T., Brodale, D. L., Grant, K. S., Elbulok-Charcape, M. M., & Barr, W. B. (2014). Utilization rates of computerized tests and test batteries among clinical neuropsychologists in the United States and Canada. *Professional Psychology: Research and Practice, 45,* 368–377.

Rabiner, D. L., Anastopoulos, A. D., Costello, E. J., et al. (2009). The misuse and diversion of prescribed ADHD medications by college students. *Journal of Attention Disorders, 13,* 144–153.

Rachman, S. (1998). A cognitive theory of obsessions. In E. Sanavio (Ed.), *Behaviour and cognitive therapy today: Essays in honour of Hans J. Eysenck* (pp. 209–222). Oxford, England: Elsevier Science Limited.

Rachman, S. (2002). A cognitive theory of compulsive checking. *Behaviour Research and Therapy, 40*, 625–639.

Rachman, S. (2003a). Compulsive checking. In R. G. Menzies & P. de Silva (Eds.), *Obsessive compulsive disorder: Theory research and treatment* (pp. 142–143). New York: John Wiley & Sons.

Rachman, S. (2003b). *The treatment of obsessions.* New York: Oxford University Press.

Rachman, S. (2012). Health anxiety disorders: A cognitive construal. *Behaviour Research and Therapy, 50*, 502–512.

Rachman, S., Gruter-Andrew, J., & Shafran, R. (2000). Post-event processing in social anxiety. *Behaviour Research and Therapy, 38*, 611–617.

Rachman, S., & Hodgson, R. J. (1980). *Obsessions and compulsions.* Englewood Cliffs, NJ: Prentice-Hall.

Rachman, S., & Shafran, R. (1998). Cognitive and behavioural features of obsessive-compulsive disorder. In R. P. Swinson, M. M. Antony, S. Rachman, & M. A. Richter (Eds.), *Obsessive-compulsive disorder: Theory, research, and treatment* (pp. 51–78). New York: Guilford.

Radomsky, A. S., Dugas, M. J., Alcolado, G. M., & Lavoie, S. L. (2014). When more is less: Doubt, repetition, memory, metamemory, and compulsive checking in OCD. *Behaviour Research and Therapy, 59*, 30–39.

Ragan, C. I., Bard, I., & Singh, I. (2013). What should we do about student use of cognitive enhancers? An analysis of current evidence. *Neuropharmacology, 64*, 588–595.

Ragland, J. D., Laird, A. R., Ranganath, C., et al. (2009). Prefrontal activation deficits during episodic memory in schizophrenia. *American Journal of Psychiatry, 166*, 863–874.

Rahe, R. H., & Lind, E. (1971). Psychosocial factors and sudden cardiac death: A pilot study. *Journal of Psychosomatic Research, 15*, 19–24.

Rahe, R. H., & Ransom, J. A. (1968). Life-change patterns surrounding illness. *Journal of Psychosomatic Research, 11*, 341–345.

Raina, P. S., et al. (2009). The Canadian Longitudinal Study on Aging (CLSA). *Canadian Journal on Aging, 28*, 221–229.

Rajkowska, G., Selemon, L. D., & Goldman-Rakic, P. S. (1998). Neuronal and glial soma size in the prefrontal cortex: A postmortem morphometric study of schizophrenia and Huntington disease. *Archives of General Psychiatry, 55*, 215–224.

Ransom, D. C., LaGuardia, J. G., Woody, E. Z., & Boyd, J. L. (2010). Interpersonal interactions on online forums addressing eating concerns. *International Journal of Eating Disorders, 43*, 161–170.

Ranta, K., Kaltiala-Heino, R., Rantanen, P., & Marttunen, M. (2009). Social phobia in Finnish general adolescent population: Prevalence, comorbidity, individual and family correlates, and service use. *Depression and Anxiety, 26*, 528–536.

Rapee, R. M. (2013). The preventative effects of a brief, early intervention for preschool-aged children at risk for internalising: Follow-up into middle adolescence. *Journal of Child Psychology and Psychiatry, 54*, 780–788.

Rapee, R. M., & Heimberg, R. G. (1997). A cognitive-behavioral model of anxiety in social phobia. *Behaviour Research and Therapy, 35*, 741–756.

Rapee, R. M., Schniering, C. A., & Hudson, J. L. (2009). Anxiety disorders during childhood and adolescence: Origins and treatment. *Annual Review of Clinical Psychology, 5*, 311–341.

Raphael, D. (2009). Poverty, human development, and health in Canada: Research, practice, and advocacy dilemmas. *Canadian Journal of Nursing Research, 41*, 7–18.

Rapoport, J., Chavez, A., Greenstein, D., et al. (2009). Autism spectrum disorders and childhood-onset schizophrenia: Clinical and biological contributions to a relation revisited. *Journal of the American Academy of Child and Adolescent Psychiatry, 48*, 10–18.

Rapp, S. R., Parisi, S. A., Walsh, D. A., & Wallace, C. E. (1988). Detecting depression in elderly medical patients. *Journal of Consulting and Clinical Psychology, 56*, 509–513.

Rappaport, J., & Chinsky, J. M. (1974). Models for delivery of service from a historical and conceptual perspective. *Professional Psychology, 5*, 42–50.

Rashid, F. L., Morris, R. D., & Sevcik, R. A. (2005). Relationship between home literacy environment and reading achievement in children with reading disabilities. *Journal of Learning Disabilities, 38*, 2–11.

Rasmussen, K. A., Slish, M. L., Wingate, L. R., Davidson, C. L., & Grant, D. M. (2012). Can perceived burdensomeness explain the relationship between suicide and perfectionism? *Suicide and Life-Threatening Behavior, 42*, 121–128.

Ratnasingham, S., Cairney, J., Rehm, J., Manson, H., & Kurdyak, P. A. (2012). *Opening eyes, opening minds: The Ontario burden of mental illness and addictions report.* An ICES/PHO report. Toronto: Institute for Clinical Evaluative Sciences and Public Health Ontario.

Rauch, S. L., et al. (1994). Regional cerebral blood flow measured during symptom provocation in obsessive-compulsive disorder using oxygen-15 labeled carbon dioxide and positron emission tomography. *Archives of General Psychiatry, 51*, 62–70.

Raupach, T., & Onno, C. P. (2011). Pharmacotherapy for smoking cessation: Current advances and research topics. *CNS Drugs, 25*, 371–382.

Ravindran, L. N., & Stein, M. B. (2010). The pharmacologic treatment of anxiety disorders: A review of progress. *Journal of Clinical Psychiatry, 71*, 839–854.

Ravindran, L., & Kennedy, S. H. (2007a). Are antidepressants as effective as claimed? Yes, but… *Canadian Journal of Psychiatry, 52*, 98–99.

Ravindran, L., & Kennedy, S. H. (2007b). In debate: Response to Dr. Moncrieff. *Canadian Journal of Psychiatry, 52*, 102.

Raymond, N. C., Coleman, E., Ohlerking, F., Christenson, G. A., & Miner, M. (1999). Psychiatric comorbidity in pedophilic sex offenders. *American Journal of Psychiatry, 156*, 786–788.

Read, J. P., Bachrach, R. L., Wright, A. G. C., & Colder, C. R. (2016). PTSD symptom course during the first year of college. *Psychological Trauma: Theory, Research, Practice, and Policy, 8*, 393–403.

Ready, R. E., & Veague, H. B. (2014). Training in psychological assessment: Current practices of clinical psychology programs. *Professional Psychology: Research and Practice, 45*, 278–282.

Reavley, N. J., Mackinnon, A. J., Morgan, A. J., & Jorm, A. F. (2014). Stigmatising attitudes towards people with mental disorders: A comparison of Australian health professionals with the general community. *Australian and New Zealand Journal of Psychiatry, 48*, 433–441.

Rechlin, T., Loew, T. H., & Joraschky, P. (1997). Pseudoseizure "status." *Journal of Psychosomatic Research, 42*, 495–498.

Rector, N. A., Bagby, R. M., Segal, Z. V., Joffe, R., & Levitt, A. (2000). Self-criticism and dependency in depressed patients treated with cognitive therapy or pharmacotherapy. *Cognitive Therapy and Research, 24*, 571–584.

Rector, N. A., Kocovski, N. L., & Ryder, A. G. (2006). Social anxiety and the fear of causing discomfort to others. *Journal of Social and Clinical Psychology, 25*, 906–918.

Rector, N. A., Richter, M. A., Lerman, B., & Regev, R. (2015). A pilot test of the additive benefits of physical exercise to CBT for OCD. *Cognitive Behaviour Therapy, 44*, 328–340.

Rector, N. A., Seeman, M. V., & Segal, Z. V. (2003). Cognitive therapy for schizophrenia: A preliminary randomized controlled trial. *Schizophrenia Research, 63*, 1–11.

Rector, N. A., Segal, Z. V., & Gemar, M. (1998). Schema research in depression: A Canadian perspective. *Canadian Journal of Behavioural Science, 30*, 213–224.

Redmond, D. E. (1977). Alterations in the function of the nucleus locus coeruleus. In I. Hanin & E. Usdin (Eds.), *Animal models in psychiatry and neurology.* New York: Pergamon.

Reed, J. C., & Reed, H. B. C. (1997). The Halstead-Reitan Neuropsychological Battery. In G. Goldstein & T. Incagnoli (Eds.), *Contemporary approaches to neuropsychological assessment* (pp. 93–130). New York: Plenum.

Regehr, C., Glancy, D., & Pitts, A. (2013). Interventions to reduce stress in university students: A review and meta-analysis. *Journal of Affective Disorders, 148*, 1–11.

Regier, D. A., Boyd, J. H., Burke, J. D., Rae, D. S., et al. (1988). One-month prevalence of mental disorders in the United States: Based on five epidemiologic catchment area sites. *Archives of General Psychiatry, 45*, 977–986.

Regier, D. A., Narrow, W. E., Clarke, D. E., Kraemer, H. C., et al. (2013). *DSM-5* field trials in the United States and Canada, Part II: Test–retest reliability of selected categorical diagnoses. *The American Journal of Psychiatry, 170*, 59–70.

Regier, D. A., Narrow, W. E., Kuhl, E. A., & Kupfer, D. J. (2009). The conceptual development of DSM-V. *American Journal of Psychiatry, 166*, 645–649.

Regina v. Chaulk, [1990] 3 SCR 1303.

Regina v. Rogers, 1990 CanLII 432 (BC CA).

Regina v. Swain, [1991] 1 SCR 933.

Regina v. Trochym, 2007 SCC 6, [2007] 1 SCR 239.

Rehm, J., Baliunas, D., Brochu, S., et al. (2006). *The costs of substance abuse in Canada 2002.* Ottawa: Canadian Centre on Substance Abuse.

Reid, J. L., Hammond, D., & Driezen, P. (2010). Socio-economic status and smoking in Canada, 1999–2006: Has there been any progress on disparities in tobacco use? *Canadian Journal of Public Health, 101*, 73–78.

Reid, J. L., Hammond, D., McCrory, C., Dubin, J. A., & Leatherdale, S. T. (2015). Use of caffeinated energy drinks among secondary school students in Ontario: Prevalence and correlates of using energy drinks and mixing alcohol. *Canadian Journal of Public Health, 106*, e101–e108.

Reid, J. L., Hammond, D., Rynard, V. L., & Burkhalter, R. (2015). *Tobacco use in Canada: Patterns and trends: 2015 edition.* Waterloo, ON: Propel Centre for Population Health Impact.

Reid, R. C., Carpenter, B. N., Hook, J. N., Garos, S., et al. (2012). Report of findings from a *DSM-5* field trial for hypersexual disorder. *Journal of Sexual Medicine, 9*, 2868–2877.

Reinders, A. A. T. S., et al. (2006). Psychobiological characteristics of dissociative identity disorder: A symptom provocation study. *Biological Psychiatry, 60*, 730–740.

Reininghaus, U., Duttka, R., Dazzan, P., Doody, G. A., et al. (2015). Mortality in schizophrenia and other psychoses: A 10-year follow-up of the AESOP first-episode cohort. *Schizophrenia Bulletin, 41*, 664–673.

Reiss, A. L. (2009). Childhood developmental disorders: An academic and clinical convergence point for psychiatry, neurology, psychology and pediatrics. *Journal of Child Psychology and Psychiatry, 50*, 87–98.

Reiss, D., Heatherington, E. M., Plomin, R., Howe, G. W., Simmens, S. J., et al. (1995). Genetic questions for environmental studies: Differential parenting and psychopathology in adolescence. *Archives of General Psychiatry, 52*, 925–936.

Reissing, E. D. (2009). Vaginismus: Evaluation and management. In A. Goldstein, C. F. Pukall, & I. Goldstein (Eds.), *Female sexual pain*

disorders: Evaluation and management (pp. 229–234). New York: Wiley-Blackwell.

Reitmanova, S., & Gustafson, D. L. (2009). Mental health needs of visible minority immigrants in a small urban center: Recommendations for policy makers and service providers. *Journal of Immigrant Minority Health, 11*, 46–56.

Renneberg, B., Goldstein, A. J., Phillips, D., & Chambless, D. L. (1990). Intensive behavioral group treatment of avoidant personality disorder. *Behavior Therapy, 21*, 363–377.

Rennie, D. L. (1998). *Person-centred counseling: An experiential approach.* London: Sage.

Renvoise, E. B., & Beveridge, A. W. (1989). Mental illness and the late Victorians: A study of patients admitted to three asylums in York, 1880–1884. *Psychological Medicine, 19*, 19–28.

Report of the Standing Committee on the Status of Women. (2014). *Eating disorders among girls and women in Canada.* Ottawa: Parliament of Canada.

Rescorla, L., Achenbach, T., Almqvist, F., Bilenberg, N., et al. (2007). Epidemiological comparisons of problems and positive qualities reported by adolescents in 24 countries. *Journal of Consulting and Clinical Psychology, 75*, 351–358.

Rescorla, L., Achenbach, T., Ivanova, M. Y., Dumenci, L., et al. (2007). Behavioral and emotional problems reported by parents of children ages 6 to 16 in 31 societies. *Journal of Emotional and Behavioral Disorders, 15*, 130–142.

Rescorla, R. A. (1988). Pavlovian conditioning: It's not what you think it is. *American Psychologist, 43*, 151–160.

Research Units on Pediatric Psychopharmacology Network. (2005). Randomized, controlled, crossover trial of methylphenidate in pervasive developmental disorders with hyperactivity. *Archives of General Psychiatry, 62*, 1266–1274.

Resick, P. A. (1993). The psychological impact of rape. *Journal of Interpersonal Violence, 8*, 223–255.

Resick, P. A., et al. (2002). A comparison of cognitive processing therapy with prolonged exposure therapy and a waiting list condition for the treatment of chronic posttraumatic stress disorder in female rape victims. *Journal of Consulting and Clinical Psychology, 70*, 867–879.

Resick, P. A., et al. (2008). A randomized clinical trial to dismantle components of cognitive processing therapy for posttraumatic stress disorder in female victims of interpersonal violence. *Journal of Consulting and Clinical Psychology, 76*, 243–258.

Resick, P. A., & Schnicke, M. K. (1993). Cognitive processing therapy for sexual assault victims. *Journal of Consulting and Clinical Psychology, 60*, 748–756.

Reuters. (1999, October 27). Pontiff says he continues to enjoy life despite aging. *Toronto Star*, p. 6.

Reynolds, C. F., et al. (2006). Maintenance treatment of major depression in old age. *New England Journal of Medicine, 354*, 1130–1138.

Reynolds, C. R., Chastain, R. L., Kaufman, A. S., & McLean, J. E. (1997). Demographic characteristics and IQ among adults: Analysis of the WAIS-R standardization sample as a function of the stratification variables. *Journal of School Psychology, 25*, 323–342.

Reynolds, C. R., & Suzuki, L. A. (2012). Bias in psychological assessment: An empirical review and recommendations. In I. B. Weiner, J. R. Graham, & J. A. Naglieri (Eds.), *Handbook of psychology, Vol. 10* (pp. 82–113). Hoboken, NJ: John Wiley & Sons.

Reynolds, S., Wilson, C., Austin, J., & Hooper, L. (2012). Effects of psychotherapy for anxiety in children and adolescents: A meta-analytic review. *Clinical Psychology Review, 32*, 251–262.

Rezendes, M., Russell, J., Helman, S., Cramer, M., & Wallack, T. (2016, June 23). The desperate and the dead: Families in fear: Closing psychiatric hospitals seemed humane, but the state failed to build a system to replace them. *The Boston Globe.*

Rheaume, G. (2000). *Remembrance of patients past: Patient life at the Toronto Hospital for the Insane, 1870–1940.* Don Mills, ON: Oxford University Press.

Rhee, S. H., & Waldman, I. D. (2002). Genetic and environmental influences on antisocial behavior: A meta-analysis of twin and adoption studies. *Psychological Bulletin, 128,* 490–529.

Rhodes, A., Goering, P., To, T., and Williams, J. (2002). Gender and outpatient mental health service use. *Social Science and Medicine, 54,* 1–10.

Rice, M. E. (1997). Violent offender research and implications for the criminal justice system. *American Psychologist, 52,* 414–423.

Rice, M. E., & Harris, G. T. (1995). Violent recidivism: Assessing predictive validity. *Journal of Consulting and Clinical Psychology, 63,* 737–748.

Rice, M. E., & Harris, G. T. (2002). Men who molest their sexually immature daughters: Is a special explanation required? *Journal of Abnormal Psychology, 111,* 329–339.

Rice, M. E., & Harris, G. T. (2003). The size and sign of treatment effects in sex offender therapy. *Annals of the New York Academy of Sciences, 989,* 428–440.

Rice, M. E., & Harris, G. T. (2013). Treatment for adult sex offenders: May we reject the null hypothesis? In K. Harrison & B. Rainey (Eds.), *The Wiley-Blackwell handbook of legal and ethical aspects* (pp. 219–235). Chichester, England: Wiley.

Rice, M. E., Harris, G. T., & Lang, C. (2013). Validation of and revision to the VRAG and SORAG: The Violence Risk Appraisal Guide-Revised. *Psychological Assessment, 25,* 951–965.

Richards, D. A. (2001). Drinking. In L. Crozier & P. Lane (Eds.), *Addicted: Notes from the belly of the beast* (pp. 105–121). Vancouver/Toronto: Greystone Books.

Richards, D., & Timulak, L. (2012). Client-identified helpful and hindering events in therapist-delivered vs. self-administered online cognitive-behavioural treatments for depression in college students. *Counselling Psychology Quarterly, 25,* 251–262.

Richardson, L. K., et al. (2009). Current directions in videoconferencing tele-mental health research. *Clinical Psychology Science and Practice, 16,* 323–338.

Rief, W., Hiller, W., & Margraf, J. (1998). Cognitive aspects of hypochondriasis and somatization syndrome. *Journal of Abnormal Psychology, 107,* 587–596.

Rief, W., & Martin, A. (2014). How to use the *DSM-5* somatic symptom disorder diagnosis in research and practice: A critical evaluation and a proposal for modifications. *Annual Review of Clinical Psychology, 10,* 339–367.

Riley, E. P., Infante, M. A., & Warren, K. R. (2011). Fetal alcohol syndrome disorders: An overview. *Neuropsychology Review, 21,* 73–80.

Riley, K. P., Snowdon, D. A., Desrosiers, M. F., & Markesberry, W. R. (2005). Early life linguistic ability, late life cognitive function, and neuropathology: Findings from the Nun Study. *Neurobiology and Aging, 26,* 341–347.

Ripke, S., Wray, N. R., Lewis, C. M., Hamilton, S. P., Weissman, M. M., Breen, G., Byrne, E. M., ..., Sullivan, P. F. (2013). A mega-analysis of genome-wide association studies for major depressive disorder. *Molecular Psychiatry, 18,* 497–511.

Ritterband, L. M., Thorndike, F. P., Gonder-Frederick, L. A., et al. (2009). Efficacy of an Internet-based behavioral intervention for adults with insomnia. *Archives of General Psychiatry, 66,* 692–698.

Rizzi, T. S., Beunders, G., Rizzu, P., Sistermans, E., et al. (2012). Supporting the generalist genes hypothesis for intellectual ability/disability: The case of SNAP25. *Genes, Brain, and Behavior, 11,* 767–771.

Roberts, S., O'Connor, K., Aardema, F., & Bélanger, C. (2015). The impact of emotions on body-focused repetitive behaviors: Evidence from a non-treatment-seeking sample. *Journal of Behavior Therapy and Experimental Psychiatry, 46,* 189–197.

Robertson, D. A., King-Kallimanis, B. L., & Kenny, R. A. (2016). Negative perceptions of aging predict longitudinal decline in cognitive functioning. *Psychology and Aging, 31,* 71–81.

Robins, L. N. (1966). *Deviant children grown up.* Baltimore: Williams & Wilkins.

Robins, L. N., Helzer, J. E., Przybec, T. R., & Regier, D. A. (1988). Alcohol disorders in the community: A report from the Epidemiologic Catchment Area. In R. M. Rose & J. E. Barrett (Eds.), *Alcoholism: Origins and outcome.* New York: Raven.

Robins, R., John, O., Caspi, A., Moffitt, T., & Stouthamer-Loeber, M. (1996). Resilient, over-controlled, and undercontrolled boys: Three replicable personality types. *Journal of Personality and Social Psychology, 70,* 157–171.

Robinson, D., Woerner, M. G., Alvir, J., Bilder, R., Goldman, R., et al. (1999). Predictors of relapse following response from a first episode of schizophrenia or schizoaffective disorder. *Archives of General Psychiatry, 56,* 241–247.

Robinson, J., Sareen, J., Cox, B. J., & Bolton, J. (2009). Self-medication of anxiety disorders with alcohol and drugs: Results from a nationally representative sample. *Journal of Anxiety Disorders, 23,* 38–45.

Robinson, L. A., Klesges, R. C., Zbikowski, S. M., & Glaser, R. (1997). Predictors of risk for different stages of adolescent smoking in a biracial sample. *Journal of Consulting and Clinical Psychology, 65,* 653–662.

Robinson, N. S., Garber, J., & Hillsman, R. (1995). Cognitions and stress: Direct and moderating effects on depression versus externalizing symptoms during the junior high school transition. *Journal of Abnormal Psychology, 104,* 453–463.

Robitaille, A., Orpana, H., & McIntosh, C. N. (2012). Reciprocal relationship between social support and psychological distress among a national sample of older adults: An autoregressive cross-lagged model. *Canadian Journal on Aging, 31,* 13–24.

Rock, A. (2015, September 24). When dealing with mental illness, help is only a phone call away. *The Globe and Mail.*

Rodgers, R. F., Lowy, A. S., Halperin, D. M., & Franko, D. L. (2016). A meta-analysis examining the influence of pro-eating disorder websites on body image and eating pathology. *European Eating Disorders Review, 24,* 3–8.

Rodgers, R. F., Skowron, S., & Chabrol, H. (2012). Disordered eating and group membership among members of a pro-anorexic online community. *European Eating Disorders Review, 20,* 9–12.

Rodin, J., McAvay, G., & Timko, C. (1988). A longitudinal study of depressed mood and sleep disturbances in elderly adults. *Journal of Gerontology: Psychological Sciences, 43,* 45–53.

Rodrigues, H., Figueira, I., Lopes, A., Goncalves, R., Mendlowicz, M. V., et al. (2014). Does d-cycloserine enhance exposure therapy for anxiety disorders in humans? A meta-analysis. *PLoS ONE, 9.7.*

Rodriguez-Murillo, Gogos, J. A., & Karayiorgou, M. (2012). The genetic architecture of schizophrenia: New mutations and emerging paradigms. *Annual Review of Medicine, 63,* 63–80.

Roesch, R., Zapf, P. A., Eaves, D., & Webster, C. D. (1999). *The fitness interview test* (Rev. ed.). Burnaby, BC: Mental Health Law and Policy Institute.

Rogalski, E. J., Gefen, T., Shi, J., Samimi, M., et al. (2013). Youthful memory capacity in older brains: Anatomic and genetic clues from the Northwestern SuperAging project. *Journal of Cognitive Neuroscience, 25,* 29–36.

Rogeberg, O. (2013). Correlations between cannabis use and IQ change in the Dunedin cohort are consistent with confounding from socioeconomic status. *Proceedings of the National Academy of Sciences of the United States of America, 110,* 4251–4254.

Rogers, C. R. (1951). *Client-centered therapy.* Boston: Houghton Mifflin.

Rogers, C. R. (1961). *On becoming a person: A therapist's view of psychotherapy.* Boston: Houghton Mifflin.

Rogers, R. (2000). The uncritical acceptance of risk assessment in forensic practice. *Law and Human Behavior, 24,* 595–605.

Rogers, R. (2003). Standardizing DSM-IV diagnoses: The clinical applications of structured interviews. *Journal of Personality Assessment, 81,* 220–225.

Rogers, S. L., Doody, R. S., Mohs, R. C., Friedhoff, L. T., & the Donepezil Study Group. (1998). Donepezil improves cognition and global function in Alzheimer disease. *Archives of Internal Medicine, 158,* 1021–1031.

Rohan, K. J. (2008). *Coping with the seasons: A cognitive-behavioral approach to seasonal affective disorder.* New York: Oxford University Press.

Rohan, K. J., Roecklein, K. A., Lacy, T. M., & Vacek, P. M. (2009). Winter depression recurrence one year after cognitive-behavioral therapy, light therapy, or combination treatment. *Behavior Therapy, 40,* 225–238.

Rohan, K. J., Roecklein, K. A., Tierney Lindsey, K., Johnson, L. G., Lippy, R. D., Lacy, T. M., & Barton, F. B. (2007). A randomized controlled trial of cognitive-behavioral therapy, light therapy, and their combination for seasonal affective disorder. *Journal of Consulting and Clinical Psychology, 75,* 489–500.

Rollnick, S., & Allison, J. (2004). Motivational interviewing. In N. Heather & T. Stockwell (Eds.), *The essential handbook of treatment and prevention of alcohol problems* (pp. 105–115). Chichester, England: John Wiley & Sons.

Roman-Urrestarazu, A., Lindholm, P., Moilanen, I., Kiviniemi, V., Mieltunen, J., et al. (2015). Brain structural deficits and working memory fMRI dysfunction in young adults who were diagnosed with ADHD in adolescence. *European Child and Adolescent Psychiatry,* 1–10.

Romano, E., Baillargeon, R. H., Wu, H.-X., et al. (2002). Prevalence of methylphenidate use and change over a two-year period: A nationwide study of 2- to 11-year old Canadian children. *Journal of Pediatrics, 141,* 71–75.

Romano, E., Tremblay, R. E., Vitaro, F., Zoccolillo, M., & Pagani, L. (2001). Prevalence of psychiatric diagnoses and the role of perceived impairment: Findings from an adolescent community sample. *Journal of Child Psychology and Psychiatry, 42,* 451–461.

Romanow, R. J. (2002). *Building on values: The future of health care in Canada.* Ottawa: Commission on the Future of Health Care in Canada.

Romanow, R. J. (2006). Canada's medicare—at the crossroads? *Canadian Psychology, 47,* 1–8.

Romanow, R. J., & Marchildon, G. P. (2003). Psychological services and the future of health care in Canada. *Canadian Psychology, 44,* 283–295.

Ronningstam, E., & Gunderson, J. (1990). Identifying criteria for narcissistic personality disorder. *American Journal of Psychiatry, 147,* 918–922.

Rooksby, M., Elouafkaoui, P., Humphris, G., Clarkson, J., & Freeman, R. (2015). Internet-assisted delivery of cognitive behavioural therapy (CBT) for childhood anxiety: Systematic review and meta-analysis. *Journal of Anxiety Disorders, 29,* 83–92.

Roos, A., Grant, J. E., Fouche, J., Stein, D. J., & Lochner, C. (2015). A comparison of brain volume and cortical thickness in excoriation (skin picking) disorder and trichotillomania (hair pulling disorder) in women. *Behavioural Brain Research, 279,* 255–258.

Rosa-Alcazar, A. I., Sanchez-Meca, J., Gomez-Consesa, A., & Marin-Martinez, F. (2008). Psychological treatment of obsessive-compulsive disorder: A meta-analysis. *Clinical Psychology Review, 28,* 1310–1325.

Rosch, P. J. (1998). Reminiscences of Hans Selye and the birth of "stress." *Stress Medicine, 14,* 1–6.

Rose, D. T., Abramson, L. Y., Hodulik, C. J., Halberstadt, L., & Gaye, L. (1994). Heterogeneity of cognitive style among depressed inpatients. *Journal of Abnormal Psychology, 103,* 419–429.

Rosen, J. L., Miller, T. J., D'Andrea, J. T., McGlashan, T. H., & Woods, S. W. (2006). Comorbid diagnoses in patients meeting criteria for the schizophrenia prodrome. *Schizophrenia Research, 85,* 124–131.

Rosen, R. C. (1991). Alcohol and drug effects on sexual response: Human experimental and clinical studies. *Annual Review of Sex Research, 2,* 119–180.

Rosen, R. C., & Leiblum, S. R. (1995). Treatment of sexual disorders in the 1990s: An integrated approach. *Journal of Consulting and Clinical Psychology, 63,* 877–890.

Rosen, R. C., Leiblum, S. R., & Spector, I. (1994). Psychologically based treatment for male erectile disorder: A cognitive-interpersonal model. *Journal of Sex and Marital Therapy, 20,* 67–85.

Rosen, R. C., & Rosen, L. (1981). *Human sexuality.* New York: Knopf.

Rosenbaum, M. (1980). The role of the term schizophrenia in the decline of diagnoses of multiple personality. *Archives of General Psychiatry, 37,* 1383–1385.

Rosenberg, D. R., Keshavan, M. S., O'Hearn, K. M., Seymour, A. B., Birmaher, B., et al. (1997). Frontostriatal measurement in treatment-naive children with obsessive-compulsive disorder. *Archives of General Psychiatry, 54,* 824–830.

Rosenfarb, I. S., Goldstein, M. J., Mintz, J., & Neuchterlein, K. H. (1994). Expressed emotion and subclinical psychopathology observable within transactions between schizophrenics and their family members. *Journal of Abnormal Psychology, 104,* 259–267.

Rosenfeld, D., Hebert, P. C., Stanbrook, M. B., et al. (2011). Time to address stimulant abuse on our campuses (Editorial). *Canadian Medical Association Journal, 183,* 1345.

Rosenheck, R., Cramer, J., Allan, E., Erdos, J., Frisman, L. K., Xu, W., ... Charney, D. (1999). Cost-effectiveness of clozapine in patients with high and low levels of hospital use. Department of Veterans Affairs Cooperative Study Group on Clozapine in Refractory Schizophrenia. *Archives of General Psychiatry, 56,* 565–572.

Rosenman, R. H., Brand, R. J., Jenkins, C. D., Friedman, M., Straus, R., & Wurm, M. (1975). Coronary heart disease in the Western Collaborative Group Study: Final follow-up experience of 8 years. *Journal of the American Medical Association, 233,* 872–877.

Rosenthal, D. (1963). *The Genain quadruplets.* New York: Basic Books.

Rosenthal, D. (1974). Genetic research in the schizophrenic syndrome. In R. J. Morris (Ed.), *Perspectives in abnormal behavior* (pp. 205–213). Oxford: Pergamon Press.

Rosenthal, N. E., Sack, D. A., Gillin, J. C., et al. (1984). Seasonal affective disorder: A description of the syndrome and preliminary findings with light therapy. *Archives of General Psychiatry, 41,* 72–80.

Rosenzweig, S. (1936). Some implicit common factors in diverse methods of psychotherapy. *American Journal of Orthopsychiatry, 6,* 412–415.

Ross, C. A. (1991). Epidemiology of multiple personality disorder and dissociation. *Psychiatric Clinics of North America, 14*, 503–517.

Ross, C. A. (1997). *Dissociative identity disorder: Diagnosis, clinical features, and treatment of multiple personality.* Toronto: John Wiley & Sons.

Ross, C. A. (2009). Errors of logic and scholarship concerning dissociative identity disorder. *Journal of Child Sexual Abuse, 18*, 221–231.

Ross, C. A. (2015). Editorial: Problems with *DSM-5* somatic symptom disorder. *Journal of Trauma and Dissociation, 16*, 341–348.

Ross, C. A., Joshi, S., & Currie, R. P. (1990). Dissociative experiences in the general population: A factor analysis. *Hospital and Community Psychiatry, 42*, 297–301.

Ross, D. M., & Ross, S. A. (1982). *Hyperactivity: Research, theory, and action.* New York: John Wiley & Sons.

Ross, S., Heath, N. L., & Toste, J. R. (2009). Non-suicidal self-injury and eating pathology in high school students. *American Journal of Orthopsychiatry, 79*, 83–92.

Ross-Gower, J., Waller, G., Tyson, M., & Elliott, P. (1998). Reported sexual abuse and subsequent psychopathology among women attending psychological clinics: The mediating role of dissociation. *British Journal of Clinical Psychology, 37*, 313–326.

Roth, W. T. (2010). Diversity of effective treatments of panic attacks: What do they have in common? *Depression and Anxiety, 27*, 5–11.

Rothbart, M. K., & Putnam, S. P. (2002). Temperament and socialization. In L. Pulkkinen & A. Caspi (Eds.), *Personality in the life course: Paths to successful development* (pp. 19–45). Mahwah, NJ: Erlbaum.

Rothe, C., Koszycki, D., Bradwejn, J., King, N., Deluca, V., Tharmalingam, S., et al. (2006). Association of the Val158Met 31Catechol OMethyltransferase genetic polymorphism with panic disorder. *Neuropsychopharmacology, 31*, 2237–2242.

Rourke, B. P. (2008). Neuropsychology as a (psycho)social science: Implications for research and clinical practice. *Canadian Psychology, 49*, 35–41.

Roussy, S., & Toupin, J. (2000). Behavioral inhibition deficits in juvenile psychopaths. *Aggressive Behavior, 26*, 413–424.

Rowa, K., Antony, M. M., Brar, S., Summerfeldt, L. J., & Swinson, R. P. (2000). Treatment histories of patients with three anxiety disorders. *Depression and Anxiety, 12*, 92–98.

Rowa, K., Paulitzki, J. R., Ierullo, M. D., Chiang, B., Antony, M. M., McCabe, R. E., & Moscovitch, D. A. (2015). A false sense of security: Safety behaviors erode objective speech performance in individuals with social anxiety disorder. *Behavior Therapy, 46*, 304–314.

Rowa, K., & Purdon, C. (2003). Why are certain intrusive thoughts more upsetting than others? *Behavioural and Cognitive Psychotherapy, 31*, 1–11.

Rowa, K., Purdon, C., Summerfeldt, L. J., & Antony, M. M. (2005). Why are some obsessions more upsetting than others? *Behaviour Research and Therapy, 43*, 1453–1465.

Rowland, D. L., Cooper, S. E., & Slob, A. K. (1996). Genital and psychoaffective responses to erotic stimulation in sexually functional and dysfunctional men. *Journal of Abnormal Psychology, 105*, 194–203.

Roxborough, H., Hewitt, P. L, Kaldas, J., Flett, G. L., Caelian, C., Sherry, S., & Sherry, D. L. (2012). Perfectionistic self-presentation, socially prescribed perfectionism, and suicide in youth: A test of the perfectionism social disconnection model. *Suicide and Life-Threatening Behavior, 42*, 217–233.

Roy, A. (1994). Recent biologic studies on suicide. *Suicide and Life Threatening Behaviors, 24*, 10–24.

Royal Commission on Aboriginal Peoples (RCAP). (1996). Residential schools. In *Report of the Royal Commission on Aboriginal Peoples* (pp. 333–385). Ottawa: Canada Communication Group.

Royal, S., MacDonald, D. E., & Dionne, M. M. (2013). Development and validation of the Fat Talk Questionnaire. *Body Image, 10*, 62–69.

Rubin, G. J., Brewin, C. R., Greenberg, N., Simpson, J., & Wessely, S. (2005). Psychological and behavioural reactions to the bombings in London on 7 July 2005: Cross sectional survey of a representative sample of Londoners. *British Medical Journal, 331*, 606–612.

Rubin, R. T., Phillips, J. J., Sadow, T. F., & McCracken, J. T. (1995). Adrenal gland volume in major depression: Increase during the depressive episode and decrease with successful treatment. *Archives of General Psychiatry, 52*, 213–218.

Rucklidge, J. J., & Kaplan, B. J. (1997). Psychological functioning in women identified in adulthood with Attention-Deficit/Hyperactivity Disorder. *Journal of Attention Disorders, 2*, 167–176.

Rucklidge, J. J., & Tannock, R. (2001). Psychiatric, psychosocial, and cognitive functioning of female adolescents with ADHD. *Journal of the American Academy of Child and Adolescent Psychiatry, 40*, 530–540.

Rudolph, K. D., Flynn, M., Abaied, J. L., Groot, A., & Thompson, R. (2009). Why is past depression the better predictor of future depression? Stress generation as a mechanism of depression continuity in girls. *Journal of Clinical Child and Adolescent Psychology, 38*, 473–483.

Rummel, C., Kissling, W., & Leucht, S. (2005). Antidepressants as add-on treatment to anti-psychotics for people with schizophrenia and pronounced negative symptoms: A systematic review of randomized trials. *Schizophrenia Research, 80*, 85–97.

Rumsey, J. M., Zametkin, A. J., Andreasen, P., et al. (1994). Normal activation of frontotemporal language cortex in dyslexia, as measured with oxygen 15 positron emission tomography. *Archives of Neurology, 51*, 27–38.

Rumstein-McKean, O., & Hunsley, J. (2001). Interpersonal and family functioning of female survivors of childhood sexual abuse. *Clinical Psychology Review, 21*, 471–490.

Ruocco, A. C., Amirthavasagam, S., Choi-Kain, L. W., & McMain, S. F. (2013). Neural correlates of negative emotionality in borderline personality disorder: An activation-likelihood-estimation meta-analysis. *Biological Psychiatry, 73*, 153–160.

Rupert, J. (2005, May 27). Mentally ill jailed despite judge's order: Province misses deadline to fix problem identified in landmark ruling. *Ottawa Citizen.*

Ruscio, A. M., Stein, D. J., Chiu, W. T., & Kessler, R. C. (2010). The epidemiology of obsessive-compulsive disorder in the National Comorbidity Survey Replication. *Molecular Psychiatry, 15*, 53–63.

Ruscio, A. Y., et al. (2005). Should excessive worry be required for a diagnosis of generalized anxiety disorder? Results from the US National Comorbidity Survey Replication. *Psychological Medicine, 35*, 1761–1772.

Ruscio, A. Y., et al. (2007). Broadening the definition of generalized anxiety disorder: Effects on prevalence and associations with other disorders in the National Comorbidity Survey Replication. *Journal of Anxiety Disorders, 21*, 662–676.

Rush, A. J. (2011). STAR-D: Lessons learned and future implications. *Depression and Anxiety, 28*, 521–524.

Rush, A. J., Beck, A. T., Kovacs, M., & Hollon, S. D. (1977). Comparative efficacy of cognitive therapy and pharmacotherapy in the treatment of depressed outpatients. *Cognitive Therapy and Research, 1*(1), 17–38.

Rush, A. J., Beck, A. T., Kovacs, M., Weissenberger, J., & Hollon, S. D. (1982). Comparison of the effects of cognitive therapy on hopelessness and self-concept. *American Journal of Psychiatry, 139*, 862–866.

Rush, C. (2012, September 26). Mobile crisis intervention team at Toronto East General to be "fast-tracked." *The Toronto Star.*

Rutherford, M. J., Cacciola, J. S., & Alterman, A. I. (1999). Antisocial personality disorder and psychopathy in cocaine-dependent women. *American Journal of Psychiatry, 156*, 849–856.

Rutter, L. A., & Brown, T. A. (2015). Reliability and validity of the dimensional features of generalized anxiety disorder. *Journal of Anxiety Disorders, 29*, 1–6.

Ruwaard, J., Lange, A., Schrieken, B., Dolan, C. V., & Emmelkamp, P. (2012). The effectiveness of online cognitive behavioral treatment in routine clinical practice. *PLoS One, 7*, e40089.

Rybstein-Blinchik, E. (1979). Effects of different cognitive strategies on chronic pain experience. *Journal of Behavioral Medicine, 2*, 93–101.

Ryding, E., et al. (2006). Regional brain serotonin and dopamine transporter binding capacity in suicide attempters relate to impulsiveness and mental energy. *Psychiatry Research: Neuroimaging, 148*, 195–203.

Rylands, A. J., McKie, S., Elliott, R., Deaki, B., & Tarrier, N. (2011). Neural response to expressed emotion in schizophrenia investigated using fMRI. *The Journal of Nervous and Mental Disease, 199*, 25–29.

Rynor, B. (2010). Value of community treatment orders remains at issue. *Canadian Medical Association Journal, 182*(8), E337–E338.

Saavedra, L. M., Silverman, W. K., Morgan-Lopez, A. A., & Kurtines, W. M. (2010). Cognitive behavioral treatment for childhood anxiety disorders: Long-term effects on anxiety and secondary disorders in young adulthood. *Journal of Child Psychology and Psychiatry, 51*(8), 924–934.

Sacher, J., Wilson, A. A., Houle, S., Rusjan, P., Hassan, S., et al. (2010). Elevated brain monoamine oxidase A binding in the early postpartum period. *Archives of General Psychiatry, 67*, 468–474.

Sacher, J., Wilson, A. A., Rusjan, P., et al. (2011). Monoamine oxidase A (MAO-A) binding in prefrontal and anterior cingulate cortex in postpartum depression. *Biological Psychiatry, 69*, 157S.

Sachs-Ericcson, N., Corsentino, E., Moxley, J., et al. (2013). A longitudinal study of differences in late- and early-onset geriatric depression: Depressive symptoms and psychosocial, cognitive, and neurological functioning. *Aging and Mental Health, 17*, 1–11.

Sackeim, H. A., Nordlie, J. W., & Gur, R. C. (1979). A model of hysterical and hypnotic blindness: Cognition, motivation and awareness. *Journal of Abnormal Psychology, 88*, 474–489.

Sadava, S. W., & Pak, A. W. (1993). Stress-related problem drinking and alcohol problems: A longitudinal study and extension of Marlatt's model. *Canadian Journal of Behavioural Science, 25*, 446–464.

Sahay, S., Piran, N., & Maddocks, S. (2000). Sexual victimization and clinical challenges in women receiving hospital treatment for depression. *Canadian Journal of Community Mental Health, 19*, 161–174.

Sakel, M. (1938). The pharmacological shock treatment of schizophrenia. *Nervous and Mental Disease Monograph, 62*, 1–133.

Sakinofsky, I. (2007a). Caring for the suicidal patient. *Canadian Journal of Psychiatry, 52* (6 Supplement 1), 5S–6S.

Sakinofsky, I. (2007b). The current evidence base for the clinical care of suicidal patients: Strengths and weaknesses. *Canadian Journal of Psychiatry, 52* (6 Supplement 1), 7S–20S.

Saklofske, D. H., & Hildebrand, D. K. (1999). The Wechsler Adult Intelligence Scale–Third Edition: The Canadian Standardization Study. *Canadian Clinical Psychologist, 9*, 11–12.

Saklofske, D. H., Hildebrand, D. K., & Gorsuch, R. L. (2000). Replication of the factor structure of the Wechsler Adult Intelligence Scale–Third Edition with a Canadian sample. *Psychological Assessment, 12*, 436–439.

Salan, S. E., Zinberg, N. E., & Frei, E. (1975). Antiemetic effect of delta-9-THC in patients receiving cancer chemotherapy. *New England Journal of Medicine, 293*, 795–797.

Salekin, R. T., Worley, C., & Grimes, R. D. (2010). Treatment of psychopathy: A review and brief introduction to the mental model approach for psychopathy. *Behavioral Sciences and the Law, 28*, 235–266.

Salkovskis, P. M. (1998). Psychological approaches to the understanding of obsessional problems. In R. P. Swinson, M. M. Antony, S. Rachman, & M. A. Richter (Eds.), *Obsessive-compulsive disorder: Theory, research, and treatment* (pp. 33–50). New York: Guilford.

Salkovskis, P. M., & Warwick, H. M. C. (1985). Cognitive therapy of obsessive-compulsive disorder: Treating treatment failures. *Behavioural Psychotherapy, 13*, 243–255.

Salkovskis, P. M., & Warwick, H. M. C. (2001). Making sense of hypochondriasis: A cognitive theory of health anxiety. In G. J. G. Asmundson, S. Taylor, & B. J. Cox (Eds.), *Health anxiety: Clinical and research perspectives on hypochondriasis and related conditions* (pp. 46–64). Toronto: John Wiley & Sons.

Salzman, L. (1985). Psychotherapeutic management of obsessive-compulsive patients. *American Journal of Psychotherapy, 39*, 323–330.

Sampson, S. M., Rome, J. D., & Rummans, T. A. (2006). Slow-frequency rTMS reduces fibromyalgia pain. *Pain Medicine, 7*, 115–118.

Samson, C., Wilson, J., & Mazower, J. (1999). *Canada's Tibet: The killing of the Innu.* London: Clement and Foster.

Samuel, D. B. (2015). A review of the agreement between clinicians' personality disorder diagnoses and those from other methods and sources. *Clinical Psychology: Science and Practice, 22*, 1–19.

Sanday, P. R. (1981). The socio-cultural context of rape: A cross-cultural study. *Journal of Social Issues, 37*, 5–27.

Sandberg, D. A., & Lynn, S. J. (1992). Dissociative experiences, psychopathology and adjustment, and child and adolescent maltreatment in female college students. *Journal of Abnormal Psychology, 101*, 717–723.

Sandercock, G., Hurtado, V., & Cardoso, F. (2013). Changes in cardiovascular fitness in cardiac rehabilitation patients: A meta-analysis. *International Journal of Cardiology, 167*, 894–902.

Sanderson, W. C., & Rego, S. A. (2000). Empirically supported treatment for panic disorder: Research, theory, and application of cognitive behavioral therapy. *Journal of Cognitive Psychotherapy, 14*, 219–244.

Sandler, J., & Steele, H. V. (1991). Aversion methods. In F. H. Kanfer & A. P. Goldstein (Eds.), *Helping people change: A textbook of methods* (4th ed., pp. 202–247). Elmsford, NY: Pergamon Press.

Sanger, T. M., Lieberman, J. A., Tohen, M., Grundy, S., et al. (1999). Olanzapine versus haloperidol in first-episode psychosis. *American Journal of Psychiatry, 156*, 787.

Sankar, T., Tierney, T. S., & Hamani, C. (2012). Novel applications of deep brain stimulation. *Surgical Neurology International, 3* (Supplement 1), S26–S33.

Santa-Mina, E. E., et al. (2006). The Self-Injury Questionnaire: Evaluation of the psychometric properties in a clinical population. *Journal of Psychiatric and Mental Health Nursing, 13*, 221–227.

Santucci, L. C., McHugh, R. K., Elkins, R. M., Schechter, B., et al. (2014). Pilot implementation of computerized cognitive behavioral therapy in a university health setting. *Administration and Policy in Mental Health and Mental Health Services Research, 41*, 514–521.

Sarason, I. G. (1984). Stress, anxiety, and cognitive interference: Reactions to tests. *Journal of Personality and Social Psychology, 46*, 929–938.

Sartorius, A., Ruf, M., Kief, C., Demirakca, T., et al. (2008). Abnormal amygdala activation profile in pedophilia. *European Archives in Psychiatry and Clinical Neuroscience, 258*, 271–278.

Sartorius, N., & Schultze, H. (2005). *Reducing stigma due to mental illness: A report from a global program of the World Psychiatric Association.* Cambridge: Cambridge University Press.

Sartorius, N., Shapiro, R., & Jablonsky, A. (1974). The International Pilot Study of Schizophrenia. *Schizophrenia Bulletin, 1,* 21–35.

Satre, D. D. (2015). Alcohol and drug use problems among older adults. *Clinical Psychology Science and Practice, 22,* 238–254.

Sattler, J. M. (1992). *Assessment of Children: Revised and Updated Third Edition.* San Diego, CA: Jerome M. Sattler, Publisher, Inc.

Sattler, S., & Wiegel, C. (2013). Cognitive test anxiety and cognitive enhancement: The influence of students' worries on their use of performance-enhancing drugs. *Substance Use & Misuse, 48,* 220–232.

Saucier, A. (1992) *Le portrait des personnes ayant des incapacités au Québec en 1986.* Quebec City: Direction de l'évaluation, Ministère de la santé et des services sociaux.

Saulsman, L. M., & Page, A. C. (2004). The five-factor model and personality disorder empirical literature: A meta-analytic review. *Clinical Psychology Review, 23,* 1055–1085.

Savage, J. E., McMichael, O., Gorlin, E., Beadel, J. R., Teachman, B., Vladimirov, V. I., … Roberson-Nay, R. (2015). Validation of candidate anxiety disorder genes using a carbon dioxide challenge task. *Biological Psychology, 109,* 61–66.

Savoy, R. L., Frederick, B. B., Keuroghlian, A. S., & Wolk, P. C. (2012). Voluntary switching between identities in dissociative identity disorder: A functional MRI case study. *Cognitive Neuroscience, 3,* 112–119.

Sawyer, M. G., Borojevic, N., Ettridge, K. A., Spence, S. H., Sheffield, J., & Lynch, J. (2012). Do help-seeking intentions during early adolescence vary for adolescents experiencing different levels of depressive symptoms? *Journal of Adolescent Health, 50,* 236–242.

Saxena, S., & Sumner, J. (2014). Venlafaxine extended-release treatment of hoarding disorder. *International Clinical Psychopharmacology, 29,* 266–273.

Schachar, R. (1999). The MTA: Child and adolescent psychiatry in a new century. *The Canadian Journal of Psychiatry, 44,* 972.

Schade, L. C., Sandberg, J. G., Bradford, A., Harper, J. M., Holt-Lunstad, J., & Miller, R. B. (2015). A longitudinal view of the association between therapist warmth and couples' in-session process: An observational pilot study of emotionally focused couples therapy. *Journal of Marital and Family Therapy, 41,* 292–307.

Schaefer, L. C., Wheeler, C. C., & Futterweit, W. (1997). Gender identity disorders (transsexualism). In G. O. Gabbard & S. D. Atkinson (Eds.), *Synopsis of treatments of psychiatric disorders* (2nd ed., pp. 843–858). Washington, DC: American Psychiatric Press.

Schaie, K. W., & Hertzog, C. (1982). Longitudinal methods. In B. B. Wolman (Ed.), *Handbook of developmental psychology.* Englewood Cliffs, NJ: Prentice-Hall.

Scharfstein, L. A., & Beidel, D. C. (2015). Social skills and social acceptance in children with anxiety disorders. *Journal of Clinical Child & Adolescent Psychology, 44,* 826–838.

Schermerhorn, A. C., D'Onofrio, B. M., Turkheimer, E., Ganiban, J. M., Spotts, E. L., Lichtenstein, P., … Neiderhiser, J. M. (2011). A genetically informed study of associations between family functioning and child psychosocial adjustment. *Development and Psychopathology, 47,* 707–725.

Schieber, K., Kollei, I., de Zwaan, M., & Martin, A. (2015). Classification of body dysmorphic disorder—What is the advantage of the new DSM-5 criteria? *Journal of Psychosomatic Research, 78,* 223–227.

Schienle, A., Hettema, J. R., Caceda, R., & Nemeroff, C. B. (2011). Neurobiology of genetics of generalized anxiety disorder. *Psychiatric Annals, 41,* 113–123.

Schieve, L. A., Blumberg, S. J., Rice, C., et al. (2007). The relationship between autism and parenting stress. *Pediatrics, 119,* S114–S121.

Schiffer, B., Kreuger, T., Paul, T., de Greiff, A., et al. (2008). Brain response to visual sexual stimuli in homosexual pedophiles. *Journal of Psychiatry and Neuroscience, 33,* 23–33.

Schiffer, B., Paul, T., Gizewski, E., Forsting, M., et al. (2008). Functional brain correlates of heterosexual paedophilia. *Neuroimage, 41,* 80–91.

Schizophrenia Society of Canada. (2002). *Schizophrenia: Youth's greatest disabler—A report on psychiatrist and patient attitudes and opinions towards schizophrenia.* Ottawa: Author.

Schizophrenia Working Group of the Psychiatric Genomics Consortium. (2014). Biological insights from 108 schizophrenia-associated genetic loci. *Nature, 511,* 421–427.

Schlundt, D. G., & Johnson, W. G. (1990). *Eating disorders: Assessment and treatment.* Needham Heights, MA: Allyn & Bacon.

Schmidt, N. B., Eggleston, A. M., Woolaway-Bickel, K., Fitzpatrick, K. K., Vasey, M. W., & Richey, J. A. (2007). Anxiety Sensitivity Amelioration Training (ASAT): A longitudinal primary prevention program targeting cognitive vulnerability. *Journal of Anxiety Disorders, 21,* 302–319.

Schmidt, N. B., Zvolensky, M., & Maner, J. K. (2006). Anxiety sensitivity: Prospective prediction of panic attacks and Axis I pathology. *Journal of Psychiatric Research, 40,* 691–699.

Schmitt, W. A., & Newman, J. P. (1999). Are all psychopathic individuals low-anxious? *Journal of Abnormal Psychology, 108,* 353–358.

Schmitz, J., Kramer, M., Blechert, J., & Tuschen-Caffier, B. (2010). Post-event processing in children with social phobia. *Journal of Abnormal Child Psychology, 38,* 911–919.

Schmitz, J., Kramer, M., & Tuschen-Caffier, B. (2011). Negative post-event processing and decreased self-appraisals of performance following social stress in childhood social anxiety: An experimental study. *Behaviour Research and Therapy, 49,* 789–795.

Schmucker, M., & Losel, F. (2008). Does sexual offender treatment work? A systematic review of outcome evaluations. *Psicothema, 20,* 10–19.

Schnall, P. L., Landsbergis, P. A., & Baker, D. (1994). Job strain and cardiovascular disease. *Annual Review of Public Health, 15,* 381–411.

Schneider, B., et al. (2006). Axis I disorders and personality disorders as risk factors for suicide. *European Archives of Psychiatry and Clinical Neuroscience, 256,* 17–27.

Schneider, K. (1959). *Clinical psychopathology.* New York: Grune & Stratton.

Schneider, R. (2001, July). Fitness to stand trial: Obligation of the court to inquire? Paper presented in a symposium chaired by R. Cooper, entitled "Adjudicating mental illness: Dilemmas in the courtroom and in practice," 26th International Congress on Law and Mental Health, Montreal, Quebec.

Schneider, R. D. (2000). *A statistical survey of provincial and territorial review boards.* Ottawa: Federal Department of Justice.

Schneider, R. D., Forestell, M., & MacGarvie, S. (2002). *Statistical survey of provincial and territorial review boards.* Ottawa: Department of Justice Canada.

Schneider, R. D., Glancy, G. D., Bradford, J. M., et al. (2000). Canadian landmark case, Winko v. British Columbia: Revisiting the conundrum of the mentally disordered accused. *Journal of the American Academy of Psychiatry and the Law, 28,* 206–212.

Schoeneman, T. J. (1977). The role of mental illness in the European witch-hunts of the sixteenth and seventeenth centuries: An assessment. *Journal of the History of the Behavioral Sciences, 13,* 337–351.

Schofield, W. (1964). *Psychotherapy: The purchase of friendship.* Englewood Cliffs, NJ: Prentice-Hall.

Schooler, C., Flora, J. A., & Farquhar, J. W. (1993). Moving toward synergy: Media supplementation in the Stanford Five-City Project. *Communication Research, 26,* 587–610.

Schopler, E., Short, B., & Mesibov, G. B. (1989). Comments. *Journal of Consulting and Clinical Psychology, 157,* 162–167.

Schreiber, F. L. (1973). *Sybil.* New York: Warner Books.

Schroeter, M. L., Stein, T., Maslowski, N., & Neumann, J. (2009). Neural correlates of Alzheimer's disease and mild cognitive impairment: A systematic and quantitative meta-analysis involving 1351 patients. *Neuroimage, 47,* 1196–1206.

Schuckit, M. A., Daeppen, J.-B., Danko, G. P., Tripp, M. L., Smith, T. L., et al. (1999). Clinical implications for four drugs of the DSM-IV distinction between substance with and without a physiological component. *American Journal of Psychiatry, 156,* 41–49.

Schulze, L., Schmahl, C., & Niedtfeld, I. (2016). Neural correlates of disturbed emotion processing in borderline personality disorder: A multimodal meta-analysis. *Biological Psychiatry, 79,* 97–106.

Schütze, R., Rees, C., Preece, M., & Schütze, M. (2010). Low mindfulness predicts pain catastrophizing in a fear-avoidance model of chronic pain. *Pain, 48,* 120–127.

Schwartz, G. E. (1973). Biofeedback as therapy: Some theoretical and practical issues. *American Psychologist, 28,* 666–673.

Schwartz, J. L. (1987). *Review and evaluation of smoking cessation methods: United States and Canada, 1978-1985.* U.S. Department of Health and Human Services, Public Health Service, National Institutes of Health. NIH Publication No. 87-2940.

Schwartz, J. M. (1998). Neuroanatomical aspects of cognitive-behavior therapy response in obsessive-compulsive disorder. *British Journal of Psychiatry, 173,* 38–44.

Schwartz, M. B., et al. (2006). The influence of one's own body weight on implicit and explicit anti-fat bias. *Obesity, 14,* 440–447.

Schwartz, P. J., Murphy, D. L., Wehr, T. A., Garcia-Borreguero, D., Oren, D. A., et al. (1997). Effects of meta-chlorphenylpiperazine infusions in patients with seasonal affective disorder and healthy control subjects. *Archives of General Psychiatry, 54,* 375–385.

Schwarz, T. (1981). *The Hillside Strangler: A murderer's mind.* Garden City, NJ: Doubleday.

Schwartz-Mette, R., & Rose, A. J. (2016). Depressive symptoms and conversational self-focus in adolescents' friendships. *Journal of Abnormal Child Psychology, 44,* 87–100.

Schweinsburg, A. D., Brown, S. A., & Tapet, S. F. (2008). The influence of marijuana use on meta-cognitive functioning in adolescents. *Current Drug Abuse Reviews, 1,* 99–111.

Schweizer, E., Rickels, K., Case, G., & Greenblatt, D. J. (1990). Long-term therapeutic use of benzodiazapines: Effects of gradual taper. *Archives of General Psychiatry, 47,* 908–915.

Schwitzgebel, R. L., & Schwitzgebel, R. K. (1980). *Law and psychological practice.* New York: John Wiley & Sons.

Scoggin, F. (1998). Anxiety in old age. In I. H. Nordhus, G. R. VandenBos, S. Berg, & P. Fromholt (Eds.), *Clinical geropsychology* (pp. 205–209). Washington, DC: American Psychological Association.

Scoggin, F., & McElreath, L. (1994). Efficacy of psychosocial treatments for geriatric depression: A quantitative review. *Journal of Consulting and Clinical Psychology, 62,* 69–74.

Scott, J. (2008). Cognitive-behavioural therapy for severe mental disorders: Back to the future? *The British Journal of Psychiatry, 192,* 401–403.

Scott, J. G., Duhig, M., Hamlyn, J., & Norman, R. (2013). Environmental contributions to autism: Explaining the rise in incidence of autistic spectrum disorders. *Journal of Environmental Immunology and Toxicology, 1,* 75–79.

Scott, J., et al. (2006). Cognitive-behavioural therapy for severe and recurrent bipolar disorders: Randomized controlled trial. *British Journal of Psychiatry, 188,* 313–320.

Scott, S. J., Stanton, B., Garland, A., & Ferrier, I. N. (2000). Cognitive vulnerability in patients with bipolar disorder. *Psychological Medicine, 30,* 467–472.

Scott, T., Mackenzie, C. S., Chipperfield, J. G., & Sareen, J. (2010). Mental health service use among Canadian older adults with anxiety disorders and clinically significant anxiety symptoms. *Aging and Mental Health, 14,* 790–800.

Scroppo, J. C., Drob, S. L., Weinberger, J. L., & Eagle, P. (1998). Identifying dissociative identity disorder: A self-report and projective study. *Journal of Abnormal Psychology, 107,* 272–284.

Sealy, P. (2012). The impact of the process of deindividualization of mental health services in Canada: An increase in accessing of health professionals for mental health concerns. *Social Work in Public Health, 27,* 229–237.

Seedat, S., Scott, K. M., Angermeyer, M. C., et al. (2009). Cross-national associations between gender and mental disorders in the World Health Organization World Mental Health surveys. *Archives of General Psychiatry, 66,* 785–795.

Seedat, S., Stein, M. B., & Forde, D. R. (2003). Prevalence of dissociative experiences in a community sample: Relationship to gender, ethnicity, and substance use. *Journal of Nervous and Mental Disease, 191,* 115–120.

Segal, Z. V., Gemar, M., Truchon, C., Guirguis, M., & Horowitz, L. M. (1995). A priming methodology for studying self-representation in major depressive disorder. *Journal of Abnormal Psychology, 104,* 205–213.

Segal, Z. V., Shaw, B. F., Vella, D. D., & Katz, R. (1992). Cognitive and life stress predictors of relapse in remitted unipolar depressed patients: Tests of the congruency hypothesis. *Journal of Abnormal Psychology, 101,* 26–36.

Segal, Z. V., Vincent, P., & Levitt, A. (2002). Efficacy of combined, sequential, and crossover psychotherapy and pharmacotherapy in improving outcomes in depression. *Journal of Psychiatry and Neuroscience, 27,* 281–290.

Segal, Z. V., Williams, M., & Teasdale, J. (2012). *Mindfulness-based cognitive therapy for depression: A new approach to preventing relapse* (2nd ed.). New York: Guilford.

Segerstrom, C., & Miller, G. E. (2004). Psychological stress and the human immune system: A meta-analytic study of 30 years of inquiry. *Psychological Bulletin, 130,* 601–630.

Segraves, K. B., & Segraves, R. T. (1991). Hypoactive sexual desire disorder: Prevalence and comorbidity in 906 subjects. *Journal of Sex and Marital Therapy, 17,* 55–58.

Segraves, R. T. (1990). Theoretical orientations in the treatment of marital discord. In F. D. Fincham & T. N. Bradbury (Eds.), *The psychology of marriage: Basic issues and applications* (pp. 281–298). New York: Guilford.

Seidman, L. J., & Bruder, G. (2003). Neuropsychological testing and neurophysiological assessment. In A. Tasman, J. Kay, & J. Lieberman (Eds.), *Psychiatry* (Vol. 1, pp. 560–572). London: John Wiley & Sons.

Sekar, A., Bialas, A. R., de Rivera, H., Davis, A., et al. (2016). Schizophrenia risk from complex variation of complement component 4. *Nature, 530,* 177–183.

Selby, P. (2013). Phase 1 study: Stop Smoking Therapy for Ontario Patients (STOP). *ClinicalTrials.gov Identifier: NCT00356993.*

Selemon, L. D., Rajkowska, G., & Goldman-Rakic, P. S. (1995). Abnormally high neuronal density in the schizophrenic cortex: A morphometric analysis of prefrontal area 9 and occipital area 17. *Archives of General Psychiatry, 52,* 805–818.

Seligman, M. E. P. (1975). *Helplessness: On depression, development, and death.* San Francisco: W. H. Freeman and Company.

Seligman, M. E. P. (1995). The effectiveness of psychotherapy: The Consumer Reports study. *American Psychologist, 50,* 965–974.

Seligman, M. E. P., & Binik, Y. M. (1977). The safety signal hypothesis. In H. Davis and H. Hurwitz (Eds.), *Pavlovian-operant interactions* (pp. 165–187). Hillsdale, NJ: Lawrence Erlbaum Associates.

Seligman, M. E., Schulman, P., & Tryon, A. M. (2007). Group prevention of depression and anxiety symptoms. *Behaviour Research and Therapy, 45,* 1111–1126.

Seltzer, A. (1983). Psychodynamics of spirit possession among the Inuit. *Canadian Journal of Psychiatry, 28,* 52–56.

Seltzer, M. M., Shattuck, P., Abbeduto, L., & Greenberg, J. S. (2004). Trajectory of development in adolescents and adults with autism. *Mental Retardation and Developmental Disabilities Research Reviews, 10,* 234–247.

Selye, H. (1950). *The physiology and pathology of exposure to stress.* Montreal: Acta.

Selye, H. (1974). *Stress without distress.* Philadelphia: J.B. Lippincott Company.

Senior, K. (2000). Bigger and better tobacco warning labels. *Lancet, 356,* 139.

Serdula, M. K., Mokdad, A. H., Williamson, D. F., Galuska, D. A., et al. (1999). Prevalence of attempting weight loss and strategies for controlling weight. *Journal of the American Medical Association, 282,* 1353–1358.

Serene, J. A., Ashtari, M., Szeszko, P. R., & Kumra, S. (2007). Neuroimaging studies of children with serious emotional disturbances: A selective review. *Canadian Journal of Psychiatry, 52,* 135–145.

Serfaty, M. A., Haworth, D., Blanchard, M., Buszewicz, M., Murad, S., & King, M. (2009). Clinical effectiveness of individual cognitive behavior therapy for depressed older people in primary care. *Archives of General Psychiatry, 66,* 1332–1340.

Serin, R. C., & Amos, N. L. (1995). The role of psychopathy in the assessment of dangerousness. *International Journal of Law and Psychiatry, 18,* 231–238.

Serin, R. C., Mailloux, D. L., & Malcolm, P. B. (2001). Psychopathy, deviant sexual arousal, and recidivism among sexual offenders. *Journal of Interpersonal Violence, 16,* 234–246.

Serras, A., Saules, K. K., Cranford, J. A., & Eisenberg, D. (2010). Self-injury, substance use, and associated risk factors in a multi-campus probability sample of college students. *Psychology of Addictive Behaviors, 24,* 119–128.

Seto, M. C. (2004). Pedophilia and sexual offenses against children. *Annual Review of Sex Research, 15,* 321–361.

Seto, M. C. (2009). Pedophilia. *Annual Review of Clinical Psychology, 5,* 391–507.

Seto, M. C., & Barbaree, H. E. (1999). Psychopathy, treatment behavior, and sex offender recidivism. *Journal of Interpersonal Violence, 14,* 1235–1248.

Seto, M. C., Cantor, J. M., & Blanchard, R. (2006). Child pornography offenses are a valid diagnostic indicator of pedophilia. *Journal of Abnormal Psychology, 115,* 610–615.

Seto, M. C., Harris, G. T., Rice, M. E., & Barbaree, H. E. (2004). The Screening Scale for Pedophilic Interests predicts recidivism among adult sex offenders with child victims. *Archives of Sexual Behavior, 33,* 455–466.

Seto, M. C., Hermann, C. A., Kjellgren, C., Priebe, C., Svedin, C. G., & Langstrom, N. (2015). Viewing child pornography: Prevalence and correlates in a representative community sample of young Swedish men. *Archives of Sexual Behavior, 44,* 67–79.

Seto, M. C., & Lalumière, M. L. (2001). A brief screening scale to identify pedophilic interests among child molesters. *Sexual Abuse: A Journal of Research and Treatment, 13,* 15–25.

Seto, M. C., Lalumière, M. L., & Blanchard, R. (2000). The discriminative validity of a phallometric test for pedophilic interests among adolescent sex offenders against children. *Psychological Assessment, 12,* 319–327.

Seto, M. C., Lalumière, M. L., Harris, G. T., & Chivers, M. L. (2012). The sexual responses of sexual sadists. *Journal of Abnormal Psychology, 121,* 739–753.

Seto, M. C., Maric, A., & Barbaree, H. E. (2001). The role of pornography in the etiology of sexual aggression. *Aggression and Violent Behavior, 6,* 35–53.

Settin, J. M. (1982). Clinical judgment in geropsychology practice. *Psychotherapy: Theory, Research and Practice, 19,* 397–404.

Sevier, M., Atkins, D. C., Doss, B. D., & Christensen, A. (2015). Up and down or down and up? the process of change in constructive couple behavior during traditional and integrative behavioral couple therapy. *Journal of Marital and Family Therapy, 41,* 113–127.

Sewitch, M. J., Blais, R., Rahme, E., Bexton, B., & Galarneau, S. (2007). Receiving guideline-concordant pharmacotherapy for major depression: Impact on ambulatory and inpatient health service use. *Canadian Journal of Psychiatry, 52,* 191–200.

Sexton, K. A., & Dugas, M. J. (2009). An investigation of factors associated with cognitive avoidance in worry. *Cognitive Therapy and Research, 33,* 150–162.

Seyfort, B., Spreen, O., & Lahmer, V. (1980). A critical look at the WISC-R with Native Indian children. *Alberta Journal of Educational Research, 26,* 14–24.

Shachnow, J., Clarkin, J., DiPalma, C.-S., Thurston, F., et al. (1997). Biparental psychopathology and borderline personality disorder. *Psychiatry—Interpersonal and Biological Processes, 60,* 171–181.

Shanmugasegaram, S., Flett, G. L., Madan, M., Oh, P., Marzolini, S., Reitav, J., … Sturman, E. C. (2014). Perfectionism, Type D personality, and illness-related coping styles in cardiac rehabilitation patients. *Journal of Health Psychology, 19,* 417–426.

Shannon, A., & Mills, J. S. (2015). Correlates, causes, and consequences of fat talk: A review. *Body Image, 15,* 158–172.

Shapiro, D., Jamner, L. D., & Goldstein, I. B. (1993). Ambulatory stress psychophysiology: The study of "compensatory and defensive counterforces" and conflict in a natural setting. *Psychosomatic Medicine, 55,* 309–323.

Shapiro, D., Tursky, B., & Schwartz, G. E. (1970). Control of blood pressure in man by operant conditioning. *Circulation Research, 26,* 127–132.

Shaw, B. F. (1999). How to use the allegiance effect to maximize competence and therapeutic outcomes. *Clinical Psychology: Science and Practice, 6,* 131–132.

Shaw, M. E., Moores, K. A., Clark, R. C., McFarlane, A. C., et al. (2009). Functional connectivity reveals inefficient working memory systems in post-traumatic stress disorder. *Psychiatric Research: Neuroimaging, 172,* 235–241.

Shaw, P., Eckstrand, K., Sharp, W., Blumenthal, J., et al. (2007). Attention-deficit/hyperactivity disorder is characterized by a delay in cortical maturation. *PNAS Proceedings of the National Academy of Sciences of the United States of America, 104,* 19649–19654.

Shaw, P., Sharp, W. S., & Morrison, M. (2009). Psychostimulant treatment and the developing cortex in attention deficit hyperactivity disorder. *American Journal of Psychiatry, 166,* 58–63.

Shaywitz, S. E., & Shaywitz, B. A. (2005). Dyslexia (specific reading disability). *Biological Psychiatry, 57,* 1301–1309.

Shedler, J. (2010). The efficacy of psychodynamic psychotherapy. *American Psychologist, 65,* 98–109.

Shedler, J. (2015). Where is the evidence for "evidence-based" therapy? *The Journal of Psychological Therapies in Primary Care, 4,* 47–59.

Shell, B. (2009, November 19). Psychologist has personal stake in Vancouver homeless project. Simon Fraser University News Online.

Shenal, B. V., Harrison, D. W., & Demaree, H. A. (2003). The neuropsychology of depression: A literature review and preliminary model. *Neuropsychology Review, 13,* 33–42.

Sheppard, D. M., Bradshaw, J. L., Purcell, R., & Pantelis, C. (1999). Tourette's and comorbid syndromes: Obsessive-compulsive and attention deficit hyperactivity disorder. A common etiology? *Clinical Psychology Review, 19,* 531–552.

Sher, K. J., Martin, E. D., Wood, P. K., & Rutledge, P. C. (1997). Alcohol use disorders and neuropsychological functioning in first-year undergraduates. *Experimental and Clinical Psychopharmacology, 5,* 304–315.

Shield, K. D., Soerjomataram, I., & Rehm, J. (2016). Alcohol use and breast cancer: A critical review. *Alcoholism: Clinical and Experimental Research, 40,* 1166–1181.

Shields, M., & Wilkins, K. (2005). *Findings from the 2005 National Survey of the Work and Health of Nurses.* Ottawa: Canadian Institute for Health Information.

Shih, J. H., Eberhart, N. K., Hammen, C. L., & Brennan, P. A. (2006). Differential exposure and reactivity to interpersonal stress predicts sex differences in adolescent depression. *Journal of Clinical Child and Adolescent Psychology, 35,* 103–115.

Shneidman, E. S. (1987). A psychological approach to suicide. In G. R. VandenBos & B. K. Bryant (Eds.), *Cataclysyms, crises, and catastrophes: Psychology in action* (pp. 147–183). Washington, DC: American Psychological Association.

Shneidman, E. S. (1993). Suicide as psychache. *Journal of Nervous and Mental Disease, 181,* 145–147.

Shorter, E. (2009). The history of lithium therapy. *Bipolar Disorders, 11* (Supplement s2), 4–9.

Siegel, L. S. (2006). Perspectives on dyslexia. *Pediatrics and Child Health, 11,* 581–587.

Siegel, S. (1991). Feedforward processes in drug tolerance and dependence. In R. G. Lister & H. J. Weingartner (Eds.), *Perspectives on cognitive neuroscience* (pp. 405–416). New York: Oxford University Press.

Siegel, S. (1999). Drug anticipation and drug addiction. The 1998 H. David Archibald lecture. *Addiction, 94,* 1113–1124.

Siegel, S., Baptista, M. A. S., Kim, J. A., McDonald, R. V., & Weise-Kelly, L. (2000). Pavlovian psychopharmacology: The associative basis of tolerance. *Experimental and Clinical Psychopharmacology, 8,* 276–293.

Siegel, S., Krank, M. D., & Hinson, R. E. (1987). Anticipation of pharmacological and nonpharmacological events. *Journal of Drug Issues, 1,* 83–110.

Siegle, G. J., Thompson, W., Carter, C. S., et al. (2007). Increased amygdala and decreased dorsolateral prefrontal bold responses in unipolar depression: Related and independent features. *Biological Psychiatry, 61,* 198–209.

Siegling, A. B., Vesely, A. K., Petrides, K. V., & Saklofske, D. H. (2015). Incremental validity of the trait emotional intelligence questionnaire–short form (TEIQue–SF). *Journal of Personality Assessment, 97,* 525–535.

Sigman, M. (1994). What are the core deficits in autism? In S. H. Broman & J. Grafman (Eds.), *Atypical cognitive deficits in developmental disorders: Implications for brain function* (pp. 139–157). Hillsdale, NJ: Lawrence Erlbaum Associates.

Sigman, M., Mundy, P., Sherman, T., & Ungerer, J. A. (1986). Social interactions of autistic, mentally retarded and normal children with their caregivers. *Journal of Child Psychology and Psychiatry, 27,* 647–669.

Sijbrandij, M., Kunovski, I., & Cuijpers, P. (in press). Effectiveness of internet-delivered cognitive behavioral therapy for posttraumatic stress disorder: A systematic review and meta-analysis. *Depression and Anxiety.*

Silberg, J., Moore, A. A., & Rutter, M. (2015). Age of onset and the subclassification of conduct/dissocial disorder. *Journal of Child Psychology and Psychiatry and Allied Disciplines, 56,* 826–833.

Silove, D. M., Marnane, C. L., Wagner, R., Manicavasagar, V. L., & Rees, S. (2010). The prevalence and correlates of adult separation anxiety disorder in an anxiety clinic. *BMC Psychiatry, 10,* 21.

Silva, J. A. (2009). Forensic psychiatry, neuroscience and the law. *Journal of the American Academy of Psychiatry and the Law, 37,* 489–502.

Silverman, K., Evans, S. M., Strain, E. C., & Griffiths, R. R. (1992). Withdrawal syndrome after the double-blind cessation of caffeine consumption. *New England Journal of Medicine, 327,* 1109–1114.

Sim, K., et al. (2006). Hippocampal and parahippocampal volumes in schizophrenia: A structural MRI study. *Schizophrenia Bulletin, 32,* 332–340.

Simeon, D., Gross, S., Guralnik, O., Stein, D. J., Schmeidler, J., & Hollander, E. (1997). Feeling unreal: 30 cases of DSM-III-R depersonalization disorder. *American Journal of Psychiatry, 154,* 1107–1112.

Simeone, J. C., Ward, A. J., Rotella, P., Collins, J., & Windisch, R. (2015). An evaluation of variation in published estimates of schizophrenia prevalence from 1990–2013: A systematic literature review. *BMC Psychiatry, 15,* 193.

Simmie, S. (1998, October 10). True reform is up to all of us. *Toronto Star.*

Simmie, S. (1998, October 3–10). Atkinson Fellowship investigation into mental health: Out of Mind (Series). *Toronto Star.*

Simmie, S., & Nunes, J. (2001). *The last taboo: A survival guide to mental health care in Canada.* Toronto: McClelland and Stewart.

Simmons, H. G. (1987). Psychosurgery and the abuse of psychiatric authority in Ontario. *Journal of Health Politics, 12,* 537–550.

Simms, L. J., & Calabrese, W. R. (2016). Incremental validity of the DSM-5 Section III personality disorder traits with respect to psychosocial impairment. *Journal of Personality Disorders, 30,* 95–111.

Simon, A. E., Borgwardt, S., Riecher-Rossler, A., Velthorst, E., et al. (2013). Moving beyond transition outcomes: Meta-analysis of remission rates in individuals at high clinical risk for psychosis. *Psychiatry Research, 209,* 366–272.

Simonsen, R. K., Giraldi, A., Kristensen, E., & Hald, G. M. (2016). Long-term follow-up of individuals undergoing sex reassignment surgery: Psychiatric morbidity and mortality. *Nordic Journal of Psychiatry, 70,* 241–247.

Simpson, J., Doze, S., Urness, D., Hailey, D., & Jacobs, P. (2001a). Evaluation of a routine telepsychiatry service. *Journal of Telemedicine and Telecare, 7,* 90–98.

Simpson, J., Doze, S., Urness, D., Hailey, D., & Jacobs, P. (2001b). Telepsychiatry as a routine service—The perspective of the patient. *Journal of Telemedicine and Telecare, 7,* 155–160.

Sinclair, C. (1993). *Comparison of CPA, APA, and ASPPB codes.* Ottawa: Canadian Psychological Association.

Sinclair, C., Poizner, S., Gilmour-Barrett, K., & Randall, D. (1987). The development of a code of ethics for Canadian psychologists. *Canadian Psychology, 28*, 1–8.

Singh, A. A., & dickey, l. m. (2016). Implementing the APA Guidelines on Psychological Practice with Transgender and Gender Nonconforming People: A call to action to the field of psychology. *Psychology of Sexual Orientation and Gender Diversity, 3*, 195–200.

Singh, A. A., & dickey, l. m. (2017). Introduction. In A. A. Singh & l. m. dickey (Eds.), *Affirmative counseling and psychological practice with transgender and gender nonconforming clients* (pp. 3–18). Washington, DC: American Psychological Association.

Singh, S., & Lee, A. S. (1997). Conversion disorders in Nottingham: Alive but not kicking. *Journal of Psychosomatic Research, 43*, 425–430.

Single, E., Brewster, J. M., MacNeil, P., Hatcher, J., & Trainor, C. (1995). The 1993 General Social Survey I: Alcohol use in Canada. *Canadian Journal of Public Health, 86*, 397–401.

Singley, D. B., & Edwards, L. M. (2015). Men's perinatal mental health in the transition to fatherhood. *Professional Psychology: Research and Practice, 46*, 309–316.

Sinha, B. K., & Watson, D. C. (2001). Personality disorder in university students: A multitrait-multimethod matrix study. *Journal of Personality Disorders, 15*, 235–244.

Sintchak, G. H., & Geer, J. H. (1975). A vaginal plethysmograph system. *Psychophysiology, 12*, 113–115.

Sisson, R. W., & Azrin, N. H. (1989). The community-reinforcement approach. In R. K. Hester & W. R. Miller (Eds.), *Handbook of alcoholism treatment approaches: Effective alternatives* (pp. 242–258). New York: Pergamon. *SMA 13-4795.* Rockville, MD: SAMSHA.

Sizemore, C. C., & Pittillo, E. S. (1977). *I'm Eve.* Garden City, NY: Doubleday.

Sizemore, R. C. (2012). How does stress affect the immune response? *Cell and Developmental Biology, 1*, 1.

Skarborn, M., & Nicki, R. (1996). Worry among Canadian seniors. *International Journal of Aging and Human Development, 43*, 169–178.

Skeem, J. L., et al. (2006). Psychiatric symptoms and community violence among high-risk patients: A test of the relationship at the weekly level. *Journal of Consulting and Clinical Psychology, 74*, 967–979.

Skilling, T. A., Harris, G. T., Rice, M. E., & Quinsey, V. L. (2002). Identifying persistently antisocial offenders using the Hare Psychopathy Checklist and DSM antisocial personality disorder criteria. *Psychological Assessment, 14*, 27–38.

Skodol, A. E., Oldham, J. M., & Gallaher, P. E. (1999). Axis II comorbidity of substance use disorders among patients referred for treatment of personality disorders. *American Journal of Psychiatry, 156*, 733–738.

Slater, E., & Glithero, E. (1965). A follow-up of patients diagnosed as suffering from hysteria. *Journal of Psychosomatic Research, 9*, 9–13.

Slaunwhite, A. K. (2015). The role of gender and income in predicting barriers to mental health care in Canada. *Community Mental Health Journal, 51*, 621–627.

Slikboer, R., Nedeljkovic, M., Bowe, S. J., & Moulding, R. (in press). A systematic review and meta-analysis of behaviourally based psychological interventions and pharmacological interventions for trichotillomania. *Clinical Psychologist.*

Slomp, M., Bland, R., Patterson, S., & Whittaker, L. (2009). Three-year physician treated prevalence rate of mental disorders in Alberta. *Canadian Journal of Psychiatry, 54*, 199–202.

Slopen, N., Williams, D. R., Fitzmaurice, G. M., & Gilman, S. E. (2011). Sex, stressful life events, and adult onset depression and alcohol dependence: Are men and women equally vulnerable? *Social Science and Medicine, 73*, 615–622.

Small, G. W., & Jarvik, L. F. (1982). The dementia syndrome. *Lancet,* 1443–1446.

Smit, Y., Huibers, M. J. H., Ioannidis, J. P. A., van Dyck, R., et al. (2012). The effectiveness of long-term psychoanalytic psychotherapy: A meta-analysis of randomized controlled trials. *Clinical Psychology Review, 32*, 81–92.

Smith v. Jones, 1999 CanLII 674 (SCC), [1999] 1 SCR 455.

Smith, G. E. (2016). Healthy cognitive aging and dementia prevention. *American Psychologist, 71*, 268–275.

Smith, I. C., Reichow, B., & Volkmar, F. R. (2015). The effects of *DSM-5* criteria on number of individuals diagnosed with autism spectrum disorder: A systematic review. *Journal of Autism and Developmental Disorders, 45*, 2241–2552.

Smith, J. M., Alloy, L. B., & Abramson, L. Y. (2006). Cognitive vulnerability to depression, rumination, hopelessness, and suicide ideation: Multiple pathways to self-injurious thinking. *Suicide and Life-Threatening Behavior, 36*, 445–456.

Smith, J. W., Frawley, P. J., & Polissar, L. (1991). Six- and twelve-month abstinence rates in inpatient alcoholics treated with aversion therapy compared with matched inpatients from a treatment registry. *Alcoholism: Clinical and Experimental Research, 15*, 862–870.

Smith, K. B., Pukall, C. F., & Boyer, S. C. (2009). Psychological and relational aspects of dyspareunia. In A. Goldstein, C. F. Pukall, & I. Goldstein (Eds.), *Female sexual pain disorders: Evaluation and management* (pp. 208–217). New York: Wiley-Blackwell.

Smith, M. E., & Farah, M. J. (2011). Are prescription stimulants "smart pills"? The epidemiology and cognitive neuroscience of prescription stimulant use by normal healthy individuals. *Psychological Bulletin, 137*, 717–741.

Smith, M. L., Glass, G., & Miller, T. (1980). *The benefits of psychotherapy.* Baltimore: Johns Hopkins University Press.

Smith, T., Groen, A. D., & Wynn, J. W. (2000). Randomized trial of intensive early intervention for children with pervasive developmental disorder. *American Journal of Mental Retardation, 105*, 269–285.

Smith, T. W., Snyder, C. R., & Perkins, S. C. (1983). Self-serving function of hypochondriacal complaints: Physical symptoms as self-handicapping strategies. *Journal of Personality and Social Psychology, 44*, 787–797.

Smits, J. A. J., Berry, A. C., Tart, C. D., & Powers, M. B. (2008). The efficacy of cognitive-behavioral interventions for reducing anxiety sensitivity: A meta-analytic review. *Behaviour Research and Therapy, 46*, 1047–1054.

Smits, J. A. J., Julian, K., Rosenfield, D., & Powers, M. B. (2012). Threat reappraisal as a mediator of symptom change in cognitive-behavioral treatment of anxiety disorders: A systematic review. *Journal of Consulting and Clinical Psychology, 80*, 624–663.

Smoller, J. W. (2016). The genetics of stress-related disorders: PTSD, depression, and anxiety disorders. *Neuropsychopharmacology, 41*, 297–319.

Smoller, J. W., Gardner-Schuster, E., & Covino, J. (2008). The genetic basis of panic and phobic anxiety disorders. *American Journal of Medical Genetics Part C (Seminars in Medical Genetics), 148C*, 118–126.

Smyth, C., et al. (1996). Further tests for linkage of bipolar affective disorder to the tyrosine hydroxylase gene of chromosome 11p15 in a new series of multiplex British affective disorder pedigrees. *American Journal of Psychiatry, 153*, 271–274.

Snow, N., & Austin, W. J. (2009). Community treatment orders: Ethical balancing act in community mental health. *Journal of Psychiatric and Mental Health Nursing, 16*, 177–186.

Snowdon, D. A., Kemper, S. J., Mortimer, J. A., Greiner, L. H., et al. (1996). Linguistic ability in early life and cognitive function and Alzheimer's disease in late life: Findings from the Nun Study. *Journal of the American Medical Association, 275,* 528–534.

Snuggs, S., McRobbie, H., Myers, H., et al. (2012). Using text messaging to prevent relapse to smoking: Intervention development, practicability, and client reactions. *Addiction, 107,* 39–44.

Snyder, C. R., Ilardi, S., Michael, S. T., & Cheavens, J. (2000). Hope theory: Updating a common process for psychological change. In C. R. Snyder & R. E. Ingram (Eds.), *Handbook of psychological change* (pp. 128–150).

Snyder, H. R., Kaiser, R. H., Warren, S. L., & Heller, W. (2015). Obsessive-compulsive disorder is associated with broad impairments in executive function: A meta-analysis. *Clinical Psychological Science, 3,* 301–330.

Snyder, J., Reid, J., & Patterson, G. (2003). A social learning model of child and adolescent antisocial behavior. In B. B. Lahey, T. E. Moffitt, & A. Caspi (Eds.), *The causes of conduct disorder and juvenile delinquency* (pp. 27–48). New York: Guilford.

Snyder, S. H. (1974). Amphetamine psychosis: A "model" schizophrenia mediated by catecholamines. *American Journal of Psychiatry, 130,* 60–67.

Snyder, S. H. (1996). *Drugs and the brain.* New York: Freeman.

Sobel, A. A., Resick, P. A., & Rabalais, A. E. (2009). The effect of cognitive processing therapy on cognitions: Impact statement coding. *Journal of Traumatic Stress, 22,* 205–211.

Sobell, L. C., Toneatto, A., & Sobell, M. B. (1990). Behavior therapy. In A. S. Bellack & M. Hersen (Eds.), *Handbook of comparative treatments for adult disorders* (pp. 479–505). New York: John Wiley & Sons.

Sobell, M. B., & Sobell, L. C. (1976). Second-year treatment outcome of alcoholics treated by individualized behavior therapy: Results. *Behaviour Research and Therapy, 14,* 195–215.

Sobell, M. B., & Sobell, L. C. (1993). *Problem drinkers: Guided self-change treatment.* New York: Guilford.

Sobell, M. B., & Sobell, L. C. (2000). Stepped care as a heuristic approach to the treatment of alcohol problems. *Journal of Consulting and Clinical Psychology, 68,* 573–579.

Sobell, M. B., & Sobell, L. C. (2005). Guided self-change model of treatment for substance use disorders. *Journal of Cognitive Psychotherapy, 19,* 199–210.

Soh, N. L., Touyz, S. W., & Surgenor, J. L. (2006). Eating and body image disturbances across cultures: A review. *Eating Disorders Review, 14,* 54–65.

Soh, N. L., & Walter, G. (2013). Publications on cross-cultural aspects of eating disorders. *Journal of Eating Disorders, 1,* 4.

Solomon, A., Ruscio, J., Seeley, J. R., & Lewinsohn, P. M. (2006). A taxometric investigation of unipolar depression in a large community sample. *Psychological Medicine, 36,* 973–985.

Solowij, N., & Battisti, R. (2008). The chronic effects of cannabis on memory in humans: A review. *Current Drug Abuse Reviews, 1,* 81–98.

Somers, J. M., Goldner, E. M., Waraich, P., & Hsu, L. (2006). Prevalence and incidence studies of anxiety disorders: A systematic review of the literature. *Canadian Journal of Psychiatry, 51,* 100–113.

Somers, J. M., Moniruzzaman, A., & Rezansoff, S. N. (2016). Migration to the Downtown Eastside neighbourhood of Vancouver and changes in service use in a cohort of mentally ill homeless adults: A 10-year retrospective study. *BMJ Open* 2016;6:e009043. doi:10.1136/bmjopen-2015-009043.

Soo, H., Burney, S., & Basten, C. (2009). The role of rumination in affective distress in people with a chronic physical illness: A review of the literature and theoretical formulation. *Journal of Health Education, 14,* 956–966.

Soor, G. S., Vukin, I., Bridgman-Acker, K., Marble, R., et al. (2012). The effects of gender on adolescent suicide in Ontario, Canada. *Journal of the Canadian Academy of Child and Adolescent Psychiatry, 21,* 179–185.

Sourander, A., Klomeck, A. B., Niemala, S., et al. (2009). Childhood predictors of completed and severe suicide attempts: Findings from the Finnish 1981 Birth Cohort Study. *Archives of General Psychiatry, 66,* 398–406.

Sowers, K. M., & Rowe, W. S. (2007). Global aging. In J. A. Blackburn & C. N. Dulmus (Eds.), *Handbook of gerontology: Evidence-based approaches to theory, practice, and policy* (pp. 3–16). New York: John Wiley & Sons.

Spaans, H., Verwijk, E., Comijs, H. C., Kok, R. M., Sienaert, P., Bouckaert, F., . . . Kho, K. H. (2013). Efficacy and cognitive side effects after brief pulse and ultrabrief pulse right unilateral electroconvulsive therapy for major depression: A randomized, double-blind, controlled study. *Journal of Clinical Psychiatry, 74,* e1029–e1036.

Spanagel, R. (2009). Alcoholism: A systems approach from molecular physiology to addictive behavior. *Physiological Review, 89,* 649–705.

Spanos, N. P. (1994). Multiple identity enactments and multiple personality disorder: A sociocognitive perspective. *Psychological Bulletin, 116,* 143–165.

Spanos, N. P. (1996). *Multiple identities and false memories: A sociocognitive perspective.* Washington, DC: American Psychological Association.

Spanos, N. P., Cross, P. A., Dickson, K., & DeBreuil, S. C. (1993). Close encounters: An examination of UFO experiences. *Journal of Abnormal Psychology, 102,* 624–632.

Spanos, N. P., Weekes, J. R., & Bertrand, L. D. (1985). Multiple personality: A social psychological perspective. *Journal of Abnormal Psychology, 94,* 362–376.

Sparks, B. F., et al. (2002). Brain structural abnormalities in children and adults with autism. *Neurology, 59,* 184–192.

Specht, K., Hugdahl, K., & Ofte, S. (2009). Brain activation on pre-reading tasks reveals at-risk status for dyslexia in 6-year-old children. *Scandinavian Journal of Psychology, 50,* 79–91.

Spector, I. P., & Carey, M. P. (1990). Incidence and prevalence of the sexual dysfunctions: A critical review of the empirical literature. *Archives of Sexual Behavior, 19,* 389–408.

Spence, S. H., Donovan, C. L., March, S., Gamble, A., et al. (2011). A randomized controlled trial of online versus clinic-based CBT for adolescent anxiety. *Journal of Consulting and Clinical Psychology, 79,* 629–642.

Spengler, A. (1977). Manifest sadomasochism of males: Results of an empirical study. *Archives of Sexual Behavior, 6,* 441–456.

Spiegel, D., Lewis-Fernández, R., Lanius, R., Vermetten, E., Simeon, D., & Friedman, M. (2013). Dissociative disorders in DSM-5. *Annual Review of Clinical Psychology, 9,* 299–326.

Spiegel, D., Lowenstein, R. J., Lewis-Fernandez, R., Sar, V., Simeon, D., et al. (2011). Dissociative disorders in DSM-5. *Depression and Anxiety, 28,* 824–852.

Spiess, W. F. J., Geer, J. H., & O'Donohue, W. T. (1984). Premature ejaculation: Investigation of factors in ejaculatory latency. *Journal of Abnormal Psychology, 93,* 242–245.

Spitzer, R. L., Endicott, J., & Gibbon, M. (1979). Crossing the border into borderline personality and borderline schizophrenia. *Archives of General Psychiatry, 36,* 17–24.

Spitzer, R. L., Gibbon, M., & Williams, J. B. W. (1996). *Structured clinical interview for DSM-IV Axis I disorders.* New York: N.Y. State Psychiatric Institute, Biometrics Research Department.

Sprague, R. L., & Gadow, K. D. (1976). The role of the teacher in drug treatment. *School Review, 85*, 109–140.

Squires-Wheeler, E., Skodal, A., Agamo, O. M., Bassett, A. S., et al. (1993). Personality features and disorder in the subjects in the New York High-Risk Project. *Journal of Psychiatric Research, 27*, 379–393.

St-Hilaire, A., Steiger, H., Liu, A., Laplante, D. P., Thaler, L., Magill, T., & King, S. (2015). A prospective study of effects of prenatal maternal stress on later eating-disorder manifestations in affected offspring: Preliminary indications based on the Project Ice Storm cohort. *International Journal of Eating Disorders, 48*, 512–516.

St-Pierre-Delorme, M., Lalonde, M. P., Perreault, V., Koszegi, N., & O'Connor, K. (2011). Inference-based therapy for compulsive hoarding: A clinical case study. *Clinical Case Studies, 10*, 291–303.

St. John, J., Krichev, A., & Bauman, E. (1976). Northwestern Ontario Indian children and the WISC. *Psychology in the Schools, 13*, 407–411.

St. John, P., & Montgomery, P. (2002). Are cognitively intact seniors with subjective memory loss more likely to develop dementia? *International Journal of Geriatric Psychiatry, 17*, 814–820.

St. John, P., Montgomery, P. R., Kristjansson, B., & McDowell, I. (2002). Cognitive scores, even within the normal range, predict death and institutionalization. *Age and Ageing, 31*, 373–378.

Stacy, A. W., Sussman, S., Dent, C. W., Burton, D., & Flay, B. R. (1992). Moderators of peer social influence in adolescent smoking. *Personality and Social Psychology Bulletin, 18*, 163–172.

Stacy, A. W., & Wiers, R. W. (2010). Implicit cognition and addiction: A tool for explaining paradoxical behavior. *Annual Review of Clinical Psychology, 6*, 551–575.

Stade, B., et al. (2009). The burden of prenatal exposure to alcohol: Revised measurement of cost. *Canadian Journal of Clinical Pharmacology, 16*, e91–e102.

Stafford, M., Newbold, B. K., & Ross, N. A. (2011). Psychological distress among immigrants and visible minorities in Canada: A contextual analysis. *International Journal of Social Psychiatry, 57*, 428–441.

Stamoulos, C., Trepanier, L., Bourkas, S., Bradley, S., Stelmaszczyk, K., Schwartzman, D., & Drapeau, M. (in press). Psychologists' perceptions of the importance of common factors in psychotherapy for successful treatment outcomes. *Journal of Psychotherapy Integration*.

Stangier, U. (2016). New developments in cognitive-behavioral therapy for social anxiety disorder. *Current Psychiatry Reports, 18*(3), 25.

Staniute, M., Brozaitiene, J., Burkauskas, J., Kazukauskiene, N., Mickuviene, N., & Bunevicius, R. (2015). Type D personality, mental distress, social support, and health-related quality of life in coronary artery disease patients with heart failure: A longitudinal observation study. *Health and Quality of Life Outcomes, 13*, 1.

Stanley, M. A., et al. (2003). Cognitive-behavioral treatment of late-life generalized anxiety disorder. *Journal of Consulting and Clinical Psychology, 71*, 309–319.

Stanley, M. A., & Novy, D. M. (2000). Cognitive-behavior therapy for generalized anxiety in late life: An evaluative overview. *Journal of Anxiety Disorders, 14*, 191–207.

Stanley, M. A., & Turner, S. M. (1995). Current status of pharmacological and behavioral treatment of obsessive-compulsive disorder. *Behavior Therapy, 26*, 163–186.

Stansfeld, S. A., Blackmore, E. R., Zagorski, B. M., et al. (2008). Work characteristics and social phobia in a nationally representative employed sample. *Canadian Journal of Psychiatry, 53*, 371–376.

Stanton, A. L., Kirk, S. B., Cameron, C. L., & Danoff-Burg, S. (2000). Coping through emotional approach: Scale construction and validation. *Journal of Personality and Social Psychology, 78*, 1150–1169.

Stanton, M. D., & Bardoni, A. (1972). Drug flashbacks: Reported frequency in a military population. *American Journal of Psychiatry, 129*, 751–755.

Starcevic, V., Portman, M. E., & Beck, A. T. (2012). Generalized anxiety disorder: Between neglect and an epidemic. *Journal of Nervous and Mental Disease, 200*, 664–667.

Starr, L. R., & Davila, J. (2009). Clarifying corumination: Associations with internalizing symptoms and romantic involvement among adolescent girls. *Journal of Adolescence, 32*, 19–37.

Starson v. Swayze, **2003 SCC 32,** [2003] 1 SCR 722.

Statistics Canada. (1995). *National Population Health Survey Overview* (Catalogue No. 82-567). Ottawa: Author.

Statistics Canada. (1999). *Sex offenders, 1997* (Catalogue No. 85-002-XIE). Ottawa: Author.

Statistics Canada. (2002). *A profile of disability in Canada* (Catalogue No. 89-577-XIE). Ottawa: Author.

Statistics Canada. (2005). *Population projections for Canada, provinces, and territories*. Ottawa: Author.

Statistics Canada. (2012a). Canadian Community Health Survey—Mental Health. Ottawa: Author.

Statistics Canada. (2012b). Canadian Vital Statistics, Death Database: Leading causes of death in Canada — 2009. Ottawa: Statistics Canada.

Statistics Canada. (2016). Leading causes of death, total population, by age group and sex, Canada, annual (CANSIM Table 102-0561). Ottawa: Author.

Steadman, H. J., Mulvey, E. P., Monahan, J., Robbins, P. C., Appelbaum, P. S., Grisso, T., et al. (1998). Violence by people discharged from acute psychiatric inpatient facilities and by others in the same neighborhoods. *Archives of General Psychiatry, 55*, 393–401.

Steele, C. M., & Josephs, R. A. (1990). Alcohol myopia: Its prized and dangerous effects. *American Psychologist, 45*(8), 921.

Steele, L. S., Glazier, R. H., & Lin, E. (2006). Inequity in mental health care under Canadian universal health coverage. *Psychiatric Services, 57*, 317–324.

Steenhuis, R. E., & Ostbye, T. (1995). Neuropsychological test performance of specific diagnostic groups in the Canadian Study of Health and Aging (CSHA). *Journal of Clinical and Experimental Neuropsychology, 17*, 773–785.

Steenkamp, M. M., Litz, B. T., Hoge, C. W., & Marmar, C. R. (2015). Psychotherapy for military-related PTSD: A review of randomized clinical trials. *Journal of the American Medical Association, 314*, 489–500.

Steiger, H., et al. (2001). Implications of impulsive and affective symptoms for serotonin function in bulimia nervosa. *Psychological Medicine, 31*, 85–95.

Steiger, H., et al. (2005). Mood- and restraint-based antecedents to binge episodes in bulimia nervosa: Possible influences of the serotonin system. *Psychological Medicine, 35*, 1553–1562.

Steiger, H., Gauvin, L., Jabalpurwala, S., Seguin, J. R., & Stotland, S. (1999). Hypersensitivity to social interactions in bulimia syndromes: Relationship to binge eating. *Journal of Consulting and Clinical Psychology, 67*, 765–775.

Steiger, H., & Israel, M. (1999). A psychodynamically informed, integrated psychotherapy for anorexia nervosa. *Journal of Clinical Psychology, 55*, 741–753.

Steiger, H., Israel, M., Gauvin, L., Ng, Y. K., & Young, S. N. (2003). Implications of compulsive and impulsive traits for serotonin status in women with bulimia nervosa. *Psychiatry Research, 120*, 219–229.

Steiger, H., Jabalpurwala, S., Champagne, J., & Stotland, S. (1997). A controlled study of trait narcissism in anorexia and bulimia nervosa. *International Journal of Eating Disorders, 22*, 173–178.

Stein, D. J., Kogan, C. S., Atmaca, M., Fineberg, N. A., Fontenelle, L. F., Grant, J. E., ... Reed, G. M. (2016). The classification of obsessive–compulsive and related disorders in the ICD-11. *Journal of Affective Disorders, 190,* 663–674.

Stein, L. I., & Santos, A. B. (1998). *Assertive community treatment of persons with severe mental illness.* New York: W. W. Norton.

Stein, L. I., & Test, M. A. (1980). Alternative to mental hospital treatment: I. Conceptual model, treatment program, and clinical evaluation. *Archives of General Psychiatry, 37,* 392–397.

Stein, M. B., Jang, K. L., & Livesley, W. J. (1999). Heritability of anxiety sensitivity: A twin study. *American Journal of Psychiatry, 156,* 246–251.

Stein, M. B., & Kean, Y. M. (2000). Disability and quality of life in social phobia: Epidemiologic findings. *American Journal of Psychiatry, 157,* 1606–1613.

Steinberg, L. (2009). Adolescent development and juvenile justice. *Annual Review of Clinical Psychology, 5,* 459–485.

Steinert, C., Kruse, J., & Leichsenring, F. (2016). Long-term outcome and non-response in psychotherapy: Are we short-sighted? *Psychotherapy and Psychosomatics, 85,* 235–237.

Steketee, G., Frost, R. O., Tolin, D. F., et al. (2010). Waitlist-controlled trial of cognitive behavior therapy for hoarding disorder. *Depression and Anxiety, 27,* 476–484.

Stephens, R. S., Roffman, R. A., & Simpson, E. E. (1993). Adult marijuana users seeking treatment. *Journal of Consulting and Clinical Psychology, 61,* 1100–1104.

Stephens, T., Dulberg, C., & Joubert, N. (1999). Mental health of the Canadian population: A comprehensive analysis. *Chronic Diseases in Canada, 20*(3), 118–126.

Stermac, L., Du Mont, J., & Dunn, S. (1998). Violence in known-assailant sexual assaults. *Journal of Interpersonal Violence, 13,* 398–412.

Stermac, L., Du Mont, J., & Kalemba, V. (1995). Comparison of sexual assaults by strangers and known assailants in an urban population of women. *Canadian Medical Association Journal, 153,* 1089–1095.

Stern, A. M., Novak, N. L., Lira, N., O'Connor, K., Harlow, S., & Kardia, S. (2017). California's sterilization survivors: An estimate and call for redress. *American Journal of Public Health, 107,* 50–54.

Stern, R. S., & Cobb, J. P. (1978). Phenomenology of obsessive-compulsive neurosis. *British Journal of Psychiatry, 132,* 233–239.

Stewart, D. E., Gagnon, A., Saucier, J.-F., et al. (2008). Postpartum depression symptoms in newcomers. *Canadian Journal of Psychiatry, 53,* 121–124.

Stewart, J. G., & Harkness, K. L. (2015). The interpersonal toxicity of excessive reassurance-seeking: Evidence from a longitudinal study of romantic relationships. *Journal of Social and Clinical Psychology, 34,* 392–410.

Stewart, M. J., Georgiou, A., & Westbrook, J. I. (2013). Successfully integrating aged care services: A review of the evidence and tools emerging from a long-term care program. *International Journal of Integrated Care, 13,* 1–14.

Stewart, R. E., & Chambless, D. L. (2009). Cognitive-behavior therapy for adult anxiety disorders in clinical practice: A meta-analysis of effectiveness studies. *Journal of Consulting and Clinical Psychology, 77,* 595–606.

Stewart, S. H., Conrod, P. J., Gignac, M. L., & Pihl, R. O. (1998). Selective processing biases in anxiety-sensitive men and women. *Cognition and Emotion, 12,* 105–133.

Stewart, S. H., & Watt, M. C. (2001). Assessment of health anxiety. In G. J. G. Asmundson, S. Taylor, & B. J. Cox (Eds.), *Health anxiety: Clinical and research perspectives on hypochondriasis and related conditions* (pp. 95–131). Toronto: John Wiley & Sons.

Stewart, S., Boase, P., & Lamble, R. W. (2000). Criminal profiles of drinking drivers in Ontario. In *Alcohol, Drugs, and Traffic Safety—T2000.* Stockholm: Swedish National Road Safety.

Stice, E., Barrera, M., & Chassin, L. (1998). Prospective differential prediction of adolescent alcohol use and problem use: Examining the mechanisms of effect. *Journal of Abnormal Psychology, 107,* 616–628.

Stice, E., Rohde, P., Durant, S., & Shaw, H. (2012). A preliminary trial of a prototype internet dissonance-based eating disorder prevention program for young women with body image concerns. *Journal of Consulting and Clinical Psychology, 80,* 907–916.

Stice, E., & Shaw, H. (2004). Eating disorder prevention programs: A meta-analytic review. *Psychological Bulletin, 130,* 206–227.

Stice, E., Shaw, H., Bohon, C., Marti, C. N., & Rohde, P. (2009). A meta-analytic review of depression prevention programs for children and adolescents: Factors that predict magnitude of intervention effects. *Journal of Consulting and Clinical Psychology, 77,* 486–503.

Stiles, W. B. (2010). Theory-building case studies as practice-based evidence. In M. Barkham, G. E. Hardy, & J. Mellor-Clark (Eds.), *Developing and delivering practice based evidence: A guide for psychological therapies* (pp. 91–108). Chichester, UK: Wiley & Sons.

Stinson, F. S., Dawson, D. A., Chou, S. P., et al. (2007). The epidemiology of DSM-IV specific phobia in the USA: Results for the National Epidemiologic Survey on Alcohol and Related Conditions. *Psychological Medicine, 37,* 1047–1059.

Stip, E., Caron, J., & Lane, C. J. (2001). Schizophrenia: People's perceptions in Quebec. *Canadian Medical Association Journal, 164,* 1299–1300.

Stip, E., Caron, J., & Mancini-Marie, A. (2006). General population perceptions and attitudes towards schizophrenia and bipolar disorder. *Primary Care and Community Psychiatry, 11,* 157–165.

Stirman, S. W., DeRubeis, R. J., Crits-Cristoph, P., & Brody, P. E. (2003). Are samples in randomized controlled studies of psychotherapy representative of community outpatients? A new methodology and initial findings. *Journal of Consulting and Clinical Psychology, 71,* 963–972.

Stirpe, T., Abracen, J., Stermac, L., & Wilson, R. (2006). Sexual offenders' state-of-mind regarding childhood attachment: A controlled investigation. *Sexual Abuse: A Journal of Research and Treatment, 18,* 289–302.

Stockwell, T., Zhao, J., Panwar, S., Roemer, A., et al. (2016). Do "moderate" drinkers have reduced mortality risk? A systematic review and meta-analysis of alcohol consumption and all-cause mortality. *Journal of Study of Alcohol and Drugs, 77,* 185–198.

Stockwell, T., Zhao, J., & Thomas, G. (2009). Should alcohol policies aim to reduce total alcohol consumption? New analyses of Canadian drinking patterns. *Addiction Research and Theory, 17,* 135–151.

Stojanovich, L., & Marisavljevich, D. (2008). Stress as a trigger of autoimmune disease. *Autoimmune Review, 7,* 209–213.

Stoléru, S. (2008). The brain, androgens, and pedophilia. In D. W. Pfaff, C. Kordon, P. Chanson, & Y. Christen (Eds.), *Research and perspectives in endocrine interactions* (pp. 163–175). Berlin: Springer Berlin Heidelberg.

Stoltenborgh, M., van Ijzendoorn, M. H., Euser, E. M., & Bakermans-Kranenburg, M. J. (2011). A global perspective on child sexual abuse: Meta-analysis of prevalence around the world. *Child Maltreatment, 16,* 79–101.

Stone, A. A., Bovbjerg, D. H., Neale, J. M., Napoli, A., Valdimarsdottir, H., et al. (1992). Development of common cold symptoms following experimental rhinovirus infection is related to prior stressful life events. *Behavioral Medicine, 18,* 115–120.

Stone, A. A., Cox, D. S., Valdimarsdottir, H., Jandorf, L., & Neale, J. M. (1987). Evidence that secretory IgA antibody is associated with daily mood. *Journal of Personality and Social Psychology, 52,* 988–993.

Stone, A. A., & Neale, J. M. (1982). Development of a methodology for assessing daily experiences. In A. Baum and J. Singer (Eds.), *Environment and health*. Hillsdale, NJ: Erlbaum.

Stone, A. A., & Neale, J. M. (1984). The effects of "severe" daily events on mood. *Journal of Personality and Social Psychology, 46*, 137–144.

Stone, A. A., Reed, B. R., & Neale, J. M. (1987). Changes in daily event frequency precede episodes of physical symptoms. *Journal of Human Stress, 13*, 70–74.

Stone, G. (1982). Health Psychology, a new journal for a new field. *Health Psychology, 1*, 1–6.

Stone, J., Smyth, R., Carson, A., Lewis, S., Prescott, R., Warlow, C., & Sharpe, M. (2005). Systematic review of misdiagnosis of conversion symptoms and "hysteria." *British Medical Journal, 331*, 989–995.

Stone, L. B., Hankin, B. L., Gibb, B. E., & Abela, J. R. Z. (2011). Co-rumination predicts the onset of depressive disorders during adolescence. *Journal of Adolescence, 32*, 19–37.

Stone, M. H. (1986). Exploratory psychotherapy in schizophrenia-spectrum patients: A reevaluation in the light of long-term follow-up of schizophrenic and borderline patients. *Bulletin of the Menninger Clinic, 50*, 287–306.

Stone, M. H. (1987). Psychotherapy of borderline patients in light of long-term follow-up. *Bulletin of the Menninger Clinic, 51*, 231–247.

Stone, M. H. (1993). *Abnormalities of personality. Within and beyond the realm of treatment*. New York: Norton.

Stone, S. V., & Costa, P. T. (1990). Disease-prone personality or distress-prone personality? The role of neuroticism in coronary heart disease. In H. S. Friedman (Ed.), *Personality and disease*. New York: John Wiley & Sons.

Stonnington, C. M., Barry, J. J., & Fisher, R. S. (2006). Conversion disorder. *American Journal of Psychiatry, 163*, 1510–1517.

Stoolmiller, M., Kim, H. K., & Capaldi, D. M. (2005). The course of depressive symptoms in men from early adolescence to young adulthood: Identifying latent trajectories and early predictors. *Journal of Abnormal Psychology, 114*, 331–345.

Stoppard, J. M. (2000). *Understanding depression: Feminist social constructionist approaches*. Florence, KY: Taylor and Francis/Routledge.

Stormer, S. M., & Thompson, J. K. (1996). Explanations of body image disturbance: A test of maturational status, negative verbal commentary, and sociological hypotheses. *International Journal of Eating Disorders, 19*, 193–202.

Strain, E. C., Bigelow, G. E., Liebson, I. A., & Stitzer, M. L. (1999). Moderate- vs low-dose methadone in the treatment of opioid dependence. *Journal of the American Medical Association, 281*, 1000–1005.

Strand, J., & Warren, R. (2014). Panic control treatment in private practice: Effectiveness and clients' perspectives. *The Behavior Therapist, 37*, 42–44.

Stratton, P., Silver, E., Nascimento, N., McDonnell, L., Powell, G., & Nowotny, E. (2015). Couple and family therapy outcome research in the previous decade: What does the evidence tell us? *Contemporary Family Therapy: An International Journal, 37*, 1–12.

Stravynski, A., & Boyer, R. (2001). Loneliness in relation to suicide ideation and parasuicide: A population-wide study. *Suicide and Life-Threatening Behavior, 31*, 32–40.

Streiner, D. L. (2005). I have the answer, now what's the question? Why meta-analyses do not provide definitive solutions. *Canadian Journal of Psychiatry, 50*, 829–831.

Striegel-Moore, R. H., Silberstein, L. R., & Rodin, J. (1993). The social self in bulimia nervosa: Public self-consciousness, social anxiety, and perceived fraudulence. *Journal of Abnormal Psychology, 102*, 297–303.

Strike, C. J., Urbanoski, K. A., & Rush, B. R. (2003). Who seeks treatment for cannabis-related problems? *Canadian Journal of Public Health, 94*, 351–354.

Strober, M., Freeman, R., & Morrell, W. (1997). The long-term course of severe anorexia nervosa in adolescents: Survival analysis of recovery, relapse, and outcome predictors over 10-15 years in a prospective study. *International Journal of Eating Disorders, 22*, 339–360.

Strober, M., Lampert, C., Morrell, W., Burroughs, J., & Jacobs, C. (1990). A controlled family study of anorexia nervosa: Evidence of family aggregation and lack of shared transmission with affective disorders. *International Journal of Eating Disorders, 9*, 239–253.

Stroebe, M., Schut, H., & Finkehauer, C. (2001). The traumatization of grief? A conceptual framework for understanding the trauma-bereavement interface. *The Israel Journal of Psychiatry and Related Sciences, 38*, 185–201.

Strunk, D. R., Brotman, M. A., DuRubeis, R. J., & Hollon, S. D. (2010). Therapist competence in cognitive therapy for depression: Predicting subsequent symptom change. *Journal of Consulting and Clinical Psychology, 78*, 429–437.

Stuart, H. L. (2003). Stigma and the daily news: Evaluation of a newspaper intervention. *Canadian Journal of Psychiatry, 48*, 651–656.

Stuart, H. L. (2006a). Reaching out to high school youth: The effectiveness of a video-based anti-stigma program. *Canadian Journal of Psychiatry, 51*, 647–643.

Stuart, H. L. (2006b). Media portrayal of mental illness and its treatments. *CNS Drugs, 20*, 99–106.

Stuart, H. L., & Arboleda-Florez, J. (2001). Community attitudes toward people with schizophrenia. *Canadian Journal of Psychiatry, 46*, 245–251.

Stuart, H. L., Arboleda-Florez, J., & Crisanti, A. J. (2001). Impact of legal reforms on length of forensic assessments in Alberta, Canada. *International Journal of Law and Psychiatry, 24*, 527–538.

Stuart, H. L., Chen, S.-P., Christie, R., Dobson, K., Kirsh, B., Knaak, S., et al. (2014). Opening Minds in Canada: Background and rationale. *Canadian Journal of Psychiatry, 59*, S8–S12.

Stuart, R. B. (1976). An operant interpersonal program for couples. In D. H. L. Olson (Ed.), *Treating relationships*. Lake Mills, IA: Graphic Publishing.

Stuart, R. B. (1978). Protection of the right to informed consent to participate in research. *Behavior Therapy, 9*, 73–82.

Stubbings, D. R., Rees, C. S., & Roberts, L. D. (2015). New avenues to facilitate engagement in psychotherapy: The use of videoconferencing and text–chat in a severe case of obsessive-compulsive disorder. *Australian Psychologist, 50*, 265–270.

Studer, L. H., Clelland, S. R., Aylwin, A. S., Reddon, J. R., & Monro, A. (2000). Rethinking risk assessment for incest offenders. *International Journal of Law and Psychiatry, 23*, 15–22.

Stuss, D. T., & Benson, D. F. (1983). Emotional concomitants of psychosurgery. In K. M. Heilman & P. Satz (Eds.), *Advances in neuropsychology and behavioural neurology: Vol. 1. Neuropsychology of human emotion* (pp. 111–140). New York: Guilford.

Substance Abuse and Mental Health Services Administration. (2013). Results from the 2012 National Survey on Drug Use and Health: Detailed tables. Rockville, MD: Author.

Suddath, R. L., Christison, G. W., Torrey, E. F., Casanova, M. F., & Weinberger, D. R. (1990). Anatomical abnormalities in the brains of monozygotic twins discordant for schizophrenia. *New England Journal of Medicine, 322*, 789–794.

Sue, D. W., & Sue, D. (2003). What is cultural competence? In D. W. Sue & D. Sue (Eds.), *Counseling the culturally diverse* (pp. 12–24). New York: John Wiley & Sons.

Suisman, J. L., O'Connor, S., Sperry, S., Thompson, K., et al. (2012). Genetic and environmental influences on thin-ideal internalization. *International Journal of Eating Disorders, 45*, 942–948.

Sullivan, P. F., Neale, M. C., & Kendler, K. S. (2000). Genetic epidemiology of major depression: Review and meta-analysis. *American Journal of Psychiatry, 157*, 1552–1562.

Suls, J., & Fletcher, B. (1985). The relative efficacy of avoidant and nonavoidant coping strategies: A meta-analysis. *Health Psychology, 4*, 249–288.

Summerfeldt, L. J., & Endler, N. S. (1998). Examining the evidence for anxiety-related cognitive biases in obsessive-compulsive disorder. *Journal of Anxiety Disorders, 12*, 579–598.

Sunderland, A., & Findlay, L. C. (2013). Perceived need for mental health care in Canada: Results from the 2012 Canadian Community Health Survey—Mental Health. *Health Reports, 24*, 3–9.

Suppes, T., Baldessarini, R. J., Faedda, G. L., & Tohen, M. (1991). Risk of recurrence following discontinuation of lithium treatment in bipolar disorder. *Archives of General Psychiatry, 48*, 1082–1087.

Supreme Court of British Columbia Vancouver Registry. (2016, September 12). Notice of civil claim: In the Supreme Court of British Columbia between Mary Louise MacLaren, D.C., and Council of Canadians with Disabilities.

Surles, R. C., Blanch, A. K., Shern, D. L., & Donahue, S. A. (1992). Case management as a strategy for systems change. *Health Affairs, 11*, 151–163.

Susser, E., Neugebauer, R., Hoek, H. W., Brown, A. S., Lin, S., et al. (1996). Schizophrenia after prenatal famine: Further evidence. *Archives of General Psychiatry, 53*, 25–31.

Sussman, S. (1998). The first asylums in Canada: A response to neglectful community care and current trends. *Canadian Journal of Psychiatry, 43*, 260–264.

Sussman, S., Stacy, A. W., Dent, C. W., Simon, T. R., & Johnson, C. A. (1996). Marijuana use: Current issues and new research directions. *Journal of Drug Issues, 26*, 695–733.

Sutcliffe, J. P., & Jones, J. (1962). Personal identity, multiple personality, and hypnosis. *International Journal of Clinical and Experimental Hypnosis, 10*, 231–269.

Sutera, S., Pandey, J., Esser, E. L., et al. (2007). Predictors of optimal outcome in toddlers diagnosed with autism spectrum disorders. *Journal of Autism and Developmental Disorders, 37*, 98–107.

Svenson, L. W., & Campbell, R. L. (1992). Perceived health status and desired health information needs of university students. *Canadian Journal of Public Health, 83*, 167–168.

Svrakic, D. M., Zorumski, C. F., Svrakic, N. M., Zwir, I., & Cloninger, C. R. (2013). Risk architecture of schizophrenia: The role of epigenetics. *Current Opinions in Psychiatry, 26*, 188–195.

Swanson, J. W., Borum, R., Swartz, M. S., Hiday, V. A., Wagner, H. R., & Burns, B. J. (2001). Can involuntary outpatient commitment reduce arrests among persons with severe mental disorder? *Criminal Justice and Behavior, 28*, 156–189.

Swanson, M. C., Bland, R. C., & Newman, S. C. (1994). Epidemiology of psychiatric disorders in Edmonton: Antisocial personality disorders. *Acta Psychiatrica Scandinavica, 376* (Suppl.), 63–70.

Swanson, J. W., Holzer, C. E., Ganju, V. K., & Jono, R. T. (1990). Violence and psychiatric disorder in the community: Evidence from the Epidemiological Catchment Area surveys. *Hospital and Community Psychiatry, 41*, 761–770.

Swartz, M. S., et al. (2001). A randomized control trial of outpatient commitment in North Carolina. *Psychiatric Services, 52*, 325–329.

Swartz, M. S., et al. (2006). Substance use in persons with schizophrenia: Baseline prevalence and correlates from the NIMH CATIE Study. *Journal of Nervous and Mental Disease, 194*, 164–172.

Swartz, M. S., Blazer, D., George, L., & Winfield, I. (1990). Estimating the prevalence of borderline personality in the community. *Journal of Personality Disorders, 4*, 257–272.

Sweet, J. J., Carr, M. A., Rossini, E., & Kasper, C. (1986). Relationship between the Luria-Nebraska Neuropsychological Battery and the WISC-R: Further examination using Kaufman's factors. *International Journal of Clinical Neuropsychology, 8*, 177–180.

Sweet, L., Savoie, J. A., & Lemyre, L. (1999). Appraisals, coping, and stress in breast cancer screening: A longitudinal investigation of causal structure. *Canadian Journal of Behavioural Science, 31*, 240–253.

Sweet, R. A., et al. (1995). Duration of neuroleptic treatment and prevalence of tardive dyskinesia in late life. *Archives of General Psychiatry, 52*, 478–486.

Swendsen, J., Burstein, M., Case, B., Conway, K. P., et al. (2012). Use and abuse of alcohol and illicit drugs in U.S. adolescents: Results of the National Comorbidity Survey — Adolescent Supplement. *Archives of General Psychiatry, 69*, 390–398.

Swift, J. K., & Derthick, A. O. (2013). Increasing hope by addressing clients' outcome expectations. *Psychotherapy, 50*, 284–287.

Sylvain, C., Ladouceur, R., & Boisvert, J.-M. (1997). Cognitive and behavioral treatment of pathological gambling: A controlled study. *Journal of Consulting and Clinical Psychology, 65*, 727–732.

Sylvia, L. G., Thase, M. E., Reilly-Harrington, N., Salcedo, S., Brody, B., Kinrys, G., . . . Deckersbach, T. (2015). Psychotherapy use in bipolar disorder: Association with functioning and illness severity. *The Australian and New Zealand Journal of Psychiatry, 49*, 453–461.

Sypeck, M. F., et al. (2006). Cultural representations of thinness in women, redux: Playboy magazine's depiction of beauty from 1979 to 1998. *Body Image, 3*, 229–235.

Szasz, T. (2005). Idiots, infants, and the insane: Mental illness and legal incompetence. *Journal of Medical Ethics, 31*, 78–81.

Szasz, T. S. (1963). *Law, liberty, and psychiatry*. New York: Macmillan.

Szoke, A., Trandafir, A., Dupont, M.-E., et al. (2008). Longitudinal studies of cognition in schizophrenia: Meta-analysis. *The British Journal of Psychiatry, 192*, 248–257.

Taillon, A., O'Connor, K., Dupuis, G., & Lavoie, M. (2013). Inference-based therapy for body dysmorphic disorder. *Clinical Psychology & Psychotherapy, 20*, 67–76.

Tam, P. (2008, August 19). Canadians suffering mental illness leaving hospitals earlier: Study. Canwest News.

Tamburri, R., & Samson, N. (2014, October 20). Ending sexual violence on campus. *University Affairs.*

Tan, W. C., et al. (2009). Marijuana and chronic obstructive lung disease: A population-based survey. *Canadian Medical Association Journal, 180*, 814–820.

Tanaka, M., Georgiades, K., Boyle, M. H., & MacMillan, H. L. (2015). Child maltreatment and educational attainment in young adulthood: Results from the Ontario Child Health Study. *Journal of Interpersonal Violence, 30*, 195–214.

Tandon, R., Keshavan, M. S., & Nasrallah, H. A. (2008). Schizophrenia, "Just the facts": What we know in 2008. Part 1: Overview. *Schizophrenia Research, 100*, 4–19.

Tanner, C., & Connan, F. (2003). Cognitive analytic therapy. In J. Treasure, U. Schmidt, & E. van Furth (Eds.), *Handbook of eating disorders* (2nd ed., pp. 279–289). Chichester, England: John Wiley & Sons.

Tanner, L. (2013, August 27). Young at heart & mind. *The National Post*, B2.

Tarter, R. E., Kirisci, L., Mezzich, A., Ridenour, T., et al. (2012). Does the "gateway" sequence increase prediction of cannabis use disorder development beyond deviant socialization? Implications for prevention practice and policy. *Drug and Alcohol Dependence, 123* (Supplement 1), S72–S78.

Tasca, G. A. (2015). What Canadian clinical psychologists want from psychotherapy research. *Canadian Psychology, 56,* 16–28.

Tasca, G. A., & Balfour, L. (2014). Attachment and eating disorders: A review of current research. *International Journal of Eating Disorders, 47,* 710–717.

Tasca, G. A., Compare, A., Zarbo, C., & Brugnera, A. (2016). Therapeutic alliance and binge-eating outcomes in a group therapy context. *Journal of Counseling Psychology, 63,* 443–451.

Tashkin, D. P. (2005). Smoked marijuana as a cause of lung injury. *Monald: Archives for Chest Disease, 63,* 93–100.

Taylor, C. T., Laposa, J. M., & Alden, L. E. (2004). Is avoidant personality disorder more than just social avoidance? *Journal of Personality Disorders, 18,* 571–594.

Taylor, G. (2016). *The Chief Public Health Officer's report on the state of public health in Canada 2015: Alcohol consumption in Canada.* Ottawa: Her Majesty the Queen in Right of Canada as represented by the Minister of Health.

Taylor, P. J. (2008). Psychosis and violence: Stories, fears, and reality. *Canadian Journal of Psychiatry, 53,* 647–659.

Taylor, S. R., & Weiss, J. S. (2009). Review of insomnia psychotherapy options for the elderly: Implications for marginal care. *Population Health Management, 12,* 317–323.

Taylor, S., Asmundson, G. J. G., & Coons, M. J. (2005). Current directions in the treatment of hypochondriasis. *Journal of Cognitive Psychotherapy: An International Quarterly, 19,* 285–304.

Taylor, S., Jang, K. L., Stewart, S. H., & Stein, M. B. (2008). Etiology of the dimensions of anxiety sensitivity: A behavioral–genetic analysis. *Journal of Anxiety Disorders, 22,* 899–914.

Taylor, S., Thordarson, D. S., Jang, K. L., & Asmundson, G. J. G. (2006). Genetic and environmental origins of health anxiety: A twin study. *World Psychiatry, 5,* 47–50.

Taylor, S., Zvolensky, M. J., Cox, B. J., et al. (2007). Robust dimensions of anxiety sensitivity: Development and initial validation of the Anxiety Sensitivity Index–3. *Psychological Assessment, 19,* 176–188.

Teachman, B. A., & Woody, S. R. (2003). Automatic processing in spider phobia: Implicit fear association over the course of treatment. *Journal of Abnormal Psychology, 112,* 100–109.

Teasdale, J. D., et al. (2002). Metacognitive awareness and prevention of relapse in depression: Empirical evidence. *Journal of Consulting and Clinical Psychology, 70,* 275–287.

Teasdale, J. D., Segal, Z. V., Williams, J. M. G., et al. (2000). Prevention of relapse/recurrence in major depression by mindfulness-based cognitive therapy. *Journal of Consulting and Clinical Psychology, 68,* 615–623.

Teglasi, H., Nebbergall, A. J., & Newman, D. (2012). Construct validity and case validity in assessment. *Psychological Assessment, 24,* 464–475.

Telch, M. J., Harrington, P. J., Smits, J. A. J., & Powers, M. B. (2011). Unexpected arousal, anxiety sensitivity, and their interaction on CO2-induced panic: Further evidence for the context-sensitivity vulnerability model. *Journal of Anxiety Disorders, 25,* 645–653.

Tellegen, A., Ben-Porath, Y. S., McNulty, J. L., Arbisi, P. A., Graham, J. R., & Kaemmer, B. (2003). *MMPI-2 Restructured Clinical (RC) Scales: Development, validation, and interpretation.* Minneapolis: University of Minnesota Press.

Tennant, C. (1999). The Ritalin racket. Accessed on Student.Com.

Tennant, C. (2001). Work-related stress and depressive disorders. *Journal of Psychosomatic Research, 51,* 697–704.

Terry, D. J., & Hynes, G. J. (1998). Adjustment to a low-control situation: Reexamining the role of coping responses. *Journal of Personality and Social Psychology, 74,* 1078–1092.

Teuscher, V. (2009). Subjective age bias: A motivational and information processing approach. *International Journal of Behavioral Development, 33,* 22–31.

Thaker, G. K. (2007). Endophenotypic studies in schizophrenia: Promise and challenges. *Schizophrenia Bulletin, 33,* 1–2.

Thapar, A., Cooper, M., Eyre, O., & Langley, K. (2013). What have we learnt about the causes of ADHD. *Journal of Child Psychology and Psychiatry, 54,* 3–16.

The Investigative Staff of the Boston Globe. (2015). *Betrayal: The crisis in the Catholic Church.* Boston: Back Bay Books.

The Lancet. (2013). Living with grief. *The Lancet, 37,* 589.

The Queen v. Louis Riel, [1886]. The Queen vs. Louis Riel, accused and convicted of the crime of high treason [electronic resource]: Report of trial at Regina. -Appeal to the Court of Queen's Bench, Manitoba. -Appeal to the Privy Council, England. -Petition for medical examination of the convict. -List of petitions for commutation of sentence, Ottawa. Ottawa: The Queen's Printer.

Thibaut, J. W., & Kelley, H. H. (1959). *The social psychology of groups.* New York: John Wiley & Sons.

Thibodeau, M. A., Welch, P. G., Sareen, J., & Asmundson, G. J. G. (2013). Anxiety disorders are independently associated with suicide ideation and attempts: Propensity score matching in two epidemiological samples. *Depression and Anxiety, 30,* 947–954.

Thielsch, B., Andor, T., & Ehring, R. (2015). Do metacognitions and intolerance of uncertainty predict worry in everyday life? An ecological momentary assessment study. *Behavior Therapy, 46,* 532–543.

Thigpen, C. H., & Cleckley, H. (1954). *The three faces of Eve.* Kingsport, TN: Kingsport Press.

Thoma, N. C., & Cecero, J. C. (2009). Is integrative use of techniques in psychotherapy the exception or the rule? Results of a national survey of doctoral-level practitioners. *Psychotherapy Theory, Research, Practice, and Training, 46,* 405–417.

Thomas, A., & Chess, S. (1989). Temperament and personality. In G. A. Kohnstamm, J. E. Bates, & M. K. Rothbart (Eds.), *Temperament in childhood* (pp. 254–261). New York: John Wiley & Sons.

Thomas, G., Stockwell, T., & Reist, D. (2009). Alcohol pricing, public health and the HST: Proposed incentives for BC drinkers to make healthy choices. Victoria, BC: University of Victoria.

Thomas, J. J., Vartanian, L. R., & Brownell, K. D. (2009). The relationship between eating disorder not otherwise specified (EDNOS) and officially recognized eating disorders: Meta-analysis and implications for DSM. *Psychological Bulletin, 135,* 407–433.

Thomas, K. S., & Applebaum, R. (2015). Long-term services and supports (LTSS): A growing challenge for an aging America. *Public Policy and Aging Report, 25,* 56–62.

Thompson and Empowerment Council v. Ontario, 2013 ONSC 5392 (CANLII).

Thompson, J. K., et al. (2003). The Sociocultural Attitudes Toward Appearance Scale-3. *International Journal of Eating Disorders, 35,* 293–304.

Thompson, J. K., & Stice, E. (2001). Thin-ideal internalization: Mounting evidence for a new risk factor for body-image disturbance and eating pathology. *Current Directions in Psychological Science, 10,* 181–183.

Thompson, L. W., Gallagher, D., & Breckenridge, J. S. (1987). Comparative effectiveness of psychotherapies for depressed elders. *Journal of Consulting and Clinical Psychology, 55,* 385–390.

Tibbo, P., Joffe, K., Chue, P., Metelitsa, A., & Wright, E. (2001). Global assessment of functioning following assertive community treatment in Edmonton, Alberta: A longitudinal study. *Canadian Journal of Psychiatry, 46*, 144–148.

Tidmarsh, L., & Volkmar, F. R. (2003). Diagnosis and epidemiology of autism spectrum disorders. *Canadian Journal of Psychiatry, 48*, 517–525.

Tiefer, L., Pedersen, B., & Melman, A. (1988). Psychosocial follow-up of penile prosthesis implant patients and partners. *Journal of Sex & Marital Therapy, 14*, 184–201.

Tienari, P., Wynne, L. C., Moring, J., & Lahti, I. (1994). The Finnish adoptive family study of schizophrenia: Implications for family research. *British Journal of Psychiatry, 23*, 20–26.

Tierney, M. C., Yao, C., Kiss, A., & McDowell, I. (2005). Neuropsychological tests accurately predict Alzheimer's disease after 5 and 10 years. *Neurology, 64*, 1853–1859.

Tighe, A., Pistrang, N., Casdagli, L., Baruch, G., & Butler, S. (2012). Multisystemic therapy for young offenders: Families' experiences of therapeutic processes and outcomes. *Journal of Family Psychology, 26*, 187–197.

Timpano, K. R., Broman-Fulks, J. J., Glaesmer, H., Exner, C., et al. (2013). A taxometric exploration of the latent structure of hoarding. *Psychological Assessment, 25*, 194–203.

Tolin, D. F., McKay, D., Forman, E. M., Klonsky, E. D., & Thombs, B. D. (2015). Empirically supported treatment: Recommendations for a new model. *Clinical Psychology: Science and Practice, 22*, 317–337.

Tolin, D. F., Witt, S. T., & Stevens, M. C. (2014). Hoarding disorder and obsessive–compulsive disorder show different patterns of neural activity during response inhibition. *Psychiatry Research: Neuroimaging, 221*, 142–148.

Tonmyr, L., Jamieson, E., Mery, L. S., & MacMillan, H. L. (2005). The relation between childhood adverse experiences and disability due to mental health problems in a community sample of women. *Canadian Journal of Psychiatry, 50*, 778–783.

Toplak, M. E., Connors, L., Shuster, J., et al. (2008). Review of cognitive, cognitive-behavioral, and neural-based interventions for Attention-Deficit/Hyperactivity Disorder (ADHD). *Clinical Psychology Review, 28*, 801–823.

Topping, K. J., & Barron, I. G. (2009). School-based child sexual abuse prevention programs: A review of effectiveness. *Review of Educational Research, 79*, 431–463.

Torgersen, S. (1986). Genetics of somatoform disorder. *Archives of General Psychiatry, 43*, 502–505.

Toronto Star. (2005, November 11). Mentally ill denied their rights: Judge, A17.

Torrey, E. F. (1995). Prevalence of psychosis among the Hutterites: A reanalysis of the 1950–53 study. *Schizophrenia Research, 16*, 167–170.

Torrey, E. F. (1996). *Out of the shadows: Confronting America's mental health crisis.* New York: John Wiley & Sons.

Torrey, E. F., Kennard, A. D., Eslinger, D., et al. (2010). *More mentally ill people are in jails and prisons than hospitals: A survey of the states.* Arlington, VA: Treatment Advising Centre.

Torrey, E. F., Taylor, E., Bowler, A., & Gottesman, I. (1994). *Schizophrenia and manic depressive disorder. The biological roots of mental illness as revealed by the landmark study of identical twins.* New York: Basic Books.

Toufexis, A. (1996). Why Jennifer got sick: The mother of a poster child is accused of causing her daughter's illness. *Time, 147*, 70.

Toughill, K. (2003, November 1). New home, same old problems: Gas-sniffing children, drunken adults still plague Innu town. *Toronto Star*, H2.

Toupin, J., Dery, M., Pauze, R., Mercier, H., & Fortin, L. (2000). Cognitive and familial contributions to conduct disorder in children. *Journal of Child Psychology and Psychiatry, 41*, 333–344.

Towbin, K., Axelson, S., Leibenluft, E., & Birmaher, B. (2013). Differentiating bipolar disorder—not otherwise specified and severe mood dysregulation. *Journal of the American Academy of Child and Adolescent Psychiatry, 52*, 466–481.

Travers, L. V., Randell, E. T., Bryant, F. B., Conley, C. S., & Bohnert, A. M. (2015). The cost of perfection with apparent ease: Theoretical foundations and development of the Effortless Perfectionism Scale. *Psychological Assessment, 27*, 1147–1159.

Trawver, K. (2010). Assertive community treatment. In A. Rubin, D. W. Springer, & K. Trawver (Eds.), *Psychosocial treatment of schizophrenia* (pp. 187–252). Hoboken, NJ: John Wiley & Sons.

Tregellas, J. (2009). Connecting brain structure and function in schizophrenia. *American Journal of Psychiatry, 166*, 134–136.

Tremblay, C., Hébert, M., & Piché, C. (2000). Type I and II posttraumatic stress disorder in sexually abused children. *Journal of Child Sexual Abuse, 9*, 65–90.

Tremblay, R. E., Masse, B., Perron, D., Leblanc, M., Schwartzman, A. E., & Ledingham, J. E. (1992). Early disruptive behavior, poor school achievement, delinquent behavior, and delinquent personality: Longitudinal analyses. *Journal of Consulting and Clinical Psychology, 60*, 64–72.

Trew, J. L., & Alden, L. E. (2015). Kindness reduces avoidance goals in socially anxious individuals. *Motivation and Emotion, 39*, 892.

Treynor, W., Gonzalez, R., & Nolen-Hoeksema, S. (2003). Rumination reconsidered: A psychometric analysis. *Cognitive Therapy and Research, 27*, 247–259.

Triano-Antidormi, L. (2013, June 5). Dr. Lori Triano-Antidormi (Psychologist, As an Individual) at the Justice and Human Rights Committee. Retrieved from http://openparliament.ca/committees/justice/41-1/76/dr-lori-triano-antidormi-1/only/.

Trocmé, N., et al. (2005). Canadian incidence study of reported child abuse and neglect 2003: Major findings. Ottawa: Minister of Public Works and Government Services Canada.

Troister, T., & Holden, R. R. (2012). A two-year prospective study of psychache and its relationship to suicidality among high-risk undergraduates. *Journal of Clinical Psychology, 68*, 1019–1027.

True, W. R., Rice, J., Eisen, S. A., Heath, A. C., Goldberg, J., et al. (1993). A twin study of genetic and environmental contributions to liability for posttraumatic stress disorder. *Archives of General Psychiatry, 50*, 257–264.

Trull, T. J. (2001). Relationships of borderline features to parental mental illness, childhood abuse, Axis I disorder, and current functioning. *Journal of Personality Disorders, 15*, 19–32.

Trull, T. J., Useda, J. D., Costa, P. T., Jr., & McCrae, R. R. (1995). Comparison of the MMPI-2 personality psychopathology five (PSY-5), the NEO-PI, and the NEO-PI-R. *Psychological Assessment, 7*, 508–516.

Truscott, D., & Crook, K. H. (1993). Tarasoff in the Canadian context: Wenden and the duty to protect. *Canadian Journal of Psychiatry, 38*, 84–89.

Tryon, W. W. (2008). Whatever happened to symptom substitution? *Clinical Psychology Review, 26*, 963–968.

Tsai, G., Gastfriend, D. R., & Coyle, J. T. (1995). The glutamatergic basis of human alcoholism. *American Journal of Psychiatry, 152*, 332–340.

Tsai, G., Parssani, L. A., Slusher, B. S., Carter, R., Baer, L., et al. (1995). Abnormal excitatory neurotransmitter metabolism in schizophrenic brains. *Archives of General Psychiatry, 52*, 829–836.

Tsertsvadze, A., et al. (2009). Oral sildenafil citrate (Viagra) for erectile dysfunction: A systematic review and meta-analysis of harms. *Urology, 74,* 831–836.

Tsuang, M. T., Lyons, M. J., Meyer, J. M., et al. (1998). Co-occurrence of abuse of different drugs in men: the role of drug specific and shared vulnerabilities. *Archives of General Psychiatry, 55,* 967–972.

Tu, J. V., Nardi, L., & Fang, J. (2009). National trends in rates of death and hospital admissions related to acute myocardial infarction, heart failure, and stroke, 1994–2004. *Canadian Medical Association Journal, 180,* E118–E125.

Tucker, J. A., Vuchinich, R. E., & Downey, K. K. (1992). Substance abuse. In S. M. Turner, K. S. Calhoun, & H. E. Adams (Eds.), *Handbook of clinical behavior therapy* (pp. 203–223). New York: John Wiley & Sons.

Tuokko, H., Garrett, D. D., McDowell, I., et al. (2003). Cognitive decline in high-functioning older adults: Reserve or ascertainment bias? *Aging and Mental Health, 7,* 259–270.

Tuokko, H., Hadjistavropoulos, T., Miller, J. A., & Beattie, B. L. (1992). The Clock Test: A sensitive measure to differentiate normal elderly from those with Alzheimer disease. *Journal of the American Geriatrics Society, 40,* 579–584.

Tuokko, H., Hadjistavropoulos, T., Rae, S., & O'Rourke, N. (2000). A comparison of alternative approaches to the scoring of clock drawing. *Archives of Clinical Neuropsychology, 15,* 137–148.

Tuokko, H., Kristjansson, E., & Miller, J. (1995). Neuropsychological detection of dementia: An overview of the neuropsychological component of the Canadian Study of Health and Aging. *Journal of Clinical and Experimental Neuropsychology, 17,* 352–373.

Tuomisto, M. T. (1997). Intra-arterial blood pressure and heart rate reactivity to behavioral stress in normotensive, borderline, and mild hypertensive men. *Health Psychology, 16,* 554–565.

Turcotte, M. (2014). *Insights on Canadian society: Canadians with unmet home care needs* (Catalogue No. 75-006-x). Ottawa: Statistics Canada.

Turecki, G., Briere, R., Dewar, K., Antonetti, T., Seguin, M., et al. (1999). Prediction of level of serotonin 2A receptor binding by serotonin receptor 2A genetic variation in postmortem brain sample from subjects who did or did not commit suicide. *American Journal of Psychiatry, 156,* 1456–1458.

Turner, B. J., Cobb, R. J., Gratz, K. L., & Chapman, A. L. (2016). The role of interpersonal conflict and perceived social support in nonsuicidal self-injury in daily life. *Journal of Abnormal Psychology, 125,* 588–598.

Turner, R. J., & Wagonfeld, M. O. (1967). Occupational mobility and schizophrenia. *American Sociological Review, 32,* 104–113.

Turner, S. M., Beidel, D. C., & Townsley, R. M. (1992). Behavioral treatment of social phobia. In S. M. Turner, K. S. Calhoun, & H. E. Adams (Eds.), *Handbook of clinical behavior therapy* (2nd ed., pp. 13–37). New York: John Wiley & Sons.

Turner, W. A., & Casey, L. M. (2014). Outcomes associated with virtual reality in psychological interventions: Where are we now? *Clinical Psychology Review, 34,* 634–644.

Twenge, J. M., & Foster, J. D. (2010). Birth cohort increases in narcissistic personality traits among American college students, 1982-2009. *Social Psychological and Personality Science, 1,* 99–106.

Twentyman, C. T., & McFall, R. M. (1975). Behavioral training of social skills in shy males. *Journal of Consulting and Clinical Psychology, 43,* 384–395.

Tyas, S. L., et al. (2007). Transitions to mild cognitive impairments, dementia, and death: Findings from the Nun Study. *American Journal of Epidemiology, 165,* 1231–1238.

Tyler, T. (2004, November 5). Pair who caged sons get longer jail terms. *The Toronto Star.*

Tyler, T. (2008, June 21). Sexual anxiety drove me: Bernardo. Killer suggests he is not a psychopath anymore. *Toronto Star.*

Tyler, T. (2009, May 29). When illness leads to prison, or worse. *The Toronto Star.*

Tyrer, P., et al. (2007). Critical developments in the assessment of personality disorder. *The British Journal of Psychiatry, 190,* s51–s59.

Uhl, G. R., Liu, Q.-R., Drgon, T., et al. (2008). Molecular genetics of successful smoking cessation: Convergent genome-wide association study results. *Archives of General Psychiatry, 65,* 683–693.

Uliaszek, A., Zinbarg, R. E., Mineka, S., Craske, M. G., et al. (2012). A longitudinal examination of stress generation in depressive and anxiety disorders. *Journal of Abnormal Psychology, 121,* 4–15.

Ullmann, L., & Krasner, L. (1975). *A psychological approach to abnormal behavior* (2nd ed.). Englewood Cliffs, NJ: Prentice-Hall.

Undheim, A. M., & Sund, A. M. (2008). Psychosocial factors and reading difficulties: Students with reading difficulties drawn from a representative population sample. *Scandinavian Journal of Psychology, 49,* 377–384.

United Way of Greater Toronto. (1997). Metro Toronto: A community at risk. Toronto: United Way.

U. S. Department of Health and Human Services. (1994). Treatment for alcohol and other drug abuse: Opportunities for coordination. Rockville, MD: U.S. Department of Health and Human Services.

U. S. Department of Health and Human Services, Centers for Disease Control and Prevention, & National Center for Chronic Disease Prevention and Health Promotion. (2014). Smoking—50 years of progress: A report of the Surgeon General. Atlanta: Authors.

U. S. Department of Health and Human Services (HHS) Office of the Surgeon General and National Action Alliance for Suicide Prevention. (2012). 2012 National strategy for suicide prevention: Goals and objectives for action. Washington, DC: HHS.

Unutzer, J. (2008). Evidence-based treatments for anxiety and depression: Lost in translation. *Depression and Anxiety, 25,* 726–729.

Usman, M. A. (1997). Frontotemporal dementias. In P. D. Nussbaum (Ed.), *Handbook of neuropsychology and aging* (pp. 159–176). New York: Plenum.

Vaidya, C. J., & Stollstorff, M. (2008). Cognitive neuroscience of attention deficit hyperactivity disorder: Current status and working hypotheses. *Developmental Disabilities Research Review, 14,* 261–267.

Vaidyanathan, U., Hall, J. R., Patrick, C. J., & Bernat, E. J. (2011). Clarifying the role of defensive reactivity deficits in psychopathy and antisocial personality using startle reflex methodology. *Journal of Abnormal Psychology, 120,* 253–258.

Vaillant, G. E. (1996). A long-term follow-up of male alcohol abuse. *Archives of General Psychiatry, 53,* 243–250.

Valtonen, H. M., et al. (2007). Suicidal behaviour during different phases of bipolar disorder. *Journal of Affective Disorders, 97,* 101–107.

Van de Velde, S., Bracke, P., & Levecque, K. (2010). Gender differences in depression in 23 European countries: Cross-national variation in the gender gap in depression. *Social Science and Medicine, 71,* 305–313.

van den Bree, M. B., Shelton, K., Bonner, A., et al. (2009). A longitudinal population-based study of factors in adolescence predicting homelessness in young adulthood. *Journal of Adolescent Health, 45,* 571–578.

van der Oord, S., Prins, P. J. M., Oosterlaan, J., & Emmelkamp, P. M. G. (2008). Efficacy of methylphenidate, psychosocial treatments and their combination in school-aged children with ADHD: A meta-analysis. *Clinical Psychology Review, 28(5),* 783–800.

van Dessel, N. C., van der Wouden, J. C., Dekker, J., & van der Horst, H. E. (2016). Clinical value of *DSM IV* and *DSM V* criteria for diagnosing the most prevalent somatoform disorders in patients with medically unexplained physical symptoms (MUPS). *Journal of Psychosomatic Research, 82,* 4–10.

van Erp, T. G. M., et al. (2004). Hippocampal volumes in schizophrenic twins. *Archives of General Psychiatry, 61,* 346–353.

Van Gundy, K., & Rebellon, C. J. (2010). A life-course perspective on the "gateway hypothesis." *Journal of Health and Social Behavior, 51,* 244–259.

van Houtem, M. H. H., Aartman, I. H. A., Boomsma, D. I., Ligthart, L., Visscher, C. M., & de Jongh, A. (2014). Is dental phobia a blood-injection-injury phobia? *Depression and Anxiety, 31,* 1026–1034.

van Ingen, D. J., Freiheit, S. R., & Vye, C. S. (2009). From the lab to the clinic: Effectiveness of cognitive-behavioral treatments for anxiety disorders. *Professional Psychology: Research and Practice, 40,* 69–74.

van Kammen, W. B., Loeber, R., & Stouthamer-Loeber, M. (1991). Substance use and its relationship to conduct problems and delinquency in young boys. *Journal of Youth and Adolescence, 20,* 399–413.

van Lier, P. A. C., Vitaro, F., Barker, E. D., Brendgen, M., Tremblay, R. E., & Boivin, M. (2012). Peer victimization, poor academic achievement, and the link between childhood externalizing and internalizing problems. *Child Development, 83,* 1175–1788.

Van Nieuwerburgh, F. C. W., et al. (2009). Response to serotonin reuptake inhibitors in OCD is not influenced by common CYP2D6 polymorphisms. *International Journal of Psychiatry in Clinical Practice, 13,* 345–348.

van Nimwegen, L. J., de Haan, L., van Beveren, N. J. M., et al. (2008). Effect of olanzapine and risperidone on subjective well-being and craving for cannabis in patients with schizophrenia or related disorders: A double-blind randomized controlled trial. *Canadian Journal of Psychiatry, 53,* 400–405.

Van Oppen, P., de Haan, E., van Balkom, A. J., Spinhoven, P., Hoogduin, K. A. L., & van Dyck, R. (1995). Cognitive therapy and exposure in vivo in the treatment of obsessive–compulsive disorder. *Behaviour Research and Therapy, 33,* 379–390.

Van Orden, K. A., Bamonti, P. M., King, D. A., & Duberstein, P. R. (2012). Does perceived burdensomeness erode meaning in life among older adults? *Aging and Mental Health, 16,* 855–860.

Van Orden, K. A., & Conwell, Y. (2016). Issues in research on aging and suicide. *Aging and Mental Health, 20,* 240–251.

Van Orden, K. A., Witte, T. K., Cukrowicz, K. C., Braithwaite, S. R., Selby, E. A., & Joiner, T. E., Jr. (2010). The interpersonal theory of suicide. *Psychological Review, 117,* 575–600.

van Praag, H., Plutchik, R., & Apter, A. (Eds.). (1990). *Violence and suicidality.* New York: Brunner/Mazel.

Van Praet, N. (2016, August 29). Ontario faces fentanyl crisis, police warn: Organizations involved in drug issues say province sadly unprepared for surge in overdoses as threat from bootleg substance grows. *The Globe and Mail,* A1, A4.

van Reekum, R., Conway, C. A., Gansler, D., White, R., & Bachman, D. L. (1993). Neurobehavioral study of borderline personality disorder. *Journal of Psychiatry and Neuroscience, 18,* 121–129.

van Stegeren, A. H. (2009). Imaging effects on memory: A review of neuroimaging studies. *Canadian Journal of Psychiatry, 54,* 16–27.

van Straten, A., Hill, J., Richards, D. A., & Cuijpers, P. (2015). Stepped care treatment delivery for depression: A systematic review and meta-analysis. *Psychological Medicine, 45,* 231–246.

van Zelst, W. H., de Beurs, E., Beckman, A. T., Deej, D. T., & van Dyck, R. (2003). Prevalence and risk factors of posttraumatic stress disorder in older adults. *Psychotherapy and Psychosomatics, 72,* 333–342.

Vancouver Sun. (2005, July 5). Morissette reveals fight with anorexia, bulimia. *Vancouver Sun,* C3.

Vandewalle, G., Hebert, M., Beaulieu, C., et al. (2011). Abnormal hypothylamic response to light in seasonal affective disorder. *Biological Psychiatry, 70,* 954–961.

Vang, Z., Sigouin, J., Flenon, A., & Gagnon, A. (2015). The healthy immigrant effect in Canada: A systematic review. *Population Change and Lifecourse Strategic Knowledge Cluster Discussion Paper Series, 3,* Issue 1.

Vasilaki, E. I., Hosier, S. G., & Cox, W. M. (2006). The efficacy of motivational interviewing as a brief intervention for excessive drinking: A meta-analytic review. *Alcohol and Alcoholism, 41,* 328–335.

Vasiliadis, H.-M., Tempier, R., Lesage, A., & Kates, N. (2009). General practice and mental health care: Determinants of outpatient service use. *Canadian Journal of Psychiatry, 54,* 468–476.

Vasquez, F. L., Torres, A., Blanco, V., Diaz, O., Otero, P., & Hermida, E. (2012). Comparison of relaxation training with a cognitive-behavioral intervention for indicated prevention of depression in university students: A randomized controlled trial. *Journal of Psychiatric Research, 46,* 1456–1463.

Vasquez, F. L., Torres, A., Otero, P., & Diaz, O. (2011). Prevalence, comorbidity, and correlates of *DSM-IV* Axis I mental disorders among female university students. *Journal of Nervous and Mental Disease, 199,* 379–383.

Veale, D., Anson, M., Miles, S., Pieta, M., Costa, A., & Ellison, N. (2014). Efficacy of cognitive behaviour therapy versus anxiety management for body dysmorphic disorder: A randomised controlled trial. *Psychotherapy and Psychosomatics, 83,* 341–353.

Veale, D., Miles, S., & Anson, M. (2015). Long-term outcome of cognitive behavior therapy for body dysmorphic disorder: A naturalistic case series of 1 to 4 years after a controlled trial. *Behavior Therapy, 46,* 775–785.

Veale, D., & Roberts, A. (2014). Obsessive-compulsive disorder. *BMJ, 348,* g2183.

Vega, W. A., Aguilar-Gaxiola, S., Andrade, L., et al. (2002). Prevalence and age of onset for drug use in seven international sites: Results from the international consortium of psychiatric epidemiology. *Drug and Alcohol Dependence, 68,* 285–297.

Velakoulis, D., Pantelis, C., McGorry, P. D., Dudgeon, P., Brewer, W., et al. (1999). Hippocampal volume in first-episode psychoses and chronic schizophrenia: A high-resolution magnetic resonance imaging study. *Archives of General Psychiatry, 56,* 133–141.

Verdoux, H., Geddes, J. R., Takei, N., Lawrie, S. M., Bovet, P., et al. (1997). Obstetric complications and age at onset in schizophrenia: An international collaborative meta-analysis of individual patient data. *American Journal of Psychiatry, 154,* 1220–1227.

Verdun-Jones, S. N. (2000). Forensic psychiatry, ethics, and protective sentencing: What are the limits of psychiatric participation in the criminal justice system? *Acta Psychiatrica Scandinavica, 101,* 77–82.

Verheul, R., & Widiger, T. A. (2004). A meta-analysis of the prevalence and usage of the personality disorder not otherwise specified (PDNOS) diagnosis. *Journal of Personality Disorders, 18,* 309–319.

Verlaan, P., & Schwartzman, A. E. (2002). Mother's and father's parental adjustment: Links to externalising behaviour problems in sons and daughters. *International Journal of Behavioral Development, 26,* 214–224.

Vermeulen-Smit, E., Verdurmen, J. E., & Engels, R. C. (2015). The effectiveness of family interventions in preventing adolescent illicit drug use: A systematic review and meta-analysis of randomized controlled trials. *Clinical Child and Family Psychology Review, 18,* 218–239.

Verona, E., Patrick, C. J., & Joiner, T. E. (2001). Psychopathy, antisocial personality disorder, and suicide risk. *Journal of Abnormal Psychology, 110,* 462–470.

Viana, A. G., Beidel, D. C., & Rabian, B. (2009). Selective mutism: A review and integration of the last 15 years. *Clinical Psychology Review, 29,* 57–67.

Vickerman, K. A., & Margolin, G. (2009). Rape treatment outcome research: Empirical findings and state of the literature. *Clinical Psychology Review, 29,* 431–448.

Viding, E., Blair, R. J., Moffitt, T. E., & Plomin, R. (2005). Evidence for substantial genetic risk for psychopathy in 7-year-olds. *Journal of Child Psychology and Psychiatry, 46,* 592–597.

Viding, E., Jones, A. P., Frick, P. J., et al. (2008). Heritability of antisocial behavior at 9: Do callous-unemotional traits matter? *Developmental Science, 11,* 17–22.

Vien, A., & Beech, A. R. (2006). Psychopathy: Theory, measurement, and treatment. *Trauma, Violence, and Abuse, 7,* 155–174.

Vienneau, D. (1999, January 10). Give Alzheimer's patients right to die, doctor says. *Toronto Star,* L8.

Viglione, D. J. (1999). A review of recent research addressing the utility of the Rorschach. *Psychological Assessment, 11,* 251–265.

Vigod, S. N., Tarasoff, L. A., Bryja, B., Dennis, C., Yudin, M. H., & Ross, L. E. (2013). Relation between place of residence and postpartum depression. *Canadian Medical Association Journal, 185,* 1129–1135.

Viljoen, J. L., Roesch, R., Ogloff, J. R. P., & Zapf, P. A. (2003). The role of Canadian psychologists in conducting fitness and criminal responsibility evaluations. *Canadian Psychology, 44,* 369–381.

Viljoen, J. L., Vincent, G. M., & Roesch, R. (2006). Assessing adolescent defendants' adjudicative competence: Interrater reliability and factor structure of the Fitness Interview Test–Revised. *Criminal Justice and Behavior, 33*(4), 467–487.

Vine, C., & Challen, P. (2002). *Gardens of shame: The tragedy of Martin Kruze and the sexual abuse at Maple Leaf Gardens.* Vancouver: Greystone Books.

Vingilis, E., Wade, T. J., & Adlaf, E. (1998). What factors predict student self-rated physical health. *Journal of Adolescence, 21,* 83–97.

Vinkers, D. J., et al. (2004). The 15-item Geriatric Depression Scale (GDS-15) detects changes in depressive symptoms after a major negative life event: The Leiden 85-plus study. *International Journal of Geriatric Psychiatry, 19,* 80–84.

Virues-Ortega, J. (2010). Applied behavior analytic intervention for autism in early childhood: Meta-analysis, meta-regression, and dose-response meta-analysis of multiple outcomes. *Clinical Psychology Review, 30,* 387–399.

Vismara, L. A., & Rogers, S. J. (2010). Behavioral treatments in autism spectrum disorder: What do we know? *Annual Review of Clinical Psychology, 6,* 447–468.

Vissia, E. M., Giesen, M. E., Chavlavi, E. R. S., Nijenhuis, N., Draijer, N., Brand, B. L., & Reinders, A. A. T. S. (2016). Is it trauma- or fantasy-based? Comparing dissociative identity disorder, post-traumatic stress disorder, simulators, and controls. *Acta Psychiatrica Scandinavica, 134*(2), 111–128.

Vitacco, M. J., Erickson, S. K., Kurus, S., & Apple, B. N. (2012). The role of the Violence Risk Appraisal Guide and Historical, Clinical, Risk-20 in U.S. courts: A case law survey. *Psychology, Public Policy, and Law, 18,* 361–391.

Vitacco, M. J., Gonsalves, V., Tomony, J., Smith, B., & Lishner, D. A. (2012). Can standardized measures of risk predict inpatient violence? *Criminal Justice and Behavior, 39,* 589–609.

Voeller, K. K. (2004). Dyslexia. *Journal of Child Neurology, 19,* 790–794.

Vogel-Sprott, M., Kartechner, W., & McDonnell, D. (1989). Consequences of behavior influence the effect of alcohol. *Journal of Substance Abuse, 1,* 369–379.

Volkmar, F. R., Cohen, D. J., & Paul, R. (1986). An evaluation of DSM-III criteria for infantile autism. *Journal of the American Academy of Child Psychiatry, 25,* 190–197.

Volkow, N. D. (2012). Inhalants. *NIDA-NIH,* 1–8.

Volkow, N. D., Wang, G. J., Fischman, M. W., & Foltin, R. W. (1997). Relationship between subjective effects of cocaine and dopamine transporter occupancy. *Nature, 386,* 827–830.

Volpicelli, J. R., Rhines, K. C., Rhines, J. S., Volpicelli, L. A., et al. (1997). Naltrexone and alcohol dependence: Role of subject compliance. *Archives of General Psychiatry, 54,* 737–743.

Volpicelli, J. R., Watson, N. T., King, A. C., Shermen, C. E., & O'Brien, C. P. (1995). Effects of naltrexone on alcohol "high" in alcoholics. *American Journal of Psychiatry, 152,* 613–617.

von Knorring, A. L., & Hagglof, B. (1993). Autism in northern Sweden: A population-based follow-up study: Psychopathology. *European Child and Adolescent Psychiatry, 2,* 91–97.

von Krafft-Ebing, R. (1902). *Psychopathia sexualis.* Brooklyn, NY: Physicians and Surgeons Books.

von Ranson, K. M., & Robinson, K. E. (2006). Who is providing what type of psychotherapy to eating disorder clients? A survey. *International Journal of Eating Disorders, 39,* 27–34.

Voshaar, R. C. O., Kapur, N., Bickley, H., Williams, A., & Purandare, N. (2011). Suicide in late life: A comparison between cases with early-onset and late-onset depression. *Journal of Affective Disorders, 132,* 185–191.

Vredenburg, K., Flett, G. L., & Krames, L. (1993). Analogue versus clinical depression: A critical re-appraisal. *Psychological Bulletin, 113,* 327–344.

Wachtel, J. R., & Strauss, C. C. (1995). Separation anxiety disorder. In A. Eise, C. Kearny, & C. Schaefer (Eds.), *Clinical handbook of anxiety disorders in children and adolescents* (pp. 53–81). Northvale, NJ: Aronson, Inc.

Waddell, C. (2007). Improving the mental health of young children: A discussion paper prepared for the British Columbia Healthy Child Developmental Alliance. Vancouver: Children's Health Policy Centre.

Waddell, C., McEwan, K., Shepherd, C. A., Offord, D. R., & Hua, J. M. (2005). A public health strategy to improve the mental health of Canadian children. *Canadian Journal of Psychiatry, 50,* 226–233.

Waddell, C., Offord, D. R., Shepherd, C. A., Hua, J. M., & McEwan, K. (2002). Child psychiatric epidemiology and Canadian public policy-making: The state of the science and the art of the possible. *Canadian Journal of Psychiatry, 47,* 825–832.

Waddell, C., Shepherd, C., Schwartz, C., & Barican, J. (2014). A research report for the British Columbia Ministry of Children and Family Development. Vancouver: Simon Fraser University.

Waddington, J. L., Brown, A. S., Lane, A., et al. (2008). Congenital anomalies and early functional impairments in a prospective birth cohort: Risk of schizophrenia-spectrum disorder in adulthood. *The British Journal of Psychiatry, 192,* 264–267.

Wagner, A. W., & Linehan, M. M. (1994). Relationship between childhood sexual abuse and topography of parasuicide among women with borderline personality disorder. *Journal of Personality Disorders, 8,* 1–9.

Wagner, D. V., Borduin, C. M., Sawyer, A. M., & Dopp, A. R. (2014). Long-term prevention of criminality in siblings of serious and violent juvenile offenders: A 25-year follow-up to a randomized clinical trial of multisystemic therapy. *Journal of Consulting and Clinical Psychology, 82*, 492–499.

Wahi, G., Zorzi, A., Macnab, A., & Panagiotopoulos, C. (2009). Prevalence of type 2 diabetes, obesity and the metabolic syndrome among Canadian First Nations children in a remote Pacific coast community. *Paediatrics and Child Health, 14*, 79–83.

Wahlsten, D. (1997). Leilani Muir versus the philosopher king: Eugenics on trial in Alberta. *Genetica, 99*, 185–198.

Wakefield, J. (1992). Disorder as dysfunction: A conceptual critique of DSM-III-R's definition of mental disorder. *Psychological Review, 99*, 232–247.

Walker, E., Kestler, L., Bollini, A., & Hochman, K. M. (2004). Schizophrenia: Etiology and course. *Annual Review of Psychology, 55*, 401–430.

Walker, E. F., Davis, D. M., & Savoie, T. D. (1994). Neuromotor precursors of schizophrenia. *Schizophrenia Bulletin, 20*, 441–451.

Walker, E. R., & Druss, B. G. (2015). Rate and predictors of persistent major depressive disorder in a nationally representative sample. *Community Mental Health Journal, 51*, 701–707.

Walkom, T. (2003, September 20). Now, medical waiting lists include health-care reform: Proposed changes collecting dust; Ottawa, provinces blamed for delay. *The Toronto Star.*

Wall, A.-M., McKee, S. A., & Hinson, R. E. (2000). Assessing variation in alcohol outcome expectancies across environmental context: An examination of the situational-specificity hypothesis. *Psychology of Addictive Behaviors, 14*, 367–375.

Wall, A.-M., Wekerle, C. & Bissonette, M. (2000). Childhood maltreatment, parental alcoholism, and beliefs about alcohol: Subgroup variation among alcohol-dependent adults. *Alcoholism and Treatment Quarterly, 18*, 49–60.

Wallace, J. (1966). An abilities conception of personality: Some implications for personality measurement. *American Psychologist, 21*, 132–138.

Wallace, S. T., & Alden, L. E. (1997). Social phobia and positive social events: The price of success. *Journal of Abnormal Psychology, 106*, 416–424.

Waller, D. A., Kiser, S., Hardy, B. W., Fuchs, I., & Feigenbaum, L. P. (1986). Eating behavior and plasma beta-endorphin in bulimia. *American Journal of Clinical Nutrition, 4*, 20–23.

Waller, G. (2009). Evidence-based treatment and therapist drift. *Behaviour Research and Therapy, 47*, 119–127.

Waller, G., et al. (2007). Narcissism and narcissistic defenses in the eating disorders. *International Journal of Eating Disorders, 40*, 143–148.

Waller, R., & Gilbody, S. (2009). Barriers to the uptake of computerized cognitive behavioural therapy: A systematic review of the quantitative and qualitative evidence. *Psychological Medicine, 39*, 705–712.

Wallerstein, R. S. (1989). The Psychotherapy Research Project of the Menninger Foundation: An overview. *Journal of Consulting and Clinical Psychology, 57*, 195–205.

Walling, M., Anderson, B. L., & Johnson, S. R. (1990). Hormonal replacement therapy for postmenopausal women: A review of sexual outcomes and related gynecologic effects. *Archives of Sexual Behavior, 19*, 119–137.

Walls, M. L., Hautala, D., & Hurley, J. (2014). "Rebuilding our community": Hearing silenced voices on aboriginal youth suicide. *Transcultural Psychiatry, 51*, 47–72.

Walsh, B. T. (2003). Eating disorders. In A. Tasman, J. Kay, & J. A. Lieberman (Eds.), *Psychiatry* (2nd ed., Vol. 2, pp. 1501–1518). Chichester, England: John Wiley & Sons.

Walter, M., et al. (2007). Pedophilia is linked to reduced activation in hypothalamus and lateral prefrontal cortex during visual erotic stimulation. *Biological Psychiatry, 62*, 698–701.

Walters, D. (1995). Mandatory reporting of child abuse: Legal, ethical, and clinical implications within a Canadian context. *Canadian Psychology, 36*, 163–182.

Walters, E., & Kendler, K. S. (1994). Anorexia nervosa and anorexia-like symptoms in a population based twin sample. *American Journal of Psychiatry, 152*, 62–71.

Wang, F., et al. (2009). The influence of childhood obesity on the development of self-esteem. *Health Reports, 20*, 21–27.

Wang, Z., Li, Z., Gao, K., & Fang, Y. (2014). Association between brain-derived neurotrophic factor genetic polymorphism Val66Met and susceptibility to bipolar disorder: A meta-analysis. *BMC Psychiatry, 14*, 366.

Wannamethee, S. G., Shaper, A. G., & Walker, M. (1998). Changes in physical activity, mortality, and incidence of coronary heart disease in older men. *The Lancet, 351*, 1603–1608.

Ward, C. H., Beck, A. T., Mendelson, M., Mock, E., & Erbaugh, J. K. (1962). The psychiatric nomenclature: Reasons for diagnostic disagreement. *Archives of General Psychiatry, 7*, 198–205.

Ward, J. A., & Fox, J. (1977). A suicide epidemic on an Indian reserve. *The Canadian Psychiatric Association Journal, 22*, 423–426.

Warren, J. I., Dietz, P. E., & Hazelwood, R. R. (2013). Offenders who preserve evidence of their crimes. *Aggression and Violent Behavior, 18*, 666–672.

Warren, S. L., Huston, L., Egeland, B., & Sroufe, L. A. (1997). Child and adolescent anxiety disorders and early attachment. *Journal of the American Academy of Child and Adolescent Psychiatry, 36*, 637–644.

Warsh, C. K. (1989). *Moments of unreason: The practice of Canadian psychiatry and the Homewood Retreat, 1883–1923.* Montreal: McGill-Queen's University Press.

Wartenberg, A. A., Nirenberg, T. D., Liepman, M. R., Silvia, L. Y., Begin, A. M., & Monti, P. M. (1990). Detoxification of alcoholics: Improving care by symptom-triggered sedation. *Alcoholism: Clinical and Experimental Research, 14*, 71–75.

Waschbusch, D. A., Walsh, T. M., Andrade, B. F., et al. (2007). Social problem solving, conduct problems, and callous-unemotional traits in children. *Child Psychiatry and Human Development, 37*, 293–305.

Waserman, J., & Criollo, M. (2000). Subjective experiences of clozapine treatment by patients with chronic schizophrenia. *Psychiatric Services, 51*, 666–668.

Wasylenki, D., Goering, P., & MacNaughton, E. (1994). Planning mental health services: Background and key issues. *New Directions in Mental Health Services, 61*, 21–29.

Watson, D., & Pennebaker, J. W. (1989). Health complaints, stress, and distress: Exploring the central role of negative affectivity. *Psychological Review, 96*, 234–254.

Watson, J. B., & Rayner, R. (1920). Conditioned emotional reactions. *Journal of Experimental Psychology, 3*, 1–14.

Watson, J. C., & Bedard, D. L. (2006). Clients' emotional processing in psychotherapy: A comparison between cognitive-behavioral and process-experiential therapies. *Journal of Consulting and Clinical Psychology, 74*, 152–159.

Watson, J. C., Goldman, R. N., & Greenberg, L. S. (2007). *Case studies in the experiential treatment of depression: A comparison of good and bad outcome.* Washington, DC: American Psychological Association.

Watson, S. M., & Westby, C. E. (2003). Strategies for addressing the executive function impairments of students prenatally exposed to alcohol and other drugs. *Communication Disorders Quarterly, 24*, 194–204.

Watt, L. M., & Cappeliez, P. (2000). Integrative and instrumental reminiscence therapies for depression in older adults: Intervention strategies and treatment effectiveness. *Aging and Mental Health, 4,* 166–177.

Watt, N. F. (1974). Childhood and adolescent roots of schizophrenia. In D. Ricks, A. Thomas, & M. Roll (Eds.), *Life history research in psychopathology* (Vol. 3). Minneapolis, MN: University of Minnesota Press.

Watzlawick, P., Beavin, J., & Jackson, D. D. (1967). *Pragmatics of human communication: A study of interactional patterns, pathologies, and paradoxes.* New York: Norton.

Webb, C. A., DeRubeis, R. J., & Barber, J. P. (2010). Therapist/adherence competence and treatment outcome: A meta-analytic review. *Journal of Consulting and Clinical Psychology, 78,* 200–211.

Webb, W. B., & Campbell, S. S. (1980). Awakenings and the return to sleep in an older population. *Sleep, 3,* 41–66.

Weber, T. (1996, December 2). Tarnishing the golden years with addiction. *Los Angeles Times,* A1, A37.

Webster, C. D., Douglas, K. S., Eaves, D., & Hart, S. D. (1997). Assessing risk of violence to others. In C. D. Webster & M. A. Jackson (Eds.), *Impulsivity: Theory, assessment, and treatment* (pp. 251–277). New York: Guilford.

Webster-Stratton, C., Reid, M. J., & Beauchaine, T. P. (2013). One-year follow-up of combined parent and child intervention for young children with ADHD. *Journal of Clinical Child and Adolescent Psychology, 42,* 251–261.

Wechsler, H., Davenport, A., Dowdell, G., Moeykens, B., & Castillo, S. (1994). Health and behavioral consequences of binge drinking in college: A national survey of students at 140 campuses. *Journal of the American Medical Association, 272,* 1672–1677.

Wechsler, H., Kelley, K., Weitzman, E. R., San Giovanni, J. P., & Seibring, M. (2000). What colleges are doing about student binge drinking: A survey of college administrators. *Journal of American College Health, 48*(5), 219–226.

Wechsler, H., Lee, J. E., Kuo, M., & Lee, H. (2000). College binge drinking in the 1990s: a continuing problem. Results of the Harvard School of Public Health 1999 College Alcohol Study. *Journal of American College Health, 48,* 199–210.

Weck, F., Grikscheit, F., Jakob, M., Höfling, V., & Stangier, U. (2015). Treatment failure in cognitive-behavioural therapy: Therapeutic alliance as a precondition for an adherent and competent implementation of techniques. *British Journal of Clinical Psychology, 54,* 91–108.

Weck, F., Neng, J. M. B., Richtberg, S., Jakob, M., & Stangier, U. (2015). Cognitive therapy versus exposure therapy for hypochondriasis (health anxiety). *Journal of Consulting and Clinical Psychology, 83,* 665–676.

Weinberger, D. R. (1987). Implications of normal brain development for the pathogenesis of schizophrenia. *Archives of General Psychiatry, 44,* 660–669.

Weinberger, D. R., Berman, K. F., & Illowsky, B. P. (1988). Physiological dysfunction of dorsolateral prefrontal cortex in schizophrenia: III. A new cohort and evidence for a monoaminergic mechanism. *Archives of General Psychiatry, 45*(7), 609.

Weinbrecht, A., Schulze, L., Boettcher, J., & Renneberg, B. (2016). Avoidant personality disorder: A current review. *Current Psychiatry Reports, 18,* 29.

Weiner, B., Frieze, L., Kukla, A., Reed, L., Rest, S., & Rosenbaum, R. M. (1971). *Perceiving the causes of success and failure.* New York: General Learning Press.

Weiner, D. B. (1994). Le geste de Pinel: The history of psychiatric myth. In M. S. Micale & R. Portern (Eds.), *Discovering the history of psychiatry.* New York: Oxford.

Weingarden, H., & Renshaw, K. D. (2015). Shame in the obsessive compulsive related disorders: A conceptual review. *Journal of Affective Disorders, 171,* 74–84.

Weinstein, N., & Ryan, R. M. (2010). When helping helps: An examination of motivational constructs underlying prosocial behavior and their influence on well-being for the helper and recipient. *Journal of Personality and Social Psychology, 98*(2), 222–224.

Weis, R., & Ash, S. E. (2009). Changes in adolescent and parent hopefulness in psychotherapy: Effects on adolescent outcomes as evaluated by adolescents, parents, and therapists. *The Journal of Positive Psychology, 4,* 356–364.

Weisman, A. G., Nuechterlein, K. H., Goldstein, M. J., & Snyder, K. S. (1998). Expressed emotion, attributions, and schizophrenia symptom dimensions. *Journal of Abnormal Psychology, 107,* 355–359.

Weissman, A. N., & Beck, A. T. (1978). Development and validation of the Dysfunctional Attitude Scale: A preliminary investigation. Paper presented at the annual meeting of the American Educational Research Association, Toronto.

Weissman, M. M. (1993). The epidemiology of personality disorders: A 1990 update. *Journal of Personality Disorders, 7,* 44–61.

Weissman, M. M. (1995). *Mastering depression: A patient's guide to interpersonal psychotherapy.* New York: Graywind.

Weissman, M. M. (2006). A brief history of interpersonal psychotherapy. *Psychiatric Annals, 36,* 553–557.

Weissman, M. M., Bland, R. C., Canino, G. J., Faravelli, C., Greenwald, S., et al. (1996). Cross-national epidemiology of major depression and bipolar disorder. *Journal of the American Medical Association, 276,* 293–299.

Weizmann, F., Wiener, N. I., Wiesenthal, D. L., & Ziegler, M. (1991). Eggs, eggplants and eggheads: A rejoinder to Rushton. *Canadian Psychology, 32,* 43–50.

Wells, A. (2010). Metacognitive theory and therapy for worry and generalized anxiety disorder: Review and status. *Journal of Experimental Psychopathology, 1.1,* 133–145.

Wells, C. E., & Duncan, G. W. (1980). *Neurology for psychiatrists.* Philadelphia: F. A. Davis.

Wells, J., & Zlomislic, D. (2012, December 13). Electroshock therapy more prevalent in Ontario but guidelines minimal. *The Toronto Star.*

Wells, S., Graham, K., & West, P. (2000). Alcohol-related aggression in the general population. *Journal of Studies on Alcohol, 61,* 626–632.

Wender, P. H., Kety, S. S., Rosenthal, D., Schulsinger, F., Ortmann, J., & Lunde, I. (1986). Psychiatric disorders in the biological and adoptive families of adopted individuals with affective disorders. *Archives of General Psychiatry, 43,* 923–929.

Wente, M. (2003, March 20). The case of the crazy professor. *The Globe and Mail.*

Werner, K. B., Few, L. R., & Bucholz, K. K. (2015). Epidemiology, comorbidity, and behavioral genetics of antisocial personality disorder and psychopathy. *Psychiatric Annals, 45,* 195–199.

West, M., Adam, K., Spreng, S., & Rose, S. (2001). Attachment disorganization and dissociative symptoms in clinically treated adolescents. *Canadian Journal of Psychiatry, 46,* 627–631.

West, S. L., & O'Neal, K. K. (2004). Project D.A.R.E. outcome effectiveness revisited. *American Journal of Public Health, 94,* 1027–1029.

West, S. L., Vinikoor, L. C., & Zolnoun, D. (2004). A systematic review of the literature on female sexual dysfunction prevalence and predictors. *Annual Review of Sex Research, 15,* 40–172.

Westen, D., Novotny, C. M., & Thompson-Brenner, H. (2004). The empirical status of empirically supported psychotherapies: Assumptions, findings, and reporting in controlled clinical trials. *Psychological Bulletin, 130,* 631–663.

Westra, H. A. (2004). Managing resistance in cognitive behavioural therapy: The application of motivational interviewing in mixed anxiety and depression. *Cognitive Behaviour Therapy, 33,* 161–175.

Westra, H. A., Constantino, M. J., & Antony, M. M. (in press). Integrating motivational interviewing with cognitive-behavioral therapy for severe generalized anxiety disorder: An allegiance-controlled clinical trial. *Journal of Consulting and Clinical Psychology.*

Westra, H. A., Constantino, M. J., Arkowitz, H. A., & Dozois, D. J. A. (2011). Therapist differences in cognitive behavioral therapy for generalized anxiety disorder: A pilot study. *Psychotherapy, 48*(3), 283–292.

Westra, H. A., Eastwood, J. D., Bouffard, B. B., & Gerritsen, C. J. (2006). Psychology's pursuit of prescriptive authority: Would it meet the goals of Canadian health care reform? *Canadian Psychology, 47,* 77–95.

Wetherell, J. L. (1998). Treatment of anxiety in older adults. *Psychotherapy, 39,* 444–458.

Wetherell, J. L., Gatz, M., & Craske, M. G. (2003). Treatment of generalized anxiety disorder in older adults. *Journal of Consulting and Clinical Psychology, 71,* 31–40.

Wexler, B. E., Zhu, H., Bell, M. D., et al. (2009). Neuropsychological near normality and brain structure abnormality in schizophrenia. *American Journal of Psychiatry, 166,* 188–195.

Whalen, C. K., & Henker, B. (1999). The child with attention-deficit/hyperactivity disorder in family contexts. In H. C. Quay & A. E. Hogan (Eds.), *Handbook of disruptive behavior disorders* (pp. 139–155). New York: Plenum Press.

Wheaton, B. (1997). The nature of chronic stress. In B. H. Gottlieb (Ed.), *Coping with chronic stress* (pp. 43–73). New York: Plenum.

Wheeler, H. A., Blankstein, K. R., Antony, M. M., McCabe, R. E., & Bieling, P. J. (2011). Perfectionism in anxiety and depression: Comparisons across disorders, relations with symptom severity, and role of comorbidity. *International Journal of Cognitive Therapy, 4*(1), 66–91.

Whelton, P. K., et al. for the TONE Collaborative Research Group. (1998). Sodium reduction and weight loss in the treatment of hypertension in older persons: A randomized controlled trial of nonpharmacologic interventions in the elderly (TONE). *Journal of the American Medical Association, 279,* 839–846.

Whiffen, V. E., & MacIntosh, H. B. (2005). Mediators of the link between childhood sexual abuse and emotional distress: A critical review. *Trauma, Violence, and Abuse, 6,* 24–39.

Whisman, M. A., Robustelli, B. L., & Sbarra, D. A. (2016). Marital disruption is associated with shorter salivary telomere length in a probability sample of older adults. *Social Science & Medicine, 157,* 60–67.

White, S. W., Oswald, D., Ollendick, T., & Scahill, L. (2009). Anxiety in children and adolescents with autism spectrum disorders. *Clinical Psychology Review, 29,* 216–229.

Whitehorn, D., Richard, J. C., & Kopala, L. (2004). Hospitalization in the first year of treatment for schizophrenia. *Canadian Journal of Psychiatry, 49,* 635–638.

Whitlock, J. L., Powers, J. P., & Eckenrode, J. E. (2006). The virtual cutting edge: Adolescent self-injury and the Internet. *Developmental Psychology, 42,* 407–417.

Wichstrom, L., Belsky, J., & Berg-Nielsen, T. S. (2013). Preschool predictors of childhood anxiety disorders: A prospective community study. *Journal of Child Psychology and Psychiatry, 54,* 1327–1336.

Wickham, M. E., Senthilselvan, A., Wild, C., Hoglund, W. L. G., & Colman, I. (2015). Maternal depressive symptoms during childhood and risky adolescent health behaviors. *Pediatrics, 135,* 59–67.

Widiger, T. A., Crego, C., & Oltmanns, J. R. (2015). The validation of a classification of psychopathology. *Psychological Inquiry, 26,* 272–278.

Widiger, T. A., Frances, A., & Trull, T. J. (1987). A psychometric analysis of the social-interpersonal and cognitive-perceptual items for schizotypal personality disorder. *Archives of General Psychiatry, 44,* 741–745.

Wiebking, C., & Northoff, G. (2013). Neuroimaging in pedophilia. *Current Psychiatry Reports, 15*(4), 351.

Wiers, R. W., & Stacy, A. W. (2006). Implicit cognition and addiction. *Current Directions in Psychological Science, 15,* 292–296.

Wildes, J. E., Harkness, K. L., & Simons, A. D. (2002). Life events, number of social relationships, and twelve-month naturalistic course of major depression in a community sample of women. *Depression and Anxiety, 16,* 104–113.

Wilfley, D., Stein, R., & Welch, R. (2003). Interpersonal psychotherapy. In J. Treasure, U. Schmidt, & E. van Furth (Eds.), *Handbook of eating disorders* (2nd ed., pp. 253–270). Chichester, England: John Wiley & Sons.

Wilgosh, L., Mulcahy, R., & Watters, B. (1986). Assessing intellectual performance of culturally different, Inuit children with the WISC-R. *Canadian Journal of Behavioural Science, 18,* 270–277.

Wilhelm, K., et al. (2006). Life events, first depression onset, and the serotonin transporter gene. *British Journal of Psychiatry, 188,* 210–215.

Wilkie, C., Macdonald, S., & Hildahl, K. (1998). Community case study: Suicide cluster in a small Manitoba community. *Canadian Journal of Psychiatry, 43,* 823–828.

Wilkins, K., Gee, M., & Campbell, N. (2012). The difference in hypertension control between older men and women. *Health Reports, 23,* 3–10.

Wilkinson, S., Waller, R., & Viding, E. (2016). Practitioner review: Involving young people with callous-unemotional traits in treatment—does it work? A systematic review. *The Journal of Child Psychology and Psychiatry, 57,* 552–565.

Williams, J. M. G., Teasdale, J. D., Segal, Z. V., & Soulsby, J. (2000). Mindfulness-based cognitive therapy reduces overgeneral autobiographical memory in formerly depressed patients. *Journal of Abnormal Psychology, 109,* 150–155.

Williams, J., Hadjistavropoulos, T., & Sharpe, D. (2006). A meta-analysis of psychological and pharmacological treatments for body dysmorphic disorder. *Behaviour Research and Therapy, 44,* 99–111.

Williams, L., et al. (2008). Type D personality mechanisms of affect: The role of heart-related behavior and social support. *Journal of Psychosomatic Research, 64,* 63–69.

Williams, L., & Wingate, A. (2012). Type D personality, physical symptoms, and subjective stress: The mediating effects of coping and social support. *Psychology and Health, 27,* 1075–1085.

Williams, L. M. (1995). Recovered memories of abuse in women with documented child sexual victimization histories. *Journal of Traumatic Stress, 8,* 649–673.

Wills, T. A., & Cleary, S. D. (1999). Peer and adolescent substance use among 6th–9th graders: Latent growth analysis of influence versus selection mechanisms. *Health Psychology, 18,* 453–463.

Wills, T. A., DuHamel, K., & Vaccaro, D. (1995). Activity and mood temperament as predictors of adolescent substance use: Test of a self-regulation model. *Journal of Personality and Social Psychology, 68,* 901–916.

Wilsnak, S. C. (1984). Drinking, sexuality, and sexual dysfunction in women. In S. C. Wilsnak & L. J. Beckman (Eds.), *Alcohol problems in women: Antecedents, consequences, and intervention* (pp. 189–227). New York: Guilford.

Wilson, C. J., & Deane, F. P. (2010). Help negative and suicide ideation: The role of depression, anxiety, and hopelessness. *Journal of Youth and Adolescence, 39,* 291–305.

Wilson, C. M., Nicholls, T. L., Charette, Y., Seto, M. C., & Crocker, A. G. (2016). Factors associated with Review Board dispositions following re-hospitalization among discharged persons found not criminally responsible. *Behavioral Sciences and the Law, 34*, 278–294.

Wilson, G. T., & Davison, G. C. (1971). Processes of fear reduction in systematic desensitization: Animal studies. *Psychological Bulletin, 76*, 1–14.

Wilson, G. T., Vitousek, K., & Loeb, K. L. (2000). Stepped care treatment for eating disorders. *Journal of Consulting and Clinical Psychology, 68*, 564–572.

Wilson, K. G., Sandler, L. S., Asmundson, G. J. G., Larsen, D. K., & Ediger, J. M. (1991). Effects of instructional set on self-reports of panic attacks. *Journal of Anxiety Disorders, 5*, 43–63.

Wincze, J. P., & Carey, M. P. (1991). *Sexual dysfunction: A guide for assessment and treatment.* New York: Guilford.

Winett, R. A., & Winkler, R. C. (1972). Current behavior modification in the classroom: Be still, be quiet, be docile. *Journal of Applied Behavior Analysis, 5*, 499–504.

Wingrove, J. (2013, March 16). Care centre can't shake sordid history. *The Globe and Mail*, A12.

Winkler, A., Dorsing, B., Rief, W., Shen, Y., & Glombiewski, J. A. (2013). Treatment of internet addiction: A meta-analysis. *Clinical Psychology Review, 33*, 317–329.

Wipfli, H., & Samet, J. M. (2016). One hundred years in the making: The global tobacco epidemic. *Annual Review of Public Health, 37*, 149–166.

Wirshing, D. A., Marshall, B. D., Green, M. F., Mintz, J., Marder, S. R., & Wirshing, W. C. (1999). Risperidone in treatment-refractory schizophrenia. *American Journal of Psychiatry, 156*, 1347–1379.

Wise, T. (1978). Where the public peril begins: A survey of psychotherapists to determine the effects of Tarasoff. *Stanford Law Review, 31*, 165–190.

Wise, T., Cleare, A. J., Herane, A., Young, A. H., & Arnone, D. (2014). Diagnostic and therapeutic utility of neuroimaging in depression: An overview. *Neuropsychiatric Disease and Treatment, 10*, 1509–1522.

Wiseheart, M., Viswanathan, M., & Bialystok, E. (2016). Flexibility in task switching by monolinguals and bilinguals. *Bilingualism: Language & Cognition, 19*, 141–146.

Wisner, K. L., Bogen, D. L., Sit, D. K., McShea, M., Hughes, C., Rizzo, D., et al. (2013). Does fetal exposure to SSRIs or maternal depression impact infant growth? *American Journal of Psychiatry, 170*, 485–493.

Wisner, K. L., Sit, D. K., Hanusa, B. H., et al. (2009). Major depression and antidepressant treatment: Impact on pregnancy and neonatal outcomes. *American Journal of Psychiatry, 166*, 557–566.

Witkiewitz, K., & Marlatt, G. A. (2006). Overview of harm reduction treatments for alcohol problems. *International Journal of Drug Policy, 17*, 285–294.

Witlox, J., Eurelings, L. S. M., de Jonghe, J. F. M., et al. (2010). Delirium in elderly patients and the risk of postdischarge mortality, institutionalization, and dementia: A meta-analysis. *The Journal of the American Medical Association, 304*, 443–451.

Wittchen, H. U., Stein, M. B., & Kessler, R. C. (1999). Social fears and social phobia in a community sample of adolescents and young adults: Prevalence, risk factors and co-morbidity. *Psychological Medicine, 29*(2), 309–323.

Witthoft, M., Fischer, S., Jasper, F., Rist, F., & Nater, U. M. (2016). Clarifying the latent structure and correlates of somatic symptom distress: A bifactor model approach. *Psychological Assessment, 28*, 109–115.

Wold, D. A. (1968). *The adjustment of siblings to childhood leukemia.* Unpublished medical thesis, University of Washington, Seattle.

Wolf, A., & Kutash, I. L. (1990). Psychoanalysis in groups. In I. L. Kutash & A. Wolf (Eds.), *The group psychotherapist's handbook: Contemporary theory and technique.* New York: Columbia University Press.

Wolf-Maier, K., et al. (2003). Hypertension prevalence and blood pressure levels in 6 European countries, Canada, and the United States. *Journal of the American Medical Association, 289*, 2363–2369.

Wolfe, V. V. (1990). Sexual abuse of children. In A. S. Bellack, M. Hersen, & A. E. Kazdin (Eds.), *International handbook of behavior modification and therapy* (2nd ed., pp. 707–729). New York: Plenum.

Wolff, P. H., & Melngailis, I. (1996). Reversing letters and reading transformed text in dyslexia: A reassessment. *Reading and Writing, 8*, 341–355.

Wolfson, C., et al. (2001). A reevaluation of the duration of survival after the onset of dementia. *New England Journal of Medicine, 344*, 1160–1161.

Wolitzky, D. L., & Eagle, M. N. (1990). Psychotherapy. In A. S. Bellack & M. Hersen (Eds.), *Handbook of comparative treatments for adult disorders* (pp. 123–143). New York: John Wiley & Sons.

Wolitzky-Taylor, K. B., Bobova, L., Zinbarg, R. E., Mineka, S., & Craske, M. G. (2012). Longitudinal investigation of the impact of anxiety and mood disorders in adolescence on subsequent substance use disorder onset and vice versa. *Addictive Behaviors, 37*, 982–985.

Wolitzky-Taylor, K. B., Castriotta, N., Lenza, E. J., Stanley, M. A., & Craske, M. G. (2010). Anxiety disorders in older adults: A comprehensive review. *Depression and Anxiety, 27*, 190–211.

Wolitzky-Taylor, K. B., Horowitz, J. D., Powers, M. B., & Telch, M. J. (2008). Psychological approaches in the treatment of specific phobias: A meta-analysis. *Clinical Psychology Review, 28*, 1021–1037.

Wolpe, J. (1958). *Psychotherapy by reciprocal inhibition.* Stanford, CA: Stanford University Press.

Wolraich, M. L., Wilson, D. B., & White, J. W. (1995). The effect of sugar on behavior or cognition in children: A meta-analysis. *Journal of the American Medical Association, 274*, 1617–1621.

Wonderlich, S. A., Rosenfeldt, S., Crosby, R. D., Mitchell, J. E., Engel, S. G., Smyth, J., et al. (2007). The effects of childhood trauma on daily mood lability and comorbid psychopathology in bulimia nervosa. *Journal of Traumatic Stress, 20*(1), 77–87.

Wong, S. C. P., & Olver, M. E. (2015). Risk reduction treatment of psychopathy and applications to mentally disordered offenders. *CNS Spectrum, 20*, 303–310.

Woo, A. (2016, August 30). The opioid crisis: As thousands die of overdoses, police are becoming front-line medics and politicians are forced to respond. *The Globe and Mail*, A6.

Wood, A. M., & Johnson, J. (in press). Schema therapy. In A. M. Wood & J. Johnson (Eds.), *The Wiley handbook of positive clinical psychology.* Chichester, UK: Wiley.

Wood, E., Tyndall, M. W., Montaner, J. S., & Kerr, T. (2006). Summary of findings from the evaluation of a pilot medically supervised safer injecting facility. *Canadian Medical Association Journal, 175*, 1399–1404.

Wood, J. M., Garb, H. N., Nezworski, M. T., Lilienfeld, S. O., & Duke, M. C. (2015). A second look at the validity of widely used Rorschach indices: Comment on Mihura, Meyer, Dumitrascu, and Bombel (2013). *Psychological Bulletin, 141*, 236–249.

Wood, J. M., Nezworski, M. T., Lilienfeld, S. O., & Garb, H. N. (2009). Projective techniques in the courtroom. In J. L. Skeem, K. S. Douglas, & S. O. Lilienfeld (Eds.), *Psychological science in the courtroom: Consensus and controversy* (pp. 202–223). New York: Guilford.

Woodhead, E. L., Emery, E. E., Pachana, N. A., Scott, T. L., Konnert, C. A., & Edelstein, B. A. (2013). Graduate students' geropsychology training opportunities and perceived competence in working with older adults. *Professional Psychology: Research and Practice, 44,* 355–362.

Woodhead, E. L., Emery-Tiburcio, E. E., Pachana, N. A., Scott, T. L., Konnert, C. A., & Edelstein, B. A. (2015). Clinical and counseling psychology graduate students' expectations for future work with older adults. *Clinical Gerontologist, 38,* 357–374.

Woodill, G. (1992). Controlling the sexuality of developmentally disabled persons: Historical perspectives. *Journal of Developmental Disabilities, 1,* 1–14.

Woodman, C. L., Noyes, R., Black, D. W., Schlosser, S., & Yagla, S. J. (1999). A 5-year follow-up study of generalized anxiety disorder and panic disorder. *Journal of Nervous and Mental Disease, 187,* 3–9.

Woodside, D. B., Shekter-Wolfson, L. F., Garfinkel, P. E., & Olmsted, M. P. (1995). Family interactions in bulimia nervosa: Study design, comparisons to established population norms and changes over the course of an intensive day hospital treatment program. *International Journal of Eating Disorders, 17,* 105–115.

Woodward, C. A., Abelson, J., Tedford, S., & Hutchison, B. (2004). What is important to continuity in home care? Perspectives of key stakeholders. *Social Science and Medicine, 58,* 177–192.

Woodworth, M., Hancock, J., Porter, S., Hare, R., et al. (2012). The language of psychopaths: New findings and implications for law enforcement. *FBI Law Enforcement Bulletin.* Retrieved from https://leb.fbi.gov/2012/july/the-language-of-psychopaths-new-findings-and-implications-for-law-enforcement.

Woodworth, M., & Porter, S. (2002). In cold blood: Characteristics of criminal homicides as a function of psychopathology. *Journal of Abnormal Psychology, 111,* 436–445.

Woody, S., Detweiler-Bedell, J., Teachman, B. A., & O'Hearn, T. (2003). *Treatment planning in psychotherapy: Taking the guesswork out of clinical care.* London: Guilford.

Woody, S. R., Kellman-McFarlane, K., & Welsted, A. (2014). Review of cognitive performance in hoarding disorder. *Clinical Psychology Review, 34,* 324–336.

Woolley, S., & Johnson, S. M. (2006). Emotionally focused interventions. In J. Lebow (Ed.), *Handbook of clinical family therapy* (pp. 384–405). New York: John Wiley & Sons.

World Health Organization (WHO). (2000). *Multi-site intervention study on suicidal behaviours—SUPRE-MISS: Components and instruments.* Geneva: WHO, Department of Mental Health and Substance Dependence.

World Health Organization (WHO). (2002). *Reducing stigma and discrimination against older people with mental disorders: A technical consensus statement.* Geneva: Author.

World Health Organization (WHO). (2004). *World health report 2004.* Geneva: Author.

World Health Organization (WHO). (2011). *Global status report on alcohol & health.* Geneva: Author.

World Health Organization (WHO). (2014). *Preventing suicide: A global imperative.* Geneva: World Health Organization.

Worling, J. R. (2001). Personality-based typology of adolescent male sexual offenders: Differences in recidivism rates, victim-selection characteristics, and personal victimization histories. *Sexual Abuse: A Journal of Research and Treatment, 13,* 149–166.

Worthington, P. (2011, September 30). Olson will not be missed. *Toronto Sun.*

Wragg, J. A., & Whitehead, R. E. (2004). CBT for adolescents with psychosis: Investigating the feasibility and effectiveness of early intervention using a single case design. *Behavioural and Cognitive Psychotherapy, 32,* 313–329.

Wright, A. C., Lukowitsky, M. R., Pincus, A. L., & Conroy, D. E. (2010). The higher order factor structure and gender invariance of the Pathological Narcissism Inventory. *Assessment, 17,* 467–483.

Wright, A. G. C., Thomas, K. M., Hopwood, C. J., Markon, K. E., Pincus, A. E., & Krueger, R. F. (2012). The hierarchical model of DSM-5 pathological personality traits. *Journal of Abnormal Psychology, 121,* 951–957.

Wright, I. C., et al. (2000). Meta-analysis of regional brain volumes in schizophrenia. *American Journal of Psychiatry, 157,* 16–25.

Wright, M. J. (1991). Identifying child sexual abuse using the Personality Inventory for Children. *Dissertation Abstracts International, 52,* 1744.

Wurtele, S. K., & Miller-Perrin, C. L. (1987). An evaluation of side-effects associated with participation in a child sexual abuse prevention program. *Journal of School Health, 57,* 228–231.

Wykes, T., Steel, C., Everitt, B., & Tarrier, N. (2008). Cognitive behavior therapy for schizophrenia: Effect sizes, clinical models, and methodological rigor. *Schizophrenia Bulletin, 34,* 523–537.

Wylie, K. R. (1997). Treatment outcome of brief couple therapy in psychogenic male erectile disorder. *Archives of Sexual Behavior, 26,* 527–545.

Xu, B., Ionita-Laza, I., Roos, J. L., Boone, B., et al. (2012). *De novo* gene mutations highlight patterns of genetic and neural complexity in schizophrenia. *Nature Genetics, 44,* 1365–1369.

Xu, B., Roos, J. L., Dexheimer, P., Boone, B., et al. (2011). Exome sequencing supports a *de novo* mutational paradigm for schizophrenia. *Nature Genetics, 43,* 864–868.

Yalom, I. D., Green, R., & Fisk, N. (1973). Prenatal exposure to female hormones: Effect on psycho-sexual development in boys. *Archives of General Psychiatry, 28,* 554–561.

Yang, X., Kirton, A., Wilkes, T. C., Pradhan, S., Liu, I., Jaworska, N., . . . MacMaster, F. P. (2014). Glutamate alterations associated with transcranial magnetic stimulation in youth depression: A case series. *The Journal of ECT, 30,* 242–247.

Yates, T. M., Tracy, A. J., & Luthar, S. S. (2008). Nonsuicidal self-injury among "privileged" youth: Longitudinal and cross-sectional approaches to developmental processes. *Journal of Consulting and Clinical Psychology, 76,* 52–62.

Yatham, L. N., Kauer-Sant'Anna, M., Bond, D. J., et al. (2009). Course and outcome after the first manic episode in patients with bipolar disorder: Prospective 12-month data from the Systematic Treatment Optimization Program for Early Mania Project. *Canadian Journal of Psychiatry, 54,* 105–112.

Yatham, L. N., Kennedy, S. H., Parikh, S. V., Schaffer, A., Beaulieu, S., Alda, M., . . . Berk, M. (2013). Canadian Network for Mood and Anxiety Treatments (CANMAT) and International Society for Bipolar Disorders (ISBD) collaborative update of CANMAT guidelines for the management of patients with bipolar disorder: Update 2013. *Bipolar Disorders, 15,* 1–44.

Yesavage, J. A., et al. (1983). Development and validation of a geriatric screening scale: A preliminary report. *Journal of Psychiatric Research, 17,* 37–49.

Yildirim, C., & Correia, A. (2015). Exploring the dimensions of nomophobia: Development and validation of a self-reported questionnaire. *Computers in Human Behavior, 49,* 130–137.

Yirmiya, N., & Sigman, M. (1991). High functioning individuals with autism: Diagnosis, empirical findings, and theoretical issues. *Clinical Psychology Review, 11,* 669–683.

Young, D. A., Zakzanis, K., Campbell, Z., Freyslinger M. G., et al. (2002). Scaffolded instruction remediates Wisconsin Card Sorting Test deficits in schizophrenia: A comparison to other techniques. *Neuropsychological Rehabilitation, 12,* 257–287.

Young, J. E. (1994). *Cognitive therapy for personality disorders: A schema-focused approach.* Sarasota, FL: Professional Resource Exchange.

Young, J. E. (1999). *Cognitive therapy for personality disorders: A schema-focused approach.* New York: Guilford Press.

Young, J. E., & Beck, A. T. (1980). *Cognitive Therapy Scale: Rating manual.* Unpublished manuscript, University of Pennsylvania, Philadelphia.

Young, J. E., Klosko, J. S., & Weishaar, M. (2003). *Schema therapy: A practitioner's guide.* New York: Guilford.

Young, J. E., & Lindemann, M. (2002). An integrated schema-focused model for personality disorders. In R. L. Leahy & E. T. Dowd (Eds.), *Clinical advances in cognitive psychotherapy: Theory and applications* (pp. 93–109). New York: Springer.

Young, K. S. (1998). Internet addiction: The emergence of a new clinical disorder. *CyberPsychology & Behaviour, 1,* 237–244.

Young, S. (1998). Risk in research: From the Nuremberg Code to the Tri-Council Code: Implications for clinical trials of psychotropic drugs. *Journal of Psychiatry and Neuroscience, 23,* 149–155.

Young, S. E., Smolen, A., Hewitt, J. K., et al. (2006). Interaction between MAO-A genotype and maltreatment in the risk for conduct disorder: Failure to confirm in adolescent patients. *American Journal of Psychiatry, 163,* 1019–1025.

Yu, D., Mathews, C. A., Scharf, J. M., Neale, B. M., Davis, L. K., Gamazon, E. R., . . . Pauls, D. L. (2015). Cross-disorder genome-wide analyses suggest a complex genetic relationship between Tourette's syndrome and OCD. *American Journal of Psychiatry, 172,* 82–93.

Yung, A. R., Phillips, L. J., Hok, P. Y., & McGorry, P. D. (2004). Risk factors for psychosis in an ultra high-risk group: Psychopathology and clinical features. *Schizophrenia Research, 67,* 131–142.

Yurgelun-Todd, D., et al. (1996). Functional magnetic resonance imagery of schizophrenia patients and comparison subjects during word production. *American Journal of Psychiatry, 153,* 200–206.

Zack, M., Poulos, C. X., Fragopoulos, F., & MacLeod, C. M. (2003). Effects of negative and positive mood phrases on priming of alcohol words in young drinkers with high and low anxiety sensitivity. *Experimental and Clinical Pharmacology, 11,* 176–185.

Zack, M., Poulos, C. X., Fragopoulos, F., Woodford, T. M., & MacLeod, C. M. (2006). Negative affect words prime beer consumption in young drinkers. *Addictive Behaviors, 31,* 169–173.

Zack, M., Toneatto, T., & MacLeod, C. M. (1999). Implicit activation of alcohol concepts by negative affective cues distinguishes between problem drinkers with high and low psychiatric distress. *Journal of Abnormal Psychology, 108,* 518–531.

Zack, S. E., Castonguay, L. G., Boswell, J. F., McAleavey, A. A., Adelman, R., Kraus, D. R., & Pate, G. A. (2015). Attachment history as a moderator of the alliance outcome relationship in adolescents. *Psychotherapy, 52,* 258–267.

Zahn-Waxler, C., Shirtcliff, E. A., & Marceau, K. (2008). Disorders of childhood and adolescence: Gender and psychopathology. *Annual Review of Clinical Psychology, 4,* 275–303.

Zai, G., et al. (2005). Evidence for the gamma-amino-butyric acid type B receptor 1 (*GABBR1*) gene as a susceptibility factor in obsessive-compulsive disorder. *American Journal of Medical Genetics Part B: Neuropsychiatric Genetics, 134B,* 25–29.

Zakzanis, K. K., & Azarbehi, R. (2014). Introducing Brainscreen: Web-based real-time examination and interpretation of cognitive functioning. *Applied Neuropsychology: Adult, 21,* 77–86.

Zakzanis, K. K., Graham, S. J., & Campbell, Z. (2003). A meta-analysis of structural and functional brain imaging in dementia of Alzheimer's type: A neuroimaging profile. *Neuropsychology Review, 13,* 1–19.

Zakzanis, K. K., Poulin, P., Hansen, K. T., & Jolic, D. (2000). Searching the schizophrenic brain for temporal lobe deficits: A systematic review and meta-analysis. *Psychological Medicine, 30,* 491–504.

Zakzanis, K. K., Troyer, A. K., Rich, J. B., & Heinrichs, W. (2000). Component analysis of verbal fluency in patients with schizophrenia. *Neuropsychiatry, Neuropsychology, and Behavioral Neurology, 13,* 239–245.

Zanarini, M. C., et al. (2005). The McLean Study of Adult Development (MSAD): Overview and implications of the first six years of prospective follow-up. *Journal of Personality Disorders, 19,* 505–523.

Zanarini, M. C., Frankenburg, F. R., Dubo, E. D., Sickel, A. E., Trikha, A., et al. (1998). Axis I comorbidity of borderline personality disorder. *American Journal of Psychiatry, 155,* 1733–1739.

Zanarini, M. C., Frankenburg, F. R., Hennen, J., Reich, D. B., & Silk, K. R. (2005). Psychosocial functioning of borderline patients and Axis II comparison subjects followed prospectively for six years. *Journal of Personality Disorders, 19,* 19–29.

Zanarini, M. C., Frankenburg, F. R., Reich, D. B., Wedig, M. M., Conkey, L. C., & Fitzmaurice, G. M. (2014). Prediction of time-to-attainment of recovery for borderline patients followed prospectively for 16 years. *Acta Psychiatrica Scandinavica, 130,* 205–213.

Zanarini, M. C., Horwood, J., Wolke, D., Waylen, A., Fitzmaurice, G., & Grant, B. F. (2011). Prevalence of DSM-IV borderline personality disorder in two community samples: 6,330 English 11-year olds and 34,653 American adults. *Journal of Personality Disorders, 25,* 607–619.

Zapf, P. A., & Roesch, R. (1997). Assessing fitness to stand trial: A comparison of institution-based evaluations and a brief screening interview. *Canadian Journal of Community Mental Health, 16,* 53–66.

Zarit, S. H. (1980). *Aging and mental disorders: Psychological approaches to assessment and treatment.* New York: Free Press.

Zarit, S. H., & Zarit, J. M. (1998). *Mental disorders in older adults: Fundamentals of assessment and treatment.* New York: Guilford.

Zavos, H. M., Gregory, A. M., & Eley, T. C. (2012). Longitudinal genetic analysis of anxiety sensitivity. *Developmental Psychology, 48,* 204–212.

Zeier, J. D., Baskin-Sommers, A. R., Racer, K. D. H., & Newman, J. P. (2012). Cognitive control deficits associated with antisocial personality disorder and psychopathy. *Personality Disorders, 3,* 283–293.

Zeifman, R. J., Atkey, S. K., Young, R. E., Flett, G. L., Hewitt, P. L., & Goldberg, J. O. (in press). When ideals get in the way of self-care: Perfectionism and self-stigma for seeking psychological help among high school students. *Canadian Journal of School Psychology.*

Zhang, Y., et al. (2013). White matter integrity alterations in first-episode, treatment-naïve generalized anxiety disorder. *Journal of Affective Disorders, 148*(2–3), 196–201.

Zhao, W., Young, R. E., Breslow, L., Michel, N. M., Flett, G. L., & Goldberg, J. O. (2015). Attachment style, relationship factors, and mental health stigma among adolescents. *Canadian Journal of Behavioural Science, 46,* 263–271.

Zilboorg, G., & Henry, G. W. (1941). *A history of medical psychology.* New York: Norton.

Zilcha-Mano, S., Muran, J. C., Hungr, C., Eubanks, C. F., Safran, J. D., & Winston, A. (in press). The relationship between alliance and outcome: Analysis of a two-person perspective on alliance and session outcome. *Journal of Consulting and Clinical Psychology.*

Zimmer, L., & Morgan, J. P. (1995). *Exposing marijuana myths: A review of the scientific evidence.* New York: The Lindemith Center.

Zimmerman, G., Favrod, J., Trieu, V. H., & Pomini, V. (2005). The effects of cognitive behavioral treatment on the positive symptoms of schizophrenia spectrum disorders: A meta-analysis. *Schizophrenia Research, 77,* 1–8.

Zimmerman, M., & Coryell, W. (1989). DSM-III personality disorder diagnoses in a nonpatient sample. *Archives of General Psychiatry, 46,* 682–689.

Zinatelli, M., & Vogel-Sprott, M. (1993). Behavioral tolerance to alcohol in humans is enhanced by prior drug-free treatment. *Experimental and Clinical Psychopharmacology, 1,* 194–199.

Zipursky, R. B., et al. (1997). Deficits in gray matter volume are present in schizophrenia but not bipolar disorder. *Schizophrenia Research, 26,* 85–92.

Zipursky, R. B., Meyer, J. H., & Verhoeff, N. P. (2007). PET and SPECT imaging in psychiatric disorders. *Canadian Journal of Psychiatry, 52,* 146–157.

Zivian, M. T., Gekoski, W., Knox, V. J., Larsen, W., & Hatchette, V. (1994). Psychotherapy for the elderly: Public opinion. *Psychotherapy, 31,* 492–502.

Zivian, M. T., Larsen, W., Knox, V. J., Gegoski, W. L., & Hatchette, V. (1992). Psychotherapy for the elderly: Psychotherapists' preferences. *Psychotherapy, 29,* 668–674.

Zoccola, P. M., Dickerson, S. S., & Zaldivar, F. P. (2008). Rumination and cortisol responses to laboratory stressors. *Psychosomatic Medicine, 70,* 661–667.

Zon, L. (2009, May 15). Apathy, stigma worsen suffering. *Toronto Star,* L6.

Zoomer.com. (1997, December 1). A tale of the Stanley Cup…. And Alzheimer's. Retrieved from: http://www.everythingzoomer.com/a-tale-of-the-stanley-cup-and-alzheimers/.

Zucker, K. J., et al. (1999). Gender constancy judgments in children with gender identity disorder: Evidence for a developmental lag. *Archives of Sexual Behavior, 28,* 475–502.

Zucker, K. J., & Blanchard, R. (1997). Transvestic fetishism: Psychopathology and theory. In D. R. Laws & W. O'Donohue (Eds.), *Sexual deviance* (pp. 280–296). New York: Guilford.

Zucker, S. H., Perras, C., Gartin, B., & Fidler, D. (2005). Best practices for practitioners. *Education and Training in Developmental Disabilities, 40,* 199–201.

Zwaigenbaum, L., Bryson, S., Lord, C., et al. (2009). Clinical assessment and management of toddlers with suspected autism spectrum disorder: Insights from studies of high-risk infants. *Pediatrics, 123,* 1383–1391.

Zwanzger, P., Domschke, K., & Bradwejn, J. (2012). Neuronal network of panic disorder: The role of the neuropeptide cholecystokinen. *Depression and Anxiety, 29,* 762–774.

Zweig-Frank, H., & Paris, J. (2002). Predictors of outcome in a 27-year follow-up of patients with borderline personality disorder. *Comprehensive Psychiatry, 43,* 103–107.

Zwisler, A.-D., Norton, R. J., Dean, S. G., Dalal, H., Tang, L. H., Wingham, J., & Taylor, R. S. (in press). Home-based cardiac rehabilitation for people with heart failure: A systematic review and meta-analysis. *International Journal of Cardiology.*

Name Index

A

Aardema, F., 160

AARP. *See* American Association of Retired Persons (AARP)

Aase, D. M., 351

Abayomio, O., 433

Abbass, A. A., 50, 186, 544, 545

Abbate-Daga, G., 300

Abbeduto, L., 487

Abbott, K. A., 134

Abe-Kim, J., 60

Abel, A., 527

Abela, J. R. Z., 205

Abelson, J., 519

Abma, D., 460

Aboujaoude, E., 558

Abracen, J., 430, 433

Abraham, C., 458

Abramowitz, J. S., 151, 153, 159, 160, 169

Abrams, R., 226

Abramson, L. Y., 119, 214, 215, 217, 236

Achenbach, T. M., 454

Achim, A. M., 307

Ad Hoc Advisory Group of Experts National Institutes of Health, 361

Adalsteinsson, E., 514

Adam, K., 191

Adams, C. E., 225

Adams, E. H., 360, 367

Adams, L. P., 238

Adams, M. R., 267

Adams, P., 11

Addington, D. E., 311, 332, 334, 339

Addington, J., 311, 334

Adelson, N., 61–62

ADHD-200 Consortium, 38

Adlaf, E. M., 254, 343, 352, 364, 368, 369

Adler, 284

Adler, A., 164

Adler, D., 106

Adrian, M., 386

Advisory Group on Suicide Prevention, 238

Affrunti, N. W., 491

Afifi, T. O., 114–115, 296

Agarwal, M., 534

Aggarwal, N. K., 100

Aggarwal, R., 427

Agid, O., 310

Agran, M., 479

Agras, S., 301

Agras, W. S., 300

Ahn, W., 530

Ahonen, T., 472

Ainsworth, M. D., 489

Akbarian, S., 323

Akerib, 274

Akers, L., 257

Akyuz, G., 192

al'Absi, 267

Alamian, A., 369

AlAqeel, B., 306

Albee, G. W., 327

Alden, L. E., 140, 153, 187, 215, 391, 409, 411

Alegria, A. A., 402

Alexander, A. W., 476

Alexander, F., 51

Alexander, F., 261

Alexander, P. C., 426

Alexopoulos, G. S., 518

Alfano, L., 291

Alfano, M. S., 215

Alfonso, J., 352

Alford, B. A., 541

Ali, J., 21, 62

Alladi, S., 504

Allan, R., 553

Allardyce, J., 314

Alldridge, P., 7

Allen, J. J. B., 192

Allison, J., 381, 381n

Alloul, K., 502, 507

Alloy, L. B., 119, 215, 217, 236

Almquist, Y., 59

Almqvist, F., 454

Alpers, G. W., 139

Alpert, J. E., 409

Altamura, C., 171

Altenburger, E. M., 173

Alterman, A. I., 404

Althof, S. E., 449

Alvarado, 274

Alzheimer Society of Canada, 501, 502

Amador, X. F., 328

Amateau, L. M., 258

American Association of Mental Retardation (AAMR), 475

American Association of Retired Persons (AARP), 506, 520

American Association on Intellectual and Developmental Disabilities (AAIDD), 475

American College Health Association (ACHA), 254, 352

The American Journal of Psychiatry, 185n

American Psychiatric Association (APA), 93, 95, 100, 102, 103, 144, 167, 170, 171, 173, 178, 180, 181, 203, 208, 246, 310, 328, 348, 390, 390n, 418, 419, 422, 431, 432, 453, 456, 464, 465, 470, 472, 474, 475, 480, 481t, 488, 501, 520

American Psychological Association, 575

Ametrano, R. M., 527

Amianto, F., 300

Amirthavasagam, S., 398

Amoo, G., 433

Amos, N. L., 576

Amsel, R., 443

Anand, A., 219

Andersen, B. L., 444, 447

Andersen, E., 170

Anderson, B. L., 448

Anderson, C., 442

Anderson, D., 425, 430

Anderson, K. K., 306

Anderson, M., 519

Anderson, P., 354, 385, 386

Anderson, P. L., 150

Anderson, T., 554, 554n

Anderssen, E., 18, 419

Andersson, B., 352

Andersson, G., 556, 557

Andor, T., 149

Andreasen, N. C., 217, 309, 315, 322

Andreason, P. J., 397

Andreescu, C., 512

Andresen, M., 24

Andress, V. R., 241

Andrew, M. K., 499

Andrews, G., 147, 221, 222

Angelakis, I., 158

Angold, A., 103

Angrist, 320, 320

Angus, L., 55

Angus, L. E., 529

Anisman, H., 248

Annunziato, B., 258

Anson, M., 172

Anthony, K. E., 460

Antoni, M. H., 260

Antony, M. M., 135, 136, 150n, 163, 210, 529

Antshel, K. M., 457

APA. *See* American Psychiatric Association (APA)

APA Presidential Task Force on Evidence-Based Practice, 538

Apfel, N., 57

Appel, L. J., 247

Appelbaum, P. S., 589

Apple, B. N., 578

Applebaum, R., 506

Apt, C., 400

Apter, A., 239

Araujo, A. B., 443

Arbisi, P. A., 79

Arboleda-Florez, J., 343, 566

Arbuthnot, J., 469

Ard, B. N., Jr., 442

Ardern, S. I., 262

Argento, E., 363

Arieti, S., 141

Arkowitz, H., 529, 530

Armony, 274

Armor, D. J., 376

Armstrong, H. E., 413

Armstrong, T., 148

Arnberg, A., 223

Arnkoff, D. B., 555

Arnold, P. D., 169

Arntz, A., 411, 543, 555

Aronson, K., 355

Arpin-Cribbie, C., 225

Arria, A. M., 460

Arseneault, L., 463

Ash, S. E., 527

Ashbaugh, A., 134

Ashbridge, M., 365

Asheron, P., 456

Ashtari, M., 88

Ashton, M. C., 391, 391n

Ashworth, F., 547

Askew, C., 41

Asmundson, 272

Asmundson, G. J. G., 4, 85, 133, 144, 146, 166, 179, 186, 541

Subject Index